MAT 011

BEGINNING ALGEBRA

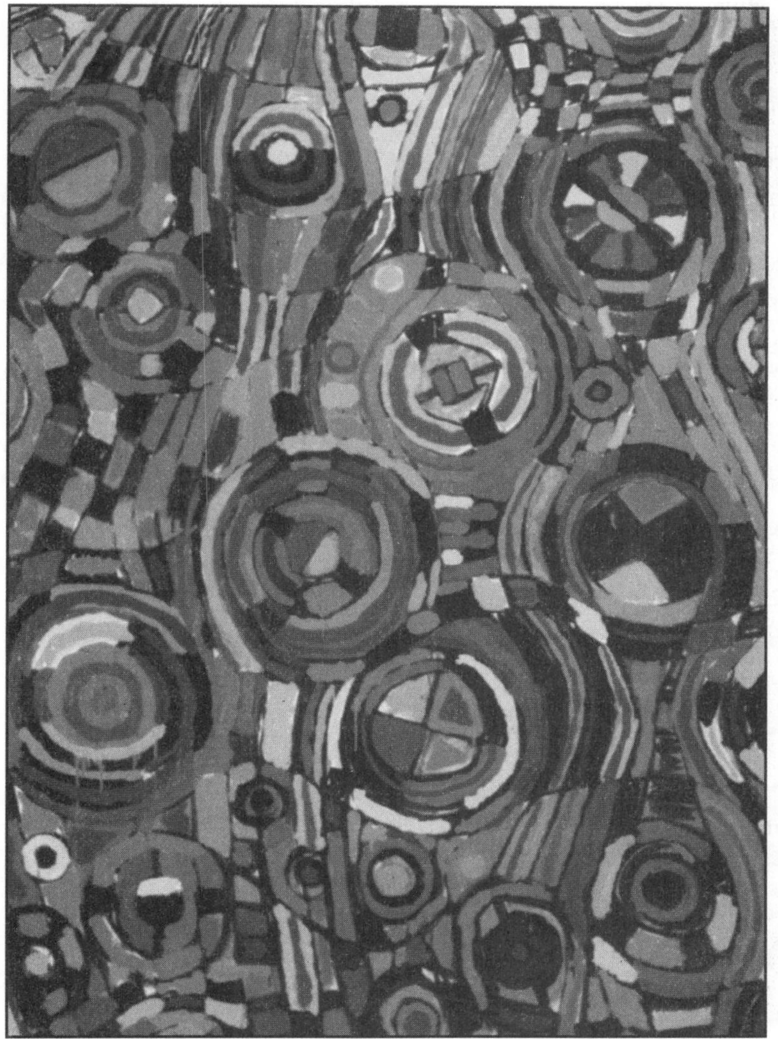

2006–2007

Custom Edition for Montgomery County Community College
2002 AMATYC Input Award Winner

DR. ROSEANNE HOFMANN, WALTER R. HUNTER, SUSAN K. YANKOSKY

Excerpts taken from:
Introductory Algebra, Tenth Edition
By Marvin L. Bittinger

Cover art: *Untitled #42* by Wayne Hopkins

Taken from:

Introductory Algebra, Tenth Edition
by Marvin L. Bittinger

Published by Addison-Wesley
Boston, Massachusetts 02116

Printed in the United States of America

10 9 8 7 6 5 4 3 2

ISBN 0-536-20165-X

2006360229

EC

Please visit our web site at *www.pearsoncustom.com*

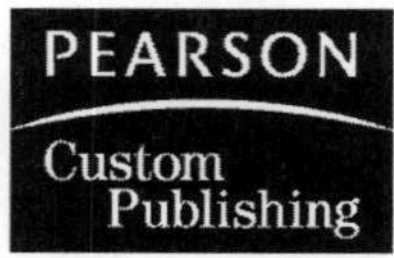

PEARSON CUSTOM PUBLISHING
75 Arlington Street, Suite 300, Boston, MA 02116
A Pearson Education Company

TABLE OF CONTENTS

MATH 011 INTRODUCTION

"I can't do math!!" " I have a calculator. Why do I need to know the multiplication tables?" "I've been working for 25 years and algebra has never come up on the job."

"I didn't take the placement test seriously. This is ridiculous to have to take non-credit math classes and waste all this time and money."

"Some people are born mathematicians and some aren't." "Computers will do all of the math I need."

As you sit in your Math 011 class this first week, you probably will hear some of the above comments being made by your classmates. You may even be uttering some of them yourself. (Interestingly enough, a student bragging about not being able to read is rare indeed.)

Please understand that placement into a non-credit course is not a punishment; it is a sincere effort on the part of the College to help you begin your math requirements at a place where you can succeed. If you are convinced that the placement results are not a true indication of your abilities, then please take a re-test. (The re-test should be taken before the first day of the semester.) However, if the re-test confirms your initial results, please return to class with a positive attitude and a willingness to work.

What would be a **true** tragedy would be to pay for the same class twice! Remember: You must earn a C to move to the next level.

Health Club Metaphor

When one joins a health club, the goal is usually a very positive one: to lose weight, to get in shape, to improve cardio-vascular health, or to look good in a bathing suit. However, good intentions and membership fees are just the easy first steps. Success depends on determination and hard work—going to work out when one does not really feel like it, doing more repetitions than are comfortable, giving up other, more enjoyable, activities to adhere to the workout routine.

No one would dispute the fact that results depend upon the individual. No health club, no personal trainer can do the sweating for the person, no matter who he or she may be.

You have just joined Club Math; your success or failure is in your own hands. Many aids are available to you, but ultimately you are the determining factor. Math muscle or math flab—you decide.

TEXTBOOK USE

This Math 011 textbook is designed to reflect an applications approach to algebra. That is, you will be required to get very involved in each class and in each assignment. Individual sections contain an overview section, class work, group work, and exercise sections. The overview section should be read by the student either before or after the section is covered by the instructor. The class work section will be done with the instructor as a guide, the group work section with the assistance of classmates, and the exercises completed at home, with a study group, or with a tutor.

Each chapter ends with a review section for an exam. This can be handled in an individual or group situation. (Groups are wonderful review tools. Ask your instructor for suggestions on forming study groups.)

The textbook is designed as a workbook. You should take notes in the class work sections. There is not enough space provided in the book to adequately do the exercises. Homework exercises should be done on separate paper from a loose leaf note book. This allows you to do the same problems again and again. Such repetition can be very helpful when reviewing for a test.

PRACTICAL SUGGESTIONS FOR MATH SUCCESS

1. Attend class faithfully (Everyone has illnesses and family emergencies; work around them. You can rarely make up material missed in a class session.)

2. Believe you can be successful even if math has not been a strength in the past. **Positive thinking does work**.

3. Read the pages assigned before attending class. Even if you don't understand the material, just seeing it begins a circuitry in the brain for future development and expansion.

4. Be aware of your learning style and the techniques you can use to manipulate the material to your best learning advantage.

5. Do some type of math work every day. The learning curve drops dramatically with even a one-day hiatus.

6. Plan on short, frequent math sessions. Twenty minutes is enough at the beginning. (Set a quiet timer and reward yourself with a pleasant activity after each session). Three periods a day is ideal.

7. Your math professor is an expert; use his or her talents both inside and outside of the classroom. Learn your instructor's name and office location. Visit during office hours to ask questions and clarify difficult problems.

8. Use lined paper for all problem solving; write on only one side and allow plenty of white space between numbers. It is imperative to keep information very organized.

9. Create note cards for important formulas and rules. They will be a great reference when studying for a test and/or doing your homework.

10. Don't write on handouts unless you make copies first. Again, these can be reused as study tools for exams.

11. We often learn more from our failures than from our successes. Don't get discouraged if it seems to be difficult. Most worthwhile human endeavors are.

12. Write key definitions and concepts on note cards; these can be easily reviewed in the car, on the bus, in the doctor's office and count as part of your study time.

12 Don't be embarrassed to ask questions in class if you need clarification on homework or on the lecture. The only stupid question is the one that goes unasked.

13 Repetition is important; keep working on problems until they become very familiar to you. Don't worry about the numbers as much as the process.

Montgomery County Community College

Learning Assistance Labs

Central Campus (Blue Bell, PA) – 215.641.6452 – College Hall Room 320
West Campus (Pottstown, PA) – 215.718.1945 – Room 159

The Learning Assistance Labs (LALs) of Montgomery County Community College provide academic support services for all MCCC students. Assistance is available for most courses offered at the college and all services are free. The purpose of the Labs is to assist all students in the pursuit of academic success. **Students enrolled in MAT 011 (Beginning Algebra) can get assistance with course topics by utilizing one or more of the following services:**

One-on-One Tutoring – Students sit with a tutor to discuss course material, review homework problems, and prepare for tests. Students should attend class and attempt assigned problems before visiting the lab for tutoring. No appointment is required. Students come to the lab, sign in, and ask to see a MAT 011 tutor. Students are usually served within 30 minutes of visiting the lab if not immediately.

Small Group Tutoring – Students sit with a tutor and other MAT 011 students to discuss course material, review homework problems, and prepare for tests. Students should attend class and attempt assigned problems before attending a group tutoring session. Contact LAL Central and LAL West respectively for details and schedules.

On-line Tutoring – Students log on to the MAT 011 tutoring site, post questions for the tutor, and check back for a response within 24 hours. To register for On-line Tutoring, contact LAL Central (215-641-6452). All MCCC students (Central, West, and Distance) may use this service.

Supplemental Instruction in the Developmental Studies Lab at Central Campus – Students may use special computer software to practice topics and problems covered in the classroom. Call the DSL (215-641-6693) for details.

Hours – Central Campus (Blue Bell)

Fall and Spring Terms

Monday through Thursday
7:30 a.m. to 9:30 p.m.
Friday
7:30 a.m. to 5:00 p.m.
Saturday
10:00 a.m. to 4:00 p.m.
Sunday
1:00 p.m. to 5:00 p.m.

Summer Sessions

Monday through Thursday
8:00 a.m. to 9:30 p.m.
Friday
8:00 a.m. to 5:00 p.m.
Saturday
10:00 a.m. to 4:00 p.m.

Hours - West Campus (Pottstown)

Fall and Spring Terms

Monday through Thursday
8:00 a.m. to 9:00 p.m.
Friday
8:00 a.m. to 5:00 p.m.
Saturday
9:00 a.m. to noon

Summer Sessions

Monday through Thursday
8:00 a.m. to 9:00 p.m.
Friday
8:00 a.m. to 5:00 p.m.

ELECTRONIC STUDENT RESOURCES

Arrays of technology tools were designed to accompany the newly created textbook. Animated ToolBook modules made available on a CD provide a different learning style that is appropriate for many students. A web page was developed with Power Point lectures, classroom videos, SmartBoard lectures with audio, and sample tests. Interactive graphical Excel spreadsheets were also developed.

ToolBook Modules

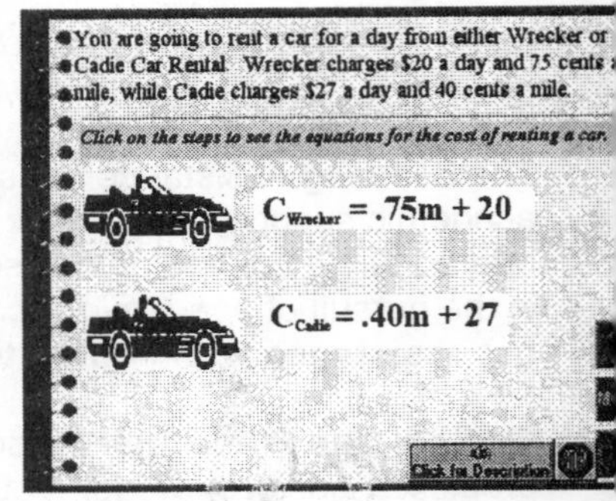

Eleven ToolBook modules were written to accompany a context based elementary algebra course. The modules are interactive, animated, audio enriched lessons. The goal of the ToolBook modules is to use another medium to present elementary algebra topics. One page from one of the eleven modules included here is just a static page. This page does not show or capture the animation, the sound, nor the interactivity required by the student. The sound is a value-added feature for English as a second language (ESL) and for on-line students. The ToolBook modules are on the CD that accompanies the book. The CD is on the inside frontcover.

Web Page

The electronic resources include classroom videos, textbook lectures, sample tests, course outline, a calculator supplement, Power Point lectures, and ToolBook modules. The web page is located at:
www.mc3.edu/aa/career/MATHSCI/mat011/mat011.htm
or enter MAT 011 Electronic Resources in the search our web site box from MCCC's web page, www.mc3.edu.

PowerPoint

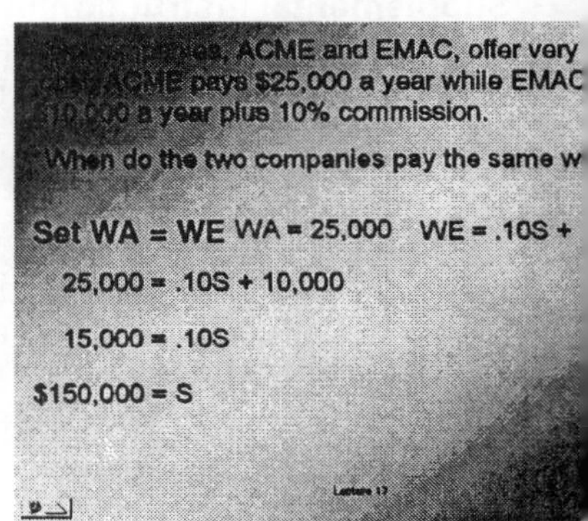

Thirty-four PowerPoint lectures were produced to provide visualizations for the materials. These PowerPoint lectures are available on the CD and on the web page.

IPTV

An instructor's class is available for students to view on the school's network. The Learning Lab will show you how to access the lectures.

What Math Course Should I Take Next?
Advising Information for Mat 011 Students

Math courses available to students who pass MAT 011:

MAT 100 Intermediate Algebra

This course is designed as a prerequisite for students who are required to take MAT 125 (Discrete Math), MAT 131 (Statistics I), MAT 140 (Finite Math), and/or MAT 161 (Precalculus I). If you think you might major in Business, Computer Science, Math, or a Science, then this is the course you should take. This course generally does not transfer. When it does transfer it is as a free elective, not as a fulfillment of a math requirement. It is fast paced and challenging.

MAT 100B Intermediate Algebra with Review

This course covers the same material as MAT 100 but also includes a review of the material in MAT 011. It is suggested that students who get a C in MAT 011 and need to take MAT 100 should consider taking MAT 100B. This course meets 4 hours a week and students receive 3 credits. Students pay for 4 credits.

MAT 103 Math for Elementary Education

This is a course designed for Elementary Education majors. You should check with a counselor or an advisor about the transferability of the course.

MAT 106 Math Applications

This course is for Liberal Arts students who need one or two college level math courses. If you think you might major in Criminal Justice, Social Science, Humanities, Secondary Education (except math or science concentrations), or Communications, then this is the course you should take. The exception is a major in Psychology which may require MAT 131 (Statistics I). Check the requirements of the four year school.

MAT 108 Mathematics Culture and Concepts

This course is for Liberal Arts students who need a second college level math. MAT 106 and MAT 108 may be taken in any order.

MAT 115 Applied Algebra/Trigonometry I

This course is for Technology majors. The course does not transfer to a four-year college. The Technology programs are designed for students to get an Associate degree and then enter the workforce.

Note: Although the numbers 103, 106, 108, and 115 are higher than 100, the courses do **<u>not</u>** need MAT 100 as a prerequisite.

General Advice:

1. It is very important to meet with a counselor or an advisor. You need to be aware of the latest transfer and graduation requirements.
2. If you have chosen a major, then you should follow the course listings for that major in the catalog. The Counseling and Advising Centers have catalogs for most of the area colleges.
3. If you know what college you are going to transfer to, then you should follow the catalog for your transfer school and find the equivalent courses offered by Montgomery County Community College. If the math course you need doesn't seem to be offered by MCCC, contact the four year college for advice.
4. If you are undecided as to what you want to do, then you may want to spend some time contemplating your career choices. The Counseling Center has many resources to help with your career options. The math course you take after MAT 011 may set the path for your career.

NOTE TO THE INSTRUCTOR: PHILOSOPHY OF THE AUTHORS

The practical application of mathematics is of paramount importance to our culture in the twenty-first century. Whether one is attempting to balance the weekly budget, to secure a well-paying job, or to advance to a higher level mathematics course, understanding the process is imperative. However, at the same time, improper use of technology has given some students the erroneous impression that calculators are the end result rather than the tools. These students fail to comprehend the human intellectual role in the process.

In an attempt to circumvent some of the negative thinking and frustrating experiences students bring to the classroom, the authors have attempted to present the beginning algebra material in this text in a non-threatening manner. We use applications not only to justify the material in the course but also to give concrete examples of the abstract concepts. At the same time, we understand the importance of imparting traditional mathematical skills.

In walking this fine line, we have intentionally chosen to present the rules of arithmetic informally, especially in the first section of the text. Our primary goal in this approach is to help the students feel successful from the beginning of the course. Additionally, we also purposely delayed presenting the formal rules for solving equations until after students were introduced to them using applications.

If we can convince the learners that simple language and concrete study strategies are effective, perhaps they will be more willing to move ahead, regardless of past negative experiences.

We have included in the appendices the more formal definitions of addition and subtraction of signed numbers. The instructor can refer to these pages whenever it seems appropriate. Also, we have included pages of exercises to use when drill seems necessary.

Acknowledgements: Aileen Conway
Rich Kern
Irene Yarbrough
Marion Graziano
Megan Malizia
Leslie Helm
Alison Sawyer

AMATYC INPUT AWARD is presented to innovative curriculum that utilizes modern technology in courses before calculus. AMATYC, American Mathematical Society of Two Year Colleges, is the leading national organization for community college mathematics teachers.

UNIT 1

SIGNED NUMBERS
OVERVIEW

Objectives: In this section, you will add, subtract, multiply, and divide signed numbers. Also, you will perform the order of operations including exponential problems.

The rules for adding and subtracting signed will be presented informally. For a formal discussion on adding and subtracting signed numbers see Appendix A page 398.

Addition and Subtraction:

Example 1. I have $40, and I owe you $75. What is my net worth?

Since I owe more than I have, the answer has to be a negative number.

To find the answer:

Having $40 is equivalent to + 40.
Owing $75 is equivalent to – 75.

My net worth will be given by 40 – 75.

or

40 – 75 = –35

My net worth is –$35.

> **Vocabulary:** What is being added or subtracted are called **terms.** In the example 40 – 75, 40 and 75 are the terms.

Informal Rule for adding unlike signs:

Find the difference (or subtract) the two numbers and use the sign of the larger number.

Alternative rule: Cover the signs of the numbers. Find the difference between the numbers with the signs covered. Use the sign of the larger number.

Example 2. I am in debt for $50, and I owe you $60. What is my net worth?

Since I am in debt and I owe you money, then my net worth has to be negative.

To find the answer:

Being in debt for $50 is equivalent to –50.
Owing $60 is equivalent to – 60.

My net worth will be given by –50 – 60.

or

–50 – 60 = –110

My net worth is –$110.

Informal Rule for adding numbers with like signs: Add the two numbers and use the common sign.

Study Tip: Make a note card with the rule for adding and subtracting signed numbers. Review notecards at least twice a week as part of your homework routine.

Multiplying and Dividing:

Vocabulary: When two numbers are multiplied, the answer is called the product. When two numbers are divided, the answer is called the quotient.

Example 3. I will lose \$9 a day for each of the next 6 days. How much money will I lose?

Since I am losing money, the answer has to be a negative number.

To find the answer:

Losing \$9 is equivalent to –9.

Since I am losing \$9 everyday for the next 6 days, I will have $-9 \cdot 6$ fewer dollars.

or

$-9 \bullet 6 = -54$

> **Vocabulary:** The numbers being multiplied are called **factors**. In the example, $-9 \bullet 6 = -54$, -9 and 6 are the factors.

I will lose \$54 in the next 6 days.

Informal Rule for multiplying or dividing numbers with unlike signs:

The product or quotient of two numbers with unlike signs is always negative.

Example 4. I lost \$8 a day for the previous 7 days. How much more money did I have 7 days ago?

Since I had more money 7 days ago, the answer has to be a positive number.

To find the answer:

Losing \$8 is equivalent to –8.
Previous 7 days is equivalent to –7

Since I have lost \$8 everyday for the past 7 days, I will have -8×-7 less dollars.

or

$-8 \bullet -7 = 56$

I had 56 more dollars 7 days ago.

Informal Rule for multiplying or dividing numbers with like signs:

The product or quotient of two numbers with like signs is always positive.

Study Tip: Make a note card with the rules for multiplying and dividing signed numbers.

Different notation for multiplication:

$$-4 \bullet 9 = (-4)(9) = -4 \times 9 = -4 * 9 = -36$$

An important vocabulary word: 3 and –3 are **opposites** because they both are the same distance from zero on the number line but in opposite directions. They are also called additive inverses because their sum is zero.

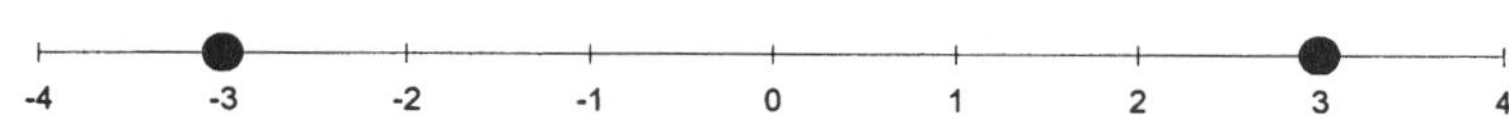

The opposite of –6 is 6. In mathematical notation, – (–6) = 6. The first negative sign means to use the opposite; the second negative sign means that 6 is negative.

An Application: The graph below shows the profit and loss of SRH Inc. for the years 1990 through 1995.

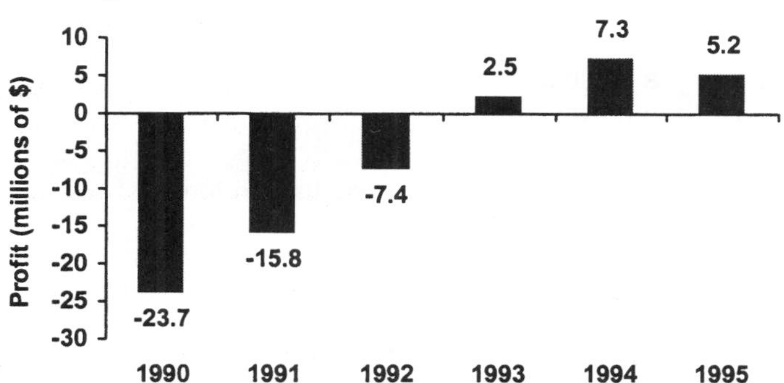

1. What was the difference between the profit in 1994 and the loss in 1991?

> Subtracting a negative number is equivalent to adding a positive number.

"Difference" means subtraction. (1994 profit) – (1991 loss).
Note: The most recent year should be first.

7.3 – (–15.8) =	– (–15.8) means, find the opposite of –15.8.
7.3 + 15.8 =	Add the two numbers.
23.1	

The difference between the profit in 1994 and the loss in 1991 was 23.1 million dollars.

2. What was the difference between the profit in 1995 and profit in1994? What is the significance of the negative sign in your answer?

5.2 – 7.3 =	Most recent year's profit minus earlier year's profit.
–2.1	Subtract 5.2 from 7.3. The answer is negative because SRH's profits decreased from years 1994 to 1995. The answer is positive in Part 1 because SRH's profits increased from years 1991 to 1994.

The difference in profit was –2.1 million dollars.

3. What is the mean (average) profit for the six years?

To find the average, add the profits and losses; then divide by the number of years, 6.

$$\frac{-23.7+(-15.8)+(-7.4)+2.5+7.3+5.2}{6} = \quad \text{Add the profits.}$$

$$-31.9/6 = \quad \text{Divide.}$$

$$-5.317$$

> **Note**: -31.9/6 does not actually equal -5.317, the answer is rounded to four digits.

The average profit for the six years was –5.317 million dollars.

Using a calculator to add, subtract, multiply, or divide:
(The TI-30X II S calculator is recommended for the course.)

Example 5. $-7.4 - 8.6 = -16$

-7.4 means that 7.4 is negative. To input a negative number into a calculator you must use the [(-)] key which is different from the subtraction key [–] .

The keys for multiplication, addition, and division are the standard ones.
Be aware that the key for multiplication on the calculator is ×, but it appears as * on the calculator screen. For division, the division key is ÷, but appears as / on the screen.

Study Tip: When using a calculator, you should take a couple of seconds to mentally estimate the answer.

Exponents: $\mathbf{b^n}$ means that the number **b** is multiplied by itself **n** times.

Example 6. $(-7)^2 = (-7)(-7)$
$= 49$

Order of Operations: When an arithmetic problem has more than one operation, the order is as follows:

First: Inside **P**arentheses, ( ).

Second: **E**xponents

Third: **M**ultiplication and **D**ivision (left to right)

Fourth: **A**ddition and **S**ubtraction (left to right)

Study Tip: **P**lease **E**xcuse **M**y **D**ear **A**unt **S**ally is a learning mnemonic used to memorize the order of operations. P is for parentheses, E is for Exponents, M is for Multiplication, D is for Division, A is for Addition, and S is for Subtraction.

Example 7. $-6(8 - 13)$
$= -6(-5)$ Perform arithmetic inside the parentheses.
$= 30$ The product of numbers with like signs is positive.

Example 8. $-6 - (-3)^2$
$= -6 - 9$ Compute the quantity $(-3)^2$
$= -15$ Subtract using the rules of signed numbers.

Summary:

Signed numbers are a key concept in Beginning Algebra. Initially, they can be confusing, but once the rules are learned and practiced, these numbers function in very predictable ways. Along with signed numbers, the order of operations must be mastered early in the semester. Answers will vary dramatically if the correct sequence is not followed.

1. Informal rules for adding and subtracting signed numbers:

   a. Unlike Signs: Find the difference (or subtract) of the two numbers and use the sign of the larger number.

   Example 9: $-9 + 12 = 3$

   b. Like Signs: Add the two numbers and use the common sign.

   Example 10: $-4 - 7 = -11$

2. Informal rules for multiplying and dividing signed numbers: (Perform the operation.)

   a. Unlike Signs: The result is always negative.

   Example 11: $(-5)(8) = -40$

   b. Like Signs: The result is always positive.

   Example 12: $\dfrac{-21}{-3} = 7$

3. Order of Operations:

   First: Inside parentheses, ( )
   Second: Exponents
   Third: Multiplication and Division (left to right)
   Fourth: Addition and Subtraction (left to right)

   Example 13: $\dfrac{-8}{2} + (-5)(3) =$

   $$-4 - 15 =$$

   $$-19$$

   Example 14: $(-4)^2(7 - 12) =$

   $$(-4)^2(-5) =$$

   $$16(-5) =$$

   $$-80$$

SIGNED NUMBERS
CLASS WORK

I. Adding and subtracting signed numbers:

1. I have \$60, and I owe you \$90. What is my net worth?

2. I am in debt for \$50, and you give me \$10. What is my net worth?

3. I am in debt for \$30, and you give me \$40. What is my net worth?

4. I am in debt for \$20, and I owe you \$50. What is my net worth?

5. Rules for adding and subtracting signed numbers.

6. Perform the operation.

a. $-7 + 5 =$ b. $6 - 10 =$

c. $2 - 11 =$ d. $-8 - 15 =$

e. $-6 + 10 =$ f. $\frac{1}{4} - \frac{5}{6} =$

II. Addition and subtraction using a calculator:

1. The subtraction key is

2. The negative key is

3. Perform the operation.

a. $-8.6 + 11.4 =$ b. $-16.85 - 28.42 =$

III. What is the opposite of a number?

IV. The graph below shows the profit and loss of Star Inc. for the years 1990 through 1995.

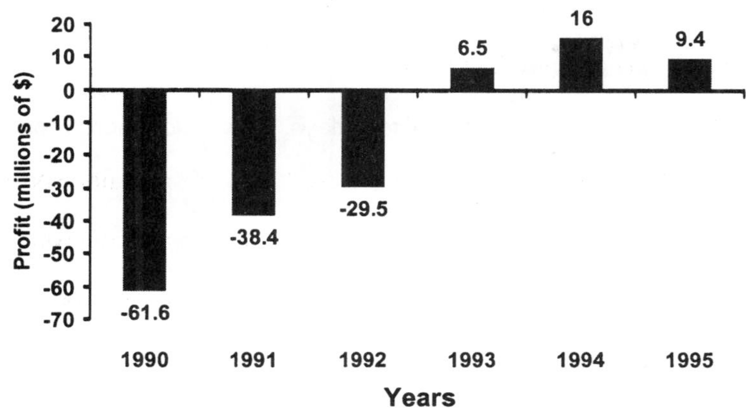

1. What was the difference between the profit in 1994 and the loss in 1990?

2. What was the difference between the profit in 1994 and the profit in 1993?

3. What was the difference between the profit in 1995 and in 1994? What is the significance of the negative sign in your answer?

4. What was the sum of the profits for 1991, 1992, and 1993?

5. What is the mean (average) for the six years?

6. Write a question that would generate –29.5 + (–38.4) as an answer.

7. Write a question that would generate –38.4 – (–61.6) as an answer.

V. Multiplication and division:

1. I will lose \$5 a day for the next three days. How much money will I lose?

2. I lost \$6 a day for the previous four days. How much more money did I have four days ago?

3. Rules for multiplying and dividing signed numbers.

4. Perform the operation.

a. $(-6)(3) =$ b. $(-7)(-2) =$ c. $(8)(-4) =$

d. $\frac{18}{-3} =$ e. $\frac{-21}{7} =$ f. $\frac{-48}{-6} =$

g. $\frac{0}{10} =$ h. $\frac{8}{0} =$ i. $\frac{0}{0} =$

5. Use a calculator to perform the operation.

a. $(-6.42)(-7.81) =$ b. $\frac{-8.42}{3.15} =$ c. $\frac{-10.81}{0} =$

6. Exponents:

a. $3^2 =$

b. $8^2 =$

c. $(-5)^2 =$

d. $(-2)^2 =$

VI. 1. List the order of operations.

2. Perform the operations.

a. $(-8)(2) - 6 =$

b. $7(8 - 10) =$

c. $(-8)(3) - \frac{-14}{2} =$

d. $(-7) - (-5)^2 =$

e. $\frac{6(-3)+(5)(-2)}{3-10} =$

f. $\frac{2(-3)^2+7}{25-5^2} =$

GROUP EXERCISE

Study Tip: Introduce yourself to other members of the group. Group success means individual success. Use only one sheet of paper for the entire group. This encourages all to participate.

The graph below shows the profit and loss of Black Paper, Inc. for the years 1992 through 1996.

Study Tip: Review the bar graphs on pages 3 and 7.

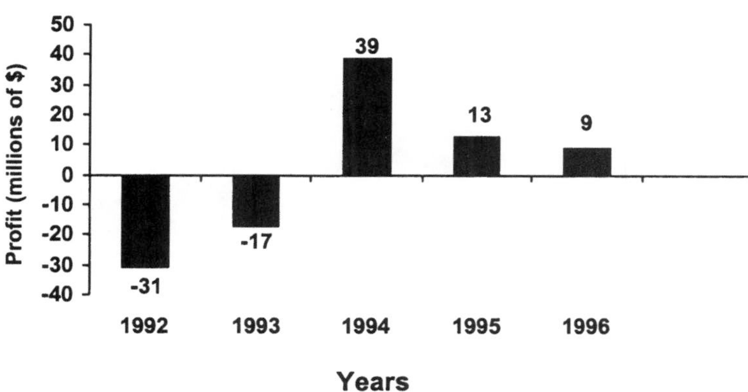

Write an arithmetic expression for each question and then answer the question.

1. What was the difference between the profit in 1994 and the loss in 1993?

2. What was the difference between the profit in 1995 and the loss in 1992?

3. What was the difference between profit in 1995 and the profit in 1994? What is the significance of the negative sign in the answer?

4. What is the sum of the profits and losses for 1993, 1994, and 1995?

5. What is the mean (average) for the five years?

6. Write a question that would generate –17 + 39 as an answer.

7. Write a question that would generate 9 – (–17) as an answer.

EXERCISES

Study Tip: If your arithmetic skills are weak, you should rewrite the problems on lined paper in a loose leaf notebook. Have all note cards handy for easy reference. Work for short periods of time, but do some math everyday. Consider doing your homework with a classmate. Two heads are better than one!

For questions 1 through 7, write an arithmetic expression for each sentence. Then find the person's net worth. There are two steps to each problem:

1. Translate the sentence into an arithmetic expression.
2. Simplify the arithmetic expression.

1. I have $80 in my checking account, and I owe RECO $100. What is my net worth?

2. I am in debt for $60, and I receive a check for $90. What is my net worth?

3. I am in debt for $210, and I owe M.C.C.C. $80. What is my net worth?

4. I have $60 in my checking account, and I owe $50 to ZZT. What is my net worth?

5. I have $97 in my checking account, and I owe ACME $155. What is my net worth?

6. What is the difference between a **2 under par on hole 12**, and a **1 over par on hole 15**?

7. What is the difference between Monday's class dismissing 7 minutes early and Wednesday's class staying 4 minutes longer?

8. What is the rule for adding numbers with the same sign?

9. What is the rule for adding numbers with different signs?

10. Perform the operation.

a. $7 - 5 =$ b. $-6 - 7 =$ c. $-15 + 6 =$

d. $-21 + 36 =$ e. $4 - 11 =$ f. $-8 + 15 =$

g. $-8 - 21 =$ h. $10 - 15 =$ i. $-11 - 21 =$

j. $-17 - (-28) =$ k. $-8 - 10 + 4 =$ l. $6 - 7 - 8 =$

m. $-3 + 6 - 11 =$ n. $7 - 11 + 4 - 15 =$ o. $(-5) - (-3) - (-5)$

11. a. What is the opposite or additive inverse of –12?

b. What is the opposite or additive inverse of 17?

12. Which key do you press to compute the opposite of a number on your calculator?

13. Use your calculator to perform the operation. Estimate if the answer will be positive or negative before you do the calculation.

Study Tip: Refer to Appendix C and the CD that accompanies the textbook to learn how to use the TI-30X IIS calculator.

a. $4.3 - 8.7 =$ b. $-6.5 + 7.21 =$

c. $-6.83 + 7.42 =$ d. $\frac{1}{4} - \frac{5}{6} =$

e. $-18.3 - (-36.5) =$ f. $-\frac{7}{8} - (-\frac{2}{3}) =$

14. The bar graph at the right shows the annual profit and loss, in millions of dollars, for The National Silver Company.

Study Tip: Review Group Work on page eleven or problem IV on page seven.

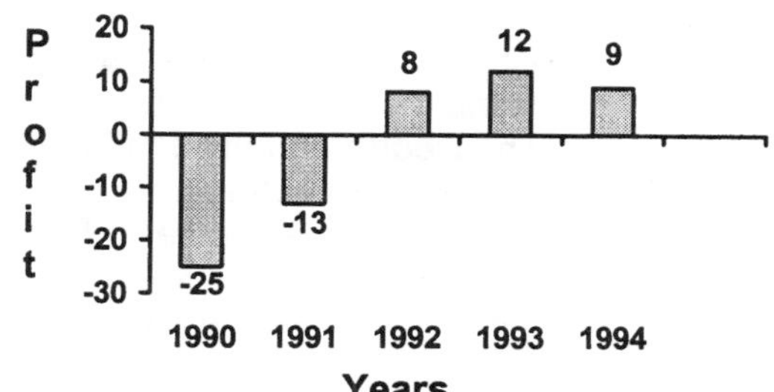

a. Determine the profit for the five years.

b. What is the difference between the profit in 1994 and 1990?

c. What is the difference between the profit in 1994 and 1993?

d. Why is the answer to question b positive but in question c negative?

e. Write a question that would generate 12 – (–13) as an answer.

f. What is the mean (average) profit for the five years?

15. Explain how you would find the mean (the average) of a set of five numbers.

16. The high temperatures for a six day period in Boise , Idaho were 10°F, 8°F, 15°F, 25°F, –10°F, and –2°F. Calculate the average daily temperature for the six-day period.

17. Find the mean of the following temperatures: –6°C, 11°C, –56°C, –22°C, 68°C, and –4°C.

18. The following are elevations at selected points around the world

Location	Elevation
Mt. Everest, Nepal	29,028 ft above sea level
Mariana Trench, Pacific Ocean	36,198 ft below sea level
The Dead Sea between Israel & Jordan	1,340 ft below sea level
Death Valley, CA	282 ft below sea level
Mt. Kilimanjara, Africa	5,895 ft above sea level

Find the mean of the elevations.

19. What is the rule for multiplying or dividing two numbers with the same sign?

20. What is the rule for multiplying or dividing two numbers with different signs?

21. Dividing by what number gives you an undefined answer?

22. Perform the operation.

a. $(-6)(7)$ b. $(-5)(-6)$ c. $3(-5)$

d. $-21(-3)$ e. $\frac{18}{-3}$ f. $\frac{-35}{7}$

g. $\frac{0}{11}$ h. $\frac{11}{0}$ i. $\frac{0}{0}$

Study Tip: It is an important mathematical fact that division by zero (zero in the denominator) is undefined. Put this on a note card.

j. $\frac{-25}{-5}$ k. $8(-5)$ l. $4(-3)(-5)$

m. $(-8)(-4)(-3)$ n. $9(-3)(-4)(0)(5)$

23. Use your calculator to perform the operation. Estimate if the answer will be positive or negative before you do the arithmetic.

a. $(-3.56)(-7.41)$

b. $-7.83(6.3)$

c. $\frac{-13.88}{4.7}$

d. $\frac{-6.21}{-3.51}$

24. List the order of operations.

Study Tip: Make a note card listing the order of operations.

25. Perform the operations.

a. $2(3-8)$

b. $-7(2)-\frac{-20}{5}$

c. $\frac{-12+14}{2}$

d. $\frac{36}{-12}-4(-8)$

e. $(-3)^2+8(-5)$

f. $-6-(-2)^2$

g. $\frac{8(-2)-5(4)}{(-3)^2}$

h. $\frac{(-5)^2+3^2}{2(-17)}$

i. $\frac{3(-5)-2(-8)}{2}$

Study Tip: The answers to the homework questions are given on page 362. Always check to see if you are doing the problems correctly. If you got a problem wrong, try to figure out what you did incorrectly. Be prepared to ask your teacher to help you do the problems you can't figure out either in class or during office hours.

INTRODUCTION TO VARIABLES
OVERVIEW

Objectives: By performing similar arithmetic steps, you will discover the need for variables.

Basic Example:

You need to rent a moving van. Class Movers charges a basic rate of $24.95 plus 32 cents per mile.

A. Calculate the cost of renting a van if you drive the following miles:

MILES	CALCULATION	COST
10	$.32 \bullet 10 + 24.95$	$28.15
20	$.32 \bullet 20 + 24.95$	$31.35
30	$.32 \bullet 30 + 24.95$	$34.55
m	$.32 \bullet m + 24.95$	C

Explanation: Since you drove 10 miles and it costs 32 cents a mile, then the cost is .32 times 10 plus 24.95, the basic rate.

Explanation: The only numbers that change in the calculation column are 10, 20, and 30. These numbers represent different miles, so we let the variable m represent the number of miles driven.

B. What is the equation that relates cost and number of miles driven?

The last row in the table above contains the answer. $C = .32 \bullet m + 24.95$

C. Another rental company, Zippo Movers, charges a flat rate of $42.95. How many miles would you have to drive for Zippo and Class to charge the same?

The cost equation for Zippo is: $C = 42.95$

To calculate when the two companies charge the same, set their cost equations equal to each other.

Cost of Zippo = Cost of Class

$$42.95 = .32m + 24.95$$

Since we don't know any algebra, we will guess at the solution. Substitute a guess for the number of miles into the equation for Class Movers,

$$C = .32m + 24.95 .$$

GUESS NUMBER OF MILES	CALCULATION OF COST	COST	TOO HIGH/ TOO LOW
50	$.32 \bullet 50 + 24.95$	$40.95	Too Low
60	$.32 \bullet 60 + 24.95$	$44.15	Too high
55	$.32 \bullet 55 + 24.95$	$42.55	Close

If you drive 55 miles, then the two companies will charge about the same. Guessing is very tedious and not precise. In two sections, we will use algebra to solve the problem. Algebra is easier and is more precise than guessing.

Summary:

Learning to generate a table is another key step in Beginning Algebra. Be sure your table contains the correct number of columns for the information you need. Use a ruler to draw the tables to ensure the information does not get confusing.

For every problem in this section, you should be able to:

1. Generate a table.

> **Explanation:** The calculation column is the most important column. It indicates how you get the equation.

2. Once you get the equation, you should understand what everything means. For example:

$$C = .32m + 24.95$$

a. C is the cost of renting a moving van.

b. .32 is how much Class Movers charges per mile.

c. m is the number of miles you drive the van.

d. 24.95 is the basic rate or fixed cost.

Study Tip: Do not use x or y as variables in applications. Use descriptive letters for variables. In the example, C was used for cost and m for number of miles driven.

CLASS WORK

1. The manager of a 33 Flavors Ice Cream Shop pays $800 per month for fixed expenses such as rent, lights, and wages. She sells ice cream cones for $1.85 each. It costs $1.40 to serve the ice cream cone.

   A. Without considering fixed expenses of $800 per month, how much profit do they make per cone?

   B. Calculate the monthly profits when they have sold the following number of ice cream cones per month. Make sure you include fixed costs in the equation for profit.

CONES	CALCULATION	PROFIT
10,000		
15,000		
20,000		
C		

   C. What is the equation that relates profit and the number of cones sold?

   D. Estimate the number of ice cream cones they must sell if they want to make $7,750 a month.

GUESS NUMBER OF CONES	CALCULATION OF PROFIT	PROFIT	TOO HIGH/ TOO LOW

   E. Suppose the expenses increase to $875 a month, and they charge $2.10 a cone ($1.40 still goes for ice cream, cone, and napkin). What will be the new equation for their monthly profits?

2. A rental car company, Wrecker, charges \$21.95 plus 41 cents a mile.

A. Calculate the cost of renting a car for one day if you drive the following miles:

MILES	CALCULATION	COST
10		
20		
30		
M		

B. What is the equation that relates cost and number of miles driven?

C. Another rental company, Limo, charges a flat rate of \$39.95 a day with unlimited miles. How many miles would you have to drive to make Limo cost the same as Wrecker?

GUESS NUMBER OF MILES	CALCULATION OF COST	COST	TOO HIGH/ TOO LOW

D. A third company, Ertz, charges \$18.95 a day and 50¢ a mile. What is the formula that calculates the cost of renting a car from Ertz for a day? When is Ertz the same price as Wrecker? (Just set up the equation; do not solve it.)

3. Farmer Nixon has 700 yards of fencing to enclose his rectangular pasture.

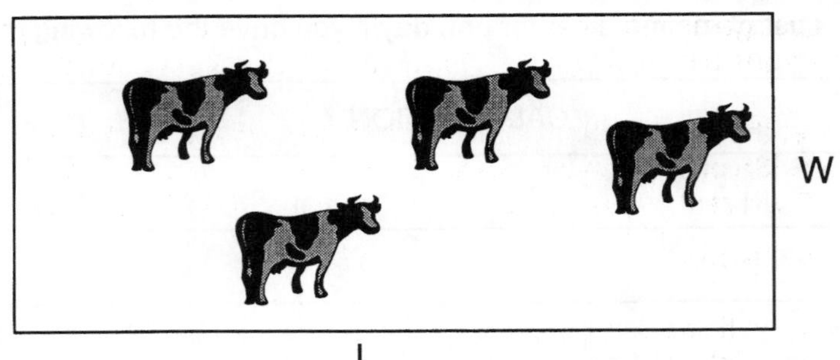

A. Complete the table below and find a formula for the area.

W yards	L yards	$A = L \bullet W$ square yards
50		
100		
175		
200		
W		

B. Use the table to find the maximum area he can enclose with 700 yards of fencing.

GROUP EXERCISE

Study Tip: Group suggestion. Use only one sheet of paper for the entire group. This encourages all to participate. Group success means individual success.

Today we will look at the cost of renting a car from three different rental companies. Elvis will rent us a car for $35 plus 25 cents a mile. Quartz rents the same model for $25 plus $0.50 a mile. AUTO will rent it to us for a flat daily rate of $55 with no mileage charge.

Study Tip: Review the problem on page 21.

1. For each company, find a formula for the cost of renting a car for a day. Complete the table below. (Pick values for the variable miles.)

Elvis			**Quartz**			**AUTO**
Miles	Calculation	Cost	Miles	Calculation	Cost	Cost
m			m			

2. What are the equations that relate cost and number of miles driven for each company?

3. From which company would you rent if you planned to drive the car 20 miles? 60 miles? 100 miles?

EXERCISES

Study Tip: You should have a separate loose leaf notebook for your math homework. This will help you organize your work and give you an opportunity to redo some of the more difficult problems. There isn't enough room in the book to adequately do the problems.

1. Complete the table for each rectangle.

WIDTH IN.	LENGTH IN.	AREA $A = L \cdot W$ SQ. IN.	PERIMETER $P = 2(L+W)$ IN.
5 in.	6 in.	$A = 6 \cdot 5 = 30\text{in}^2$	$P = 2(6+5) = 22$ in.
7 in.	8 in.		
9 in.	12 in.		
8 in.		80 in^2	
11 in.			60 in.

Study Tip: The first three problems should help you get comfortable replacing the variables with numbers in the formulas.

2. The area of a circle is indicated by the formula

$$A = \pi r^2$$

($\pi \approx 3.14$ or use the pi key on your calculator and the radius is half the diameter.)

a. One pizza has a diameter of 10 inches. Another has a diameter of 14 inches. How much larger is the 14 inch pizza than the 10 inch one? If the 10 inch pizza costs $5.95 and the 14 inch pizza costs $6.95, which size pizza is the better buy? Write a sentence explaining why.

b. One pizza has a diameter of 28 inches. Another pizza has a diameter of 32 inches. How much larger is the 32 inch pizza than the 28 inch pizza? If the 28 inch pizza costs $10.95 and the 32 inch pizza costs $11.95, which pizza is the better buy? Write a sentence explaining why.

c. If a 12 inch (diameter) pizza costs $7.99, what is a fair price for a 6 inch pizza?

3. The formula $C = \frac{5}{9}(F - 32)$ converts temperature in Fahrenheit to Celsius.

a. If it is 32° F, find the temperature in Celsius.

b. If it is -5° F, find the temperature in Celsius.

c. If it is 98.6° F, find the temperature in Celsius.

4. A server at the gourmet restaurant, Slow Eddie's, earns $80 per week in salary and averages $7.50 in tips per table.

Study Tip: This problem is similar to problem 1 from Class Work on page 20.

a. Calculate the server's wages when he has served the following number of tables per week.

TABLES	CALCULATION	WAGES
10	7.50(10) + 80	$155
15		
20		
t		

b. What is the equation that relates wages and number of tables serviced?

c. If he waited on 36 tables, how much money would he make?

d. Estimate how many tables he would have to serve if he wanted to make $215 for the week.

e. If he averaged $8.50 per table, how would the equation change?

f. If he averaged $7.00 per table and earned $95 in salary, how would the equation change?

5. Megan's making plans for a summer business. She wants to enter the lawn-mowing business. She can buy a power mower for $160, and she hopes to charge $8 an hour for her work.

a. Calculate Megan's income for the summer if she has worked the following number of hours.

Hours	Calculation	Income
40		$160
60		
80		
h		

b. What is the equation that relates income and hours worked?

c. Estimate the number of hours Megan would have to work if she wants to earn $280 for the summer.

d. What would the income equation be if she buys a lawn mower for $200 and charges $9 an hour?

6. a. A phone company, Ringer, charges $7.46 per month plus 13 cents a call. Calculate your phone bill if you make the following number of calls per month:

Study Tip: This problem is similar to problem 2 from Class Work on page 21.

CALLS	CALCULATION	PHONE BILL
10		$8.76
15		
20		
c		

b. What is the equation that relates the phone bill and the number of calls?

c. A second phone company, Busy, charges $6.17 per month plus 17 cents per call. What is the equation for your phone bill if your phone company is Busy?

d. Fill in a table to estimate when Ringer charges less than Busy?

CALLS	RINGER	BUSY

e. For what number of calls is the cost the same for both companies?

7. A 10 cm stick is broken into two pieces. One is placed at a right angle to form an upside down "T" shape. By attaching wires from the ends of the base to the end of the upright piece, a framework for a sail will be formed.

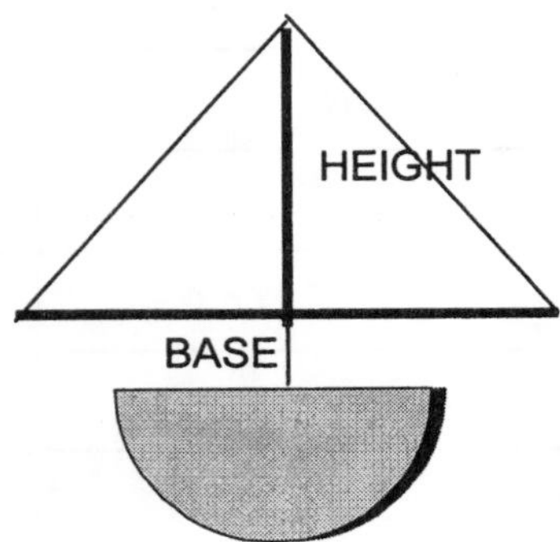

Additional discussion about the problem: The 10 cm stick that is broken into two pieces is described by the diagram below. The slash mark represents where the stick is broken.

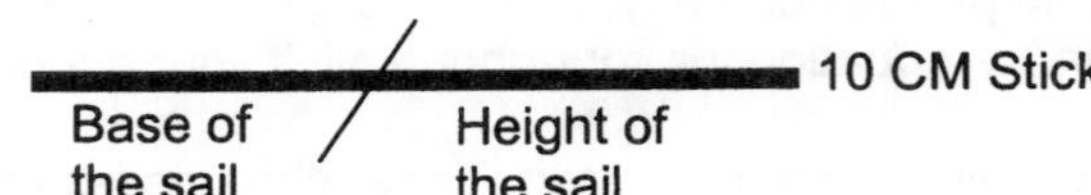

So the base of the sail plus the height of the sail equals 10. If the base is 4 cm then the height of the sail must be 10 – 4 or 6 cm.

a. Calculate the area of the sail for the given length of the base.

Base cm b	Height cm h	Area cm^2 $A = \frac{1}{2} b \bullet h$
4	10 - 4 = 6	$\left(\frac{1}{2}\right) \cdot (4)(6) = 12\,cm^2$
5		
8		
b		

b. What is the equation that relates area and the base of the sail?

c. Why can't the base be 15 cm long?

d. Use the table to determine what base gives the maximum area.

e. Could the base that gives the maximum area be a fractional number?

8. A farmer has 1800 feet of fencing. She wants to fence her pasture. The pasture borders on a river. How should she do it if she wants to maximize the area of her pasture? Find a formula for the area of her pasture. The problem assumes that the animals can't swim.

Study Tip: This problem is similar to problem 3 from Class Work on page 22.

Hint: You have to find a formula for L involving W. You do not have to enlarge the table to find the maximum area.

River

W W

L

Width ft.	**Length** ft.	**Area** $(A = L \bullet W)$
300	1200	$1200 \cdot 300 = 360{,}000 \text{ ft}^2$
400		$= 400{,}000 \text{ ft}^2$
500		
450		
W		

Study Tip: The answers to the homework questions are given on page 362. Always check to see if you are doing the problems correctly. If you got a problem wrong, try to figure out what you did incorrectly. Be prepared to ask your teacher to help you do the problems you can't figure out.

SIMPLIFLYING ALGEBRAIC EXPRESSIONS OVERVIEW

Objectives: This section begins the process of solving equations. You will understand how to **combine like terms** and use the **distributive property**.

Combining Like Terms:

Explanation: 3x means that you adding an unspecified number th times.

Example 1. $3x + 7x =$
$(x + x + x) + (x + x + x + x + x + x + x) = 10x$

Vocabulary:

Terms: terms are parts of an algebraic expression separated by addition or subtraction signs.

Example 2. For $3 + 5 = 8$, 3 and 5 are terms while for $4 \bullet 2 = 8$, 4 and 2 are called **factors**.

Coefficient: the number multiplying the variable.

Example 3. For the expression $7x - 2y + z$, 7 is the coefficient of x; -2 is the coefficient of y, and 1 is understood to be the coefficient of z.

Like Terms: terms which have the same variable and exponent.

Example 4. For the expression $4x + 7y - 3x + 4z$, $4x$ and $-3x$ are like terms.

Rule: To combine like terms, add their coefficients. $4x + (-3x) = x$ or $1x$.

Study Tip: Write these important definitions on note cards and use them to do your homework.

Example 5. Combine like terms.

$3x - 5 - 6x + 7 =$	Identify the like terms, $3x$ and $-6x$, -5 and 7.
$-3x + 2$	Add the coefficients of the like terms.

Distributive Property: Definition $a(b + c) = a \bullet b + a \bullet c$

Example 6. Consider the two arithmetic problems

a. $2(5+7) =$
$2 \bullet 12 =$
24

b. $2 \bullet 5 + 2 \bullet 7 =$
$10 + 14 =$
24

Explanation: In both problems, you ge the same answer. In part a, you add fir and multiply second; while in part b, yo multiply first and add second. The distributive property allows you to chan the order of operations and still get the same answer.

Study Tip: You may want to review the order of operations on page 4.

Explanation: Always work inside parentheses first. Only use the distributive property when you cannot simplify what is inside the parentheses.

Example 7. Use the distributive property.

$3(6x - 5) =$	Can't combine terms inside the parentheses.
$3 \bullet 6x - 3 \bullet 5 =$	Using the distributive property, multiply 6x and –5 by 3.
$18x - 15$	Multiply.

> **Explanation:** 3(6x – 5) means that we are making each term inside the parentheses 3 times bigger.

Simplifying Algebraic Expressions:

Example 8. Use the distributive property.

$-3(4x - 2) =$	Can't combine terms inside the parentheses.
$(-3) \bullet 4x - (-3) \bullet 2 =$	Using the distributive property, multiply 4x and –2 by -3.
$-12x + 6$	Multiply.

Example 9. Simplify the expression.

$8x - 14 - 3(4x - 2) =$	
$8x - 14 - 12x + 6 =$	Using the distributive property, multiply 4x and –2 by –3.
$-4x - 8$	Combine like terms, 8x and –12x, and –14 and 6.

Summary: Simplifying Algebraic Expressions

We are now ready to do the real work of algebra. Key definitions include:

1. The distributive property.

   $a(b + c) = a \bullet b + a \bullet c$
   The factor "a" multiplies both "b" and "c" inside the parentheses.

2. Like terms have the same variable and exponent.

3. Coefficient is the number multiplying the variable.

4. Items being multiplied are called factors.

Example 10. Simplify the expression.

$4 - (2x - 3) =$	In the same way that –x means -1*x, -(2x – 3) means -1(2x – 3)
$4 - 2x + 3 =$	Using the distributive property; multiply 2x and –3 by –1.
$-2x + 7$	Combine Like terms.

CLASS WORK

What are like terms?

How do we add or subtract like terms?

Combine like terms:

1. $3x + 7 + 2x + 5$
2. $6x - 8 - 11x + 2$
3. $-\frac{1}{2}x - \frac{3}{4}x + \frac{7}{5}$

Use the distributive property:

1. $2(3x + 5)$
2. $-(x - 8)$
3. $-6(2x + 4)$

Simplify:

1. $4x + 2(3x + 8)$
2. $6x - (5x + 7)$
3. $9 - 3(4x + 6)$

GROUP EXERCISE

Study Tips: 1. Review pages 30 and 32.
2. Remember good group principles.

Simplify

1. $\frac{1}{5}x - \frac{2}{3} + \frac{2}{15}x - 4$

2. $3(2x - 5) - 7x$

3. $4(6 - x) - 3(4x + 5)$

4. Describe what is wrong with the following problems.

a. $6x - 7 + 4x + 8 =$
$10x + 1 =$
$11x$

b. $4(3x + 5) - 9x =$
$12x + 5 - 9x =$
$3x + 5$

c. $5(3x - 8) - 4x =$
$15x - 40 - 4x =$
$19x - 40$

d. $4x + 2x = 8x$

e. $6 - 2(4x + 5) =$
$4(4x + 5) =$
$16x + 20$

EXERCISES

Study Tip: Do these exercises and then go to the the Learning Assistance Lab (L. A. L.), in College Hall at the Central campus or room 159 at West for help. The L. A. L. is a service provided by the college that includes individual tutoring, group tutoring sessions, and study skills tips free of charge to all Montgomery County Community College students. See page iii for L. A. L. hours at Central and West campuses.

1. What are like terms?
2. How are like terms combined?
3. State the distributive property.
4. Simplify.

   a. $9x - 4x$
   b. $6x + 11x - 13$
   c. $\frac{1}{2}x - \frac{3}{5} + \frac{2}{3}x$
   d. $3(2x + 5)$
   e. $6 - 4(3x - 8)$
   f. $4(2x - 5) + 3(7 - 2x)$
   g. $4x + 5(3x + 1)$
   h. $9x - 18x + 2(4x - 8)$
   i. $4 - 2(3x + 4) - (x - 8)$

5. Describe what is wrong with the following problems.

   a. $6x + 5x = 30$

   b. $5x - 3 + 4x - 8 =$
   $9x - 11 =$
   $-2x$

   c. $6(4x - 5) - 7x =$
   $24x - 5 - 7x =$
   $17x - 5$

   d. $2(5x - 8) - 3(2x - 4) =$
   $10x - 16 - 6x - 12 =$
   $4x - 28$

   e. $4x - (x - 7) =$
   $4x - x - 7 =$
   $3x - 7$

   f. $3(4x - 8) - (3x - 5) =$
   $12x - 24 - 3x + 5 =$
   $15x - 19$

Study Tip: The answers to the homework questions are given on page 363. Always check to see if you are doing the problems correctly. If you got a problem wrong, try to figure out what you did incorrectly. Be prepared to ask your teacher to help you do the problems you can't figure out. Remember to use your loose leaf homework notebook.

SOLVING EQUATIONS PART I
OVERVIEW

Objectives: In Introduction to Variables, we solved equations by guessing. In this section, you will learn how to solve equations using algebra. Algebra is easier and more precise than guessing.

Basic Examples: The example below is from Introduction to Variables, page 18.

Example 1. You need to rent a moving van. Class Movers charges a basic rate of $24.95 plus 32 cents per mile.

a. . Calculate the cost of renting a van if you drive the following miles.

MILES	CALCULATION	COST
10	$.32 \bullet 10 + 24.95$	28.15
20	$.32 \bullet 20 + 24.95$	31.35
30	$.32 \bullet 30 + 24.95$	34.55
m	$.32 \bullet m + 24.95$	C

Explanation: Since you drove 10 miles and it costs 32 cents a mile, then the cost is .32 times 10 plus 24.95, the basic rate.

Explanation: The only numbers that change in the calculation column are 10, 20, and 30. These numbers represent different miles, so we let m represent the number of miles driven.

The cost equation is. $C = .32m + 24.95$

b. Use the equation to calulate how many miles you can drive at a cost of $42.87.

The problem can be solved logically. The cost $42.87 contains the basic rate $24.95. Subtracting $24.95 from $42.87 yields $17.92. This is how much of the cost is attributed to the number of miles driven. Since it costs 32 cents per mile, dividing 17.92 by .32 determines the number of miles driven or 56 miles. This same logic is algebra. Below is how the problem is done algebraically.

Find m when C = 42.87.

$42.87 = .32m + 24.95$	Substitute 42.87 for C.
$42.87 - 24.95 = .32m$	Subtract 24.95 from 42.87 because the cost, 42.87, contains the basic rate, 24.95.
$17.92 = .32m$	Combine like terms, 42.87 and 24.95.
$\frac{17.92}{.32} = m$	The miles driven cost 17.92. Since it costs 32 cents per mile, divide 17.92 by .32.
$56 = m$	Answer.

You can drive 56 miles for $42.87.

Study Tip: You should answer the problem with a sentence, like the one above, that refers to both variables in the problem.

c. Check your answer.

Substitute m = 56 into the equation $C = .32m + 24.95$,the cost should be $42.87.

$$C = .32 \bullet 56 + 24.95$$
$$C = 17.92 + 24.95$$
$$C = 42.87$$

How to solve an equation:

1. The first goal is to write the equation in the form:

   Variable term = constant

   This is done by performing the opposite operation to both sides of the equation. For example, if 27 is being added on one side of the equation, then 27 should be subtracted from both sides of the equation.

Explanation: a variable term contains a letter that can represent different values. A constant is a number that never changes value.

2. Divide both sides by the coefficient (the number multiplying the variable) of the variable or if the coefficient is a fraction, multiply by the reciprocal of the fraction.

   Definition: Two numbers are reciprocals if their product is one. The reciprocal of $\frac{2}{5}$ is $\frac{5}{2}$.

Study Tip: You should write the steps on a note card along with an example.

Example 2. Solve.

$$42.87 = 0.32 \bullet m + 24.95$$

$$42.87 - 24.95 = 0.32 \bullet m + 24.95 - 24.95$$

Subtract 24.95 from both sides since –24.95 is the opposite of 24.95.

$$17.92 = 0.32m$$

Combine like terms, 42.87 – 24.95, 24.95 – 24.95. This is our first goal in solving the problem.

$$\frac{17.92}{0.32} = \frac{0.32m}{0.32}$$

Divide both sides by the coefficient of m, .32.

$$56 = m$$

Answer

Example 3. Solve.

$$\frac{4}{5}x + 21 = -15$$

$$\frac{4}{5}x + 21 - 21 = -15 - 21$$

Subtract 21 from both sides since –21 is the opposite of +21.

$$\frac{4}{5}x = -36$$

Combine like terms, 21 – 21 and –15 – 21. This is our first goal in solving the problem.

$$\left(\frac{5}{4}\right)\frac{4}{5}x = -36\left(\frac{5}{4}\right)$$

Since the coefficient of x is a fraction $\frac{4}{5}$, multiply both sides by its reciprocal, $\frac{5}{4}$

$$x = -45$$

Answer

Summary: The basic procedure to solve an equation:

1. Add the opposite to get a variable on one side of the equation and a constant on the other or perform the opposite operation to both sides of the equation.

2. Divide by the coefficient of the variable or multiple by the reciprocal.

CLASS WORK

1. A rental car company, Wrecker, uses the formula $C = .41m + 21.95$ to calculate the cost, C, of renting a car driven m miles. If your vacation budget allows you to spend $100 for car rental, how far can you drive?

2. Consider the equation $5x - 2 = 13$

   Is $x = 2$ a solution?

   Is $x = 3$ a solution?

   Is $x = 22$ a solution?

3. Solve each equation.

   a. $x + 8 = -3$

   b. $x - 2 = 5$

   c. $4x = -12$

   d. $\frac{-2}{5}x = 4$

4. Solve the equation and describe each step.

a. $4x - 7 = -27$

b. $\frac{1}{3}x + 4 = 6$

5. Solve each equation.

a. $-\frac{4}{5}x = 12$

b. $5x - 11 = 4$

GROUP EXERCISES

1. Describe each step.

	Step
$\frac{2}{5}x - 8 = 12$	
$\frac{2}{5}x - 8 + 8 = 12 + 8$	____________________
$\frac{2}{5}x = 20$	____________________
$\frac{5}{2} * \frac{2}{5}x = \frac{5}{2} * 20$	____________________
$x = 50$	____________________

2. Find where the first mistake occurs.

$6x - 11 = 35$

$6x - 11 + 11 = 35 - 11$

$6x = 24$

$x = 4$

3. Solve.

a. $x - 5 = -2$

b. $3x + 8 = -13$

c. $\frac{3}{5}x = -18$

d. $5x - 3 = 8$

EXERCISES

Study Tip: Remember your homework tips.

1. Describe each step.

a.

	Step
$6x + 7 = 31$	
$6x + 7 - 7 = 31 - 7$	________________
$6x = 24$	________________
$\frac{6x}{6} = \frac{24}{6}$	________________
$x = 4$	________________

b.

	Step
$\frac{1}{5}x - 4 = 3$	
$\frac{1}{5}x - 4 + 4 = 3 + 4$	________________
$\frac{1}{5}x = 7$	________________
$5\left(\frac{1}{5x}\right) = 5 \bullet 7$	________________
$x = 35$	________________

2. Find where the first mistake occurs.

a.

$$3x + 5 = 4$$
$$3x + 5 - 5 = 4 + 5$$
$$3x = 9$$
$$\frac{3x}{3} = \frac{9}{3}$$
$$x = 3$$

b.

$$\frac{2}{3}x - 4 = 5$$
$$\frac{2}{3}x - 4 + 4 = 5 + 4$$
$$\frac{2}{3}x = 9$$
$$\frac{2}{3} \bullet \frac{2}{3}x = \frac{2}{3} \bullet 9$$
$$x = 6$$

3. a. Is $x = 2$ a solution to $4x - 8 = 0$?

b. Is $x = -3$ a solution to $2x + 5 = -1$?

c. Is $x = 8$ a solution to $4x - 12 = -16$?

4. Describe the procedure to solve an equation.

5. Solve.

a. $6x = 18$

b. $-2x = 5$

c. $\frac{x}{4} = -10$

d. $\frac{2}{3}x = 21$

e. $x + 8 = 10$

f. $x - 15 = 21$

g. $6x - 5 = 31$

h. $\frac{1}{7}x + 4 = -3$

i. $-3x - 4 = 11$

6. A company uses the equation V = C - 500t to determine the depreciated value V, after t years, of a printing press that originally cost C dollars. If a printing press originally cost $22,000, in how many years will the depreciated value be $10,000?

Study Tip: In addition to your instructor and the Learning Assistance Lab, the CD that accompanies the textbook is another excellent source of information available outside of class.

SOLVING EQUATIONS PART II
OVERVIEW

Objectives: This section will expand on the skills presented in the previous section. You will learn to solve harder algebraic equations and encounter ones without a solution as well as ones that have every number as a solution.

Basic Examples:

Example 1. Solve

$7x - 4 = 5(2x + 9) + 3x$	
$7x - 4 = 10x + 45 + 3x$	Use the **distributive property**; multiply 2x and 9 by 5.
$7x - 4 = 13x + 45$	**Combine like terms**; add 10x and 3x.
$7x - 4 + 4 = 13x + 45 + 4$	Want a variable term equal to a constant term. Since we have a constant term on both sides of the equation, **add the opposite** of –4 to both sides, +4.
$7x = 13x + 49$	**Combine like terms**, 45 and 4.
$7x - 13x = 13x - 13x + 49$	Want a variable term equal to a constant term. Since we have a variable term on both sides of the equation, **add the opposite** of 13x to both sides, -13x.
$-6x = 49$	**Combine like terms**, 7x and –13x.
$\frac{-6x}{-6} = \frac{49}{-6}$	Now there is a variable term equal to a constant term, so divide both sides by the **coefficient** of x, –6.
$x = -8.167$	Answer, rounded to four significant digits. Four digits of accuracy is fine for the entire course.

Example 2. Solve

$4 - 2(6x - 7) = -12x + 10$	
$4 - 12x + 14 = -12x + 10$	Use the distributive property; multiply 6x and –7 by –2.
$-12x + 18 = -12x + 10$	Combine like terms.
$-12x + 12x + 18 = -12x + 12x + 10$	Want a variable term equal to a constant term. Since we have a variable term on both sides of the equation, add the opposite of –12x to both sides, 12x.
$18 = 10$	Combine like terms.
No solution.	18 can never equal 10.

Example 3. Solve

$21x - 10 + 10x = 5(6x - 2) + x$	
$21x - 10 + 10x = 30x - 10 + x$	Use the distributive property; multiply 6x and –2 by 5.
$31x - 10 = 31x - 10$	Combine like terms.
$31x - 31x - 10 = 31x - 31x - 10$	Want a variable term equal to a constant term. Since we have a variable term on both sides of the equation, add the opposite of 31x to both sides, –31x.
$-10 = -10$	Combine like terms.
Every number is a solution.	–10 is always equal to –10.

Definitions: a. A **conditional equation** has a finite number of solutions. In this section, a conditional equation will have one solution. Example 1 is a conditional equation.

b. When an equation doesn't have a solution, it is called a **contradiction**. Example 2 is a contradiction.

c. When an equation has every number as a solution, then it is called an **identity**. Example 3 is an identity.

Example 4. This example will demonstrate a more mathematically formal approach.

Solve.
$$\begin{aligned} 6x-5&=2x+11. \\ 6x-5+5&=2x+11+5 \\ 6x&=2x+16 \\ 6x-2x&=2x-2x+16 \\ 4x&=16 \\ \frac{4x}{4}&=\frac{16}{4} \\ x&=4 \end{aligned}$$

Explanation: Solving equations rests on the **principle of equality.** The principle of equality states: in order to preserve the equality, what ever you do to one side of the equation you must do to the other. In this example, 5 was added to both sides; 2x was subtracted from both sides, and both sides were divided by 4.

Summary: It is important to know the difference between algebra and arithmetic. Arithmetic involves operations with numbers. Algebra has variables that represent many different numbers. If you think back to the section, Introduction to Variables, in the last row of the tables we created, we used variables to represent all of the arithmetic in the previous rows. Algebra is the generalization of repeated arithmetic operations. The equations from Introduction to Variables contained two variables. If you know a value for one of the variables, then you can use the procedures in this section to find the value of the other. Solving equations is a basic function of algebra.

How to solve equations:

1. Simplify both sides of the equation by using the distributive property, $a(b + c) = ab + ac$, and combining like terms; then add their coefficients.

2. The first goal is to write the equation in the form:

   Variable term = constant

   This is done by adding the opposite to both sides of the equation.

3. Divide both sides by the coefficient, the number multiplying the variable.

   If the coefficient is a fraction, multiply by the reciprocal. The reciprocal of $\frac{2}{5}$ is $\frac{5}{2}$.

4. Three possible outcomes to solving an equation:
   a. One solution.
   b. No solution.
   c. Every number is a solution, or the problem has an infinite number of solutions.

Study Tip: You should write the steps on a note card along with an example.

CLASS WORK

1. Consider the equation $5x + 6 = 3x - 2$

   Is $x = 4$ a solution?

   Is $x = -4$ a solution?

2. Solve the equation and describe each step.

   a. $8x - 2 = 11x + 7$

   b. $2(4x + 5) - 3x = 24 - 2x$

3. Solve each equation.

a. $3x + 5 = 4 - 5x$

b. $3x - 8 = 4(5 - 3x) + 9$

c. $3(2x + 8) = 6x - 7$

d. $3(2x + 8) = 8x + 24 - 2x$

4. A company determines that the cost, C, of making x items is $C = 2.2x + 78$ and the revenue, R, is $R = 2.25x$. Find the break even point.

GROUP EXERCISES

Study Tips: 1. Group suggestion: Use only one sheet of paper for the entire group. This encourages all to participate.

2. For help, see page 45 or your notes from the Class Work section.

1. Describe each step.

	Step
$5(4x - 8) - 13x = 2x + 10$	
$20x - 40 - 13x = 2x + 10$	__________
$7x - 40 = 2x + 10$	__________
$7x - 2x - 40 = 2x - 2x + 10$	__________
$5x - 40 = 10$	__________
$5x - 40 + 40 = 10 + 40$	__________
$5x = 50$	__________
$\frac{5x}{5} = \frac{50}{5}$	__________
$x = 10$	__________

2. Find where the first mistake occurs.

$$3(4x - 5) + 4 = 3x + 47$$
$$12x - 15 + 4 = 3x + 47$$
$$12x - 11 = 3x + 47$$
$$12x - 11 + 11 = 3x + 47 - 11$$
$$12x = 3x + 36$$
$$12x - 3x = 3x - 3x + 36$$
$$9x = 36$$
$$\frac{9x}{9} = \frac{36}{9}$$
$$x = 4$$

3. Solve each equation.

a. $6x - 5 = 8 - 4(2x + 7)$

b. $5(3 + 2x) = 10x - 11$

EXERCISES

Study Tip: Use your loose leaf homework notebook; review your notecards; work with a friend.

1. Describe each step.

a.

	Step
$4(2x + 5) - 11x = 3x - 4$	
$8x + 20 - 11x = 3x - 4$	______________
$-3x + 20 = 3x - 4$	______________
$-3x - 3x + 20 = 3x - 3x - 4$	______________
$-6x + 20 = -4$	______________
$-6x + 20 - 20 = -4 - 20$	______________
$-6x = -24$	______________
$\frac{-6x}{-6} = \frac{-24}{-6}$	______________
$x = 4$	______________

b.

	Step
$7x + 2 = 2(5x - 3) - 3x$	
$7x + 2 = 10x - 6 - 3x$	______________
$7x + 2 = 7x - 6$	______________
$7x - 7x + 2 = 7x - 7x - 6$	______________
$2 = -6$	______________
no solution	______________

2. Find where the first mistake occurs.

a.

$$2(3x - 8) - 4x = 6 - 7x$$
$$6x - 8 - 4x = 6 - 7x$$
$$4x - 8 = 6 - 7x$$
$$4x + 7x - 8 = 6 - 7x - 7x$$
$$11x - 8 = 6$$
$$11x - 8 + 8 = 6 + 8$$
$$11x = 14$$
$$\frac{11x}{11} = \frac{14}{11}$$
$$x = \frac{14}{11}$$

b.

$$4 - (x + 6) = 4x + 7$$
$$4 - x - 6 = 4x + 7$$
$$-x - 2 = 4x + 7$$
$$-x - 4x - 2 = 4x - 4x + 7$$
$$-5x - 2 = 7$$
$$-5x - 2 + 2 = 7 - 2$$
$$-5x = 5$$
$$\frac{-5x}{-5} = \frac{5}{-5}$$
$$X = -1$$

Study Tip: Review page 45 or your Class Work notes.

3. Describe the procedure to solve an equation.

4. When does an equation not have a solution?

5. When does an equation have every number as a solution?

6. Solve each equation.

a. $6x - 8 = 3x + 7$

b. $-2x + 5 = 7x - 31$

c. $3(2x - 5) = 6 + 6x$

d. $6 - (x+4) = 2x - 5$

e. $4 + 3x = 2(5x + 2) - 7x$

f. $4 - 3(2x + 6) = -(x - 5)$

7. A phone company, Ringer, charges $7.46 per month plus 13 cents a call. A second company, Busy, charges $6.17 per month plus 17 cents per call. How many calls does it take for the two companies to charge the same for a month?

Study Tip: Review the problem on page 27.

APPLICATIONS OF LINEAR EQUATIONS PART I
OVERVIEW

Objective: This section is a review of the course to date. You will create tables to find equations and then solve them using algebra.

Study Tip: If you have trouble with this section, review Introduction to Variables and Solving Equations Part I and II.

Basic Example:

Class Truck rental company charges a basic rate of 34.99 plus 20 cents a mile after the first 15 miles.

a. Write an equation for the cost of renting from Class.

Miles	Calculation	Cost
25	$.20(25-15)+34.99$	\$36.99
40	$.20(40-15)+34.99$	\$39.99
55	$.20(55-15)+34.99$	\$42.99
m	$.20(m-15)+34.99$	C

Explanation: They charge 20 cents after 15 miles, so if you drive for 25 miles you are only charged 20 cents for 10 miles, 25 – 15. Since you subtracted 25 – 15 before you multiplied by .20, you need parentheses.

b. Simplify the equation.

$C=.20(m-15)+34.99$

$C=.20m-3+34.99$ Use the distributive property; multiply m and –15 by .20, $.20m$ and $.20\bullet-15=-3$.

$C=.20m+31.99$ Combine like terms, -3 and 34.99.

c. How many miles can you go if the cost is \$85?

Find m when C = 85.

$85=.20m+31.99$ Substitute 85 for C.

$53.01=.20m$ Subtract 31.99 from both sides.

$265.05=m$ Divide both sides by .20.

You can drive 265 miles for \$85.

Study Tip: In the last problem, we wrote down fewer steps. You should take a couple of minutes to work out the problem in detail. It is important that you know how each step was done. Use your homework notebook. Allow plenty of space so you don't get confused.

Summary: This section reviews most of the material presented thus far in the course and therefore, is <u>extremely</u> important. You should be able to:

1. Read the problem and create a table in order to find the equation.
2. Incorporate parentheses into the equation.

Variable	Calculation	Variable
	The calculation column contains the process of how the answer was computed.	
	Accurately write down how you got an answer. Think about the order of operations. Do you need parentheses or not?	
	This line should contain the equation.	

3. Use algebra to solve equations. It is easier and more accurate than guessing.

Study Tips: 1. If any of the above steps is not clear to you, ask questions in the next class session, see your instructor during office hours, or go to the Learning Assistance Lab.

2. Do not proceed until you have mastered this section.

3. Another source of information available to you outside of class is IPTV. IPTV has videos of a teacher's class lectures. The Learning Assistance Lab can help you get access to IPTV.

CLASS WORK

A. Two women want to enter the lawn-mowing business for the summer. They plan to buy a lawn mower for $180, and they hope to charge $8 an hour.

1. If they work for 20 hours, how much money will they make?

HOURS	CALCULATION	PROFIT
20		
h		

2. What is the equation that relates profit and hours worked?

3. How many hours will they have to work in order to break even?

4. How many hours will they have to work in order to make $780 for the summer?

B. You are offered two very similar jobs selling math textbooks. One pays 8% commission plus $10,000 a year, and the other pays 12% commission.

1. If you sell $200,000 for the year, which job would pay you more?

COMPANY A		
Sales	Calculation	Wages
200,000		
S		

COMPANY B		
Sales	Calculation	Wages
200,000		
S		

What are the equations that relate wages and sales for Companies A and B?

2. How much would you have to sell for the two companies to pay you the same amount of money for the year?

C. The women's recommended weight formula from the Managed Health Care Plan says:

"Give yourself 100 lbs. plus 5 lbs. for every inch over 5 ft. or 60 inches tall."

1. Complete the table:

HEIGHT	CALCULATION	WEIGHT
61 inch		
64 inch		
72 inch		
h inches		

What is the equation that relates weight and height? Simplify the equation.

2. How tall should you be if you weigh 135 lbs.?

3. How tall should you be if you weigh 85 lbs.?

4. How tall should you be if you weigh zero lbs.?

GROUP EXERCISES

Study Tip: Review the example on page 53 or the problem on page 57.

A. A company pays $10,000 a year plus 10% commission on sales over $50,000.

1. Complete the table below.

SALES	CALCULATION	WAGES
80,000		
100,000		
S		

What is the equation that relates wages and sales? Simplify the equation.

2. If you want to earn $30,000 a year, how much do you have to sell?

3. Solve for the variable S from the formula in Part 1.

B. Rental Car Company, Silver Star, charges 21 cents a mile plus $31 a day.

1. Complete the table below.

MILES	CALCULATION	COST
20		
m		

What is the equation that relates cost and miles?

2. If you spent $44.02 renting a car for the day, how many miles did you drive?

3. A second company, Limo, charges 11 cents a mile and $42 a day. How many miles do you have to drive for both companies to charge you the same amount of money?

Study Tip: You should be able to interpret the cost equation for Silver Star to get the cost equation for Limo.

EXERCISES

Study Tip: Do homework in short intervals, 20 to 30 minutes. Then do something else and return to your math homework a little later.

1. You plan to rent a car for the day; you are told it costs $25.00 for the day and 16 cents a mile.

Study Tip: Review the problem on page 55 or 60.

a. Complete the table below.

MILES	CALCULATION	COST
20		
m		

b. What is the equation that relates cost and miles?

c. If you drive 31 miles, how much will it cost?

d. If you want to spend $31 on renting a car, how far can you drive?

e. If you want to spend $65 on renting a car, how far can you drive?

2. A phone company charges 80 cents a call and 15 cents a minute.

a. Complete the table below.

MINUTES	CALCULATION	COST
10		
m		

b. What is the equation that reflects cost and minutes?

c. If you are on the phone for 32 minutes, how much did it cost?

d. If it costs $1.85, how long were you on the phone?

e. If it costs $2.50, how long were you on the phone?

3. Phone Company Ringer, charges 8¢ per minute and 50¢ per call while Company Busy charges 10¢ per minute and 25¢ per call.

a. Complete the table below.

RINGER			BUSY		
MIN.	CALCULATION	COST	MIN.	CALCULATION	COST
10			10		
m			m		

b. What are the equations that relate cost and minutes on the phone for the two companies?

c. How long would you have to talk if the cost of the phone call were the same for both Ringer and Busy?

4. You are offered two very similar jobs selling encyclopedias. One job pays 7.5% commission and $5,000 a year while the second company pays 5% commission and $9,000 a year.

Study Tip: Review the problem on page 56.

a. If you sold $100,000 for the year, which job would pay more?

Company A			Company B		
Sales	Calculation	Wages	Sales	Calculation	Wages
100,000			100,000		
s			s		

b. What are the equations that relate wages and sales for the two companies?

c. How much would you have to sell for the two companies to pay you the same amount of money for the year?

5. A job pays 15% commission on sales over $1,000 a week.

Study Tip: This problem is like the example in the Overview Section on page 53 or question A on page 59.

a. Complete the table below.

SALES	CALCULATION	WAGES
1,500		$75
2,000		
s		

b. What is the equation that relates wages and sales? Simplify the equation.

c. If you sell $10,000 in a week, how much money will you earn?

d. If you earned $270 in a week, how much did you sell?

e. If you earned $3,372 in a week, how much did you sell?

6. The men's recommended weight formula from the MONTCO HMO says: "Give yourself 160 lbs. plus 7 lbs. for every inch over 6 ft."

Study Tip: Review the problem on page 57.

a. Complete the table.

HEIGHT	CALCULATION	WEIGHT
74 in.		174
78 in.		
h		

b. What is the equation that relates weight and height? Simplify the equation.

c. How tall should a man be if he weighs 216 lbs.?

d. How tall should a man be if he weighs 220 lbs.?

7. Phone Company Hook charges 22 cents a call and 10 cents a minute after the first 5 minutes.

a. Complete the table below.

MINUTES	CALCULATION	COST
2		
5		
7		
12		
m		

b. What is the equation that relates cost and minutes? Simplify the equation.

c. If it costs $2.02 for a phone call, how long were you on the phone?

d. If it costs $3.81 for a phone call, how long were you on the phone?

8. Nader Rental car company charges 27 cents per mile plus $25.95 while Trump Rental car agency charges 33 cents per mile plus $31.95. How many miles do you have to drive for both companies to cost the same.

Study Tip: Construct a table which contains all the information you need.

APPLICATIONS OF LINEAR EQUATIONS PART II
LITERAL EQUATIONS
OVERVIEW

Objectives: In this section, you will learn how to solve equations that have two variables. The algebra is the same as in the previous sections. The difference is that the solution will be an equation, not a number.

Basic Example:
A phone company charges a basic rate of $1.25 plus 15 cents per minute after the first 10 minutes.

a. Complete the table to find the cost of making a phone calls that last longer than ten minutes.

Minutes	Calculation	Cost
20	$.15(20-10)+1.25$	$2.75
30	$.15(30-10)+1.25$	$4.25
m	$.15(m-10)+1.25$	C

Explanation: Parentheses are needed because they don't charge 15 cents per minute until after 10 minutes.

b. What is the equation that relates cost and minutes? Simplify the equation.

$C=.15(m-10)+1.25$

$C=.15m-1.50+1.25$ Distributive property: multiply m and –10 by .25

$C=.15m-.25$ Combine like terms, –1.50 + 1.25

c. If it costs $2.90, how long were you on the phone?

Find m when C = 2.90

$2.90=.15m-.25$ Substitute 2.90 for C.

$3.15=.15m$ Add .25 to both sides.

$21=m$ Divide both sides by .15

d. Solve for m in the equation from Part b.

(This is the only new information in this section.)

Why would you want to do this? Imagine a situation where you know the cost of ten different calls. Instead of solving for C ten separate times, you can solve for C once and then use arithmetic to find the ten different values of m.

$C=.15m-.25$

$C+.25=.15m$ Add .25 to both sides.

$\dfrac{C+.25}{.15}=m$ Divide both sides by .15

Explanation: The algebraic steps are the same as in Part c. The difference is that the solution is not a number.

Summary: To solve a literal equation, a problem involving more than one variable, the algebraic steps are the same as the problems in the previous two sections. The only difference is the solution is not a number but an algebraic formula.

Example 2. Solve for y.

Traditional Equation Solve for y.		Literal Equation Solve for y.
$6 + 3y = 24$		$6x + 3y = 24$
$3y = 18$	Subtract 6 from both sides.	$3y = 24 - 6x$
$y = 6$	Divide both sides by 3.	$y = \dfrac{24 - 6x}{3}$

Study Tip: Have you tried reviewing Cisco IPTV for extra practice? If not, tune in today. The Learning Assistance Lab can help you log in.

NOTES:

CLASS WORK

1. An appliance repair store charges $50 for the first hour and $18 an hour for each additional hour.

   a. Complete the table to find the cost of repairing an appliance.

HOURS	CALCULATION	COST
3		
8		
h		

   b. What is the equation that relates cost and hours? Simplify the equation.

   c. If the repair cost $230, how long did it take?

   d. Solve for h in the equation from Part b.

2. Scientists use the length of the femur, the bone from the hip to the knee, to approximate the height of a person. The equation below is used to approximate the height of a man knowing the length of the femur

$$h = 69.1 + 2.24f,$$

where f is the length of the femur and h is the length of the person, are measured in centimeters. Solve the equation for f.

3. $FV = P(1 + rt)$ is used to compute the future value of an investment that earns simple interest.

FV is the future value of the investment.
P is the principal or the amount invested.
r is the annual interest rate.
t is the number of years the money is invested.

a. Find t if \$1,000 is invested at an annual interest rate of 6% and the future value is \$1,420.

b. Solve the formula for t.

GROUP EXERCISE

The accompanying bar graph shows the number of registered shareholders (in thousands) of PPG Company stock at the end of each year between 1986 and 1990. The data in this figure can be modeled by the equation *s* = 788 - 28t, where s is the number of registered shareholders (in thousands) of stock at the end of year *t*, and *t* is the number of years since 1985. The equation is derived from the data using the linear regression command on the TI 83 plus calculator. If you take MAT 100, Intermediate Algabra, you will learn how to do this.

Study Tip: Make sure you understand what the variables t and s mean in the equation.

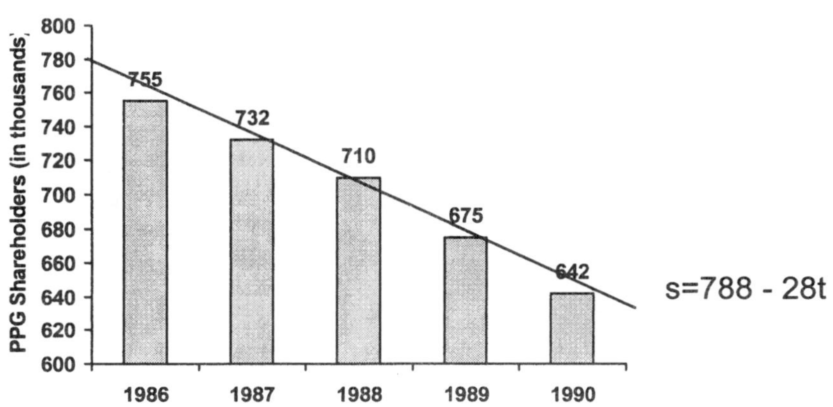

1. When will there be 600,000 PPG Company shareholders?
   (Hint: Because the units for shareholders is in thousands, s = 600)

2. When will there be 544,000 PPG Company shareholders?
   (Hint: Because the units for shareholders is in thousands, s = 544)

3. Solve for the variable t in the formula s = 788 - 28t.

Study Tip: Review Part d on page 65 or 1d on page 67.

EXERCISES

Study Tip: Remember your guidelines for meaningful homework time.

1. From a modest beginning, Q-Mart Stores have risen to become one of the largest retailing chains in America. The accompanying bar graph shows the number of stores at the end of selected years in the period 1983-1991. The figure also shows the graph of s = 118t +146, where s represents the number of stores at the end of year t, and t is the number of years since 1982. The equation is derived from the data using the linear regression command on the TI 83 Plus calculator. If you take MAT 100, Intermediate Algabra, you will learn how to do this.

Study Tip: Make sure you understand what the variables t and s mean in the equation. Review the group work problem on page 69 for a similar problem.

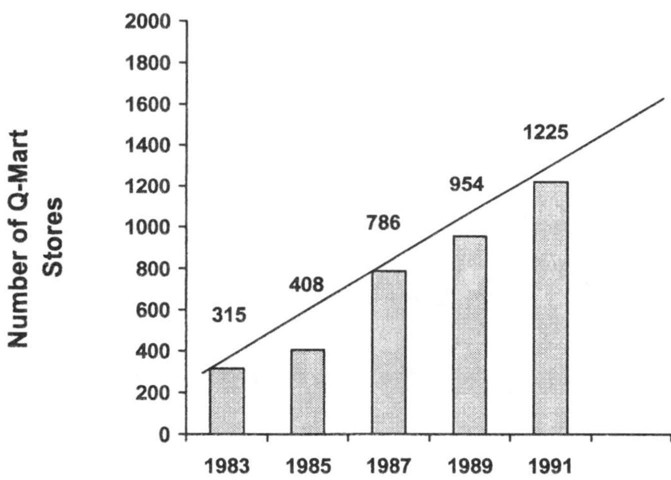

a. According to the equation, when will Q-Mart have 1,500 stores?

b. According to the equation, when will Q-Mart have 1,600 stores?

c. Solve for t in the equation s = 118t + 146.

2. The wind chill produced by a 45 mph wind can be approximated by the formula:

$$W = 1.6T - 54.6,$$

where w is the wind chill and T is the temperature. Solve the above equation for T.

3. $FV = P(1 + rt)$ is used to compute the future value of an investment that earns simple interest.

FV is the future value of the investment.
P is the principal or the amount invested.
r is the annual interest rate.
t is the number of years the money is invested.

a. Find r if $1,500 is invested for 6 years and the future value is $1,950.
b. Solve the formula for r.

Study Tip: Review the problem on page 68 for a similar problem.

4. Solve for the indicated variable.

a. $P = 2L + 2W$, solve for L.

b. $D = rt$, solve for r.

c. $3x - 4y = 12$, solve for y.

d. $6x + 3y = 9$, solve for y.

5. The equation $C = \frac{5}{9}(F - 32)$ converts temperature in Fahrenheit, F, to Celsius, C.

a. If the temperature is 72° Fahrenheit, what is the corresponding temperature in Celsius?

b. If the temperature is 11° Celsius, what is the corresponding temperature in Fahrenheit?

Study Tip: To deal with the fraction, $\frac{5}{9}$, multiply both sides of the equation by $\frac{9}{1}$. Multiplying by the denominator 9 will eliminate the fraction in the equation. This is different from multiplying by the reciprocal of $\frac{5}{9}$. Multiplying by the reciprocal was the last step in solving an equation. Multiplying by 9 should be your first step in solving this equation.

c. If the temperature is –6° Celsius, what is the corresponding temperature in Fahrenheit?

d. If the temperature is 63° Celsius, what is the corresponding temperature in Fahrenheit?

e. Try to solve the equation $C = \frac{5}{9}(F - 32)$ for the variable F.

APPLICATIONS OF LINEAR EQUATIONS PART III
PERCENTAGES
OVERVIEW

Overview: This section will explain how to apply algebra to percentage problems.

Basic Examples:

Example 1. Sink Hardware store is having a 15% off sale. The sale price of a toilet is $97; find the cost of the toilet before the sale.

To find the solution:

a. Complete the table to find an equation relating the sale price to the retail price (the price before the sale).

Visualization

15% Discount
85% Sale Price

al Price (00%)

Write percentages as a decimal, 15% = .15.

Sale Price is equal to the retail price minus the discount.

Retail Price	Discount	Sale Price
$110	$.15 \bullet 110 = 16.50$	$110 - .15 \bullet 110 = 93.50$
$140	$.15 \bullet 140 = 21.00$	$140 - .15 \bullet 140 = 119$
R	$.15 \bullet R$	$R - .15 \bullet R = SP$

b. Simplify the equation.

$R - .15 \bullet R = SP$
$.85 \bullet R = SP$

Explanation: The coefficient of R is one, so the arithmetic for combining like terms is 1 - .15 = .85. In English, the sale price is 85% of the retail price.

c. Solve the equation when the Sale Price is $97.

$.85 \bullet R = 97$ Substitute 97 in for SP
$R = 114.12$ Divide both sides by .85.

The retail price for the toilet was $114.12.

Note: the answer was rounded to the nearest cent.

Study Tip: Remember to use descriptive letters to describe the variables.

Example 2. A math teacher, Dr. Pi, computes a student's grade for the course as follows:

20% for homework
50% for the average of 5 tests
30% for the final exam

a. Compute Darrel's grade for the course if he has a 91 on the homework, 84 for his test average, and a 98 on the final exam.

$.20 \bullet 91 + .50 \bullet 84 + .30 \bullet 98 = G$	Write percents as decimals.
$18.2 + 42 + 29.4 = G$	Multiply
$89.6 = G$	Add

Darrel's grade for the course is an 89.6, or a B.

b. Suppose Selena has an 89 homework average and a 97 test average. What does Selena have to get on the final exam to get a 90 for the course?

The difference between Part a and Part b is that in Part b we don't know Selena's grade on the final exam.

So instead of multiplying 30% times a number, multiply 30% times E. E is the variable that represents what Selena has to get on the final exam to get a 90 for the course.

$.20 \bullet 89 + .50 \bullet 97 + .30 \bullet E = 90$	Set up the equation.
$66.3 + .30E = 90$	Simplify
$.30E = 23.7$	Subtract 66.3 from both sides.
$E = 79$	Divide both sides by .30.

Because Selena studied all semester, she only has to get a 79 on the final to get a 90 for the course.

Summary: Percentages play an integral role in our every day lives, including computing discounts, calculating mortgages, savings, investments, and estimating final grades.

When working with percentages, remember to write them as decimals, to create tables to derive equations, and to follow the proper procedures to solve equations.

CLASS WORK

1. Review of basic percentage problems.

   a. Write the percentage as a decimal.
   1. 5% 2. 0.45% 3. 33 1/3 % 4. 500%

   b. What is 72% 0f 200?

   c. 63 is what percent of 72?

   d. 120 is 15% of what number?

   e. You get 9 out of 12 questions right on a quiz. What percentage did you get right?

   f. If you got 75% of the questions on a test correct, and there were 52 questions, how many did you get right?

2. Phillip's Hardware Store is having a 20% off sale. What is the sale price of a mower that is usually priced at $380?

3. Phillip's Hardware Store is having a 20% off sale.

   a. Complete the table.

Retail Price	Discount	Sale Price
60		
50		
R		

   b. A stepladder has a sale price of $44. What was the retail price before the sale? Set up the appropriate equation and solve it.

4. SRH Inc. gave everyone a 4% raise. The wages are per hour.

a. Complete the table below.

Current hourly wage	Calculation	New hourly wage
$12.50		
$14.75		
C		N

b. What is Joyce's current hourly wage if her new hourly wage will be $21.55.

c. Suppose Mark's new hourly wage will be $10.07 and his current hourly wage is $9.50. What percent increase did he receive?

d. Find a formula for the percent increase.

5. a. Walden Department Store computes retail prices (the price Walden charges its customers for an item) by marking up the wholesale price (the price Walden pays for the item) by 40%. Complete the table. Recall that wholesale price plus markup equals retail price.

WHOLESALE PRICE ($)	MARK UP ($)	RETAIL PRICE ($)
$10		
$20		
$40		
w		

b. What is the equation that relates retail price to wholesale price and markup?

c. Suppose an item costs $82 at the Walden Department store. How much did Walden pay for the item?

6. A math teacher, Dr. Kay, computes a student's grade for the course as follows:

10% for homework
65% for the average of 4 tests
25% for the final exam

a. Compute Bill's grade for the course if he has a 78 on the homework, 81 for his test average, and a 79 on the final exam.

b. Suppose Sue has an 82 homework average and a 63 test average. What does Sue have to get on the final exam to get a 70 for the course?

GROUP EXERCISE

Study Tip: Group suggestion: Use only one sheet of paper for the <u>entire group</u>. This encourages all to participate.

1. A grocer purchases a can of fruit juice for $.68. Find the selling price if the markup is 30%.

2. A grocer marks up his produce by 25% of the wholesale price.

   a. Complete the table.

WHOLE SALE	MARKUP	RETAIL PRICE
.85		
1.00		
s		

   b. If the grocer sells a bunch of bananas for $1.15, how much did the grocer pay for the bananas?

3. Professor Passall computes his grades as follows:

   15% for homework
   55% for the average of 3 tests
   30% for the final exam

   a. Compute Howie's grade if he has a 71 homework average, an 83 test average, and a 68 final exam.

   b. Nancy wants to get an 80 for the course. She has an 82 homework average and a 74 test average. What does Nancy have to get on the final exam to get an 80 for the course?

EXERCISES

Study Tip: Remember to use your homework notebook.

1. a. If 98 girls and 87 boys attended a dance, what percentage of the attendees were female?

   b. If 60% of the people at a dance were girls, and 125 people attended the dance, how many were girls?

2. Dairy Prince has given each employee a 12% raise.

   a. Complete this table.

Employee	Susan	Joe	Mary	Pat
Current earnings per hour	\$3.35	\$3.50		
New earnings per hour			\$4.48	\$4.20

Study Tip: To find Mary's current earnings per hour, answer Part b first.

   b. What is the equation that relates new earnings to current?

Study Tip: For problems 3 and 4 use the formula $P = \frac{\text{New} - \text{Old}}{\text{Old}} * 100$.

3. Your employer increases your hourly wages by \$1.35 per hour. Find the percent increase in your salary if your old salary was \$9.00 an hour.

4. An item originally listed as \$14.50 is on sale for \$11.60, find the sale percentage.

5. Harry's Hardware Store is having a 32% off sale. Complete the table.

Current Price (\$)	Discount (\$)	Sale Price (\$)
25	0.32(25) = 8	25 - 0.32(25) = 17
35		
45		
C		
		37.40

Study Tip: This problem is like example 1 from Overview on page 73.

6. A math teacher, Dr. Pi, computes a student's grade for the course as follows:

10% for Homework
65% for the average of the 5 tests
25% for the Final Exam

Compute the following students' grades for the course.

Study Tip: Review pages 74 and 77.

a. George: 78 homework, 88 for the 5 tests, 71 for the final

b. Darrel: 87 for homework, his 5 test scores of 89, 71, 95, 97, 88, and a 90 for the final

c. Rachel wants an 80 for the course. She has an 81 homework average and a 75 test average. What does Rachel have to get on the final exam to get an 80 for the course?

7. An English teacher, Dr. Austin, computes a student's grade for the course as follows:

15% for a research paper
15% for short essays
50% for the average of 4 tests
20% for the final

a. Harold wants a 75 for the course. He has an 82 for the research paper, 61 for the short essays, and a 71 for the 4 tests. What does Harold need to get on the final exam to get a 75 for the course?

b. Thomas wants a 90 for the course. He has a 78 for the research paper, 80 for the short essays, and a 69 for the 4 tests. What does Thomas need to get on the final exam to get a 90 for the course? What do you conclude about Thomas' chances of getting a 90?

8 a. To compute the retail price, a store owner uses the formula R = 1.20W. What was the markup? Explain what the coefficient (the number multiplying the variable)means.

b. To compute the sale price, a store owner uses the formula S = .85R. What was the percent off for the sale?

c. Why is the coefficient in Part a greater than 1?

d. Why is the coefficient in Part b less than 1?

REVIEW I

This unit introduces algebra by examining similar models. You should be able to read a problem and create a table to find an equation that relates two variables. If you are given information about one of the variables, you should be able to use algebra to find the other variable.

Signed Numbers:

Informal Rules: (See Appendix A for formal presentation)

Adding or subtracting like signs: Add the two numbers and use the common sign.

Example 1. a. $-3 - 5 = -8$ b. $+3 + 5 = +8$

Adding or subtracting unlike signs: Subtract the two numbers and use the sign of the larger.

Example 2. a. $-5 + 2 = -3$ b. $+5 - 2 = +3$

Multiplying or dividing unlike signs: The product or quotient of two numbers with unlike signs is always negative.

Example 3. a. $-6 \bullet 9 = -54$

Multiplying or dividing like signs: The product or quotient of two numbers with like signs is always positive.

Example 4. a. $\frac{-35}{-7} = 5$ b. $\frac{+20}{+5} = +4$

Order of operations: **P**lease **E**xcuse **M**y **D**ear **A**unt **S**ally

1. Inside **P**arentheses, ( ).
2. **E**xponents.
3. **M**ultiplication and **D**ivision (left to right)
4. **A**ddition and **S**ubtraction (left to right)

Example 5. $-4(7-10) = 12$ Example 6. $7 - 5^2 = -18$

Introduction to Variables:

Generate a table to find an equation that relates two variables.

Example 7. A car company charges $14.95 plus 35 cents per mile.

Miles	Calculation	Cost
15	$0.35 \bullet 15 + 14.95$	$20.20
25	$0.35 \bullet 25 + 14.95$	$23.70
m	$0.35m + 14.95$	C

Simplifying Algebraic Equations:

Distributive property: $a(b + c) = a \bullet b + a \bullet c$

Combine like terms:

Example 8. Simplify.

$$8x - 2(3x - 5) =$$
$$8x - 6x + 10 =$$
$$2x + 10$$

Solving Equations Part I and II

Solving Equations

1. Simplify both sides of the equation.
2. Write the equation as a variable term equal to a constant.
3. Divide both sides by the coefficient or multiply by the reciprocal.
4. Three possible outcomes to solving an equation.
   a. One solution (a conditional equation)
   b. No solution (a contradiction)
   c. Every number is a solution (an identity)

Example 9. Solve

$$3x - 5(4x + 12) = 23 - 9x$$
$$3x - 20x - 60 = 23 - 9x$$
$$-17x - 60 = 23 - 9x$$
$$-17x + 17x - 60 = 23 - 9x + 17x$$
$$-60 = 23 + 8x$$
$$-60 - 23 = 23 - 23 + 8x$$
$$-83 = 8x$$
$$-10.375 = x$$

Applications of Linear Equations Part I:

This section summarizes the major skills taught in this unit.

Study Tip: Review pages 53 and 54.

Example 10. A phone company charges $12.50 plus 15 cents per minute after the first six minutes.

a. Create a table to find the equation that relates cost and minutes.

Minutes	Calculation	Cost
10	$0.15(10-6)+12.50$	$13.10
20	$0.15(20-6)+12.50$	$14.60
m	$0.15(m-6)+12.50$	C

b. Simplify the equation.

$$0.15(m - 6) + 12.50 = C$$
$$0.15m - .90 + 12.50 = C$$
$$0.15m + 11.60 = C$$

c. If it costs $23.50, how long were you on the phone?

$$0.15m + 11.60 = 23.50$$
$$0.15m = 11.90$$
$$m = 79.33$$

If it costs $23.50, then you were on the phone for approximately 79 minutes.

Applications of Linear Equations Part II, Literal Equations:

A literal equation involves solving an equation for one of two variables.

Example 11. Solve for y.

$$2x + 5y = 8$$
$$5y = 8 - 2x$$
$$y = \frac{8 - 2x}{5}$$

Applications of linear Equations Part III, Percentages:

Write percentages as decimals.

Example 12. An English teacher computes his grades as follows:
30% short essays
15% research paper
55% final exam.
Sue has a 87 on the short essays and a 72 on the research paper. If she wants an 80 for the course, what grade does Sue have to get on the final?

$$.30 \bullet 87 + .15 \bullet 72 + .55E = 80$$
$$36.90 + .55E = 80$$
$$.55E = 43.10$$
$$E = 78.36$$

Sue has to get a 78.36 in the final exam to get an 80 for the course.

Study Tips:

1. Practice the review test starting on the next page by placing yourself under realistic exam conditions.

2. Find a quiet place and use a timer to simulate the test period.

3. Write your answers in your homework notebook. You may then re-take the exam for extra practice.

4. Check your answers. The answers to the review test are on page 365.

5. There is an additional exam available on the MAT 011 web page, **www.mc3.edu/aa/ac/MATHSCI/mat011/mat011.htm**

6. Do NOT wait until the night before the exam to study.

REVIEW TEST I

1. Water Witch Well Drillers charge their customers $350.00 to come to the well site and $20.00 per foot to drill a well.

   a. Complete the table.

DEPTH OF THE WELL (Feet)	CALCULATION	COST ($)
50		
70		
90		
d		

   b. What is the equation that relates cost and depth of the well?

   c. If a person is charged $2,150.00 for a well, how deep is the well?

2. Take-Taxi Co. charges $1.35 immediately upon entering the cab. The first 3 miles are free, and after that it costs $1.80 per mile.

   a. Complete the table.

MILES	CALCULATION	COST ($)
10		
15		
20		
m		

   b. What is the equation that relates cost and miles?

   c. If the taxi fare is $27.50, how far was your ride?

Study Tip: If you don't remember how to do a problem look through the Unit for a similar problem.

3. Professor Newton computes his grades as follows:

Test Average: 60%
Homework: 15%
Final Exam: 25%

a. Otto has a test average of 82, a homework average of 99, and a final exam score of 71. What is Otto's grade for the course?

b. Tito has a test average of 71 and a homework average of 76. What does Tito have to get on the final to get a 70 for the course?

4. The equation

$$G = .022B + .359$$

relates the price per gallon, G, of gasoline with the price per barrel, B, of crude oil.

a. Find the price per gallon if the price per barrel of crude oil is $47.50.

b. Find the price per barrel of crude oil if the price per gallon of gasoline is $1.27.

5. Clancy's Burgers has given a 12% raise to all of its employees. Complete the table.

a.

CURRENT SALARY	CALCULATION	NEW SALARY
$1.00 per hr.		
$3.00 per hr.		
CS per hr.		NS

b. What is the equation that relates current salary to new salary?

c. If your new salary will be $5.25 per hour, what is your current salary?

6. Stats' Department Store is having a 20% off sale.

a. Complete the table.

ORIGINAL PRICE	CALCULATION	SALE PRICE
10.00		
20.00		
OP		SP

b. What is the equation that relates the original price to the sale price?

c. If the sale price is $81.00, what was the original price?

7. The net profits and losses for Rose Stores for the years 1990 through 1993 are shown in the graph below.

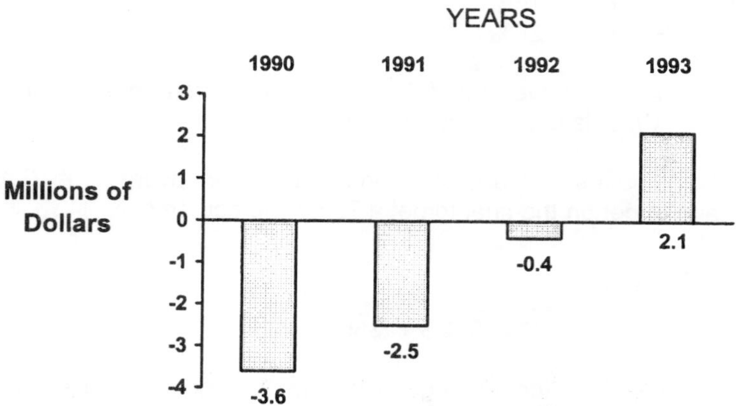

a. What is the difference between the profit or loss in 1990 and that in 1992?

b. What is the difference between the profit or loss in 1993 and that in 1991?

8. Simplify. $-2(x-3)+2(4-x)$

9. Is -3 a solution of $x^2+6x+9=x+3$

10. Solve. a. $7x-8=-29$

b. $8x-3(4x-5)=-2x-11$

11. A business manager has determined that the cost per unit for a camera is \$70 and that the fixed costs per month are \$3,500. Find the number of cameras that are produced during a month in which the total cost was \$21,000. Use the equation

$$T = U \cdot N + F,$$

where T is the total cost, U is the cost per unit, N is the number of units produced, and F is the fixed cost.

12. $P = 2W + 2L$, solve for W.

UNIT 2

INEQUALITIES
OVERVIEW

Objectives: In this section you will solve inequality algebra problems and represent the answers on a number line. Also, you will identify quantities as being greater than, less than or equal to each other.

Basic Examples:

The following example comes from the section, Applications of Linear Equations Part III, page 74.

Example 1. A math teacher, Dr. Pi, computes a student's grade for the course as follows:

20% for homework
50% for the average of 5 tests
30% for the final exam

Suppose Selena has an 89 homework average and a 97 test average. What does Selena have to get on the final exam to get a 90 for the course?

Let E be the variable that represents what Selena has to get on the final exam to get a 90 for the course.

$.20 \bullet 89 + .50 \bullet 97 + .30 \bullet E = 90$	Set up the equation.
$66.3 + .30E = 90$	Simplify.
$.30E = 23.7$	Subtract 66.3 from both sides.
$E = 79$	Divide both sides by .30.

Because Selena studied all semester, she only has to get a 79 on the final to get a 90 for the course.

But this problem isn't practical. What Selena really wants for the course is an A. So she would be happy with a grade of 90 or higher. The more realistic question would be:

What does Selena have to get on the final exam to get a 90 or higher for the course?

Let E be the variable that represents what Selena has to get on the final exam to get a 90 or higher for the course.

Explanation: We use the symbol $\geq$ to mean greater than or equal to. So instead of setting Selena's grade = to 90, we set Selena's grade $\geq$ 90.

$.20 \bullet 89 + .50 \bullet 97 + .30 \bullet E \geq 90$	Set up the equation.
$66.3 + .30E \geq 90$	Simplify.
$.30E \geq 23.7$	Subtract 66.3 from both sides.
$E \geq 79$	Divide both sides by .30.

Because Selena studied all semester, she only has to get a 79 or higher on the final to get a 90 or higher for the course.

Inequality Notation:

1. > means **greater than**.

   For example, $x > 3$ represents all the numbers larger than 3, but not 3.

2. < means **less than**.

   For example, $x < 5$ represents all the numbers smaller than 5, but not 5.

3. ≥ means **greater than or equal to**.

   For example, $x \geq 7$ represents all the numbers larger than 7, including 7.

4. ≤ means **less than or equal to**.

   For example, $x \leq 6$ represents all the numbers smaller than 6, including 6.

Graphing Inequalities on the number line:

Graphing an inequality often conveys its meaning more clearly than just writing the inequality.

Two rules for graphing inequalities:

1. For ≥ and ≤ we use a dot, •,to show that we are including the number. (sometimes called a shaded circle.)

2. For > and < we use a small circle, ∘, to show that we are not including the number. (sometimes called an open circle.)

Example 2. Graph $x \leq -4$.

This means that we want the numbers smaller than and including –4. We put a dot at –4 since we have ≤ and we draw an arrow going to the left of –4.

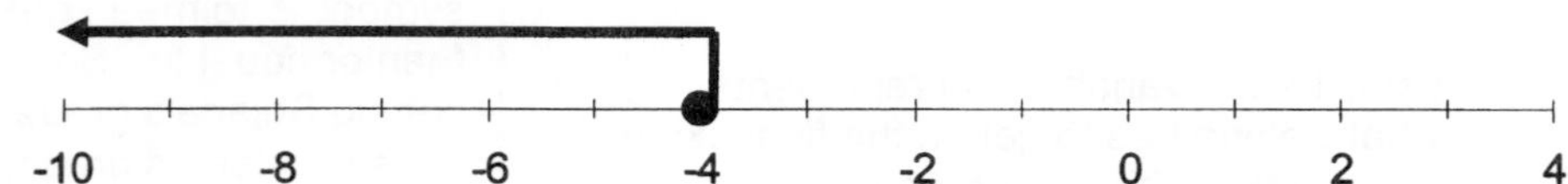

Example 3. Graph $-5 < x \leq 3$.

This means that we want numbers between –5 and 3, including 3 but not including –5. We will put a dot at 3 and a circle at –5 and draw a line between –5 and 3.

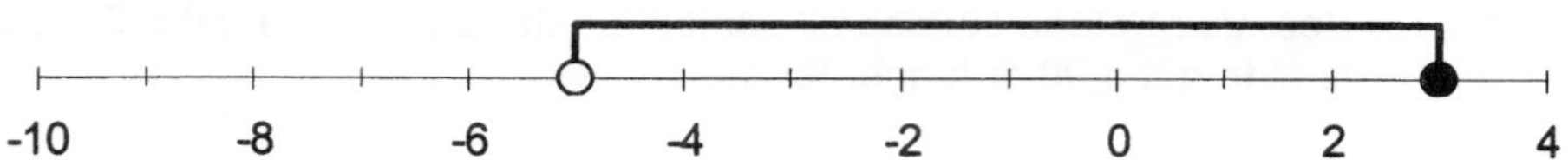

Solving Inequalities:

The only difference between solving equality problems and inequality problems is:

When you multiply or divide by a negative number you must change the direction of the inequality.

Study Tip: This should be written down on a note card and memorized.

Explanation: Consider the two numbers 3 and 7. $3 < 7$ because 3 is to the left of 7 on the number line.

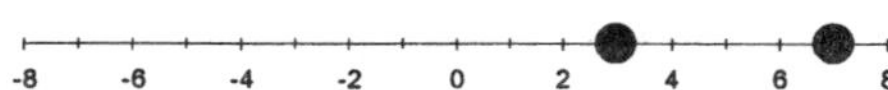

If we multiply both numbers by a negative 1, then we get –3 and –7. Graphing –3 and –7 on the number line:

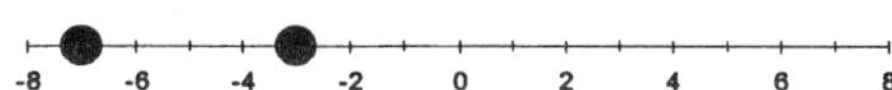

You can see that –7 is to the left of –3, so $-3 > -7$. By multiplying by a negative you switch the order of the numbers.

Example 4. Solve and graph the solution on the number line.

$5 - 3x \le -13$

$-3x \le -18$ Subtract –5 from both sides.

$x \ge 6$ Divide both sides by –3. Since we divide both sides by a negative, we change the direction of the inequality.

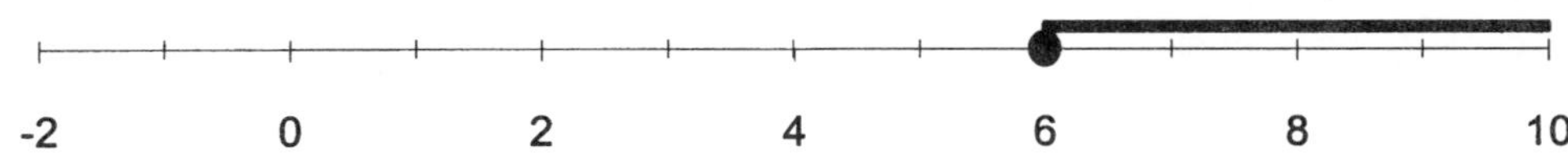

Example 5. Solve and graph the solution on the number line.

$-7 < 4x - 5 \le 3$

This problem has three parts

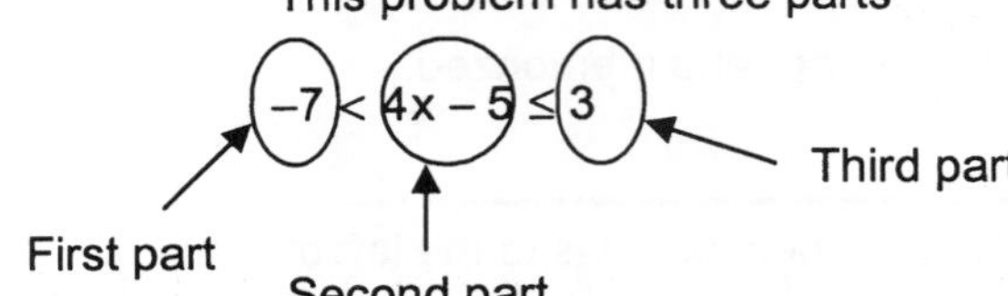

$$-7 < 4x - 5 \le 3$$

$$-7 + 5 < 4x - 5 + 5 \le 3 + 5$$ Add 5 to all three parts.

$$-2 < 4x \le 8$$ Combine like terms.

$$\frac{-2}{4} < \frac{4x}{4} \le \frac{8}{4}$$ Divide all three parts by 4.

$$-.5 < x \le 2$$ Answer.

Explanation: This problem has two inequalities. The solution should contain x in the middle. Whatever we do to one part we must do to all three parts.

-4 -2 0 2 4 6

Summary: Adding inequalities to your algebra repertoire allows you to find when one quantity is more or less than another.

Major ideas:

1. When solving inequalities, if you multiply or divide by a negative number, then you must change the direction of the inequality.

2. When graphing inequalities on the number line, $\le$, $\ge$ are represented by a small dot or shaded circle.

3. When graphing inequalities on the number line, $<$, $>$ are represented by a small circle or open circle.

4. When solving a problem with more than one inequality:

    a. Perform the same algebraic step to all three parts of the inequality.
    b. The answer should have x in the middle.

CLASS WORK

1. An English teacher, Bill Shakespeare, computes a student's grade for a course as follows:

   20% for a research paper
   40% for the average of 4 tests
   15% for short essays
   25% for the final exam

   A student, Rosetta Stone (author of *Because a Little Bug Went Ka-Choo*), wants to get a C for the course. This means that Rosetta's grade must be greater than or equal to 70, but less than 80. Rosetta has an 85 on the research paper, a 68 average for the tests, and a 62 average on the short essays. What does Rosetta have to get on the final exam to get a C?

2. Is $x = 3$ a solution to $x + 5 \geq 1$?

   Is $x = -2$ a solution to $x + 5 \geq 1$?

   Is $x = -4$ a solution to $x + 5 \geq 1$?

   Is $x = -8$ a solution to $x + 5 \geq 1$?

3. Use the number line to describe the solutions to an inequality equation.

a. $x \leq 5$

b. $x > -3$

c. $5 \geq x$

d. $-2 < x \leq 5$

4. Solve the inequality and graph the solution on the number line. Describe each step.

a. $4 - 3x \geq 22$

b. $-6 \leq 15 + 7x < 50$

5. Solve each inequality and graph the solution on the number line.

a. $4x - 11 > 15x + 25$

b. $3(2 - 8x) \leq 3x - 5$

c. $-2 \leq 7 + 2x < 8$

d. $-8 < 7 - 3x < 31$

GROUP EXERCISE

Study Tip: Group Suggestion: Use one piece of paper and have each group member decide a step and then pass the sheet to the next person. If someone gets stuck, the previous person should try to explain. If no one in the group can help, ask the professor for assistance.

1. Describe each step.

	Step
$4 - 8x > 19 - 3x$	
$-8x > 15 - 3x$	____________
$-5x > 15$	____________
$x < -3$	____________

2. Find where the first mistake occurs.

$-6 \leq 4 + 5x \leq 15$

$-10 \leq 5x \leq 15$

$-2 \leq x \leq 3$

3. Solve and graph the solutions on the number line.

a. $8x - 5 \leq 4x + 23$

b. $-6 \leq 10 - 2x < 22$

Study Tip: Review example 5 on page 92 or 4b, page 94.

4. A math teacher, Mrs. Lincoln computes a student's grade for the course as follows:

15% for homework
55% for the average of 4 tests
30% for the final exam

Sue wants to get a B for the course. This means that her grade must be greater than or equal to 80 but less than 90. Sue has a 68 on the homework and an 84 test average. What does Sue have to get on the final to get a B for the course?

EXERCISES

Study Tip: Remember all of the homework suggestions:

1. Lined paper and ruler.
2. Short homework sessions.
3. Learning Assistance Lab.
4. The CD that accompanies the book.
5. IPTV.

1. Describe each step.

a. | | Step
---|---
$6 - 3x \leq 30 + x$ |
$-3x \leq 24 + x$ | ______________
$-4x \leq 24$ | ______________
$x \geq -6$ | ______________

b. | | Step
---|---
$-4 < 6 - 2x \leq 14$ |
$-10 < -2x \leq 8$ | ______________
$5 > x \geq -4$ | ______________

2. Find where the first mistake occurs.

a.
$$5 - 7x > 19$$
$$-7x > 14$$
$$x > -2$$

b.
$$-15 \leq 4x + 9 < 12$$
$$-24 \leq 4x < 12$$
$$-6 \leq x < 3$$

3. a. Is $x = 5$ a solution to $3x - 4 > 8$?

b. Is $x = 21$ a solution to $3x - 4 > 8$?

c. Is $x = 1$ a solution to $3x - 4 > 8$?

4. a. Describe the procedure to solve a simple inequality equation.

b. Describe the procedure to solve a multiple inequality problem.

5. Solve and graph the solutions on the number line.

a. $-6x > 54$

b. $\frac{1}{5}x < 4$

c. $7 - x \leq 15$

d. $15 - 2x \geq 21$

e. $5x - 11 < 2x + 8$

f. $2(4x - 5) - 11 \leq 41$

 **Study Tip:** Review example 4 on page 91 or 4a on page 94.

g. $5 < x + 11 \leq 15$

h. $-6 \leq 5 - 2x \leq 11$

i. $0 \leq 4x - 8 < 18$

 **Study Tip:** Review example 5 on page 92 or 4b, page 94

j. $-7 \leq \frac{1}{3}x + 5 \leq 15$

k. $-6 < 8 - \frac{2}{3}x < 24$

APPLICATIONS OF INEQUALITIES OVERVIEW

Objective: This section merges inequalities with the applications from the previous unit.

Basic Examples:

Example 1. You are offered two sales positions after graduating from college. One, Math Inc., pays $10,000 plus 8% commission. The other, Hunter Company, pays $5,000 plus 12% commission. When does Math Inc. pay more than Hunter Company?

We first have to find the equations for each company. Create a table for each. Since both jobs are sales positions, we need a column for sales, a calculation column, and a wage column. (You might be able to find the equations by just reading the problem.)

Math Inc.			**Hunter Company**		
Sales	Calculation	Wage	Sales	Calculation	Wage
15,000	$.08 \bullet 15{,}000 + 10{,}000$	11,200	15,000	$.12 \bullet 15{,}000 + 5{,}000$	6,800
40,000	$.08 \bullet 40{,}000 + 10{,}000$	13,200	40,000	$.12 \bullet 40{,}000 + 5{,}000$	9,800
S	$.08S + 10{,}000$	W	S	$.12S + 5{,}000$	W

The equation for Math Inc: $W = .08S + 10{,}000$

The equation for Hunter Company: $W = .12S + 5{,}000$

Now we get to answer the question: When does Math Inc. pay more than Hunter Company?

Wages from Math Inc. > Wages from Hunter Co.

$.08S + 10{,}000 > .12S + 5{,}000$	Set up the inequality.
$.08S > .12S - 5{,}000$	Subtract 10,000 from both sides.
$-.04S > -5{,}000$	Subtract .12S from both sides.
$S < 125{,}000$	Divided both sides by -.04 and change the direction of the inequality.

Math Inc. pays more than Hunter Company for sales less than $125,000.

Example 2. A phone company charges a basic rate of 30 cents plus 8 cents after the first seven minutes.

a. Find the equation for the cost of making phone calls for calls over seven minutes. Simplify the equation.

The company doesn't start charging a per minute rate until after the first seven minutes. You will have to subtract 7 from the number of minutes you were on the phone before multiplying by .08. This means you will have to use parentheses in the calculation column of the table.

Minutes	Calculation	Cost
10	$.08(10-7)+.30$	.54
15	$.08(15-7)+.30$	.94
m	$.08(m-7)+.30$	C

The equation for the cost is: $C = .08(m-7)+.30$

Simplify the equation.

$C = .08(m-7)+.30$

$C = .08m-.56+.30$ Use the Distributive Property.

$C = .08m-.26$ Combine Like terms.

b. How many minutes were you on the phone if the cost was more than $3.00.

$\text{Cost} > 3.00$ Cost is more than $3.00.

$.08m-.26 > 3.00$ Set up the inequality.

$.08m > 3.26$ Add .26 to both sides.

$m > 40.75$ Divide both sides by .08.

If the cost is more than $3.00, then you were on the phone for more than 40.75 minutes.

c. How many minutes were you on the phone if the cost was between $2.50 and $3.25?

$2.50 < \text{Cost} < 3.25$ Cost is between $2.50 and $3.25.

$2.50 < .08m-.26 < 3.25$ Set up inequality.

$2.76 < .08m < 3.51$ Add .26 to all three parts.

$34.50 < m < 43.9$ Divide all three parts by .08.

If the cost is between $2.50 and $3.25 then you were on the phone between 34.5 and 43.9 minutes.

Summary: This section allows us to expand the applications from the previous unit to problems that deal with quantities greater than, less than, or equal to each other. The procedures include the following steps:

1. Creating tables that include all necessary information.
2. Setting up the inequality.
3. Using algebraic skills to solve the inequality.

CLASS WORK

1. The equation $S = 118t + 146$ represents the number of stores, S, ZZ-Mart has opened at the end of t years, where t is the number of years since 1982. A model like this usually comes from a sample of data. Using the linear regression capability of a calculator or computer generates the equation. This is covered in MAT 100, Intermediate Algebra.

   a. When will ZZ-Mart have more than 1500 stores?

   b. When will ZZ-Mart have between 1000 and 1300 stores? (Make sure your interval truly expresses the time described.)

2. Two companies offer you very similar sales positions. Haunted House will pay you $10,000 a year plus 7% commission on the dollar amount of book sales. Reader Publishing Co. will pay you $8,000 a year plus 11% commission. For what dollar amount of book sales does Haunted House pay more than Reader Publishing Co.?

3. Pop Bell charges 20 cents per phone call and 11 cents for each minute over 3 minutes.

   a. Find an equation for the cost of making a phone call. Simplify the equation.

   b. How many minutes were you on the phone if the cost was more than \$2.50?

   c. How many minutes were you on the phone if the cost was between \$3.00 and \$4.50?

GROUP EXERCISE

Study Tips: 1. Review the problems on pages 100 and 102.
2. Quietly go to the board and do the problem there. (You should ask the teacher first.)

1. Graphic Inc. offers you a sales position. They will pay you $18,000 a year plus 13% commission on sales over $100,000.

   a. Find an equation for your yearly salary. (You may need to make a table.) Simplify the equation.

   b. How much do you have to sell if you want to make more than $50,000 a year?

   c. How much do you have to sell if you want to make between $45,000 and $75,000 a year?

EXERCISES

1. The equation $C = \frac{5}{9}(F - 32)$ converts temperature in Fahrenheit, F, to Celsius, C. For each problem set up an equation and solve it.

Study Tip: See homework problem 1 on page 71.

   a. If the temperature is above 8° Celsius, what must the corresponding temperature in Fahrenheit be?

   b. If the temperature is between -2° Celsius and 12° Celsius, what is the corresponding temperature in Fahrenheit?

2. Two companies have offered you very similar jobs selling cars. Company A pays \$30,000 a year, and Company B pays 8% commission plus \$10,000 a year. When will Company A pay more than Company B? Set up an inequality and solve.

Study Tip: Refer to problem 1 on page 99 for a similar problem.

3. The accompanying bar graph shows the population growth of the United States since 1980.

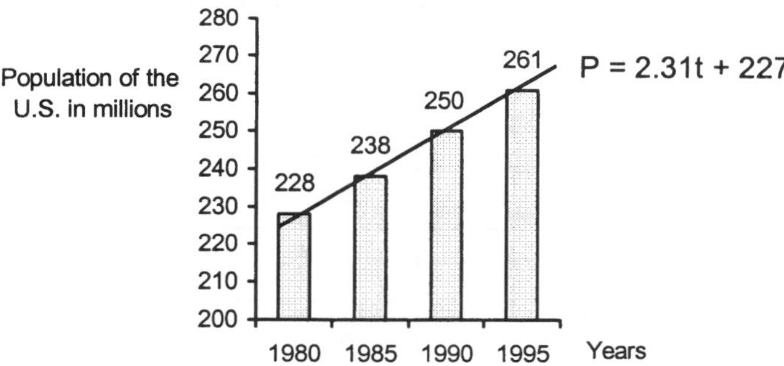

The equation P = 2.31t + 227 can be used to approximate the population of the U.S. In the equation, P represents the population in millions and t is the number of years since 1980.

   a. Use the equation to estimate the population in 1989.

   b. Use the equation to find when the population will be more than 266,500,000. Use P = 266.5 (Set up an inequality and solve it.)

   c. When will the population of the U.S. be between 270 million and 300 million? (Set up an inequality and solve it.)

4. Two girls want to enter the lawn-mowing business for the summer. They plan to buy a power mower for $200, and they hope to charge $8.50 an hour.

a. Use the table below to help you find a formula for the girls' profit.

HOURS	CALCULATION	PROFIT ($)
30		
h		

b. What is the equation that relates profit and hours worked?

c. Find out how many hours the girls will have to work to make more than $200 for the summer.

d. Find out how many hours the girls will have to work to break even but not earn more than $500.

5. You are planning to rent a car. Wrecker charges 50 cents a mile and $28 for a day while Ertz charges 75 cents a mile and $20 for a day.

a. Use the table below to help you set up a formula for finding the cost of renting a car for the day.

WRECKER			ERTZ		
MILES	CALCULATION	COST ($)	MILES	CALCULATION	COST (
20			20		
m			m		

b. What are the equations that relate cost and miles for each of the two companies?

c. When will Wrecker cost more than Ertz? Set up an inequality and solve it.

6. Two companies have offered you very similar jobs selling appliances. Company A pays 12% commission on sales over $50,000 a year plus $8,000, and Company B pays 5% commission plus $15,000 a year.

Study Tip: Review similar problems on pages 99, 101, and 103.

a. Use the table below to find a formula for your wages.

COMPANY A			COMPANY B		
ALES	CALCULATION	WAGES	SALES	CALCULATION	WAGES
),000			50,000		
0,000			100,000		
5,000			125,000		
s			s		

b. What are the equations that relate wages and sales for the two companies? Simplify them.

c. When does Company A pay more than Company B? Set up an inequality and solve it.

d. For Company A, why is the formula not valid for s = 20,000?

7. You are trying to decide which long distance phone company to choose. Company WHAT?! charges 15 cents a call and 11 cents a minute after the first 4 minutes. Company Disconnect charges 10 cents a call and 14 cents after the first 5 minutes. Which company will you choose? Why? Find equations for both companies and state some limitations on the variable m by writing inequalities. (Hint: You may have to use a table to find the equation.)

Study Tip: The following section begins graphing. For the next class, you should bring graph paper, colored pencils, and a ruler.

SCATTER PLOTS
OVERVIEW

Objectives: This section describes how to create a graph. A graph provides a visualization of the relationship between two quantities. It can be used easily to answer many questions. The term "scatter plot" is used in statistics to describe graphs of data.

Basic Example:

When NASA sends a rocket into space, they monitor the temperature of certain gases. The table below gives a sample of the data collected. Note that negative time represents time before takeoff.

Time (minutes)	–6	–4	–2	0	2	4	6	8
Temperature (Celsius)	–27	–13	–4	4	43	21	9	-2

a. Create a graph based on the data.

Before we graph our data we must decide:

- What are the **independent** and **dependent** variables?
  Since the temperature depends on when the rocket is in the air, temperature is the dependent variable, and time is the independent variable. It is important to decide what the independent and dependent variables are because they determine how the graph is oriented. In a basic math problem, x is the independent variable, and y is the dependent variable. For this class, the set of numbers that make up the values of the independent variable is called the **domain** and the set of numbers that make up the values of the dependent variable is called the **range**.

- How to write the **ordered pairs**.
  In a nonapplication problem, ordered pairs are the x and y coordinates written in parentheses and separated by a comma (x, y). Always write the ordered pair as (independent variable, dependent variable).
  In our example, (time, temperature). The points we will graph are:
  (–6, –27), (–4, –13), (–2, –4), (0, 4), (2, 43), (4, 21), (6, 9), and (8, –2).

- What variable represents the **horizontal axis**?
  The independent variable is always the horizontal axis. In our example, time is the horizontal axis. In a basic math problem, x is the horizontal axis.

- What variable represents the **vertical axis**?
  The dependent variable is always the vertical axis. In our example, temperature is the vertical axis. In a basic math problem, y is the vertical axis.

- What **scale** should we use along the horizontal axis?
  To decide the scale, find the lowest and highest value for time and think about the easiest way to count between them. Since time ranges between –6 and 8, we will count by twos. So the scale will be by 2.

- What **scale** should we use along the vertical axis?
  To decide the scale, find the lowest and highest value for temperature and think about the easiest way to count between them. Since temperature ranges between –27 and 43, we will count by fives, starting at –30 and going to 45. The scale will be by 5.

The graph of the data is given below.

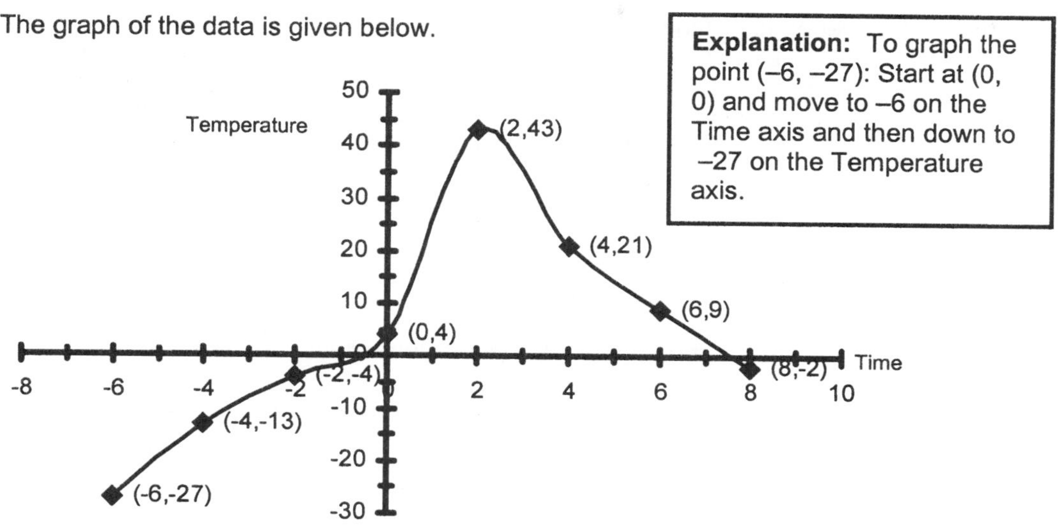

Explanation: To graph the point (–6, –27): Start at (0, 0) and move to –6 on the Time axis and then down to –27 on the Temperature axis.

b. Answer the following questions based on your graph.

1. Estimate the temperature one minute into the flight.

   One minute is half way between zero and two on the horizontal axis, Time. If you lightly draw a vertical line up from 1, the point where the vertical line intersects the graph is the answer. Put a dot at this point and read the temperature on the vertical axis. The temperature of the gas at one minute is approximately 30 degrees Celsius.

2. What was the temperature at takeoff?

   When the rocket takes off, the time is zero. The point that represents the temperature of the gas is the point on the Temperature axis. This point is called the **Temperature intercept** because it is on the Temperature axis. Put a dot at this point and read the temperature on the vertical axis. The temperature at takeoff is 4 degrees Celsius.

3. When was the temperature zero?

   The temperature is zero when the graph crosses the Time axis. These points are called the **Time intercepts** because they are on the Time axis. Put a dot at these points and read the time on the horizontal axis. The temperature is 0 around –2 seconds (just before takeoff) and about 7 minutes.

4. When did the temperature increase the fastest?

   The temperature increased the fastest between 0 minutes and 2 minutes. This is where the graph is steepest.

Summary: This section covers the basic process of graphing. It is important that you master this because the rest of the unit involves graphing lines.

Definitions:

1. Independent Variable.
   The independent variable was the first column in the tables made in previous sections. Miles, time, and sales are usually independent variables.
2. Dependent Variable.
   The dependent variable is the quantity that is contingent on the independent variable. The dependent variable was the third column in the tables made in previous sections. Cost and wages are usually dependent variables.

Example 2. It costs 10 cents per mile plus $20.00 a day to rent a van. The equation that relates miles and cost is $C = .10m + 20$. The cost depends on the number of miles driven, so C is the dependent variable, and m is the independent variable.

3. Ordered Pair.
   The ordered pair indicates the coordinates of a point on the graph. It always has the form:
   (Independent Variable, Dependent Variable) or (x, y).
4. Scale.
   The scale is the distance between the tick marks on the axis.
5. Intercept.
   The intercept is where the graph crosses an axis.

Example 3. In the graph below:

- The x axis is the horizontal axis, and x is the independent variable.
- The scale of the x axis is 5.
- The y axis is the vertical axis, and y is the dependent variable.
- The scale of the y axis is 25.
- The ordered pair is indicated by (x, y).
- The x intercepts are approximately (-2.5, 0) and (27.5, 0).
- The y intercept is approximately (0, 75).

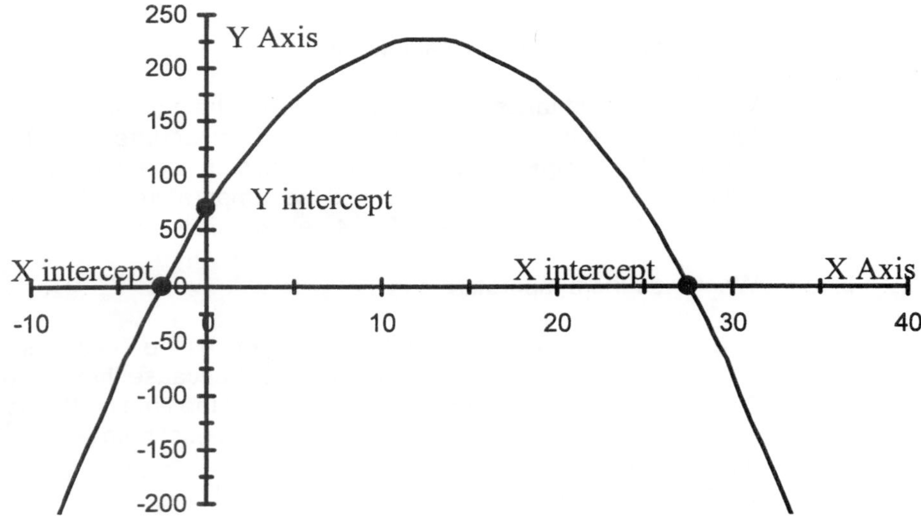

6. This type of graph uses the **Cartesian Coordinate System**.

Study Tip: The CD that accompanies the textbook has a good explanation of this section.

CLASS WORK

Sarah has a job that pays her 8% commission plus $10,000 per year. She has computed her possible wages in the table below.

Wages	$11,600	$12,400	$14,000	$15,600	$18,000	$19,600
Sales	$20,000	$30,000	$50,000	$70,000	$100,000	$120,000

Since Sarah is interested in her wages, then we can say that her wages depend on her sales. Wages are called the dependent variable, and sales are called the independent variable.

The General Rules:

1. The independent variable, S, goes on the horizontal axis. (In a basic algebra problem, x is the independent variable.)
2. The dependent variable, W, goes on the vertical axis. (In a basic algebra problem, x is the independent variable.)
3. The ordered pair is written as (S,W) or (Independent, Dependent) or (x, y).

W

S

In each problem below, find the equation and then identify the independent and dependent variables, label the axes, and write down the ordered pair. These are problems from Unit 1.

1. It costs $25 plus 16 cents a mile to rent a car.

2. A phone company charges 15 cents a minute plus 80 cents for the call.

3. The equation S = 114t + 146 represents the number of ZZ-Mart stores, S, at the end of the year t, where t is the number of years since 1982.

4. When NASA sends a rocket into space, they monitor the temperature of certain gases. The table below gives a sample of the type of data collected. Time is the independent variable, and temperature is the dependent variable. Notice that negative time is used to denote time before lift off.

Time	**Temperature** (C°)
-20	-20
-15	-20
-10	-10
-5	0
0	15
5	40
10	80
15	130
20	90
25	25
30	5
35	-15

a. Graph the data pairs, (time, temperature) and connect the dots.

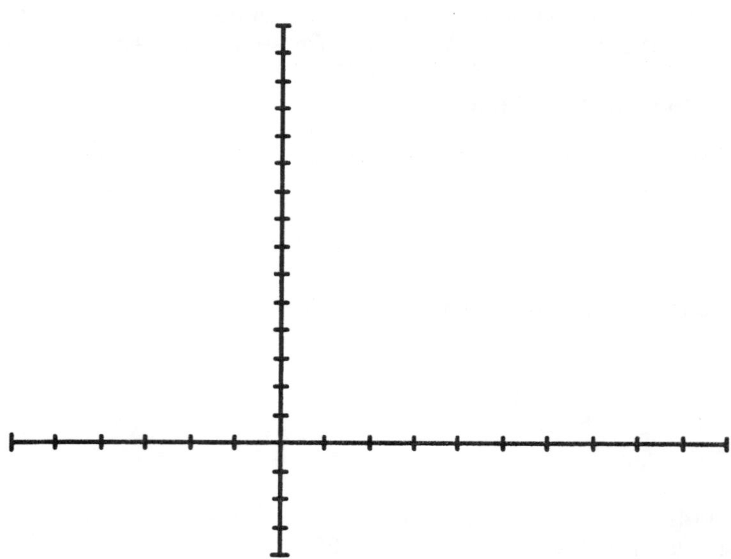

b. Answer each of the following questions about the temperature of the nose cone of the space shuttle and give the coordinates you used to get the answer. Estimate where needed.

1) What was the temperature at take off?

2) What was the temperature 5 minutes into the flight?

3) What was the temperature 17 minutes into the flight?

4) At what times was the temperature 90°?

5) At what times was the temperature 0°?

6) What was the change in temperature for the first 15 min. of the flight?

7) What was the change in temperature of the flight between 15 min. and 35 min.?

8) What was the maximum temperature?

9) At what times was the temperature rising most quickly?

10) At what times was the temperature falling most quickly?

2. Animal populations tend to rise and fall in cycles. Suppose the following data shows how squirrel populations in a central Pennsylvania city varied from 1975 to 1984.

Year 19	75	76	77	78	79	80	81	82	83	84
Population	750	700	520	680	730	650	550	625	780	700

a. Graph the data on graph paper using the two different scales.

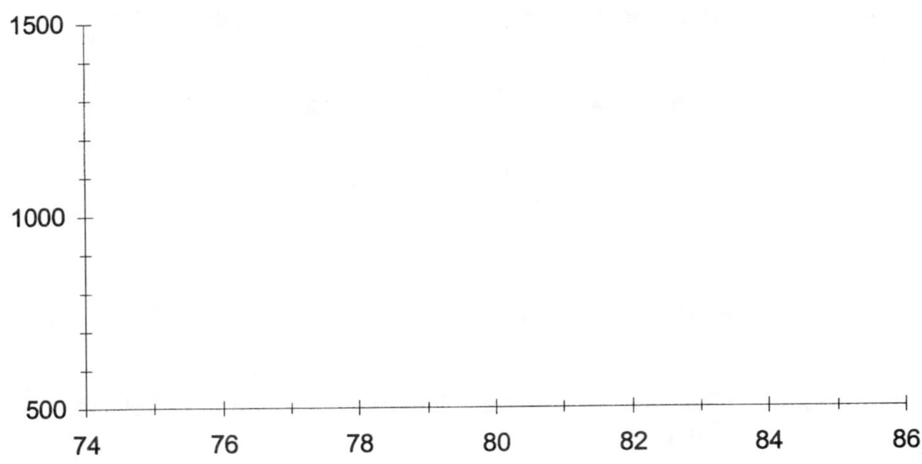

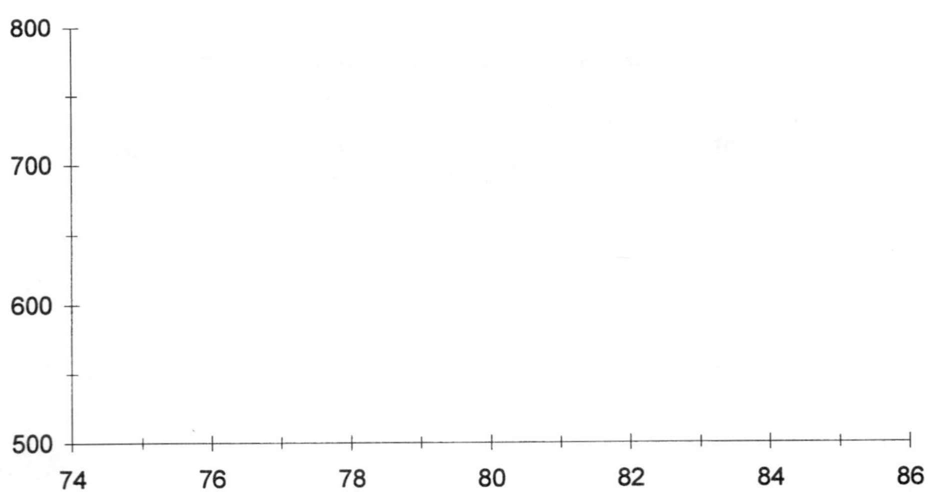

b. Which graph best describes the data? Why?

GROUP EXERCISE

Study Tips: 1. Review the material on pages 111 and 112.
2. Use a ruler and colored pencils.

1. You are given data relating two variables. Choose reasonable scales for axes on a graph and plot the given data. Then write a sentence describing the pattern in the graph and what it says about the relationship between the two variables.

Price per Barrel of Crude Oil, *X*	Price per Gallon of Gasoline, Y
$ 3.35	$ .38
3.75	.40
4.29	.43
5.80	.57
18.00	.80
21.30	.85
30.00	.98
35.75	1.20
37.05	1.15
42.50	1.35
45.75	1.40
45.75	1.25

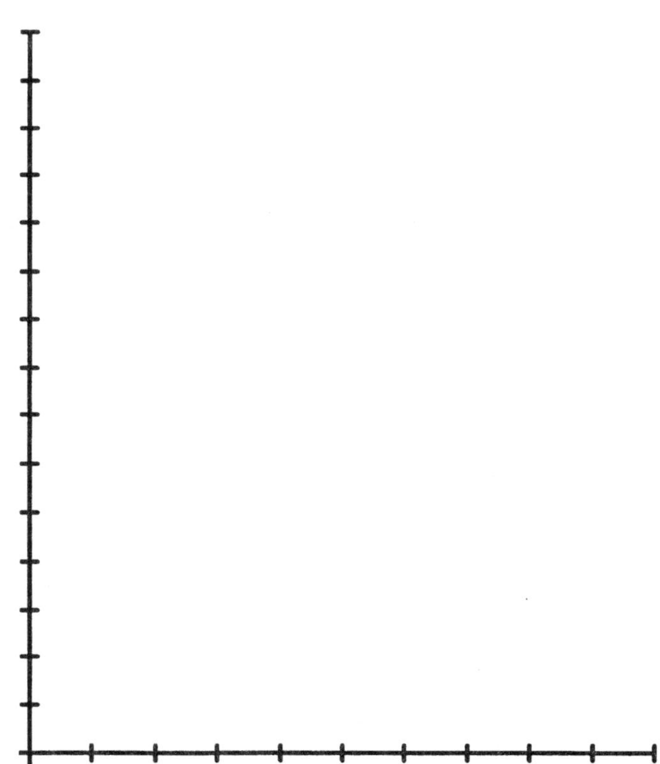

2. A 10 cm. stick is broken into two pieces. One is placed at a right angle to form an upside down "T" shape. By attaching wires from the ends of the base to the end of the upright piece, a frame work for a sail will be formed. This problem was first introduced on page 28.

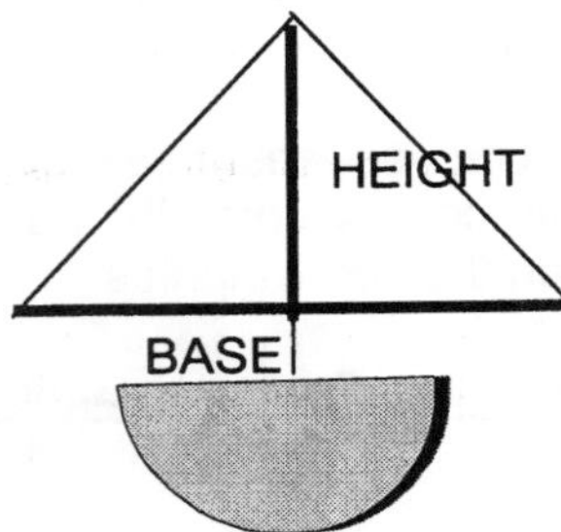

a. Calculate the area of the sail for the given length of the base.

Base b cm	Height h cm	Area $A = \frac{1}{2} b \cdot h$ cm^2	Point (base, area)
0			
2			
4 cm	10 - 4 = 6 cm	$\frac{1}{2}(4)(6) = 12\ cm^2$	(4, 12)
5			
8			
9			
10			
b			

b. What is the equation that relates area to the base?

c. Use the graph to estimate the maximum area.

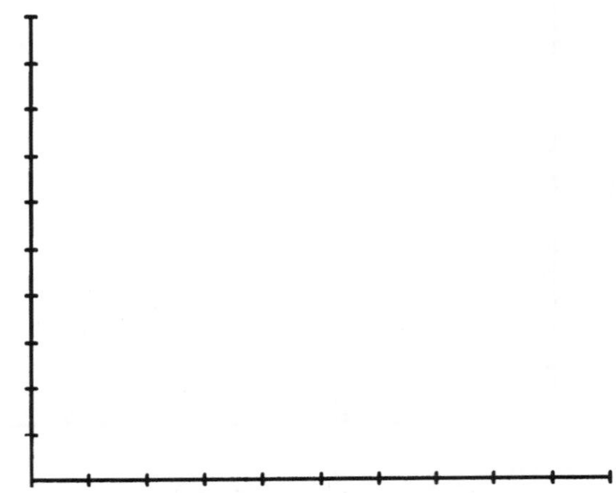

EXERCISES

Study Tips: 1. Review page 110 and, if your teacher did the Class Work section, page 114.
2. Have all necessary materials available: graph paper, ruler, and colored pencils.
3. Work for 20 minutes and then do something else. Complete your homework in short intervals.

You are given data relating two variables. Choose reasonable scales for axes on a graph and plot the given data. Then write a sentence describing the pattern in the graph and the relationship between the two variables.

1. The following table shows the school year and total revenue spent for public elementary and secondary schools.

School Year	1930	1946	1954	1966	1974	1985	1990
Revenues (millions of dollars)	2	3	8	25	58	137	208

Source: *Digest of Educational Statistics.*

2. The following table shows the number of insurance establishments in Montgomery County.

Year	1990	1991	1992	1993	1994
Number of Establishments	519	523	536	552	554

Source: *Pennsylvania County Industry Trends 1990-1994.*

3. At a pizza store, Sarah is in charge of scheduling workers. To help make these decisions, Sarah collected the following data on the number of people waiting for pizzas each hour on the hour for three days.

Time	Day 1	Day 2	Day 3	Average
11:00	11	9	8	
12:00	15	18	19	
1:00	18	21	20	
2:00	9	11	13	
3:00	5	4	6	
4:00	6	8	7	
5:00	12	11	15	
6:00	22	4	21	
7:00	15	17	9	
8:00	8	7	7	

a. Average the values for the different times and plot them on a graph.

b. Write a paragraph interpreting the data and the graph.

c. Suppose you were told that on the second day at 6:00 pm a water repair crew blocked the pizza shop's driveway. Would you change your interpretation of the graph? How?

4. Suppose that a baseball player hits a high pop-up straight above home plate. If the bat meets the ball 1.5 meters above the ground and sends it up at a velocity of 30 meters per second, then the height of the ball, in meters, *t* seconds later is indicated by the table.

t seconds	0	1	2	3	4	5	6
h meters	1.5	27	42	47	43	29	5

a. Use the table to make a graph. Choose your scales so that you can answer the questions that follow. Be sure to indicate time and height scales along the axes.

b. What point shows the starting height of the ball? Give its coordinates.

c. What point shows the height of the ball at 2 seconds? Label this point *B* and give its coordinates.

d. What point(s) show a height of 20 meters? Label it (or them) *C* and give the coordinates.

e. What point shows where the ball reaches its maximum height? Label this point *D* and give its coordinates.

f. What point shows when the ball hits the ground? Label this point *E* and give its coordinates.

g. When is the ball more than 40 meters above ground?

h. When is the ball exactly 35 meters above the ground? (Be careful!)

i. What is the height of the ball when the time is zero seconds?

j. What is the height of the ball when the time is 4.5 seconds?

k. When is the ball less than 50 meters above the ground?

l. What was the change in height for the first two seconds?

m. What was the change in height between 2 seconds and 3 seconds?

n. What was the change in height between 4 seconds and 6 seconds?

o. At what times was the ball rising most quickly?

p. At what times was the ball falling most quickly?

INTERPRETING GRAPHS
OVERVIEW

Objective: This section covers the basic properties of graphs. You will learn about intercepts, vertices, and intersections. In order to answer questions properly, it is very important to pay attention to the scale of the graph.

Basic Example: The graph below shows the profit of two toy companies, Radio Control Inc. and Turbo Car Co.

Labeling the variables:

Let N represent the number of toys sold. The units for N are millions.
Let P represent the profit of the companies. The units for P are thousands.

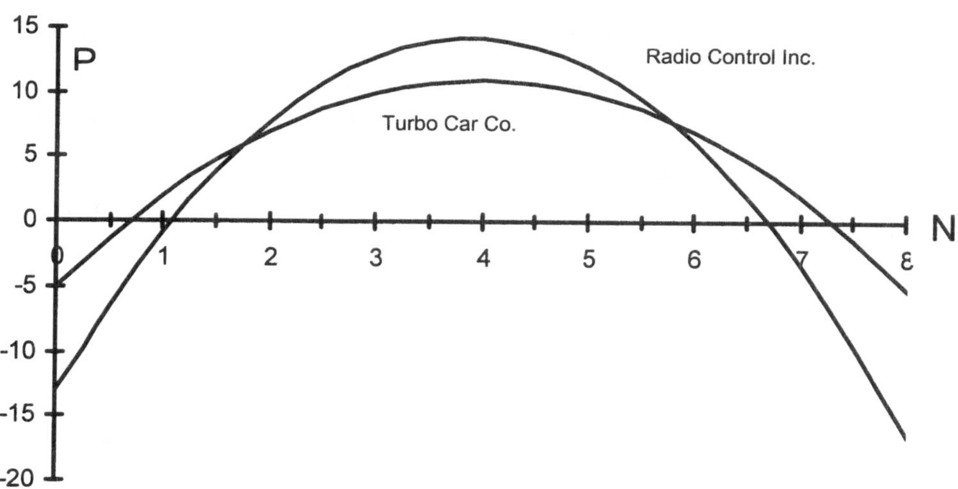

1. What is the independent variable?
   The independent variable is the horizontal axis, which in this example, is the number of toy cars sold, N.

2. What is the dependent variable?
   The dependent variable is the vertical axis, which in this case is profit, P.

3. How many toy cars does Radio Control Inc. have to sell to break even?
   A company breaks even when their profit is zero. So the break even points are on the horizontal axis. The graph of Radio Control Inc. crosses the N axis at approximately 1.1 and 6.6. The break-even points for Radio Control Inc. are 1,100,000 and 6,600,000 toy cars. The break-even points are the N **intercepts**.

4. For what number of cars sold is the profit the same for both companies?
   The two companies have the same profit where the two graphs **intersect** or cross. Put a dot where the two graphs intersect. The answer to the question is the independent variable, number of cars sold, N. The values for the independent variable are approximately 1.6, and 5.9. The two companies make the same profit when they sell 1,600,000 or 5,900,000 toy cars.

Study Tip: You need to know the difference between intercepts and intersection.

5. How much money does Turbo Car Co. lose if they don't sell any cars?

   If Turbo Car Co. doesn't sell any cars, then the independent variable, N, is zero. So the answer to the question is the **Profit intercept**. The profit coordinate of the Profit intercept is –5. Turbo Co. loses $5,000 if they don't sell any toy cars.

6. For what number of cars does Radio Control Inc have a maximum profit?

   The maximum profit is at the top of the graph. This point is called the **vertex** of the graph. The N (number of cars sold) coordinate is approximately 4. Radio Control Inc. will have a maximum profit if they sell 4,000,000 cars.

7. What is the maximum profit of Radio Control Inc.?

   The maximum profit occurs when Radio Control Inc. sells 4 million toy cars, N = 4. At that point, their profit will be $14,000.

Summary: Interpreting graphs is an extremely important skill in the work world. Visual representation of data is expected by both supervisors and customers. You must be comfortable with key graphing concepts. See page 110 for definitions and examples

1. Horizontal axis. (In a nonapplication problem the x axis.)

2. Vertical axis. (In a nonapplication problem the y axis.)

3. Independent variable.

4. Dependent variable.

5. Intercepts.

6. Intersection.

7. Vertex.

CLASS WORK

1. The graph below shows the temperature during a winter day in Chicago, Illinois.

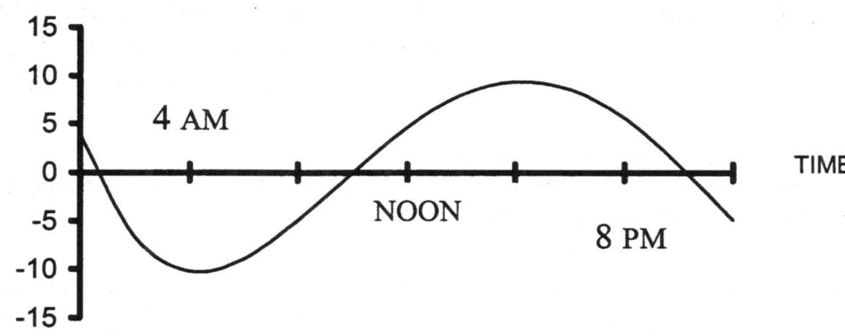

a. What was the temperature at noon?

b. When was the temperature 0°?

c. What was the high temperature for the day?

d. When was the high temperature?

e. What was the low temperature for the day?

f. When was the low temperature for the day?

g. When was the temperature rising?

h. When was the temperature decreasing?

2. The graphs below show the profit for the calculator companies, PA Instruments and Hewett Luggage.

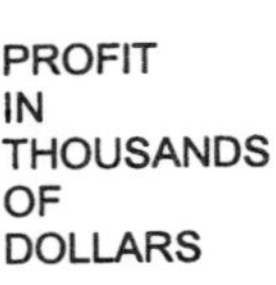

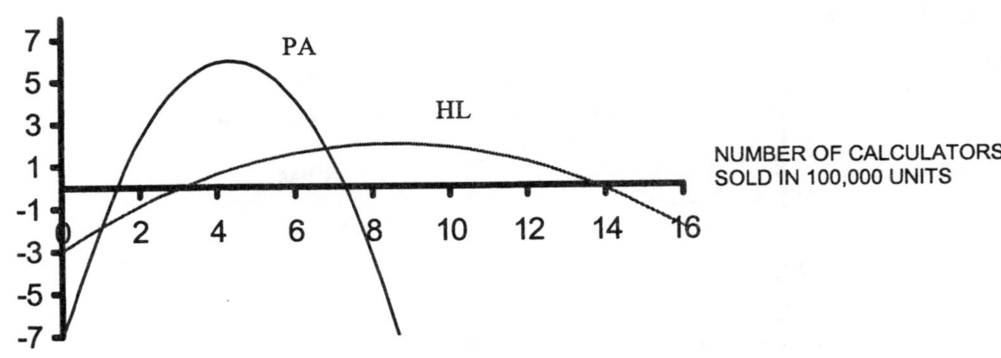

a. How many calculators does Hewett Luggage have to sell to break even?

b. How many calculators does PA Instruments have to sell to break even?

c. For what number of calculators sold is the profit the same for both companies?

d. How much profit does PA Instruments make (or lose) if they don't sell any calculators?

e. How much profit does Hewett Luggage make (or lose) if they don't sell any calculators?

GROUP EXERCISE

Study Tips: 1. Practice good group techniques.
2. If your teacher did the Class Work problems, review the problem on page 122.

1. The graph below shows the temperature during a winter day in Snowbound, Montana.

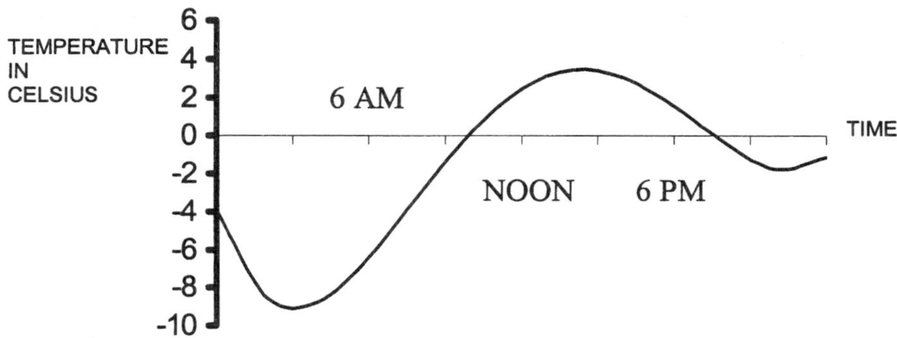

a. What was the temperature at 9 a.m.?

b. When was the temperature 0°

c. What was the high temperature for the day?

d. When was the high temperature for the day?

e. What was the low temperature for the day?

f. When was the low temperature for the day?

g. When was the temperature rising?

h. When was the temperature falling?

2. The graph below shows the profit for two companies, AMATYC and PSMATYC.

Study Tip: Review pages 120 and 121.

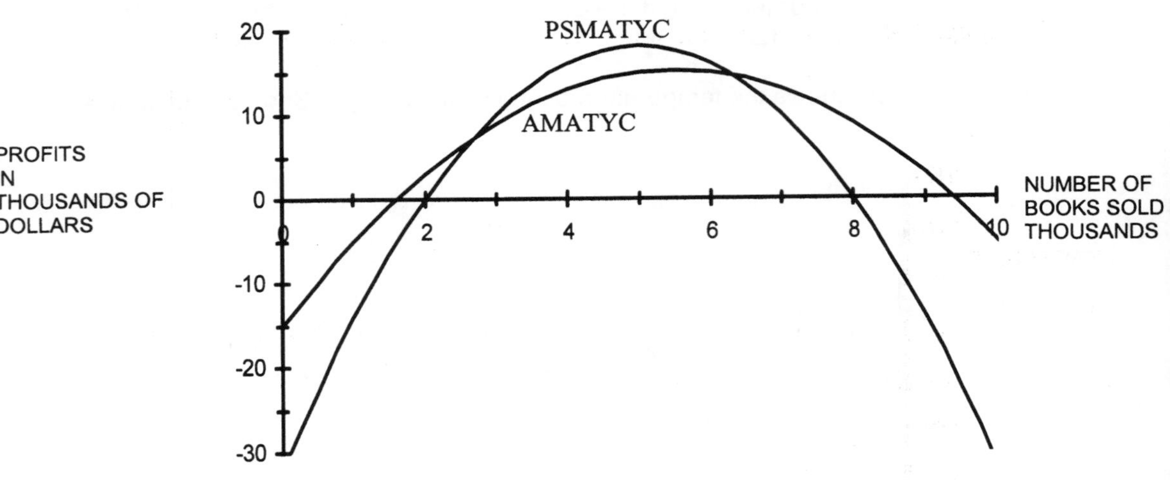

a. How many books does AMATYC have to sell to break even?

b. How many books does PSYMATYC have to sell to break even?

c. For what number of books is the profit the same for both companies?

d. What is the maximum profit for AMATYC?

e. How many books does AMATYC have to sell to maximize its profits?

f. How much profit does PSYMATYC make (or lose) if they don't sell any books?

g. How much profit or loss does AMATYC experience if they don't sell any books?

h. How much profit or loss does PSYMATYC experience if they don't sell any books?

i. When are AMATYC's profits decreasing?

EXERCISES

Study Tips: 1. Have you tried doing homework with a friend?
2. If your teacher covered the Class Work, review page 122.

1. The graph below shows the temperatures during a winter day in Killington, Vermont.

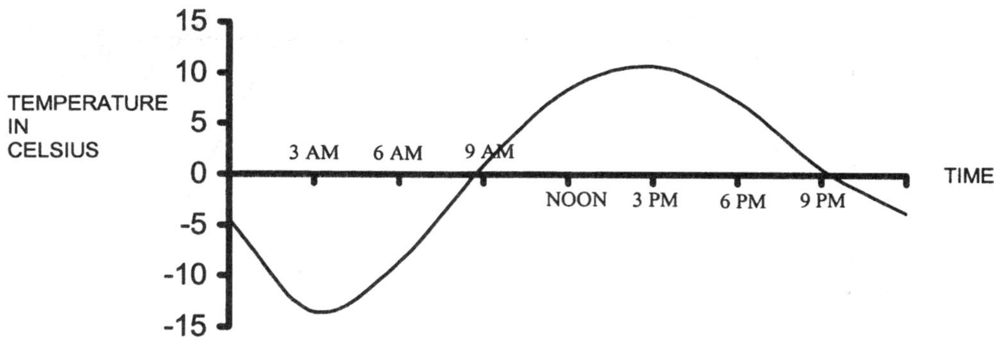

a. What were the high and low temperatures recorded during the day?

b. When were the high and low temperatures recorded?

c. During what time intervals was the temperature above 0° C?

d. During what time intervals was the temperature below 0° C?

e. When was the temperature 10° C?

f. What was the temperature at noon?

g. When was the temperature rising?

h. When was the temperature falling?

2. The graph below shows the fish population of a lake.

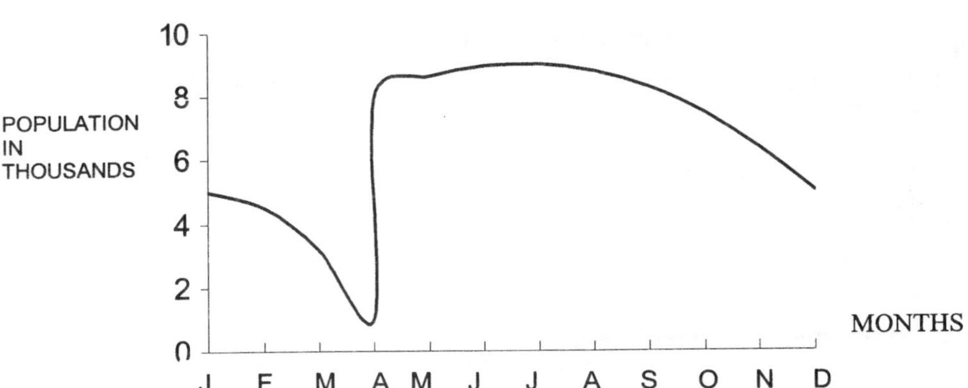

a. How many fish are there at the beginning of June?

b. When is the fish population the greatest?

c. What is the maximum number of fish in the lake?

d. When is the population of the fish increasing?

e. When is the population of the fish decreasing?

f. What do you think happened on April 1?

3. The graphs below show the cost of making a phone call for two different companies, WRONG # and BUZZ.

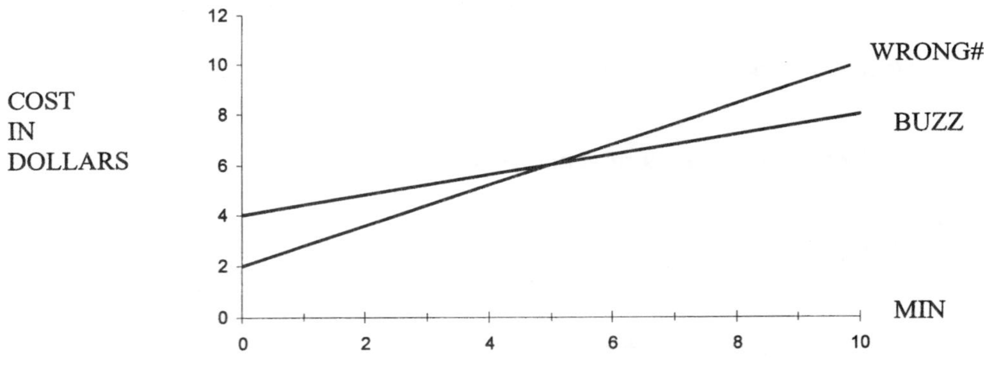

a. When do the two companies charge the same amount for a phone call?

b. Which company charges the most per minute?

c. Which company charges the most just to pick up the phone?

d. When is Buzz cheaper than Wrong #?

GRAPHING LINES BY PLOTTING POINTS
OVERVIEW

Objective: In this section we will graph lines by finding three points.

Basic Examples:

Example 1. You need to rent a moving van. Class Movers charges a basic rate of $24.95 plus 32 cents per mile.

(This example is from Introduction to Variables, page18 and Solving Equations Part I, page 36.)

a. Calculate the cost of renting a van if you drive the following miles.

MILES	CALCULATION	COST
10	$.32 \bullet 10 + 24.95$	28.15
20	$.32 \bullet 20 + 24.95$	31.35
30	$.32 \bullet 30 + 24.95$	34.55
m	$.32 \bullet m + 24.95$	C

The cost equation is. $C = .32 \bullet m + 24.95$

b. What are the independent and dependent variables?

The cost depends on the number of miles driven. So cost is the dependent variable and miles are the independent variable.

c. What are the ordered pairs generated by the table?

The ordered pairs have the form (miles, cost) because ordered pairs have the form (independent variable, dependent variable).

The points are (10, 28.15), (20, 31.35), (30, 34.55).

d. Graph the equation $C = .32m + 24.95$.

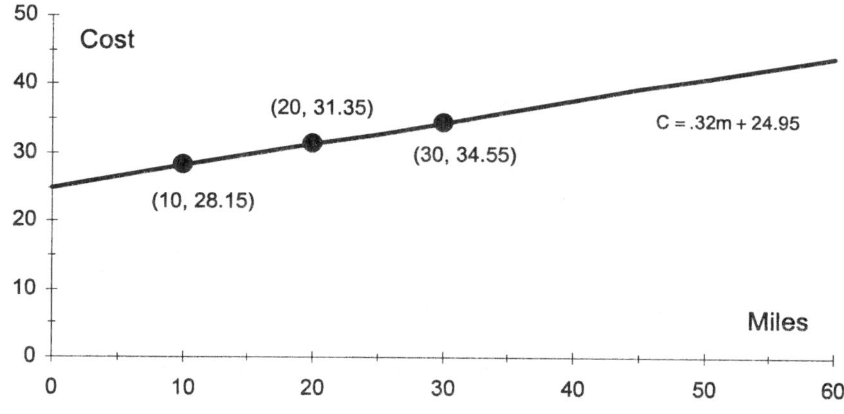

Example 2. Graph $2x + 5y = 26$

a. For a basic math problem like this, x is always the independent variable.

b. For a basic math problem like this, y is always the dependent variable.

c. You must have two points to graph a line, but we will find three. We use the third point to check our work. All three points must be on the line.

> **Explanation:** It doesn't matter what 3 values you pick for x, but don't choose numbers too close together.

1. Choose three values for x; then use algebra to find y.

2. Choose x = – 5.

$2(-5) + 5y = 26$	Substitute –5 for x.
$-10 + 5y = 26$	Multiply
$5y = 36$	Add 10 to both sides.
$y = 7.2$	Divide both sides by 5.

One point is (–5, 7.2).

3. Choose x = 2.

$2(2) + 5y = 26$	Substitute 2 for x.
$4 + 5y = 26$	Multiply
$5y = 22$	Subtract 4 from both sides.
$y = 4.4$	Divide both sides by 5.

The second point is (2, 4.4).

4. Choose x = 10.

$2(10) + 5y = 26$	Substitute 10 for x.
$20 + 5y = 26$	Multiply
$5y = 6$	Subtract 20 from both sides.
$y = 1.2$	Divide both sides by 5.

The third point is (10, 1.2).

d. Graph the three points.

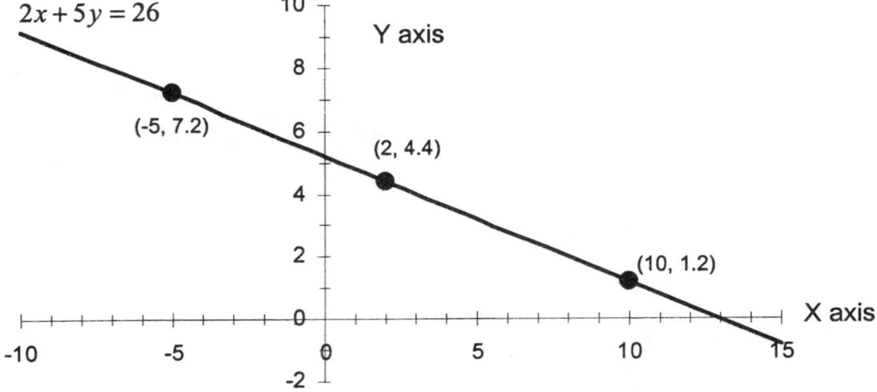

Summary: Graphing is a very important topic in algebra. A graph gives a visualization of data or of an equation. For example a graph allows you to see how the cost of renting a van is increasing as you drive more miles.

To graph a line:

1. Choose three values of the independent variable. A minimum of two points is needed to graph a line. A third point is used to check the work.

2. For each value of the independent variable, use algebra to find the value of the dependent variable.

3. Plot and connect the three points. If the points are not forming a line, then you have made a mistake.

4. When graphing an application, you need to think about the restrictions on the variables. In Example 1, it wouldn't make any sense to have negative values for miles or cost.

5. When graphing a basic math problem, x is always the independent variable, and y is always the dependent variable.

6. When graphing a basic math problem, you don't have any restrictions on the variables. Your graph should include both positive and negative values for x and y.

Study Tip: Note card for graphing

1. Construct a table of values.
2. Plot the points.
3. Connect the points.

Review the card as homework at least twice a week and use the card as a reference when you do the homework from this section..

CLASS WORK

1. An appliance repair shop charges an initial fee of \$30 plus \$15 per hour to fix an appliance.

   a. Complete the table to find the cost of repairing an appliance.

Hours	Calculation	Costs
3		
5		
10		
h		

   b. What is the equation that relates cost and hours?

   c. Use the results in Part a. to graph the equation in Part b. Choose an appropriate scale and only graph the portion that makes sense to the problem. Label the axes.

Hours	**Cost**	**Point (h, c)**
3		
5		
10		

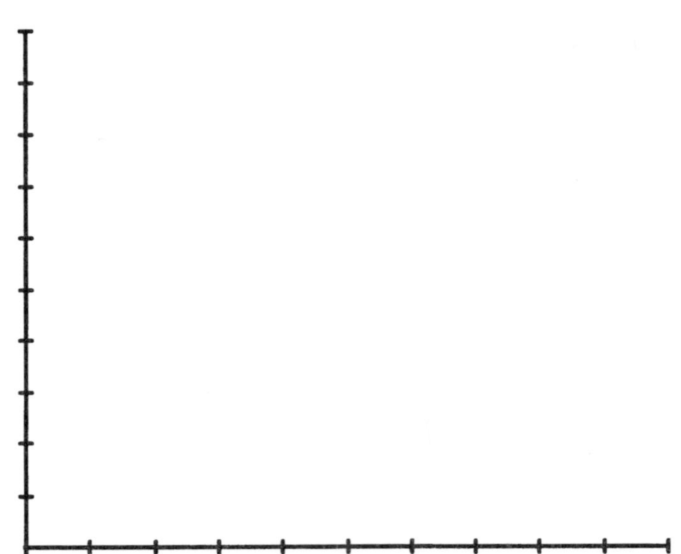

2. Given $y = 3x - 4$

Is $x = 2, y = -1$ a solution?

Is $x = 5, y = 11$ a solution?

Is $x = -2, y = -10$ a solution?

Is $x = 3, y = 2$ a solution?

3. Represent all of the solutions by graphing a line using the Cartesian Coordinate system.

a. $y = 3x - 4$

x	y	Point (x, y)

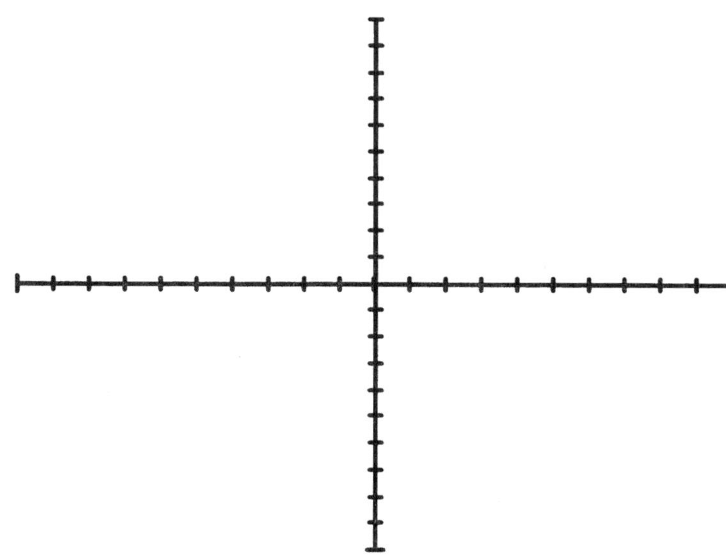

b. $6x - 4y = 18$

x	y	Point (x, y)

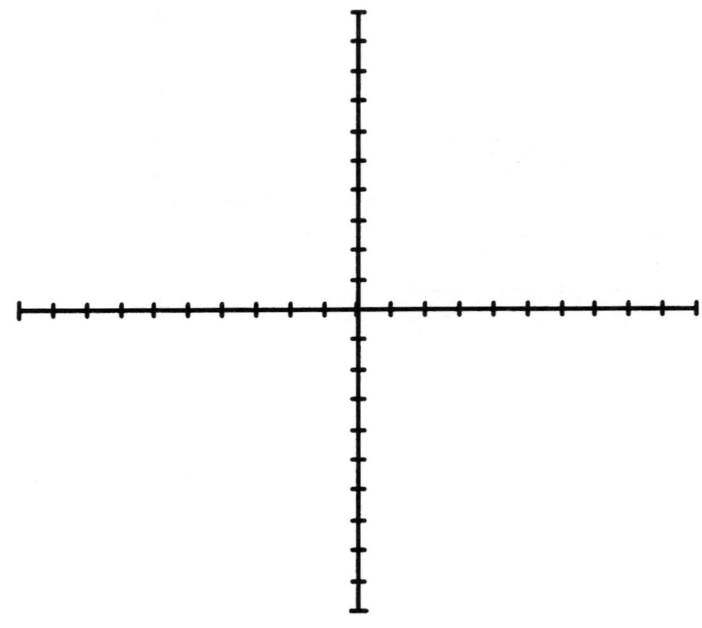

4. Graph the line by plotting points.

a. $y = \frac{-1}{2}x + 5$

x	y	Point (x, y)

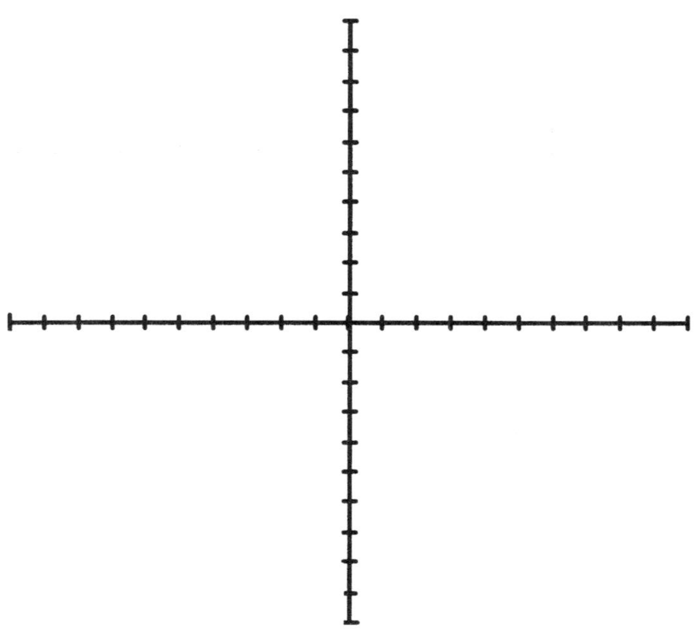

b. $6x + 5y = 35$

x	y	Point (x, y)

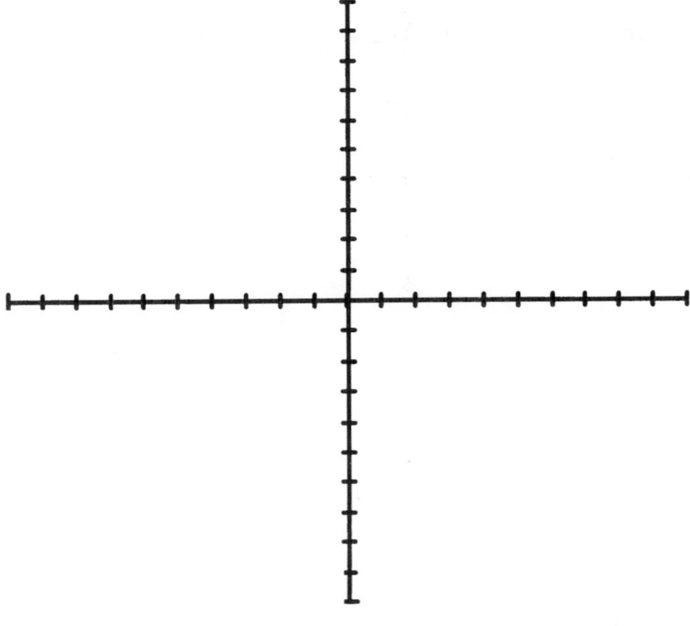

GROUP EXERCISE

Study Tip:
1. Choose one person to draw the graph.
2. Other group members should work on the table of values to guide the grapher.
3. All are responsible for knowing the complete process.

1. A sales position pays 12% commission plus $200 per week.

   a. Complete the table below.

Sales	Calculation	Wages
500		
1000		
2000		
s		

   b. What is the equation that relates wages and sales?

   c. Use the results in Part a. to graph the equation in Part b. Choose an appropriate scale and only graph the portion that makes sense to the problem. Label the axes.

Sales	**Wages**	**Point (s, w)**
500		
1,000		
2,000		

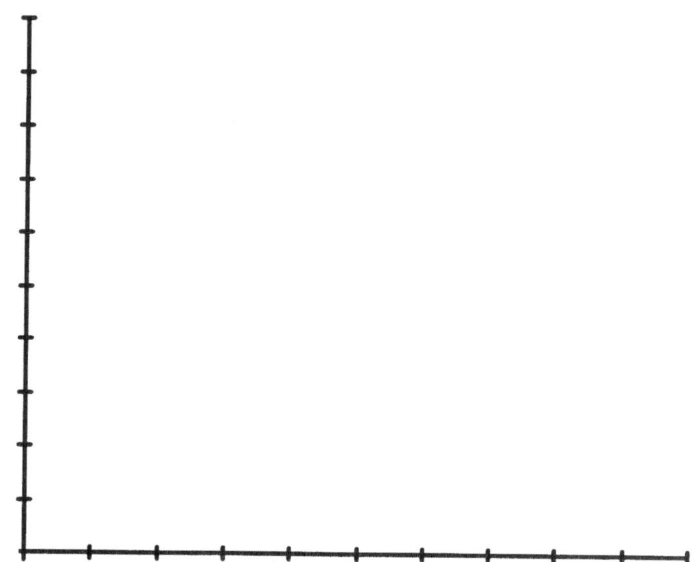

2. Graph the line by plotting points.

Study Tip: Not enough space is provided to adequately do the algebra necessary to compute the points for the graphs. Use notebook paper to help organize your work.

a. $y = \frac{2}{3}x - 7$

x	y	Point (x, y)

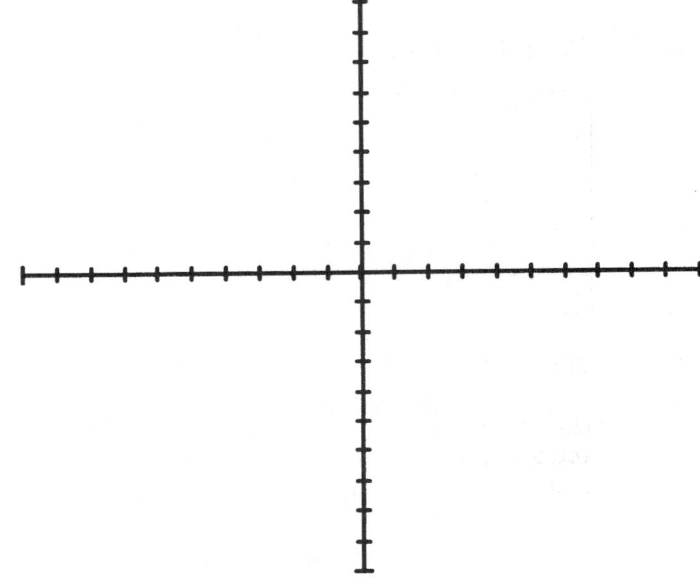

b. $8x - 3y = 24$

Study Tip: Review Example 2 on page 130.

x	y	Point (x, y)

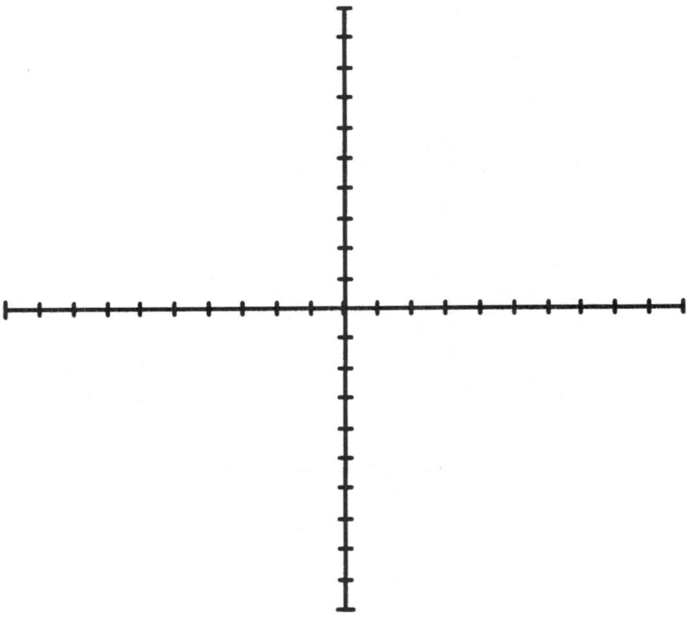

EXERCISES

Study Tip: Necessary materials: pencils, colored pencils, ruler, eraser, graph paper, and notecards.

1. An internet provider, Wild Web, charges $15 per month plus 50 cents an hour.

   a. Complete the table below.

Hours	Calculation	Cost
20		
50		
100		
h		

   b. What is the equation that relates cost and hours?

   c. Use the results in Part a. to graph the equation in Part b. Choose an appropriate scale and only graph the portion that makes sense to the problem. Label the axes.

Hours	**Cost**	**Point (h, c)**
20		
50		
100		

2. A car rental company, 4Wheels, charges 35 cents a mile plus $15 a day.

   a. Complete the table below. (You must pick values for hours.)

Miles	Calculation	Cost
m		

   b. What is the equation that relates cost and miles?

   c. Use the results in Part a. to graph the equation in Part b. Choose an appropriate scale and only graph the portion that makes sense to the problem. Label the axes.

Miles	**Cost**	**Point (m, c)**
20		
50		
100		

3. Find the mistake. Write a sentence describing what the student did wrong.

Graph y = 2x – 5

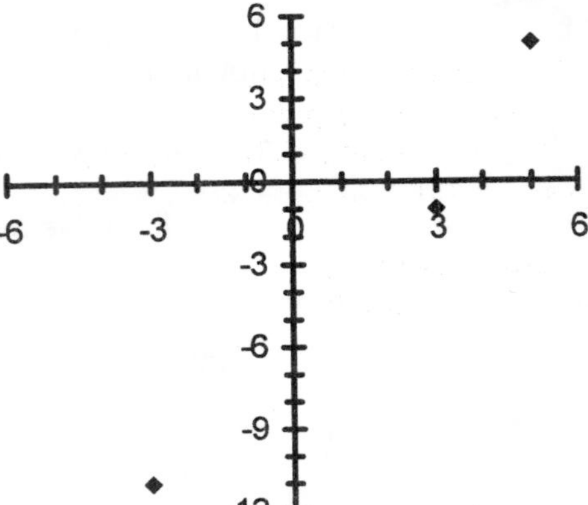

Let x = 3	Let x = 5	Let x = -3
y = 2(3)–5	y = 2(5)–5	y = 2(-3)-5
y = -1	y = 5	y = -11
(3, -1)	(5, 5)	(-3, -11)

This is why we usually graph three points.

4. Given y = 2x + 7

Is x = 2, y = 11 a solution?
Is x = 5, y = 15 a solution?
Is x = -1, y = 5 a solution?
Is x = 7, y = 21 a solution?

5. Graph the line by plotting points.

Study Tips: 1. Make the table below for each problem. The table helps organize your work.

x	y	Point (x, y)

2. Use graph paper, colored pencils, and a ruler to create the graphs.

a. y = 2x + 7

b. $y = \frac{-1}{2}x + 5$

c. 3x – 8y = 32

d. 6x + 4y = 18

Study Tips: 1. Always check your homework by looking up the answers in the back of the book.
2. If you had difficulty with the homework, be prepared to ask your teacher for help. Ask your teacher to go over specific problems.
3. For further assistance:
   a. See your instructor during his/her office hours.
   b. Go to the L. A. L.
   c. Review the section using the CD that accompanies the textbook.
   d. View the appropriate lecture on IPTV. The L. A. L. can help you do this.

GRAPHING LINES BY FINDING THE INTERCEPTS
OVERVIEW

Objectives: This section presents an additional way to graph a line. To graph a line, you need a minimum of two points. Two special points can be used. They are the intercepts of each axis. Often the intercepts have special meanings in a mathematical model. Also covered in this section are horizontal and vertical lines.

Basic examples:

Example 1. Your 8-year-old son plans to open a lemonade stand. All of his supplies cost \$18.00, and he charges 50 cents per glass. The equation that relates profit and number of glasses sold is

$$P = .50g - 18.00$$

a. What are the independent and dependent variables?

His profit depends on the number of glasses sold. So P is the dependent variable, and g is the independent variable. The points on the graph will have the form (g, P).

b. How many glasses does he have to sell to break even?

Breaking even means that his profit will be zero.
Find g when P = 0.

$0 = .50g - 18.00$	Substitute 0 for P.
$18.00 = .50g$	Add 18.00 to both sides.
$36 = g$	Divide both sides by .50.

He needs to sell 36 glasses to break even.
Graph the point (36, 0).

c. How much money will he make if he doesn't sell any lemonade?

If he doesn't sell any, then g = 0. Find P when g = 0.

$P = .50 \bullet 0 - 18.00$	Substitute 0 for g.
$P = -18.00$	Compute P.

He will lose \$18.00 if he doesn't sell any glasses of lemonade.
Graph the point (0, -18).

Explanation: Parts b and c complete the table below.

g	P	Point (g, P)
36	0	(36, 0)
0	-18	(0, -18)

d. Graph the line $P = .50g - 18.00$ by plotting the points obtained in Parts b and c. Choose an appropriate scale and only graph the portion which makes sense in the problem. Label the axes.

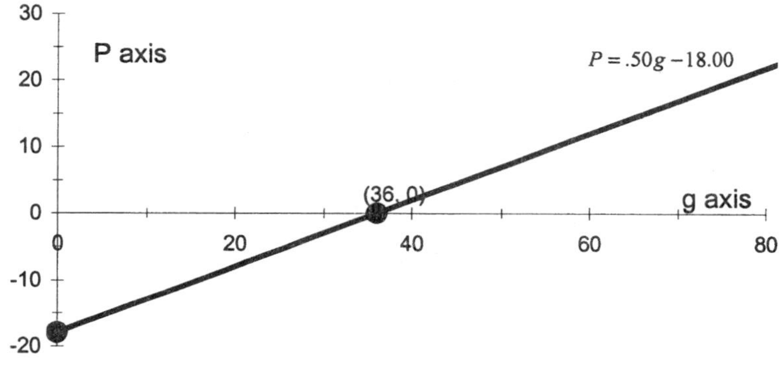

Explanation:
The point (36, 0) is the **g intercept** because the point is on the g axis.

The point (0, -18) is the **P intercept** because the point is on the P axis.

The significance of the previous example is:

The point (36, 0) is the g intercept. The P coordinate of the point (36, 0) is zero.

The point (0, -18) is the P intercept. The g coordinate of the point (0, -18) is zero.

To find the intercept of one of the axes, set the other variable equal to zero.

Example 2. Graph the line $25x + .04y = 50$ by finding the intercepts.

a. Find the y intercept. **Set x = 0**.

$25 \bullet 0 + .04y = 50$ Substitute x = 0.

$.04y = 50$ Multiply. $25 \bullet 0 = 0$.

$y = 1250$ Divide both sides by .04.

The y intercept is (0, 1250).

b. Find the x intercept. **Set y = 0**.

$25x + .04 \bullet 0 = 50$ Substitute y = 0.

$25x = 50$ Multiply. $.04 \bullet 0 = 0$.

$x = 2$ Divide both sides by 25.

The x intercept is (2, 0).

c. Graph the points (0, 1250) and (2, 0).

You have to think about the scale of the y axis. The scale of the y axis is 250. It is nice, but not necessary, to have the intercept correspond to an interval on the axis. Also, you don't want the intercept to be at the very top or bottom of the graph. There are other possibilities.

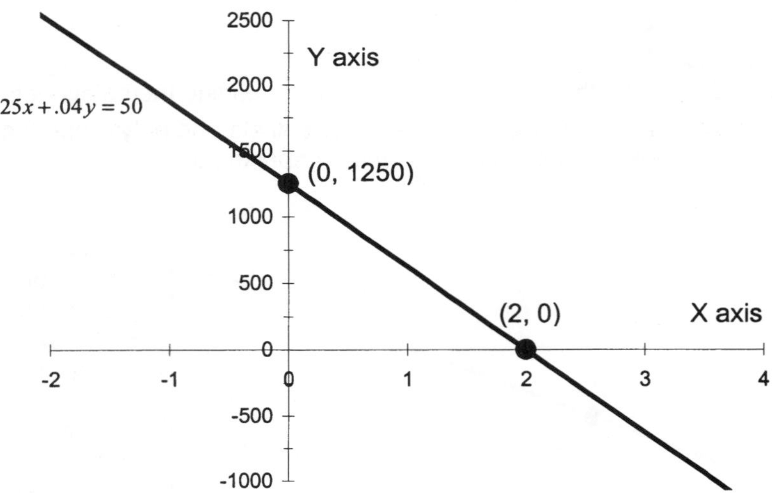

Study Tip: Write a note card describing the process of graphing by finding the intercepts. Review regularly.

Horizontal Lines:

Example 3. Today we will look at the cost of renting a car from three different rental companies. Elvis will rent us a car for $35 plus $0.25 a mile. Quartz rents the same model for $25 plus $0.50 a mile. AUTO will rent it to us for a flat daily rate of $55 with no mileage charge.

(This is the group work problem from Introduction to Variables on page 23.)

The equations for the three companies are:

Elvis: $C = .25m + 35.00$

Quartz: $C = .50m + 25.00$

AUTO: $C = 55.00$

The independent variable is m and the dependent variable is C.

The company AUTO charges $55.00 no matter how many miles you go.

If you drive, 10 miles it costs $55.

If you drive, 30 miles it costs $55.

If you drive, 90 miles it costs $55.

The graph of $C = 55.00$

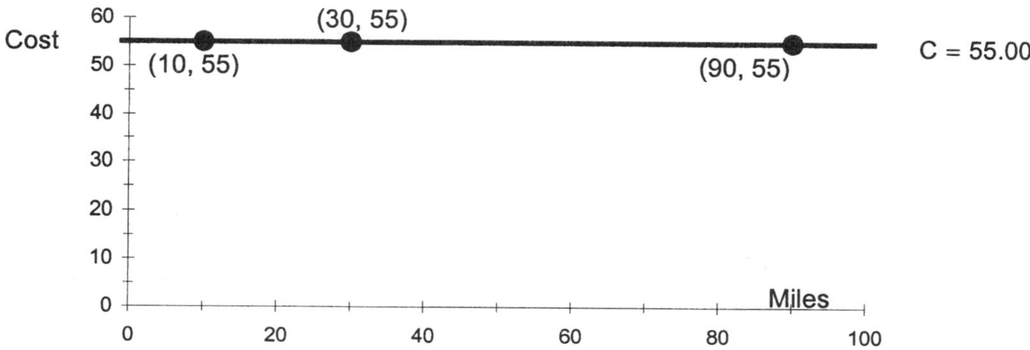

The equation of a horizontal line is the dependent variable equal to a constant. The graph of y = k, k a constant, is a horizontal line.

Study Tip: You should write the equation for a horizontal line on a note card. You will need to graph horizontal lines in the section Applications of Graphs. You should review this card at least twice a week.

Example 4. Graph y = -4.

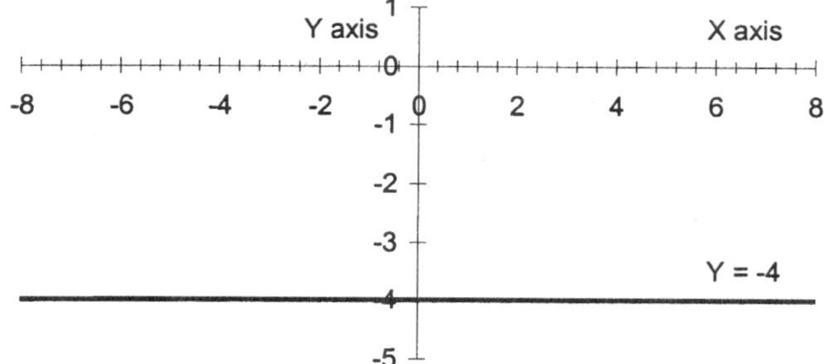

Explanation: Every point on the graph has a y coordinate of – 4.

Points on the graph: (– 6, – 4), (0, – 4), (3, – 4).

Vertical Lines:

The equation of a vertical line is the independent variable equal to a constant. The graph of x = h, h a constant, is a vertical line.

Study Tip: You should write the equation for a vertical line on a note card.

Example 5. Graph x = 3.

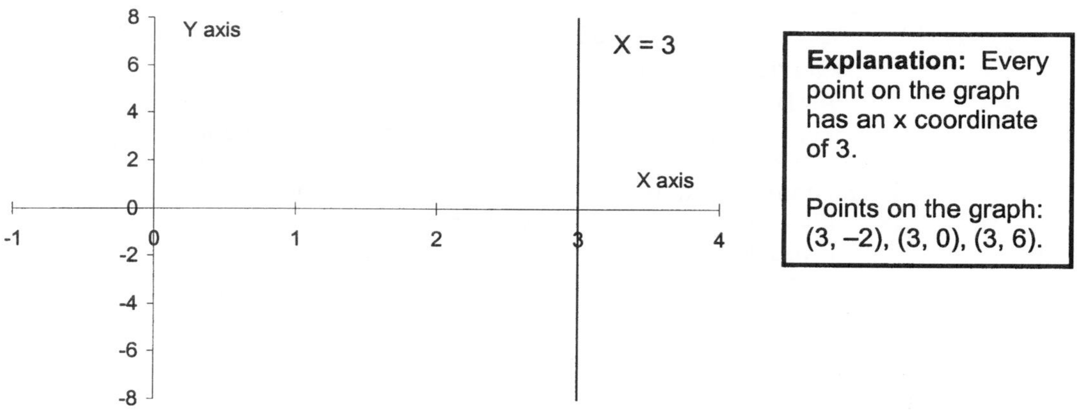

Explanation: Every point on the graph has an x coordinate of 3.

Points on the graph: (3, –2), (3, 0), (3, 6).

Summary: Graphs allow you to visualize the equation. You now know two ways to graph a line, plotting any two points or finding the intercepts. Sometimes you will have to decide which way is easier.

a. To graph a line by plotting two points.
   1. Choose two values of the independent variable.
   2. For each value of the independent variable, use algebra to find the value of the dependent variable.
   3. Plot and connect the two points.
   4. Choose a third value of the independent variable to check your work.

b. Graphing lines by finding the intercepts.
   1. To find the x intercept, set y = 0 and solve for x.
   2. To find the y intercept, set x = 0 and solve for y.

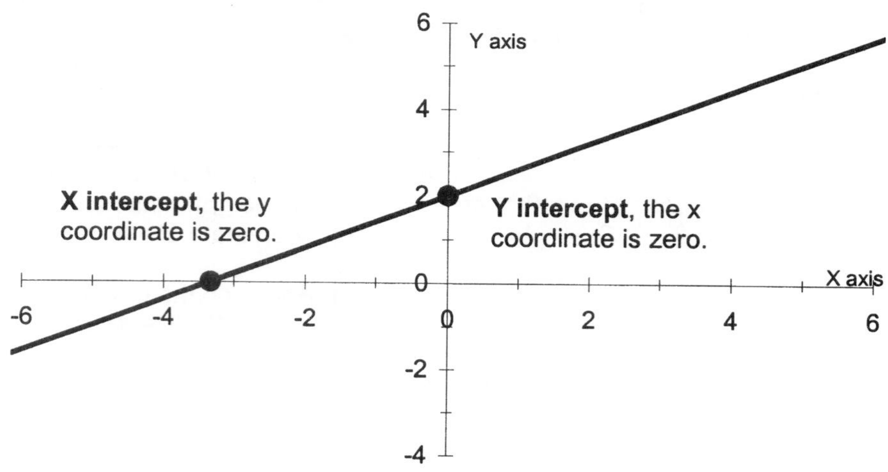

c. Horizontal lines.

The equation of a horizontal line is:

$$y = \text{a number}$$

The graph of a horizontal line:

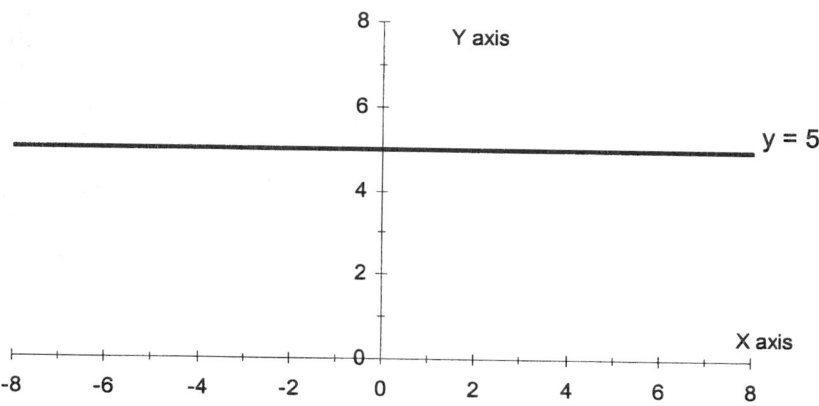

d. Vertical lines.

The equation of a vertical line is:

$$x = \text{a number}$$

The graph of a vertical line is:

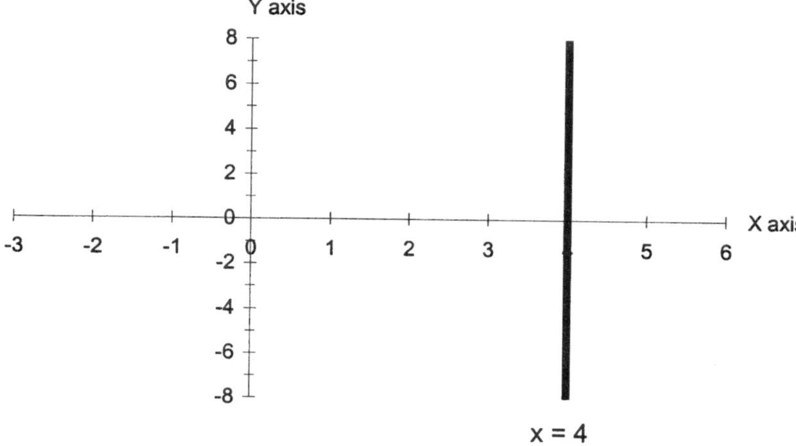

CLASS WORK

1. Sally started a lawn-mowing business for the summer. She bought a lawn mower for \$200, and she charges \$5 an hour. The equation that relates profit and hours worked is

$$p = 5h - 200$$

a. How many hours does she have to work to break even?

b. How much money will she make if she doesn't work any hours?

c. Graph the line $p = 5h - 200$ by plotting the points obtained in Parts a. and b. Choose an appropriate scale and only graph the portion that makes sense to the problem. Label the axes.

p intercept	
h intercept	

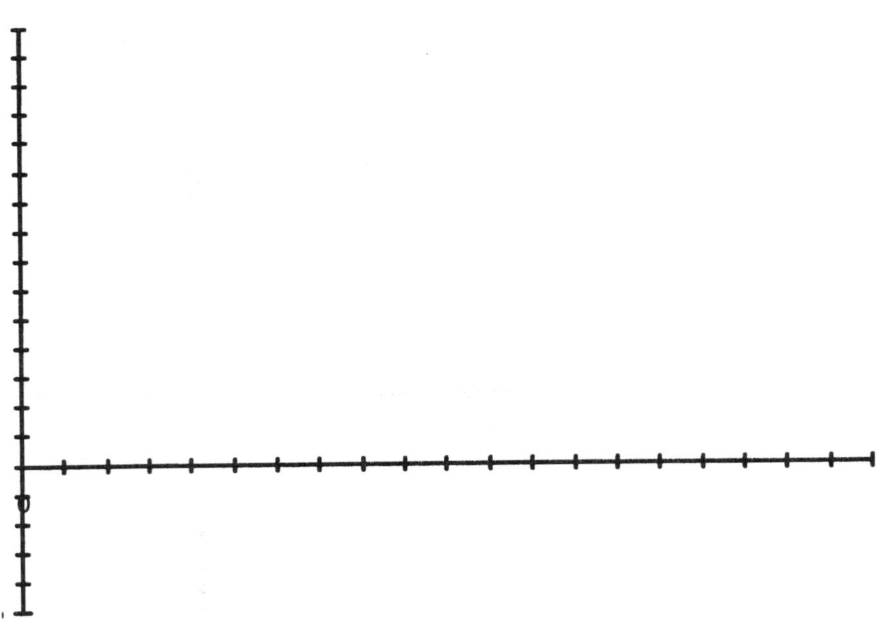

2. Graph the line by finding the x and y intercepts. Choose an appropriate scale and label the axes.

a. $y = \frac{2}{3}x - 5$

x intercept	
y intercept	

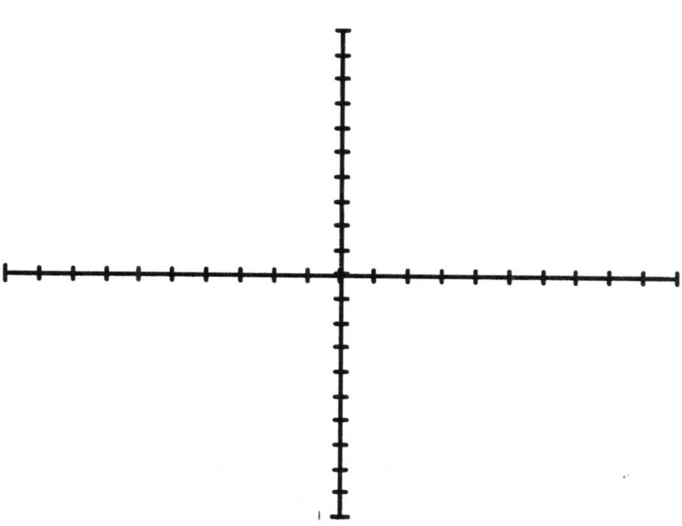

b. $.03x - 4y = 16$

xintercept	
y intercept	

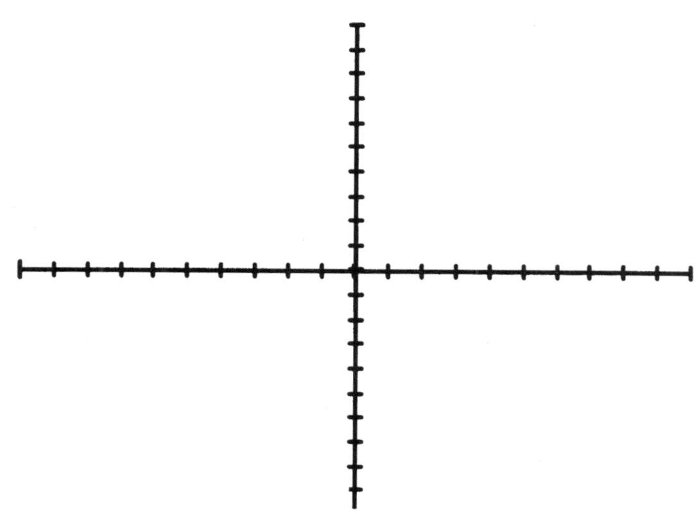

3. Define vertical and horizontal lines.

4. Graph the lines.

a. $y = 18$

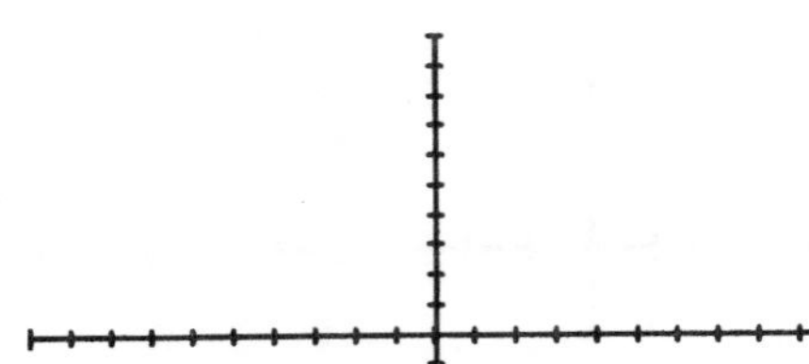

b. $x = -4$

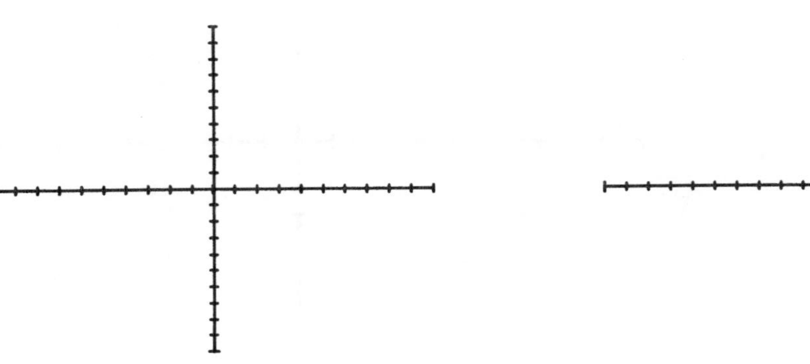

c. $28x - .13y = 15$

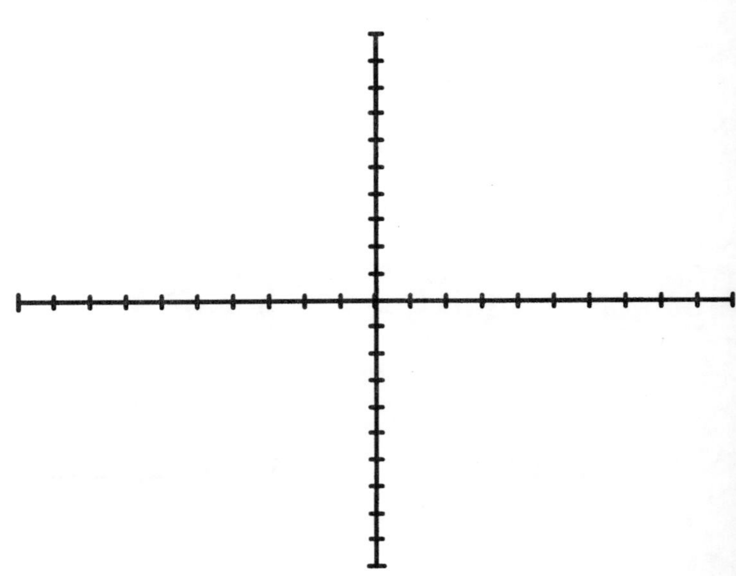

GROUP EXERCISES

1. Johnny Lift runs a snow clearing business for the winter. He bought a snow blower for $310 and charges $10 per hour. The equation that relates profit and hours is

$$p = 10h - 310$$

a. How many hours does he have to work to break even?

b. How much money will he make or lose if he doesn't work any hours?

c. Graph the line $p = 10h - 310$ by plotting the points obtained in Parts a. and b. Choose an appropriate scale and only graph the portion that makes sense to the problem. Label the axes.

p intercept	
h intercept	

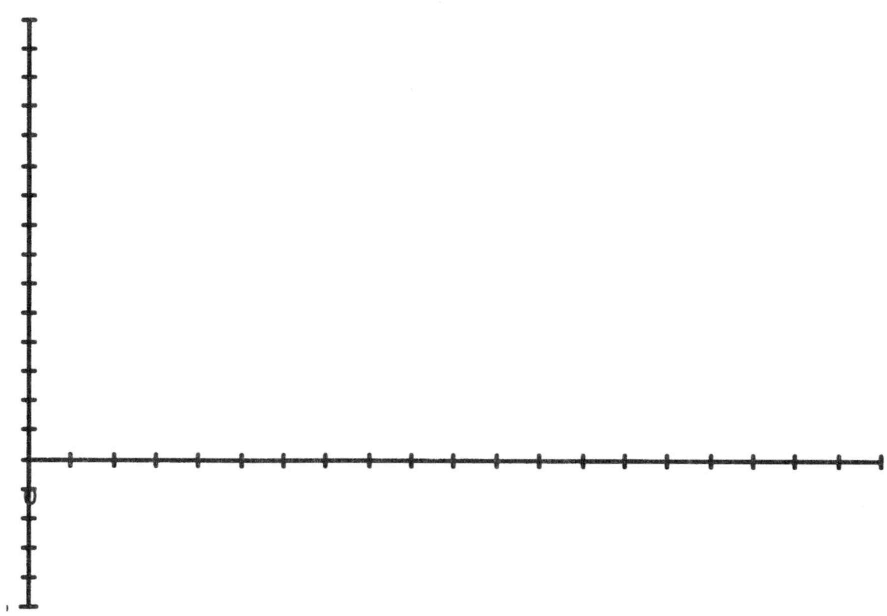

3. Graph the line. If possible, find the x and y intercepts. Choose an appropriate scale and label the axes.

a. $.02x - 15y = 8$

x intercept	
y intercept	

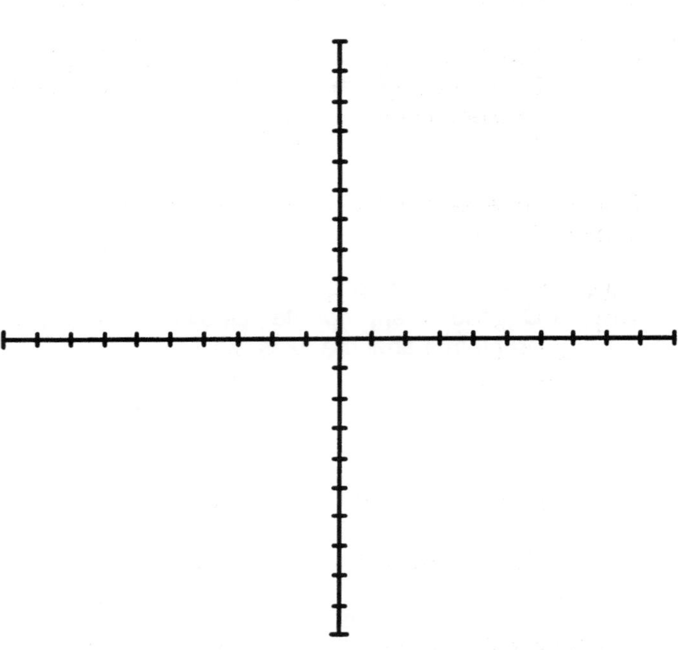

b. $y = 7$

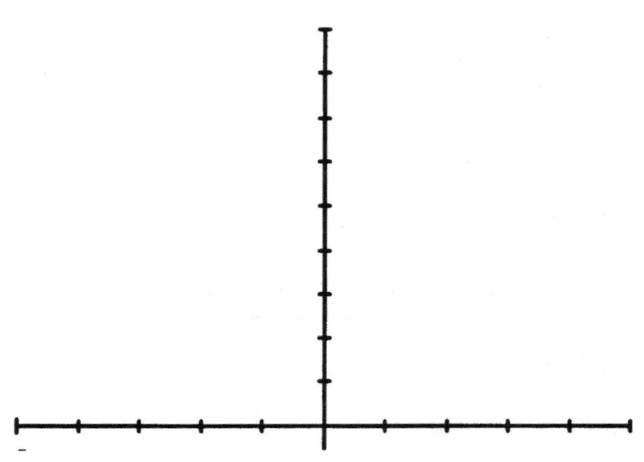

EXERCISES

Study Tip: Necessary materials: pencils, colored pencils, ruler, eraser, graph paper, and note cards. Review the example on page 141.

1. Joe Skuppy runs a pool cleaning service. The equipment costs \$1095, and he charges \$15 an hour. The equation that relates profit and hours is

$$p = 15h - 1095$$

   a. How many hours does he have to work to break even?

   b. How much money will he make if he doesn't work any hours?

   c. Graph the line $p = 15h - 1095$ by plotting the points obtained in parts a. and b. Choose an appropriate scale and only graph the portion that makes sense to the problem. Label the axes.

2. Find the mistake. Write a sentence describing what the student did wrong.
Graph $3x - 2y = 6$

Let $x = 0$	Let $y = 0$
$3(0) - 2y = 6$	$3x - 2(0) = 6$
$-2y = 6$	$3x = 6$
$y = -3$	$x = 2$

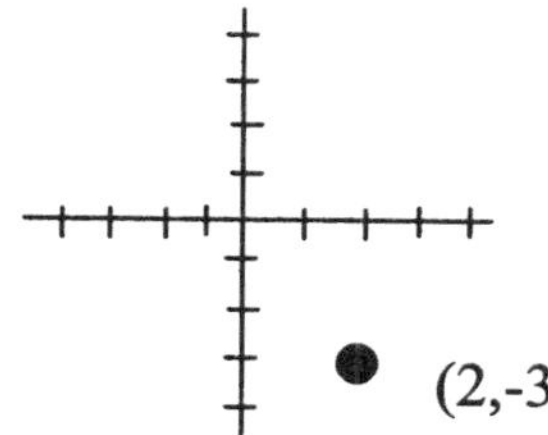

3. a. How do you find the x intercept?

   b. How do you find the y intercept?

4. Graph each line by finding the x and y intercepts. Choose an appropriate scale and label the axes.

   a. $y = \frac{3}{5}x + 11$ b. $11x + 1241y = 100$

   c. $3x - .02y = 12$ d. $y = \frac{-3}{4}x - 5$

5. a. Write an equation for a horizontal line.

   b. Write an equation for a vertical line.

6. Graph each line.

   a. $y = -3$ b. $x = 6$

   c. $x = \frac{-1}{2}$ d. $y = 8$

8. Graph the line y = 0.2x + 70 by finding the x and y intercepts. Use the scale from the two graphs below. Which graph is steeper? Should one graph be steeper than the other? Why or why not? (You will need to use graph paper.)

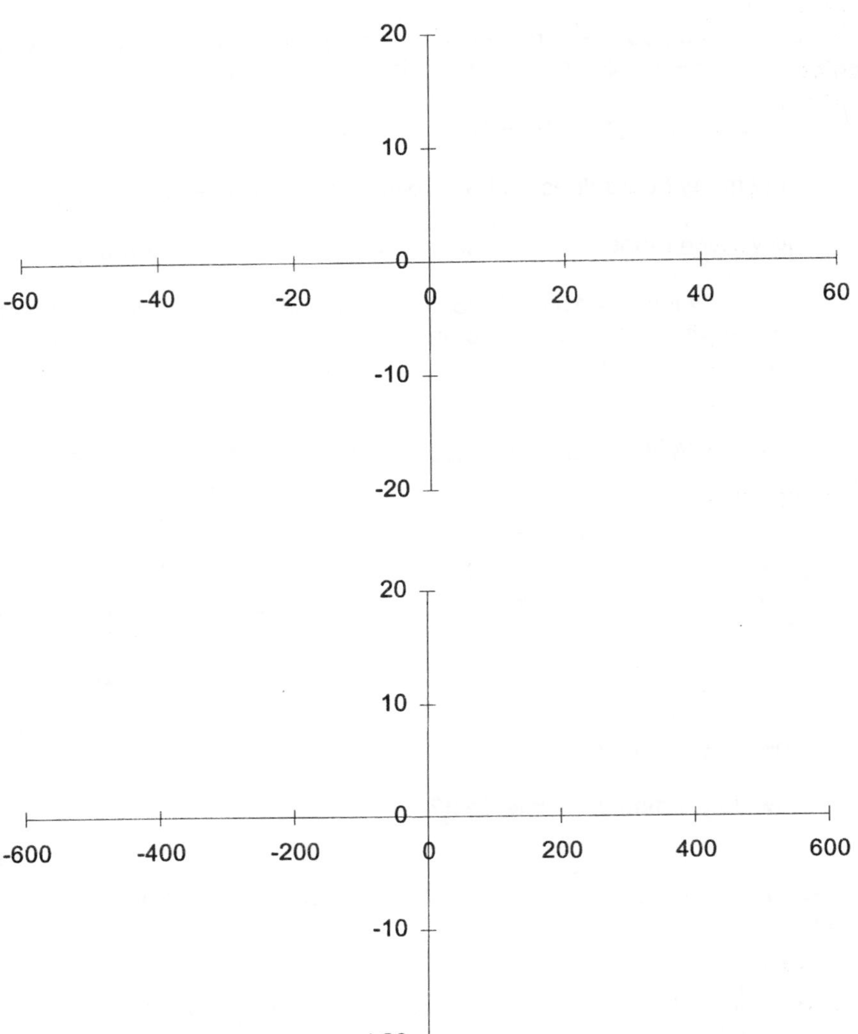

INTRODUCTION TO SLOPE
OVERVIEW

Objectives: This section introduces the important concept of slope using applications from previous sections. Slope describes how a line changes.

Basic Examples:

Example 1. You need to rent a moving van. Class Movers charges a basic rate of $24.95 plus 32 cents per mile.

(This example is from Graphing Lines by Plotting Points, page 129.)

a. Calculate the cost of renting a van if you drive the following number of miles.

MILES	CALCULATION	COST
10	.32(10) + 24.95	28.15
20	.32(20) + 24.95	31.35
30	.32(30) +24.95	34.55
m	.32m + 24.95	C

b. Graph of the equation $C = .32m + 24.95$

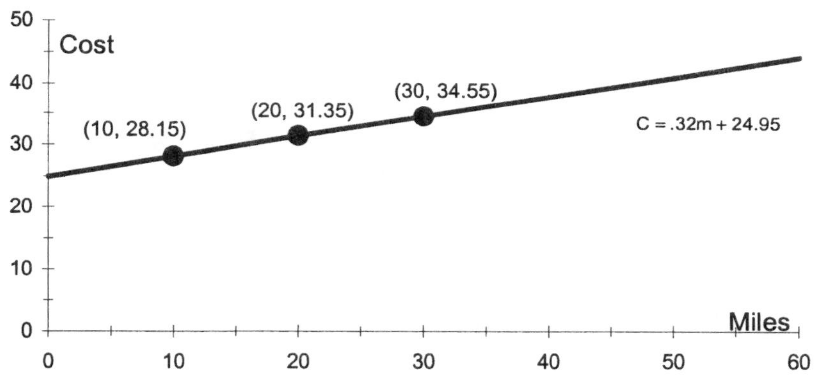

c. The **slope** of this line is computed by selecting any two points to find $\frac{\text{change in cost}}{\text{change in miles}}$. For example, $\frac{34.55 - 28.15}{30 - 10}$.

This formula can be interpreted as:

- $\frac{\text{Change in Cost}}{\text{Change in Miles}}$
- $\frac{\text{Change in Dependent Variable}}{\text{Change in independent variable}}$
- $\frac{\text{Vertical Change}}{\text{Horizontal Change}}$
- $\frac{\text{Rise}}{\text{Run}}$

Explanation:
34.55 – 28.15 represents how the cost changed. Cost is the dependent variable and the vertical axis.

30 – 10 represents how the miles changed. Miles are the independent variable and the horizontal axis.

d. Compute $\frac{34.55 - 28.15}{30 - 10}$ and interpret what it means.

$\frac{34.55 - 28.15}{30 - 10} = .32$, .32 is the cost per mile and is the coefficient of m, the independent variable. This is not a coincidence. In this problem slope is the cost per mile.

e. Suppose Class Movers begins to charge 55 cents per mile. Then the new equation is $C = .55m + 24.95$. The slope is still the cost per mile, so the slope of this line is .55. The graph of both equations is given below.

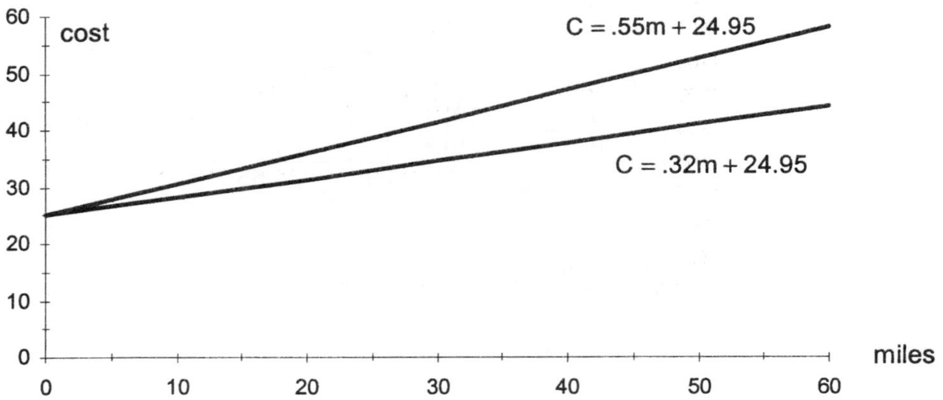

The line representing the equation $C = .55m + 24.95$ is steeper than the line representing $C = .32m + 24.95$ because they now charge more per mile. The slope of the line $C = .55m + 24.95$ is greater than the slope of the line $C = .32m + 24.95$.

Slope measures how steep a line is.

Example 2. Which plant grows faster: Hybrid A sunflower which grew 26 inches in 10 days or Hybrid B sunflower which grew 24 inches in 9 days.

To answer the question we will compute $\frac{\text{growth}}{\text{time}}$.

Hybrid A: $\frac{26}{10} = 2.6$. Hybrid A grew 2.6 inches per day.

Hybrid B: $\frac{24}{9} = 2.667$. Hybrid B grew 2.667 inches per day.

Hybrid B grew faster than Hybrid A. Since plants grow at different rates depending on the weather, the numbers 2.6 and 2.667 represent the average growth per day. The numbers 2.6 and 2.667 also represent the idea of slope, $\frac{\text{Change in Dependent Variable}}{\text{Change in independent variable}}$.

Slope also means the average rate of change. The slope of Hybrid B Is steeper than the slope of hybrid A.

Example 3. The average cost of a personal computer is given in the table below.

YEAR	COST
1987	$1,678
2001	$1,076

a. Make a graph of year versus cost.

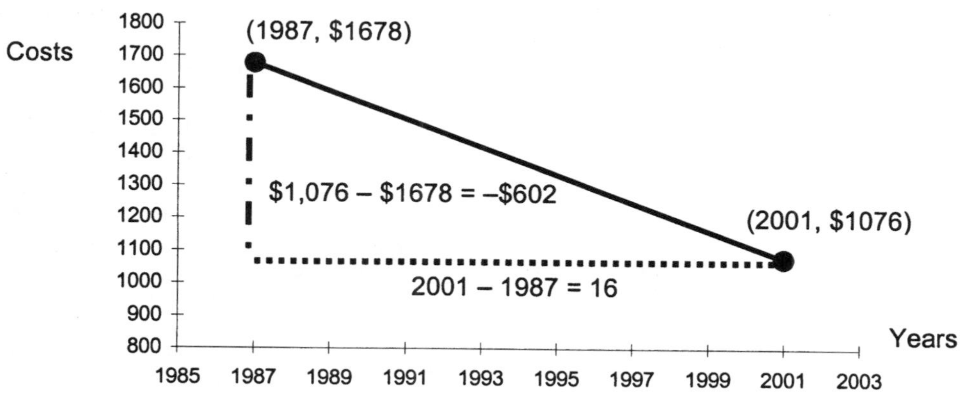

b. Calculate the average rate of change.

Average Rate of Change = slope

$$= \frac{\text{Vertical Change}}{\text{Horizontal Change}}$$

$$= \frac{\text{Change in Cost}}{\text{Change in Years}}$$

$$= \frac{1{,}076 - 1{,}678}{2001 - 1987}$$

$$= \frac{-602}{14}$$

$$= -43$$

> **Explanation:** Look at the graph above:
>
> 1,076 – 1,678 represents the vertical change.
>
> 2001 – 1987 represents the horizontal change.

On the average, the cost of personal computers decreased $43 per year between 1987 and 2001.

If the slope of the line is negative, then the line is decreasing. Also, if the slope is positive then the line is increasing.

Example 4. Use the data from Example 3 to calculate the percent change in the cost of personal computers.

Percent change is a similar idea to slope. It also measures how a quantity changes, except that percent change only involves one variable. In our problem, the change only involves the cost.

The formula for percent change is:

$$\text{Percent Change} = \frac{\text{New - Old}}{\text{Old}} \bullet 100$$

Study Tip: You should write this formula on a note card and memorize it.

The variable New is the cost of personal computers in 2001, $1,076.

The variable Old is the cost of personal computers in 1987, $1,678.

$$\text{Percent Change} = \frac{1{,}076 - 1{,}678}{1{,}678} \bullet 100$$

$$\text{Percent Change} = -35.88$$

> **Explanation:**
> Notice that the numerator of the formula for percent change is the same as the numerator for the formula for slope.

The cost of personal computers decreased 35.88% from 1987 to 2001.

Summary: Slope is a very important topic in algebra. It measures how things change. The following are different interpretations of slope:

- $\frac{\text{Change in dependent variable}}{\text{Change in independent variable}}$ or $\frac{\text{Change in y}}{\text{Change in x}}$
- $\frac{\text{Vertical Change}}{\text{Horizontal Change}}$
- $\frac{\text{Rise}}{\text{Run}}$
- Slope measures the steepness of a line.
- Slope is the average rate of change.
- If the slope of the line is negative, then the line is decreasing.
- If the slope of the line is positive, then the line is increasing.

Percent Change also measures how a quantity changes. The formula for Percent Change is:

$$\text{Percent Change} = \frac{\text{New - Old}}{\text{Old}} \bullet 100$$

CLASS WORK

1. A rental car company, Wrecker, charges $21.95 per day plus 41 cents a mile.

   a. Calculate the cost of renting a car for one day.

Miles	Calculation	Cost
10	.41*10 + 21.95	26.05
20	.41*20 + 21.95	30.15
30	.41*30 + 21.95	34.25
m	.41*m + 21.95	*C*

   b. The graph of the equation C = .41M + 21.95 is given below.

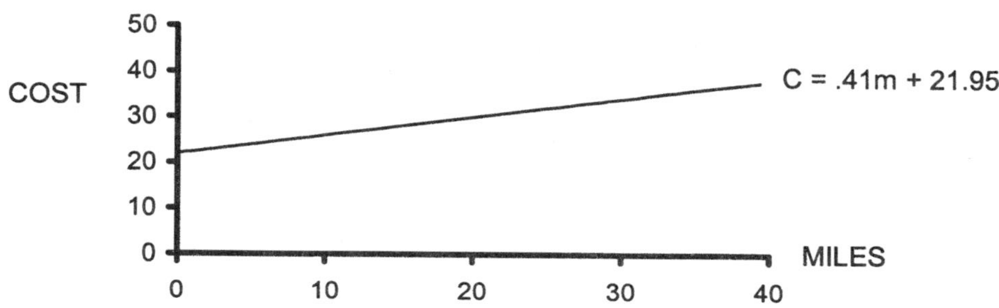

   c. What does $\dfrac{34.25 - 26.05}{30 - 10}$ mean?

   d. Suppose Wrecker starts charging 61 cents a mile. Graph the new cost equation C = .61m + 21.95 using the axis in Part b.

2. Which grows faster: Hybrid A corn seedlings, which grow 14.6 centimeters in 15 days, or Hybrid B, which grow 11.2 centimeters in 12 days?

3. What does the highway sign mean?

Average Rate of Change and Percent Change

4. Using the information in the table:

Year	Time Spent in Supermarket
1991	32 min.
1996	78.3 min.

a. Make a graph of year versus average time spent by women in a supermarket. Make sure you label your axes.

b. Calculate the average rate of change. (Be sure to include the correct units.)

c. Calculate the percent increase in the time spent in the supermarket.

Percent Change = $\left(\frac{\text{New} - \text{Old}}{\text{Old}}\right) \times 100$

d. What is the slope of the line through the two points?

5. Using the information in the table:

a. Make a graph of year versus U.S. Trade Deficit. Make sure you label your axes.

Year	U.S. Trade Deficit in Billions of Dollars
1983	.70
1984	1.20
1985	1.25
1986	1.45
1987	1.60
1988	1.20

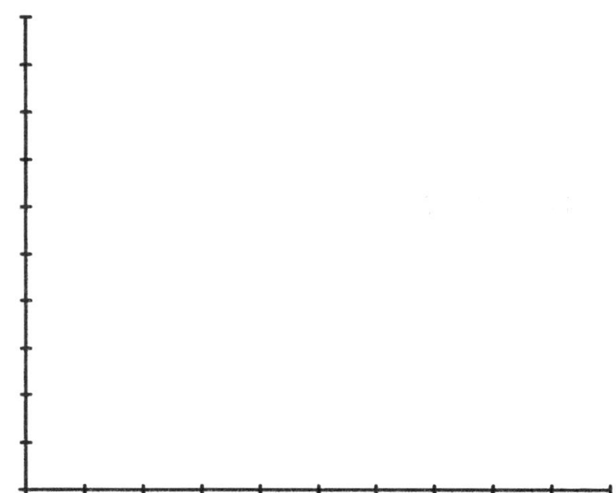

b. Calculate the average rate of change between 1983 and 1987 (include the correct units). Write a sentence describing your results.

c. Calculate the average rate of change between 1987 and 1988 (include the correct units). Write a sentence describing your results.

d. What is the percent change between 1983 and 1987. Write a sentence describing your results.

6. The graph and the table illustrate men's average Math SAT scores.

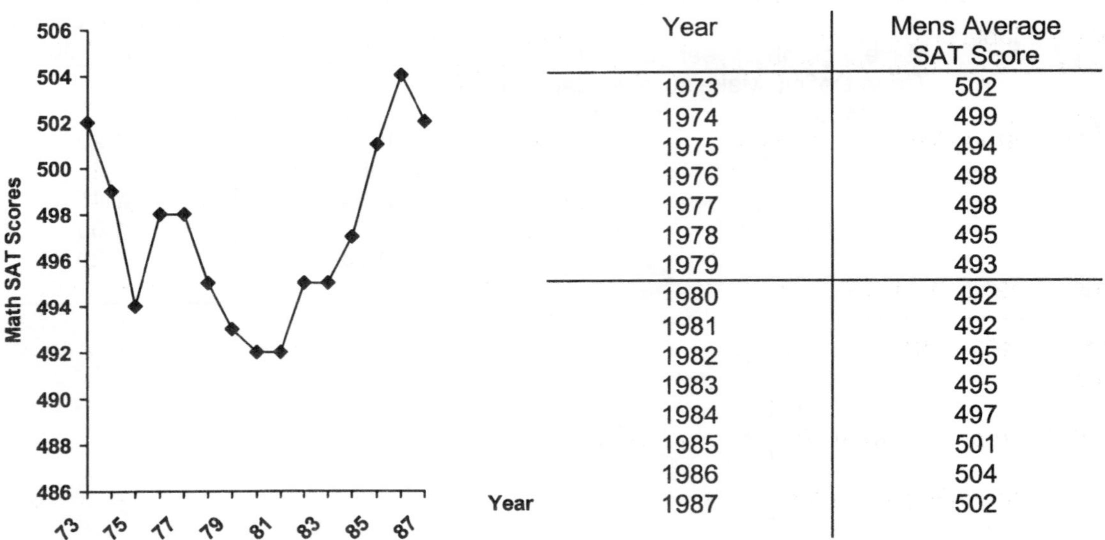

Year	Mens Average SAT Score
1973	502
1974	499
1975	494
1976	498
1977	498
1978	495
1979	493
1980	492
1981	492
1982	495
1983	495
1984	497
1985	501
1986	504
1987	502

a. According to the graph, what was the longest time period for declining Math SAT scores?

b. According to the graph, over what year did Math SAT scores decrease the most?

c. Use the table to find the average rate of change for your answer in Part b.

d. According to the graph, over what year did the Math SAT scores increase the most?

e. Use the table to find the average rate of change for your answer in Part d.

f. According to the graph, over what years did the Math SAT scores remain constant?

GROUP EXERCISE

Use the table below to make a very accurate graph of year versus women's Math SAT scores. Make sure you label your axes and choose a correct scale.

Study Tips: 1. If your teacher covered the Class Work, review pages 159 and 160.
2. Your group should make one graph on graph paper. When you have answered all of the questions, then have each person make a graph.
3. Use a ruler and colored pencils.

Year	1973	1974	1975	1976	1977	1978	1979	1980	1981	1982	1983	1984	1985	1986	1987
SAT Score	463	461	461	450	447	445	444	444	444	444	446	451	449	450	452

A blank graph is provided for you on page 162.

a. According to the graph, over what year did the women's Math SAT scores decline the most?

b. Use the table to find the average rate of change for your answer in Part a.

c. Use the table to find the percent decrease for your answer in Part a.

d. According to the table, over what year did the Math SAT scores increase the most?

e. Use the table to find the average rate of change for your answer in Part d.

f. Use the table to find the percent increase for your answer in Part d.

g. According to the graph, over what time period did women's math SAT scores remain constant?

EXERCISES

Study Tip: Do your homework everyday but for short time periods.

1. Acme sells a dozen grade A eggs for \$1.89. The Fresh Stop sells 18 eggs for \$2.68. Which store is the better buy?

2. Which is steeper: the car ramp for U-Haul rental company, which rises 5 feet for every horizontal distance of 9 feet, or Darrel's toy garage which rises 3 inches for every horizontal distance of 8 inches?

Study Tip: Questions 1 and 2 are similar to Example 2 page 154 and Problem 2 page 157.

3. Use the table to answer the following questions.

   a. Make a graph of year versus number of employees. Make sure you label your axes.

Study Tip: You should use graph paper, a ruler, and colored pencils.

Year	Number of Employees in Chemical and Allied Products in Montgomery County
1990	13,329
1991	14,486
1992	15,132
1993	17,355
1994	18,072

Source: Pennsylvania County Industry Trends 1994-95

   b. Calculate the average rate of change between 1990 and 1994 (include the correct units).

   c. Calculate the average rate of change between 1993 and 1994 (include the correct units).

   d. Use Parts b. or c. to estimate the numbers of employees in 1995. Write a sentence that describes your logic.

   e. What is the percent change between the years 1990 and 1994?

   f. Write a topic sentence summarizing what you think is the central idea to be drawn from this data.

4. Use the table to answer the following questions.

Source: <u>95 Statistical Yearbook by the United Nations Educational, Scientific and Cultural Organization</u>

Year	Number of Daily Newspapers in the U.S.
1980	1,745
1985	1,676
1990	1,611
1992	1,570

a. Make a graph of year versus number of newspapers.

a. Calculate the average rate of change between the years 1980 and 1992 (include the correct units).

c. Calculate the average rate of change between the years 1990 and 1992 (include the correct units).

d. What is the percent change between the years 1990 and 1992?

e. Write a topic sentence summarizing what you think is the central idea to be drawn from this data.

5. Use the table below to make a very accurate graph of year versus men's median age of first marriage. Make sure you label your axes and choose a correct scale.

Year	Men's Median age of First Marriage
1890	26.1
1900	25.9
1910	25.1
1920	24.6
1930	24.3
1940	24.3
1950	22.8
1960	22.8
1970	23.2
1980	24.7
1990	26.1

a. According to the graph, over what 10 year period was there the greatest decrease in men's median age of first marriage?

b. Use the table to find the average rate of change over the 10 year period for your answer in Part a.

c. According to the graph, over what 10 year period did the greatest increase in men's median age of first marriage occur? Why are you not sure you have the correct answer?

d. Use the table to find the average rate of change over the 10 year period for your answer in Part c. Find the average rate of change over the 10 year period in men's median age of first marriage for your "other" answer in Part c.

e. According to the graph, over what 10 year period was there no change in men's median age of first marriage?

f. Use slope to predict the men's median age of first marriage in the year 2000. Write a sentence explaining what you did.

Study Tip: In Question f, what does the slope tell you about how the marriage age of men is changing in 1990?

6. Below is an approximation of the cost of doctors' bills and Medicare between 1963 and 1979.

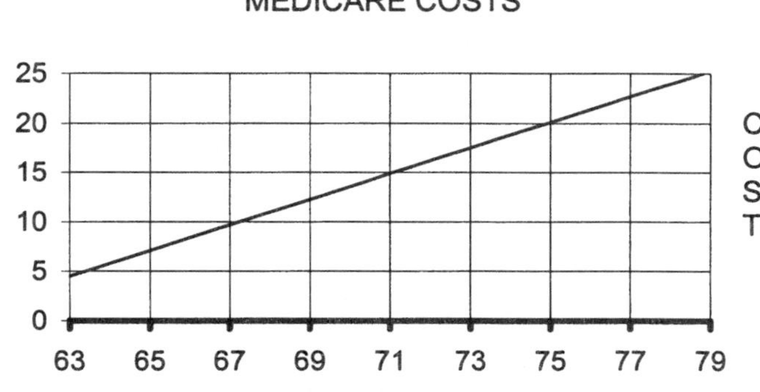

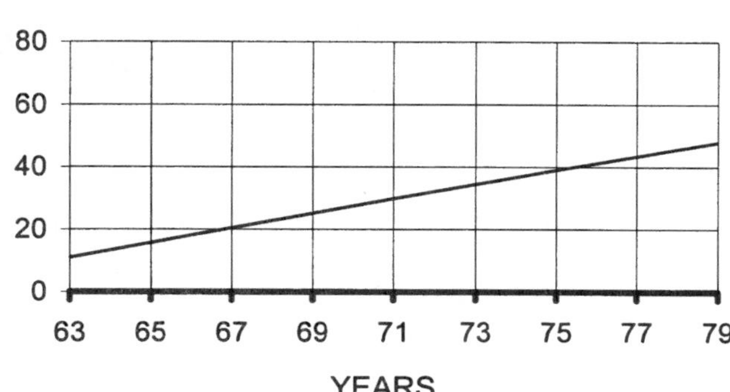

Study Tip: Review slope and pay attention to the scales.

a. Which *appears* to have been growing at a faster rate: doctors' bills or Medicare costs? Why?

b. Which actually grew at a faster rate, and how can you tell?

7.

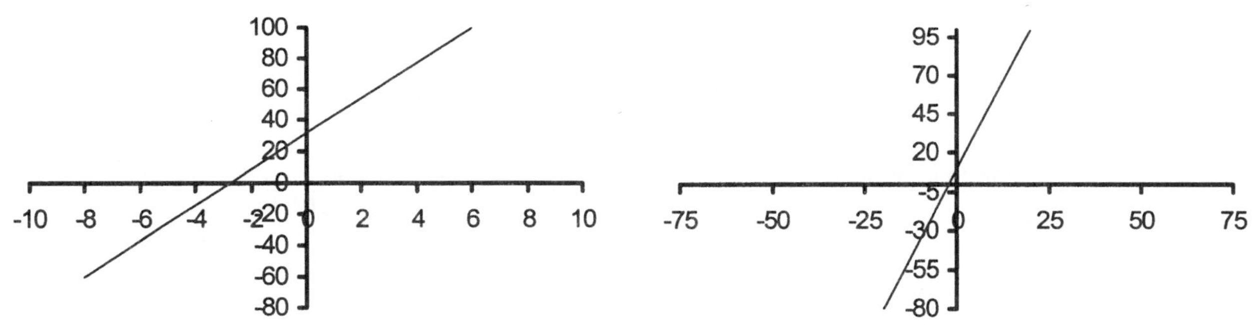

a. Which line appears to have the greater slope?

b. Estimate the slope of both lines by finding two points from both lines.

8. The table below appeared in the Morning Call newspaper on Sunday, October 16, 2000.

UTILITY COMPLAINTS RISE Change in "justified" consumer complaints from 1998 to 1999:		
UTILITY	**1998**	**1999**
BELL ATLANTIC	1,078	3,443
COMMONWEALTH TELEPHONE	28	44
GTE	163	227
PPL	55	390

a. Look at the data and estimate which company had the largest increase in complaints and which company had the least increase in complaints.

b. Compute the percent increase in complaints for each company.

 **Study Tip:** Review the percent change formula.

c. Based on your results in Part b, which company actually had the largest increase in complaints, and which company actually had the least increase in complaints?

d. The actual table that appeared in the newspaper is given below.

UTILITY COMPLAINTS RISE Change in "justified" consumer complaints from 1998 to 1999 for selected utilities:			
	COMPLAINTS		
UTILITY	**1998**	**1999**	**INCREASE**
PPL	55	390	Up 609%
BELL ATLANTIC	1,078	3,443	Up 219%
COMMONWEALTH TELEPHONE	28	44	Up 57%
GTE	163	227	Up 39%

How did the newspaper compute the increase column?

SLOPE
OVERVIEW

Objective: This section will cover the algebraic formula for slope, the slope of horizontal and vertical lines, and the slope-intercept equation.

Algebraic formula for slope:

Let (x_1, y_1) and (x_2, y_2) be any two points on the line; then the formula for slope is:

$$m = \frac{y_2 - y_1}{x_2 - x_1}.$$

Study Tip: Write the formula on a note card for easy reference.

Explanation: Slope is $\frac{\text{vertical change}}{\text{horizontal change}}$.
$y_2 - y_1$ represents the vertical change.
$x_2 - x_1$ represents the horizontal change.

Basic examples:

Example 1. Graph the line that passes through the two points (-2, -1), (3, 5) and find the slope.

a. To graph the line just plot the two points.

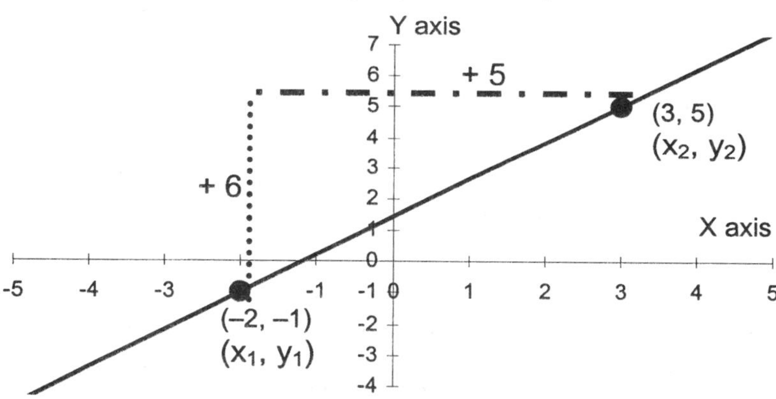

b. Use the formula $m = \frac{y_2 - y_1}{x_2 - x_1}$ to find the slope.

$y_2 = 5$
$y_1 = -1$
$x_2 = 3$
$x_1 = -2$

Explanation: It doesn't matter which y value you choose to equal y_1 as long as you are consistent. If $y_1 = 5$ then x_1 has to be 3. (3, 5) is a point on the graph.

$$m = \frac{y_2 - y_1}{x_2 - x_1} = \frac{5-(-1)}{3-(-2)}$$

$$m = \frac{5+1}{3+2}$$

Explanation:
$-(-1) = +1$

$-(-2) = +2$

$m = \frac{6}{5}$, The slope of the line is $\frac{6}{5}$.

Since the slope is positive the line is increasing. The line starts at the bottom left and rises to the top right.

Example 2. Given the graph below, find the slope.

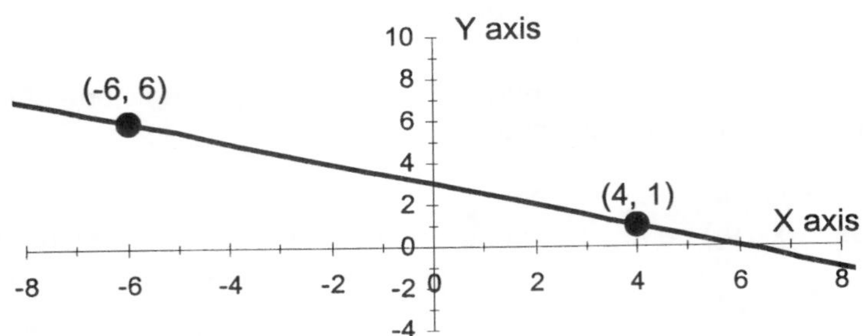

Use the formula $m = \frac{y_2 - y_1}{x_2 - x_1}$ to find the slope.

$y_2 = 6$ $\quad y_1 = 1$

$x_2 = -6$ $\quad x_1 = 4$ $\quad m = \frac{y_2 - y_1}{x_2 - x_1} = \frac{6-1}{-6-4}$

$m = \frac{5}{-10}$

$m = -\frac{1}{2}$, The slope of the line is $-\frac{1}{2}$.

Since the slope is negative, the line is decreasing from left to right.

Example 3. Graph the line that passes through the two points (–3, 4), (5, 4) and find the slope.

a. To graph the line just plot the two points.

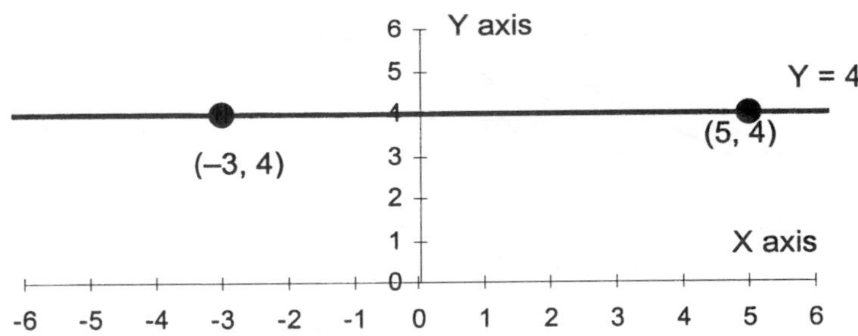

b. Use the formula $m = \frac{y_2 - y_1}{x_2 - x_1}$ to find the slope.

$y_2 = 4$ $\quad y_1 = 4$
$x_2 = -3$ $\quad x_1 = 5$

Explanation: The slope of a horizontal is zero because there is no vertical change.

$m = \frac{y_2 - y_1}{x_2 - x_1} = \frac{4-4}{-3-5}$

$m = \frac{0}{-8}$

$m = 0$ The slope of a horizontal line is zero.

Study Tip: This is an important fact that will be significant in a later section.

Example 4. Graph the line that passes through the two points (3, –4), (3, 2) and find the slope.

a. To graph the line just plot the two points.

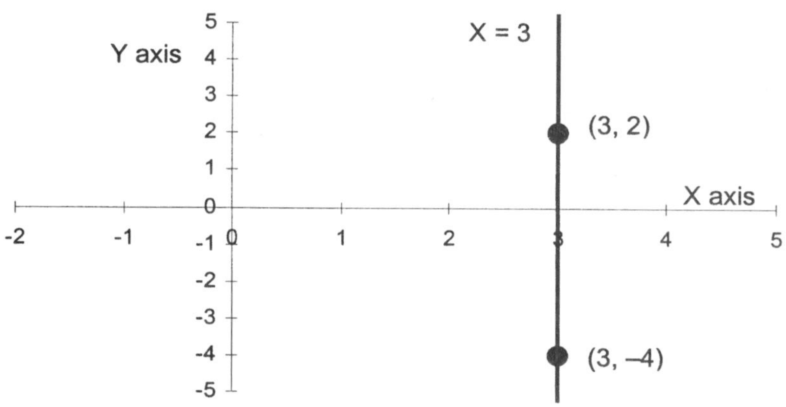

b. Use the formula $m = \dfrac{y_2 - y_1}{x_2 - x_1}$ to find the slope.

$y_2 = -4 \quad y_1 = 2$

$x_2 = 3 \quad x_1 = 3$

$$m = \frac{y_1 - y_0}{x_1 - x_0} = \frac{-4 - 2}{3 - 3}$$

$$m = \frac{-6}{0}$$

The slope of a vertical line is undefined since division by zero is undefined.

The Slope-Intercept Equation

Definition: The equation **y = mx + b** is called the slope-intercept form of a line. The coefficient of x, m, is the slope and (0, b) is the y intercept. The equation is called a first degree polynomial because x is raised to the first power.

Study Tip: This is an important formula you need to know.

All of our applications are in the form of the slope-intercept equation.

Example 5. You need to rent a moving van. Class Movers charges a basic rate of $24.95 plus 32 cents per mile.

This is the basic problem for the first half of the course, and we know its equation relating cost and miles is:

C = .32m + 24.95

The slope of the line is .32 since .32 is the coefficient of m.

The C intercept is (0, 24.95).

> **Explanation:** The letter m is used differently in the definition than it is used in the example. In the definition, m represents slope. In the example, m is the variable for number of miles.

Summary: Slope is a fundamental concept in mathematics. It measures how things change.

The basic ideas in this section are:

- The formula for the slope of a line is $m = \frac{y_2 - y_1}{x_2 - x_1}$.
- If the slope of a line is positive, then the line is increasing from left to right.
- If the slope of a line is negative, then the line is decreasing from left to right.
- The slope of a horizontal line is zero.
- The slope of a vertical line is undefined.
- In the slope-intercept equation y = mx + b, m is the slope and (0,b) is the y intercept.

CLASS WORK

Definition: a. $m = \dfrac{\text{Change in } y}{\text{Change in } x}$

b. $m = \dfrac{y_2 - y_1}{x_2 - x_1}$ (x_2, y_2) and (x_1, y_1) are two points on the line.

Graph the line that passes through the two given points and find the slope of the line.

1. (6, –2) and (5, 7)
2. (8, 2) and (4, –12)

3. (2, 4) and (2, –5)

4. (7, –3) and (–2, –3)

The equation **y = mx + b** is called the slope-intercept equation. The coefficient of x, m, is the slope of the line and (0, b) is the y intercept.

5. Identify the slope and y-intercept of the equation of the line. Graph the line.

a. $y = -\frac{3}{4}x - 5$

b. $y = 4x + 5$

6. Mr. McNab started a lawn-mowing business for the summer. He bought a lawn mower for $350, and he charges $6.50 an hour. The equation that relates profit and hours worked is

$$p = 6.50h - 350$$

Identify the slope and p intercept of the equation above.

GROUP EXERCISE

Study Tips:
1. Discuss the problem. Don't have each person solve it separately.
2. Review the slope formula.
3. Review addition/subtraction of signed numbers.

1. Find the mistake in the problems below. Write a sentence describing the mistake.

a. (6, 4) and (–7, 2)

$$m = \frac{6-(-7)}{4-2}$$

$$m = \frac{13}{2}$$

b. (–3, 5) and (2, 6)

$$m = \frac{5-6}{2-(-3)}$$

$$m = \frac{-1}{5}$$

c. (4, –2) and (–5, 1)

$$m = \frac{-2-1}{4-5}$$

$$m = \frac{-3}{-1}$$

2. Graph the line that passes through the two points and find the slope of the line.

a. (–1, 5) and (3, –2)

b. (–2, 4) and (5, 4)

EXERCISES

Study Tip: Review group work.

1. Find the slope of the lines.

a.

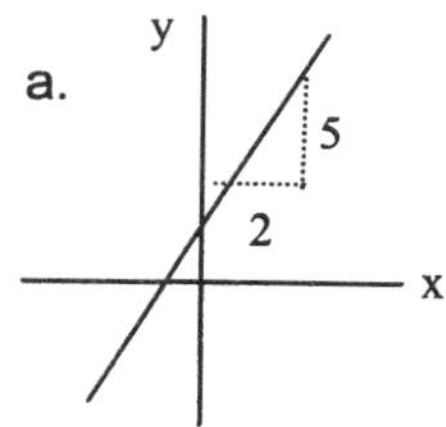

b.

y
-3
7
x

c.

y
x

2. Find the mistake in the problems below. Write a sentence describing the mistake.

a. (–6, 1) and (–2, 3)

$$M = \frac{1-(-2)}{3-(-6)}$$

b. (5, –1) and (3, 7)

$$M = \frac{5-3}{-1-7}$$

3. Graph the line that passes through the two points and find the slope of the line.

a. (8, –1) and (–2, 4)

b. (3, 5) and (7, 5)

c. (–3, 1) and (6, 5)

d. (6, –2) and (6, 4)

e. (9, 6) and (–1, –2)

4. Identify the slope and y intercept of the equation of the line.

a. $y = 7x + 5$

b. $Y = \frac{-2}{3}x - 2$

Study Tip: Don't wait until the night before to study for a test. Begin to review now. The next section is very important. It summarizes the material of the course.

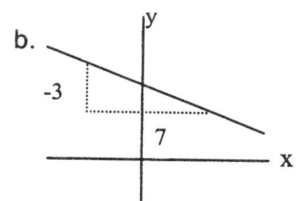

APPLICATION OF GRAPHS
OVERVIEW

Objectives: This section summarizes the course thus far. You will create **tables** to find equations, apply your knowledge of graphing lines by finding the **intercepts** and **plotting points,** interpret **slope**, understand **inequalities** graphically, and **solve equations**.

Vocabulary Review and Appropriate Sections

- **Tables:** A systematic arrangement of information using rows and columns. (Section: Introduction to Variables)
- **Intercept:** The point where the graph crosses either the x or y axis. (Section: Graphing Lines by Finding the Intercepts)
- **Plotting Points:** Using numbers generated by the table to graph the line. (Section: Graphing Lines by Plotting Points)
- **Slope:** (Steepness of a line.) Change in the dependent variable divided by change in the independent variable. Often it has the phrase cost per mile or something similar. (Section: Introduction to Slope)
- **Inequalities:** The use of less than (<) and greater than (>) symbols to show relationships. (Section: Applications of Inequalities)
- **Solving Equations:** Algebraic technique used to determine the point when two quantities are equal. (Section: Applications of Linear Equations)

Basic Example:

You are going to rent a car for a day. You have two choices, Speed Car Rental and Honest Car Rental. Speed charges $18 plus 85¢ per mile while Honest charges $42 plus 45¢ per mile.

a. Write an equation for the cost of renting a car from Speed.

Study Tip: Draw a chart similar to those in earlier problems.

Miles	Calculation	Cost
10	$.85 \bullet 10 + 18$	$26.50
30	$.85 \bullet 30 + 18$	$43.50
m	.85m + 18	C

Suggestion: By now, you may be a to derive the cost equation by readi the problem. Using descriptive variable names like m for the numb of miles driven should help you interpret what the formula means.

The equation for Speed is **C = .85m + 18.**

b. Write an equation for the cost of renting a car from Honest.

Miles	Calculation	Cost
10	$.45 \bullet 10 + 42$	$46.50
30	$.45 \bullet 30 + 42$	$55.50
m	.45m + 42	C

Suggestion: Instead of making a table, you could have recognized th the cost per mile multiplies the varia m, and the flat cost is the constant.

The equation for Honest is **C = .45m + 42.**

c. Find the intersection of two lines. Label the point.

Study tip: This is the same question as finding how many miles you have to drive for The two companies to charge the same. (Section: Applications of Linear Equations, Part I)

Step 1. Find the number of miles that give the same cost.

Cost of Speed = Cost of Honest

$.85m + 18 = .45m + 42$	Set the cost equations equal to each other.
$.40m + 18 = 42$	Subtract .45m from both sides.
$.40m = 24$	Subtract 18 from both sides.
$m = 60$	Divide both sides by .40

Step 2. Find the cost of going 60 miles
Choose one of the equations and plug in 60 for m.
Speed: $C = .85 \bullet 60 + 18$
$C = 69$
The two lines intersect at (60, 69).

> **Explanation:** It doesn't matter which company you choose to substitute 69 in for miles; you will get the same cost.

d. Graph both equations on the same set of axes. Label each axis and choose an appropriate scale. Only graph the portion that is relevant to the problem.

Study Tips
1. Parts c and d are like the chicken and the egg. You don't know which to do first. The answer in Part c is the most important point on the graph.
2. You should use graph paper and ruler when you make a graph.
3. You should use different colored pencils, and you should label Each line, their intersection, and the cost intercepts.

Step 1. We need to decide what the independent and dependent variables are to be.

Since cost depends on miles, cost is the dependent variable, and miles are the independent variable. So we will write our points as (miles, cost), and our graph will be:

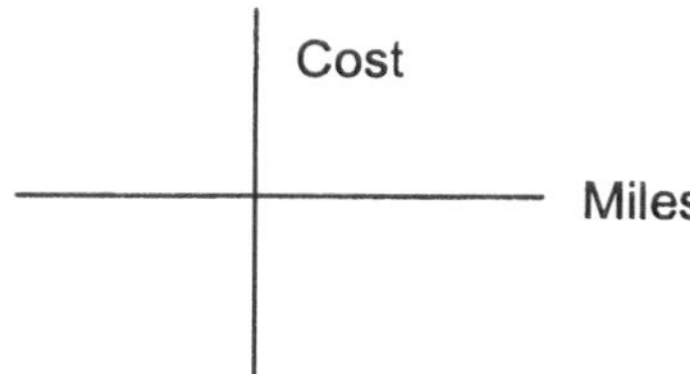

Step 2. Find at least two points for each line, Speed and Honest.

Point 1. From Part c, we know that the lines intersect at (60, 69). This point will be used to graph both lines.

Point 2. Find the cost intercept for Speed and Honest. We find the cost intercept by assuming m = 0.

Study Tip: Organize your work in tables to see this more easily.

Where the lines intersect. → row 1 (60)

Cost intercept → row 2 (0)

SPEED				HONEST			
Miles	**Calculation**	**Cost**	**Point**	**Miles**	**Calculation**	**Cost**	**Point**
60	$.85 \bullet 60 + 18$	\$69.0	(60, 69)	60	$.45 \bullet 60 + 42$	\$69.00	(60, 69)
0	$.85 \bullet 0 + 18$	\$18.00	(0, 18)	0	$.45 \bullet 0 + 42$	\$45.00	(0, 42)

Study Tip: Note that the intersection and the intercept are two different points.

Step 3. Plot the points and label the graph.

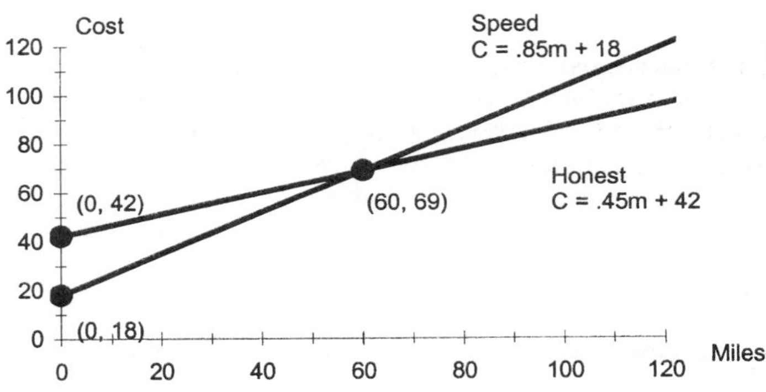

e. Use the graph to find when Speed costs more than Honest.

Speed is more expensive than Honest when the graph of Speed is above the graph of Honest. This is when m is greater than 60, ($m > 60$) . So Speed costs more than Honest for $m > 60$.

f. Use the graph to determine when Honest costs more than Speed.

Honest is more expensive than Speed when the graph of Honest is above the graph of Speed. This is when m is less than 60, ($0 < m < 60$). So Honest costs more than Speed for $0 < m < 60$.

g. What do the cost intercepts mean in terms of the problems?

The cost intercept of Speed is where the line for Speed hits the Cost axis. This is the point (0, 18). It means the cost of going zero miles is \$18.

The cost intercept of Honest is where the line for Honest hits the Cost axis. This is the point (0, 42). It means the cost of going zero miles is \$42.

h. What does the slope of each line mean in terms of the problem?

We can find the slope of each line by using the **slope-intercept** equation

$$y = mx + b.$$

The number multiplying X (the coefficient) is the slope of the line.

For Speed, $C = .85m + 18$, so the slope of the line is .85.
For Honest, $C = .40\,m + 42$, so the slope of the line is .40.

In both cases, the slope of the line is the cost per mile and indicates the steepness of the line.

Summary: This section reviews most of the material presented thus far in the course. You should be able to look at the equation

$$C = .85m + 18$$

and understand:

a. .85 is the **slope** of the line, measures its steepness, and the cost per mile.
b. 18 is the cost **intercept,** and it represents the cost of going 0 miles.
c. **Intersection** (where two lines meet) and **intercept** (where the line touches the axis) are two different terms.

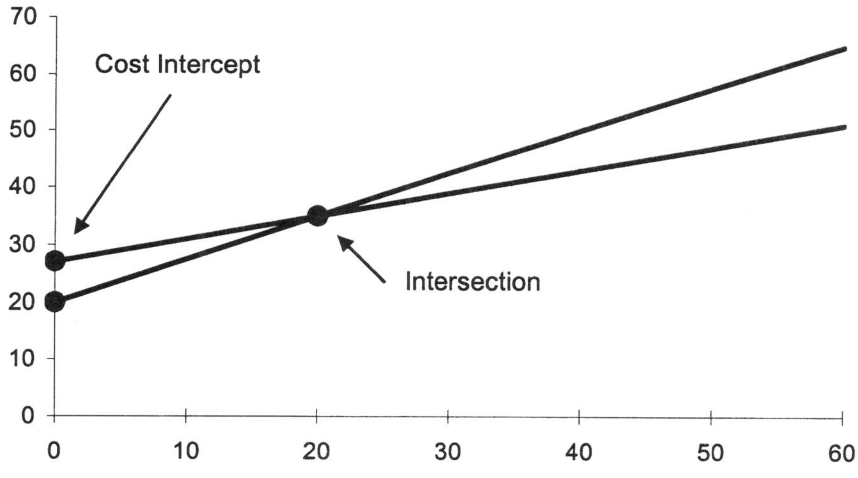

Study tip: Write the definitions of intercepts and intersection on the same note card so that you realize that they are different.

CLASS WORK

1. Two women want to start a lawn mowing business for the summer. They buy a lawn mower for $400 and plan to charge $8.75 an hour.

   a. Write an equation for the amount of profit they plan to make in terms of the number of hours they work.

   b. Graph the equation. Label your axes and use an appropriate scale. Only graph the portion that is relevant to the problem.

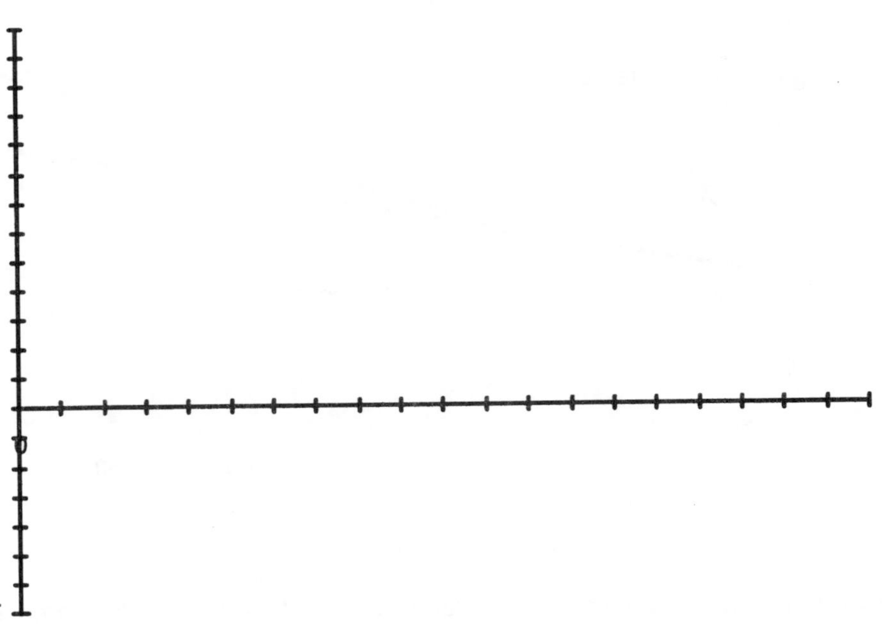

c. What is the profit intercept? Label the point on the graph. What does the profit intercept mean? What does it mean in terms of the problem?

d. What is the hour intercept? Label the point on the graph. What does the hour intercept mean? What does it mean in terms of the problem?

e. What is the slope? What does it mean in terms of the problem?

f. How much profit will they make if they work 100 hours for the summer?

g. Use the equation to determine how many hours they have to work to make $500.

2. Two companies, ACME and EMAC, offer you very similar sales positions. ACME pays $25,000 a year while EMAC pays $10,000 a year plus 10% commission.

a. Write an equation for your yearly wages from ACME.

Write an equation for your yearly wages from EMAC.

b. Graph both equations on the same set of axes. Label your axes and choose an appropriate scale. Only graph the portion that is relevant to the problem. (Answering question c before question b may be helpful.)

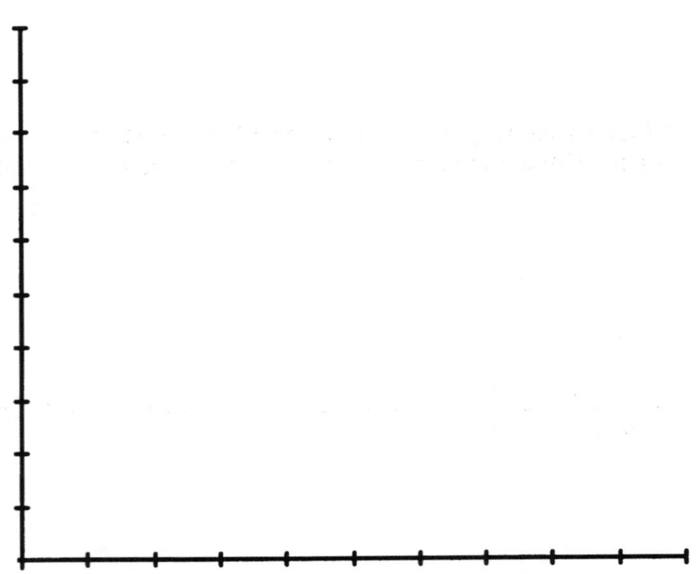

c. Where do the two lines intersect? This is the same question as finding the sales amount where each company pays the same amount, except you have to also find the wage. Label this point.

d. Use the graph to determine when ACME pays more than EMAC.

e. Use the graph to determine when EMAC pays more than ACME.

f. What are the wages intercepts for ACME and EMAC? Label the points on the graph. What does the wages intercept mean in terms of the problem?

g. What is the slope for each line? What does the slope of each line mean in terms of the problem?

3. You are going to rent a car for a day. You have two choices, Lemon Car Rental and Go Kart Car Rental. Lemon charges $20 a day and 75 cents a mile while Go Kart charges $27 a day and 40 cents a mile.

a. Write an equation for the cost of renting a car from Lemon.

Write an equation for the cost of renting a car from Go Kart.

b. Graph both equations on the same set of axes. Label each axis and choose an appropriate scale. Only graph the portion that is relevant to the problem. (Answering question c before question b may be helpful.)

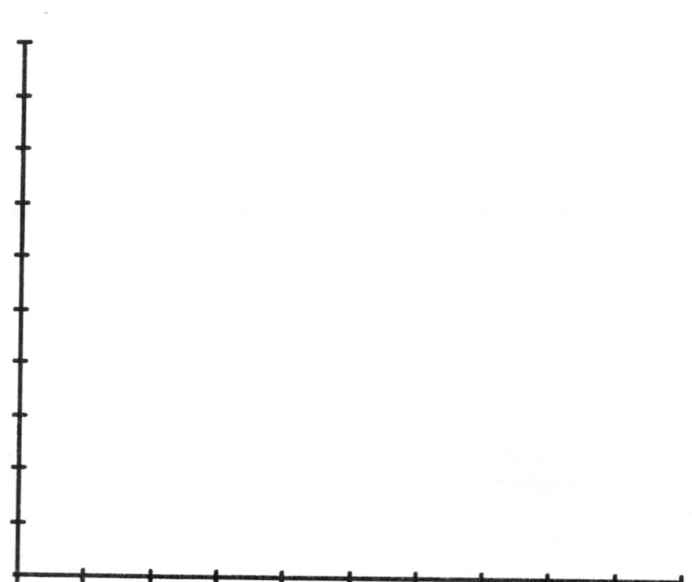

c. Where do the two lines intersect? This is the same question as finding how many miles you have to drive for the two companies to charge the same, except you have to also find the cost. Label the point.

d. Use the graph to determine when Lemon costs more than Go Kart.

e. Use the graph to determine when Go Kart costs more than Lemon.

f. What is the cost intercepts for Lemmon and Go Kart? Label the points on the graph. What does the cost intercept mean in terms of the problems?

g. What is the slope for each line? What does the slope of each line mean in terms of the problem?

4. A phone company, DADBELL, charges 75 cents a phone call and 15 cents per minute after the first three minutes.

a. Write an equation for the cost of a phone call that lasts longer than 3 minutes.

b. What is the cost of a phone call 2 minutes long?

c. What is the cost of a phone call 1 minute long?

d. What is the cost of a phone call 10 minutes long?

e. What is the equation of a phone call that lasts fewer than 3 minutes?

f. Graph the cost of a phone call. Make sure you include the first three minutes in your graph. Label the axes and choose an appropriate scale.

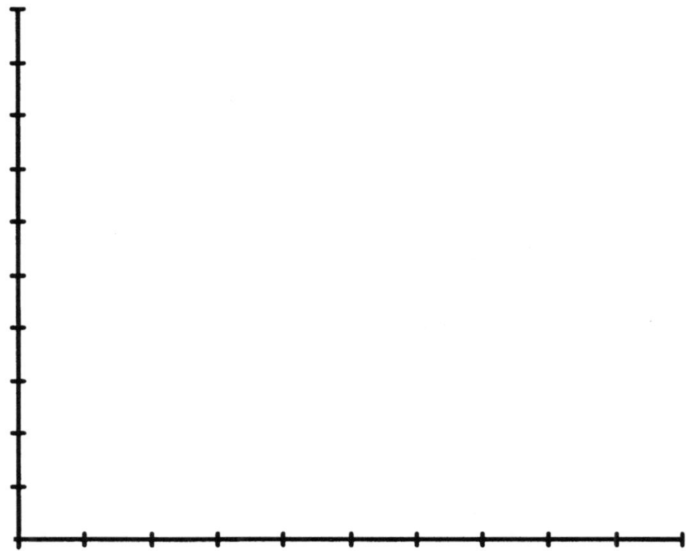

GROUP EXERCISE

 **Study Tip:** 1. Construct a table for the information.
2. Have all of your graphing materials available.

Two companies offer you a similar sales position. Brisk Inc. will pay you $40,000 a year while Bipton Tea Co. will pay you $18,000 plus 8.8% commission.

a. Write an equation for your yearly wages from Brisk Inc.

Write an equation for your yearly wages from Bipton Tea Co.

b. Graph both equations on the same set of axes. Label your axes and choose an appropriate scale. Only graph the portion that is relevant to the problem. (Answering question c before question b may be helpful.)

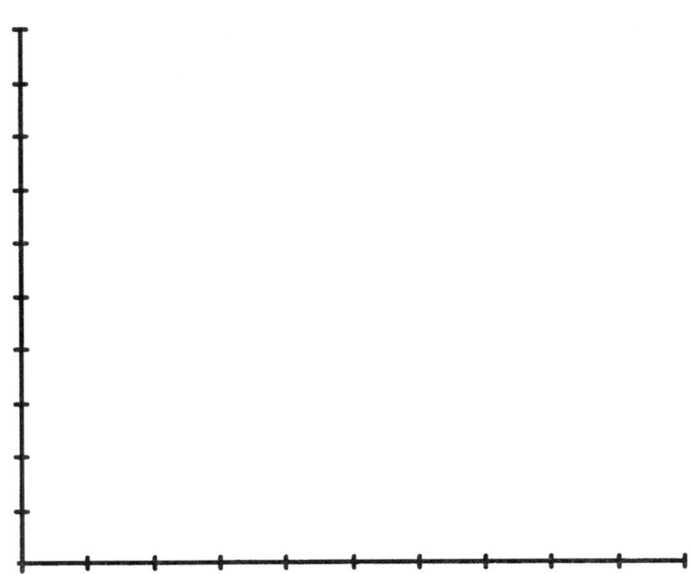

c. Where do the two lines intersect? This is the same question as finding the sales amount where each company pays the same amount, except you have to also find the wage Label this point. (Use Algebra, <u>NOT</u> "guesstimation".)

d. Use the graph to determine when Brisk Inc. pays more than Bipton Tea Co.

e. Use the graph to determine when Bipton Tea Co. pays more than Brisk Inc.

f. What is the cost intercepts for Brisk and Bipton? Label the points on the graph. What does the wages intercept mean in terms of the problem?

g. What is the slope for each line? What does the slope of each line mean in terms of the problem?

EXERCISES

Study Tip: Necessary materials: pencils, colored pencils, ruler, eraser, graph paper, and note cards.

1. Darrel plants sunflower seedlings, each 4 inches tall. With plenty of water and sunlight, they will grow approximately 1.7 inches a day.

   a. Write an equation for the height of the plants in terms of the number of days since they were planted. (If you don't recognize the equation, construct a table.)

   b. Graph the equation. Label your axes and use an appropriate scale. Only graph the portion that is relevant to the problem.

   c. How tall is the sunflower after two weeks? (14 days)

   d. How tall is the sunflower after two months? (60 days)

   e. How tall is the sunflower after four months? Why does this not make sense? How can your graph reflect this idea?

   f. Use the equation to find out how long it will take before the sunflower is 5 feet tall. Does your answer agree with your graph?

2. You are going to rent a car for a day. You have two choices, Golden Car Rental and Classic Car Rental. Golden Car Rental will rent you the car for $35 a day and unlimited mileage while Classic Car Rental will rent you the car for $15 a day plus 80 cents a mile.

   a. Write an equation for the cost of renting a car from Golden Car Rental. Write an equation for the cost of renting from Classic Car Rental.

Study Tip: 1. Review a similar problem on page 176.
2. Construct tables before deriving equations and before graphing.

   b. Graph both equations on the same set of axes. Label your axes and choose an appropriate scale. Only graph the portion that is relevant to the problem. (Answering question c before question b may be helpful.)

   c. Use the equation to find the point where the two lines intersect. This is the same question as finding how many miles you have to drive for the two companies to charge the same, except you have to also find the cost. Label this point on the graph.

   d. Use the graph to find when Golden Car Rental is more expensive than Classic Car Rental.

   e. Use the graph to find when Classic Car Rental is more expensive than Golden Car Rental.

   f. What is the cost intercepts for Golden and Classic? Label the points on the graph. What does the cost intercept mean?

   g. What is the slope of each line? What does the slope of each line mean?

3. You have a choice of two phone companies, Ringer and Buzz. Ringer charges 50 cents a phone call and 18 cents a minute. Buzz charges 25 cents a phone call and 27cents a minute.

Study Tip: 1. Remember to use graph paper, ruler, and colored pencils.
2. Refer to the example from Overview on page 176.

a. Write an equation for the cost of making a phone call using Ringer. Write an equation for the cost of making a phone call using Buzz. (If you don't recognize the equations, construct a table.)

b. Graph both equations on the same set of axes. Label your axes and choose an appropriate scale. Only graph the portion that is relevant to the problem. (Answering question c before question b may be helpful.)

c. Use the equations to find the point where the two lines intersect. This is the same question as finding how many minutes you have to drive for the two companies to charge the same, except you have to also find the cost. Label this point on the graph.

d. Use the graph to determine when Ringer is more expensive than Buzz.

e. Use the graph to determine when Buzz is more expensive than Ringer.

f. What is the cost intercepts for Ringer and Buzz? Label the points on the graph. What does the cost intercept mean in terms of the problem?

g. What is the slope of each line? What does the slope of each line mean in terms of the problem?

4. Two companies offer you very similar sales positions, MATHCO and CALCCO. MATHCO will pay $5,000 a year and 8% commission while CALCCO will pay $10,000 a year and 4% commission.

Study Tip: Refer to your Group Work notes on page 189 or example 2 on page 182.

a. Write an equation for your yearly wages from MATHCO. Write an equation for your yearly wages from CALCCO.

b. Graph both equations on the same set of axes. Label your axes and choose an appropriate scale. Only graph the portion that is relevant to the problem. (Answering question c before question b may be helpful.)

c. Use the equations to determine where the two lines intersect. This is the same question as finding the sales amount where each company pays the same amount, except you have to also find the wage. Label this point on the graph.

d. Use the graph to determine when MATHCO will pay more than CALCCO.

e. Use the graph to determine when CALCCO will pay more than MATHCO.

f. What is the wage intercepts for MATHCO and CALCO? Label the points on the graph. What does the wages intercept mean in terms of the problem?

g. What is the slope of each line? What does the slope of each line mean in terms of the problem?

5. The phone company, Hook, charges 50 cents a call and 20 cents per minute after the first three minutes.

 **Study Tip:** Refer to your notes on example 4 on page186 from Class Work.

a. Write an equation for the cost of a phone call. (You may need to construct a table.)

b. When is the formula in Part a. <u>not</u> valid?

c. What is the cost of a phone call for the first three minutes?

d. Graph the cost of a phone call. Make sure you include the first three minutes in your graph. Label the axes and choose an appropriate scale.

6. A company, Mathematics, Inc., will pay you $10,000 a year plus 10% commission on sales over $50,000.

a. Write an equation for your yearly salary. (You may need to make a table.)

b. When is the formula in Part a. <u>not</u> valid?

c. What is your pay if you sell under $50,000 worth of merchandise?

c. Graph your salary for the year. Make sure you include the possibility of selling less than $50,000 worth of merchandise. Label the axes and choose an appropriate scale.

REVIEW II

This unit interprets algebra and inequalities graphically. You should be able to read a problem and construct a graph that displays all of the important features of the problem.

Inequalities:

Solving equations of inequalities is similar to solving traditional algebraic equations except, when you multiply or divide by a negative, you must change the direction of the inequality symbol.

Example 1. Solve.

$$12 - 3x \leq 27$$
$$-3x \leq 15$$
$$x \geq -5$$

Some inequality equations have three parts. The variable is to be isolated in the middle.

Example 2. Solve.

$$-5 \leq 7 + 2x < 15$$
$$-12 \leq 2x < 8$$
$$-6 \leq x < 4$$

When graphing inequalities on the number line use • for $\leq$ or $\geq$ and ∘ for $<$ or $>$.

Example 3. Graph $-4 \leq x < 3$.

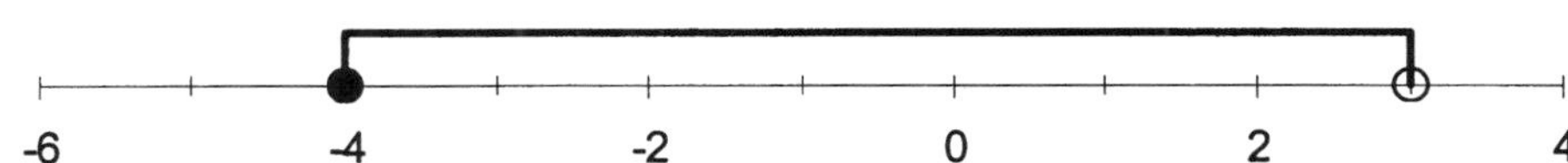

Applications of Inequalities:

Interpret phrases like "more than" and "less than" in mathematical models studied in the previous unit.

Example 4. The equation $C=.12m+.40$ represents the cost of making a long distance phone call. m is the number of minutes on the phone. If the cost was more than \$1.25 and less than \$1.40, how long were you on the phone?

$$1.25 < C < 1.40$$
$$1.25 < .12m + .40 < 1.40$$
$$.85 < .12m < 1.00$$
$$7.08 < m < 8.333$$

If the phone call cost between \$1.25 and \$1.40, then you were on the phone between 7.08 minutes and 8.333 minutes.

Scatter Plots:

Important vocabulary words:

The **independent variable** is the one represented by the first column of a table and is the horizontal axis. In a basic math problem it is x.

The **dependent variable** is the one represented by the last column of the tables and is the vertical axis. In a basic math problem it is y.

Since there are two variables on our graph, we must be consistent in how we describe a point on the graph. An **ordered pair** describes this point. It always has the form (independent variable, dependent variable) or in a nonapplication (x, y).

Example 5. The equation $C = .12m + .40$ represents the cost of making a long distance phone call. m is the number of minutes on the phone.

Construct a table.

Minutes	**Calculation**	**Cost**
10	$.12 \bullet 10 + .40$	\$1.60
20	$.12 \bullet 20 + .40$	\$2.80
30	$.12 \bullet 30 + .40$	\$4.00
M	$.12 \bullet M + .40$	C

Since the cost of making a phone call depends on how long you were on the phone, C is the dependent variable and m is the independent variable.

An ordered pair will have the form (m, C).

The graph will look like

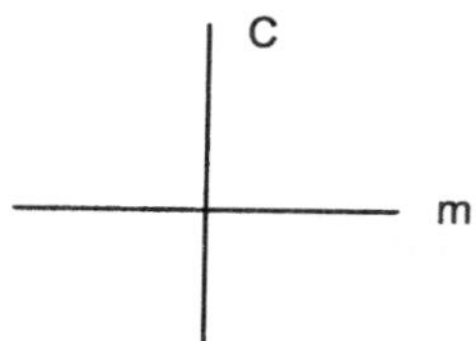

Interpreting Graphs:

The important features of a graph are:

- **Vertex:** The high or low point.
- **Intercept:** Where the graph crosses the horizontal or vertical axis.
- **Intersection:** Where two graphs meet.
- **Slope:** Where the graph is very steep or flat.
  Where the graph is increasing or decreasing.

Graphing Lines By Plotting Points:

Use the points from a table to generate a graph.

Example 6. A math textbook company, Calculate Inc., offers you a job selling textbooks. They pay $15,000 plus 9% commission. Complete the table below and make a graph of your possible wages.

Sales	Calculation	Wages
50,000	$.09 \bullet 50{,}000 + 15{,}000$	19,500
100,000	$.09 \bullet 100{,}000 + 15{,}000$	24,000
200,000	$.09 \bullet 200{,}000 + 15{,}000$	33,000
S	$.09S + 15{,}000$	W

Graph the points (50000, 19500), (100000, 24000), and (200000, 33000).

Choosing the scale of the graph:

For the Sales axis:

Start at zero and go past \$200,000. Perhaps \$250,000.
Count by ten thousands.

For the Wages axes:

Start at zero and go past \$33,000. Perhaps \$40,000.
Count by five thousands.

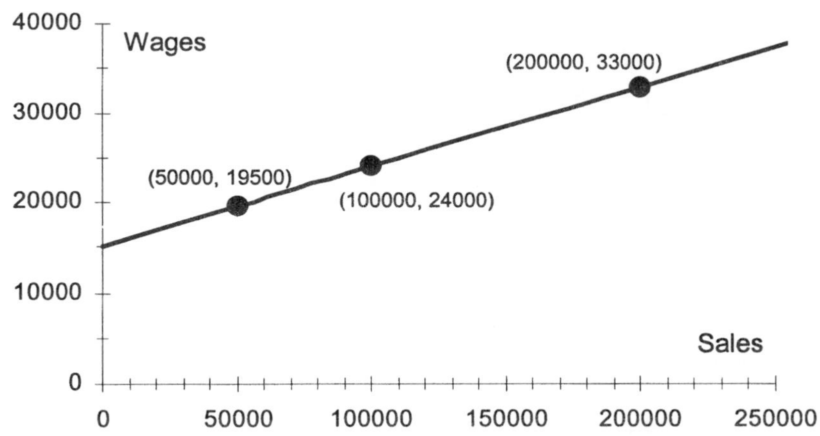

Graphing Lines By Finding the Intercepts:

To find the x intercept, set y = 0.
To find the y intercept, set x = 0.

Example 7. Graph $.02x + 30y = 15$

Find the x intercept; set y = 0.

$$.02x + 30 \bullet 0 = 15$$
$$.02x = 15$$
$$x = 750$$

The x intercept is (750, 0).

Find the y intercept; set x = 0.

$$.02 \bullet 0 + 30y = 15$$
$$30y = 15$$
$$y = .5$$

The y intercept is (0, .5).

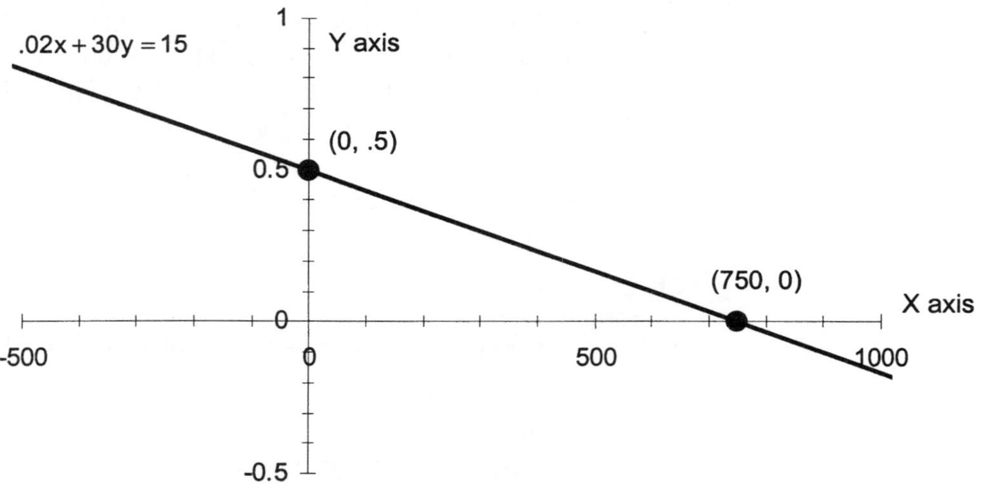

Introduction to Slope:

Slope measures how things change. Slope is:

- $\dfrac{\text{Change in Dependent Variable}}{\text{Change in Independent Variable}}$
- $\dfrac{\text{Vertical Change}}{\text{Horizontal Change}}$
- $\dfrac{\text{Rise}}{\text{Run}}$

- Slope measures how steep a line is.
- Slope is the average rate of change.
- If the slope of the line is negative, then the line is decreasing.
- If the slope of the line is positive, then the line is increasing.

Percent Change also measures how a quantity changes. The formula for Percent Change is:

$$\text{Percent Change} = \frac{\text{New - Old}}{\text{Old}} \bullet 100$$

Example 8. Use the information in the table below to answer the questions.

Year	Number of Radio Stations with a Jazz Format
1999	243
2001	213

a. Find the average rate of change.
(This is the same as the slope of a line.)

Year is the independent variable, and number of stations is the dependent variable.

$$\text{Average Rate of Change } = \frac{213-243}{2001-1999}$$

Average Rate of Change = –15.

On the average, there was a decrease of 15 radio stations per year.

b. Find the percent change.

$$\text{Percent Change} = \frac{\text{New - Old}}{\text{Old}} \bullet 100$$

$$\text{Percent Change} = \frac{213 - 243}{243} \bullet 100$$

Percent Change = -12.35

The number of jazz radio stations decreased by 12.35% between 1999 and 2001.

Slope:

The algebraic formula for slope is $m = \frac{y_2 - y_1}{x_2 - x_1}$.

The slope of a horizontal line is zero.

The slope of a vertical line is undefined.

The slope-intercept equation is y = mx + b.

Example 9. Find the slope of the line that contains the points (-3, 5) and (2, -1).

$$m = \frac{5-(-1)}{-3-2}$$

$$m = \frac{-6}{5}$$

The slope of the line is $\frac{-6}{5}$.

Applications of Graphs:

This section summarizes the major concepts of the course thus far.

Example 10. You need to rent a moving van. One company, Quick Movers, charges a basic rate of \$24.95 plus 32 cents a mile. A second company, Silver Glove Movers, charges a basic rate of \$19.95 plus 40 cents a mile.

The equations are: Quick: $C = .32m + 24.95$
Silver: $C = .40m + 19.95$

To find where the two lines intersect:

$$.40m + 19.95 = .32m + 24.95$$
$$.40m = .32m + 5.00$$
$$.08m = 5.00$$
$$m = 62.5$$

Find C when m = 62.5.

$$C = .32 \bullet 62.5 + 24.95$$
$$C = 44.95$$

The two lines intersect at (62.5, 44.95).

Explanation: You can use either company's equation.

Graph the two equations.

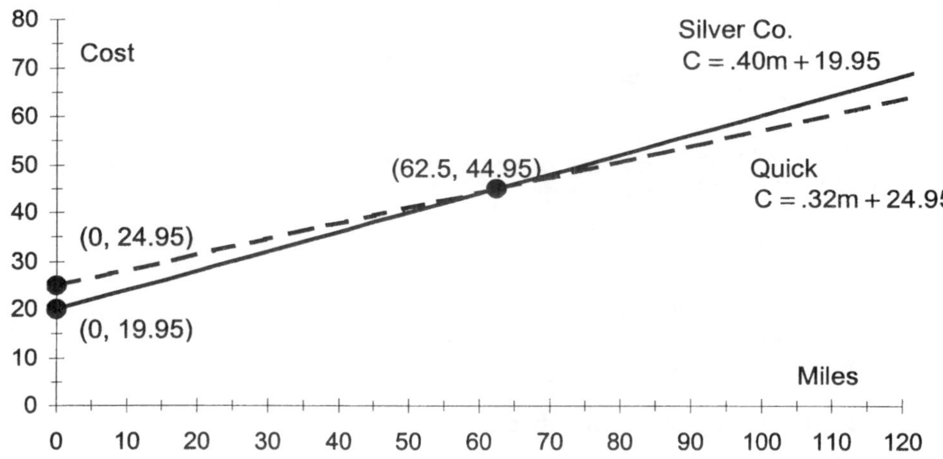

Silver Co. costs more if you drive over 62.5 miles.
Quick costs more if you drive under 62.5 miles.

The cost intercept of Quick is (0, 24.95). It will cost you \$24.95 to drive nowhere.

The slope of $C = .40m + 19.95$ is .40. Silver company charges 40 cents per mile.

Study Tips:

1. Practice the review test starting on the next page by placing yourself under realistic exam conditions.
2. Find a quiet place and use a timer to simulate test conditions.
3. Write your answers in your homework notebook. You may then re-take the exam for extra practice.
4. Check your answers. The answers to the review test are on page 369.
5. There is an additional exam available on the MAT 011 web page, **www.mc3.edu/aa/career/MATHSCI/mat011/mat011.htm**
6. Do NOT wait until the night before to study.

TEST II

1. The following table shows the temperature, in Celsius, of a microwave dinner while it is in the freezer, taken out to defrost, cooked in the oven and served at the table. The food was removed from the freezer at t = 0 min.

   a. Make a graph of temperature versus time. Make sure you label your axes and choose an appropriate scale.

   b. When do you think the microwave dinner was placed in the oven?

   c. When do you think the microwave dinner was taken out of the oven?

   d. From the graph, when was the microwave dinner 100°?

Time in Minutes	Temperature Celsius
-15	-10°
0	-10°
10	-5°
20	3°
25	23°
30	45°
35	90°
50	125°
60	160°
65	90°
70	55°
75	40°

2. Graph the lines

   a. $y = -4$ b. $x = 7$

3. Find the x and y intercepts and graph the following lines. Label your axes and choose an appropriate scale.

   a. $y = 0.1x + 210$ b. $76x + 2y = 4$

   c. $4x + 7y = 20$ d. $y = \frac{4}{3}x + 8$

4. SITUATION: The following diagram shows the temperature in Frostburg, Maryland for a typical December day. The temperature is a function of the time of day.

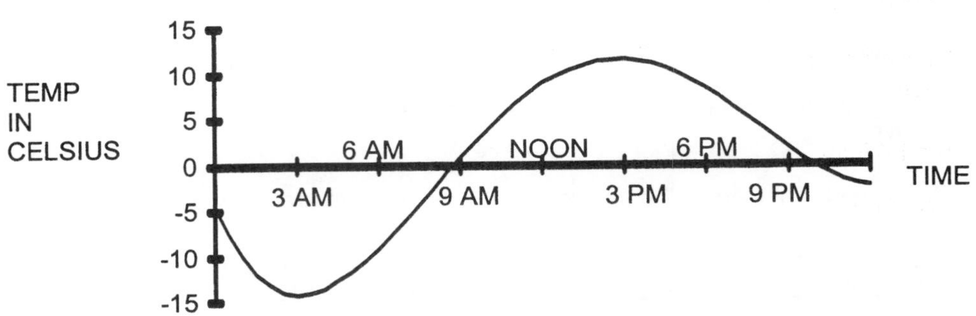

For each of the following questions, list the coordinates of the point(s) that give the answer. Then write your answer in a sentence. Estimate where necessary.

a. What was the temperature at 3 a.m.?

b. What was the temperature at 9 p.m.?

c. When was the temperature –2°C?

d. When was the temperature 3°C?

e. What was the maximum temperature, and when did it occur?

f. What was the minimum temperature, and when did it occur?

g. When was the temperature rising?

h. When was the temperature falling?

Study Tip: If you don't remember how to do a problem, look through the unit until you find an example similar to the one which is giving you difficulty.

5. Use the table to answer the following questions.

a. Find the average rate of change of corn produced in Nebraska between 1980 and 1984.

Year	Millions of Tons of Corn Produced in Nebraska
1980	62.4
1984	78.5

b. Find the percent increase of corn produced in Nebraska between 1980 and 1984.

c. Find the slope of the line created by the data.

6. Solve.

a. $8x - 3 \le 7$

b. $4 - 2x \ge -2$

c. $-3 \le 7x - 15 < 10$

7. An electric company has a fleet of trucks. The annual operating cost per truck is

$$C = 0.26m + 3100$$

where m is the number of miles traveled in a year.

a. How many miles can a truck travel in a year and still cost less than $4000?

b. How many miles can a truck travel in a year and still cost between $3500 and $5000?

8. Given the equation, find the slope and y intercept.

a. $y = -3x + 7$ b. $y = .15x - 6$

9. Find the slope of the line containing the two points.

a. (5, –8) and (–3, 5) b. (2, 6) and (–9, 6)

10. P.M.A. offers you a sales position. They pay 10% commission plus $20,000 a year. The equation that models this situation is $W = .1S + 20000$. W is your wages for the year, and S is the dollar amount of your sales.

a. What is the slope of the line? What does the slope mean in terms of the problem?

b. If you don't sell anything for P.M.A., how much money will you make for the year? If you were to graph this point, what would it be called?

11. You want to rent a car for a day. Limo will charge you $32.00 for the day while Ultra will charge you $19 for the day plus 26 cents a mile.

a. Write an equation for the cost of renting a car from Limo. Write an equation for the cost of renting a car from Ultra.

b. Graph both equations on the same set of axes. Label your axes and choose an appropriate scale. Only graph the portion that is relevant to the problem. (Answering question c before question b may be helpful.)

c. Use the equations to find where the two lines intersect. This is the same question as finding how many miles you have to drive for the two companies to charge the same, except you have to also find the cost. Label this point on the graph.

d. Use the graph to find when Limo is more expensive than Ultra.

e. Use the graph to find when Ultra is more expensive than Limo.

f. What is the cost intercepts for Limo and Ultra? Label the points on the graph. What do the intercepts mean in terms of renting a car?

g. What is the slope of each line and explain what they mean in terms of the problem.

UNIT 3

INTRODUCTION TO POSITIVE EXPONENTS
OVERVEIW

Objectives: In this section, you will define exponents and perform computations with a calculator. In addition, you will solve problems using the formula for compound interest and tables for demonstrating bacteria growth to illustrate the applications of exponents.

Definition: $\mathbf{b}^{\mathbf{n}}$ means **b** times itself **n** times; **b** is called the base and **n** is called the exponent.

Basic Examples:

Example 1. Write 3^5 using the definition of exponents.

Three is the base and five is the exponent.

$3^5 = 3 \bullet 3 \bullet 3 \bullet 3 \bullet 3$

Example 2. Use a calculator to compute the following.

The exponent key for the TI-30X II S, the recommended calculator for the course, is ^. For other calculators, the exponent key is y^x. The explanation below is for the TI-30x II S.

a. 7.6^8

Type 7.6, then the [^] key. Press 8 and [=]

$7.6^8 = 11{,}130{,}347.87$

b. -6.2^4

Use the [(-)] key. Press 6.2, then the [^] key. Press 4 and [=]

$-6.2^4 = -1{,}477.6336$

> **Explanation:** Why is -6.2^4 negative while $(-6.2)^4$ is positive?
>
> $-6.2^4 = -1 \bullet 6.2 \bullet 6.2 \bullet 6.2 \bullet 6.2$
> Recall the order of operations, exponents before multiplication.
> So -6.2^4 means $(-1) \bullet 6.2^4$.
>
> $(-6.2)^4 = (-6.2) \bullet (-6.2) \bullet (-6.2) \bullet (-6.2)$
> A negative times a negative four times is positive.

c. $(-6.2)^4$

Use the [(] key then the [(-)] key; press 6.2, [)] key, then the [^] key. Press 4, and [=]

$(-6.2)^4 = 1{,}477.6336$

d. -5.6^3

$-5.6^3 = -175.616$

e. $(-5.6)^3$

$(-5.6)^3 = -175.616$

> **Explanation:** Why are both answers negative?
> $-5.6^3 = (-1) \bullet 5.6 \bullet 5.6 \bullet 5.6$
>
> $(-5.6)^3 = (-5.6) \bullet (-5.6) \bullet (-5.6)$
> A negative times a negative three times is negative.

Study Tip: It is important to recognize when parentheses make a difference in the answer. Make a note card with examples with and without parentheses and with even and odd exponents. Review the card as homework.

For many transactions interest is added to the principal, the amount invested, at regular time intervals so that the interest itself earns interest. Examples of accounts that use compound interest are: savings accounts, certificates of deposit, savings bonds and money market accounts.

Example 3. When the interest is compounded monthly, the formula below computes how much money will be in your account at sometime in the future.

$$FV = P(1 + i)^n$$

where FV is Future Value
P is amount invested
i is interest rate per month
n is the number of times compounded

a. If you invest $3,500 at an annual interest rate of 6%, how much money will you have after 20 years?

Make a table of the information and variables in the problem.

Variables	Values
FV	What you need to find.
P	$3,500
i	$\frac{.06}{12} = .005$
n	$20 \bullet 12 = 240$

Explanation:
You need to divide .06 by 12 because annual interest is per year and the formula is per month.

You need to multiply 20 by 12 because there are 12 months in a year.

Substitute the values into the formula, $FV = P(1 + i)^n$.

$FV = 3,500(1+.005)^{240}$	Substitute the values into the variables.
$FV = 3,500(1.005)^{240}$	Add inside parentheses.
$FV = 3,500 \bullet 3.310$	Compute the exponent.
$FV = 11,585$	Multiply.

You will have $11,585 in twenty years.

b. How much money should you invest at an annual interest rate of 3% if you want $15,000 in 10 years?

Make a table of the information and variables in the problem.

Variables	Values
FV	15,000
P	What you need to find.
i	$\frac{.03}{12} = .0025$
n	$10 \bullet 12 = 120$

Substitute the values into the formula, $FV = P(1 + i)^n$.

$15{,}000 = P(1+.0025)^{120}$	Substitute the values into the variables.
$15{,}000 = P(1.0025)^{120}$	Add inside parentheses.
$15{,}000 = P1.349$	Compute the exponent.
$11{,}119.35 = P$	Divide both sides by 1.349.

You need to invest $11,119.35 now in order to have $15,000 in ten years.

Example 4. There are 5,000 bacteria initially present in a culture. The culture grows at a rate of 8% each day.

a. Complete the table below.

Time	**Calculation**	**Number Of Bacteria**
Initial day		5,000
1 day later	$5{,}000 \bullet 1.08$	5,400
2 days later	$5{,}000 \bullet 1.08^2$	5,832
3 days later	$5{,}000 \bullet 1.08^3$	6,299
4 days later	$5{,}000 \bullet 1.08^4$	6,802
N days later	$5{,}000 \bullet 1.08^n$	B

Explanation of Calculation:

1 day later:

Initial amount + increase =

$5{,}000 + .08 \bullet 5{,}000 =$

(The increase is 8% of 5,000.)

$5{,}000 \bullet 1.08 = 5{,}400$

(This is 108% of 5,000.)

2 days later:

$5{,}400 \bullet 1.08 =$

(This is 108% of 5,400.)

$5{,}000 \bullet 1.08 \bullet 1.08 =$

(Replace 5,400 with the original number and increase the exponent.)

$5{,}000 \bullet 1.08^2 = 5{,}832$

3 days later:

$5{,}832 \bullet 1.08 =$

(This is 108% of 5,832.)

$5{,}000 \bullet 1.08^2 \bullet 1.08 =$

(Replace 5,832 with the original number and increase the exponent.)

$5{,}000 \bullet 1.08^3 = 6{,}299$

Study Tip: It is important to see the logic of the calculation column.

b. What is the equation that relates the number of bacteria to time?

$B = 5{,}000 \bullet 1.08^n$, where n is the number of days.

c. Use the equation to find the number of bacteria present after 35 days.

$B = 5{,}000 \bullet 1.08^{35}$	Substitute 35 into n.
$B = 5{,}000 \bullet 14.79$	Compute the exponent.
$B = 73{,}900$	Multiply.

There will be 73,900 bacteria in 35 days.

Summary: Not everything grows at a constant rate as shown in Unit II. In this section, we examined what happens when something grows as a percentage of itself. Savings accounts, populations, and radioactive decay all increase in this way. Equations with the variable as an exponent model this behavior. Such equations are called exponential equations.

Definition of exponents:

a^n means "a" times itself "n" times; "a" is called the base and "n" is called the exponent.

When computing exponents:

Know why -6.7^8 is negative.

Know why $(-6.7)^8$ is positive.

Know why the answer doesn't change if the exponent is odd whether or not you have parentheses.

Know how to use your calculator.

Know the logic of how the equation in Example 4 was derived.

CLASS WORK

1. What is the definition of an exponent?

2. Complete the following using a calculator.

   a. $(-6)^2$ b. $(-8.2)^4$ c. 7^0 d. -6^2

   e. -8.2^4 f. 8.6^0 g. $(-3.1)^3$ h. -3.1^3

Compound Interest

For many transactions interest is added to the principal, the amount invested, at regular time intervals so that the interest itself earns interest. Examples of accounts that use compound interest are: savings accounts, certificates of deposit, savings bonds, and money market accounts.

3. Assuming that the interest is compounded monthly, the formula below computes how much money will be in your account at sometime in the future.

$$FV = P(1 + i)^n$$

where FV is Future Value
P is amount invested
i is interest rate per month
n is the number of months

   a. A couple invests \$2000 at an annual interest rate of 12%. How much money will they have after 10 years?

   b. How much money should you invest at an annual interest rate of 6% if you want \$10,000 in 20 years?

4. a. The population of Shanghai was 10,820,000 in 1974. If the population increased by 1% each year, complete the table below.

Compute Shanghai's population in 1975.

Compute Shanghai's population in 1976.

YEAR	CALCULATION	POPULATION
1974		10,820,000
1975		
1976		
1977		
1978		
n		

b. What is the equation that relates Shanghai's population and the year?

c. Use the equation to find Shanghai's population in 1985.

5. a. When a ball is dropped, it may bounce but not up to its original height. Call the ratio of the rebound height to the original height the resiliency of the ball for whatever surface on which it is being dropped. A ball is dropped from two meters, and for that surface resiliency is .6. Complete the table below.

BOUNCE	CALCULATION	HEIGHT OF BOUNCE
1st		
2nd		
3rd		
4th		
B		

b. What is the equation that relates the height of the bounce to the number of times the ball has bounced?

c. Use the equation to find the height of the 15th bounce.

6. Many MAT 011 students take AST 120, Introduction to Astronomy, to satisfy their science requirement at MCCC. The following problem comes from AST 120.

The formula below is used to approximate a star's luminosity (the total amount of energy a star radiates in 1 second) in terms of the sun's luminosity:

$$L = M^{3.5}$$

How a variable is measured, or its units, is very important in science classes. M is called solar masses and L is luminosity of a star in terms of the sun's luminosity. For example, to approximate the luminosity of a star two times the mass of the sun, M = 2 and $L = 2^{3.5} = 11.3$. So the luminosity of a star with twice the mass of the sun will be 11.3 times the luminosity of the sun.

a. Approximate the luminosity of a star five times the mass of the sun. (M = 5.)

b. Approximate the luminosity of a star half the mass of the sun. (M = 0.5)

GROUP EXERCISE

1. There are 2,000 bacteria present initially in a culture. The culture grows at 13% each day.

Study Tip: Review example 4 on page 206 or problem 4 on page 209. If you won't disturb the class, do this table on the board. Ask the teacher first.

a. Complete the table.

TIME	CALCULATION	NUMBER OF BACTERIA
Initial Day		2000
1 Day Later		
2 Days Later		
3 Days Later		
4 Days Later		
n Days Later		

b. What is the equation that relates number of bacteria to time?

c. Use the equation in 1b to find how many bacteria there will be in

1) 15 days

2) 20 days

d. Use the table below to find out when there will be 16,000 bacteria.

TIME (GUESS)	NUMBER OF BACTERIA	TOO LOW/TOO HIGH

EXERCISE

Study Tip: Review pertinent note cards first.
Review example 2 on page 204 or problem 2 on page 208.
Refer to Appendix C and the CD that accompanies the textbook to learn how to use the TI-30X IIS calculator.

1. Use a calculator to compute the following.

   a. 6^5 b. 7.82^3 c. 8.51^4

2. Use a calculator to compute the following. First decide if the answers should be positive or negative.

   a. $(-6)^2$ b. $(-7.4)^6$ c. $(-3.2)^4$

   d. $(-8.1)^2$ e. $(-6.8)^4$ f. $(-2.4)^8$

   g. $(\text{a negative})^{12}$

3. Use a calculator to compute the following. First decide if the answers should be positive or negative.

   a. -8.2^2 b. -6.7^4 c. -2.5^2

   d. -6^3 e. $(-6)^3$ f. -7^5

   g. $(-7)^5$ h. $(\text{a negative})^5$

   i. Explain why $(-5)^6$ is positive and -5^6 is negative.

4. There are 1000 bacteria present initially in a culture. The culture grows at 5% each day.

Study Tip: Review example 4 on page 206 or problem 4 on page 209.

a. Complete the table.

TIME	CALCULATION	NUMBER OF BACTERIA
Initial day		1000
1 day later	1000(1.05)	1050
2 days later		
3 days later		
4 days later		
n days later		

b. What is the equation that relates number of bacteria to time?

c. Use the equation in 4b. to find how many bacteria there will be (round to the nearest whole number)
1) 20 days later 2) 40 days later

d. Use the table below to find when there will be 2000 bacteria.

TIME (GUESS)	NUMBER OF BACTERIA	TOO HIGH/TOO LOW

5. The population of Farmington in 1980 was 1,052,000. The population is decreasing by 3.5% each year.

a. Complete the table.

YEAR	CALCULATION	POPULATION
1980		1,052,000
1981	1,052,000(.965)	
1982		
1983		
1984		
n Years after 1980		

b. What is the equation that relates population to time?

c. Use the equation from 5b. to find the population of Farmington. (Round to the nearest whole number.)
1) in 1990 2) in 1996

d. Use the table below to find when there will be 900,000 people living in Farmington.

YEAR (GUESS)	POPULATION	TOO HIGH/TOO LOW

6. Assuming that the interest is compounded monthly, the formula below computes how much money will be in your account at sometime in the future.

$$FV = P(1 + i)^n$$

where: FV is Future Value
P is the amount invested
i is the interest per period
n is the number of times compounded

a. Find the Future Value of a $1,000 deposit if the annual rate is 8% compounded monthly for 20 years. (Hint: $i = .08/12$, $n = 12 \bullet 20$)

b. Find the Future Value of a $3,000 deposit if the annual rate is 7.5% compounded monthly for 10 years. (Hint: $i = .075/12$, $n = 12 \bullet 10$)

c. Find the Future Value of a $5,000 deposit if the annual rate is 6% compounded monthly for 10 years. (Hint: i = .06/12, n = 12•10)

d. Determine how much money must be invested today at an annual rate of 6% compounded monthly if the sum of $15,000 is desired fifteen years from now. (Hint: i = .06/12, n = 12•15)

e. Determine how much money must be invested today at an annual rate of 7.5% compounded monthly if the sum of $10,000 is desired 20 years from now. (i = .075/12, n = 240)

f. Use the table below to find how long it will take for $5,000 to grow to $15,000 if it is invested at 9.5% compounded annually. (Hint: i = .095/12)

GUESS N	$5000(1.0079)^n$	TOO HIGH/TOO LOW (COMPARE TO 15,000)
10 years		

NEGATIVE EXPONENTS AND SCIENTIFIC NOTATION OVERVIEW

Objectives: This section will introduce negative exponents and scientific notation. We will use negative exponents to compute monthly mortgage payments. Scientific notation is used to write very large or very small numbers in a convenient and informative way.

Definition: A negative exponent must be changed to its reciprocal.

$$a^{-n} = \frac{1}{a^n} \text{ or}$$

$$\frac{1}{a^{-n}} = a^n$$

Example 1. Compute 5^{-2} using your calculator and the definition.
(The explanation is for the TI-30X II S calculator.)

By the definition: $5^{-2} = \frac{1}{5^2}$

$= \frac{1}{25}$

$= 0.04$

With your calculator: Press 5, the exponent key [^], the opposite key [(-)],
And then 2, [=] .

$5^{-2} = 0.04$

Example 2. Compute the following using your calculator.

a. -4.2^{-6}

Start with the opposite key [(-)], press 4.2, [^] , [(-)] , 6, [=] .

$-4.2^{-6} = -0.0001822$

b. $(-4.2)^{-6}$

Start with the [( ]; then enter −4.2 as above, close parentheses, then enter the exponent.

$(-4.2)^{-6} = 0.0001822$

Parts a and b illustrate the importance of parentheses when you have even exponents.

c. 0.24^{-5}

$0.24^{-5} = 1{,}256$

If the base is less than one and the exponent is negative, then the answer will be large.

Example 2. Use the following formula to find the monthly payment of a loan.

$$P = A\left[\frac{i}{1-(1+i)^{-n}}\right]$$

P is the monthly payment
A is the amount of the loan
n is the number of monthly payments
i is the interest rate per month

Find the monthly payments on a 48-month car loan of $14,500 at 3% annual interest.

Make a table of the information and variables in the problem.

Variables	Values
P	What you need to find.
A	$14,500
i	$\frac{.03}{12} = .0025$
n	48

Explanation:
You need to divide .03 by 12 because annual interest is per year, and the formula is per month.

Substitute values into the formula $P = A\left[\frac{i}{1-(1+i)^{-n}}\right]$.

$$P = 14,500\left[\frac{0.0025}{1-(1+0.0025)^{-48}}\right]$$ Substitute values into the formula.

$$P = 14,500\left[\frac{0.0025}{1-(1.0025)^{-48}}\right]$$ Add inside the parentheses.

$$P = 14,500\left[\frac{0.0025}{1-.8871}\right]$$ Compute the exponent.

$$P = 14,500\left[\frac{0.0025}{.1129}\right]$$ Simplify the denominator by subtracting.

$$P = 14,500 \bullet .0221$$ Divide to obtain .0221.

$$P = 320.45$$ Multiply to obtain 320.45.

The monthly payments are $320.45.

Scientific Notation: Scientific notation writes very large or extremely small numbers conveniently.

Example 3. How far can you see at night?

The farthest object that can be seen with the naked eye from North America in is the Andromeda Galaxy. The Andromeda Galaxy is 2,300,000 light years away. A light year is 10,000,000,000,000 kilometers. To answer the question, multiply the two numbers together. The zeros are annoying. Writing the numbers in scientific notation eliminates the zeros.

$10{,}000{,}000{,}000{,}000 = 1.0 \bullet 10^{13}$ in scientific notation.

$2{,}300{,}000 = 2.3 \bullet 10^{6}$

The farthest you can see at night is $(1.0 \bullet 10^{13})(2.3 \bullet 10^{6}) = 2.3 \bullet 10^{19}$ km. Scientific notation is an easy way to write the answer.

Definition: A number is in scientific notation if it is in the form

$$P \bullet 10^{n}$$

where $1 \le P < 10$ and n is an integer.
An integer is one of the following numbers ....–3, –2, –1, 0, 1, 2, 3, ...

The idea of scientific notation is based on our number system being base 10. Consider the number 2,453.0678

Each digit has its own value depending on its position.

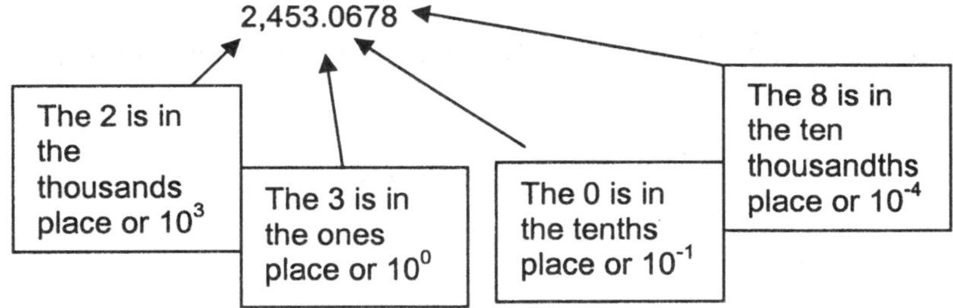

2,453.0678
The 2 is in the thousands place or 10^{3}
The 3 is in the ones place or 10^{0}
The 0 is in the tenths place or 10^{-1}
The 8 is in the ten thousandths place or 10^{-4}

Example 4. Convert each number to scientific notation.

a. 2,340,000,000

Using the definition above, P = 2.34.
The 2 is in the 10^{9} place. Remember that the ones place (the first zero) is 10^{0}.

$2{,}340{,}000{,}000 = 2.34 \bullet 10^{9}$

b. 0.0000967

Using the definition above, P = 9.67.
The 9 is in the 10^{-5} place. Remember that the first zero to the right of the decimal point is 10^{-1}.

$0.0000967 = 9.67 \bullet 10^{-5}$

Example 5. Convert from scientific notation to decimal notation.

a. $5.97 \bullet 10^{6}$

The 5 is in the 10^{6} place.
$5.97 \bullet 10^{6} = 5{,}970{,}000$

b. $2.53 \bullet 10^{-6}$

The 2 is in the 10^{-6} place.
$2.53 \bullet 10^{-6} = 0.00000253$

Example 6. Use your calculator to multiply
$(6.732 \bullet 10^{8})(4.67 \bullet 10^{12})$.

We use the [EE] key to enter a scientific notation number into your calculator. This key is equivalent to $\bullet 10$.

To enter the number $6.732 \bullet 10^{8}$, type 6.732, then the [EE] key followed by the exponent, 8.

The number should look like 6.732E8.

$(6.732 \bullet 10^{8})(4.67 \bullet 10^{12}) = 3.144 \bullet 10^{21}$

Summary: Negative exponents and scientific notation play key roles in the fields of business and science. You must feel comfortable manipulating these principles to solve very important practical problems.

Remember:

A negative exponent must be changed to its reciprocal.

$$a^{-n} = \frac{1}{a^{n}} \text{ or } \frac{1}{a^{-n}} = a^{n}$$

Scientific notation is in the form of $P \bullet 10^{n}$ where $1 \leq P < 10$ and n is an integer.

To enter a number in scientific notation into your calculator, use the [EE] key.

Study Tip: Record on notecards the keys for computing exponents on your calculator and the key to compute arithmetic with numbers in scientific notation. For the TI-30x II S, the [^] is used to compute exponents, and the [EE] is used for scientific notation.

CLASS WORK

1. What does a negative exponent mean?

2. Use a calculator to compute the following.

   a. 8^{-2} b. -6^{-4} c. $(-6)^{-4}$ d. 0.08^{-5}

3. Use the following formula to find the monthly payment of a loan.

$$P = A\left[\frac{i}{1-(1+i)^{-n}}\right]$$

P is the monthly payment
A is the amount of the loan
n is the number of monthly payments
i is the interest rate per month

   a. Find the monthly payments on a 48-month car loan of $18,000 at 3% annual interest. (Hint i = .03/12).

   b. The Clintons can afford a $1,000 monthly payment for a house. They find a loan for 7.2% annual interest rate for 360 months. How expensive of a home can they afford? (Hint: i = .072/12)

4. A number in Scientific Notation has the form

$$P \bullet 10^n$$

where $1 \leq P < 10$ and n is an integer.

a. Write the number in Scientific Notation.

1) 8,200,000

2) 0.000517

3) The weight of an oxygen atom is 0.000000000000000000000026561 grams. Write this weight in scientific notation.

b. Write the number in decimal form.

1) $7.3 \bullet 10^6$

2) $3.141 \bullet 10^{-4}$

3) $8.14 \bullet 10^3$

c. Use your calculator to compute the following.

1) $(6.3 \bullet 10^8)(4.2 \bullet 10^9)$

2) $\dfrac{2.8 \bullet 10^{-5}}{8.6 \bullet 10^{-3}}$

d. Light travels at a rate of 1.86×10^5 miles per second. How far does light travel in a day? (There are 8.64×10^4 seconds in a day.)

e. The distance from the sun to the earth is 93,000,000 miles. How long does it take for the light of the sun to reach the earth?

GROUP EXERCISE

 **Study Tip:** Review pages 217 – 220.

1. Compute the following using your calculator

   a. 2^{-4} b. -2^{-4} c. $(-2)^{-4}$

2. Use the following formula to find the monthly payment of a loan.

$$P = A\left[\frac{i}{1-(1+i)^{-n}}\right]$$

P is the monthly payment
A is the amount of the loan
n is the number of monthly payments
i is the interest rate per month

 **Study Tip:** Review problem 2 on page 218 or example 3 on page 221.

   a. Find the monthly payments on a 36-month car loan of $7,800 at 4% annual interest. (Hint: i = .04/12)

   b. Eddie Nerder can afford a $250 car payment at 6% annual interest for 36 months. How expensive a car can he afford? (Hint: i = .06/12)

3. The average amount of water flowing past the mouth of the Amazon River is 4.2×10^{6} cubic feet per second. How much water flows past in a day? (Hint: You first have to find the number of seconds in a day.)

EXERCISES

Study Tip: Refer to Appendix C and the CD that accompanies the textbook to learn how to use the TI-30X IIS calculator.

1. Compute the following using a calculator.

   a. 8^{-3} b. 3.1^{-2} c. $\left(\frac{1}{5}\right)^{-4}$ d. -3^{-4}

   e. $(-3)^{-4}$ f. -8^{-3} g. $(-8)^{-3}$ h. $.2^{-5}$

2. Compute using a calculator.

   a. $(3.8\text{x}10^{5})(6.2\text{x}10^{7})$ b. $\dfrac{8.7\text{x}10^{-3}}{2\text{x}10^{5}}$ c. $(7.3\text{x}10^{-8})(9.3\text{x}10^{20})$

3. Use the following formula to find the monthly payments of a loan.

   Payment of Debts $P = A\left[\dfrac{i}{1-(1+i)^{-n}}\right]$

   P is the monthly payment
   A is the amount of the loan
   n is the number of monthly payments
   i is the interest rate per month

   a. Find the monthly payments on a 36-month auto loan of $2,500 at 15% annual interest compounded monthly. (Hint: i = .15/12)

   b. Jackson Pollock can afford a $300 a month car payment at 12% annual interest for 36 months. How expensive a car can he afford? (Hint: i = .12/12, find A.)

   c. Find the monthly payments of a 30-year home mortgage of $100,000 at 9% annual interest compounded monthly. (Hint: i = .09/12, and n = 30(12).)

   d. The Bush's can afford a $1,000 monthly mortgage payment for a house. How large a 15-year mortgage can they afford at 8% annual interest compounded monthly. Hint: i = .08/12 and n = 15(12). Suppose they have a 30-year mortgage?

4. Write each number in scientific notation.

   a. 78,000 b. 0.00000167 c. 0.00635 d. 1,160,000

5. Write each number in decimal notation.

   a. $7.86 \bullet 10^{8}$ b. $8.673 \bullet 10^{-10}$ c. $3.3 \bullet 10^{-2}$ d. $2.032 \bullet 10^{4}$

6. The distance light travels in 1 year is 9.460×10^{12} kilometers. Write this number in decimal notation.

7. A beam of light travels 9.460×10^{12} kilometers in one year. How far does it travel in 10,000 years?

PROPERTIES OF EXPONENTS
OVERVIEW

Objectives: This section examines the algebraic properties of exponents. This is an important section for students who plan to take Intermediate Algebra, MAT 100.

Properties of Exponents:

Property		English Description
Property 1.	$a^n \bullet a^m = a^{n+m}$	When multiplying with the same bases, add the exponents.
Property 2.	$(a^n)^m = a^{nm}$	When there is an exponent raised to a power, multiply the exponents.
Property 3.	$(ab)^n = a^n b^n$	When two bases are being multiplied and are raised to the same power, then each base is raised to that power.
Property 4.	$a^{-n} = \frac{1}{a^n}$	A negative exponent means use the reciprocal. If the base is in the numerator, then when you compute the reciprocal the base goes to the denominator.
Property 5.	$\frac{1}{a^{-n}} = a^n$	A negative exponent means use the reciprocal. If the base is in the denominator, then when you compute the reciprocal the base goes to the numerator.
Property 6.	$\frac{a^n}{a^m} = a^{n-m}$	When dividing bases with the same bases, subtract the exponents.
Property 7.	$a^0 = 1$	Any base other than zero raised to the zero power is one.
Property 8.	$\left(\frac{a}{b}\right)^n = \frac{a^n}{b^n}$	When two bases are being divided and are raised to the same power, then each base is raised to that power.

Study Tip: Write the properties on separate note card and review them frequently.

Basic Examples:

Example 1. Simplify. $x^3 \bullet x$.

$$x^3 \bullet x = x^4 \quad \text{Add the exponents.} \quad x = x^1$$

Example 2. Simplify $(x^3y)^5$

$(x^3y)^5 = (x^3)^5 y^5$ Use property $(ab)^n = a^n b^n$

$= x^{15}y^5$ Multiply the exponents.

Example 3. Simplify $(5x^4)^3$

$(5x^4)^3 = 5^3(x^4)^3$ Use property $(ab)^n = a^n b^n$

$= 125x^{12}$ Multiply the exponents.

Example 4. Simplify $9x^{-4}$. Write the expression with positive exponents.

$9x^{-4} = \frac{9}{x^4}$ Only x was raised to the –4 power because no parentheses were present .

Example 5. Simplify $\frac{1}{(5x^3)^{-7}}$. Write the expression with positive exponents.

$\frac{1}{(5x^3)^{-7}} = (5x^3)^7$ Raised the entire denominator to the numerator because of the negative exponent.

$= 5^7(x^3)^7$ Use property $(ab)^n = a^n b^n$

$= 78{,}125x^{21}$ Use property $(a^n)^m = a^{nm}$

Example 6. Simplify $\frac{x^3}{x^7}$. Write the expression with positive exponents.

$\frac{x^3}{x^7} = x^{3-7}$ Use property $\frac{a^n}{a^m} = a^{n-m}$

$= x^{-4}$ Subtract exponents.

$= \frac{1}{x^4}$ Use property $a^{-n} = \frac{1}{a^n}$

Example 7. Simplify $\frac{2x^{-3}}{5x^{-9}}$. Write the expression with positive exponents.

$\frac{2x^{-3}}{5x^{-9}} = \frac{2x^9}{5x^3}$ Use properties $a^{-n} = \frac{1}{a^n}$ and $\frac{1}{a^{-n}} = a^n$. Only the variables are raised to the negative exponents.

$= \frac{2x^{9-3}}{5}$ Use property $\frac{a^n}{a^m} = a^{n-m}$

$= \frac{2x^6}{5}$ Subtract the exponents.

Summary: Manipulating exponents is an important skill in MAT 100, Intermediate Algebra. In MAT 011 you should be able to understand the basic problems and to learn the properties.

CLASS WORK

Property 1. $a^n \bullet a^m = a^{n+m}$

Simplify each expression.

1. $x^5 \bullet x^3$

2. $x^4 \bullet x^2$

Property 2. $(a^n)^m = a^{nm}$

Simplify each expression.

3. $\left(x^3\right)^4$

4. $\left(x^5\right)^3$

Property 3. $(ab)^n = a^n b^n$

Simplify each expression.

5. $\left(3x^2\right)^4$

6. $\left(x^2y^5\right)^3$

Property 4. $a^{-n} = \dfrac{1}{a^n}$

Simplify each expression. Write the expression with positive exponents only.

7. $8x^{-3}$

8. $(2x)^{-4}$

Property 5. $\dfrac{1}{a^{-n}} = a^n$

Simplify each expression. Write the expression with positive exponents only.

9. $\dfrac{1}{4x^{-3}}$

10. $\dfrac{1}{\left(7x^2\right)^{-3}}$

Property 6. $\dfrac{a^n}{a^m} = a^{n-m}$

Simplify each expression. Write the expression with positive exponents only.

11. $\dfrac{x^8}{x^3}$

12. $\dfrac{x^2}{x^5}$

Property 7. $a^0 = 1$

Simplify each expression.

13. $8x^0$

14. $(7x^3)^0$

Property 8. $\left(\dfrac{a}{b}\right)^n = \dfrac{a^n}{b^n}$

Simplify each expression.

15. $\left(\dfrac{4}{x^2}\right)^3$

16. $\left(\dfrac{x^2}{3}\right)^2$

Simplify each expression. Write the expression with positive exponents only.

17. $3x^2x^3$

18. $4(-3x^2)^2$

19. $6xy^2(-2x^2y)^3$

20. $\dfrac{8x^5}{x^{-3}}$

21. $\dfrac{4x^{-3}}{8x^{-1}}$

22. $\left(\dfrac{-2xy^4}{x^2y}\right)^3$

23. Many MAT 011 students take AST 120, Introduction to Astronomy, to satisfy their science requirement at MCCC. The following problem comes from AST 120 and is a follow up to problem 6 from Introduction to Positive Exponents on page 210.

The life expectancy of a star, T, is proportional to its mass divided by its luminosity or

$$T = \frac{M}{L} * 10^{10} \text{ years.}$$

a. From problem 6 page 210, $L = M^{3.5}$. Substitute this formula into the formula for T and use properties of exponents to simplify the formula for T.

b. How long can a 4 solar mass star live? (This is a star whose mass is 4 times that of the sun's. M = 4.)

c. How long can a 0.5 solar mass star live? (This is a star whose mass is half of the sun's. M = 0.5.)

GROUP EXERCISE

Study Tip: Review your exponent note cards first.

1. Find the mistake.

   Simplify each expression. Write the expression with positive exponents only.

   a. $x^3 \bullet x^2 = x^6$

   b. $\frac{1}{6x^{-3}} = 6x^3$

2. Simplify each expression. Write the expression with positive exponents only.

   a. $(5x^2)^3$

   b. $(-6x^3)^2$

   c. $\frac{9x^5}{3x^2}$

   d. $4x^{-5}$

   e. $\left(\frac{3x^3y}{5xy^3}\right)^2$

   f. $\frac{1}{(3x^2)^{-4}}$

EXERCISES

Study Tips: 1. Review your exponent note cards.
2. Work for a half hour and take a break.

1. State the eight properties of exponents.

2. Find the mistake.

Simplify each expression. Write the expression with positive exponents only.

a. $(3x^2)^4 = 81x^6$

b. $(3x^2)(4x) = 12x^2$

c. $-7x^{-2} = 7x^2$

3. Simplify each expression. Write the expression with positive exponents only.

a. $8x^5x^3$

b. $2x^3x^{-2}$

c. $(x^2y^5)^3$

d. $(5x^{-3})^4$

e. $6x^{-1}$

f. $\dfrac{5}{2x^{-3}}$

g. $\dfrac{9x^5}{18x^2}$

h. $\dfrac{x^4y^3}{9x^6y}$

i. 9^0

j. $\left(\dfrac{6}{x^2}\right)^3$

k. $\left(\dfrac{x^4}{2y^5}\right)^{-3}$

l. $(7x^5)^{-2}$

INTRODUCTION TO ALGEBRAIC FRACTIONS
OVERVIEW

Objectives: This section will introduce fractions with a simple application and then explain reducing, multiplying, and dividing algebraic fractions.

Basic examples:

Example 1. Suppose the cost of removing p percent of the particle pollution from the water of a polluted lake is given by the equation:

$$C = \frac{4,300p}{100 - p}$$

a. Find the cost for p = 70.

$C = \frac{4,300 \bullet 70}{100 - 70}$ Substitute 70 for p.

$C = \frac{301,000}{30}$ Multiply in the numerator and subtract in the denominator.

$C = 10,033.33$ Divide.

The cost of removing 70% of the pollution from the lake is $10,033.33.

b. Find the cost for p = 80.

$C = \frac{4,300 \bullet 80}{100 - 80}$ Substitute 80 for p.

$C = \frac{344,000}{20}$ Multiply in the numerator and subtract in the denominator.

$C = 17,200$ Divide.

The cost of removing 80% of the pollution from the lake is $17,200.

c. Find the cost for p = 90.

$C = \frac{4,300 \bullet 90}{100 - 90}$

$C = 38,700$

The cost of removing 90% of the pollution from the lake is $38,700. The cost does not increase at a constant rate. The cost went up approximately $7,000 when p increased from 70 to 80 percent while the cost went up approximately $21,000 when p increased from 80 to 90 percent. If you compute the cost for 95% and 99%, you will see that the cost increased dramatically.

d. Find the cost for p = 100.

$C = \frac{4,300 \bullet 100}{100 - 100}$

$C = \frac{430,000}{0}$

Division by zero is undefined, so we cannot find the cost of removing all of the pollution.

Study Tip: You should write on a note card that a numerator divided by zero is undefined and review it at least twice a week.

Reducing Algebraic Fractions: The basic idea behind reducing fractions is $\frac{8}{8}=1$ or more generally $\frac{x}{x}=1$ when x is not zero.

Example 2. Reduce to lowest terms.

a. $\frac{24x}{9x}$

$\frac{24x}{9x}=\frac{8 \bullet 3x}{3 \bullet 3x}$ Write 24 as $8 \bullet 3$ and 9x as $3 \bullet 3x$. Writing a term as a product is called **factoring**. 8 and 3 are **factors** of 24 and 3 and 3 are factors of 9. We must choose factors which have a common number. Other factors of 24, such as 4 and 6 or 2 and 12, are not desireable.

$=\frac{8 \bullet \mathbf{3x}}{3 \bullet \mathbf{3x}}$ Identify the like factors.

$=\frac{8}{3}$ Cancel the 3x because $\frac{3x}{3x}=1$.

Multiplying and Dividing Fractions: The rules for multiplying and dividing fractions are:

$\frac{a}{b} \bullet \frac{c}{d}=\frac{ac}{bd}$, multiply the numerators and denominators then reduce,

$\frac{a}{b} \div \frac{c}{d}=\frac{ad}{bc}$, use the reciprocal of the second fraction (invert the divisor) then multiply.

Study Tip: Write these formulas on a note card and review them at least twice a week.

Example 3. Multiply and reduce to lowest terms.

$\frac{30x^3}{14} \bullet \frac{7}{6x^2}$

$\frac{30x^3}{14} \bullet \frac{7}{6x^2}=\frac{5 \bullet 6 \bullet x \bullet x \bullet x \bullet 7}{7 \bullet 2 \bullet 6 \bullet x \bullet x}$ Factor 30 as $5 \bullet 6$, x^3 as $x \bullet x \bullet x$, 14 as $7 \bullet 2$, and x^2 as $x \bullet x$. No need to factor 6 since it is a factor of 30.

$=\frac{5 \bullet \mathbf{6} \bullet \mathbf{x} \bullet \mathbf{x} \bullet x \bullet \mathbf{7}}{\mathbf{7} \bullet 2 \bullet \mathbf{6} \bullet \mathbf{x} \bullet x}$ Identify the factors that are in the numerator and denominator.

$=\frac{5 \bullet x}{2}$ Cancel like factors.

$=\frac{5x}{2}$

Example 4. Divide and reduce to lowest terms.

$$\frac{18}{15x^2} \div \frac{12}{25x^4}$$

$$\frac{18}{15x^2} \div \frac{12}{25x^4} = \frac{18}{15x^2} \bullet \frac{25x^4}{12}$$

Take the reciprocal of $\frac{12}{25x^2}$.

$$= \frac{6 \bullet 3 \bullet 5 \bullet 5 \bullet x \bullet x \bullet x \bullet x}{5 \bullet 3 \bullet x \bullet x \bullet 6 \bullet 2}$$

Factor 18 as $6 \bullet 3$, 25 as $5 \bullet 5$, x^4 as $x \bullet x \bullet x \bullet x$, 15 as $5 \bullet 3$, x^2 as $x \bullet x$, and 12 as $6 \bullet 2$.

$$= \frac{\mathbf{6 \bullet 3 \bullet 5} \bullet 5 \bullet \mathbf{x \bullet x} \bullet x \bullet x}{\mathbf{5 \bullet 3 \bullet x \bullet x \bullet 6} \bullet 2}$$

Identify the factors that are in the numerator and denominator.

$$= \frac{5 \bullet x \bullet x}{2}$$

Cancel like factors.

$$= \frac{5x^2}{2}$$

Common Errors: The following problems are **NOT** correct.

1. $\frac{x-2}{x} = -2.$ 2. $\frac{4x-5}{4} = x-5.$ 3. $\frac{9}{3-x} = \frac{3}{-x}$

In each problem, **terms** (what is being added or subtracted) are cancelled. Only **factors** (what is being multiplied) can be cancelled. In problem 1,the x is wrongly cancelled. In problem 2, the fours are wrongly cancelled. In problem 3, the 9 and the 3 are reduced incorrectly.

Summary: This section should help you better understand the arithmetic of fractions. For students who are planning on taking MAT 100, Intermediate Algebra, you will see this topic again but with harder problems.

- You cannot divide by zero. (The answer is undefined.)
- The **factors** of a quantity are any two expressions that when multiplied together result in that quantity.
- To **reduce a fraction**, factor the numerator and denominator and then cancel all the factors that are in both the numerator and denominator.
- To **multiply two fractions**, multiply the numerators and denominators and then reduce.
  $$\frac{a}{b} \bullet \frac{c}{d} = \frac{ac}{bd}$$
- To **divide two fractions**, use the reciprocal of the second fraction and then multiply.
  $$\frac{a}{b} \div \frac{c}{d} = \frac{ad}{bc}$$

CLASS WORK

I. Evaluating an algebraic fraction.

1. Suppose the cost of removing p percent of the particulate pollution from the exhaust gases at an industrial site is given by

$$C = \frac{6800p}{100 - p}$$

Find the cost for

a. $p = 75$

b. $p = 85$

c. $p = 95$

d. $p = 100$

e. Use the results from parts a through d along with the points given in the table below to graph $C = \frac{6800p}{100 - p}$.

P	C	Point
0	0	(0, 0)
25	2,267	(25, 2267)
50	6800	(50, 6800)

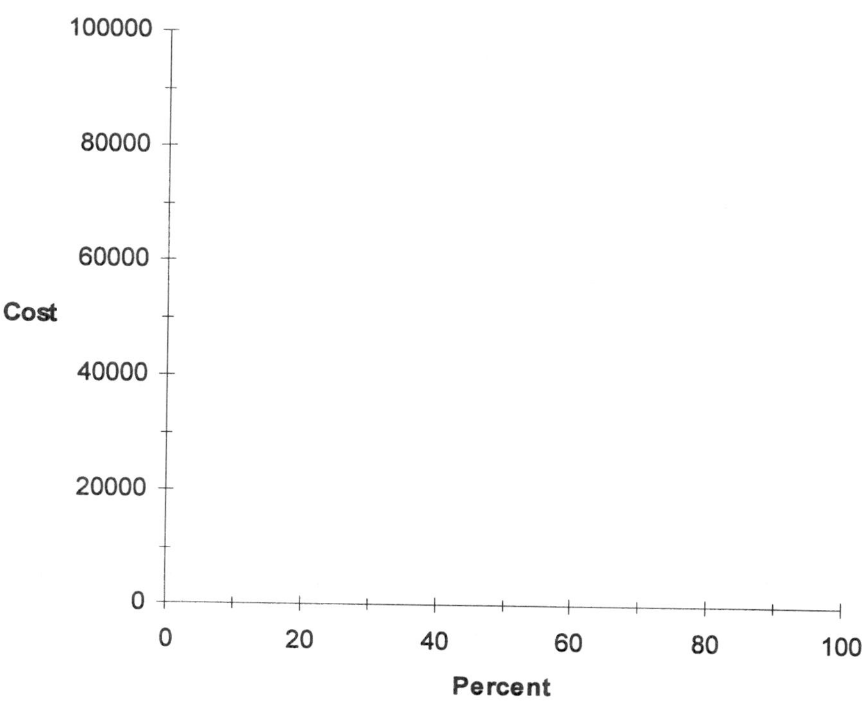

II. Reduce to lowest terms.

2. $\dfrac{12y}{8y}$

3. $\dfrac{-5x}{15x^2}$

4. $\dfrac{24x^3}{32x}$

III. Multiply or divide as indicated and reduce to lowest terms.

5. $\dfrac{8x}{5} \bullet \dfrac{15}{16x}$

6. $\dfrac{21x^2}{10} \div \dfrac{7x^3}{15}$

7. $\dfrac{-24x^3}{8} \div \dfrac{3}{5x^3}$

8. $\dfrac{9x^2}{14} \bullet \dfrac{7}{27x^3}$

GROUP EXERCISE

1. Suppose the cost of removing p percent of the particulate pollution from the exhaust gases at an industrial site is given by

$$C = \frac{7200p}{100 - p}$$

Find the cost for

a. $p = 85$

b. $p = 95$

c. $p = 99$

d. $p = 100$ (What does this say about removing all of the exhaust gases at the industrial site?)

e. Use the results from parts a through d along with the points given in the table below to graph $C = \frac{7200p}{100 - p}$.

P	C	Point
0	0	(0, 0)
25	2,400	(25, 2267)
50	7200	(50, 6800)
65	13,371	(65, 13371)
75	21,600	(75, 21600)

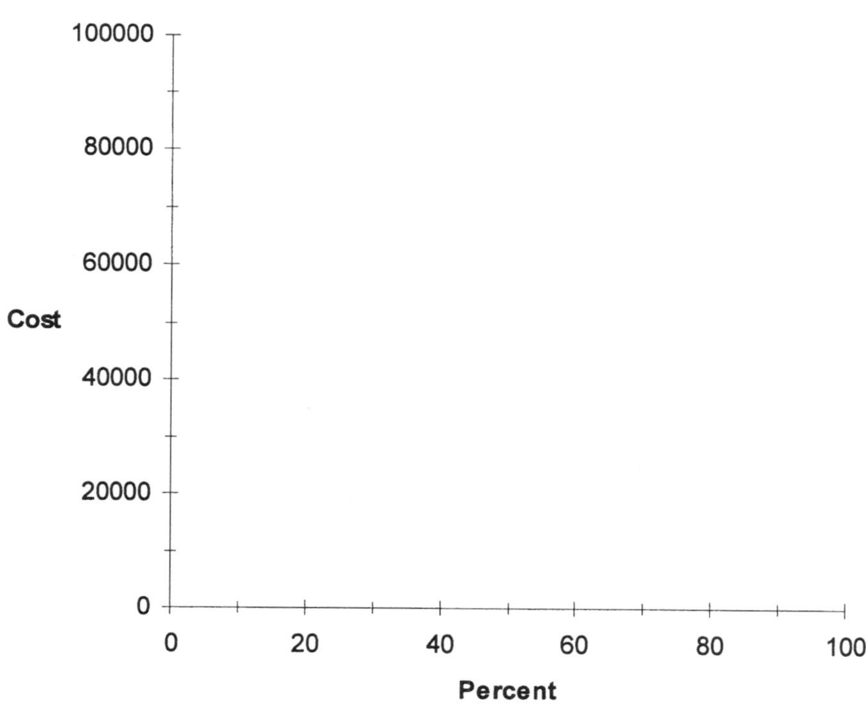

2. Reduce to lowest terms.

$$\frac{9x^3}{27x}$$

3. Multiply or divide as indicated and reduce to lowest terms.

a. $\frac{16x}{20} \bullet \frac{8x^2}{3}$

b. $\frac{-81x}{10} \div \frac{9x^3}{5}$

EXERCISES

Study Tips: 1. Review your note cards.
2. Use your loose leaf notebook.
3. Take difficult problems to the Learning Assistance Lab.

1. Suppose for a certain city the cost C of obtaining drinking water with *p* percent impurities is given by

$$C = \frac{120000}{p} - 1200$$

Find the cost for

a. $p = 15$ b. $p = 5$ c. $p = 1$

d. $p = 0$ (What does this say about the drinking water in this town?)

2. Suppose the cost C of removing *p* percent of the particulate pollution from the exhaust gases at an industrial site is given by

$$C = \frac{8300p}{100 - p}$$

Find the cost for

a. $p = 80$ b. $p = 90$ c. $p = 95$

d. $p = 100$ (What does this say about removing all of the exhaust gases at the industrial site?)

3. Reduce to lowest terms.

a. $\frac{9x}{6x}$ b. $\frac{27y}{15y}$ c. $\frac{2x^2}{8x^3}$

d. $\frac{6y^3}{15x}$ e. $\frac{-2x}{8x^2}$ f. $\frac{16x^3}{-32x}$

4. Multiply or divide as indicated and reduce to lowest terms.

a. $\frac{2x}{3} \bullet \frac{6}{3x}$ b. $\frac{6x}{5} \div \frac{3x}{10}$ c. $\frac{7}{3y} \div 3y$

d. $\frac{2x^2}{9} \bullet \frac{18}{4x}$ e. $\frac{3x^2}{4} \bullet \frac{16}{12x^3}$ f. $\frac{-6x^3}{5} \div \frac{18x}{10}$

ADDING AND SUBTRACTING ALGEBRAIC FRACTIONS
OVERVIEW

Objectives: This section will explain how to add and subtract fractions.

Procedure:

1. Find the least common denominator, LCD.
   a. For numbers, the least common denominator is the smallest number that all of the denominators divide into evenly.
   b. For variables, the least common denominator is the variable with the highest exponent.
2. Convert each fraction to a fraction with the least common denominator.
   a. Decide what you need to multiply each denominator by to get the LCD.
   b. Multiply the numerator and denominator by this quantity.
3. Combine the numerators and write as a single fraction.

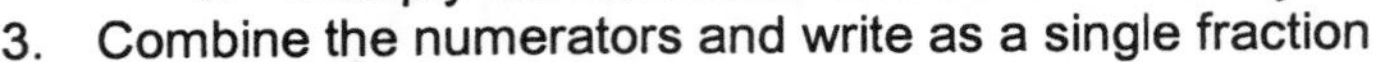

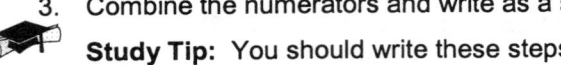

Study Tip: You should write these steps on a note card, along with an example, so you can understand what they mean.

Basic examples:

Example 1. Add $\dfrac{7}{4x}-\dfrac{3}{10}$.

$\dfrac{7}{4x}-\dfrac{3}{10}=$ The LCD is 20x. — The smallest number 4 and 10 divide into without a remainder is 20. The variable with the highest exponent is x.

$\dfrac{7}{4x}\left(\dfrac{5}{5}\right)-\dfrac{3}{10}\left(\dfrac{2x}{2x}\right)=$ — You need to multiply 4x by 5 to get 20x. You need to multiply 10 by 2x to get 20x.

$\dfrac{35}{20x}-\dfrac{6x}{20x}=$ — Multiply each fraction

$\dfrac{35-6x}{20x}$ — Write as a single fraction. Note that 35 and 6x are unlike terms and can't be combined.

Example 2. $\dfrac{5}{6x^2}+\dfrac{8}{15x^3}$.

$\dfrac{5}{6x^2}+\dfrac{8}{15x^3}=$ The LCD is$30x^3$ — The smallest number both 6 and 15 divide into without a remainder is 30. The variable with the highest exponent is x^3.

$\dfrac{5}{6x^2}\left(\dfrac{5x}{5x}\right)+\dfrac{8}{15x^3}\left(\dfrac{2}{2}\right)=$ — You need to multiply $6x^2$ by 5x to get $30x^3$. You need to multiply $15x^3$ by 2 to get $30x^3$.

$\dfrac{25x}{30x^3}+\dfrac{16}{30x^3}=$ — Multiply each fraction.

$\dfrac{25x+16}{30x^3}=$ — Write as a single fraction.

Summary: This section should help you better understand how to add and subtract numerical fractions. Learning to find the least common denominator (LCD) is imperative when working with fractions. For students planning on taking MAT 100, Intermediate Algebra, you will see these and harder examples again.

CLASS WORK

Combine into single fractions and reduce to lowest terms.

1. $\frac{9x}{10}+\frac{3x}{5}$

2. $\frac{9y}{8}+3y$

3. $\frac{7}{8x}-\frac{5}{6x}$

4. $\frac{3}{2x}-\frac{7}{5}$

5. $\frac{2}{9x}+\frac{5}{6x^2}$

6. $\frac{9}{5x}-\frac{1}{15x^3}$

GROUP EXERCISE

Describe the mistake:

1. $$\frac{6x}{5}+\frac{3x}{2}=\frac{9x}{7}$$

2. $$\frac{3x}{8}+\frac{5}{2x}=$$

$$\left(\frac{3x}{8}\right)\left(\frac{x}{x}\right)+\left(\frac{5}{2x}\right)\left(\frac{4x}{4x}\right)=$$

$$\frac{3x^2}{8x}+\frac{20x}{8x}=$$

$$\frac{3x^2+20x}{8x}$$

Describe each step.

3. $$\frac{3}{4y^2}-\frac{5}{6y^3}=$$

$$\left(\frac{3}{4y^2}\right)\left(\frac{3y}{3y}\right)-\left(\frac{5}{6y^3}\right)\left(\frac{2}{2}\right)=$$ ____________________

$$\frac{9y}{12y^3}-\frac{10}{12y^3}=$$ ____________________

$$\frac{9y-10}{12y^3}$$ ____________________

Combine into single fractions and reduce to lowest terms.

4. $$6x+\frac{3x}{5}$$

5. $$\frac{7}{4x^3}-\frac{9}{10x}$$

EXERCISES

Study Tip: Review your fraction note cards.

Describe the mistake.

1. $\frac{2x}{9}+\frac{5}{6x}=$

$\left(\frac{2x}{9}\right)\left(\frac{2x}{2x}\right)+\left(\frac{5}{6x}\right)\left(\frac{3}{3}\right)=$

$\frac{4x^2}{18x}+\frac{15}{18x}=$

$\frac{19x^2}{18x}=$

$\frac{19x}{18}$

2. $\frac{7x}{5}+\frac{2x}{3}=\frac{9x}{8}$

Describe each step.

3. $\frac{11}{2y}+\frac{8}{3y^2}=$

$\left(\frac{11}{2y}\right)\left(\frac{3y}{3y}\right)+\left(\frac{8}{3y^2}\right)\left(\frac{2}{2}\right)=$

$\frac{33y}{6y^2}+\frac{16}{6y^2}=$

$\frac{33y+16}{6y^2}$

Combine into single fractions and reduce to lowest terms.

4. $\frac{3}{5x}-\frac{2}{5x}$

5. $\frac{3}{5x}-\frac{2}{3}$

6. $\frac{4m}{3}+\frac{m}{7}$

7. $\frac{2}{3}-\frac{3}{4y}$

8. $\frac{5}{8m^3}-\frac{1}{12m}$

9. $\frac{5}{3y}+\frac{3}{4y^2}$

10. $\frac{2}{9n^2}-\frac{5}{12n^4}$

11. $\frac{3}{2x^2}+\frac{4}{3x}$

12. $\frac{x^2}{4}-\frac{x}{3}$

13. $\frac{1}{5x^3}+7$

Study Tips:
1. If any of the problems are not clear to you, ask questions in the next class session, see your instructor during office hours, or go to the Learning Assistance Lab.
2. Do not proceed until you have mastered this section.
3. Another source of information available to you outside of class is IPTV. IPTV has videos of a teacher's class lectures. The Learning Assistance Lab can help you get access to IPTV.

SOLVING EQUATIONS WITH FRACTIONS
OVERVIEW

Objective: This section will add fractions to our ability to solve equations.

Procedure: To solve an equation with fractions, multiply all the terms by the least common denominator, LCD, and reduce the fractions. This will eliminate them. Then use your skills from Unit I to solve the equation.

Basic Examples:

Example 1. Solve

$\frac{5}{6x}-\frac{2}{9x}=\frac{7}{3}$	The LCD is 18x.
$(18x)\frac{5}{6x}-(18x)\frac{2}{9x}=(18x)\frac{7}{3}$	Multiply all the terms by 18x.
$(3)\frac{5}{1}-(2)\frac{2}{1}=(6x)\frac{7}{1}$	Reduce. $18x \div 6x = 3$, $18x \div 9x = 2$, $18x \div 3 = 6x$. Note that all of the denominators are one. You don't need to write the one.
$15-4=42x$	Multiply.
$11=42x$	Combine like terms.
$\frac{11}{42}=x$	Divide both sides by 42.

The traditional answer to fractional equations is a fraction. However, there isn't anything wrong with dividing and writing the answer as a decimal.

Study Tip: You should write the procedure on a note card, along with an example, so you can understand how to solve equations involving fractions.

Example 2. Solve

$\frac{x-5}{10}-\frac{x+2}{5}=6$	The LCD is 10.
$(10)\frac{x-5}{10}-(10)\frac{x+2}{5}=(10)6$	Multiply all the terms by 10.
$(x-5)-2(x+2)=(10)6$	Reduce the fractions.
$x-5-2x-4=60$	Use the distributive property.
$-x-9=60$	Combine like terms.
$-x=69$	Add nine to both sides.
$x=-69$	Divide both sides by negative one.

Summary: The only new concept in this section is: When solving equations with fractions, multiply all of the terms by the LCD and then reduce.

Students often confuse the procedures for adding or subtracting fractions (simplifying expressions) and solving equations with fractions. When adding fractions, you want the LCD in your answer. When solving equations, you use the LCD to eliminate the fractions.

CLASS WORK

Solve each equation and describe each step.

1. $\frac{3x}{5}+\frac{7}{2}=\frac{x}{10}$

2. $\frac{4}{x}-\frac{4}{3}=\frac{8}{5x}$

Solve each equation.

3. $\frac{2x}{5}=\frac{x+2}{6}$

4. $\frac{y-4}{2}-\frac{y-3}{9}=\frac{5}{18}$

GROUP EXERCISE

1. Describe each step.

$$\frac{5x}{8}-\frac{3}{16}=\frac{7x}{24}$$

Step

$$\left(\frac{5x}{8}\right)\left(\frac{48}{1}\right)-\left(\frac{3}{16}\right)\left(\frac{48}{1}\right)=\left(\frac{7x}{24}\right)\left(\frac{48}{1}\right)$$ ____________________

$(5x)(6) - (3)(3) = (7x)(2)$ ____________________

$30x - 9 = 14x$ ____________________

$-9 = -16x$ ____________________

$\frac{9}{16} = x$ ____________________

2. Find the mistake.

$$\frac{x+5}{4}-\frac{x-3}{6}=\frac{7}{12}$$

$$\left(\frac{12}{1}\right)\left(\frac{x+5}{4}\right)-\left(\frac{12}{1}\right)\left(\frac{x-3}{6}\right)=\left(\frac{12}{1}\right)\left(\frac{7}{12}\right)$$

$$3(x+5)-2(x-3)=7$$

$$3x + 15 - 2x - 6 = 7$$

$$x + 9 = 7$$

$$x = -2$$

Solve each equation.

3. $\frac{6}{5}+\frac{8x}{15}=\frac{7x}{3}$

4. $\frac{x-2}{2}-\frac{3x+5}{4}=\frac{3}{8}$

EXERCISES

Study Tip: Make sure your homework problems are well organized. Don't be afraid to redo problems.

Describe each step.

1. $$\frac{5x}{9}-\frac{7}{36}=\frac{11x}{6}$$ Step

$$\left(\frac{5x}{9}\right)\left(\frac{36}{1}\right)-\left(\frac{7}{36}\right)\left(\frac{36}{1}\right)=\left(\frac{11x}{6}\right)\left(\frac{36}{1}\right)$$ ______________________

$$(5x)(4) - 7 = (11x)(6)$$ ______________________

$$20x - 7 = 66x$$ ______________________

$$-7 = 46x$$ ______________________

$$\frac{-7}{46} = x$$ ______________________

2. $$\frac{2x+5}{8}-\frac{x-3}{2}=\frac{7}{4}$$ Step

$$\left(\frac{2x+5}{8}\right)\left(\frac{8}{1}\right)-\left(\frac{x-3}{2}\right)\left(\frac{8}{1}\right)=\left(\frac{7}{4}\right)\left(\frac{8}{1}\right)$$ ______________________

$$2x + 5 - 4(x - 3) = (7)(2)$$ ______________________

$$2x + 5 - 4x + 12 = 14$$ ______________________

$$-2x + 17 = 14$$ ______________________

$$-2x = -3$$ ______________________

$$x = \frac{3}{2}$$ ______________________

Find the mistake.

3.
$$\frac{2}{x}-\frac{7}{5}=\frac{6}{15}$$
$$\left(\frac{2}{x}\right)\left(\frac{15x}{1}\right)-\left(\frac{7}{5}\right)\left(\frac{15x}{1}\right)=\frac{6}{15}\left(\frac{15x}{1}\right)$$
$$30x-35x=6$$
$$-5x=6$$
$$x=\frac{-6}{5}$$

4.
$$\frac{3x-2}{2}-\frac{x-5}{4}=\frac{7}{12}$$
$$\left(\frac{12}{1}\right)\left(\frac{3x-2}{2}\right)-\frac{12}{1}\left(\frac{x-5}{4}\right)=\left(\frac{12}{1}\right)\left(\frac{7}{12}\right)$$
$$6(3x-2)-3(x-5)=7$$
$$18x-12-3x-15=7$$
$$15x-27=7$$
$$15x=34$$
$$x=\frac{34}{15}$$

Solve each equation.

Study Tip: Do not confuse the procedure to add or to subtract fractions (simplifying expressions) with solving equations involving fractions.

5. $\frac{5}{18}-\frac{4x}{3}=\frac{11}{6}$

6. $\frac{2x}{21}+\frac{4}{7}=\frac{5x}{3}$

7. $\frac{8}{5x}+\frac{4}{3}=\frac{1}{15}$

8. $\frac{5}{12}-\frac{1}{3x}=\frac{7}{6}$

9. $2x-\frac{7}{5}=\frac{3x}{10}$

10. $\frac{9}{8}+3x=\frac{5x}{12}$

11. $\frac{x+1}{3}-\frac{3x+2}{2}=\frac{7}{6}$

12. $\frac{3x+5}{4}-\frac{x-2}{20}=\frac{9}{5}$

Study Tips:

1. If any of the problems are not clear to you, ask questions in the next class session, see your instructor during office hours, or go to the Learning Assistance Lab.

2. Review the CD.

3. Another source of information available to you outside of class is IPTV. IPTV has videos of a teacher's class lectures. The Learning Assistance Lab can help you get access to IPTV.

RATIO AND PROPORTION PROBLEMS
OVERVIEW

Objective: This section will cover applications involving fractions.

Definitions:

Ratios: A ratio is the comparison of two quantities that have the same units. A ratio is usually expressed as a fraction.

Rate: A rate is the comparison of two quantities that have different units A rate is usually expressed as a fraction.

Example 1. Which is the better buy? 10 ounces of peanut butter for $1.24 or 16 ounces of peanut butter for $1.89?

To answer the question, form the ratio, $\frac{\text{cost}}{\text{ounces}}$.

$\frac{1.24}{10} = .124$ For 10 ounces, the cost is 12.4 cents per ounce.

$\frac{1.89}{16} = .1181$ For 16 ounces, the cost is 11.81 cents per ounce.

The 16 ounce jar of peanut butter is the better buy because it is cheaper per ounce.

The two ratios in the problem are $\frac{1.24}{10}$ and $\frac{1.89}{16}$.

Proportions: A proportion is a statement that two ratios or rates are equal. (Or two equal fractions.)

Basic examples:

Example 2. Solve the proportion problem. $\frac{8}{x} = \frac{12}{17}$

The basic procedure for solving a proportion problem is to cross multiply.

$$\frac{8}{x} \nearrow\!\!\!\!\nwarrow \frac{12}{17}$$

Study Tip: You should write the procedure on a note card, along with an example, so you can understand how to solve proportion problems. Review the card frequently.

$\frac{8}{x} \nearrow\!\!\!\!\nwarrow \frac{12}{17}$ Cross multiplying means to multiply the denominator of one fraction with the numerator of the other fraction. This can only be done when solving a proportion problem.

$17 \bullet 8 = 12x$ Cross multiply.

$136 = 12x$ Multiply.

$11.33 = x$ Divide both sides by 12.

Example 3. Two people pooled their money to buy lottery tickets. Darrel put in $25 while Selena put in $20. If they won 8.2 million dollars, how much should each person receive?

Organize the information in a table for each person.

Darrel

	Tickets	**Winnings**
Share	25	?
Total	25 + 20	8.2 million

The ratio will be $\frac{\text{Share}}{\text{Total}}$. There are two ratios, one for tickets and one for their winnings. These two ratios should be equal.

$\frac{25}{45} = \frac{W}{8.2}$

$25 \bullet 8.2 = 45W$ Cross multiply.

$205 = 45W$ Multiply.

$4.556 = W$ Divide both sides by 45.

Darrel should win 4.556 million dollars.

Selena

	Tickets	**Winnings**
Share	20	?
Total	25 + 20	8.2 million

The ratio will be $\frac{\text{Share}}{\text{Total}}$. There are two ratios, one for tickets and one for their winnings. These two ratios should be equal.

$\frac{20}{45} = \frac{W}{8.2}$

$20 \bullet 8.2 = 45W$ Cross multiply.

$164 = 45W$ Multiply.

$3.644 = W$ Divide both sides by 45.

Selena should win 3.644 million dollars.

Example 4. In order to estimate the number of fish in a lake, 85 fish are caught, tagged, and released. Later, 64 fish are caught, and 23 have been tagged. Estimate the total number of fish in the lake.

Let T represent the total number of fish in the lake. For the second catch, 23 fish were tagged out of a total of 64. When the information is organized in a table, the rows should be labeled **Tagged** and **Total**. Since fish are caught twice, the columns should be labeled **First Catch** and **Second Catch**.

	First Catch	Second Catch
Tagged	85	23
Total	T	64

Explanation: The first catch, 85 fish are tagged out of the lake's total fish population.

The ratio is $\frac{\text{tagged}}{\text{total}}$. The first catches' ratio should equal the second catches' ratio.

$$\frac{85}{T} = \frac{23}{64}$$

$85 \bullet 64 = 23T$ Cross Multiply.

$5{,}440 = 23T$ Multiply.

$237 = T$ Divide both sides by 23.

We estimate that there are 237 fish in the lake.

Summary: Ratio and proportion problems can occur in everyday life. Maybe you don't divide lottery winnings or count fish in a lake everyday, but this application can be used to fairly divide something based on each person's input, estimate something based on a sample, convert recipes, and determine cost per unit.

Definitions:

Ratios: A ratio is the comparison of two quantities that have the same units. A ratio is usually expressed as a fraction.

Rate: A rate is the comparison of two quantities that have different units. A rate is usually expressed as a fraction.

Proportions: A proportion is a statement that two ratios or rates are equal. (Or two equal fractions.)

To solve proportion problems, cross multiply.

To solve applications:

- Create a table that organizes the information in the problem.
- Decide what units make up the ratio.
- Set up the proportion and solve.

CLASS WORK

Ratios and Rates:

1. Bob earns $250 each week, but $15 is withheld for medical insurance. Find the ratio of medical insurance to total pay.

2. Which is the better buy?

   8 oz. of jelly for $1.59 or 12 oz. of jelly for $1.80?

3. If a line rises 8 units for every 2 horizontal units, what is the slope of the line?

4. A ratio is:

   A rate is:

Proportions

5. A proportion is:

Solve:

6. $\frac{x}{5} = \frac{7}{15}$

7. $\frac{6}{x} = \frac{5}{7}$

8. In order to establish the number of fish in a lake, 30 fish are caught, tagged, and released. Later 70 fish are caught, and 14 are found to have been tagged. Estimate the number of fish in the lake.

9. Two people put their money together to buy lottery tickets. The first person put in $15, and the second person put in $25. If they won 2.4 million dollars, how much does each person win?

10. Many successful MAT 011 students take CHE 121 General Chemistry Inorganic to fulfill their science requirement at MCCC. The following problem comes from CHE 121.

Charles' Law: The volume of gas is directly proportional to its Kelvin temperature for a fixed amount of gas at a constant pressure. That is, V (volume) divided by T (temperature) is constant. Charles' Law can be stated as a proportion problem

$$\frac{V_1}{T_1} = \frac{V_2}{T_2}$$

Where V_1 is the volume of the gas at temperature T_1 and V_2 is the volume of the gas at temperature T_2.

Note: Kelvin is a temperature scale similar to Celsius. Kelvin = C° + 273.15. The temperature of 0 Kelvin or -273.15° Celsius is considered the coldest possible temperature.

An average adult inhales a volume of 0.50 L of air with each breath. If the air is warmed from room temperature (20° C = 293 K) to body temperature (37° C = 310 K) while in the lungs, what is the volume of the air when exhaled?

GROUP EXERCISE

1. Three people pooled their money to buy lottery tickets. The first person put in $20, the second put in $30 and the third put in $35. If they won 7.8 million dollars, how much did each person win?

Study Tip: Review Example 3 on page 256 or Problem 8 on page 259. Also, make sure you practice good group work habits. Make sure everyone is involved in solving the problems.

2. To determine the number of people who voted for Al Gore in Florida during the 2000 presidential election, CBS polled 160 people when they exited their polling place. Of 160 people, 82 said that they voted for Gore. If there are 5,816,000 registered voters in Florida and assuming they all vote, use a proportion to predict the total number of people who voted for Gore in Florida.

EXERCISES

Study Tips: 1. Do your homework with a friend.
2. Review your note cards.

1. Which is the better buy?

75 ounces of laundry detergent for $2.10 or
90 ounces of laundry detergent for $2.70

Study Tip: Review example 1 on page 255 or problem 1 on page 258.

2. Which is the better buy?

10 ounces of tuna for $1.09 or
15 ounces of tuna for $1.61

3. To estimate the number of bears in a forest, 8 are caught, tagged, and released. Later 9 bears are caught, and 2 are found to have been tagged. Estimate the number of bears in the forest.

Study Tip: Review example 4 on page 257 or problem 7 on page 259.

4. If a car can go 110 miles on 5 gallons of gas, how far can it go on 12 gallons of gas?

5. To estimate the number of people in Reading, population 27,000, who have no health insurance, 160 people were polled, and 18 said they had no health insurance. Estimate the number of people in Reading who don't have any health insurance.

6. A laser printer can print 7 pages every 2 minutes. How long will it take to print 81 pages?

7. Three people pooled their money to buy lottery tickets. The first person put in $20, the second put in $24, and the third put in $31. If they won 12.6 million dollars, how much did each person win?

Review example 3 on page 256 or problem 8 on page 259.

8. Solve each proportion problem:

a. $\frac{6}{x}=\frac{9}{4}$ b. $\frac{7x}{2}=\frac{6}{5}$

REVIEW III

This unit introduces exponents and algebraic fractions. Many of these skills are needed in MAT 100, Intermediate Algebra. Since the content is so important and can be confusing, plan to spend extra time in test preparation.

Introduction to Positive Exponents:

Definition: a^n means a times itself n times.

Example 1. Compute -5.8^6 using your calculator.
$-5.8^6 = -38{,}068.69254$

Explanation:
Use the ^ key.

Example 2. Compute $(-5.8)^6$ using your calculator.
$(-5.8)^6 = 38{,}068.69254$

Example 3. There are 1,000 bacteria initially present in a culture. The culture grows at a rate of 4% an hour. Complete the table below to find an equation that models the number of bacteria.

Hours	Calculation	Number of Bacteria
initially		1,000
1	$1{,}000 \bullet 1.04$	1,040
2	$1{,}000 \bullet 1.04^2$	1,082
3	$1{,}000 \bullet 1.04^3$	1,125
4	$1{,}000 \bullet 1.04^4$	1,170
h	$1{,}000 \bullet 1.04^h$	B

The equation is $B = 1{,}000 \bullet 1.04^h$.

Negative Exponents and Scientific Notation:

Definition: A negative exponent requires the use of the reciprocal.

Example 4. $\left(\dfrac{2}{3}\right)^{-5} = \left(\dfrac{3}{2}\right)^5$

Example 5. Compute -3.5^{-4} using your calulator.
$-3.5^{-4} = -0.006664$

Example 6. Use the formula $P = A\left[\dfrac{i}{1-(1+i)^{-n}}\right]$ to find the monthly payments on a 60 month car loan of $22,000 at an annual interest rate of 4%.

P is what we want to find.
A = 22,000
i = .003333 (.04/12)
n = 60

$$P = 22{,}000\left[\frac{.003333}{1-(1+.003333)^{-60}}\right]$$

$$P = 22{,}000\left[\frac{.003333}{1-(1.003333)^{-60}}\right]$$

$$P = 22{,}000\left[\frac{.003333}{1-.8190}\right]$$

$$P = 22{,}000\left[\frac{.003333}{.181}\right]$$

$$P = 22{,}000[.01841]$$

$$P = 405.02$$

The monthly payment for the car loan is $405.02.

Definition: A number in scientific notation has the form $P \bullet 10^n$ where $1 \leq P < 10$.

Example 7. Write 2,450,000,000,000 in scientific notation.

$$2{,}450{,}000{,}000{,}000 = 2.45 \bullet 10^{12}$$

Explanation: The 2 is in the 10^{12} place.

Example 8. Write $5.38 \bullet 10^{-7}$ in decimal notation.

$$5.38 \bullet 10^{-7} = 0.000000538$$

Example 9. Use your calculator to compute $\dfrac{4.89 \bullet 10^{12}}{1.56 \bullet 10^{-7}}$.

$$\frac{4.89 \bullet 10^{12}}{1.56 \bullet 10^{-7}} = 3.135 \bullet 10^{19}$$

Explanation: Use the EE key.

Properties of Exponents:

The properties of exponents are:

Property 1.	$a^n \bullet a^m = a^{n+m}$	Property 5.	$\dfrac{1}{a^{-n}} = a^n$
Property 2.	$(a^n)^m = a^{nm}$	Property 6.	$\dfrac{a^n}{a^m} = a^{n-m}$
Property 3.	$(ab)^n = a^n b^n$	Property 7.	$a^0 = 1$
Property 4.	$a^{-n} = \dfrac{1}{a^n}$	Property 8.	$\left(\dfrac{a}{b}\right)^n = \dfrac{a^n}{b^n}$

Example 10. Simplify $(4x^5)^3$. Write with positive exponents.

$$(4x^5)^3 = 4^3(x^5)^3$$
$$= 64x^{15}$$

Example 11. Simplify $\frac{6x}{2x^{-4}}$. Write with positive exponents.

$$\frac{6x}{2x^{-4}} = \frac{6xx^4}{2}$$
$$= 3x^5$$

Introduction to Algebraic Fractions:

To reduce fractions: Factor the numerator and denominator and then cancel like factors.

Example 12. Reduce $\frac{18x^3}{10x^5}$.

$$\frac{18x^3}{10x^5} = \frac{2 \bullet 9 \bullet x \bullet x \bullet x}{2 \bullet 5 \bullet x \bullet x \bullet x \bullet x \bullet x}$$
$$= \frac{9}{5x^2}$$

To multiply fractions: $\frac{a}{b} \bullet \frac{c}{d} = \frac{ac}{bd}$ multiply the numerators and denominators and then reduce.

Example 13. Multiply $\frac{15x^2}{6} \bullet \frac{8}{5x^4}$.

$$\frac{15x^2}{6} \bullet \frac{8}{5x^4} = \frac{5 \bullet 3 \bullet x \bullet x}{3 \bullet 2} \bullet \frac{4 \bullet 2}{5 \bullet x \bullet x \bullet x \bullet x}$$
$$= \frac{4}{x^2}$$

To divide fractions: $\frac{a}{b} \div \frac{c}{d} = \frac{ad}{bc}$, invert the divisor, then reduce.

Example 14. Divide $\frac{12}{27x^2} \div \frac{4x}{9}$.

$$\frac{12}{27x^2} \div \frac{4x}{9} = \frac{4 \bullet 3}{9 \bullet 3 \bullet x \bullet x} \bullet \frac{9}{4x}$$
$$= \frac{1}{x^3}$$

Adding and Subtracting Fractions:

To add and subtract fractions:

1. Find the least common denominator, LCD.
   a. For numbers, the least common denominator is the smallest number all of the denominators divide into evenly.
   b. For variables, the least common denominator is the variable with the highest exponent.
2. Convert each fraction to a fraction with the least common denominator.
   a. Decide what you need to multiply each denominator by to get the LCD.
   b. Multiply the numerator and denominator by this quantity.
3. Combine the numerators and write as a single fraction.

Example 15. Add $\frac{5}{4x^2}+\frac{7}{6x}$.

$$\frac{5}{4x^2}+\frac{7}{6x}= \qquad \text{LCD } 12x^2.$$

$$\frac{5}{4x^2}\left(\frac{3}{3}\right)+\frac{7}{6x}\left(\frac{2x}{2x}\right)=$$

$$\frac{15}{12x^2}+\frac{14x}{12x^2}=$$

$$\frac{15+14x}{12x^2}$$

Solving Equations with Fractions:

To solve an equation involving fractions, multiply all the terms by the LCD and then reduce.

Example 16. Solve $\frac{2x}{9}-\frac{4x-5}{6}=2$.

$$\frac{2x}{9}-\frac{4x-5}{6}=2 \qquad \text{The LCD is 18}$$

$$\left(\frac{18}{1}\right)\frac{2x}{9}-\left(\frac{18}{1}\right)\frac{4x-5}{6}=(18)2 \qquad \text{Multiply all the terms by 18.}$$

$$(2)2x-3(4x-5)=(18)2 \qquad \text{Reduce.}$$

$$4x-12x+15=36 \qquad \text{Distributive property.}$$

$$-8x+15=36 \qquad \text{Combine like terms.}$$

$$-8x=21 \qquad \text{Subtract 15 from both sides.}$$

$$x=\frac{-21}{8} \qquad \text{Divide both sides by 8.}$$

Ratio and Proportion Problems:

Definitions:

Ratios: A ratio is a fraction that compares two different units.

Proportions: A proportion is two equal ratios.

To solve proportion problems, cross multiply.

Example 17. Two school clubs have a car washing fundraiser. Eight members from the Math Club and 5 members from the Astronomy Club participate. If they raise $462, how much should the Math Club receive?

- Organize the information into a table.

Math Club

	Money	**Participants**
Share	?	8
Total	462	8 + 5

- Set up the proportion problem.

$$\frac{M}{462} = \frac{8}{13}$$

$13M = 3{,}696$ Cross Multiply.

$M = 284.31$ Divide both sides by 13.

The Math Club should receive $284.31.

Study Tips:

1. Practice the review test starting on the next page by placing yourself under realistic exam conditions.

2. Find a quiet place and use a timer to simulate test conditions.

3. Write your answers in your homework notebook. You may then re-take the exam for extra practice.

4. Check your answers. The answers to the review test are on page 371.

5. There is an additional exam available on the MAT 011 web page, **www.mc3.edu/aa/career/MATHSCI/mat011/mat011.htm**

6. Do NOT wait until the night before to study. This test can be very challenging.

TEST III

1. Simplify. Write with positive exponents.

   a. $x^5 \cdot x^2$ b. $\dfrac{x^3}{x^5}$ c. y^0

   d. $\left(x^5\right)^2$ e. $\left(2x^2\right)^3$ f. $x^{-7}x^2$

   g. $\dfrac{x^2}{x^{-5}}$ h. $\dfrac{9x^{-2}}{x^3}$

2. Compute using a calculator.

   a. 2.5^{-3} b. -3.6^4 c. $(-3.6)^4$

3. Compute using a calculator.

   a. $\left(2.5\text{x}10^5\right)\left(8.6\text{x}10^7\right)$ b. $\left(8.1\text{x}10^{-3}\right)\left(6.2\text{x}10^{-11}\right)$

4. Write in scientific notation.

   a. 8300000 b. 0.000614

5. Write in decimal notation.

   a. $4.2\text{x}10^5$ b. $3.1\text{x}10^{-3}$

6. Perform the indicated operation.

   a. $\dfrac{4x^5}{3y^2} \cdot \dfrac{9x}{2y^3}$ b. $\dfrac{4x^2}{7} \div 14x^5$

   c. $\dfrac{5}{2x} - \dfrac{7}{3x^2}$ d. $\dfrac{11}{5x} + \dfrac{1}{3}$

7. Solve.

   a. $\dfrac{x}{3} + 9 = \dfrac{3x-3}{2}$ b. $\dfrac{x}{4} - \dfrac{x-3}{2} = 2$

Study Tip: If you don't remember how to do a problem, look through the unit until you find an example similar to the one giving you difficulty.

8. There are 500 bacteria in a culture. The culture grows at 7% a day. Complete the table.

a.

DAY	CALCULATION	POPULATION
0		
1		
2		
3		
n		

b. What is the equation that relates population to number of days?

c. Find how many bacteria there are after 30 days.

d. Find how many bacteria there are after 60 days.

9. Use the formula:

Payment of Debts $P = A\left[\frac{i}{1-(1+i)^{-n}}\right]$

P is the monthly payment

A is the amount of the loan

n is the number of payments

i is the interest rate per month

a. Find the monthly payments of a 30 year mortgage at 9% annual interest on a \$200,000 home. (Hints: $i = \frac{.09}{12}$ and $n = 12 \bullet 30$.)

b. Find out what price car you can buy if you can afford a \$300 car payment for 36 months at 4.5% annual interest. (Hint: $i = \frac{.045}{12}$.)

UNIT 4

INTRODUCTION TO QUADRATICS
OVERVIEW

Objectives: In this section, you will add, subtract, multiply and graph quadratics.

What is a quadratic? The basic equation of a quadratic is $y = ax^2 + bx + c$; a, b, c are numbers; x is the independent variable, and y is the dependent variable. Quadratics are also called **second degree polynomials** because the highest exponent is 2. The slope-intercept equation from the second unit, $y = mx + b$, is called a **first degree polynomial** because the highest exponent is one.

Why study quadratics? The graphs of quadratic equations result in parabolas (curves which go up and down). This feature of quadratics makes them good models for describing the path of a ball thrown in the air or describing the profit of a company (examples of which you may see in MAT 140, Finite Mathematics, or Microeconomics.)

Basic Examples:

Example 1. A boy lying on his back uses a sling shot to fire a rock straight up in the air with an initial velocity (the force the boy uses to fire the rock) of 64 feet per second. The quadratic equation that models the height of the rock is

$$h = -16t^2 + 64t.$$

a. Find the height of the rock when t = 0.

In the formula $h = -16t^2 + 64t$, replace t with 0.

$h = -16(0)^2 + 64(0)$

$h = 0$

The rock is zero feet in the air at zero seconds.
(This is the point right before he shoots the rock in the air.)

b. Find the height of the rock when t = 1.

In the formula $h = -16t^2 + 64t$, replace t with 1.

$h = -16(1)^2 + 64(1)$

$h = -16(1) + 64(1)$

$h = 48$

> **Explanation:** Only the "1" is being squared; the –16 multiplies 1^2.

The rock is 48 feet in the air at one second.

c. Find the height of the rock when t = 2.

In the formula $h = -16t^2 + 64t$, replace t with 2.

$h = -16(2)^2 + 64(2)$

$h = -16(4) + 64(2)$

$h = -64 + 128$

$h = 64$

> **Explanation:** Order of operations means that you apply exponents before multiplying.

The rock is 64 feet in the air at 2 seconds.

d. Find the height of the rock when t = 3.

In the formula $h = -16t^2 + 64t$, replace t with 3.

$h = -16(3)^2 + 64(3)$

$h = -16(9) + 64(3)$

$h = -144 + 192$

$h = 48$

The rock is 48 feet in the air at 3 seconds.

e. Find the height of the rock when t = 4.

In the formula $h = -16t^2 + 64t$, replace t with 4.

$h = -16(4)^2 + 64(4)$

$h = -16(16) + 64(4)$

$h = -256 + 256$

$h = 0$

The rock is zero feet in the air at 4 seconds.

f. Graph the points obtained in parts a through e.

The height of the rock depends on the time, so h is the dependent variable, and t is the independent variable. The points have the form (t, h).

The points to graph are (0, 0), (1, 48), (2, 64), (3, 48), (4, 0).

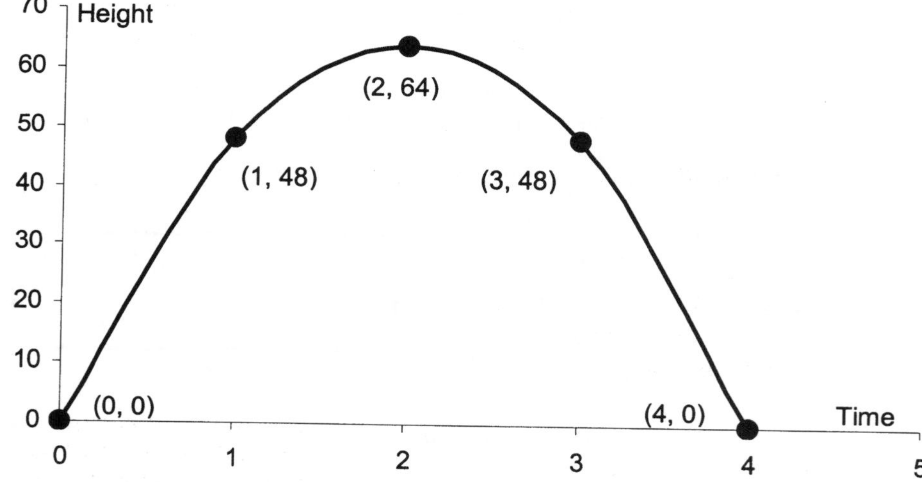

From the graph, the rock reaches its greatest height at 2 seconds. The maximum height is 64 feet. The maximum or minimum point of a quadratic is called the **vertex**. You will learn how to find the vertex in the section Quadratic Applications and their Graphs.

From the graph, the rock is on the ground at zero seconds (right before he shoots it) and at 4 seconds (when the rock lands). These points are the **time intercepts**. You will learn how to find them in the next section, Applications of the Quadratic Formula.

Adding and subtracting quadratics:

To add or subtract quadratics, combine like terms. Remember like terms have the same variable and the same exponent.

Example 2. Simplify $4x + 7x^2 - 3x + 4x^2$.

$4x$, $-3x$ and $7x^2$, $4x^2$ are like terms.

$$4x + 7x^2 - 3x + 4x^2 = x + 11x^2$$

Recall the distributive property: Definition $a(b + c) = ab + ac$.

Example 3. Simplify $3(6x - 5)$.

$3(6x-5) =$	Can't combine terms inside the parentheses.
$3 \bullet 6x - 3 \bullet 5 =$	Use the distributive property; multiply 6x by 3 and then and –5 by 3.
$18x - 15$	

Example 4. Simplify $2(4x^2 + 3x) - 5(2x^2 - 3)$.

$2(4x^2 + 3x) - 5(2x^2 - 3) =$	
$8x^2 + 6x - 10x^2 + 15 =$	Use the distributive property.
$-2x^2 + 6x + 15$	Combine like terms.

Example 5. The equation for profit is: Profit = Revenue – Cost

If the revenue equation for a company is:

$R = -2x^2 + 45x$

and the cost equation is:

$C = 2x^2 - 23x + 56$.

Find the profit equation for the company.

$P = (-2x^2 + 45x) - (2x^2 - 23x + 56)$	Substitute the revenue and cost equations into the formula for profit. It is important to use parentheses.
$= 1(-2x^2 + 45x) - 1(2x^2 - 23x + 56)$	Use the distributive property. Multiply the revenue equation by 1 and the cost equation by –1.
$= -2x^2 + 45x - 2x^2 + 23x - 56$	
$= -4x^2 + 68x - 56$	Combine like terms.

Multiplying two binomials.

A **binomial** has two terms (just like a bicycle has two wheels).

To multiply two binomials, multiply each term of the first by each term of the second.

Example 7. Multiply $(x+2)(5x+3)$.

$$(x+2)(5x+3)=$$

$$x\bullet 5x+x\bullet 3+2\bullet 5x+2\bullet 3=$$ Multiply x by 5x and 3 and multiply 2 by 5x and 3.

$$5x^2+3x+10x+6=$$

$$5x^2+13x+6$$ Combine like terms.

FOIL is a simple mnemonic to remember how to multiply two binomials.

Example 8. Multiply $(8x+6)(x+7)$.

F indicates the product of the **First** terms, $8x\bullet x=8x^2$.
O indicates the product of the **Outer** terms, $8x\bullet 7=56x$.
I indicates the product of the **Inner** terms, $6\bullet x=6x$.
L indicates the product of the **Last** terms, $6\bullet 7=42$.

$$(8x+6)(x+7)=8x\bullet x+8x\bullet 7+6\bullet x+6\bullet 7$$
$$=8x^2+56x+6x+42$$
$$=8x^2+62x+42$$

Example 9. Multiply $(2x-5)^2$.

$$(2x-5)^2=(2x-5)(2x-5)$$

F O I L

$$=2x\bullet 2x-2x\bullet 5-5\bullet 2x-5\bullet(-5)$$
$$=4x^2-10x-10x+25$$
$$=4x^2-20x+25$$

Study Tip: Write a notecard explaining the mnemonic FOIL. Review the card frequently.

Summary: Quadratics are important equations in physics and microeconomics. The technique for adding and subtracting quadratics is the same as we have been doing all semester; just add or subtract the like terms. To multiply use the distributive property or FOIL. The vertex of the quadratic will be explained in more detail in the section on Graphing Quadratics. The vertex is the maximum or minimum point on the graph of the quadratic. (We do not graph quadratics that have a minimum vertex in this class.)

CLASS WORK

I. Evaluating quadratics:

William Tell shoots an arrow straight up with an initial velocity of 160 feet per second. The height (in feet) of the arrow is given by the equation

$$h = -16t^2 + 160t,$$

where t is the number of seconds the arrow is in the air.
Find the height of the arrow for

a. $t = 2$

b. $t = 5$

c. $t = 8$

d. $t = 10$

e. According to the calculations above, when will the arrow reach its maximum height (vertex)?

f. According to the calculations above, when will the arrow hit the ground?

g. Graph the points obtained in a through d.

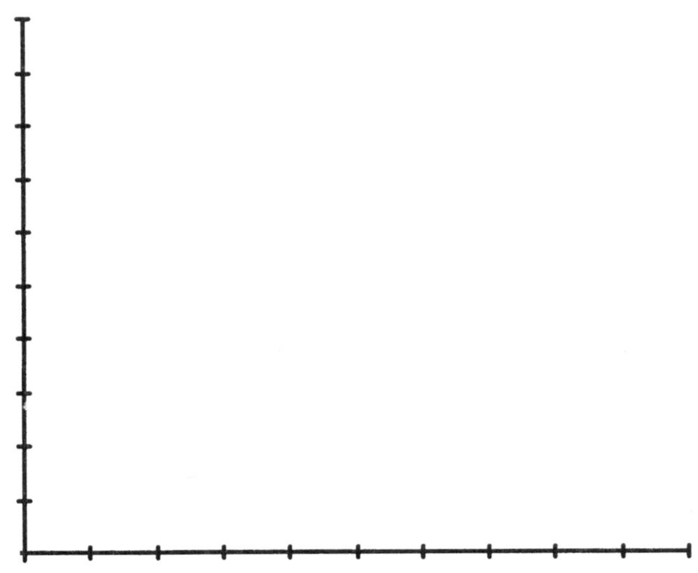

II. Combining Like Terms

1. What are like terms?

2. How do we combine like terms?

3. Simplify.

   a. $-8x^2 + 2x - 8 - 6x^2 + 10x + 2 =$

   b. $2(3x^2 + 5x - 10) - 4(x^2 - 6x + 3) =$

   c. $5(2x^2 + 5) - (8x^2 + 2x - 4) =$

   d. The equation for profit is, Profit = Revenue – Cost. If the revenue equation for a company is

   $$R = -5x^2 + 17x$$

   and the cost equation for a company is

   $$C = 3x^2 - 27x + 40.$$

   Find the equation for profit.

III. Multiplying Two Binomials (FOIL)

1. What is a binomial?

2. Multiply.

   a. $(x + 5)(x + 3)$

   b. $(x - 6)(x + 2)$

   c. $(x - 7)(x - 5)$

   d. $(2x + 5)(3x - 8)$

   e. $(3x + 4)^2$

GROUP EXERCISE

Study Tips:
1. Review pertinent notecards first.
2. Have one person record the problem as the group solves it.
3. Have another person do the graphing as the group explains it.

For Triple Bubble Gum Company, the cost of making x thousand pieces of gum a day is $C = x^2 - 19x + 48$, and the revenue from selling x thousand pieces of gum a day is $R = -x^2 + 9x$.

1. Find the profit equation for Triple Bubble Gum Co.
   (Profit = Revenue – Cost)

2. Find the profit for

   a. $x = 2$ b. $x = 3$ c. $x = 7$

   d. $x = 10$ e. $x = 12$

   f. When will the company make no profit? (The break even point or x intercepts)

   g. When will the company make the most profit?

   h. Graph the points obtained in Parts a through e.

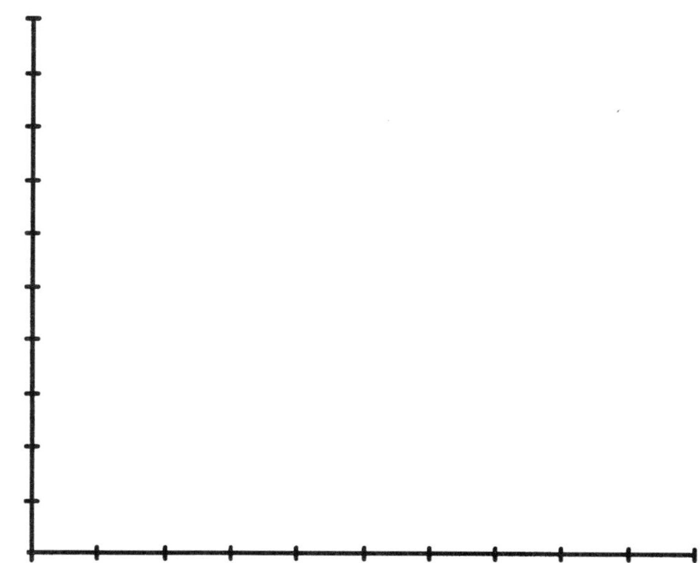

EXERCISE

Study Tips:
1. Remember to use your loose leaf notebook.
2. Have all of your graphing materials at hand.
3. Review problems from Overview, Class Work, and Group Exercise.

1. A rocket is launched from the top of a cliff with an initial velocity of 256 feet per second. The height (in feet) of the rocket is given by the equation:

$$h = -16t^2 + 256t + 80,$$

where t is the number of seconds the rocket is in the air.
Find the height of the rocket for

a. $t = 0$ b. $t = 3$ c. $t = 8$ d. $t = 10$ e. $t = 16$ f. $t = 17$

g. According to the calculations above, when will the rocket reach its maximum height?

h. According to the calculations above, estimate when the rocket hits the ground?

i. Graph the points a through f.

2. What are like terms?

3. How do you combine like terms?

4. Simplify

a. $-2x^2 + 8x - 10 - 2x^2 + 4x + 7$ b. $3(2x^2 + 5x - 8) - 2(5x^2 + 6x - 2)$

c. $(-16x^2 + 8x - 5) - (3x^2 - 5x + 2)$ d. $3(-2x^2 + 6) + 2(3x^2 - 9x)$

e. $2(3x^2 - 8x - 5) + 3(-4x^2 - 3x + 8)$ f. $(-3x^2 + 4x - 10) - (8x^2 - 2x + 5)$

5. The equation for profit is, Profit = Revenue – Cost. If the revenue equation for a company is

$$R = -3x^2 + 8x$$

and the cost equation for a company is

$$C = x^2 - 9x + 72.$$

Find the equation for profit.

6. Multiply.

a. $(x + 2)(x + 3)$ b. $(x + 4)(x - 3)$

c. $(x - 7)(x - 4)$ d. $(x + 8)(x - 8)$

e. $(x + 9)(x - 9)$ f. $(3x - 1)(2x + 3)$

g. $(x + 3)^2$ h. $(x - 5)^2$

APPLICATIONS OF THE QUADRATIC FORMULA
OVERVIEW

Objective: This section will show you how to solve quadratic equations.

Procedure: The quadratic equation is $ax^2 + bx + c = 0$. a, b and c are numbers, and x is the variable. The quadratic formula, $x = \frac{-b \pm \sqrt{b^2 - 4ac}}{2a}$, is used to solve the quadratic equation.

What does $x = \frac{-b \pm \sqrt{b^2 - 4ac}}{2a}$ mean?

- a, b, and c are numbers that will be substituted into the formula.

  a is the coefficient of the squared variable.

  b is the coefficient of the variable to the first power.

  c is the constant.

- The symbol $\pm$ gives two solutions to the equation. One solution is with the + sign, $x = \frac{-b + \sqrt{b^2 - 4ac}}{2a}$ and the other solution is with the – sign, $x = \frac{-b - \sqrt{b^2 - 4ac}}{2a}$.

- $\sqrt{\ }$ is the square root symbol.

  1. The $\sqrt{16} = 4$ because $4^2 = 16$.
  2. The $\sqrt{35} \approx 5.916$ because $5.916^2 \approx 35$.
  3. Your calculator is essential for this section. Make sure you can find the $\sqrt{\ }$ button on your calculator.
  4. You can only compute the square root of nonnegative numbers.
  5. If you try to compute $\sqrt{-5}$ your calculator will give an error message.

Study Tip: Write the quadratic equation and quadratic formula on a notecards, so you can reference them when you do your homework.

Basic Examples:

Example 1. Suppose you are standing on top of a cliff 375 feet above the canyon floor, and you throw a rock up in the air with an initial velocity of 82 feet per second. The equation that models the height of the rock above the canyon floor is:

$$h = -16t^2 + 82t + 375.$$

Find how long it takes the rock to hit the canyon floor.

Find t when h = 0.

Solve $0 = -16t^2 + 82t + 375$.

a = -16, b = 82, c = 375

Use the quadratic formula

$$t = \frac{-b \pm \sqrt{b^2 - 4ac}}{2a}$$

with a = -16, b = 82, and c = 375.

Explanation:
One side of the quadtratic equation must be zero.

a is the coefficient of the variable that is squared.

b is the coefficient of the variable to the first power.

c is the constant.

$$t = \frac{-82 \pm \sqrt{82^2 - 4(-16)(375)}}{2(-16)}$$

Substitute a, b, and c into the quadratic formula.

$$t = \frac{-82 \pm 175.3}{2(-16)}$$

Use your calculator to simplify the square root. You should see $\sqrt{(}$ when you use the square root key.

Then type $82^2 + 4 \bullet 16 \bullet 375)$ and =.

It is + because -4(-16)(375) = 4(16)(375).
The directions are for the TI-30X IIS.

$$t = \frac{-82 + 175.3}{2(-16)} \text{ or } t = \frac{-82 - 175.3}{2(-16)}$$

Separate the formula into the + and – parts.

$t = \frac{93.3}{-32}$ or $t = \frac{-257.3}{-32}$

Combine the numerators.

$t = -2.916$ or $t = 8.041$

Divide.

$t = -2.916$ is a meaningless answer since t is how long it takes the rock to hit the canyon floor, and you can't have negative time.

$t = 8.041$ is how long it takes the rock to hit the ground.

The rock will hit the canyon floor in 8.041 seconds.

Example 2. A rancher has 500 yards of fencing to enclose two adjacent pig pens that rest against the barn. If the area of the two pens must total 20,700 square feet, what should the dimensions of the pens be?

BARN

W W W

L represents the length of both pens.

a. Use the table to find the equation for the area of the pens.

Width	Length		Area
50	$500-3\bullet 50=350$	**Explanation:** Since there are 3 widths, we multiply 50 times 3. The rancher has 500 yards of fencing, so subtract $3\bullet 50$ from 500 to find the length.	$50\bullet 350=17{,}500$
75	$500-3\bullet 75=275$		$75\bullet 275=20{,}625$
85	$500-3\bullet 85=245$		$85\bullet 245=20{,}825$
W	$500-3\bullet W=L$		$W(500-3W)$

b. Simplify the equation for area.

$A=W(500-3W)$

$=500W-3W^2$ Use the distributive property.

$=-3W^2+500W$ Write the squared term first.

c. Find W when A = 20,700.

$20{,}700=-3W^2+500W$ Substitute 20,700 for A.

$0=-3W^2+500W-20{,}700$ Subtract 20,700 from both sides. The quadratic equation MUST have one side equal to zero.

a = -3, b = 500, c = -20,700 a is the coefficient of W^2. b is the coefficient of W. c is the constant.

$$W=\frac{-b\pm\sqrt{b^2-4ac}}{2a}$$ The quadratic formula.

$$W=\frac{-500\pm\sqrt{500^2-4(-3)(-20{,}700)}}{2(-3)}$$ Substitute the values of a, b, and c into the quadratic formula.

$$W = \frac{-500 \pm 40}{2(-3)}$$

Use your calculator to simplify the square root. You should see $\sqrt{(}$ when you use the square root key. Then type $500^2 - 4 \bullet 3 \bullet 20{,}700)$ and =. The directions are for the TI-30X IIS.

$$W = \frac{-500 + 40}{2(-3)} \text{ or } W = \frac{-500 - 40}{2(-3)}$$

Separate the formula into the + and – parts.

$$W = \frac{-460}{-6} \text{ or } W = \frac{-540}{-6}$$

Simplify the numerator and denominator.

$$W = 76.67 \text{ or } W = 90$$

Divide.

The width is 76.67 or 90 yards.

d. Find the length of the pens.

From the table in Part b, $L = 500 - 3W$.

Substitute $W = 76.67$	Substitute $W = 90$
$L = 500 - 3 \bullet 76.67$	$L = 500 - 3 \bullet 90$
$L = 270$	$L = 230$

The dimensions of the pig pens that yield an area of 20,700 square yards are 76.67 by 270 yards and 90 by 230 yards.

Summary: This section shows us how to solve a new set of equations, the quadratics. These have important applications in many fields, such as business, physics, and engineering. Learn the difference between the quadratic equation and the quadratic formula.

The quadratic equation is $ax^2 + bx + c = 0$.

- One side of the equation must be zero.
- a is the number multiplying x^2 or the coefficient of x^2.
- b is the number multiplying x or the coefficient of x.
- c is the constant term.

The quadratic formula, $x = \dfrac{-b \pm \sqrt{b^2 - 4ac}}{2a}$ solves the quadratic equation.

- The formula gives two solutions.
- Use your calculator to find the answers.
- The first step in evaluating the formula is to simplify the square root.

NOTES

CLASS WORK

1. Suppose you are standing on top of the 1600 feet tall Sears Tower, and you drop a rock. The height of the rock from the ground is given by the equation:

$$h = -16t^2 + 1600,$$

h is in feet and t is in seconds. How long until the rock hits the ground?

2. The revenue generated by selling *x* items is indicated by

$$R = 280x - 0.4x^2,$$

and the cost of making *x* items is indicated by

$$C = 5000 + 0.6x^2.$$

a. Find the profit function.

b. How many items must be sold (and made) if a profit of $439 is to be generated?

3. Suppose you want to enclose a rectangle with a 40 inch string, and you use a wall of the room for one side of the rectangle.

a. Make a table and find the formula for the area of the rectangle.

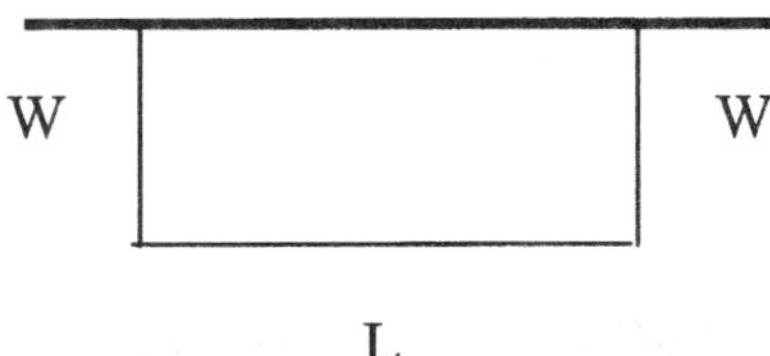

WIDTH	LENGTH	AREA

b. Find the dimensions of the rectangle if the area is 65 square inches.

4. A 10 cm stick is broken into two pieces. One is placed at a right angle to form an upside down "T" shape. By attaching wires from the ends of the base to the end of the upright piece, a framework for a sail will be formed.

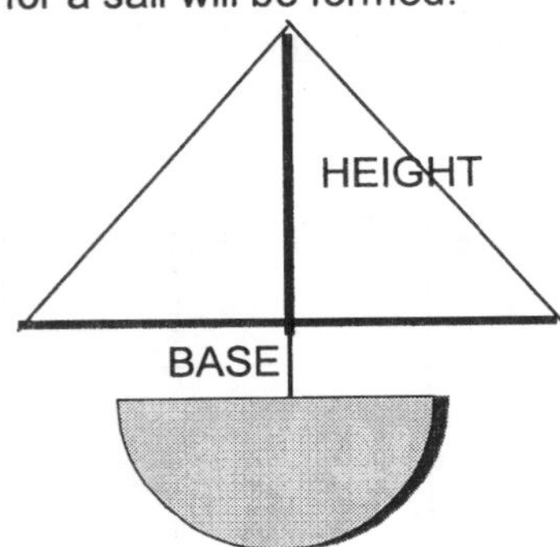

a. Complete the table below.

BASE	HEIGHT	AREA $\left(A=\frac{1}{2}bh\right)$
0	10-0 = 10	$\frac{1}{2}(0 \cdot 10)=0$ sq cm
2	10-2 = 8	$\frac{1}{2}(2 \cdot 8)=8$ sq cm
4		
6		
8		
10		
b		

b. Simplify the formula for area.

c. What should the base of the sail be if the area must be 10 sq. cm?

GROUP EXERCISE

Study Tip: This section is the foundation for the next part of your work this semester. Make sure everyone in your group understands the quadratic formula and the quadratic equation.

1. King Co. computes the revenue for making x refrigerators per month by:

$$R = -0.7x^2 + 800x \text{ dollars.}$$

The cost from selling x refrigerators per month is:

$$C = 0.3x^2 - 100x + 5250.$$

Study Tip: Review problem 2 on page 288.

a. Find the equation for profit. (P = R - C)

b. Find how many refrigerators King Co. would have to sell if they want to have a profit of $100,000.

EXERCISES

Study Tips:
1. Review pertinent note cards.
2. Review class notes from this section.
3. Some of the problems are long. Have plenty of paper ready in your loose leaf notebook.
4. Refer to Appendix C and the CD that accompanies the textbook to learn how to use the TI-30X IIS calculator.

1. Quadratic Formula

   a. State the formula.

   b. Write a sentence describing how the formula is used.

2. A rancher has 360 yards of fence to enclose a rectangular pasture. If the pasture should be 8000 square yards in area, what should the dimensions of the pasture be? (Hint: You may need a table to find the equation.)

Study Tip: Review Example 2 on page 284 or Problem 3 on page 289 except in this problem there are two lengths.

L

W PASTURE W

L

WIDTH	LENGTH	AREA

3. A flare is fired from the bridge of the Titanic. The height in feet of the flare is indicated by the equation where t is measured in seconds

$$h = -16t^2 + 140t + 40.$$

How long is the flare in the air?

Study Tip: Review Example 1 on page 283 or Problem 1 on page 287.

4. The total cost (in dollars) for a company to manufacture and sell x items per week is:

$$C = 0.6x^2 - 140x + 6200$$

and the revenue (in dollars) by selling all x items is:

$$R = -0.4x^2 + 130x$$

How many items must be sold to obtain a weekly profit of $10,000?
(Hint: Profit = revenue minus cost. Don't forget parentheses.)

Study Tip: Review Problem 2 on page 288.

5. The table below represents the percent of 18-25 year olds who reported using marijuana in the past 30 days.

Year	1974	1976	1977	1979	1982	1985	1988	1990	1991	1992	1993
% of Teenagers	34.2	35	38.7	46.9	40.4	36.3	27.9	24.6	24.5	22.7	22.9

Source: Digest of Educational Statistics.

The quadratic equation $P = -0.12t^2 + 1.46t + 35.5$ can be used to approximate the percent of teenagers who reported using marijuana in the past 30 days. P is the percentage and t is the number of years since 1974. Use the equation to:

a. Find the percentage of teenagers who used marijuana in the past 30 days for the year 1997.

b. When will the percentage of teenagers who used marijuana in the past 30 days be 10 percent?

6. The total cost (in dollars) for a company to manufacture and sell x items per week is:

$$C = 60x + 300,$$

while the revenue (in dollars) from selling all x items is:

$$R = 100x - 0.5x^2.$$

How many items must be sold to obtain a weekly profit of $300?
(Hint: $P = R - C$.)

QUADRATIC APPLICATIONS AND THEIR GRAPHS
OVERVIEW

Objectives: This section introduces key points in the graph of a quadratic. They are the vertex and the intercepts. These points will be interpreted in applications.

The basic graph:

Example 1. A boy lying on his back uses a sling shot to fire a rock straight up in the air with an initial velocity (the force the boy uses to throw the rock) of 64 feet per second. The quadratic equation that models the height of the rock is

$$h = -16t^2 + 64t.$$

(This example comes from the Introduction to Quadratics, page 271.)

On Page 272, we generated the following values:

Time	Height	Point on Graph
0	0	(0, 0)
1	48	(1, 48)
2	64	(2, 64)
3	48	(3, 48)
4	0	(4, 0)

We used the points to obtain the graph below. The important points are also labeled on the graph.

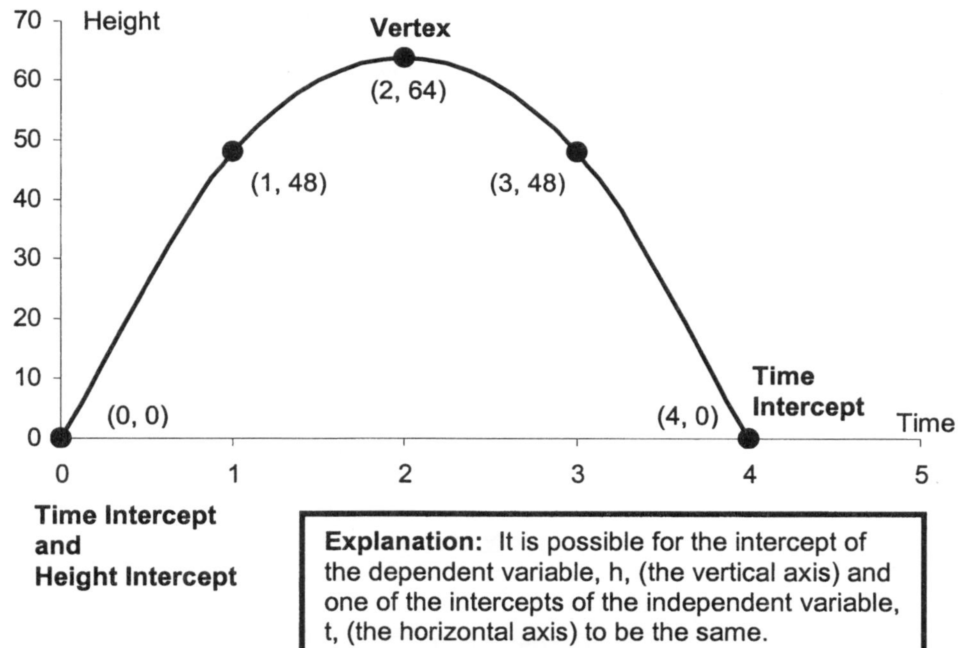

Explanation: It is possible for the intercept of the dependent variable, h, (the vertical axis) and one of the intercepts of the independent variable, t, (the horizontal axis) to be the same.

The **vertex,** (2,64) represents the maximum height of the rock. The rock reaches a maximum height of 64 feet in 2 seconds.

The **Time Intercepts,** (0, 0) and (4, 0) represent when the rock is on the ground. The rock is on the ground at zero seconds, before it is shot, (which is the **Height Intercept**) and at 4 seconds, it hits the ground.

Procedure and Definitions:

To graph a quadratic indicated by the equation, $y = ax^2 + bx + c$, master the following terms:

Vertex: The vertex is the maximum or minimum point on the graph.

To find the vertex :

a. Find the x coordinate: $x = \frac{-b}{2a}$.

b. Find the y coordinate: Substitute the value for x obtained in Part a into the formula $y = ax^2 + bx + c$.

x intercept: Set y = 0 and solve $0 = ax^2 + bx + c$ using the quadratic formula,

$$x = \frac{-b \pm \sqrt{b^2 - 4ac}}{2a}.$$

y intercept: Set x = 0 and find y. y will always be c, the constant.

Study Tip: Write the procedure and definitions on three note cards for easy reference.

Example 2. The company D+++ makes computer games. The cost of making g games per month is $C = 0.4g^2 - 32g + 625$. The revenue from selling g games per month is $R = -0.6g^2 + 52g$. The units for g are hundreds, and C and R are in thousands of dollars.

a. Find the profit equation.

Profit = Revenue - Cost	Profit formula.
$P = (-0.6g^2 + 52g) - (0.4g^2 - 32g + 625)$	Substitute equations for revenue and cost. You must use parentheses around the revenue and cost equations.
$P = -0.6g^2 + 52g - 0.4g^2 + 32g - 625$	Use the distributive property. Multiply the revenue equation by one, and the cost equation by negative one.
$P = -g^2 + 84g - 625$	Combine like terms.

b. Graph the equation. Explain what the vertex and the g and p intercepts mean in terms of making computer games. Label the axes and use an appropriate scale.

- Find the **vertex** of $P = -g^2 + 84g - 625$.

  The formula for the g coordinate is $g = \frac{-b}{2a}$.

  From the equation for profit, a = -1, b = 84.

  $$g = \frac{-84}{2(-1)} = 42$$

  Find the P coordinate:

$P = -g^2 + 84g - 625$	Equation for profit.
$P = -(42)^2 + 84(42) - 625$	Substitute 84 for g.
$P = -1{,}764 + 84(42) - 625$	Square 42, not –42.
$P = 1{,}139$	Simplify.

  The vertex is (42, 1134).

- Find the **g intercepts** of $P = -g^2 + 84g - 625$.
  To find the g intercept, set P = 0.
  Solve $0 = -g^2 + 84g - 625$.

Use the quadratic formula, a = -1, b = 84, c = -625.

$$g = \frac{-b \pm \sqrt{b^2 - 4ac}}{2a}$$ The quadratic formula.

$$g = \frac{-84 \pm \sqrt{84^2 - 4(-1)(-625)}}{2(-1)}$$ Substitute the values for a, b, and c.

$$g = \frac{-84 \pm 67.5}{2(-1)}$$ Simplify the square root. Enter $\sqrt{(84^2 - 4 * 625)}$ into your calculator.

$$g = \frac{-84 + 67.5}{-2} \text{ or } \frac{-84 - 67.5}{-2}$$ Write as two answers.

g = 8.25 or 75.75. Simplify.

Explanation: The reason there are two break even points is because the equation models the profit of a monopoly. They have control over the price of the games. If they charge a lot for a game, then they can only sell a few games while, if they sell the games cheaply, then they will sell many games.

The g intercepts are (8.25, 0) and (75.75, 0).

- Find the **P intercept** of $P = -g^2 + 84g - 625$.
  To find the P intercept, set g = 0.
  $P = -0^2 + 84 \bullet 0 - 625$
  $P = -625$
  The P intercept is (0, -625).

Plot the points:

Vertex. (42, 1139).
The **g intercepts**. (8.25, 0) and (75.75, 0).
The **P intercept**. (0, -625).

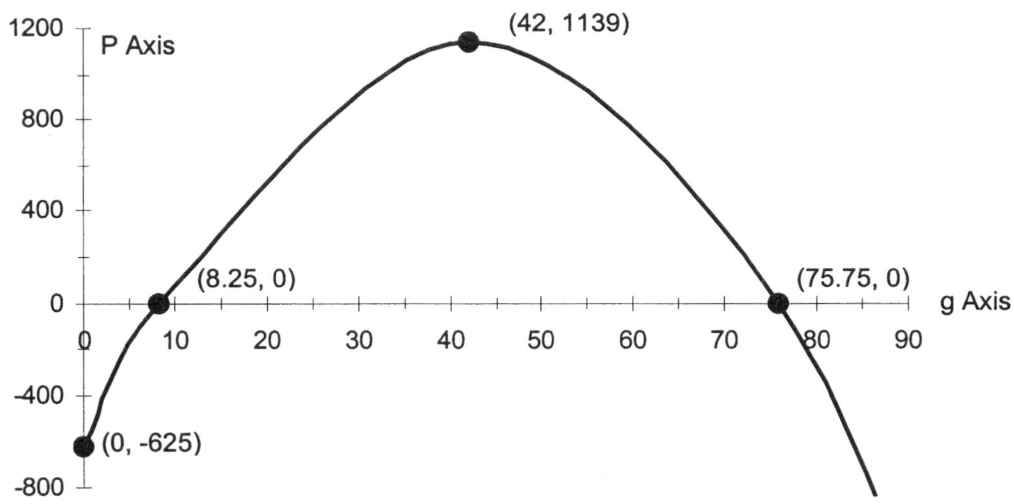

Vertex: If they sell 4,200 games, then they will earn a maximum profit of $1,139,000.
g intercepts: If they sell 825 or 7,575 games, then they will break even.
P intercept: The company's start up costs are $625,000.
Remember that the units for g are hundreds, and the units for P are thousands.

c. Suppose D+++ needs to make a profit of \$500,000 (P = 500) a month. Sketch this line on the graph obtained in Part b and find where the line intersects the graph of the quadratic. Write a sentence explaining what the answers mean.

Sketch P = 500 on the graph from the previous page.

P = 500 is a horizontal line.

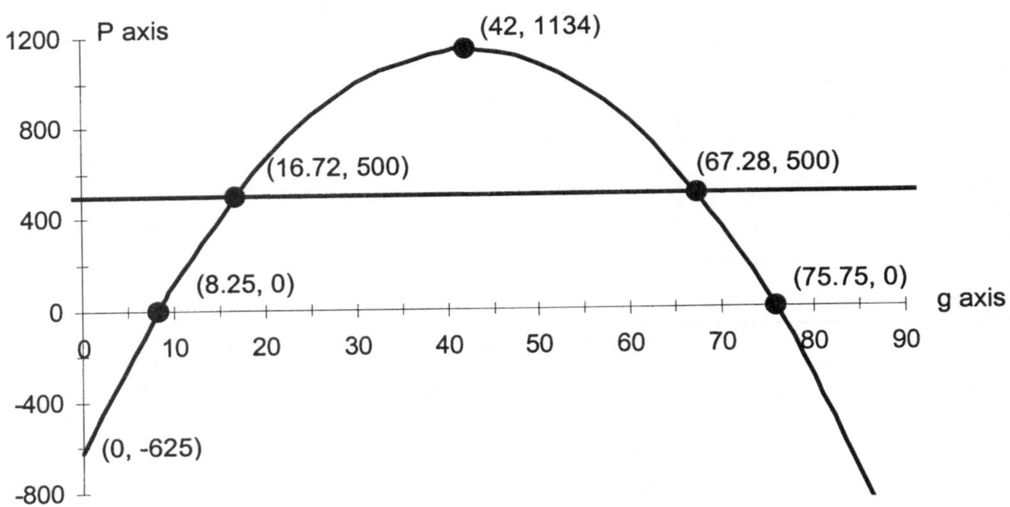

$500 = -g^2 + 84g - 625$	Substitute 500 for P.
$0 = -g^2 + 84g - 1{,}125$	Subtract 500 from both sides.
a = -1, b = 84, c = -1,125	Identify a, b and c.
$g = \dfrac{-b \pm \sqrt{b^2 - 4ac}}{2a}$	Use the quadratic formula.
$g = \dfrac{-84 \pm \sqrt{84^2 - 4(-1)(-1{,}125)}}{2(-1)}$	Substitute the values for a, b and c.
$g = \dfrac{-84 \pm 50.56}{2(-1)}$	Simplify the square root.
$g = \dfrac{-84 + 50.56}{2(-1)}$ or $g = \dfrac{-84 - 50.56}{2(-1)}$	Write as two answers.
g = 16.72 or 67.28.	Simplify.

If D+++ wants a profit of \$500,000, then they need to make and sell 1,672 or 6,728 games.

> **Explanation:** The graph gives an estimate of where the horizontal line, P = 500, and the equation for profit, $P = -g^2 + 84g - 625$ intersect. The algebra gives the exact point where they intersect.

d. Using the graph and the answers to Part c, determine how many computer games must be made and sold to guarantee a profit greater than \$500,000.

The company will earn a profit of more than \$500,000 when the profit graph is above the horizontal line P = 500.

This occurs between the points g = 16.72 and g = 67.28 or

$$16.72 < g < 67.28.$$

The company will earn more than \$500,000 when they make and sell between 1,672 and 6,728 computer games.

Example 3. A farmer wants to enclose three adjacent pig pens of equal size against a barn wall. He has 96 meters of fence.

a. Find the formula for area.

BARN WALL

W W W W

L

Width	Length	Area $A = L \bullet W$
10	$96 - 4 \bullet 10 = 56$	$56 \bullet 10 = 560$ sq. meters
15	$96 - 4 \bullet 15 = 36$	$36 \bullet 15 = 540$ sq. meters
20	$96 - 4 \bullet 20 = 16$	$16 \bullet 20 = 320$ sq. meters
W	$96 - 4 \bullet W$	$W(96 - 4 \bullet W)$

Explanation: The most difficult part of the table is finding the value for length. If the farmer uses 10 meters for the width of the pens, and there are 4 widths, then he has used $4 \bullet 10$, or 40 meters of fencing. To find how much fencing he has left for the length, subtract 40 from 96, the total amount of fencing available to the farmer.

The formula for the area of the pigpens is

$A = W(96 - 4 \bullet W)$

$A = 96W - 4 \bullet W^2$ Use the distributive property.

$A = -4W^2 + 96W$ Write the squared term first.

b. Graph the formula in Part a. Explain what the vertex, W-intercepts, and A-intercept mean in terms of the pigpens.

- Find the **vertex** of $A = -4W^2 + 96W$.

  The formula for the W coordinate is $W = \frac{-b}{2a}$.

  From the equation for profit, a = -4, b = 96.

  $$W = \frac{-96}{2(-4)} = 12$$

  Find the A coordinate:

$A = -4W^2 + 96W$	Equation for area.
$A = -4(12^2) + 96 \bullet 12$	Substitute 12 for W.
$A = -4(144) + 96 \bullet 12$	Square 12.
$A = 576$	Simplify.

  The vertex is (12, 576).

- Find the **W intercepts** of $A = -4W^2 + 96W$.

  To find the W intercept, set A = 0.
  Solve $0 = -4W^2 + 96W$.

  Use the quadratic formula, a = -4, b = 96, c = 0.

$W = \frac{-b \pm \sqrt{b^2 - 4ac}}{2a}$	The quadratic formula.
$W = \frac{-96 \pm \sqrt{96^2 - 4(-4)(0)}}{2(-4)}$	Substitute the values for a, b, and c.
$W = \frac{-96 \pm 96}{2(-4)}$	Simplify the square root. 96 is the "obvious" answer because $\sqrt{96^2} = 96$.
$W = \frac{-96 + 96}{-8}$ or $W = \frac{-96 - 96}{-8}$	Write as two answers.
W = 0 or 24	Simplify.

  The W intercepts are (0, 0) and (24, 0).

- Find the **A intercept** of $A = -4W^2 + 96W$.
  To find the P intercept, set W = 0.
  $A = -4(0)^2 + 96 \bullet 0$
  $A = 0$

  Explanation: If the width of a rectangle is zero, then the area has to be zero.

  The A intercept is (0, 0).

Plot the points:

Vertex. (12, 576).

The **W intercepts**. (0, 0) and (24, 0).

The **A intercept**. (0, 0).

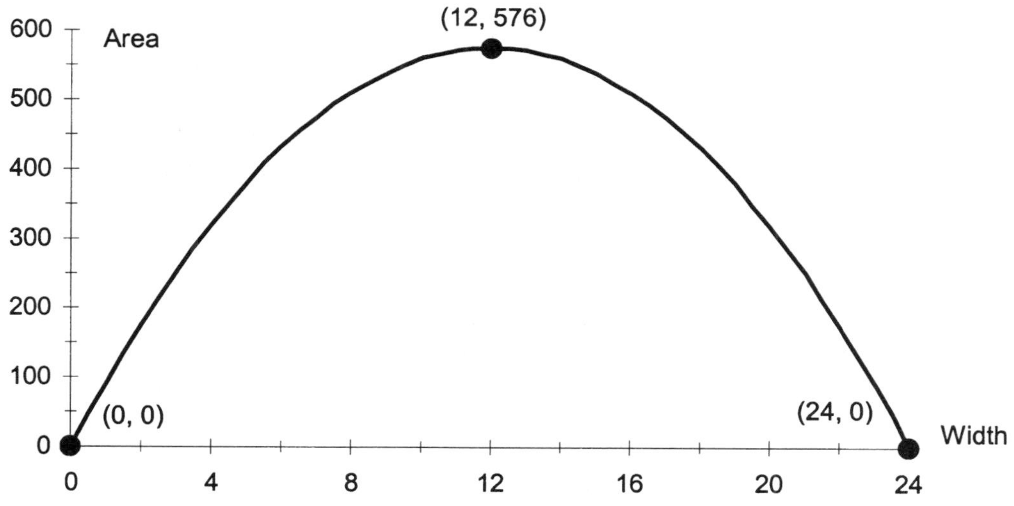

The **vertex**, (12, 576) represents the maximum area of the three pigpens. When W = 12, the maximum area will be 576. (The length of all three pigpens will be 48 or the length of one pig pen will be 16.)

The **W intercepts**, (0, 0) and (24, 0) represent the widths of the pigpens that will yield zero area.

The **A intercept**, (0, 0) is the area when W = 0.

c. Suppose the total area has to be 400 square meters. Graph A = 400 and find the dimensions of the pig sties.

Sketch A = 400 on the graph from the previous page.

A = 400 is a horizontal line.

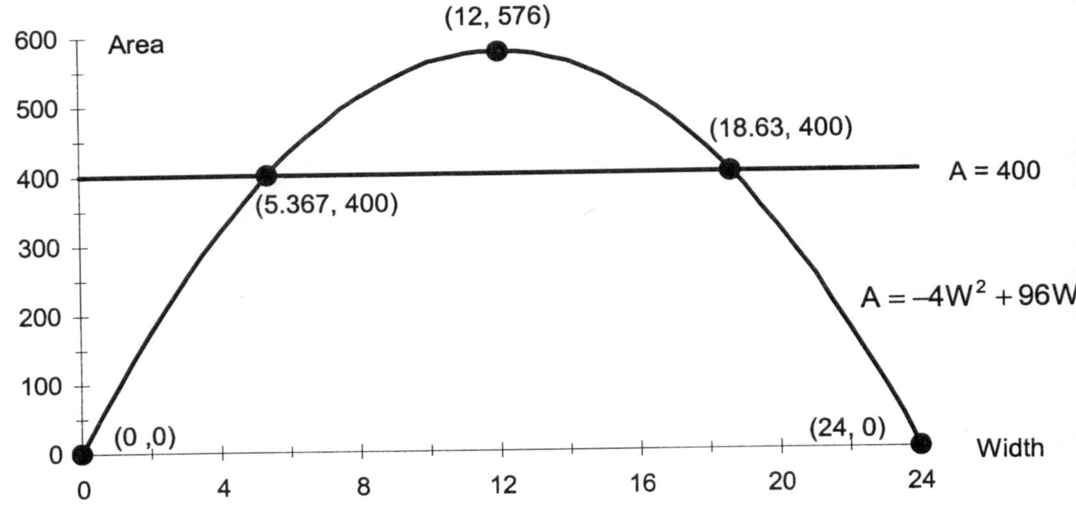

$400 = -4W^2 + 96W$	Substitute 400 for A.
$0 = -4W^2 + 96W - 400$	Subtract 400 from both sides.
a = -4, b = 96, c = -400	Identify a, b and c.
$W = \dfrac{-b \pm \sqrt{b^2 - 4ac}}{2a}$	Use the quadratic formula.
$W = \dfrac{-96 \pm \sqrt{96^2 - 4(-4)(-400)}}{2(-4)}$	Substitute the values for a, b and c.
$W = \dfrac{-96 \pm 53.07}{2(-4)}$	Simplify the square root.
$W = \dfrac{-96 + 53.07}{2(-4)}$ or $W = \dfrac{-96 - 53.07}{2(-4)}$	Write as two answers.
W= 5.367 or 18.63	Simplify.

The dimensions of the pigpens that will give an area of 400 square meters are 5.367 by 74.53 and 18.63 by 21.47.

(To find the length of the pigpens divide 400 by 5.367 and 18.63.)

Summary: Graphs of quadratics appear in subjects as diverse as microeconomics and physics. This section summarizes the major ideas of the unit.

To graph a quadratic, $y = ax^2 + bx + c$, you should find:

- The **vertex.**

  The formula for the x coordinate is
  $$x = \frac{-b}{2a}.$$

  To find the y coordinate, substitute your answer for the x coordinate in the equation $y = ax^2 + bx + c$.

- The **x intercepts.**

  Set y = 0 and solve the equation $0 = ax^2 + bx + c$ using the quadratic formula
  $$y = \frac{-b \pm \sqrt{b^2 - 4ac}}{2a}.$$

- The **y intercepts.**

  Set x = 0 in the equation $y = ax^2 + bx + c$ and find y.

The basic graph looks like this:

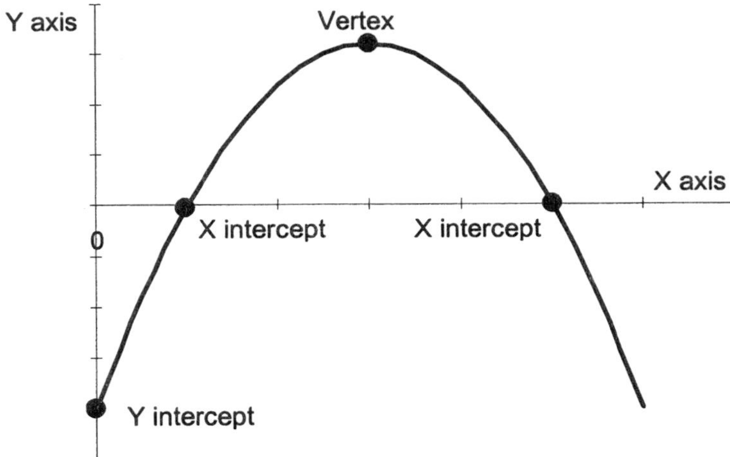

CLASS WORK

1. Earl Black makes tea bags. The cost of making x million tea bags per month is

$$C = x^2 - 38x + 400 .$$

The revenue from selling x million tea bags per month is

$$R = -x^2 + 78x.$$

C and R are in thousands of dollars.

a. Find the equation for profit.

b. Graph the profit equation. Explain what the vertex x and p intercepts mean in terms of making tea bags. Make sure you label the axes and use an appropriate scale.

Vertex	
x intercepts	
P intercept	

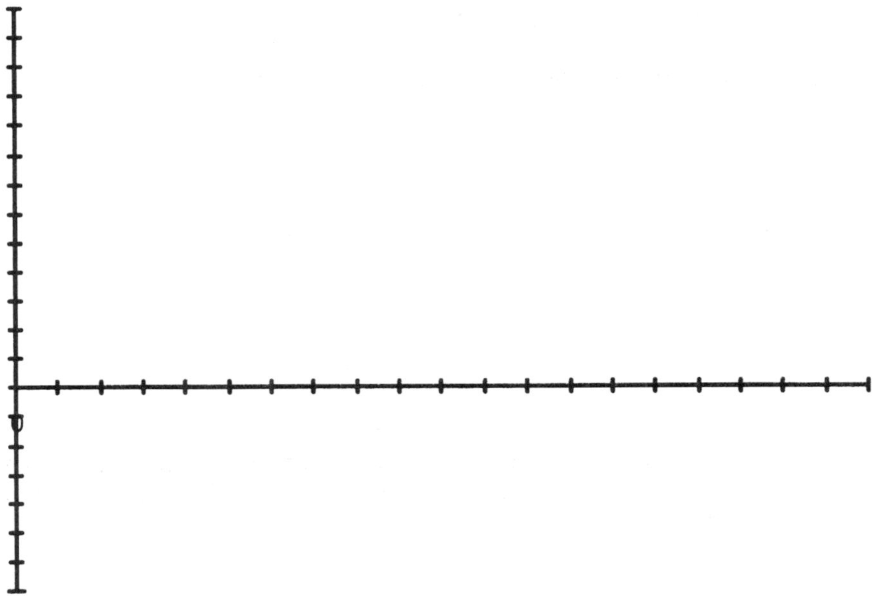

c. Suppose Earl Black needs to make $500,000 in profit (P = 500). Graph this line on the graph above and find where the line intersects the graph of the quadratic. Explain what the answers mean.

d. Using the graph and the answers to Part c, determine how many tea bags must be made and sold that will guarantee a profit of greater than $500,000.

2. An angry algebra student stands at the top of a 250 foot cliff and throws his algebra book upward with a velocity of 64 feet per second. The height of the book above the floor of the canyon t seconds after the book is thrown is indicated by

$$h = -16t^2 + 64t + 250 \text{ feet.}$$

Graph the equation. Explain what the vertex t and h intercepts mean in terms of the book being thrown off the cliff. Why should there be only one t intercept? Make sure you label the axes and choose an appropriate scale.

Vertex	
t intercept	
h intercept	

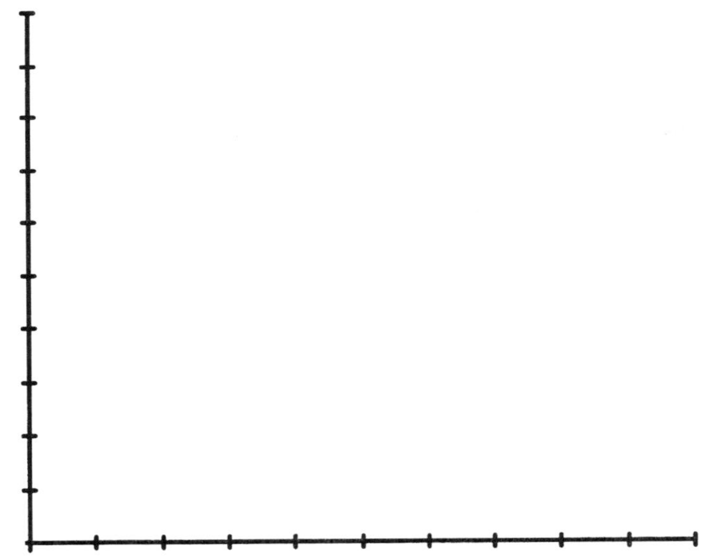

3. Ms. Farmer wants to enclose two adjacent chicken coops of equal size against the hen house wall. She has 66 feet of chicken-wire fencing and would like the chicken coop to be as large as possible.

a. Find the formula for the area of the chicken coops.

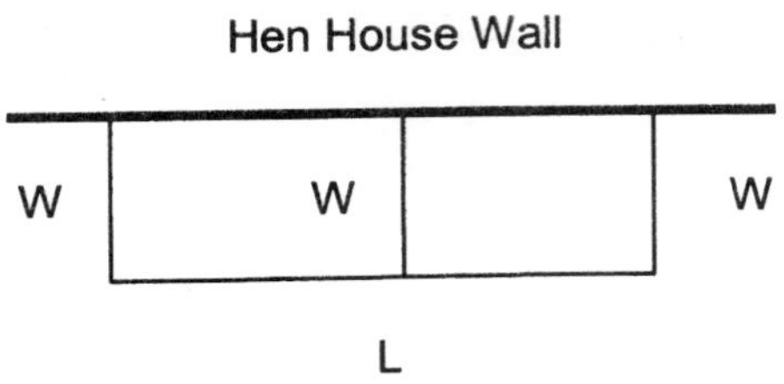

Hen House Wall

W W W

L

WIDTH	LENGTH	AREA

b. Graph the formula in Part a. Explain what the vertex, the w-intercept, and the A-intercept mean in terms of Ms. Farmer's problem.

Vertex	
W intercept	
A intercept	

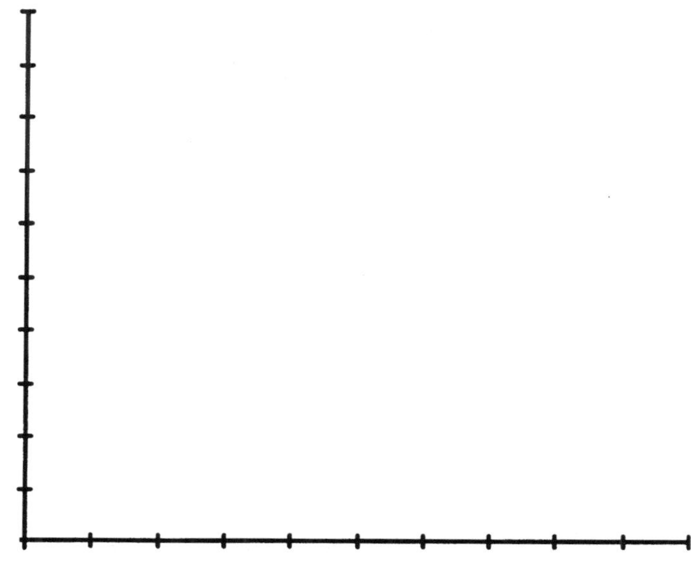

c. Mr. Urban comes along and tells Ms. Farmer that the chicken coops should only have an area of 360 square feet. Represent this idea in the graph of Part b by graphing the line $A = 360$ and find the dimensions of the chicken coop.

GROUP EXERCISE

Study Tips: 1. Review Example 2 on page 296 or Problem 1 on page 304.
2. Take your time and make sure everyone in your group understands how to do each part.

1. Soul Shoe Co. makes x thousand shoes per week. The cost of making x thousand shoes per week is

$$C = 0.3x^2 - 11x + 13$$

and the revenue from selling x thousand shoes per week is

$$R = -0.7x^2 + 7x.$$

C and R are in thousand dollar units.

a. Find the equation for profit. ($P = R - C$)

b. Graph the equation for profit. Explain what the vertex, x-intercepts, and P-intercept mean in terms of making shoes. Label your axes and choose an appropriate scale.

Vertex	
x intercepts	
P intercept	

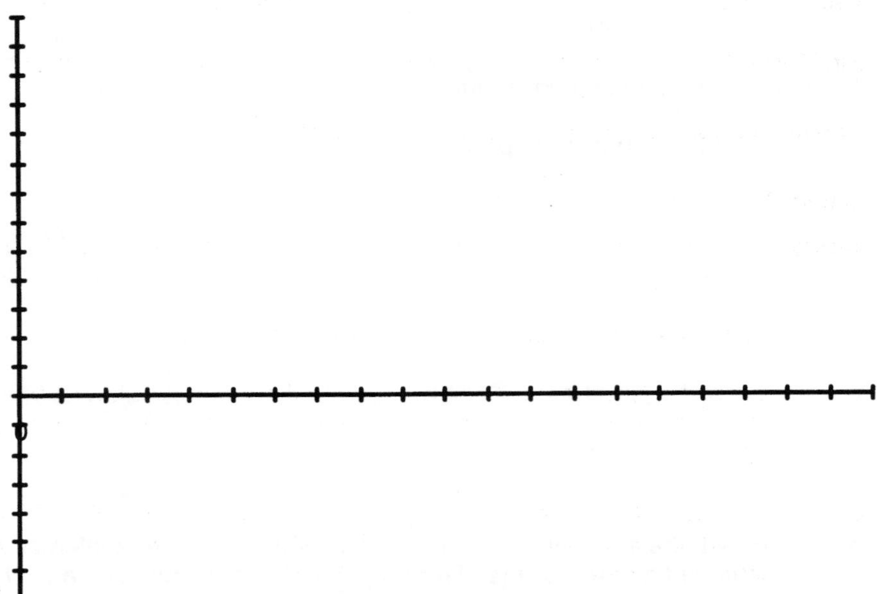

c. Suppose Soul Shoe Co. needs to make $50,000 in profit for the week (P = 50). Graph this line on the graph above and find where the line intersects the graph of the quadratic. Explain what the answers mean in terms of making shoes.

d. Using the graph and the answers to Part c, determine how many shoes must be made and sold that will guarantee a profit of greater than $50,000.

EXERCISE

Study Tips: 1. Make sure you have all of the materials needed to create a graph: graph paper, colored pencils, and a ruler.
2. Have your note cards handy for easy reference.

1. Write a sentence describing the vertex of a graph of the quadratic.

2. What is the formula for the x coordinate of the vertex?

3. Write a sentence describing how to find the y coordinate of the vertex.

4. List the important points you need to find to graph a quadratic.

5. Mr. Twisted makes pretzels. The cost of making x thousands of pretzels per week is

$$C = 0.4x^2 - 28x + 87 .$$

The revenue from selling x thousands of pretzels per week is

$$R = -0.6x^2 + 8x .$$

C and R are in thousands of dollars.

Study Tip: Review Example 2 on page 296 or Problem 1 on page 304 or the group work problem.

a. Find the equation for profit. (Profit = Revenue - Cost)

b. Graph the profit equation. Explain what the vertex, x-intercepts, and P-intercept mean in terms of making pretzels. Make sure you label the axes and use an appropriate scale.

c. Suppose Mr. Twisted needs to make $40,000 in profits (P = 40). Graph this line on the graph above and find out where the line intersects the graph of the quadradic. Explain what the answers mean.

6. Dr. Torus makes doughnuts. The cost of making x thousands of doughnuts a month is

$$C = 4x^2 - 62x + 35$$

and the revenue from selling x thousand doughnuts a month is

$$R = -3x^2 + 15x .$$

C and R are in hundreds of dollars.

a. Find the equation for profit. (Profit = Revenue - Cost).

b. Graph the profit equation. Explain what the vertex, x-intercepts, and p-intercept mean in terms of making doughnuts. Make sure you label the axes and use an appropriate scale.

c. Suppose Dr. Torus needs to make $80,000 a day in profit (P = 80). Graph this line on the graph above and find out where the line intersects the graph of the quadratic. Explain what the answers mean.

7. The Star Spangle Banner Fireworks Company launches its Liberty Bell rocket every Labor Day (the company is a little confused). The height of the rocket is given by the equation

$$h = -16t^2 + 200t \text{ feet.}$$

Study Tip: Review Example 2 on page 306.

a. Graph the equation. Explain what the vertex, t-intercepts, and h-intercept mean in terms of the Liberty Bell rocket. Make sure you label the axes and choose an appropriate scale.

b. Suppose the Liberty Bell rocket must be ignited 300 feet above the ground. Graph this requirement on the graph above. Find where the line intersects the graph of the quadratic and explain what the answers mean.

8. A farmer has 1800 feet of fencing. She wants to fence a rectangular pasture. The pasture borders on a river.

Study Tip: Review Example 3 on page 308.

a. Find an equation for the area of the pasture.

RIVER

W W

L

WIDTH	LENGTH	AREA

b. Graph the equation for area. Explain what the vertex, W-intercepts, and A-intercept mean in terms of the area of the pasture.

c. What are the dimensions of the pasture that give the maximum area?

FACTORING
OVERVIEW

Objectives: Factoring is an algebraic technique used to separate an expression into its component parts. When the component parts are multiplied together, the result is the original expression. This can sometimes be used to solve quadratic equations. Factoring is an important skill in MAT 100, Intermediate Algebra.

Definition: An algebraic expression is factored if the last operation in evaluating the expression is multiplication.

Example 1. Which expression is factored, $x^2 - 5x - 24$ or $(x-8)(x+3)$?

Pick a value for x and substitute it into the expression.

Let x = 3.

For $x^2 - 5x - 24$

$$= 3^2 - 5(3) - 24$$
$$= 9 - 5(3) - 24$$
$$= 9 - 15 - 24$$
$$= -30$$

Last operation was subtraction.

For $(x-8)(x+3)$

$$= (3-8)(3+3)$$
$$= (-5)(6)$$
$$= -30$$

Last operation was multiplication.

Since the last operation for $(x-8)(x+3)$ was multiplication, then $(x-8)(x+3)$ is factored.

Study Tip: Less formally, an algebraic expression is factored when it has parentheses.

Common Factors: The distributive property is a(b + c) = ab + ac. The left hand side is factored and a is the common factor.

Example 2. Factor $6x^2 + 12x$.

$6x^2 + 12x = 6 \bullet x \bullet x + 6 \bullet 2 \bullet x$ Find factors of $6x^2$ and $12x$.

$= \mathbf{6} \bullet \mathbf{x} \bullet x + \mathbf{6} \bullet 2 \bullet \mathbf{x}$ Identify the common factors, 6 and x.

$= 6x(x+2)$ Factor out 6x.

You should be able to check by using the distributive property.

Example 3. Factor $8x^3 + 4x$.

$8x^3 + 4x = 2 \bullet 4 \bullet x \bullet x \bullet x + 4 \bullet 1 \bullet x$ Find factors of $8x^3$ and $4x$.

$= 2 \bullet \mathbf{4} \bullet \mathbf{x} \bullet x \bullet x + \mathbf{4} \bullet 1 \bullet \mathbf{x}$ Identify the common factors, 4, x.

$= 4x(2x^2 + 1)$ Factor out 4x.

Factoring Trinomials: (A trinomial has three terms.) To factor a trinomial, recall FOIL.

Study Tip: Check your notecards for the definition of FOIL.

Example 4. Multiply $(x+3)(x+5)$.

$$(x+3)(x+5) = x^2 + 5x + 3x + 15$$
$$= x^2 + 8x + 15$$

$(x+3)(x+5)$ is factored while $x^2 + 8x + 15$ is not. To factor trinomials, you need to know how the 8x and the 15 were computed. The 8x came from adding 5x and 3x while 15 came from multiplying 5 and 3.

Example 5. Factor $x^2 + 8x + 15$. (This is from Example 4.)

We need two numbers that when added equal 8 and when multiplied equal 15.

3 and 5 add up to 8 and when multiplied are15.

So $x^2 + 8x + 15 = (x+3)(x+5)$.

Example 6. Factor $x^2 - 4x - 12$.

We need two numbers that when added equal –4 and when multiplied equal –12.

–6 and 2 add up to –4 and when multiplied are –12.

So $x^2 - 4x - 12 = (x-6)(x+2)$.

Example 7. Factor $x^2 - 64$.

This is not a trinomial, but it can become one by adding 0x.

$$x^2 - 64 = x^2 + 0x - 64$$

We need two numbers that when added equal 0 and when multiplied equal –64.

–8 and 8 add to 0 and when multiplied are –64.

So $x^2 - 64 = (x-8)(x+8)$.

This example is called factoring the difference of perfect squares and you will see this again in MAT 100, Intermediate Algebra.

Solving Quadratic Equations by Factoring: If you multiply two quantities and the result is zero, then you know that one of the quantities must be zero. In mathematical notation

$$\text{if } a \bullet b = 0 \text{ then } a = 0 \text{ or } b = 0.$$

Example 8. Solve $x^2 - 11x + 30 = 0$.

$x^2 - 11x + 30 = 0$	
$(x-5)(x-6) = 0$	Factor $x^2 - 11x + 30$.
$(x-5) = 0$ or $(x-6) = 0$	Set each factor equal to zero.
$x = 5$ or $x = 6$	Solve each equation.

Example 9. Solve $9x^2 + 15x = 0$.

$9x^2 + 15x = 0$	
$3 \bullet 3 \bullet x \bullet x + 5 \bullet 3x = 0$	Factor $9x^2$ and $15x$.
$3x(3x+5) = 0$	Factor out the common factor of $3x$.
$3x = 0$ or $3x + 5 = 0$	Set each factor equal to zero.
$x = 0$ or $x = \frac{-5}{3}$	Solve each equation.

Before you think that factoring to solve quadratics is a lot easier than using the quadratic formula, you need to know that factoring almost never works. Consider changing Example 8 by just one to $x^2 - 11x + 31 = 0$. You cannot find two numbers that when added equal –11 and when multiplied equal 31. In fact, to factor $x^2 - 11x + 31$ you must use the quadratic formula. You will learn how to factor any quadratic equation in Precalculus I, MAT 161.

Summary: There are two techniques for factoring presented in this unit. The first is common factors which use the distributive property, ab + ac = a(b + c). The other one is factoring trinomials. To factor trinomials, you need to know how FOIL works. If you take MAT 100, Intermediate Algebra, you will see much factoring.

CLASS WORK

1. When is an algebraic expression in factored form?

2. Which expression is factored?

   a. $x^2 + 7x - 30$ or $(x + 10)(x - 3)$

   b. $6x^2 + 3x$ or $3x(2x + 1)$

3. Identify the common factors and factor the expression.

   a. $2x + 8$ b. $8x + 4$ c. $16x^2 - 24x$

4. Factor these trinomials.

   a. $x^2 + 7x + 12$ b. $x^2 + 11x + 28$

   c. $x^2 - 5x + 6$ d. $x^2 - 36$

5. Solve by factoring.

   a. $x^2 - 6x - 16 = 0$ b. $20x^2 + 10x = 0$

GROUP EXERCISES

Factor.

1. $8x^2 + 20x$

2. $x^2 - 5x - 14$

3. $x^2 - 121$

Solve.

4. $x^2 + 11x + 30 = 0$

EXERCISES

Study Tips: 1. Review Class Work, Overview, and Group Exercises.
2. Have your note cards ready for important definitions.

1. What does it mean for an algebraic expression to be factored?

2. Which expression is factored?

   a. $2x^2 + 8x$ or $2x(x + 4)$

   b. $(x - 3)(x + 1)$ or $x^2 - 2x - 3$

3. Describe the mistake.

   a. $6x^2 + 3x = 3x(2x)$

   b. $x^2 - 9 = x - 3$

4. Factor.

   a. $6x + 9$
   b. $14x - 7$
   c. $-10x + 50$
   d. $8x^2 - 6x$
   e. $27x^2 - 18x$
   f. $15x^3 - 5x^2$
   g. $x^2 + 7x + 6$
   h. $x^2 - 8x + 15$
   i. $x^2 - 6x + 9$
   j. $x^2 - 3x - 18$
   k. $x^2 + 13x + 30$
   l. $x^2 - 15x + 50$
   m. $x^2 - 100$
   n. $x^2 - 36$
   o. $x^2 - 81$

5. Solve by factoring.

   a. $x^2 + 7x + 6 = 0$
   b. $x^2 - 5x - 50 = 0$
   c. $12x^2 + 20x = 0$

REVIEW IV

This unit introduces you to quadratics. The two major topics are the quadratic formula and graphs of quadratics. These topics have many applications in business, physics, and geometry. Factoring is an important topic in MAT 100, Intermediate Algebra.

Introduction to Quadratics:

Example 1. Simplify: $3(2x^2 - 5x + 7) - 5(6x^2 - 4)$

$3(2x^2 - 5x + 7) - 5(6x^2 - 4)$

$= 6x^2 - 15x + 21 - 30x^2 + 20$ Use the distributive property.

$= -24x^2 - 15x + 41$ Combine like terms.

Example 2. Multiply: $(2x - 5)(3x + 7)$.

$(2x - 5)(3x + 7) = 6x^2 + 14x - 15x - 35$ Multiply using FOIL.

$= 6x^2 - 1x - 35$ Combine like terms.

Example 3. Multiply: $(x - 6)^2$.

$(x - 6)^2 = (x - 6)(x - 6)$ Write the square as a product.

$= x^2 - 6x - 6x + 36$ Multiply using FOIL.

$= x^2 - 12x + 36$ Combine like terms.

Applications of the Quadratic Formula:

Definition: $ax^2 + bx + c = 0$ is the quadratic equation.

Definition: $x = \dfrac{-b \pm \sqrt{b^2 - 4ac}}{2a}$ is the quadratic formula.

Example 4. A farmer wants to enclose two adjacent chicken coops against a barn. He has 125 feet of fence. What should the dimensions be if he wants the total area to be 700 square feet.

a. Complete the table to find the equation for area.

Barn

W W W

L

WIDTH	LENGTH	AREA
10	$125 - 3 \bullet 10 = 95$	$10 \bullet 95 = 950$
15	$125 - 3 \bullet 15 = 80$	$15 \bullet 80 = 1{,}200$
30	$125 - 3 \bullet 30 = 35$	$30 \bullet 35 = 1{,}050$
W	$125 - 3 \bullet W$	$W(125 - 3 \bullet W)$

$A = W(125 - 3W)$

$= 125W - 3W^2$ Use the distributive property.

$= -3W^2 + 125W$ Write the squared term first.

b. Find W when A = 700.

$700 = -3W^2 + 125W$	Substitute 700 for A.
$0 = -3W^2 + 125W - 700$	Subtract 700 from both sides.
a = -3, b = 125, c = -700	Identify a, b, and c.
$W = \frac{-b \pm \sqrt{b^2 - 4ac}}{2a}$	The quadratic formula.
$W = \frac{-125 \pm \sqrt{125^2 - 4(-3)(-700)}}{2(-3)}$	Substitute the values of a, b, and c into the quadratic formula.
$W = \frac{-125 \pm 85}{2(-3)}$	Simplify the square root.
$W = \frac{-125 + 85}{2(-3)}$ or $W = \frac{-125 - 85}{2(-3)}$	Write as two solutions.
$W = 6.667$ or $W = 35$	Simplify.

The dimensions of the chicken coop that will yield an area of 700 square feet are 35 by 20 feet and 6.667 by 105 feet. (To get the length divide 700 by 6.667 and 35.)

Quadratic Applications and Their Graphs:

To graph a quadratic, $y = ax^2 + bx + c$ you must find:

1. The vertex:

   The x coordinate is computed with the formula $x = \frac{-b}{2a}$.
   The y coordinate is computed by substituting the x coordinate into $y = ax^2 + bx + c$.

2. The x intercept:

   Set y = 0 and solve $0 = ax^2 + bx + c$ using the quadratic formula.

3. The y intercept:

   Substitute x = 0 into $y = ax^2 + bx + c$.

Example 5. The cost equation for making Juice Boxes is $C = .6B^2 - 24B + 36$, and the revenue equation is given by $R = -.4B^2 + 18B$. B is in millions, and C and R are in thousands of dollars.

a. Find the profit equation.

Profit = Revenue - Cost	Formula for profit.
$P = (-.4B^2 + 18B) - (.6B^2 - 24B + 36)$	Substitute the equations for revenue and cost. Note the need for parentheses.
$P = -.4B^2 + 18B - .6B^2 + 24B - 36$	Use the distributive property.
$P = -B^2 + 42B - 36$	Combine like terms.

b. Graph the profit equation and explain what the vertex, B, and P intercepts mean in terms of the problem.

- Find the vertex of $P = -B^2 + 42B - 36$.

  The formula for the B coordinate is $B = \dfrac{-b}{2a}$.

  a = -1, b = 42.

  $$B = \frac{-42}{2(-1)}$$
  $$B = 21$$

  Find the P coordinate. Substitute B = 21 into $P = -B^2 + 42B - 36$.

  $$P = -21^2 + 42 \bullet 21 - 36$$
  $$P = 405$$

The vertex is (21, 405).

- Find the B intercept. Set P = 0.

  Solve $0 = -B^2 + 42B - 36$.

  a = -1, b = 42, c = -36.

  $$B = \frac{-42 \pm \sqrt{42^2 - 4(-1)(-36)}}{2(-1)}$$
  $$B = \frac{-42 \pm 40.25}{2(-1)}$$
  $$B = \frac{-42 + 40.25}{-2} \text{ or } B = \frac{-42 - 40.25}{-2}$$
  $$B = .875 \text{ or } B = 41.13$$

The B intercepts are (.875, 0) and (41.13, 0).

- Find the P intercept. Set B = 0.

$$P = -(0)^2 + 42 \bullet 0 - 36$$
$$P = -36$$

The P intercept is (0, -36).

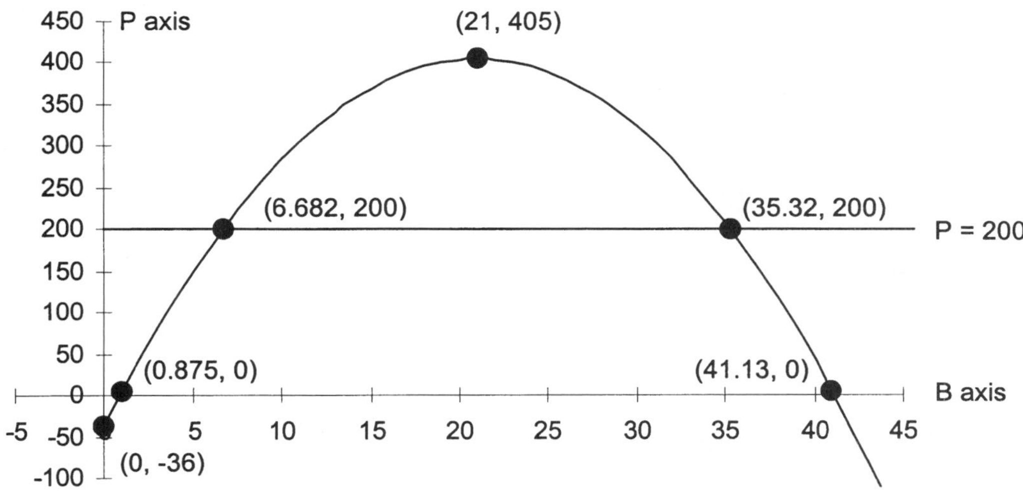

The vertex (21, 405) represents the maximum profit. The company will obtain its maximum profit of $405,000 when they sell 21 million juice boxes.

The B intercepts (0.875, 0), (41.13, 0) tell us that the company will break even if they sell .875 or 41.13 million juice boxes.

The P intercept (0. –36) represents the company's start up costs of $36,000.

c. Suppose the company needs to earn $200,000 in profit (P = 200). Graph the line P = 200 and find how many juice boxes the company needs to make to earn $200,000.

$$200 = -B^2 + 42B - 36$$
$$0 = -B^2 + 42B - 236$$
$$a = -1,\ b = 42,\ c = -236$$
$$B = \frac{-42 \pm \sqrt{42^2 - 4(-1)(-236)}}{2(-1)}$$
$$B = \frac{-42 \pm 28.64}{2(-1)}$$
$$B = 6.682,\ 35.32$$

The company needs to make 6.682 or 35.32 million juice boxes in order to earn $200,000 in profits.

Factoring:

Common Factors:

Example 6. Factor $24x^3 + 30x$.

$$24x^3 + 30x = 6 \bullet 4 \bullet x \bullet x \bullet x + 6 \bullet 5 \bullet x$$
$$= 6x(4x^2 + 5x)$$

Trinomials:

Example 7. Factor $x^2 - 4x - 12$.

$x^2 - 4x - 12$, need two numbers that when added equal –4 and when multiplied equal –12.

$(x-6)(x+2)$.

Example 8. Factor $x^2 - 81$.

$x^2 - 81 = x^2 + 0x - 81$, need two numbers that when added equal 0 and when multiplied equal –81.

$= (x-9)(x+9)$

Solving quadratic equations by factoring.

If $a \bullet b = 0$ then $a = 0$ or $b = 0$.

Example 9. Solve $x^2 + 5x - 14 = 0$.

$$x^2 + 5x - 14 = 0$$
$$(x+7)(x-2) = 0$$
$$x - 2 = 0 \text{ or } x + 7 = 0$$
$$x = 2 \text{ or } x = -7$$

Study Tips:

1. Practice the review test starting on the next page by placing yourself under realistic exam conditions.
2. Find a quiet place and use a timer to simulate test conditions.
3. Write your answers in your homework notebook. You may then re-take the exam for extra practice.
4. Check your answers. The answers to the review test are on page 373.
5. There is an additional exam available on the MAT 011 web page, **www.mc3.edu/aa/career/MATHSCI/mat011/mat011.htm**
6. Do NOT wait until the night before to study. This test can be very challenging.

TEST IV

Study Tip: Make sure you have all of your graphing materials: colored pencils, ruler, and graph paper.

1. Titanic Ship Company makes yachts. The cost of making x yachts per month is

$$C = x^2 - 32x + 12,$$

and the revenue from selling x yachts per month is

$$R = -x^2 + 8x.$$

C and R are in thousands of dollars.

   a. Find the equation for profit. (Profit = Revenue - Cost)

   b. Graph the profit equation. Explain what the vertex, x-intercepts, and p-intercept mean in terms of making yachts. Make sure you label the axes and use an appropriate scale.

   c. Suppose the Titanic Ship Company needs $35,000 in profits (P = 35). Graph this line on the graph above and find out where the line intersects the graph of the quadratic. Explain what the answers mean.

2. A rabbit breeder has 80 meters of chicken wire. He wants to form two rectangular hutches for his rabbits. One side of the hutch will be against a wall. (See the diagram below.)

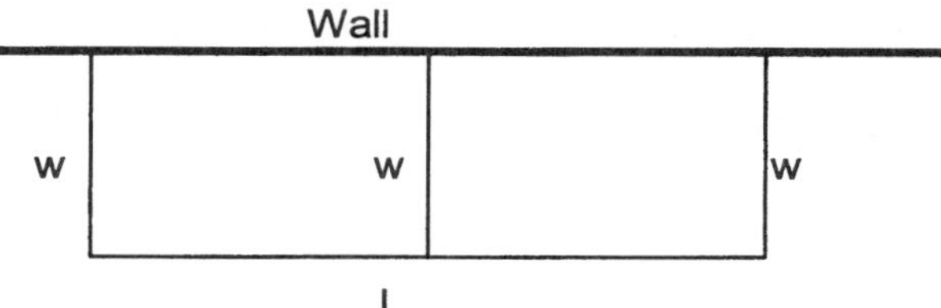

   a. Find a formula for the area of the rabbit hutches. (Make a table.)

   b. Graph the equation for area. Explain what the vertex, w-intercepts, and a-intercept mean in terms of the area of the rabbit hutch.

   c. Suppose the breeder reads in *Breeding Rabbits Magazine* that he should have an area of 477 feet (A = 477) Represent this idea in the graph of Part b. Find where the line intersects the graph of the quadratic and explain what the solutions represent.

3. Simplify. $3(x^2 + 4x - 8) - 2(3x^2 - 5x + 3)$

4. Multiply.

   a. $(3x + 5)(x - 8)$ b. $(x - 5)^2$

5. Factor.

   a. $4x^2 + 8x$ b. $x^2 + 7x - 18$

6. Solve. $x^2 - 8x + 12 = 0$

FINAL EXAM REVIEW
STUDY TIPS

1. Know when and where your final exam is being held. It may not be at the same time as your class and may not be in the same room.

   My final is in Room ______________________________

   at ______________________________

2. Arrive at least 15 minutes early for the final.

3. Make sure you have several sharpened pencils, your calculator, a ruler, and colored pencils.

4. Know what score you have to get on the final to get the grade you want for the course. If necessary, make an appointment with your teacher to discuss your grade.

5. Know when your teacher will be on campus during final exam week.

   My teacher will be in his/her office at ______________________________

6. Try to organize a study group with some of your classmates.

7. Find out if the Learning Assistance Lab is having a group study session for finals.

8. Study an hour or so a day. Do not try to pull an "all nighter" for the final.

9. To prepare for the final exam:
   a. Organize your note cards.
   b. Review the sample tests.
   c. Go over the tests you took. Go back and review the difficult sections; re-do the ones you had wrong.
   d. Review the sample problems starting on the next page.
   e. Practice the review final starting on page 342 by placing yourself under realistic exam conditions.
   f. Find a quiet place and use a timer to simulate test conditions.
   g. Write your answers in your homework notebook. You may then re-take the exam for extra practice.
   h. Check your answers. The answers to the review test are on page 374.
   i. Do NOT wait until the night before to study. The final can be very challenging.

SAMPLE PROBLEMS

Solving Equations: Solving equations is perhaps the most important skill taught in an algebra course. There were five types of equations covered this semester, linear, literal, inequalities, rational (equations with fractions), and quadratic.

- Linear Equations (Sections: Solving Equations Part I & II)

Example 1. Solve $4x-2(5x-8)=4x+12$

$4x-2(5x-8)=4x+12$

$4x-10x+16=4x+12$ Use the distributive property.

$-6x+16=4x+12$ Combine like terms.

$16=10x+12$ Add 6x to both sides.

$4=10x$ Subtract 12 from both sides.

$.4=x$ Divide both sides by 10.

- Literal Equations (Section: Applications of Linear Equations Part II, Literal Equations)

Example 2. Solve $6x+7y=15$ for y.

$6x+7y=15$

$7y=15-6x$ Subtract 6x from both sides.

$y=\dfrac{15-6x}{7}$ Divide both sides by 7.

- Inequalities (Section: Inequalities)

Example 3. Solve $24-7x\le 108$.

$24-7x\le 108$

$-7x\le 84$ Subtract 24 from both sides.

$x\ge -12$ Divide both sides by –7 and change the inequality.

Example 4. Solve $-5<7+3x<32$.

$-5<7+3x<32$

$-12<3x<25$ Subtract 7 from all three parts.

$-4<x<8.333$ Divide all three parts by 3.

- RationalEquations (Section: Solving Equations with Fractions)

Example 5. Solve $\dfrac{5}{3x}+\dfrac{7}{6}=\dfrac{26}{15}$.

$\dfrac{5}{3x}+\dfrac{7}{6}=\dfrac{26}{15}$ The LCD is 30x.

$\dfrac{5}{3x}\bullet\dfrac{30x}{1}+\dfrac{7}{6}\bullet\dfrac{30x}{1}=\dfrac{26}{15}\bullet\dfrac{30x}{1}$ Multiply all the terms by 30x

$5\bullet 10+7\bullet 5x=26\bullet 2x$ Reduce.

$50+35x=52x$ Multiply.

$50=17x$ Subtract 35x from both sides.

$\dfrac{50}{17}=x$ Divide both sides by 17.

- Quadratic Equations (Section: Applications of the Quadratic Formula)

Example 6. Solve $-2x^2+41x+27=14$.

$-2x^2+41x+27=14$	
$-2x^2+41x+13=0$	Subtract 14 from both sides.
a = -2, b = 41, c = 13	Identify a, b, and c.
$x=\dfrac{-b\pm\sqrt{b^2-4ac}}{2a}$	Recall the quadratic formula.
$x=\dfrac{-41\pm\sqrt{41^2-4(-2)(13)}}{2(-2)}$	Substitute a, b, and c into the quadratic formula.
$x=\dfrac{-41\pm 42.25}{2(-2)}$	Simplify the square root.
$x=\dfrac{-41+42.25}{2(-2)}$ or $x=\dfrac{-41-42.25}{2(-2)}$	Write as two solutions.
$x=-.3125$ or $x=20.81$	Simplify.

Graphing: Graphing is a way of visualizing a problem. A graph shows the "big" picture. There were two types of graphs presented in the course, lines (including horizontal and vertical) and quadratics.

- Graphing Lines

Example 7. Graph $y=-4x+13$ by finding three points.
(Section: Graphing Lines by Plotting Points)

Pick three values for x and find their y coordinates.
(Two points are necessary to graph a line; a third point is used to check the work.)

1. x = -5, find y.
   $y=-4(-5)+13$
   $y=33$
   Plot the point (-5, 33).

2. x = 3, find y.
   $y=-4(3)+13$
   $y=1$
   Plot the point (3, 1).

3. x = 15 find y
   $y=-4(15)+13$
   $y=-47$
   Plot the point (15, -47).

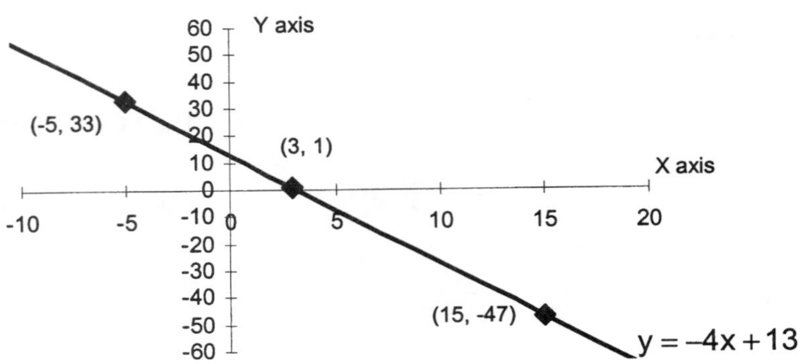

Example 8. Graph the line $4x + 0.2y = 64$ by finding the intercepts.
(Section: Graphing Lines by Finding the Intercepts)

Find the x intercept; set y = 0.

$$4x + 0.2(0) = 64$$
$$4x = 64$$
$$x = 16$$

The x intercept is (16, 0).

Find the y intercept; set x = 0.

$$4(0) + 0.2y = 64$$
$$0.2y = 64$$
$$y = 320$$

The y intercept is (0, 320).

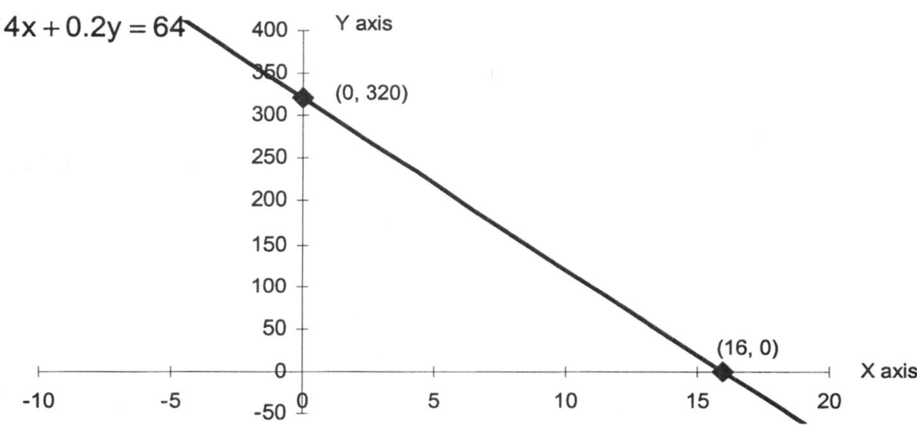

Example 9. Graph y = 8. (Section: Slope)

Since y is equal to a constant, then y = 8 is a horizontal line.

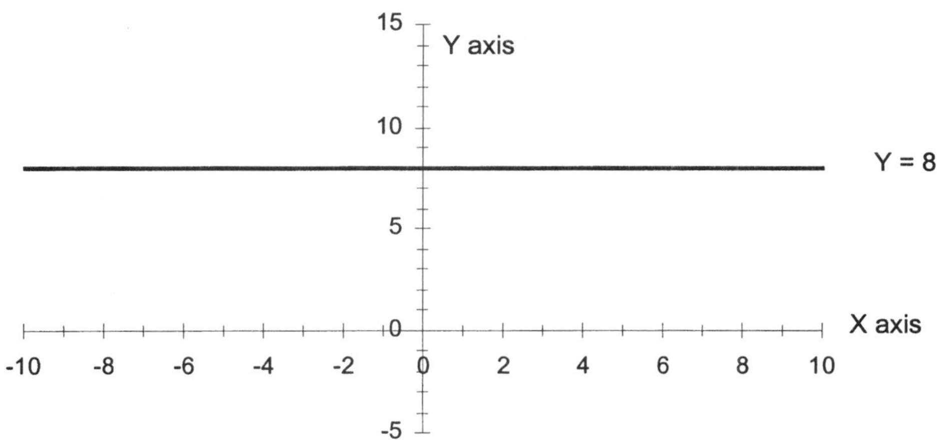

Example 10. Graph the line x = –3. (Section: Slope)

Since x is equal to a constant, then the line is vertical.

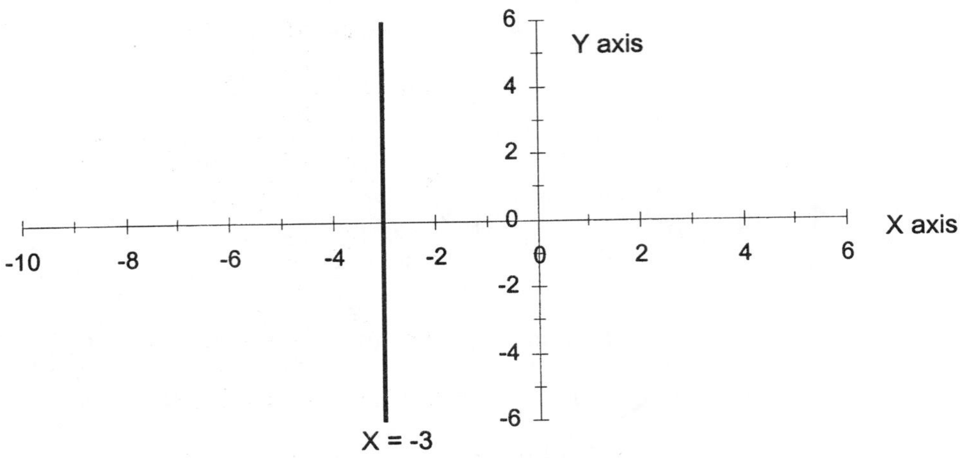

- Quadratics (Section: Quadratic Applications and Their Graphs)

Example 11. Graph $y = -2x^2 + 18x - 25$.

Find the vertex.

x coordinate:

$$x = \frac{-b}{2a}.$$

a = –2, b = 18

$$x = \frac{-18}{2(-2)}$$

$$x = 4.5$$

y coordinate:

$$y = -2(4.5^2) + 18(4.5) - 25$$

$$y = 15.5$$

The vertex is (4.5, 15.5).

Find the y intercept; set x = 0.

$$y = -2(0^2) + 18(0) - 25$$

$$y = -25$$

The y intercept is (0, –25).

Find the x intercept; set y = 0.

Solve $0 = -2x^2 + 18x - 25$

$$a = -2,\ b = 18,\ c = -25$$
$$x = \frac{-b \pm \sqrt{b^2 - 4ac}}{2a}$$
$$x = \frac{-18 \pm \sqrt{18^2 - 4(-2)(-25)}}{2(-2)}$$
$$x = \frac{-18 \pm 11.14}{2(-2)}$$
$$x = \frac{-18 + 11.14}{2(-2)} \text{ or } x = \frac{-18 - 11.14}{2(-2)}$$
$$x = 1.715 \text{ or } x = 7.285$$

The x intercepts are (1.715, 0) and (7.285, 0).

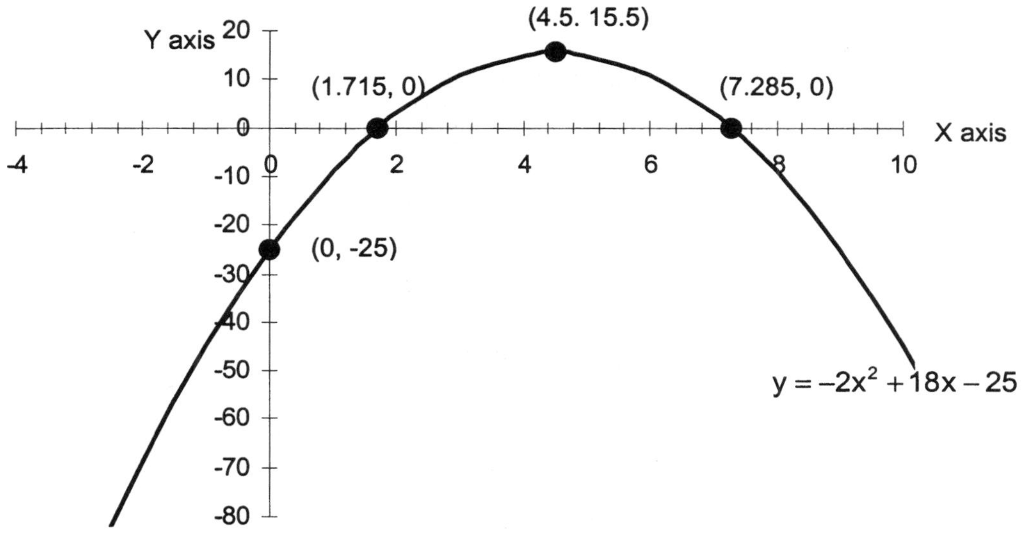

Applications: There are two reasons why applications were used in this course. One reason was to show you how algebra can be used in everyday life. The other reason was to give concrete examples to the mathematical ideas of the course.

- Tables

Example 12. A cell phone company charges $3.75 for the first 100 minutes and then 2 cents a minute after that.
(Sections: Introduction to Variables and Applications of Linear Equations, Part I)

a. Complete the table below and find an equation for the cost of the cell phone.

Minutes	**Calculation**	**Cost**
200	$.02(200-100)+3.75$	$5.75
500	$.02(500-100)+3.75$	$11.75
600	$.02(600-100)+3.75$	$13.75
m	$.02(m-100)+3.75$	C

$$C=.02(m-100)+3.75$$

b. If your cell phone bill were $4.25, how long were you the phone?

Find m when C = 4.25.

$$4.25=.02(m-100)+3.75$$
$$4.25=.02m-2+3.75$$
$$4.25=.02m+1.75$$
$$2.50=.02m$$
$$125=m$$

Since the cost was $4.25, then you were on the phone for 125 minutes.

Example 13. Storm Cloud Umbrella Company is having a 20% off sale because of a prolonged drought. If the sale price is $7.45, what was the price of the umbrella before the sale?
(Section: Percentages)

Pre-Sale Price	**Calculation**	**Sale Price**
10.00	$10.00-.20\bullet 10.00$	$8.00
9.00	$9.00-.20\bullet 9.00$	$7.20
P	$P-.20P$	S

$$S=P-.20P$$
$$S=.80P$$

Find P when S = 7.45.

$$7.45=.80P$$
$$9.31=P$$

The pre-sale price of the umbrella was $9.31.

Example 14. 500 bacteria are initially present. If the bacteria grow at a rate of 4% a day, find a formula for the number of bacteria.
(Section: Introduction to Positive Exponents)

Day	Calculation	Number of Bacteria
1	$500 \bullet 1.04$	520
2	$500 \bullet 1.04^2$	541
3	$500 \bullet 1.04^3$	562
4	$500 \bullet 1.04^4$	585
D	$500 \bullet 1.04^D$	N

$$N = 500 \bullet 1.04^D$$

- Percentage (Section: Percentages)

Example 15. Dr. Scholastic computes her grades as follows:

Homework Average	20%
Group Work Average	10%
Test Average	50%
Project Average	5%
Final Exam	15%

Selena has a 92 homework grade, 88 group work grade, 98 test average, and a 95 project average. If Selena wants a 90 for the course, how well does she have to do on the final?

$$\begin{aligned} .20 \bullet 92 + .10 \bullet 88 + .50 \bullet 98 + .05 \bullet 95 + .15E &= 90 \\ 80.95 + .15E &= 90 \\ .15E &= 9.05 \\ E &= 60.33 \end{aligned}$$

Because Selena did well all semester, she just has to get a 60.33 to get a 90 for the year.

- Inequalities (Section: Applications of Inequalities)

Example 16. Smith/Jones offers you a sales position upon graduation from M.C.C.C. They will pay $12,000 a year plus 8% commission. If your wages need to be between $45,000 and $62,000, then how much do you have to sell?

The equation that relates wages and sales is

$$W = .08S + 12{,}000 .$$

Wages need to be between 45,000 and 60,000.

$$45{,}000 < .08S + 12{,}000 < 60{,}000$$

$$33{,}000 < .08S < 48{,}000$$

$$412{,}500 < S < 600{,}000$$

If wages have to be between $45,000 and $60,000, then you sales have to be between $412,500 and $600,000.

- Slope and Percent Change (Section: Introduction to Slope)

Example 17. Use the table to answer the following questions.

Year	Number of CD Players Sold
1998	2,345,000
2002	3,789,000

a. Find the slope or average rate of change for the given years.

$$A.R.C. = \frac{3{,}789{,}000 - 2{,}345{,}000}{2002 - 1998}$$
$$A.R.C. = 361{,}000$$

The average rate of change for the years 1998 to 2002 was 361,000 CD players per year.

b. Find the percent change in the number of CD players sold.

$$A.R.C. = \frac{3{,}789{,}000 - 2{,}345{,}000}{2{,}345{,}000} \bullet 100$$
$$A.R.C. = 61.6\%$$

CD sales increased by 61.6% from 1998 to 2002.

Proportions (Section: Ratio and Proportion Problems)

Example 18. Two people pool their money to buy lottery tickets. Dave contributes $35 while Sue puts in $45. If they win 3.78 million dollars, how much should Dave get?

Dave

	Tickets	Winnings
Share	35	?
Total	80	3.78

$$\frac{35}{80} = \frac{W}{3.78}$$
$$132.3 = 80W$$
$$1.654 = W$$

Dave's fair share is 1.654 million dollars.

Scientific Notation (Section: Negative Exponents and Scientific Notation)

Example 19. a. Write 3,400,000,000 in Scientific Notation.

The 3 is in the 10^9 place. Remember that the first zero on the right is the 10^0 place.

$3{,}400{,}000{,}000 = 3.4 \times 10^9$

b. Write 5.3×10^{-4} in decimal notation.

The 5 is in the 10^{-4}. Remember that the first zero to the left of the decimal point is the 10^{-1}place.

$5.3 \times 10^{-4} = 0.00053$

- Summary of Linear Equations (Section: Applications of Graphs)

Example 19. You are going to rent a moving truck for the day. One company, Lite Trucks, charges 23.95 plus 35 cents per mile while a second company, Spacious Vans, charges a flat rate of 64.95.

a. Write the cost equations for each company.

Lite Trucks: $C = .35m + 23.95$
Spacious Vans: $C = 64.95$

b. Graph both equations on the same set of axes. Label each axis and choose an appropriate scale. Only graph the portion relevant to the problem.

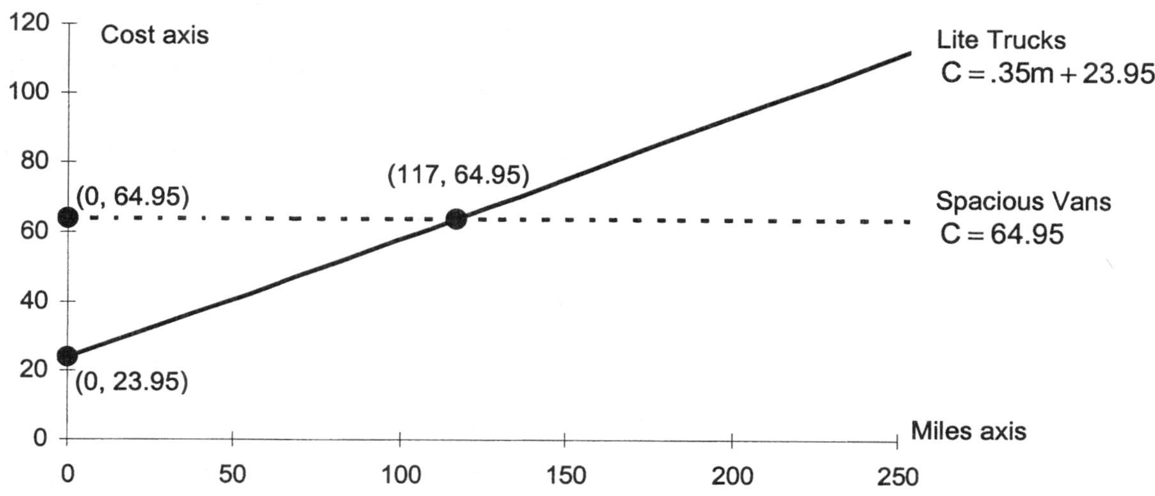

c. Find where the two lines intersect.

Solve $64.95 = .35m + 23.95$
$41 = .35m$
$117 = m$
The two companies will charge the same when you drive 117 miles.
The two lines intersect at (117, 64.95).

d. Use the graph to find when Lite Trucks costs more than Spacious Vans.

$m < 117$

e. What does the C intercept mean in terms of the problem?

For Spacious Vans the C intercept is (0, 64.95).
For Lite Trucks the C intercept is (0, 23.95).
The C intercept is the cost of going zero miles.

f. What is the slope of each line, and what does it mean in terms of the problem?

The slope of Spacious Vans is zero.
The slope of Lite Trucks is .35.
The slope is the cost per mile.

- Summary of Quadratic Applications (Section: Quadratic Applications and their Graphs)

Example 20. Q-Bees makes quilts. The cost equation for making quilts is represented by the equation $C = .7q^2 - 34q + 89$, and the revenue is represented by the equation $R = -.3q^2 + 24q$. The units for q are thousands, and C and R are in hundreds.

a. Find the profit equation.

Profit = Revenue – Cost

$$P = (-.3q^2 + 24q) - (.7q^2 - 34q + 89)$$
$$P = -.3q^2 + 24q - .7q^2 + 34q - 89$$
$$P = -q^2 + 58q - 89$$

b. Graph the profit equation. Explain what the vertex, q intercepts, and P intercept mean in terms of the problem.

Find the vertex.

Find the q coordinate.

$$q = \frac{-b}{2a}$$

a = –1, b = 58

$$q = \frac{-58}{2(-1)}$$
$$q = 29$$

Find the P coordinate.

$$P = -(29)^2 + 58(29) - 89$$
$$P = 752$$

The vertex is (29, 752).

Find the q intercepts. Set P = 0.

Solve $0 = -q^2 + 58q - 89$

a = –1, b = 58, c = -89.

$$q = \frac{-b \pm \sqrt{b^2 - 4ac}}{2a}$$
$$q = \frac{-58 \pm \sqrt{58^2 - 4(-1)(-89)}}{2(-1)}$$
$$q = \frac{-58 \pm 54.85}{2(-1)}$$
$$q = \frac{-58 + 54.85}{2(-1)} \text{ or } q = \frac{-58 - 54.85}{2(-1)}$$
$$q = 1.577 \text{ or } q = 56.42$$

The q intercepts are (1.577, 0) and (56.42, 0).

Find the P intercept. Set q = 0.

$$P = -(0^2) + 58(0) - 89$$
$$P = -89$$

The P intercept is (0, –89).

(The graph contains the answer to Part c.)

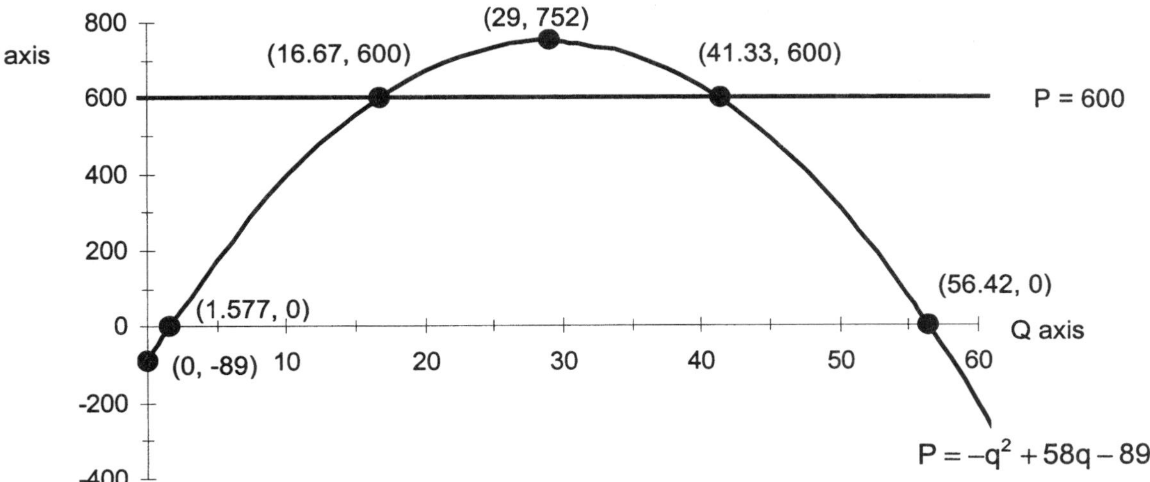

The vertex is (29, 752). If Q-Bees sell 29,000 quilts, then they will earn a maximum profit of $75,200.

The q intercepts are (1.577, 0) and (56.62, 0). If Q-Bees sells 1,577 or 56,62 quilts, then they will break even.

The P intercept is (0, –89). The start up costs for Q-Bees is $8,900.

c. Suppose that the company needs to earn a profit of $60,000, P = 600. Sketch the line P = 600 on the graph above and find where the line intersects the graph.

Solve $600 = -q^2 + 58q - 89$

$$0 = -q^2 + 58q - 689$$

a = –1, b = 58, c = –689.

$$q = \frac{-b \pm \sqrt{b^2 - 4ac}}{2a}$$

$$q = \frac{-58 \pm \sqrt{58^2 - 4(-1)(-689)}}{2(-1)}$$

$$q = \frac{-58 \pm 24.66}{2(-1)}$$

$$q = 16.67 \text{ or } q = 41.33$$

Q-Bees will earn $60,000 if they sell 16,670 or 41,330 quilts.

Algebra Skills: Manipulation of algebraic expressions is good exercise for the mind. It forces you to follow abstract rules and perform prescribed actions.

- Exponents (Section: Properties of Exponents)

Example 21. Simplify each expression. Write with positive exponents only.

a. $(3x^4)^2$

$$(3x^4)^2 = 3^2(x^4)^2$$
$$= 9x^8$$

b. $\dfrac{7x^{-4}}{x}$

$$\frac{7x^{-4}}{x} = \frac{7}{x(x^4)}$$
$$= \frac{7}{x^5}$$

c. $\dfrac{4x^5}{8x^2}$

$$\frac{4x^5}{8x^2} = \frac{x^3}{2}$$

- Multiplying and Dividing Fractions (Section: Introduction to Algebraic Fractions)

Example 22. Multiply or divide as indicated. Reduce to lowest terms.

a. $\dfrac{9x^2}{5} \bullet \dfrac{10}{6x^3}$

$$\frac{9x^2}{5} \bullet \frac{10}{6x^3} = \frac{3 \bullet 3 \bullet x \bullet x}{5} \bullet \frac{5 \bullet 2}{3 \bullet 2 \bullet x \bullet x \bullet x}$$

$$= \frac{3}{x}$$

b. $\dfrac{8}{21x^3} \div \dfrac{16x^2}{7}$

$$\frac{8}{21x^3} \div \frac{16x^2}{7} = \frac{8}{21x^3} \bullet \frac{7}{16x^2}$$
$$= \frac{8}{7 \bullet 3x^3} \bullet \frac{7}{8 \bullet 2x^2}$$
$$= \frac{1}{6x^5}$$

- Factoring (Section: Factoring)

Example 23. Factor each of the following.

a. $8x^3 + 24x$

$$8x^3 + 24x = 8 \bullet x \bullet x \bullet x + 8 \bullet 3 \bullet x$$
$$= 8x(x^2 + 3)$$

b. $x^2 - 7x - 18$

We need two numbers that when added equal –7 and when multiplied equal –18.

$$x^2 - 7x - 18 = (x - 9)(x + 2)$$

c. $x^2 - 25$

$$x^2 - 25 = x^2 + 0x - 25$$

We need two numbers that when added equal 0 and when multiplied equal –25.

$$x^2 - 25 = (x - 5)(x + 5)$$

SAMPLE FINAL

I. Find an algebraic equation for each situation. (A table may be helpful.)

1. Two students want to open up a gift wrapping store in the mall. They spend $800 on wrapping paper, boxes, and ribbons; and they plan on charging $1.25 per package. Find an equation for the amount of money they will earn.

2. There are 400 bacteria growing in a culture. The culture grows at 8% a day. Find a formula for the number of bacteria n days later.

3. A farmer wants to build a rectangular pig sty off his barn. He has 150 feet of fencing. Find a formula for the area of the pig sty.

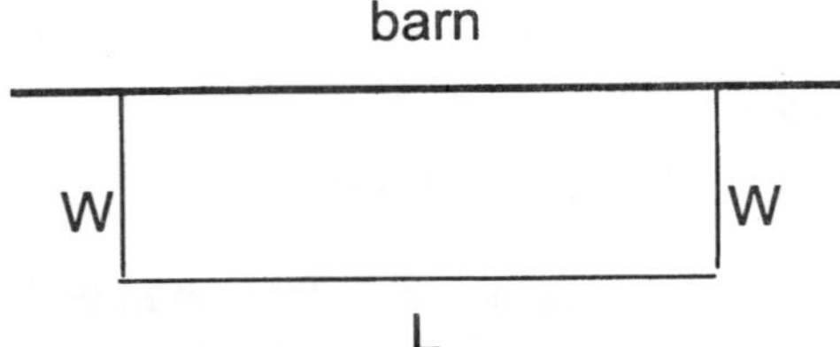

II. Solve each problem.

4. The following equation represents the average time of people commuting to work on public transportation. T is the time it takes to get to work, and D is the distance from home to work.

$$T = 2.9D - .3 \text{ (T is in minutes, and D is in miles)}$$

   a. Find out how long it will take you to get to work if you live 15 miles from your job.

   b. Find out how far away you live from work if it takes you 30 minutes to get there.

5. A math teacher, Dr. Ki, computes a student's grade for the course as follows:

   10% for homework
   65% for the average of 4 tests
   25% for the final exam

   a. Compute Sue's grade for the course if she has a 72 on the homework, 86 for the test average, and a 78 on the final exam.

   b. Suppose Salena has an 82 homework average and a 67 test average. What does Salena have to get on the final exam to get a 70 average for the course?

6. The equation

$$S = 23t + 71$$

represents the number of stores, *S*, Z-Mart has opened at the end of *t* years, where *t* is the number of years since 1985.

a. When will Z-Mart have more than 278 stores? (You must set up an inequality.)

b. When will Z-Mart have between 232 and 416 stores? (You must set up an inequality.)

7. The height of an arrow shot straight up into the air from 6 feet above the ground with an initial velocity of 95 feet per second is represented by the equation

$$h = -16t^2 + 95t + 6$$

where h is the height in feet at *t* seconds.

a. How high is the arrow at 3 seconds?

b. When will the arrow be 100 feet above the ground?

8. Use the formula to fund the monthly payment of a loan.

$$P = A\left[\frac{i}{1-(1+i)^{-n}}\right]$$

P is the monthly payment
A is the amount of the loan
n is the number of payments
i is the interest rate per month

a. Find the monthly payments of a 36-month auto loan of $3,000 at 9% annual interest. (Hint: i = .09/12)

b. I can only afford $150 a month car payment. How expensive a car can I buy if my loan is for 36 months and the annual interest rate is 15%? (Hint: i = .15/12)

III. Graphs

9. Graph the following equation by finding the x and y intercepts. Choose an appropriate scale and label the axes.

$$y = 0.2x + 41$$

10. Graph: $y = -8$

11. Graph: $x = 3$

12. The graph below shows the temperature during a winter day in Bismarck, North Dakota.

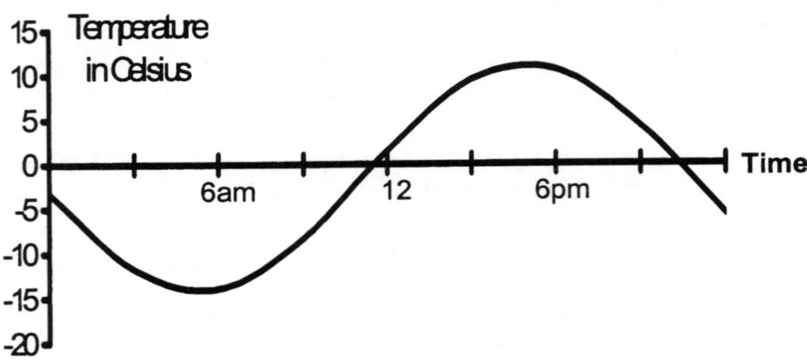

a. When was the temperature 0°?

b. What was the high temperature for the day?

c. When was the temperature rising?

13. You have the choice of two phone companies, Ringer and Buzz. Ringer charges 35¢ a phone call and 10¢ a minute while Buzz charges 15¢ a phone call and 14¢ a minute. The equation for the cost of making a phone call using Ringer is

$$C = 10m + 35 \text{ cents.}$$

The equation for the cost of making a phone call using Buzz is

$$C = 14m + 15 \text{ cents.}$$

a. Graph both equations on the same set of axes. Label your axes and choose an appropriate scale. Only graph the portion that is relevant to the problem.

b. Use the equations to find where the two lines intersect. Label this point on the graph.

c. What is the C intercept of the Ringer equation? What does it mean in terms of the problem?

d. What is the slope of the Ringer equation? What does it mean in terms of the problem?

14. AIE makes printing presses. The cost of making x presses in a month is

$$C = .5x^2 - 10x + 60$$

and the revenue from selling x printing presses a month is

$$R = -.5x^2 + 14x$$

C and R are in thousands of dollars.

a. Find the equation for profit. (P = R - C)

b. Graph the profit equation. Explain what the vertex, x intercepts, and p intercept mean in terms of making printing presses. Make sure you label the axes and use an appropriate scale.

15. The table below gives the population of the U.S. from 1800 to 1810.

YEAR	POPULATION IN MILLIONS
1800	5.3
1810	7.5

a. Calculate the percent increase.

b. Calculate the average rate of change (slope).

IV. Algebra

16. Solve the equations.

a. $3x + 7 = 4(2x - 8)$

b. $\frac{x}{3} - \frac{5}{6} = 2$

17. Factor.

a. $8x^2 + 16x$

b. $x^2 - 4x - 21$

18. Multiply: $(x + 7)^2$

19. Simplify using properties of exponents.

a. $x^5 \cdot x^2$

b. $(3x^4)^2$

c. $\frac{x^3}{x^6}$

d. $\frac{9x^{-3}}{x^2}$

20. Perform the operation.

a. $\frac{x^2}{8} \div \frac{x^3}{2}$

b. $\frac{x+5}{3} - \frac{x-2}{2}$

21. Simplify. $3\left(x^2 - 4x + 5\right) - 5\left(2x^2 + 8x - 4\right)$

22. Write in Scientific Notation.

4,300,000

23. Write in Decimal Notation.

2.4×10^{-4}

24. $3x + 5y = 10$, solve for y.

SIGNED NUMBERS

Perform the operations.

1. $-9 + 8 =$
2. $5 - 9 =$
3. $-3 - 4 =$
4. $7 - 11 =$
5. $8 - 3 =$
6. $-6 + 3 =$
7. $2 - 9 =$
8. $3 - 5 =$
9. $-7 + 2 =$
10. $12 - 15 =$
11. $-18 + 4 =$
12. $21 - 30 =$
13. $-24 + 30 =$
14. $18 - 22 =$
15. $-11 - 12 =$
16. $5 - 7 =$
17. $(-2) + (+5) + (-7) + (+3) + (-8) =$
18. $(+3) - (-4) + (-6) - (+5) + (-9) =$
19. $(+6) + (-3) - (-7) + (+2) - (+5) =$
20. $(+7) - (-2) - (+6) - (+8) + (-3) =$
21. $(-8) - (+2) + (-3) - (+5) + (+3) =$
22. $(-6) + (+3) - (-9) - (+4) + (-5) =$
23. $(-4) \bullet 5 =$
24. $-3 \bullet (-5) =$
25. $6 \bullet (-9) =$
26. $-3 \bullet (-7) =$
27. $7 \bullet (-5) =$
28. $9 \bullet (-8) =$
29. $-6 \bullet (-9) =$
30. $7 \bullet (-8) =$
31. $-8 \bullet 5 =$
32. $6 \bullet (-6) =$
33. $3 \bullet 8 =$
34. $-7 \bullet (-2) =$
35. $-4 \bullet 5 \bullet 8 \bullet -3 \bullet 0 \bullet 2 =$
36. $(-5)(+7)(+8)(-2) =$
37. $\frac{6}{-2} =$
38. $\frac{-24}{-8} =$
39. $\frac{-72}{-8} =$
40. $\frac{-27}{3} =$
41. $\frac{36}{6} =$
42. $\frac{-54}{6} =$
43. $\frac{-25}{-5} =$
44. $\frac{24}{-3} =$
45. $\frac{0}{-2} =$
46. $\frac{-48}{-8} =$
47. $\frac{6}{0} =$
48. $\frac{-35}{-7} =$
49. $(-3)^2$
50. $(-5)^2$
51. $(8)^2$
52. $(-4)^2$
53. $(7)^2$
54. $(0)^2$
55. $(-9)^2$
56. $(10)^2$
57. $6 \bullet (-4) + 12 =$
58. $2 - 3 \bullet 7 =$
59. $-4 - \frac{12}{-2} =$
60. $-6 - (+3)(-7) =$
61. $-6(7 - 3) =$
62. $5 - 8(9 - 2) =$
63. $-4(6 - 3) - 7 =$
64. $\frac{15}{-3} + 6 =$
65. $4^2 - 7^2 =$
66. $8^2 - 7(3 - 5) =$
67. $5^2 - 9(4 - 1) =$
68. $-3(-7) - 6^2 =$
69. $\frac{4(-2) - 7}{5 - 2} =$
70. $\frac{3^2 - 6}{12 - 2(8 - 2)} =$
71. $\frac{(-6)(+5) - (-2)(+15)}{6^2 - 7} =$

SIMPLIFYING ALGEBRAIC EXPRESSIONS

Simplify.

1. $9x - 5 + 3x - 4 =$
2. $3 + 6x - x + 2 =$
3. $4x - 6 - 7 - 5x =$
4. $3 + 2(4x + 5) =$
5. $5 - 3(2x - 1) =$
6. $8(4 - 5x) + 2x =$
7. $4x + 5(2 - x) =$
8. $9 - (7 - 2x) =$
9. $x + 3(5 - 2x) =$
10. $3x - 4x + 6(2 - 3x) =$
11. $2 - 7(2x + 5) - 6x =$
12. $6(5 - 2x) - (x + 5) =$
13. $4(3x - 5) - 7(2 + 2x) =$
14. $7 - 3(2x + 6) + 2(5 - 2x) =$
15. $8(4x - 1) - (3 + 2x) =$
16. $3x + 2y - 5 + y - 2x =$
17. $x + 2y - 5y + 6x - 3 =$
18. $6(3x - 2y) + 2(4y + x) =$
19. $6z - 3(5 + x) - 4x + z =$
20. $4(3y + 2z) - 5(z - 2y) =$
21. $3 - 4z + 6y - 7 + 2y - 3z =$
22. $5x - 6x + 2(3x - 7) =$
23. $8y + 3y - 6(3 + 3x) =$
24. $3z - 6(4z - 7) + z =$

SOLVING LINEAR EQUATIONS

Solve.

1. $6x + 2 = 26$
2. $5x - 15 = 2x$
3. $8 - 5x = 18$
4. $3x + 7 = 5x - 2$
5. $6 - 3x = 8 - 7x$
6. $21x + 6 = 3x - 33$
7. $9 - 3x = 7x - 1$
8. $11x + 6 = -3x + 18$
9. $-4x + 5 = 7 - 6x$
10. $3(4x + 5) + 2 = 7$
11. $-7 - (3x + 8) + 3x = 5x$
12. $6(x - 5) + 5x - 7 = 23$
13. $4(3 - 2x) + 6x = 12 - 3(4x + 1)$
14. $7x - 2(6 - 5x) + 11 = 4(x + 5) - 3x + 8$
15. $\frac{x}{4} = 5$
16. $\frac{2x}{3} = 9$
17. $\frac{-5x}{2} = -15$
18. $3 + 4x = -6$
19. $9 - 5x = 11x$
20. $7x + 9 = -4x$
21. $9x - 1 = 3 + 5x$
22. $10 - x = 21 + 5x$
23. $35x + 21 = -48 + 21x$
24. $2(4 - 5x) = 3x - 12$
25. $5 - 7(2x + 4) = 21 + 4x$
26. $3x - 5(2x + 7) = 11 + x$
27. $32x + 11(5 - 12x) = 21$
28. $3(8x - 2x) + 21 - x = 7x$
29. $3 - 5(3x - 11) = 3x + 7$
30. $2(x - 3) - 5(11 - 2x) + 3 = 3x + 12$

INEQUALITIES

Solve and graph the solution on the number line.

1. $3x + 5 > -7$
2. $7 - 5x < 24$
3. $12x + 45 > -23$
4. $23 - 4x \leq -24$
5. $12 \geq 21 - 2x$
6. $21 + 7x \geq -45$
7. $2(3x - 5) > -21$
8. $5x - 3(2x + 7) < -21$
9. $4x + 2(4x - 21) \geq 32$
10. $2x + 14 \geq 4x - 21$
11. $4x - 23 > 31 - 5x$
12. $3(4 - 3x) < 4x + 8$
13. $4 - 3(2x + 5) > 4x + 9$
14. $12 + 7x \geq 15 - 6(3 - 2x)$
15. $5x - 4(3x + 9) \leq -5$
16. $-5 \leq 3x + 9 < 8$
17. $21 \leq 4x + 12 < 45$
18. $-12 < 4x + 12 \leq -1$
19. $-24 < 5x + 15 < 24$
20. $-2 < 24 + 6x < 4$
21. $-5 \leq 5 + 4x < 15$
22. $12 \geq 5x + 24 \geq -1$
23. $34 > 4 + 7x \geq 21$
24. $-3 < 5 + 2x < 6$

GRAPHING LINES BY PLOTTING POINTS

Graph the line by finding two points. Find a third point to check.

1. $y = 2x + 5$
2. $y = -5x + 12$
3. $y = .25x - 6$
4. $y = 4.2x - 11$
5. $y = -.6x - 21$
6. $y = .01x + 46$
7. $y = 23x + 45$
8. $y = 6x - 21$
9. $y = -4x - 12$
10. $y = \frac{2}{3}x - 5$
11. $y = \frac{-4}{5}x - 9$
12. $y = \frac{7}{2}x + 6$
13. $y = \frac{-4}{7}x - 9$
14. $y = \frac{-5}{8}x - 4$
15. $y = \frac{2}{3}x + 5$
16. $3x + 5y = 14$
17. $6x - 5y = -6$
18. $7y + 4x = -23$
19. $6y - 4x = 21$
20. $.5x + 7y = -45$
21. $.6y - 5x = 42$
22. $4x - 7x = 32$
23. $6x + 2y = 23$
24. $12y - 11x = 45$

GRAPHING LINES BY FINDING THE INTERCEPTS

Graph the lines by finding the x and y intercepts.

1. $y = 2x + 6$
2. $y = -4x + 12$
3. $y = .2x - 8$
4. $y = 3.2x - 10$
5. $y = -16x - 20$
6. $y = .01x + 32$
7. $y = 23x - 45$
8. $y = 6x - 28$
9. $y = -4x + 12$
10. $y = \frac{1}{3}x - 5$
11. $y = \frac{-4}{5}x + 9$
12. $y = \frac{-5}{2}x + 6$
13. $y = \frac{-3}{7}x + 9$
14. $y = \frac{-3}{8}x + 4$
15. $y = \frac{2}{3}x + 27$
16. $3x + 7y = 14$
17. $12x - 5y = -6$
18. $7y - 4x = -28$
19. $6y - 4x = 24$
20. $.5x - 6y = -45$
21. $.06y - 5x = 42$
22. $4x - 7x = -32$
23. $6x + 2y = 84$
24. $12y - 15x = 45$

Graph the horizontal or vertical line.

25. $y = -4$
26. $x = 6$
27. $y = 5$
28. $y = 15$
29. $y = -4$
30. $x = -4$
31. $x = 12$
32. $y = 1$
33. $y = 0$

SLOPE

Find the slope of the line that contains the two points.

1. (4, 8) and (–7, 9)
2. (5, 9) and (6, –1)
3. (0, –1) and (–2, –6)
4. (–3, 6) and (–3, 9)
5. (4, 7) and (9, 12)
6. (–2, 8) and (5, 8)
7. (4.25, 6) and (–3, 1.22)
8. (1, 5) and (–4, 3.1)
9. (2.73, –.05) and (23, 19)
10. (4, 8) and (–3, 8)
11. (–23, 16) and (13, 39)
12. (–3, – 6) and (3, 9)

Use the slope intercept equation to find the slope of the line and the y intercept.

13. $y = 3.2x - 10$
14. $y = -16x - 20$
15. $y = .01x + 32$
16. $y = 23x - 45$
17. $y = 6x - 28$
18. $y = -4x + 12$
19. $y = \frac{1}{3}x - 5$
20. $y = \frac{-4}{5}x + 9$
21. $y = \frac{-5}{2}x + 6$

PROPERTIES OF EXPONENTS

Simplify. Write with positive exponents only.

1. $x^3 \bullet x^4 =$
2. $x^{-3} \bullet x^2 =$
3. $3x \bullet x^2 =$
4. $x^3 \bullet x^{-4} =$
5. $7x^5 \bullet x^3 =$
6. $x \bullet 5x =$
7. $(3x^2)^4 =$
8. $(5x^3)^2 =$
9. $(-3x^5)^4 =$
10. $(-4x^5)^2 =$
11. $(6x^3)^5 =$
12. $(-5x^{-3})^2 =$
13. $4x^{-3} =$
14. $2x^{-1} =$
15. $21x^{-7} =$
16. $\frac{2}{3x^{-4}} =$
17. $\frac{2x^{-4}}{5} =$
18. $\frac{1}{7x^{-5}} =$
19. $\frac{3x^4}{12x^2} =$
20. $\frac{30x^5}{6x^3} =$
21. $\frac{24x^2}{8x^2} =$
22. $\frac{7x^2}{56x^6} =$
23. $\frac{36x^8}{72x^5} =$
24. $\frac{21x}{7x^4} =$
25. $\frac{18x^{-4}}{12x^{-2}} =$
26. $\frac{9x^{-3}}{36x^{-5}} =$
27. $\frac{6x^{-2}}{42x^{-3}} =$
28. $(-4x^4)^{-2} =$
29. $(-2x^{-5})^{-3} =$
30. $(3x^2)^{-2} =$
31. $(7x^{-3})^{-1} =$
32. $(3x^{-7})^{-3} =$
33. $(6x^2)^{-3} =$
34. $\left(\frac{2}{x^3}\right)^4 =$
35. $\left(\frac{3x^2}{5}\right)^3 =$
36. $\left(\frac{6}{5x^2}\right)^{-4} =$
37. $\left(\frac{7x^{-3}}{3}\right)^2 =$
38. $\left(\frac{6x^{-1}}{5}\right)^{-3} =$
39. $\left(\frac{5x^{-2}}{4}\right)^{-2} =$
40. $(3x^9)^0 =$
41. $4y^3 \bullet 3x^4 \bullet 2x^3 \bullet 5y =$
42. $(3xy^2)(2x^3y^2) =$
43. $(3x^2y^4)^3 =$
44. $(5x^3y^2)^4 =$
45. $2x^2(4xy^2)^4 =$
46. $\frac{21x^3y^2}{7xy^3} =$
47. $\left(\frac{3x^{-5}y^2}{2x^{-3}y^4}\right)^3 =$
48. $\left(\frac{5x^2y^{-3}}{3x^{-3}y^3}\right)^{-2} =$

INTRODUCTION TO ALGEBRAIC FRACTIONS

Reduce.

1. $\frac{6x^3}{12x^2} =$

2. $\frac{-18x^4}{6x^2} =$

3. $\frac{24x^3}{4x^3} =$

4. $\frac{8x^3}{56x^5} =$

5. $\frac{9x^9}{72x^4} =$

6. $\frac{-21x}{3x^3} =$

7. $\frac{4yx^3}{12x^5y^2} =$

8. $\frac{32x^3y^2}{16x^4y} =$

9. $\frac{5x^3y^4}{25x^2y} =$

Multiply or divide as indicated and reduce to lowest terms.

10. $\frac{1}{6} \bullet \frac{2}{5} =$

11. $\frac{2}{3} \div \frac{8}{9} =$

12. $\frac{6}{15} \bullet \frac{25}{8} =$

13. $\frac{2x}{5} \div \frac{15x}{4} =$

14. $\frac{6}{5x} \bullet \frac{15}{2x^2} =$

15 $\frac{18}{7x} \bullet \frac{21x^3}{6} =$

16. $\frac{12}{x^3} \bullet \frac{4}{x} =$

17. $\frac{81}{2x^3} \div \frac{27}{4x} =$

18. $\frac{6x^2}{25} \div \frac{4x^3}{15} =$

19. $\frac{30}{21x^4} \div \frac{15}{7x^2} =$

20. $\frac{16}{3x^2} \bullet \frac{9x}{8} =$

21. $\frac{32x}{4} \bullet \frac{5x^2}{15} =$

22. $\frac{28x^3}{4} \bullet \frac{1}{7x} =$

23. $\frac{45}{5x^2} \div \frac{9}{2x^2} =$

24. $\frac{16x^3}{32} \bullet \frac{8}{2x^5} =$

25. $\frac{9}{2x} \bullet \frac{10x^3}{5} =$

26. $\frac{5}{27x^4} \bullet \frac{18x^2}{15} =$

27. $\frac{4x^3}{3x} \div \frac{x}{14} =$

28. $\frac{18}{x^3} \div \frac{6}{5x^2} =$

29. $\frac{x}{3} \div \frac{x}{15} =$

30. $\frac{4x}{6x^3} \bullet \frac{12x}{15} =$

31. $\frac{3x}{2y^2} \bullet \frac{8y}{x} =$

32. $\frac{7x}{4y} \div \frac{21x^2}{16y^3} =$

33. $\frac{y^3}{4x^2} \bullet \frac{8x}{y} =$

34. $\frac{27x^3}{15y^2} \div \frac{3y}{x^2} =$

35. $\frac{6x^4}{8y^2} \bullet \frac{16x^2}{4y} =$

36. $\frac{30y^2}{40x} \div \frac{9y^3}{8x^2} =$

ADDING AND SUBTRACTING ALGEBRAIC FRACTIONS

Combine into a single fraction and reduce to lowest terms.

1. $\frac{4}{5}+\frac{7}{5}=$
2. $\frac{4}{9}-\frac{1}{9}=$
3. $\frac{6}{11}+\frac{5}{11}=$
4. $\frac{3}{x}-\frac{4}{x}=$
5. $\frac{5}{2x}+\frac{1}{2x}=$
6. $\frac{8}{3x^2}-\frac{4}{3x^2}=$
7. $\frac{5}{9}-\frac{1}{6}=$
8. $\frac{3}{6}+\frac{5}{8}=$
9. $\frac{5}{9}-\frac{5}{12}=$
10. $\frac{x}{4}-\frac{x}{6}=$
11. $\frac{3x}{2}+\frac{5x}{8}=$
12. $\frac{x}{18}-\frac{5x}{12}=$
13. $\frac{3}{x}+\frac{5}{x^2}=$
14. $\frac{5}{4x}+\frac{1}{2x}=$
15. $\frac{5}{8x}-\frac{3x}{10}=$
16. $\frac{7}{12y^3}+\frac{2}{20y}=$
17. $\frac{3}{24m^3}-\frac{5}{16m}=$
18. $\frac{y^2}{14}-\frac{y}{21}=$
19. $\frac{5w}{27}+\frac{4w}{36}=$
20. $\frac{5}{12x^2}+\frac{9}{20x}=$
21. $\frac{15}{16z^2}+\frac{2}{40z^3}=$
22. $\frac{2}{x^2}+3=$
23. $7-\frac{4}{w^3}=$
24. $\frac{7x}{15}-\frac{1}{3x^2}=$
25. $\frac{x-5}{6}-\frac{7}{9}=$
26. $\frac{5}{2x}+\frac{6+x}{6x}=$
27. $\frac{9}{16y}+\frac{7y-5}{20}=$
28. $\frac{11+w}{9w}-\frac{4}{w^3}=$
29. $\frac{1}{4}-\frac{7+y}{10y}=$
30. $\frac{x+4}{30x}-\frac{7-x}{24}=$

SOLVING EQUATIONS WITH FRACTIONS

Solve each equation.

1. $\frac{2}{3}+\frac{5}{6}=\frac{x}{9}$

2. $\frac{x}{6}-\frac{x}{8}=\frac{1}{12}$

3. $\frac{x}{4}+\frac{x}{2}=6$

4. $\frac{2}{3x}+\frac{1}{x}=10$

5. $\frac{1}{2x}+\frac{1}{x}=-12$

6. $\frac{x}{4}-\frac{x}{6}=\frac{1}{8}$

7. $\frac{3}{5}-\frac{2}{3}=\frac{x}{9}$

8. $\frac{2}{3}+\frac{1}{6}=\frac{1}{x}$

9. $\frac{1}{x}=\frac{1}{3}-\frac{5}{6}$

10. $\frac{1}{8}+\frac{1}{12}=\frac{1}{x}$

11. $\frac{4}{7}-\frac{7}{x}=0$

12. $\frac{3}{5}+\frac{5}{3}=\frac{x}{9}$

13. $\frac{5}{x}=\frac{6}{x}-\frac{1}{3}$

14. $\frac{5}{3x}+\frac{2}{x}=1$

15. $\frac{5}{2x}+\frac{7}{6}=5$

16. $\frac{4}{15x}-\frac{7}{20}=\frac{23}{5x}$

17. $\frac{5x}{24}-\frac{3}{8}=\frac{x}{3}$

18. $\frac{7}{2x}+\frac{1}{5x}=\frac{4}{5}$

19. $\frac{x+1}{5}-\frac{x-2}{4}=1$

20. $\frac{x+1}{3}-\frac{x-1}{2}=3$

21. $\frac{x+3}{18}+\frac{x-2}{6}=\frac{5}{3}$

22. $2-\frac{3}{5x}=\frac{3}{2}$

23. $\frac{7}{6}-3x=\frac{x}{10}$

24. $\frac{4x+5}{12}-\frac{2x-1}{24}=\frac{5}{6}$

INTRODUCTION TO QUADRATICS

Simplify.

1. $3x^2 + 5x - 7 - x^2 + 3x - 6$
2. $-4x^2 + 7x + 8 + 3x^2 - 7x + 1$
3. $-2x^2 + 6 - 5x^2 - 4x + 5$
4. $x^2 - 11x + 21 - 3x^2 - 9x + 16$
5. $2(x^2 - 9x + 3) + 5(3x^2 + x - 8)$
6. $5(2x^2 + 5x - 6) + 4(x^2 - 7x - 3)$
7. $4(9x^2 + 2x + 1) - 7(5x^2 + 3)$
8. $6(2x^2 + 3x - 5) - 3(7x^2 - 6x + 1)$
9. $4(3x^2 + 5x - 1) - (6x^2 - 3x + 28)$
10. $(5x^2 + x - 12) - (2x^2 + 11x - 12)$

Multiply.

11. $(x + 3)(x + 1)$
12. $(x + 6)(x + 2)$
13. $(x + 4)(x + 8)$
14. $(x + 7)(x + 9)$
15. $(2x + 5)(x + 7)$
16. $(x + 5)(3x + 4)$
17. $(x - 4)(x - 2)$
18. $(x - 6)(x - 3)$
19. $(5x - 1)(x - 7)$
20. $(5x - 7)(3x - 5)$
21. $(x + 2)(x - 7)$
22. $(x + 9)(x - 9)$
23. $(2x + 1)(2x - 1)$
24. $(6x + 3)(7x - 8)$
25. $(x + 4)^2$
26. $(x + 3)^2$
27. $(x - 2)^2$
28. $(5x - 8)^2$
29. $(3x + 9)^2$
30. $(x - 11)^2$

THE QUADRATIC FORMULA

Solve using the quadratic formula.

1. $-2x^2 - 4x + 30 = 0$
2. $3x^2 - 4x = 0$
3. $x^2 - 9x + 20 = 0$
4. $x^2 - 2x - 14 = 0$
5. $-x^2 + 5x - 3 = 0$
6. $-4x^2 - 11x - 6 = 0$
7. $6x^2 - 39 = 0$
8. $-3x^2 + 6x + 9 = 0$
9. $x^2 + 6x - 17 = -26$
10. $x^2 - 8x - 4 = -20$
11. $12x^2 + 7x - 12 = 0$
12. $30x^2 - 11x - 30 = 0$
13. $18x^2 - 33x + 130 = -136$
14. $-9x^2 - 6x - 3 = 1$

GRAPHING QUADRATICS

Graph each quadratic by finding the vertex, x intercepts, and y intercept.

1. $y = x^2 - 6x + 8$
2. $y = -x^2 + x + 2$
3. $y = -x^2 + 2x + 3$
4. $y = x^2 + 5x + 4$
5. $y = x^2 + 7x + 10$
6. $y = -x^2 + 4x + 3$
7. $y = -x^2 + 4x$
8. $y = x^2 + 2x - 8$

FACTORING

Factor.

1. $3x + 6$
2. $18x - 12$
3. $30x - 15$
4. $42x - 7$
5. $24x^2 - 18x$
6. $25x^4 - 15x^2$
7. $-15x^3 + 9x$
8. $32x - 18x^2$
9. $40x^2 - 16x$
10. $-21x^4 + 49x^2$
11. $6x^5 - 40x^3$
12. $-4x^2 + x$
13. $x^2 + 7x + 6$
14. $x^2 + 6x + 8$
15. $x^2 + 9x + 20$
16. $x^2 + 13x + 30$
17. $x^2 - 8x + 15$
18. $x^2 - 10x + 9$
19. $x^2 - 6x + 9$
20. $x^2 - 3x - 18$
21. $x^2 - x - 30$
22. $x^2 - 3x - 4$
23. $x^2 - 4x - 77$
24. $x^2 - 13x + 30$
25. $x^2 - 9x + 14$
26. $x^2 - 9x + 20$
27. $x^2 - x - 56$
28. $2x^2 + 20x + 32$
29. $3x^2 + 30x + 63$
30. $2x^3 + 14x^2 + 12x$
31. $x^2 - 49$
32. $x^2 - 36$
33. $x^2 - 4$
34. $x^2 - 1$
35. $x^2 - 100$
36. $x^2 - 121$
37. $3x^2 - 75$
38. $5x^2 - 45$
39. $x^3 - 16x$

ANSWERS TO HOMEWORK AND REVIEW TESTS

Signed Numbers page 13

1. $-20	2. $30	3. $-290	4. $10	5. $-58	6. 3	7. 11	10. a. 2
b. -13	c. –9	d. 15	e. –7	f. 7	g. –29	h. -5	i. –32
j. 11	k. –14	l. -9	m. –8	n. -15	o. 3	11.a. 12	b. -17
13. a. –4.4	b. 0.71	c. 0.59	d. -7/12	e. 18.2	f. -5/24	14. a. –9	b. 34
c. –3	d. The profit increased in b but decreased in c.				e. What is the difference betwe the profit in 1993 and 1991?		
f. -1.8	15. Add the 5 numbers then ÷ by 5.				16. 7.667	17. -1.5	
18. –579.4 ft	21. zero	22.a. –42	b. 30	c. –15	d. 63	e. –6	f. -5
g. 0	h.undefined	i. indeterminent		j. 5	k. –40	l. 60	m. –9
n. 0	23.a 26.37	b. 49.32	c.–2.953	d. 1.769	24.See pg 4	25. a.-10	b. -10
c. 1	d. 29	e. –31	f. -10	g. –4	h. -1	i. .5	

Introduction to Variables page 25

1.

Width	Length	Area	Perimeter
9 in.	12 in.	108 in^2	42 in.
8 in.	10 in.	80 $in.^2$	36. in.
11 in.	19 in.	209 $in.^2$	60 in.

2. a. 75.36 sq. in., 7 inch pizza is cheaper. It costs 4.5 cents per sq. inch.

3. a. 0°C c. 37°C

4.a

Table	Calculation	Wages
15	7.50(15) + 80	$192.50
20	7.50(20) + 80	$230.00
t	7.50t + 80	W

b. W = 7.50t + 80
c. 350
d. 18 tables
e. W = 8.50t + 80
f. W = 7.00t + 95

5.a

Hours	Calculation	Income
40	8(40) – 160	160
60	8(60) – 160	320
80t	8(80) – 160	480
h	8h – 160	I

b. I = 8h - 160
c. 55 hours
d. I = 9h - 200

6.a

Calls	Calculation	Phone Bill
10	.13(10) + 7.46	8.76
15	.13(15) + 7.46	9.41
20	.13(20) + 7.46	10.06
C	.13C + 7.46	B_r

b. B_r = .13C + 7.46
c. B_B = .17C + 6.17
e. about 32

7. a

Base	Height	Area
5	10 - 5	$(1/2)(5)(5) = 12.5$
8	10 – 8	$(1/2)(8)(2) = 12.5$
b	10 - b	$(1/2)(10-b)(b)$

b. $A = (1/2)b(10-b)$

c. 5

Simplifying Algebraic Expressions page 35

4. a. 5x b. 17x – 13 c. $\frac{7}{6}x - \frac{3}{5}$
   d. 6x + 15 e. -12x + 38 f. 2x + 1
   g. 19x + 5 h. -x – 16 i. -7x + 4

5. a. Multiplied the coefficients
   b. Combined unlike terms
   c. Did not multiply the 6 and the –5
   d. -3 * -4 = 12
   e. A negative times a negative is a positive
   f. 12x – 3x = 9x

Solving Equations – Part I page 43

1. a. Subtract 7 from both sides.
   Combine like terms.
   Divide both sides by 6.
   Simplify.
   b. Add 4 to both sides.
   Combine like terms.
   Multiply both sides by 5.
   Simplify.
2. a. 4 + 5, should be 4 – 5.
   b. Multiply both sides by $\frac{3}{2}$, not $\frac{2}{3}$.
3. a. yes b. yes c. no
5. a. x = 3 b. $x = \frac{-5}{2}$ c. x = -40
   d. $x = \frac{63}{2}$ or 31.5 e. x = 2 f. x = 36
   g. x = 6 h. x = -49 i. x = -5
6. The printing press will be worth 10,000 in 24 years.

Solving Equations – Part II page 51

1. a. Distributive Property
   Combine like terms
   Subtract 3X from both sides
   Combine like terms
   Subtract 20 from both sides
   Combine like terms
   Divide both sides by –6
   Simplify
   b. Distributive Property
   Combine like terms
   Subtract 7X from both sides
   Combine like terms
   Conclusion
2. a. 2 * – 8 = -16 b. 7 – 2 should be 7 + 2
3. a. x = 5 b. x = 4 c. no solution
   d. x = 7/3 e. The solution is any number f. x = -3.8

Applications of Linear Equations (Part I) page 61

1. b. $C = .16M + 25$ c. $C = 29.96$ d. $M = 37.5$ e. $M = 250$
2. b. $C = .15m + .80$ c. $C = 5.60$ d. $M = 7$ e. $M = 11.33$
3. b. $C_R = .08M + .5$ $C_B = .10M + .25$ c. $M = 12.5$
4. b. $C_A = .075S + 5000$ $C_B = .05S + 9000$ $S = 160{,}000$
5. b. $W = .15S – 150$ c. $W = 1350$ d. $S = 2800$ e. $S = 23{,}480$
6. b. $W = 7h – 344$ c. $h = 80$ d. $h = 80.57$
7. b. $C = .1M - .28$ c. $M = 23$ d. $M = 40.9$

Applications of Linear Equations Part II (Literal Equations) page 71

1. a. t = 11.47, 1994 b. t = 12.3, 1994 or 1995 c. $t = \dfrac{s-146}{118}$

2. $T = \dfrac{W + 54.6}{1.6}$ 3. a. r = 5% b. $r = \dfrac{FV - P}{Pt}$

4. a. $L = \dfrac{P - 2W}{2}$ b. $r = \dfrac{D}{t}$ c. $Y = \frac{3}{4}x – 3$

d. $Y = \dfrac{9-6x}{3}$ or $Y = 3 – 2x$

5. a. 22.2 b. 51.8 c. 21.2 d. 145.4

e. $F = \dfrac{9C}{5} + 32$ or $\dfrac{9}{5}\left(C + \dfrac{160}{9}\right)$

Applications of Linear Equations Part III (Percentages) page 81

1. a. 53% b. 75 girls

2. a.

Susan	Joe	Mary	Pat
3.35	3.50	4.00	3.75
3.75	3.92	4.48	4.20

b. N = 1.12 OLD

3. 15% 4. 20% 5.

OLD	Discount	Sales
45	14.4	30.60
X	.32X	.68X
55	17.6	37.40

6. a. 82.75 b. 88.4 c. 92.6
7. a. 90 b. 159

Review for Test I page 86

1. b. $C = 20d + 350$ c. $d = 90$
2. b. $C = 1.8M – 4.05$ c. $M = 17.53$
3. a. 81.8 b. 64
4. a. 1.40 b. 41.41
5. b. N = 1.12 C c. 4.69
6. b. SP = .8 OP c. OP = 101.25
7. a. –3.2 b. 4.6
8. -4X + 14
9. Yes
10. a. –3 b. 13 11. 250 12. $W = \dfrac{P - 2L}{2}$

Inequalities page 97

1. a. Subtract 6 from both sides
Subtract x from both sides
Divide both sides by –4 and change the direction of the inequality
   b. Subtract 6 from all three parts
Divide all three parts by –2 and change the directions of the inequalities
2. a. Didn't change the direction of the inequality
   b. Didn't subtract 9 from 12
3. a. yes b. yes c. no
5. a. $x< -9$ b. $x< 20$ c. $x\leq 8$
   d. $x\leq -3$ e. $x< 6.33$ f. $x\leq 7.75$
   g. $-6<x\leq 4$ h. $5.5\geq x\geq -3$ i. $2\leq x< 6.5$
   j. $-36\leq x\leq 30$ k. $21>x>-24$

Applications of Inequalities page105

1. a. $F > 46.4$ b. $28.4 < F < 53.6$
2. $C < 250{,}000$
3. a. 247.79 b. $t > 17.09$, after 1997
   c. $18.61 < t < 31.60$, $1999 \leq \text{Year} \leq 2011$
4. b. $h > 47.05$, $23.5 \leq h \leq 82.35$
5. b. $C_W = .50M + 28$, $C_E = .75M + 20$ c. $M < 32$
6. b. $W_A = .12(S - 50{,}000) + 8000$, $W_B = .05S + 15000$ c. $S > 185{,}714$
7. $C_W = .11(M\text{-}4) + .15$, $C_D = .14(M\text{-}5) + .10$, $M < 10.3$

Scatter Plots page117

2. Averages: 9.3, 17.3, 19.6, 11, 5, 7, 12.6, 15.6, 13.6, 5
3. b. (0, 1.50) c. (2, 42) d. (.5, 20) (5.5, 20) e. (3, 47) f. (6.5, 0)
   g. $2 < t < 4$ h. 1.5 and 4.5 secs. i. (4.5, 35) j. 35 k. always
   l. 40.5 m. 5 n. 38 o. between 0 and 1 sec.

Interpreting Graphs page 127

1. a. -14°, 11° c. 8:30,9:30 e. 3:00 g. 3 AM to 3 PM
2. a. 8500 c. 9000 e. Jan. to April and July to Dec.
3. a. 5 min 30 sec b. WRONG # c. Buzz d. Min > 5.5

Graphing Lines by Plotting Points page 139

1.

a. (Hours,Cost) (20,25) (50,40) (100,65)
b. $C = .50H + 15$

c.

80
60
40
20
0
0 20 40 60 80 100

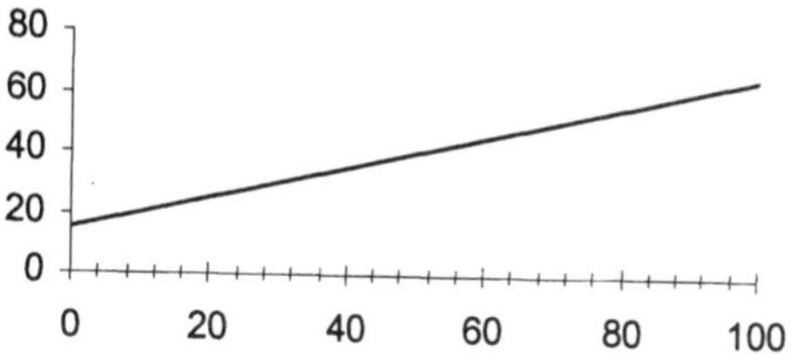

2. a. (Hours,Cost)
   b. C = .35M + 15
3. Switched the x and y coordinates when graphing
4. Yes, No, Yes, Yes
5. a.

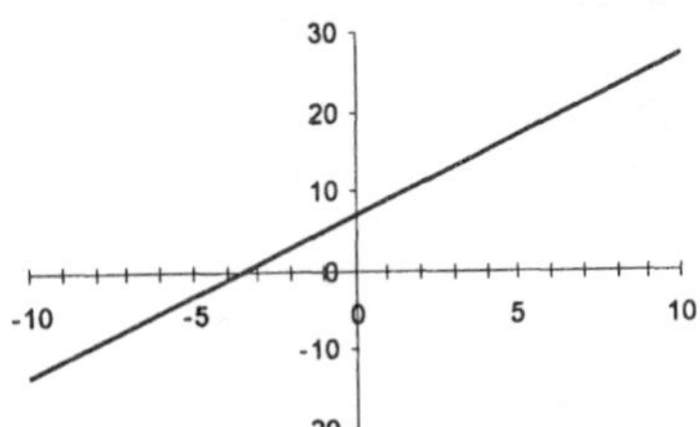

b. 

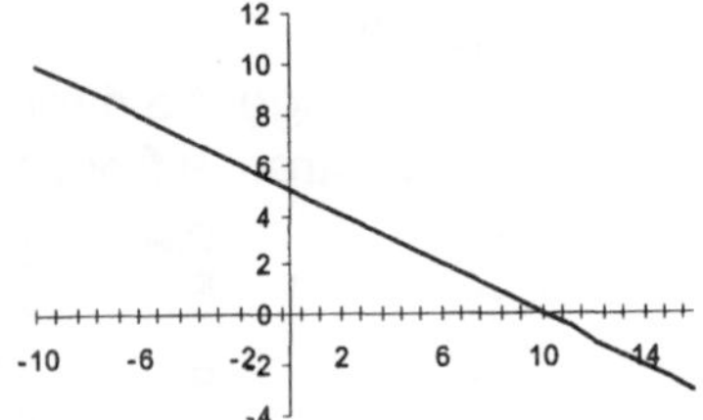

c.

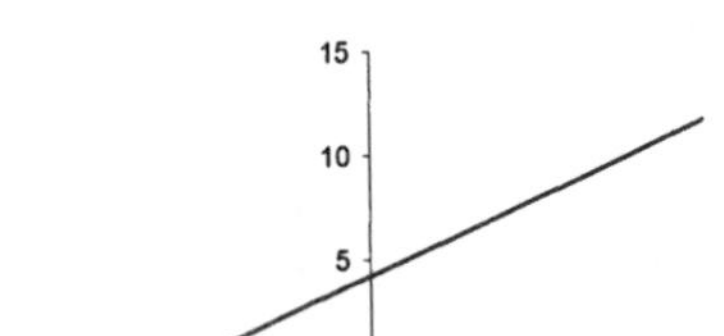

d.

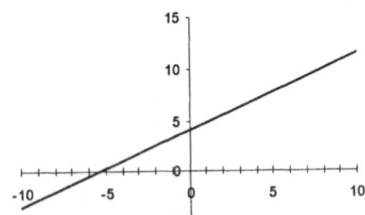

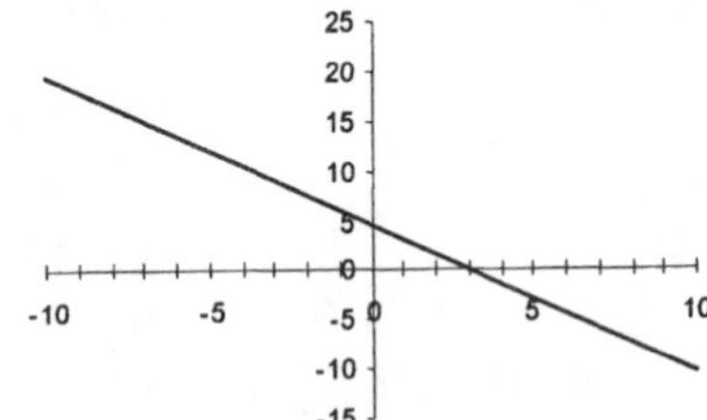

Graphing Lines by finding the Intercepts page 151

1. a. (73,0) b. (0,-1095)
   c.

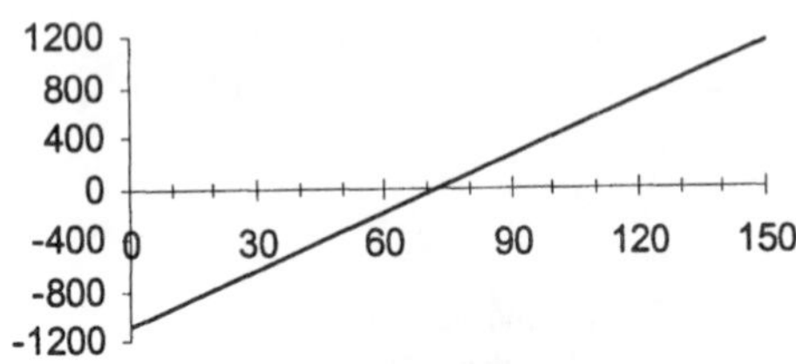

2. Did not graph the intercepts
4.
   a. (-18.33,0) (0,11) b. (9.09,0) (0,.0806)

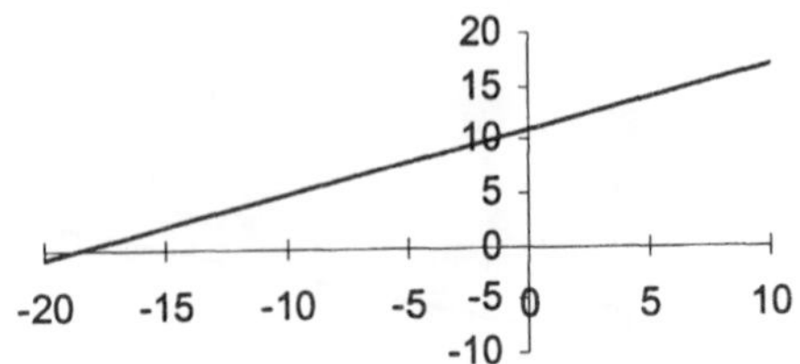

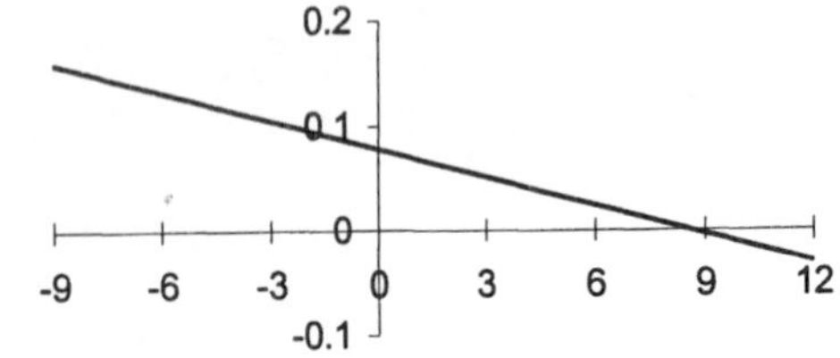

c. (4,0) (0,-600)

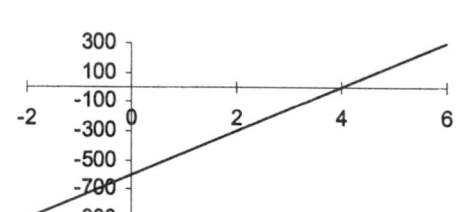

d. (-6.66,0) (0,-5)

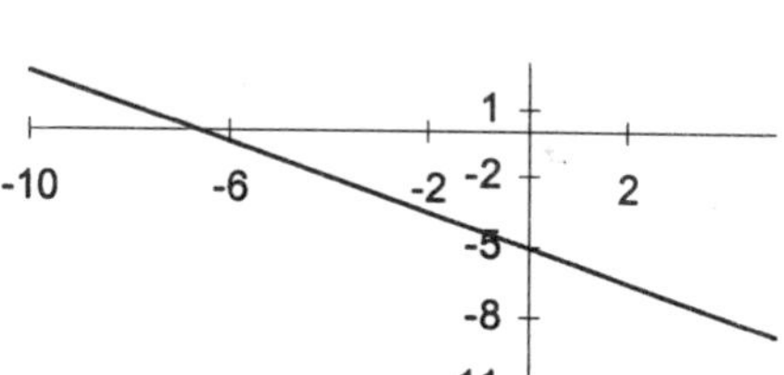

6 a.

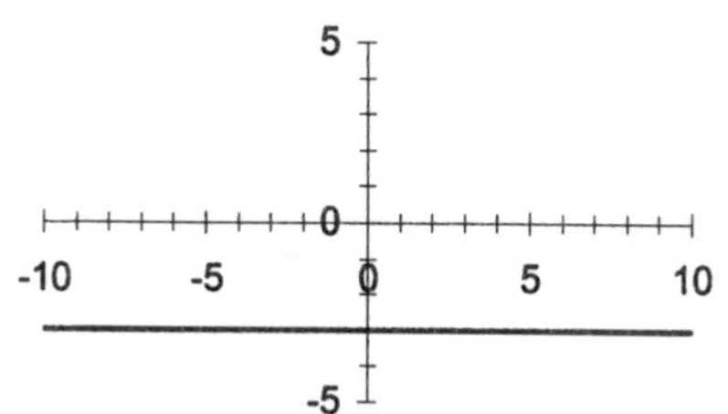

b.

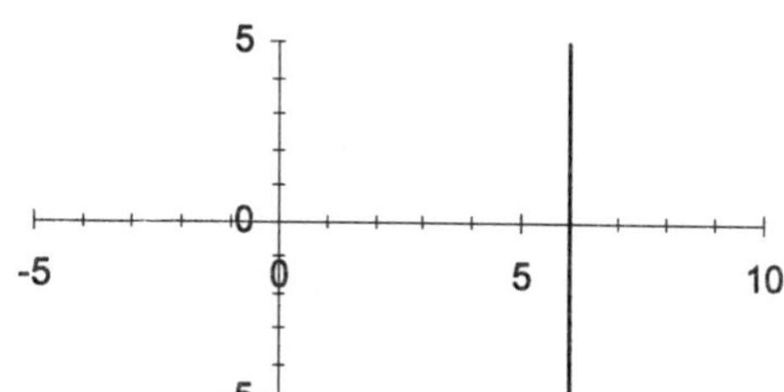

7.

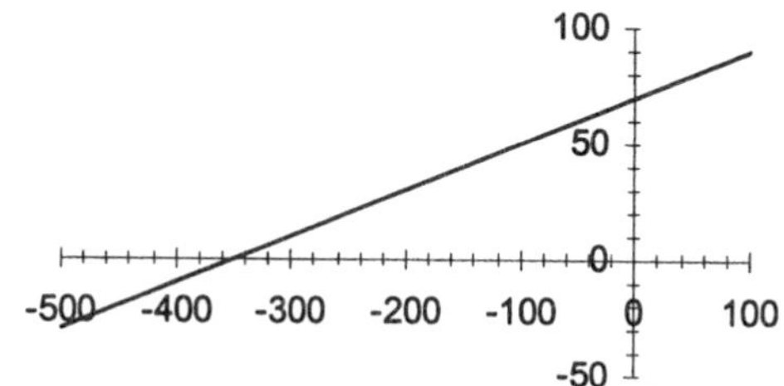

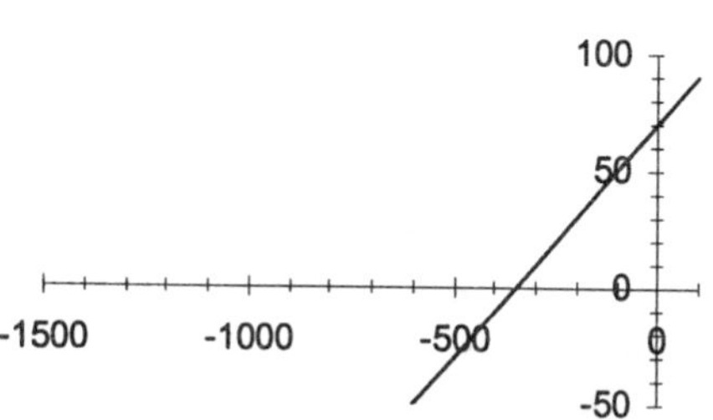

Introduction to Slope page 163

1. Acme = $\frac{1.89}{12}$, F.S. = $\frac{2.68}{18}$
3. b. 1185.75 emp. per yr. c. 717 emp. per yr. d. 18,639 (answer not unique)
   e. 35.6%
4. b. –14.58 papers per yr. c. –20.5 papers per yr. d. –2.5%
5. a. 1940 to 1950 b. -.15 f. 27.5 (answer not unique)
6. b. Dr. bills: $\frac{22.5-11}{5}$ = 2.3 billion per yr., Medicare: $\frac{11-4.5}{5}$ = 1.3 billion per yr.

Slope page 175

1. a. $M=\frac{5}{2}$ b. $M=\frac{-3}{7}$ c. $M=0$
2. a. should be $\frac{1-3}{-6-(-2)}$ b. they did x over y
3. a. M = -.5 b. M = 0 c. M = .44
   d. undefined e. M = .8
4. a. M = 7, (0,5) b. M = -2/3, (0,-2)

Applications of Graphs page 191

1. a. $h = 1.7d + 4$

   b.

   100
   50
   0
   0 20 40 60

   c. 27.8
   d. 106
   e. 208
   f. 30
   g. 33

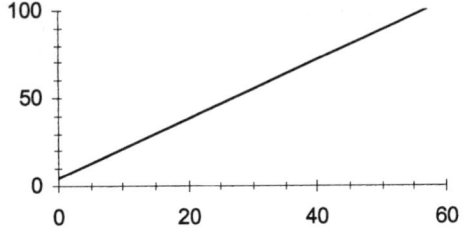

2.
   a. Golden: $C = 35$, Classic: $C = .80M + 15$

   b.

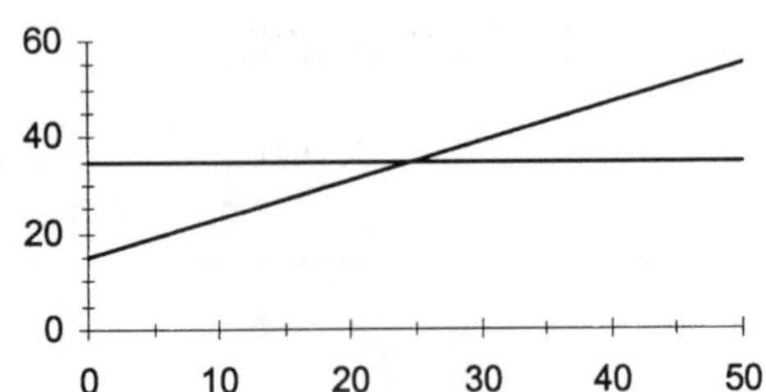

   c. $M = 25$, $C = 35$
   d. $0 \leq M < 25$
   e. $M > 25$
   f. Cost if you don't drive anywhere.
   g. Slope is .80 for Classic and 0 for Golden

3.
   a. $C_R = .18M + .50$
      $C_B = .27M + .25$
   c. $M = 27$, $C = 5.36$
   d. $0 \leq M < 2.7$
   e. $M > 2.7$
   f. initial charge for the phone call
   g. slope for ringer is .18 and the slope for Buzz is .27

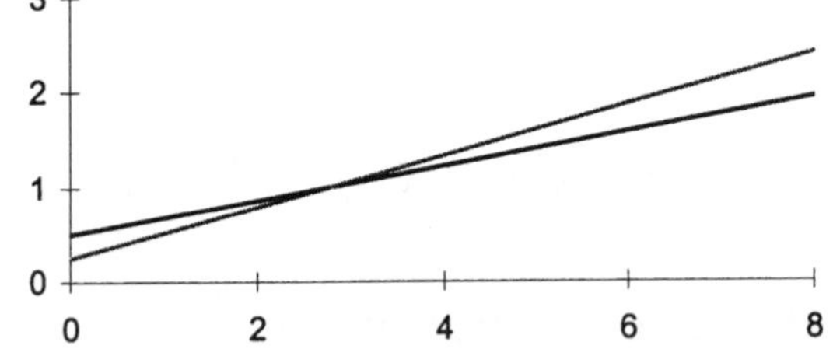

4.
   a. $W_M = .08\ S + 5000$
      $W_R = .04\ S + 10000$
   c. $S = 125{,}000$, $W = 15000$
   d. $S > 125{,}000$
   e. $0 \leq S < 125000$
   f. base pay without any sales
   g. slope for MATHCO is .08 and the slope for CALCO is .04

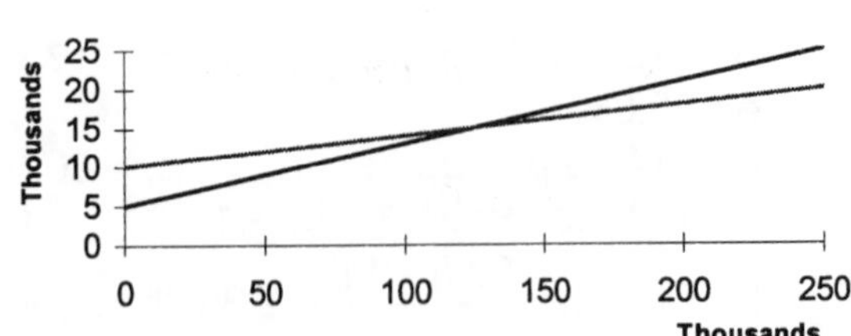

5.

a. C = .20(M-3) + .50
b. M < 3
c. C = .50

d.

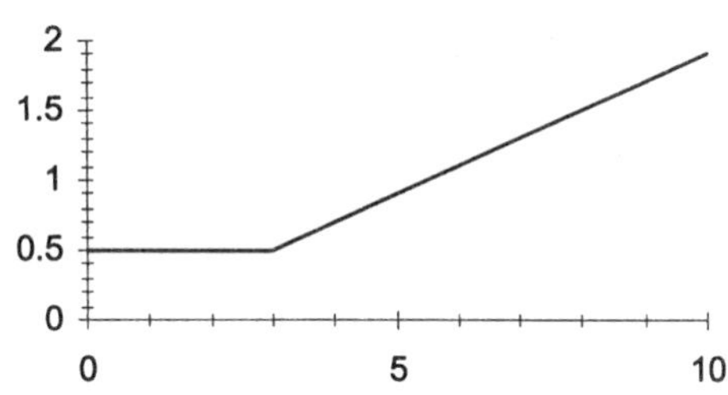

6. a. W = .10(S-50000) + 10000 b. S < 50000 c. C = .50, W = 10,000

Review for Test II page 201

1. b. 20 c. 65 d. 45 min. to 62 min.

2.

a.

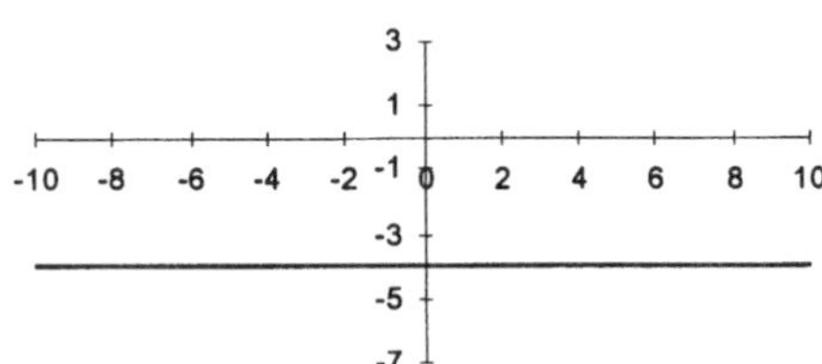

b.

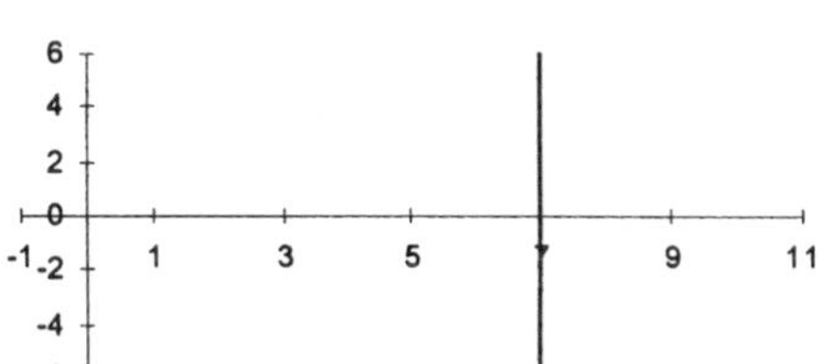

3.

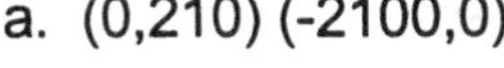

a. (0,210) (-2100,0)

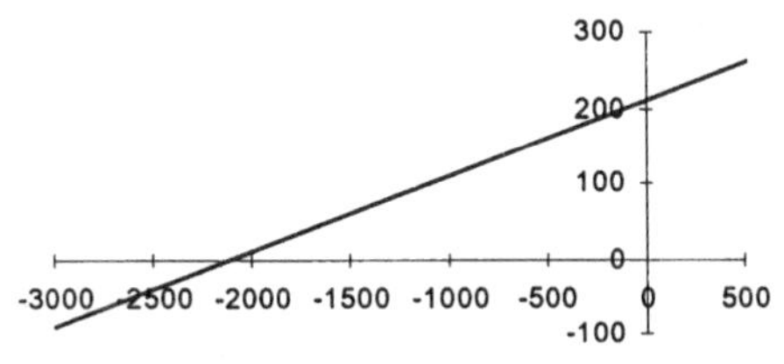

b. (0,2) (.05263,0)

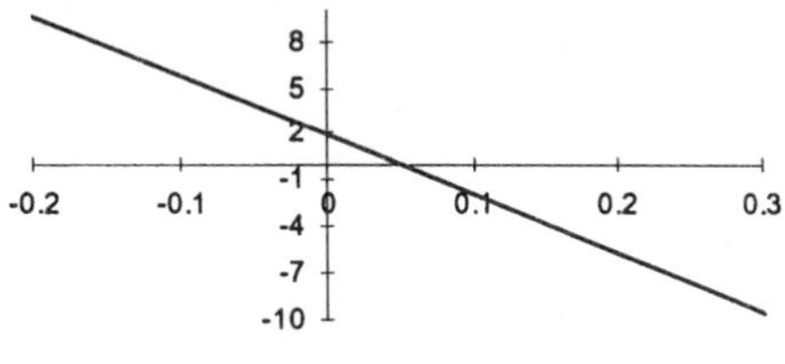

c. (0,2.85) (5,0)

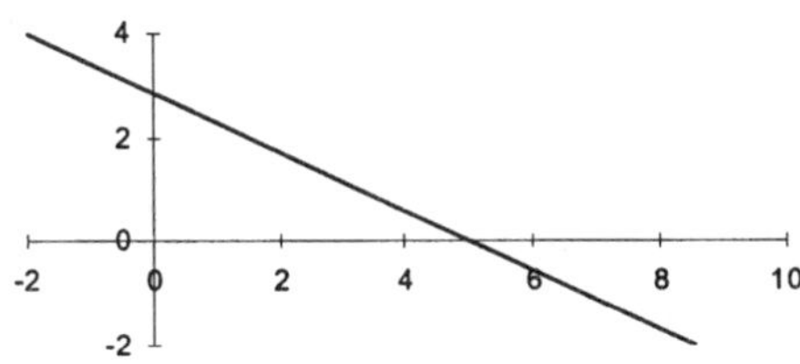

d. (0,8) (-6,0)

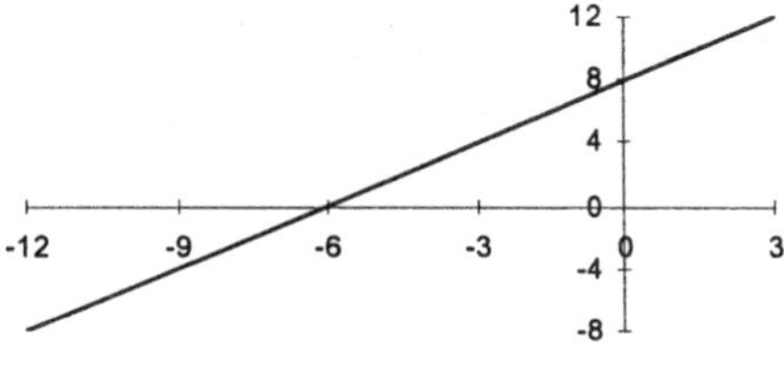

4. a. -12º b. 5º c. 8:30 AM, 11:00PM g. 3 AM TO 3 PM

5. a. 4.025 b. 25.8% c. M = 4.025
6. a. $x \le 1.25$ b. $x \le 3$ c. $1.71 \le x\ 3.57$
7. a. M < 3461 b. 1538 < M < 7307
8. a. M = -3, (0,7) b. M = .15, (0,-6)
9. a. m = -13/8 b. m = 0
10. a. slope is .1, the slope represents the commission
    b. $20,000, (0, 20000), w intercept.
11.
    a. Limo: C = 32
       Lemmon: C = .26M + 19
    b.

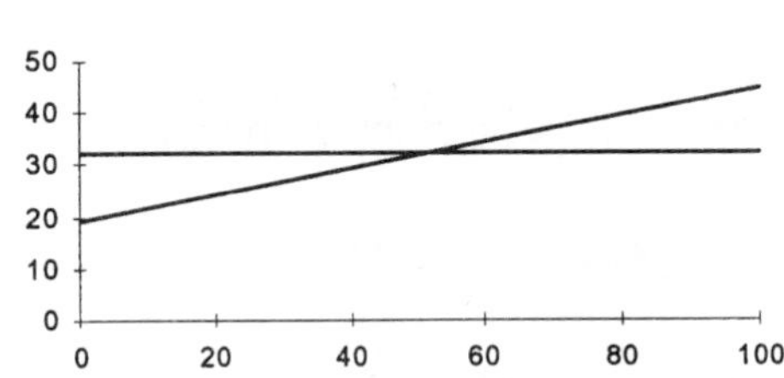

    c. M = 50, C = 32
    d. $0 \le M \le 50$
    e. M > 50
    f. Rental charge without any miles
    g. Slope of Limo is 0, Slope of Ultra is 0.26

Introduction to Exponents page 213

1. a. 7776
2. a. 36 d. 65.61 g. positive
3. a. –67.24 c. –6.25 e. –216 g. –16807 h. negative
4. b. $p = 1000(1.05)^n$ c. 2653,7040 d. 14.2
5. b. $p = 1{,}052{,}000\ (.965)^n$ c. 736,697, 594,912 d. 4.4
6. a. $4926.80 b. $6336.19 c. $9096.98 d. $6112.24 e. $2241.74
   f. Approximatly 139 months

Negative Exponents and Scientific Notation page 225

1. a. .00195 d. -.01235 e. .01234 h. 3125
2. a. 2.356×10^{13} b. 4.35×10^{-8}
3. a. $86.66 b. $9032.25 c. $804.62 d. $104,640.59, $136,283.49
4. a. 7.8×10^4 b. 1.67×10^{-6} c. 6.35×10^{-3} d. 1.16×10^6
5. a. 786,000,000 b. .0000000008673 c. .033 d. 20,320
6. 9,460,000,000,000
7. 9.460×10^{16} Kilometers
8. $1093.81

Properties of Exponents page 233

2. a. Should be $81x^8$ b. Should be $12x^3$ c. Should be $-7/x^2$

3. a. $8x^8$ b. $2x$ c. x^6y^{15} d. $\frac{625}{x^{12}}$ e. $\frac{6}{x}$ f. $\frac{5x^3}{2}$

   g. $\frac{x^3}{2}$ h. $\frac{y^2}{9x^2}$ i. 1 j. $\frac{216}{x^6}$ k. $\frac{8y^{15}}{x^{12}}$ l. $\frac{1}{49x^{10}}$

Introduction to Algebraic Fractions page 241

1. a. 6800 b. 22800 c. 118800 d. undefined
2. a. 33200 b. 74700 c. 157700 d. undefined
3. a. $\frac{3}{2}$ b. $\frac{9}{5}$ c. $\frac{1}{4x}$ d. $\frac{2y^3}{5x}$ e. $-\frac{1}{4x}$ f. $-\frac{x^2}{2}$
4. a. $\frac{4}{3}$ b. 4 c. $\frac{7}{9y^2}$ d. x e. $\frac{1}{x}$ f. $-\frac{2x^2}{3}$

Adding and Subtracting Fractions page 247

4. $\frac{1}{5x}$ 5. $\frac{9-10x}{15x}$ 6. $\frac{31m}{21}$ 7. $\frac{8y-9}{12y}$ 8. $\frac{15-2m^2}{24m^3}$

9. $\frac{20y+9}{12y^2}$ 10. $\frac{8n^2-15}{36n^4}$ 11. $\frac{9+8x}{6x^2}$ 12. $\frac{3x^2-4x}{12}$ 13. $\frac{1+35x^3}{5x^3}$

Solving Equations with Fractions page 253

5. $x = -1.1\overline{6}$ 6. $x = .\overline{36}$ 7. x = -1.263 8. x = -9/4 9. x = .8235
10. x = -.4355 11. x = -1.5714 12. x = .6429

Ratio and Proportion Problems page 263

1. 75 ounces is the better buy.
2. 15 ounces is the better buy.
3. The number of bears in the forest is approximately 36.
4. The car can go 264 miles on 12 gallons.
5. The number of people in Reading without medical insurance is approximately 3,038.
6. It will take about 23 minutes to print 81 pages.
7. One person should get 3.36 million, the second person should get 4.032 million and the third person should get 5.208 million.
8. a. 8/3 b. 12/35

Review for Test III page 269

1. a. x^7 b. $\frac{1}{x^2}$ c. 1 d. x^{10} e. $8x^6$ f. $\frac{1}{x^5}$
   g. x^7 h. $\frac{9}{x^5}$
2. a. .064 b. –167.96 c. 167.96
3. a. 2.15×10^{13} b. 5.022×10^{-13}
4. a. 8.3×10^6 b. 6.14×10^{-4}
5. a. 420000 b. .0031
6. a. $\frac{6x^6}{y^5}$ b. $\frac{2}{49x^3}$ c. $\frac{15x-14}{6x^2}$ d. $\frac{33+5x}{15x}$
7. a. x = 9 b. x = -2

8. b. $p = 500(1.07)^n$ c. 3806 d. 28973 9. a. 1609.25 b. 10,085

Introduction to Quadratics page 281

1. a. 80 b. 704 c. 1104 d. 1040 e. 80 f. –192 g. t = 8
   h. 16.3 secs.
4. a. $-4x^2 + 12x - 3$ b. $-4x^2 + 3x - 20$ c. $-19x^2 + 13x - 7$
   d. $-18x + 18$ e. $-6x^2 - 25x + 14$ f. $-11x^2 + 6x - 15$
5. $-4x^2 + 17x - 72$
6. a. $x^2 + 5x + 6$ b. $x^2 + x - 12$ c. $x^2 - 11x + 28$ d. $x^2 - 64$
   e. $x^2 - 81$ f. $6x^2 + 7x - 3$ g. $x^2 + 6x + 9$ h. $x^2 - 10x + 25$

Applications of Quadratic Formula page 293

2. 80 yards by 100 yards 3. 9.026 sec. 4. 90 or 180
5. a. 5.6% b. 21.875 = t or 1996
6. 60 or 20

Quadratic Applications and Their Graphs page 313

2. $x = \frac{-b}{2a}$ 4. x intercepts, y intercepts, vertex
5.
   a. $P = -x^2 + 36x - 87$
   b. vertex (18,237)
      y intercept (0, -87)
      x intercepts (2.605, 0) (33.39, 0)
   c. (3.964, 40), (32.04, 40)

6.
   a. $P = -7x^2 + 77x - 35$
   b. vertex (5.5, 176.75)
      y intercept (0, -35)
      x intercepts (.475, 0)(10.52, 0)
   c. (9.217, 80) or (1.78, 80)

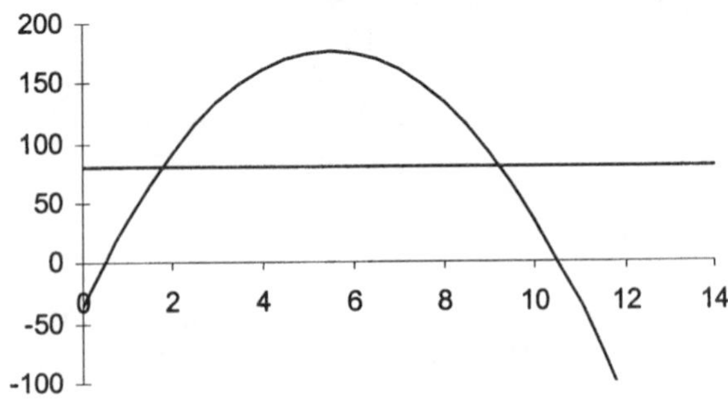

7.

a. vertex (6.25, 625)
   y intercept (0, 0)
   x intercepts (0, 0), (12.5, 0)
b. (1.75, 300) and (10.75, 300)

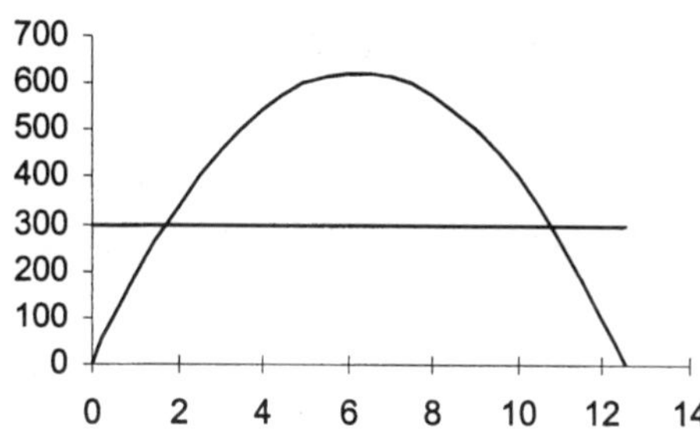

8.

a. $A = x(1800 - 2x)$
   $= -2x^2 + 1800x$
b. vertex (450, 405000)
   intercepts (0, 0) and (900, 0)
c. 450 by 900

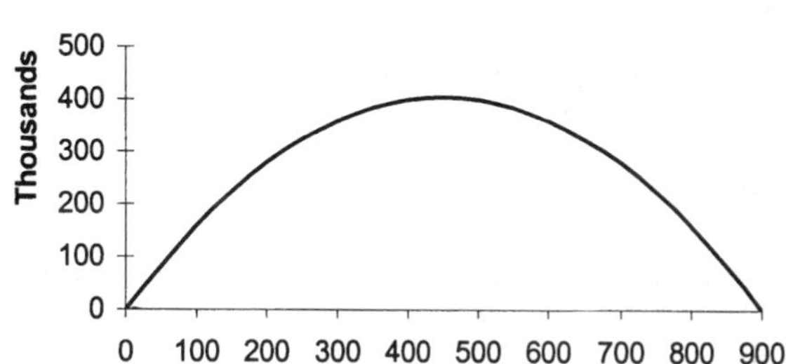

Factoring page 321

					5.	
2.	a.	$2x(x + 4)$	b.	$(x - 3)(x + 1)$	5. a.	$x = -1, -6$
4.	a.	$3(2x + 3)$	c.	$-10(x - 5)$	b.	$x = -5, 10$
	e.	$9x(3x - 2)$	g.	$(x + 6)(x + 1)$	c.	$x = -1.667, 0$
	i.	$(x - 3)(x - 3)$	k.	$(x + 10)(x + 3)$		
	m.	$(x - 10)(x + 10)$	o.	$(x - 9)(x + 9)$		

Review for Test IV page 327

1.

a. $P = -2x^2 + 40x - 12$
b. vertex (10,188)
   y intercept (0, -12)
   x intercepts (.305, 0)
   and (19.70, 0)
c. (1.25, 35)(18.75, 35)

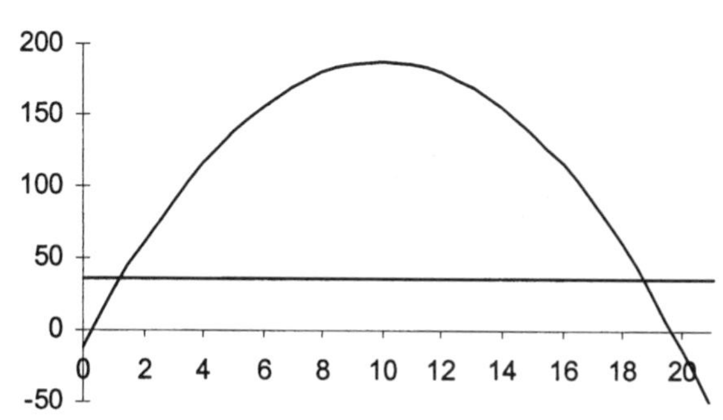

2.

a. $A = W(80-3W)$
$= -3W^2 + 80W$
b. vertex (13.3, 533.3)
intercepts (0, 0) (26.67, 0)
c. (9,477)(17.67, 477)

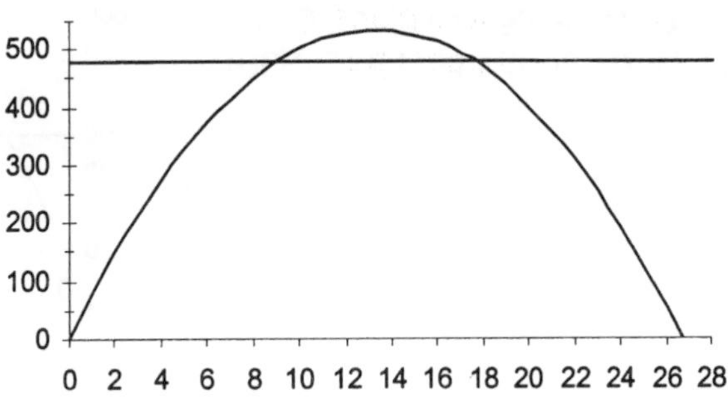

3. $-3x^2 + 22x - 30$
4. a. $3x^2 - 19x - 40$ b. $x^2 - 10x + 25$
5. a. $4x(x+2)$ b. $(x+9)(x-2)$
6. $x = 6, 2$

Review for Final Exam page 342

1. $S = 1.25p - 800$ 2. $p = 400(1.08)^n$ 3. $A = W(150-2W) = -2W^2 + 150W$
4. a. 43.2 min. b. 10.45 miles
5. a. 82.6 b. 73
6. a. $t > 9$, 1994 b. $7 < t < 15$ or $1992 < \text{years} < 2000$
7. a. 147 ft b. 1.25 or 4.68
8. a. P = \$95.40 b. A = 4327.09
9.

Y intercept (0, 41)
X intercept (-205, 0)

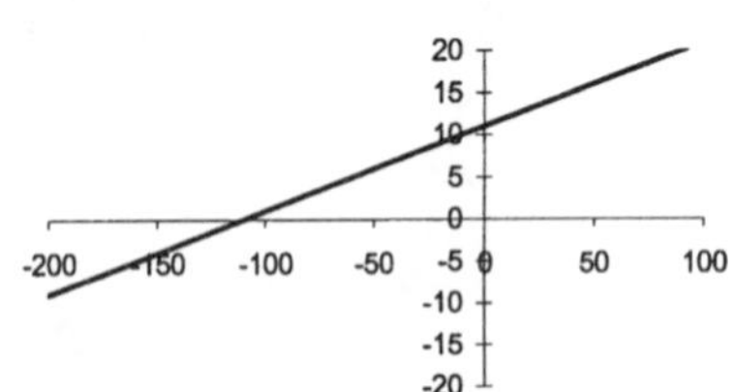

10.

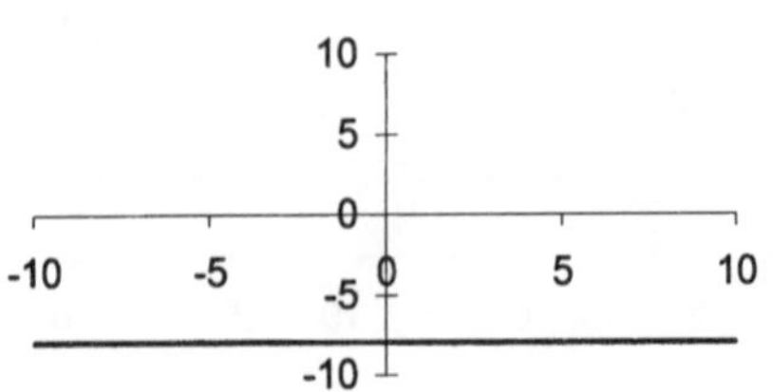

11.

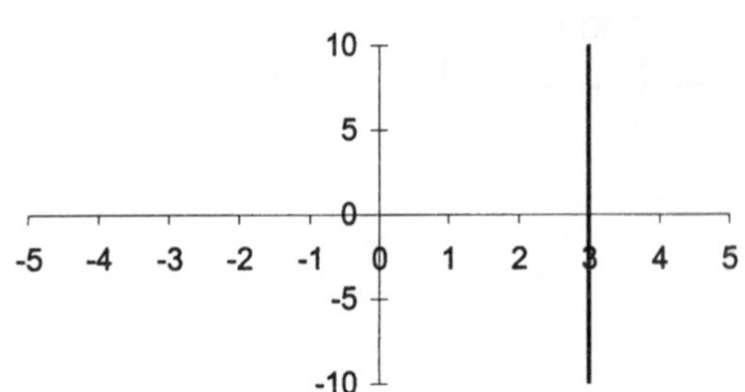

12. a. 11:30 AM and 10:30 PM b. 10° c. 6 AM until 5:00 PM

13.

b. (5, 85)
c. (0, 35), cost to place the call
d. slope is 10, cost per minute

a.

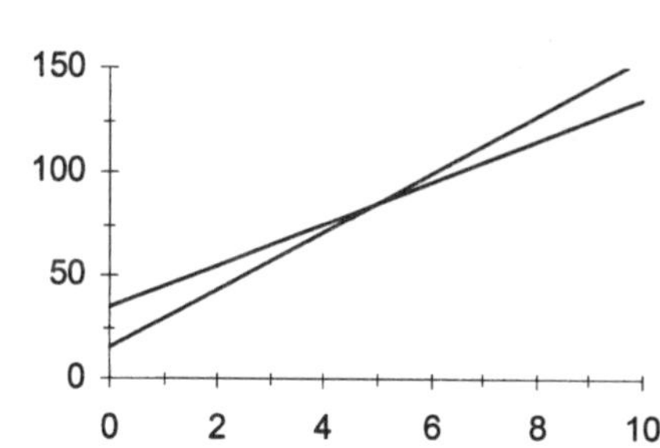

14.

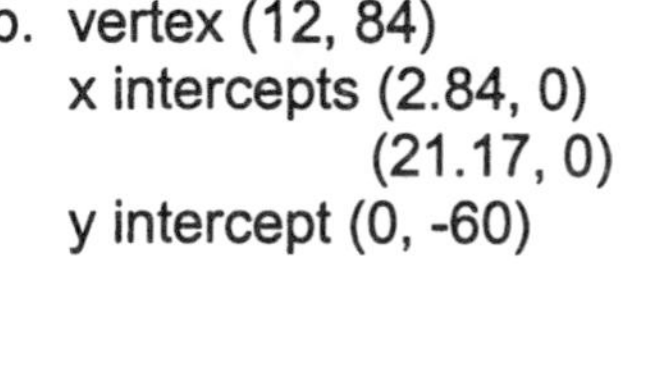
a. $P = -x^2 + 24x - 60$
b. vertex (12, 84)
   x intercepts (2.84, 0)
   (21.17, 0)
   y intercept (0, -60)

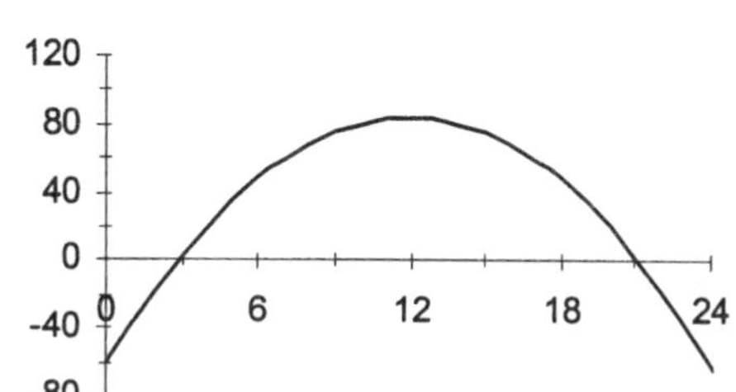

15. a. 41.5% b. .22 million per year
16. a. x = 7.8 b. x = 8.5
17. a. 8x(x+2) b. (x-7)(x+3)
18. $x^2 + 14x + 49$
19. a. x^7 b. $9x^8$ c. $\frac{1}{x^3}$ d. $\frac{9}{x^5}$
20. a. $\frac{1}{4x}$ b. $\frac{-x+16}{6}$
21. $-7x^2 - 52x + 35$
22. 4.3×10^6
23. .00024
24. $y = \frac{10-3x}{5}$ or $y = \frac{-3}{5}x + 2$

Signed Numbers, Drill and Practice page 347

1. -1 2. -4 3. -7 4. -4 5. 5 6. -3 7. -7 8. -2 9. -5 10. -3 11. -14

12. -9 13. 6 14. -4 15. -23 16. -2 17. -9 18. -13 19. 7 20. -8 21. -15

22. -3 23. -20 24. 15 25. -54 26. 21 27. -35 28. -72 29. 54 30. -56 31. -40

32. -36 33. 24 34. 14 35. 0 36. 560 37. -3 38. 3 39. 9 40. -9 41. 6 42. -9

43. 5 44. -8 45. 0 46. 6 47. undefined 48. 5 49. 9 50. 25 51. 64 52. 16

53. 49 54. 0 55. 81 56. 100 57. -12 58. -19 59. 2 60. 15 61. -24 62. -51

63. -19 64. 1 65. -33 66. 78 67. -2 68. -15 69. -5 70. undefined 71. 0

Simplifying Algebraic Expressions, Drill and Practice page 348

1. $12x-9$ 2. $5x+5$ 3. $-x-13$ 4. $8x+13$

5. $-6x+8$ 6. $-38x+32$ 7. $-x+10$ 8. $2x+2$

9. $-5x+15$ 10. $-19x+12$ 11. $-20x-33$ 12. $-13x+25$

13. $-2x-34$ 14. $-10x-1$ 15. $30x-11$ 16. $x+3y-5$

17. $7x-3y-3$ 18. $20x-4y$ 19. $-7x+7z-15$ 20. $22y+3z$

21. $8y-7z-4$ 22. $5x-14$ 23. $11y-18x-18$ 24. $-20Z+42$

Solving Linear Equations, Drill and Practice page 349

1. x = 4 2. x = 5 3. x = -2 4. x = 4.5

5. x = .5 6. x = -2.167 7. x = 1 8. x = 0.8571

9. x = 1 10. x = -0.8333 11. x = -3 12. x = 5.455

13. x = -0.3 14. x = 1.813 15. x = 20 16. x = 13.5

17. x = 6 18. x = -2.25 19. x = 0.5625 20. x = 0.8182

21. x = 1 22. x = -1.833 23. x = -4.929 24. x = 1.538

25. x = --2.444 26. x = -5.75 27. x = 0.34 28. x = -2.1

29. x = 2.833 30. x = 7.777

Inequalities, Drill and Practicepage 350

1. $x>-4$ 2. $x>-3.4$ 3. $x>-5.667$ 4. $x\geq-11.75$

5. $x\geq4.5$ 6. $x\geq-9.429$ 7. $x>1.833$ 8. $x>0$

9. $x>6.167$ 10. $x\leq17.5$ 11. $x>6$ 12. $x>0.3077$

13. $x<-2$ 14. $x\leq3$ 15. $x\geq-4.429$ 16. $-4.667\leq x<-0.3333$

17. $2.25\leq x<8.25$ 18. $-6<x\leq-3.25$

19. $-7.8<x<1.8$ 20. $-4.333<x<-3.333$

21. $-2.5 \le x < 2.5$

22. $-2.4 \ge x \ge -5$

23. $4.286 > x > 2.429$

24. $-4 < x < 0.5$

Graphing Lines by Plotting Points, Drill and Practice page 351

1.

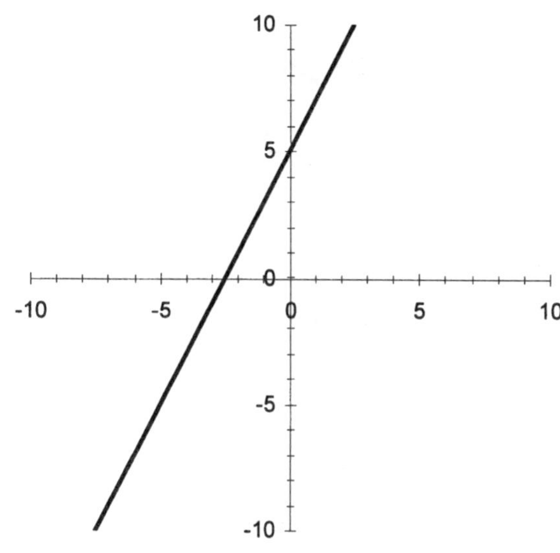

2.

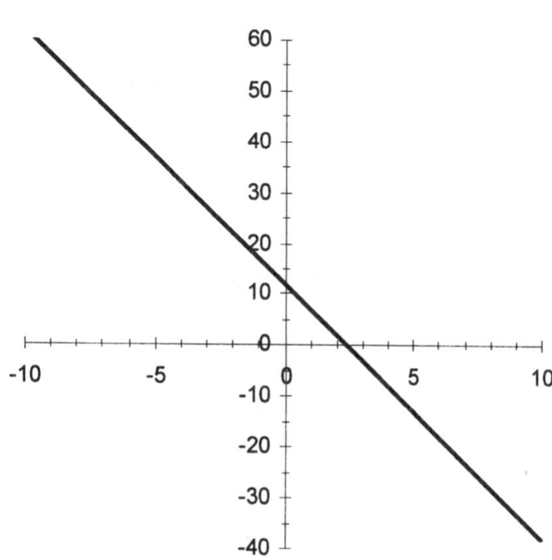

3.

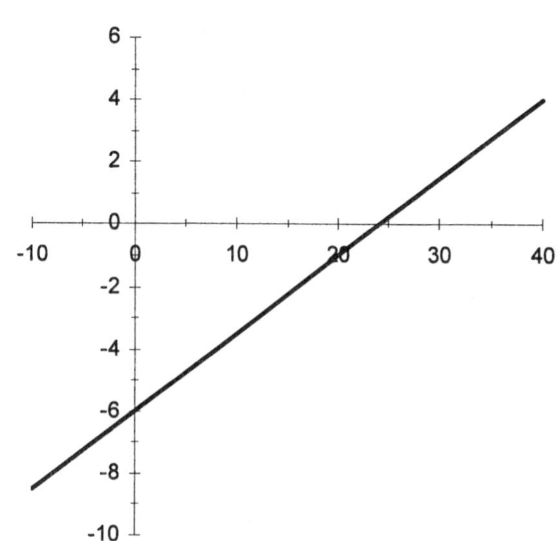

4.

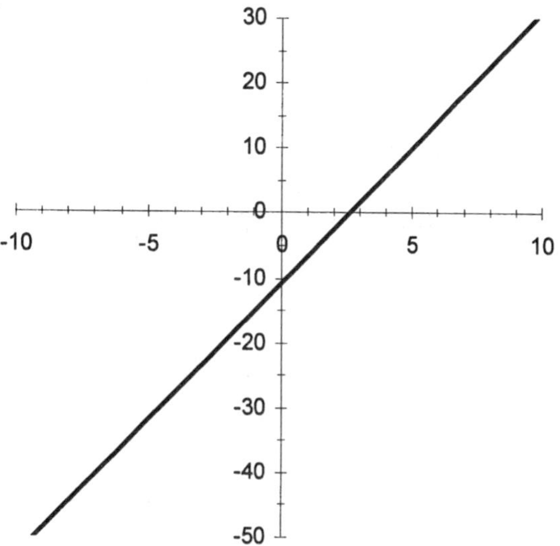

5.

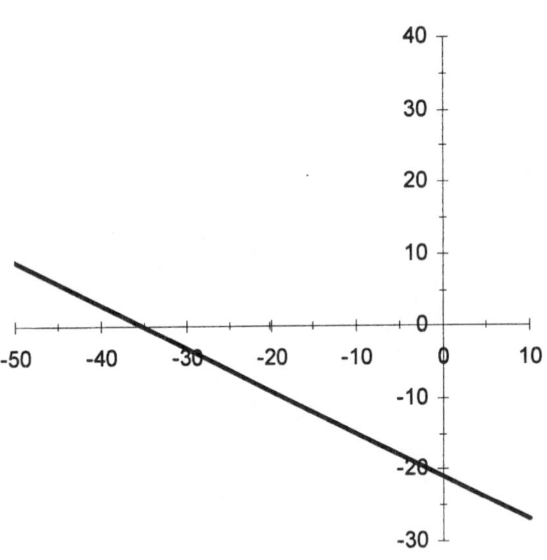

40
30
20
10
0
-10
-20
-30
-50
-40
-30
-20
-10
0
10

6.

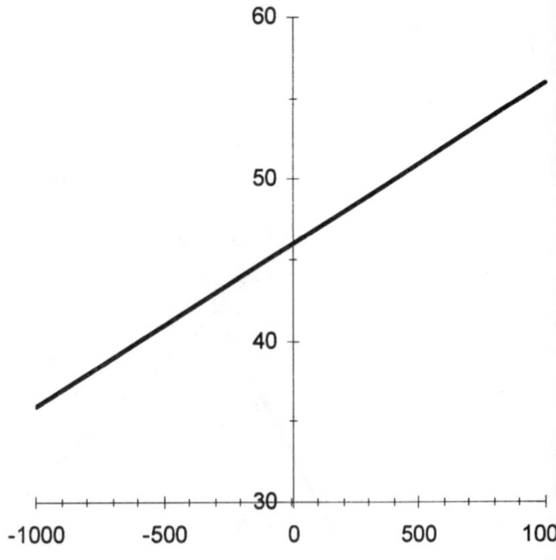

60
50
40
30
-1000
-500
0
500

7.

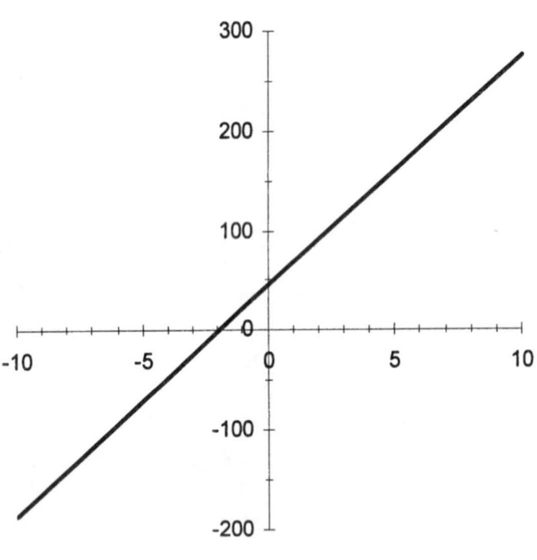

300
200
100
0
-100
-200
-10
-5
0
5
10

8.

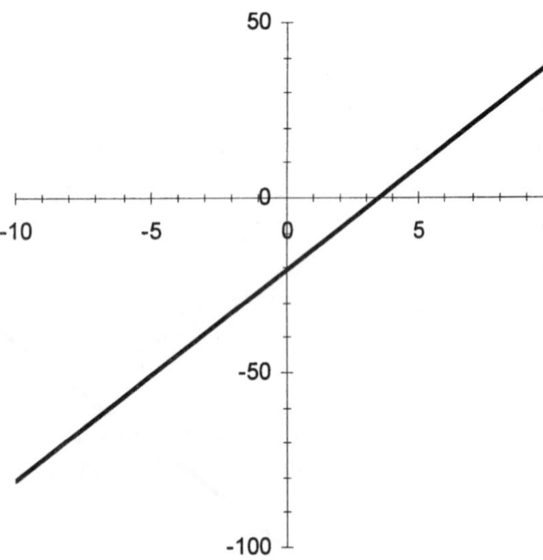

50
0
-50
-100
-10
-5
0
5

9.

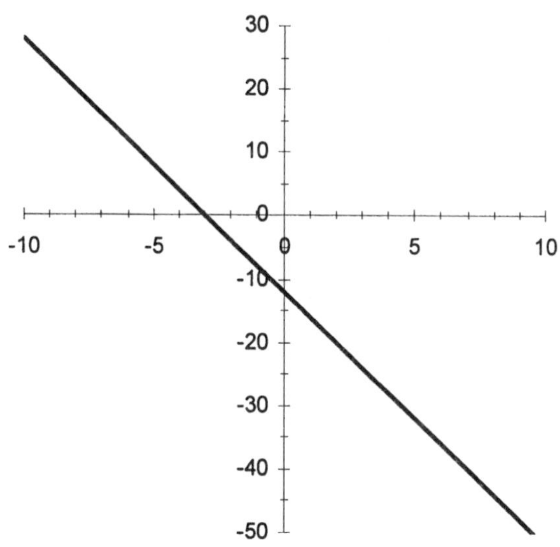

30
20
10
0
-10
-5
0
5
10
-10
-20
-30
-40
-50

10.

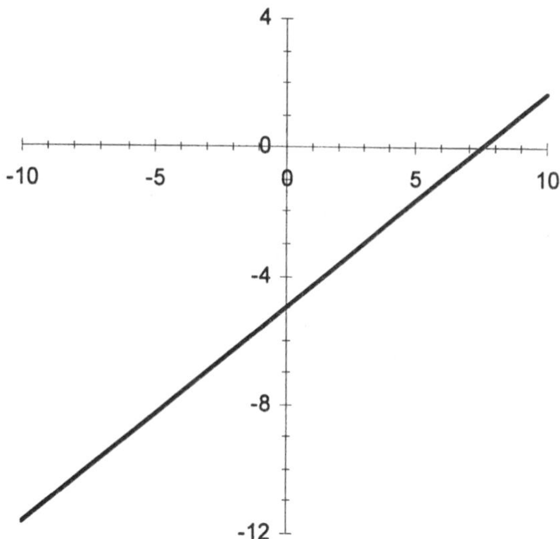

4
0
-10
-5
0
5
10
-4
-8
-12

11.

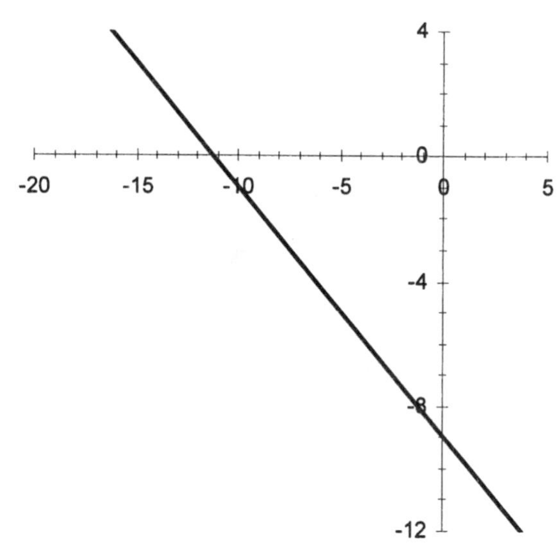

4
0
-20
-15
-10
-5
0
5
-4
-8
-12

12.

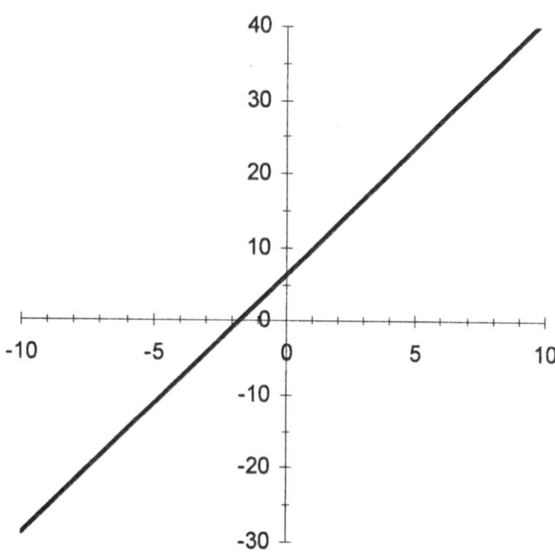

40
30
20
10
0
-10
-5
0
5
10
-10
-20
-30

13.

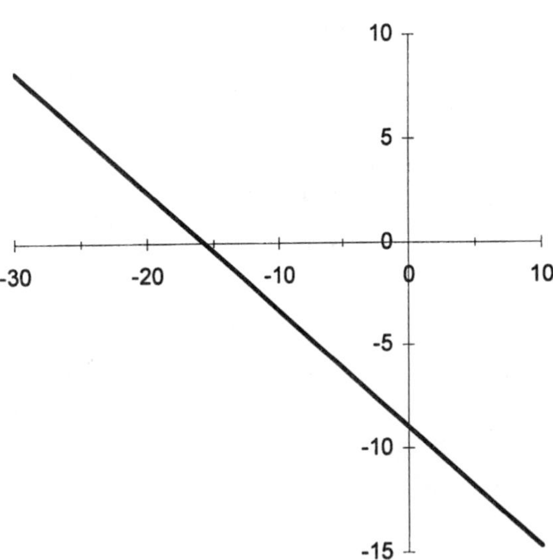
10
5
0
-5
-10
-15
-30
-20
-10
0
10

14.

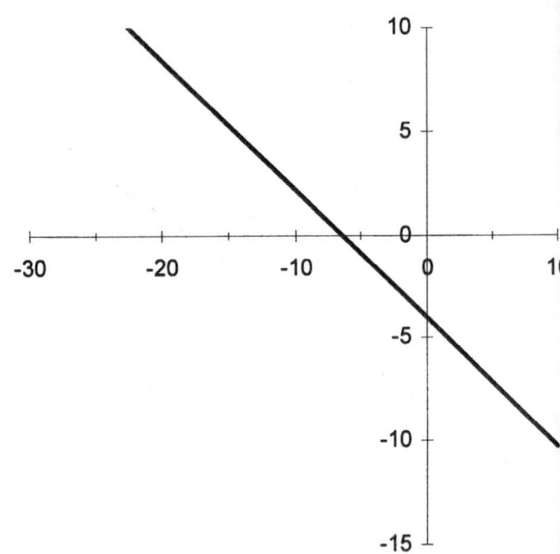
10
5
0
-5
-10
-15
-30
-20
-10
0

15.

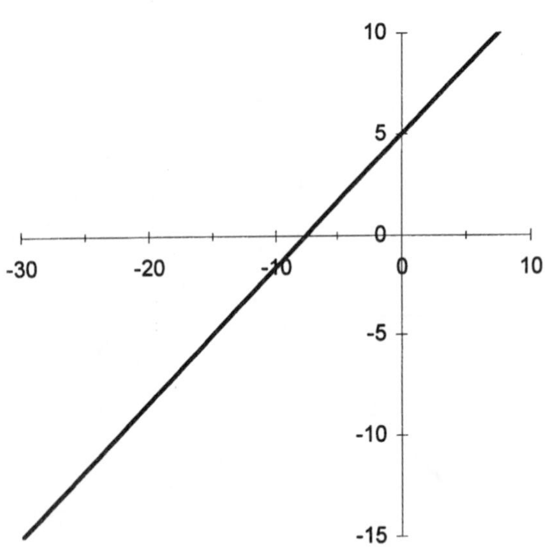
10
5
0
-5
-10
-15
-30
-20
-10
0
10

16.

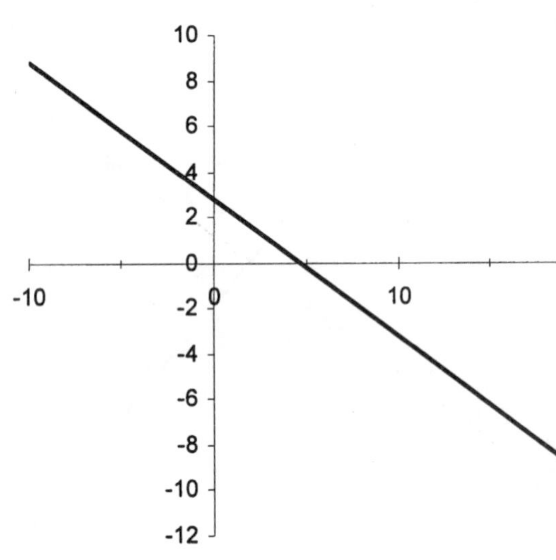
10
8
6
4
2
0
-2
-4
-6
-8
-10
-12
-10
0
10

17.

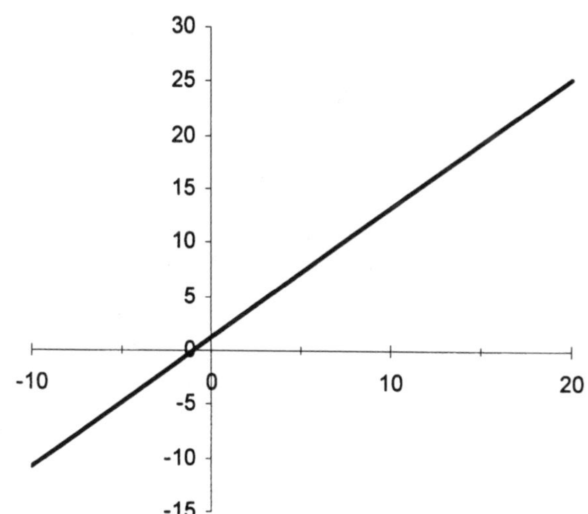
30
25
20
15
10
5
0
-10
0
10
20
-5
-10
-15

18.

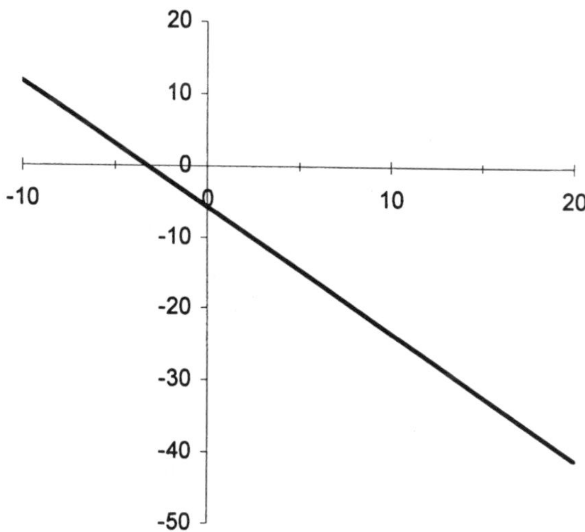
20
10
0
-10
0
10
20
-10
-20
-30
-40
-50

19.

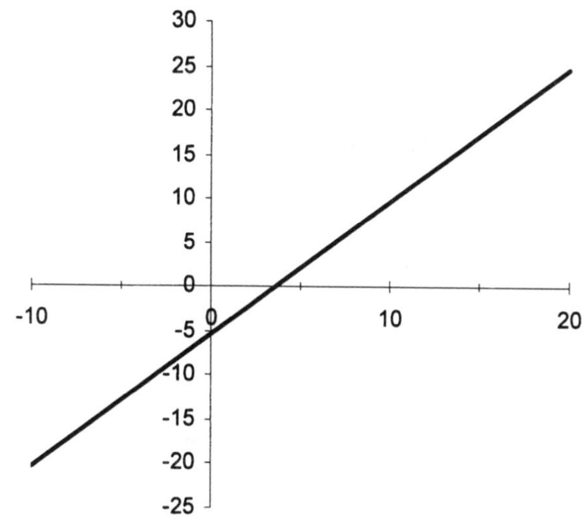
30
25
20
15
10
5
0
-10
0
10
20
-5
-10
-15
-20
-25

20.

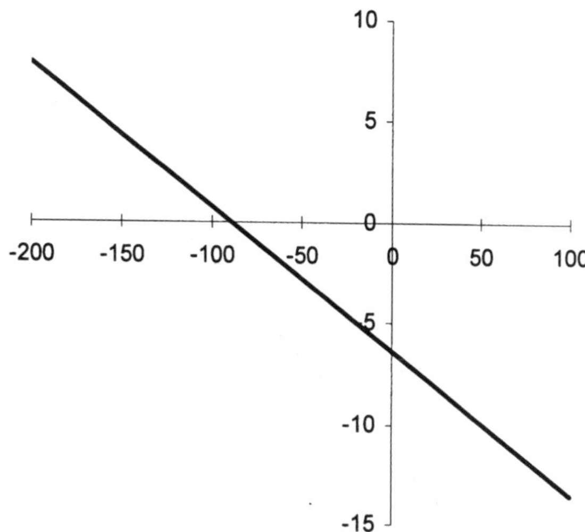
10
5
0
-200
-150
-100
-50
0
50
100
-5
-10
-15

21.

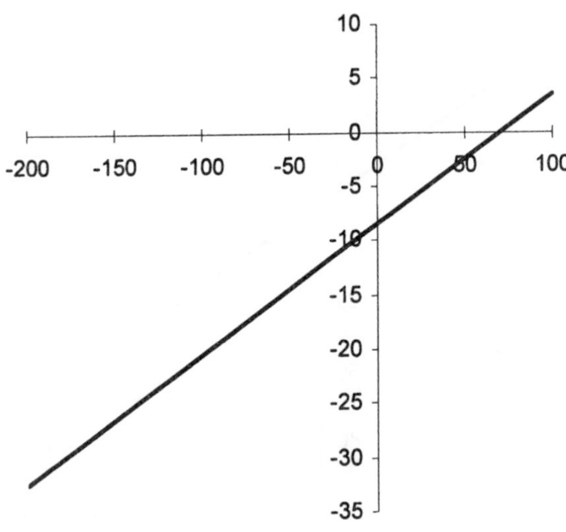
10
5
0
-5
-10
-15
-20
-25
-30
-35
-200
-150
-100
-50
0
50
100

22.

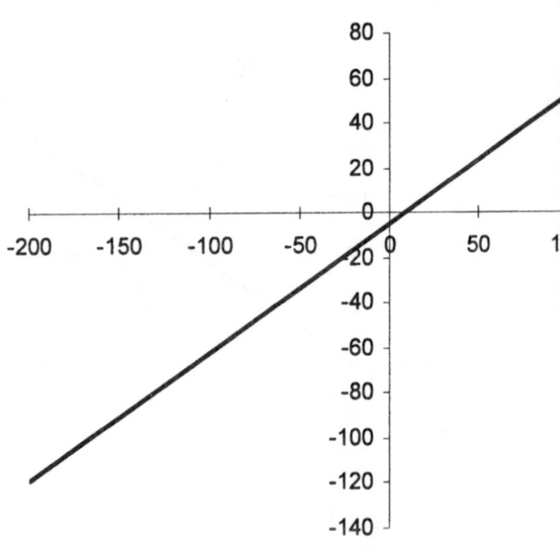
80
60
40
20
0
-20
-40
-60
-80
-100
-120
-140
-200
-150
-100
-50
0
50

23.

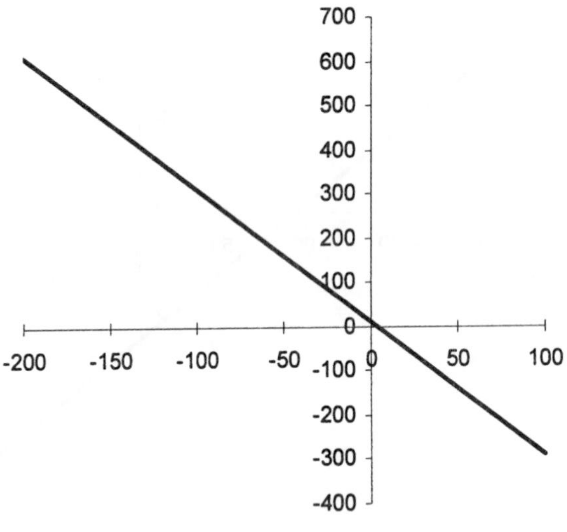
700
600
500
400
300
200
100
0
-100
-200
-300
-400
-200
-150
-100
-50
0
50
100

24.

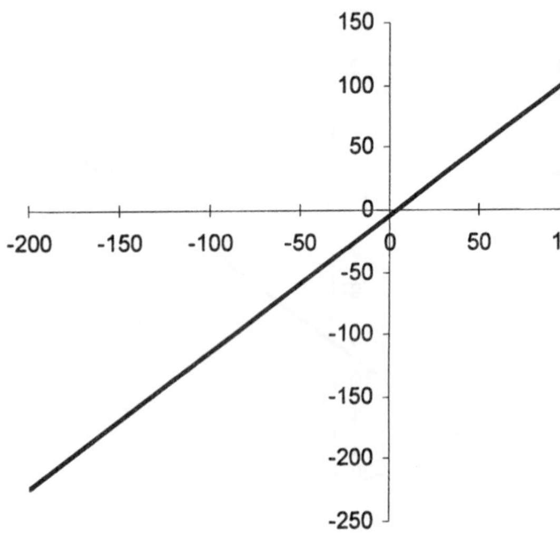
150
100
50
0
-50
-100
-150
-200
-250
-200
-150
-100
-50
0
50

Graphing Lines By finding The Intercepts, Drill and Practice page 352

1.

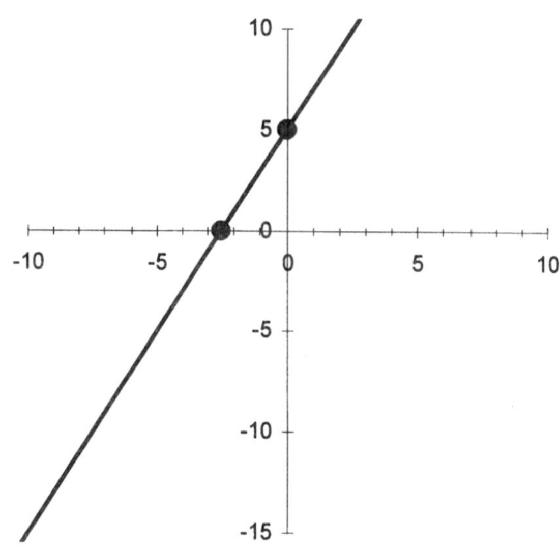

2.

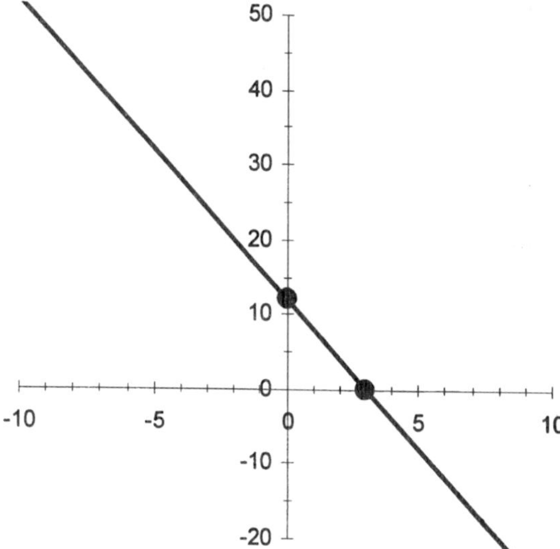

3.

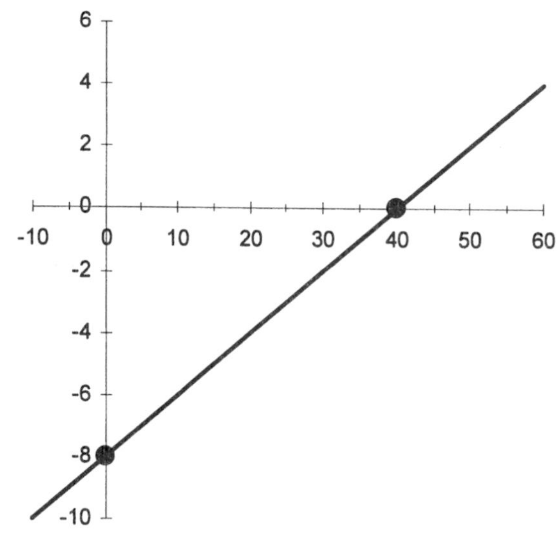

4.

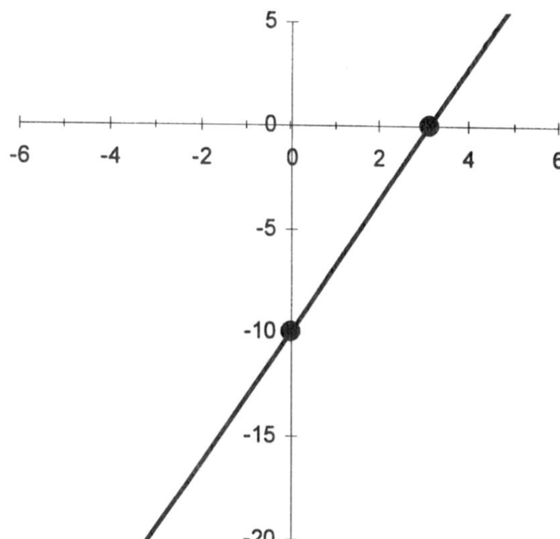

5.

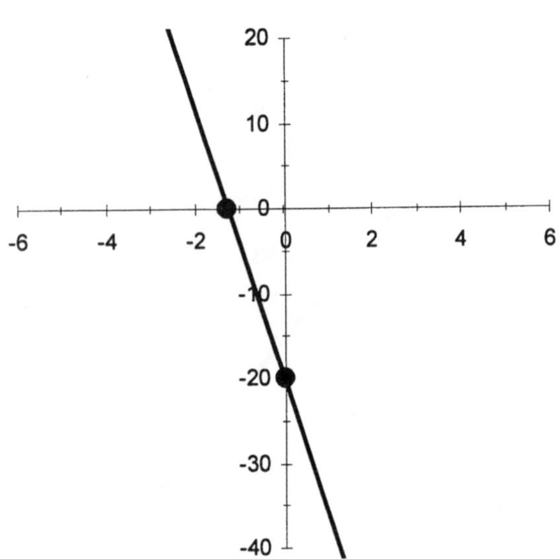
20
10
0
-6
-4
-2
0
2
4
6
-10
-20
-30
-40

6.

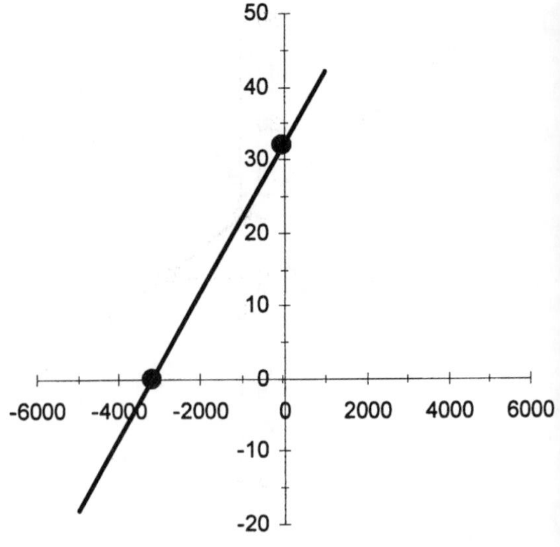
50
40
30
20
10
0
-6000
-4000
-2000
0
2000
4000
6000
-10
-20

7.

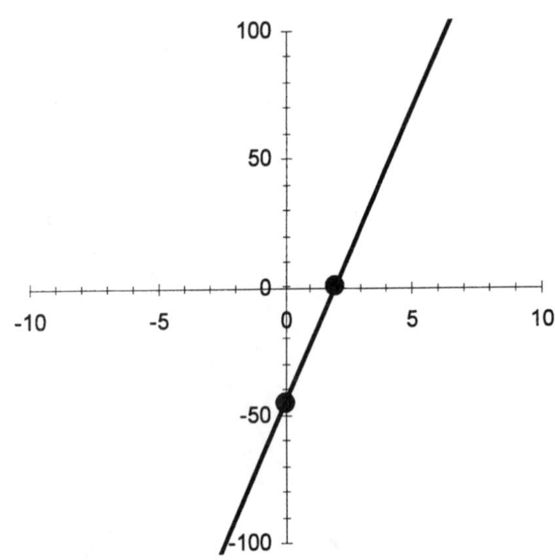
100
50
0
-10
-5
0
5
10
-50
-100

8.

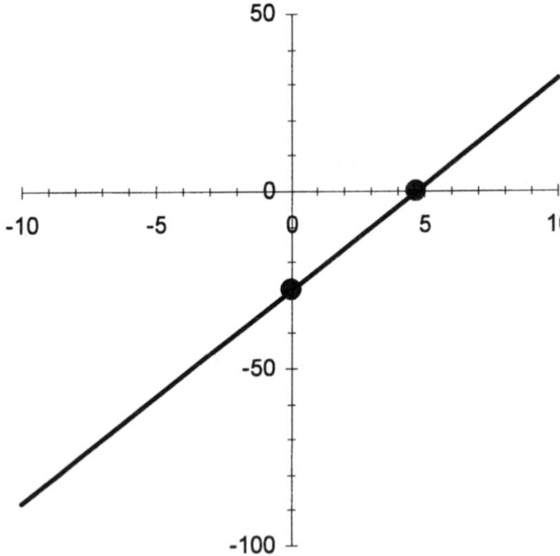
50
0
-10
-5
0
5
10
-50
-100

9.

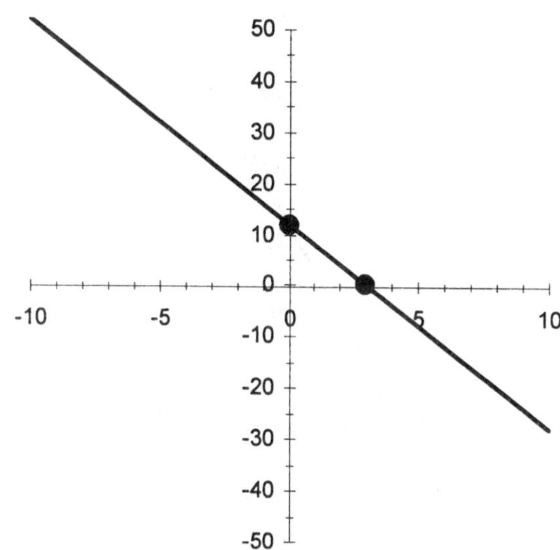

50
40
30
20
10
0
-10
-20
-30
-40
-50
-10
-5
0
5
10

10.

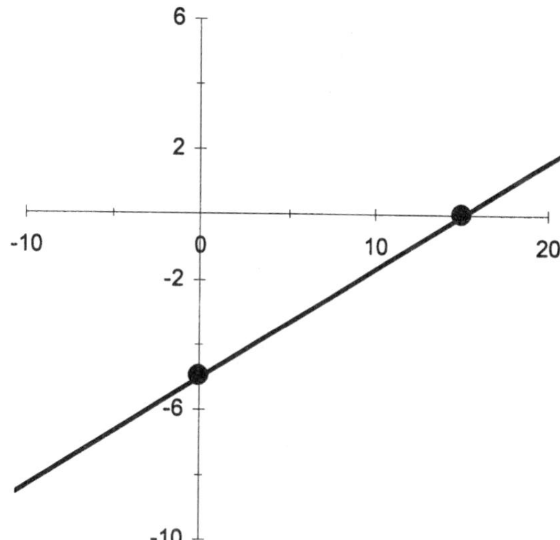

6
2
-2
-6
-10
-10
0
10
20

11.

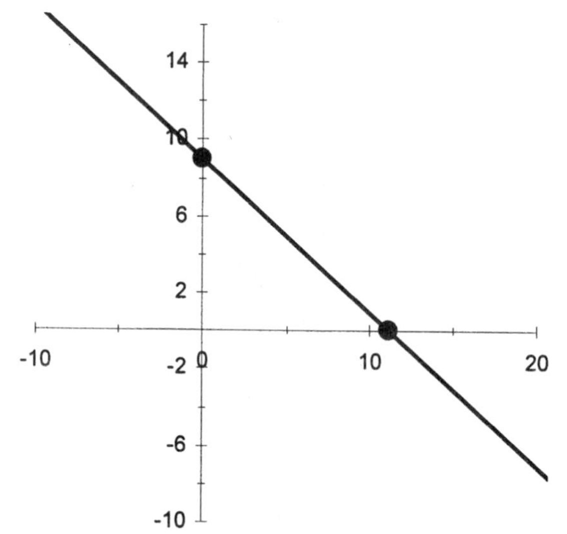

14
10
6
2
-2
-6
-10
-10
0
10
20

12.

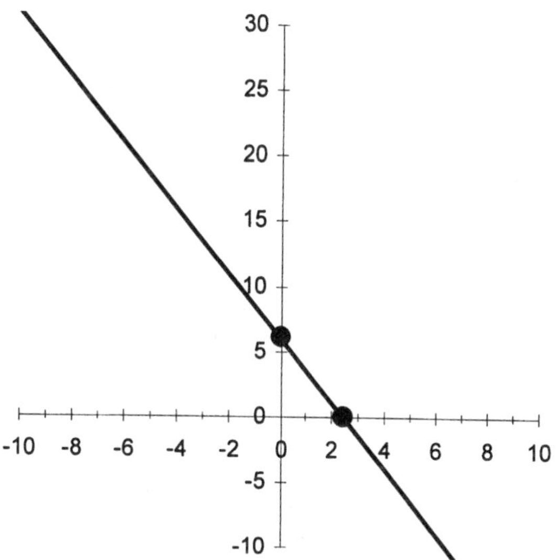

30
25
20
15
10
5
0
-5
-10
-10
-8
-6
-4
-2
0
2
4
6
8
10

13.

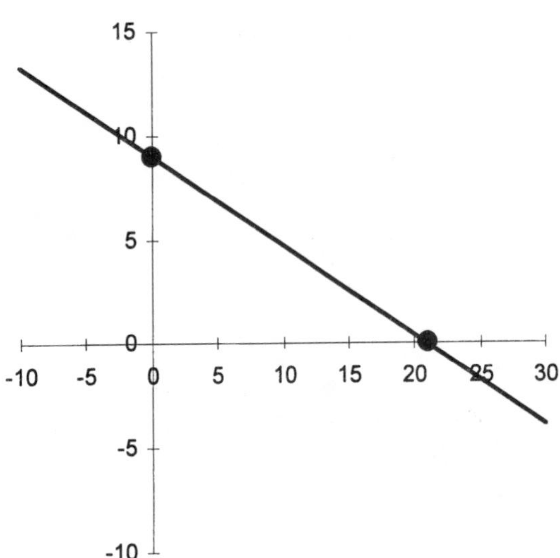
15
10
5
0
-5
-10
-10
-5
0
5
10
15
20
25
30

14.

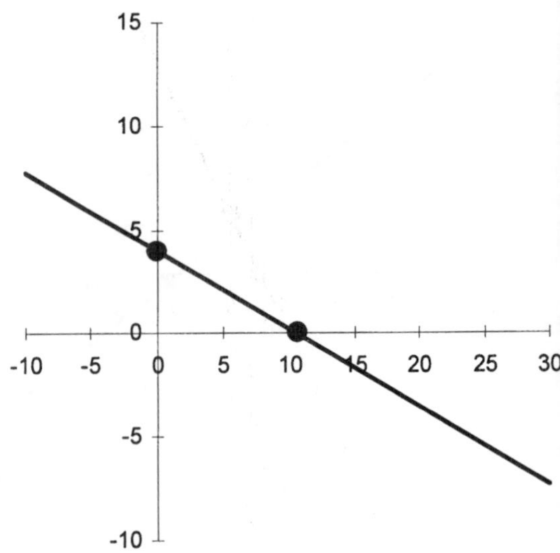
15
10
5
0
-5
-10
-10
-5
0
5
10
15
20
25
30

15.

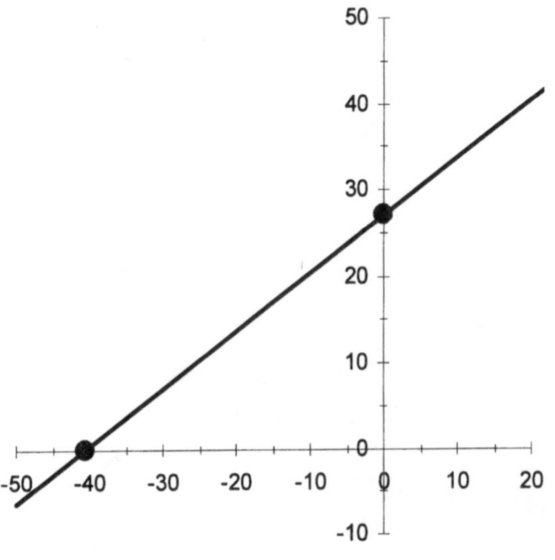
50
40
30
20
10
0
-10
-50
-40
-30
-20
-10
0
10
20

16.

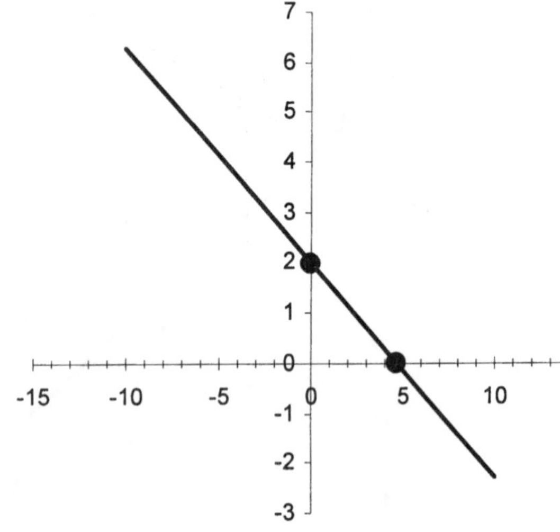
7
6
5
4
3
2
1
0
-1
-2
-3
-15
-10
-5
0
5
10

17.

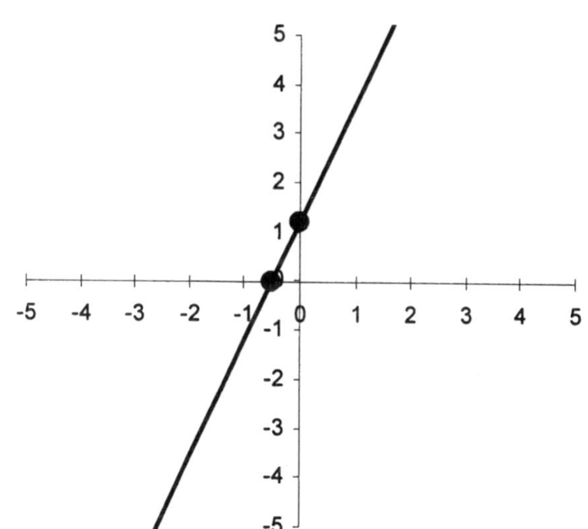
5
4
3
2
1
0
-1
-2
-3
-4
-5
-5 -4 -3 -2 -1 0 1 2 3 4 5

18.

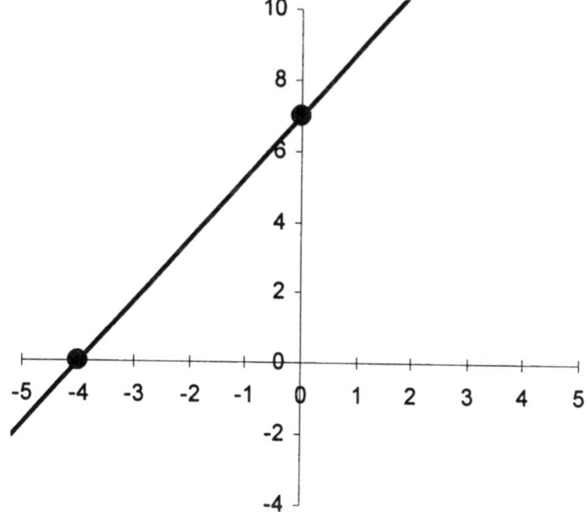
10
8
6
4
2
0
-2
-4
-5 -4 -3 -2 -1 0 1 2 3 4 5

19.

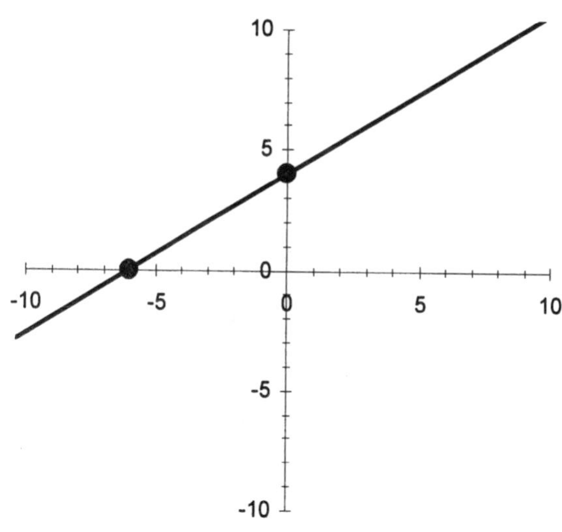
10
5
0
-5
-10
-10 -5 0 5 10

20.

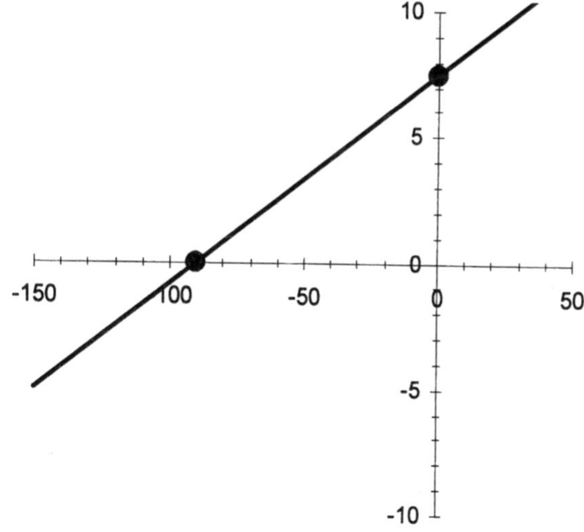
10
5
0
-5
-10
-150 100 -50 0 50

21.

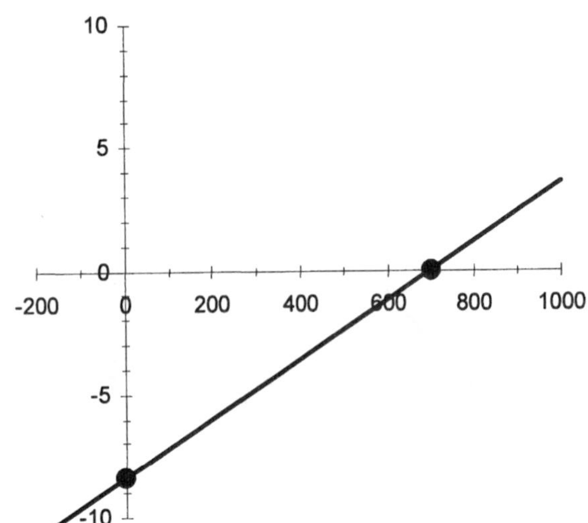

10
5
0
-5
-10
-200
0
200
400
600
800
1000

22.

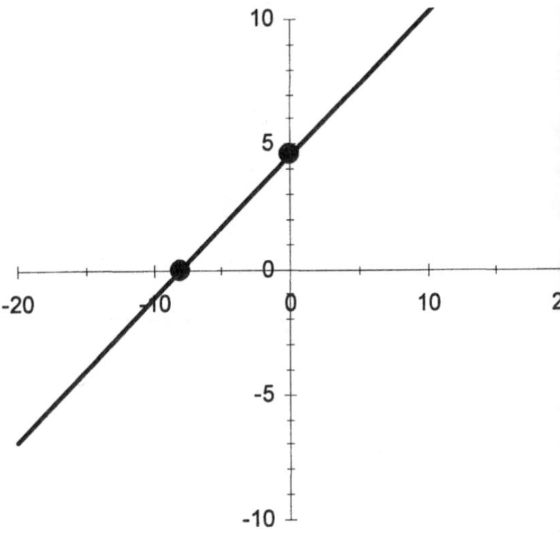

10
5
0
-5
-10
-20
-10
0
10

23.

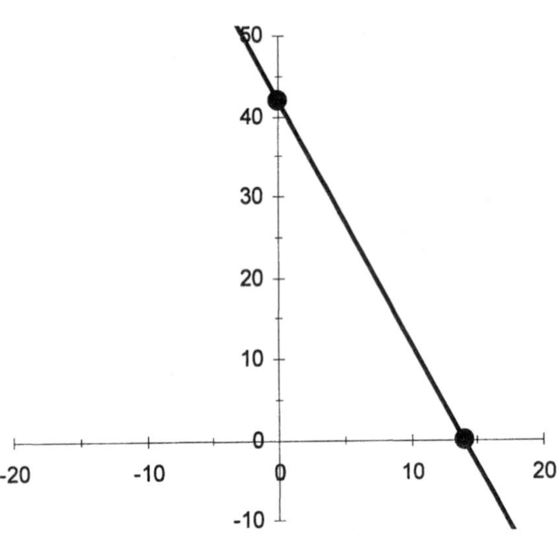

50
40
30
20
10
0
-10
-20
-10
0
10
20

24.

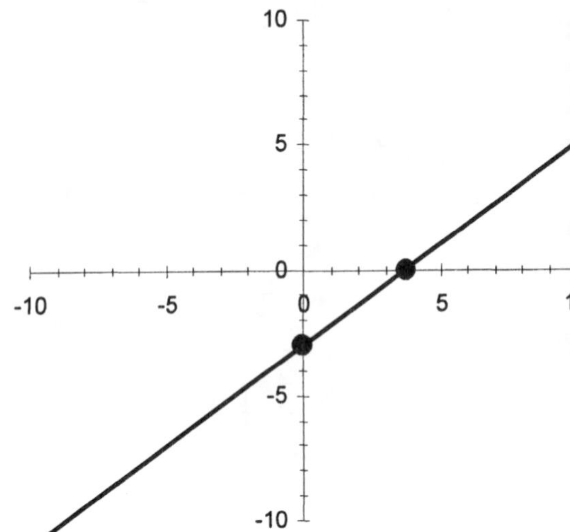

10
5
0
-5
-10
-10
-5
0
5

25.

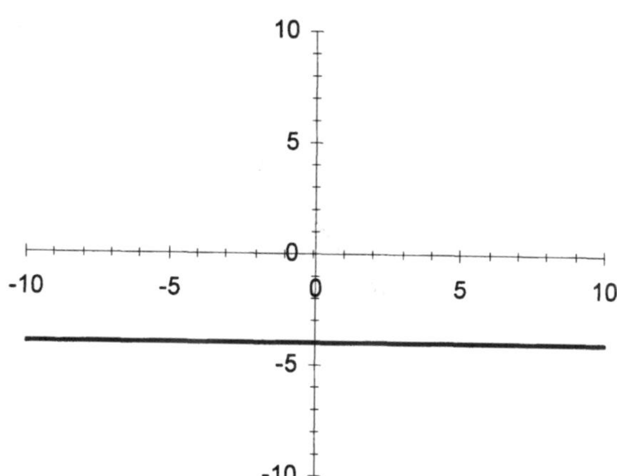

26.

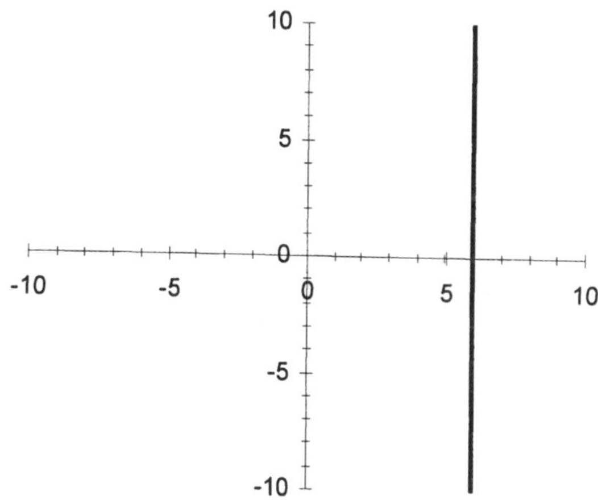

27.

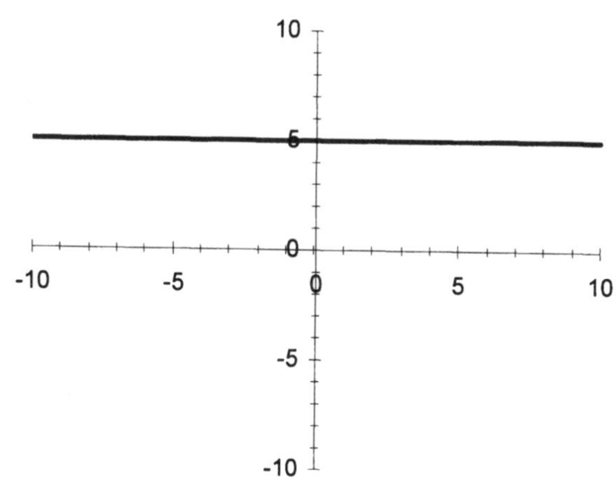

28.

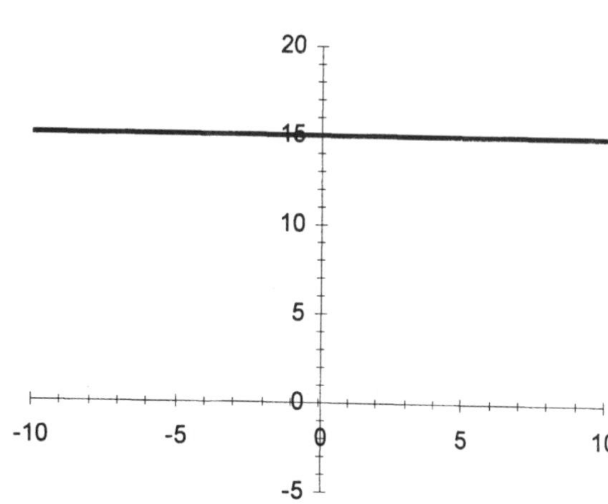

29.

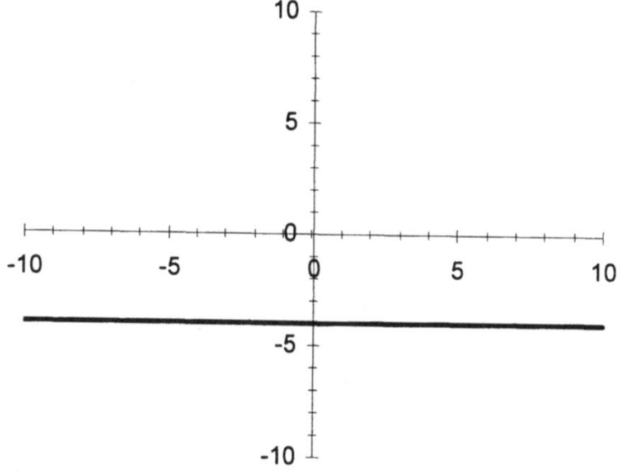

30.

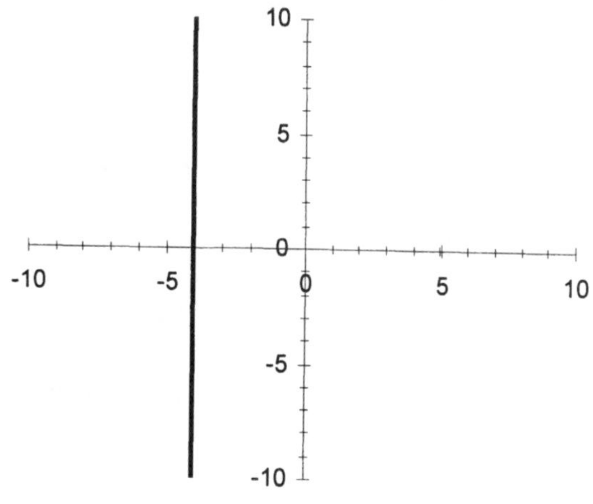

31.

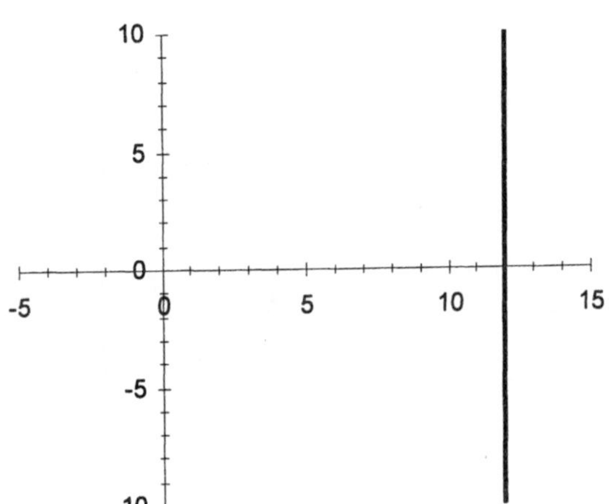

32.

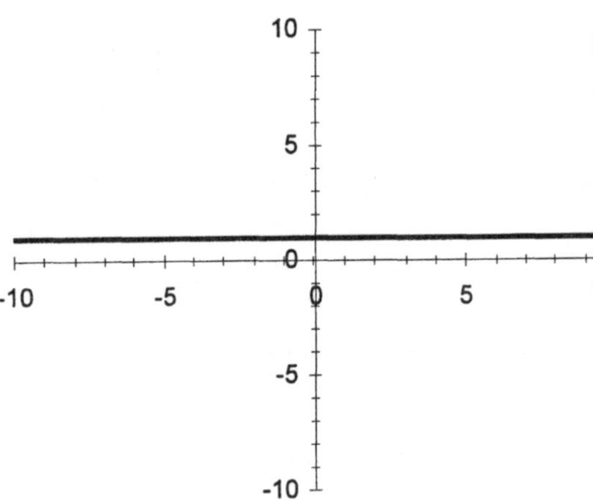

33.

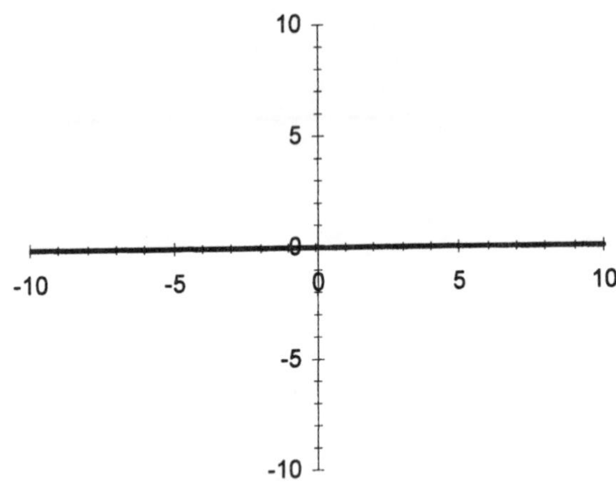

Slope, Drill and Practice page 353

1. m = -0.0909
2. m = -10
3. m = 2.5
4. undefined
5. m = 1
6. m = 0
7. m = 0.6953
8. m = 0.38
9. m = 0.9398
10. m = 0
11. m = 0.6389
12. m = 1.597
13. m = 3.2, (0, -10)
14. m = -16, (0. -20)
15. m = 0.01, (0, 32)
16. m = 23, (0, -45)
17. m = 6, (0, -28)
18. m = -4, (0, 12)
19. $m = \frac{1}{3}$, (0, -5)
20. $m = \frac{-4}{5}$, (0, 9)
21. $m = \frac{-5}{2}$, (0, 6)

Properties of Exponents, Drill and Practice page 354

1. x^7 2. $\frac{1}{x}$ 3. $3x^3$ 4. $\frac{1}{x}$ 5. $7x^8$ 6. $5x^2$

7. $81x^8$ 8. $25x^6$ 9. $81x^{20}$ 10. $16x^{10}$ 11. $7{,}776x^{15}$ 12. $\frac{25}{x^6}$

13. $\frac{4}{x^3}$ 14. $\frac{2}{x}$ 15. $\frac{21}{x^7}$ 16. $\frac{2x^4}{3}$ 17. $\frac{2}{5x^4}$ 18. $\frac{x^5}{7}$

19. $\frac{x^2}{4}$ 20. $5x^2$ 21. 3 22. $\frac{1}{8x^4}$ 23. $\frac{x^3}{2}$ 24. $\frac{3}{x^3}$

25. $\frac{3}{2x^2}$ 26. $\frac{x^2}{4}$ 27. $\frac{x}{7}$ 28. $\frac{1}{16x^8}$ 29. $\frac{-x^{15}}{8}$ 30. $\frac{1}{9x^4}$

31. $\frac{x^3}{7}$ 32. $\frac{x^{21}}{27}$ 33. $\frac{1}{216x^6}$ 34. $\frac{16}{x^{12}}$ 35. $\frac{27x^6}{125}$ 36. $\frac{625x^8}{1{,}296}$

37. $\frac{49}{9x^6}$ 38. $\frac{125x^3}{216}$ 39. $\frac{16x^4}{25}$ 40. 1 41. $120x^7y^4$ 42. $6x^4y^4$

43. $27x^6y^{12}$ 44. $625x^{12}y^8$ 45. $512x^6y^8$ 46. $\frac{3x^2}{y}$ 47. $\frac{27}{8x^6y^6}$ 48. $\frac{9y^{12}}{25x^{10}}$

ntroduction to Algebraic Fractions page 355

1. $\frac{x}{2}$ 2. $-3x^2$ 3. 6 4. $\frac{1}{7x^2}$ 5. $\frac{x^5}{8}$ 6. $\frac{-7}{x^2}$

7. $\frac{1}{3x^2y}$ 8. $\frac{2y}{x}$ 9. $\frac{xy^3}{5}$ 10. $\frac{1}{15}$ 11. $\frac{3}{4}$ 12. $\frac{5}{4}$

3. $\frac{8}{75}$ 14. $\frac{9}{x^3}$ 15. $9x^2$ 16. $\frac{48}{x^4}$ 17. $\frac{6}{x^2}$ 18. $\frac{9}{10x}$

9. $\frac{2}{3x^2}$ 20. $\frac{6}{x}$ 21. $\frac{8x^3}{3}$ 22. x^2 23. 2 24. $\frac{2}{x^2}$

5. $9x^2$ 26. $\frac{2}{9x^2}$ 27. $\frac{56x}{3}$ 28. $\frac{15}{x}$ 29. 5 30. $\frac{8}{15x}$

31. $\frac{12}{y}$ 32. $\frac{4y^2}{3x}$ 33. $\frac{2y^2}{x}$ 34. $\frac{3x^5}{5y^3}$ 35. $\frac{3x^6}{y^3}$ 36. $\frac{2x}{3y}$

Adding and Subtracting Algebraic Fractions, Drill and Practice page 356

1. $\frac{11}{5}$ 2. $\frac{1}{3}$ 3. 1 4. $\frac{-1}{x}$ 5. $\frac{3}{x}$ 6. $\frac{4}{3x^2}$

7. $\frac{7}{18}$ 8. $\frac{9}{8}$ 9. $\frac{5}{36}$ 10. $\frac{x}{12}$ 11. $\frac{17x}{8}$ 12. $\frac{-13x}{36}$

13. $\frac{3x+5}{x^2}$ 14. $\frac{7}{4x}$ 15. $\frac{25-12x^2}{40x}$ 16. $\frac{35+6y^2}{60y^3}$ 17. $\frac{6-15m^2}{48m^3}$

18. $\frac{3y^2-2y}{42}$ 19. $\frac{32w}{108}$ 20. $\frac{25+27x}{60x^2}$ 21. $\frac{75z+4}{80z^3}$

22. $\frac{2+3x^2}{x^2}$ 23. $\frac{7w^3-4}{w^3}$ 24. $\frac{7x^3-5}{15x^2}$ 25. $\frac{3x-29}{18}$

26. $\frac{21+x}{6x}$ 27. $\frac{28y^2-20y+45}{80y}$ 28. $\frac{w^3+11w^2-36}{9w^3}$

29. $\frac{3y-14}{20y}$ 30. $\frac{5x^2-31x+16}{120x}$

Solving Equations with Fractions, Drill and Practice page 357

1. x = 13.5 2. x = 2 3. x = 8 4. x = 0.1667 5. x = -0.125 6. x = 1.5

7. x = -0.6 8. x = 1.2 9. x = -2 10. x = 4.8 11. x = 12.25 12. x = 20.4

13. x = 3 14. x = 3.667 15. x = 0.6522 16. x = -12.38 17. x = -3 18. x = 4.625

19. x = -6 20. x = -13 21. x = 8.25 22. x = 1.2 23. x = 0.3763 24. x = 1.5

Introduction to Quadratics, Drill and Practice page 358

1. $2x^2+8x-13$ 2. $-x^2+9$ 3. $-7x^2-4x+11$ 4. $-2x^2-20x+37$

5. $17x^2-13x-34$ 6. $14x^2-3x-42$ 7. $x^2+8x-17$ 8. $-9x^2+36x-33$

9. $6x^2+23x-32$ 10. $3x^2-10x$ 11. x^2+4x+3 12. $x^2+8x+12$

13. $x^2+12x+32$ 14. $x^2+16x+63$ 15. $2x^2+19x+35$ 16. $3x^2+19x+20$

17. $x^2 - 6x + 8$

18. $x^2 - 9x + 18$

19. $5x^2 - 36x + 7$

20. $15x^2 - 46x + 35$

21. $x^2 - 5x - 14$

22. $x^2 - 81$

23. $4x^2 - 1$

24. $42x^2 - 27x - 24$

25. $x^2 + 8x + 16$

26. $x^2 + 6x + 9$

27. $x^2 - 4x + 4$

28. $25x^2 - 80x + 64$

29. $9x^2 + 54x + 81$

30. $x^2 - 22x + 121$

The Quadratic Formula, Drill and Practice page 359

1. x = 3, -5
2. x = 0, 1.333
3. x = 4, 5
4. x = -2.873, 4.873
5. x = 4.303, 0.6972
6. x = -0.75, -2
7. x = -1.307, 4.974
8. x = 3, -1
9. x = -3, 3
10. x = 4, 4
11. x = -1.333, 0.75
12. x = -0.833, 1.2
13. No solution
14. No solution

Graphing Quadratics, Drill and Practice page 360

1.

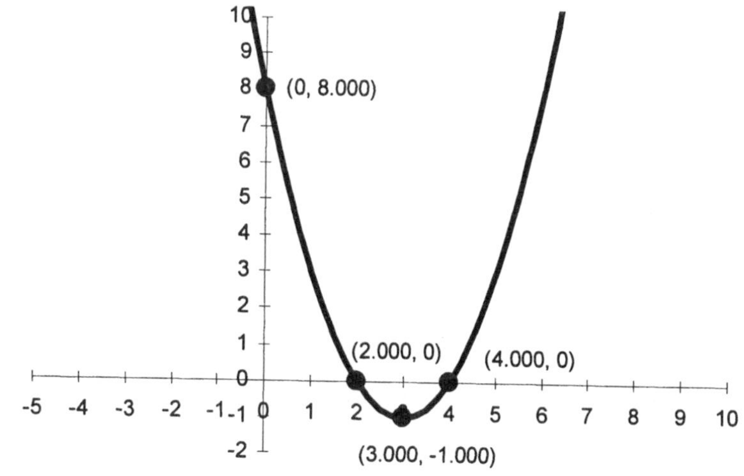

2.

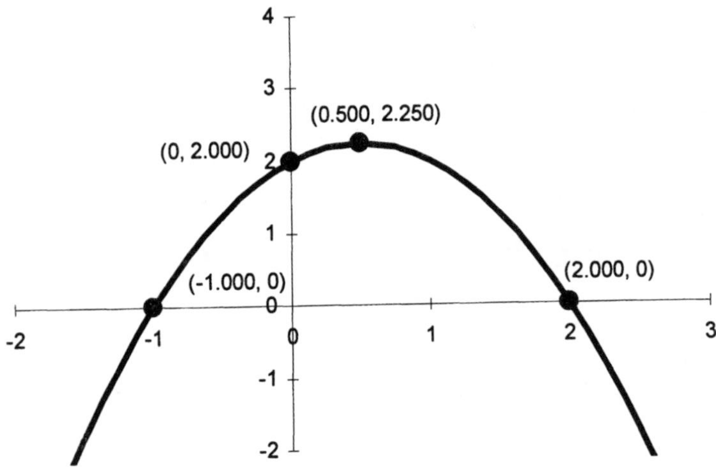
(0.500, 2.250)
(0, 2.000)
(-1.000, 0)
(2.000, 0)
4
3
2
1
0
-1
-2
-2
-1
0
1
2
3

3.

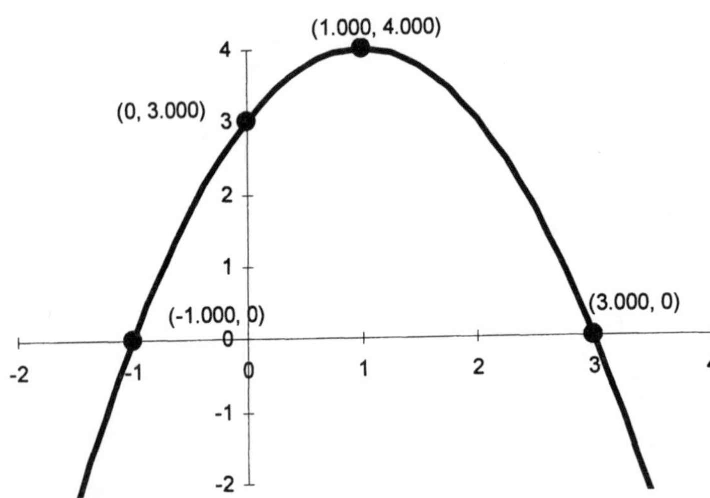
(1.000, 4.000)
(0, 3.000)
(-1.000, 0)
(3.000, 0)
4
3
2
1
0
-1
-2
-2
-1
0
1
2
3
4

4.

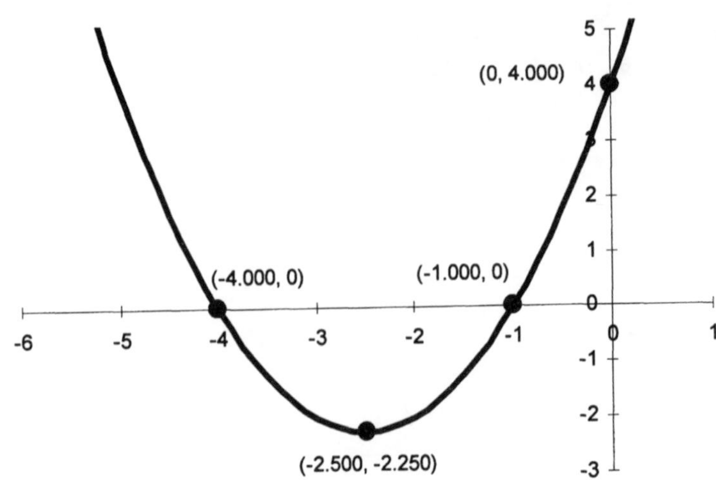
(0, 4.000)
(-4.000, 0)
(-1.000, 0)
(-2.500, -2.250)
5
4
2
1
0
-1
-2
-3
-6
-5
-4
-3
-2
-1
0
1

5.

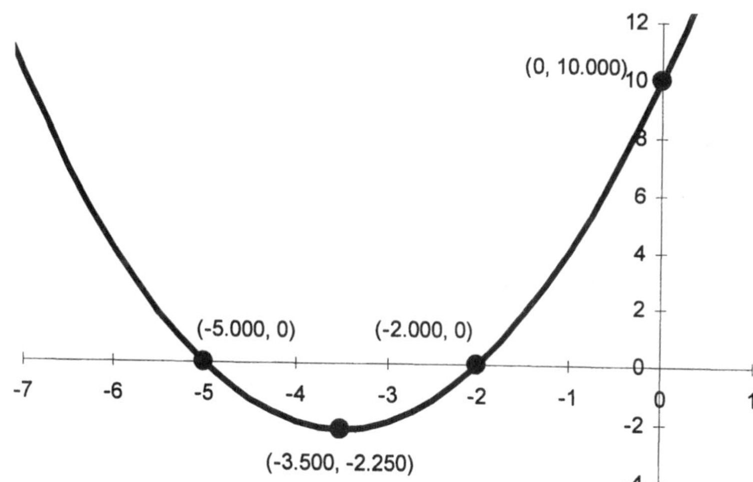

(0, 10.000)
(-5.000, 0)
(-2.000, 0)
(-3.500, -2.250)
12
10
8
6
4
2
0
-2
-4
-7
-6
-5
-4
-3
-2
-1
0
1

6.

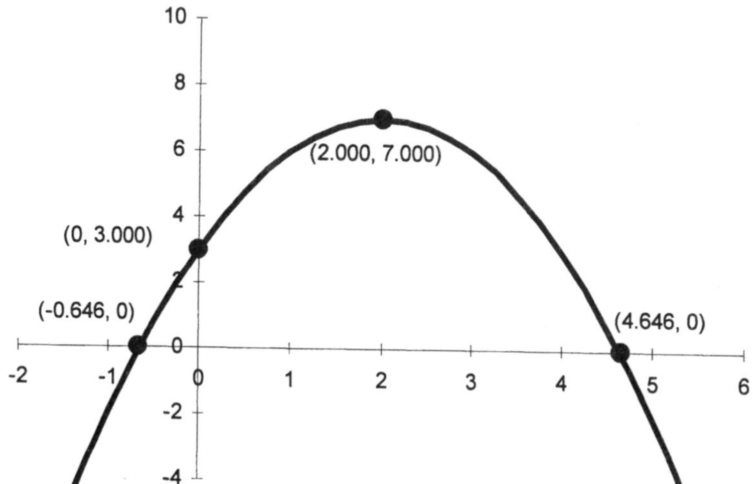

(2.000, 7.000)
(0, 3.000)
(-0.646, 0)
(4.646, 0)
10
8
6
4
2
0
-2
-4
-2
-1
0
1
2
3
4
5
6

7.

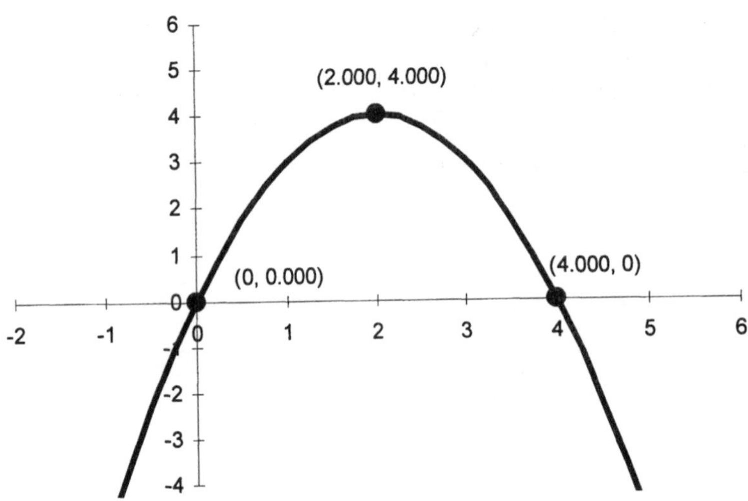

8.

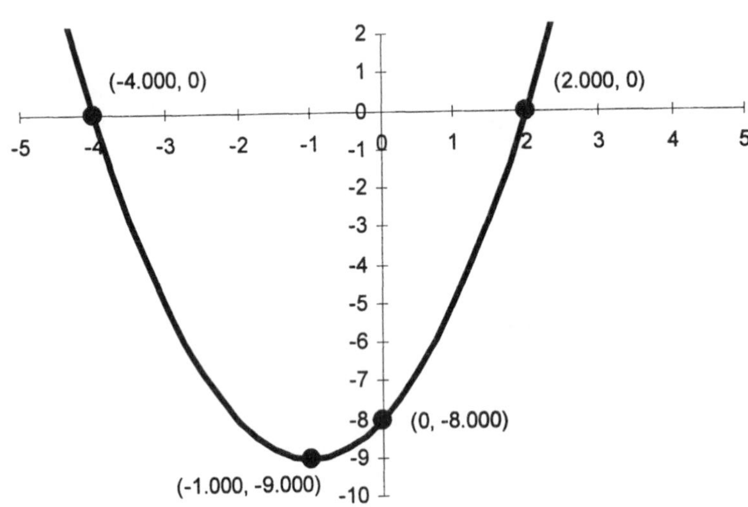

<u>**Factoring, Drill and Practice page 361**</u>

1. $3(x + 2)$	2. $6(3x - 2)$	3. $15(2x - 1)$	4. $7(6x - 1)$
5. $6x(4x - 3)$	6. $5x^2(5x^2 - 3)$	7. $3x(-5x^2 + 3)$	8. $2x(16 - 9x)$
9. $8x(5x - 2)$	10. $7x^2(-3x^2 + 7)$	11. $2x^3(3x^2 - 20)$	12. $x(-4x + 1)$
13. $(x + 6)(x + 1)$	14. $(x + 4)(x + 2)$	15. $(x + 5)(x + 4)$	16. $(x + 10)(x + 3)$
17. $(x - 5)(x - 3)$	18. $(x - 9)(x - 1)$	19. $(x - 3)(x - 3)$	20. $(x - 6)(x + 3)$
21. $(x - 6)(x + 5)$	22. $(x - 4)(x + 1)$	23. $(x - 11)(x + 7)$	24. $(x - 10)(x - 3)$

25. $(x - 7)(x - 2)$
26. $(x - 5)(x - 4)$
27. $(x - 8)(x + 7)$
28. $2(x + 8)(x + 2)$
29. $3(x + 3)(x + 7)$
30. $2x(x + 6)(x + 1)$
31. $(x - 7)(x + 7)$
32. $(x + 6)(x - 6)$
33. $(x - 2)(x + 2)$
34. $(x - 1)(x + 1)$
35. $(x - 10)(x + 10)$
36. $(x - 11)(x + 11)$
37. $3(x - 5)(x + 5)$
38. $5(x - 3)(x + 3)$
39. $x(x - 4)(x + 4)$

Appendix A
Formal Rules for Adding and Subtracting Signed Numbers

Addition of Signed Numbers

To understand addition of signed numbers you first need to know two important concepts, the **number line** and **absolute value**.

Definition: The number line is a graphical representation of numbers. Negative numbers are located to the left of zero while positive numbers are located to the right.

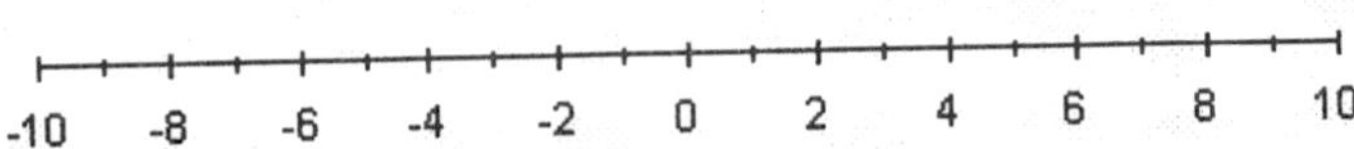

Example 1. Locate -5 on the number line.

Since the number is negative, move 5 units to the left of zero, starting from zero.

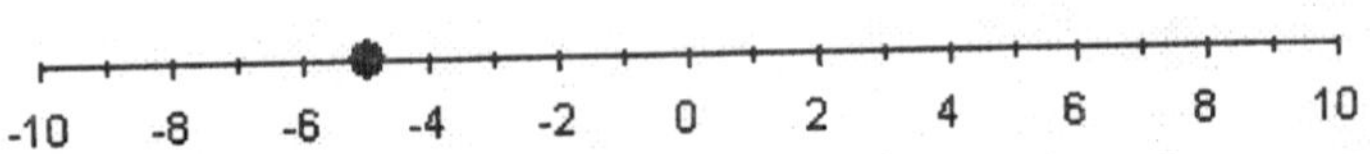

Example 2. Locate 8 on the number line.

Since the number is positive, move 8 units to the right of zero, starting from zero.

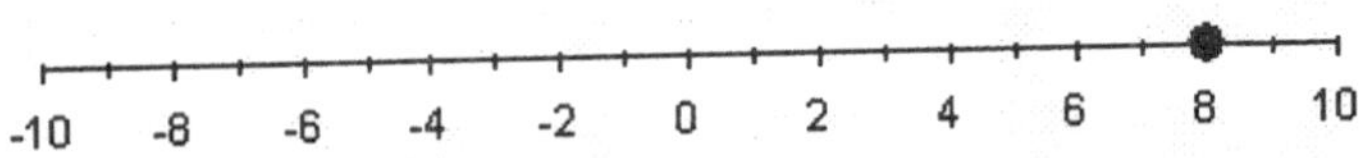

Definition: The **absolute value** of a number is the distance from the number to zero on the number line. Since absolute value is distance, the **absolute value** of a number must be positive. The **absolute value** of **b** number is denoted using the symbol $|b|$.

Example 3. $|-7|$ means:

The absolute value is the distance between the number -7 and zero on the number line.

Summary: The sign of the number gives the direction on the number line and the absolute value of the number gives the distance.

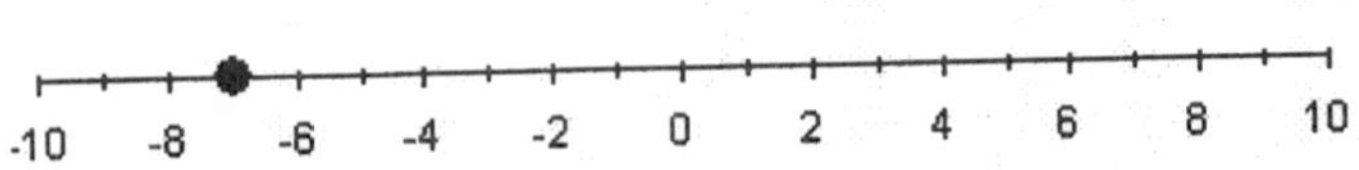

-7 is 7 units away from 0 on the number line, so $=|-7|=7$. The negative sign means move to the left on the number line.

Addition on the Number Line

To add a + b on the number line:

1. Start at zero and move to **a**.
2. From **a** move **b** units to the left if **b** is negative and to the right if **b** is positive.

Example 4. Add: 3 + 5

Start at zero and move 3 units to the right, then move 5 units to the right.

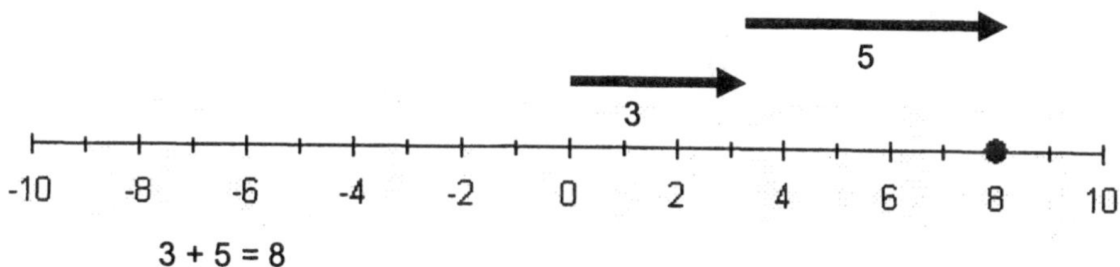

3 + 5 = 8

Example 5. Add: 4 + (-6)

Start at zero and move 4 units to the right, then 6 units to the left.

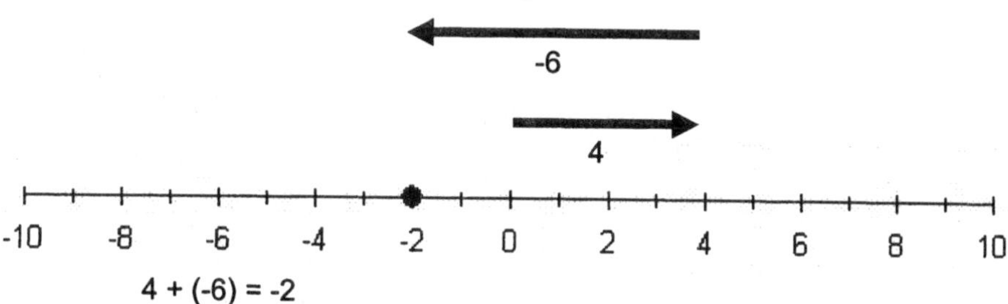

4 + (-6) = -2

Example 6. Add: (-2) + (-5)

Start at zero and move 2 units to the left, then 5 units to the left.

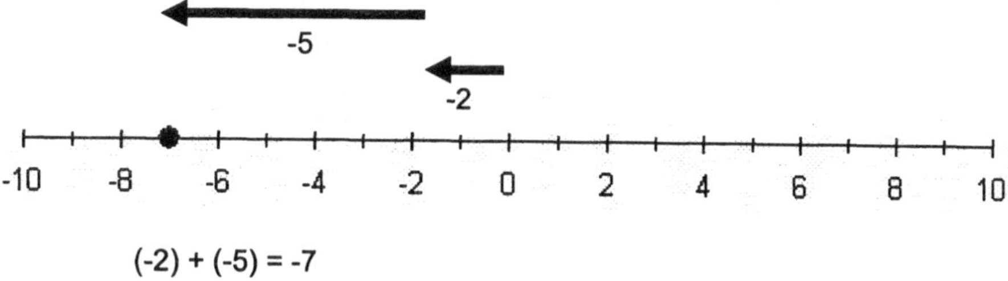

(-2) + (-5) = -7

Rules for Addition of Signed Numbers

1. Like signs: Add the absolute values of the numbers and use the common sign.

2. Unlike signs: Subtract the smaller absolute value from the larger and use the sign of the larger absolute value.

Study Tip: Make a note card with the rule for adding signed numbers. Review notecards at least twice a week as part of your homework routine.

Example 7. Add -11 + (-4) = -15

Since both numbers have the same sign, add their absolute values,
$|-11|+|-4|=11+4=15$.
Since both numbers are negative then the answer must be negative.

Example 8. Add -8 + 5 = -3

Since the numbers have unlike signs, subtract the smaller absolute value from the larger,
$|-8|-|5|=8-5=3$.
Since the negative number has the larger absolute value, the answer is negative.

Example 9. Add 9 + (-5) + 6 + (-3) + (-2)

We can change the grouping and the order of the numbers; thus we can group all of the positive numbers together and all of the negative numbers together, and then add like signs.

$$\begin{aligned} 9 + (-5) + 6 + (-3) + (-2) &= 9 + 6 + (-5) + (-3) + (-2) \\ &= 15 + (-12) \\ &= 3 \end{aligned}$$

Subtraction of Signed Numbers

Definition: 3 and –3 are **opposites** because they both are the same distance from zero on the number line but in opposite directions. They are also called **additive inverses** because their sum is zero.

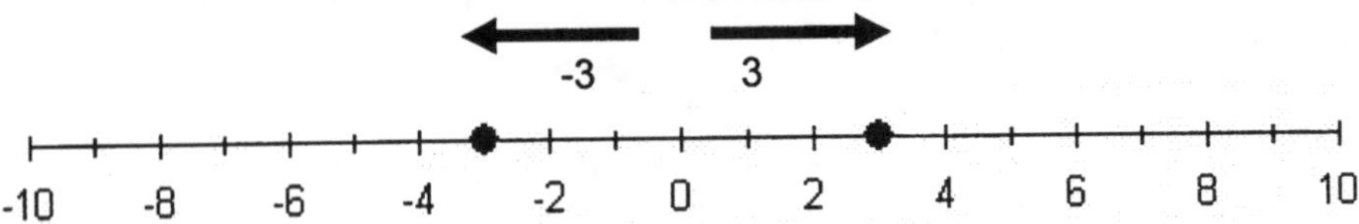

The opposite of –6 is 6. In mathematical notation, – (–6) = 6.

An important property of opposites, or additive identities, is that their sum is zero. For example, add (-6) + 6 on the number line.

Start at 0 and move 6 units to the left, then 6 units to the right.

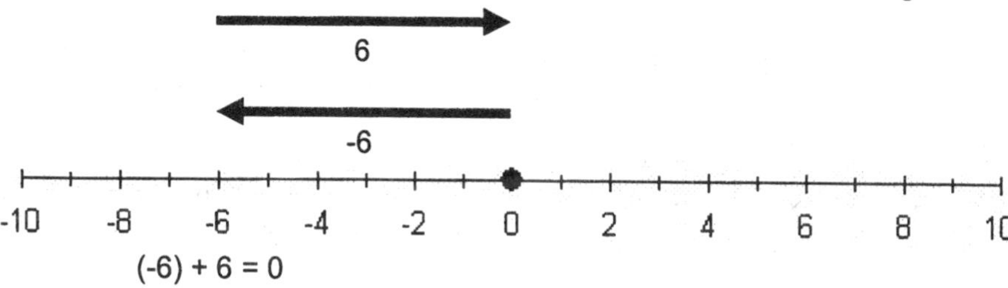

(-6) + 6 = 0

Rule for Subtraction of Signed Numbers

For any numbers **a**, and **b**, a – b = a + (-b).
To subtract, add the opposite (additive inverse) of the number being subtracted.

Study Tip: Make a note card with the rule for subtracting signed numbers.

Example 10. Subtract 4 – (-6) = 4 + 6 = 10

To subtract, add the opposite of -6 which is 6.

Example 11. Subtract -2 – 7 = -2 + (-7) = -9

To subtract, add the opposite of 7 which is -7. Since the signs are alike, add their absolute values. Since both numbers are negative the answer must be negative.

Example 12. Subtract 8 – 12 = 8 + (-12) = -4

To subtract, add the opposite of 12, -12. Since the signs are alike, subtract the smaller absolute value from the larger,

$$|-12| - |8| = 4.$$

Since the negative number has the larger absolute value, the answer is negative.

Summary: Adding and subtracting signed numbers are basic skills that you must master in order to do well in Beginning Algebra. Go back and review the section entitled "Signed Numbers" on page one. Do the homework exercises starting on page 13 and on page 347.

Rules for adding signed numbers:

1. Like signs: Add the absolute values of the numbers and use the common sign.

2. Unlike signs: Subtract the smaller absolute value from the larger and use the sign of the larger absolute value.

Rule for subtracting numbers:

For any numbers **a**, and **b**, a – b = a + (-b).
To subtract, add the opposite (additive inverse) of the number being subtracted.

Weekly Cumulative Review Problems

Week One Review Problems

1. The bar graph below shows the annual profit and lose, in millions of dollars for the Blue Bell Publishing Company.

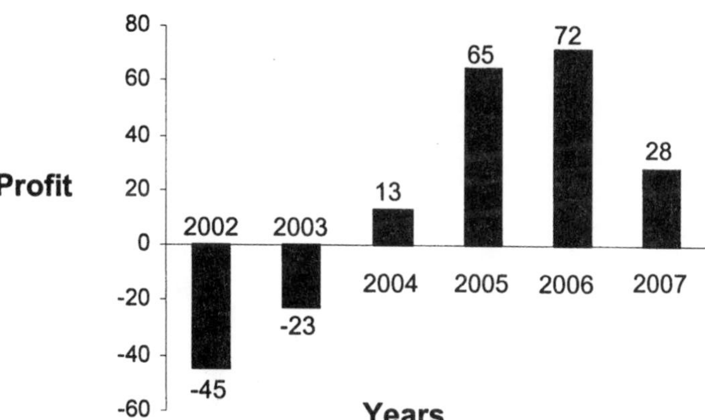

a. What is the difference between the profit in 2003 and 2002?

b. What is the difference between the profit in 2005 and 2002?

c. What is the difference between the profit in 2007 and 2006?

d. Determine the profit for the six years.

2. Duce Stanley wants to start a cabinet business. He spends $9,250 on supplies and plans to charge $575 a cabinet.

a. Complete the table below.

Cabinet	Calculation	Profit
10		
50		
c		

b. What is the equation that relates profit and number of cabinets made?

3. Simplify the algebraic expression.

a. $6x - 7 - 9x + 4$

b. $2x - 3(4x - 5)$

Week Two Review Problems

Solve each equation.

a. $6x - 11 = -112$

b. $-7x + 28 = 5x - 12$

c. $2(5-3x) = 85 - 2x$

d. $\frac{5x}{8} = 17$

e. $6(2 - 4x) + 10x = -8x + 21 - 6x$

Week Three Review Problems

1. Two companies offer you very similar jobs. CSI Company pays 6% commission on your sales plus $16,000 a year. Survivor Company B pays 13% commission on your sales.

a. Complete the table below.

Company CSI

Sales	Calculation	Wages
100,000		
250,000		
s		

Company Survivor

Sales	Calculation	Wages
100,000		
250,000		
s		

b. How much do you have to sell to earn the same amount in wages?

2. Rotor Ring Phone Company charges \$.45 per call and \$1.00 a minute after the first 5 minutes.

a. Create a table and find the formula for the cost of a phone call.

Minutes	Calculation	Cost
5		
15		
M		C

b. If it costs \$10.50, how long did you talk?

3. Solve for y

$3x + 2y = 11$

Week Four Review Problems

1. Professor Hunter computes his grades as follows:

   45% for the average of 4 tests
   20% for the average of homework assignments
   35% for the final exam

   a. Find Selena's average if she has a 93 test average, 88 homework average and a 99 final exam score.

   b. What does George Bush have to get on his final exam if he has a 68 test average, a 79 homework average, and he wants a 70 for the grade of the course?

2. The bookstore is having a 15% off sale.

   a. Complete the table below.

Cost	Calculation	Sales Price
15.00		
42.00		
c		

   b. If an item had a sales price of $65.85, what was the original cost of the item?

3. Describe each step.

	Step
$3x + 2(4x-1) = 4x - 3$	
$3x + 8x - 2 = 4x - 3$	______________
$11x - 2 = 4x - 3$	______________
$11x - 2 + 2 = 4x - 3 + 2$	______________
$11x = 4x - 1$	______________
$11x - 4x = 4x - 4x - 1$	______________
$7x = -1$	______________
$\frac{7x}{7} = \frac{-1}{7}$	______________
$x = -.1429$	______________

4. Find the mistake.

$$4(2x-5) = 3x + 7$$
$$8x - 20 = 3x + 7$$
$$8x - 20 + 20 = 3x + 7 + 20$$
$$8x = 3x + 27$$
$$8x + 3x = 3x + 3x + 27$$
$$11x = 27$$
$$\frac{11x}{11} = \frac{27}{11}$$
$$X = 2.\overline{45}$$

Week Five Review Problems

1. The graph below represents the annual rainfall that fell at Death Valley's Ranger Station.

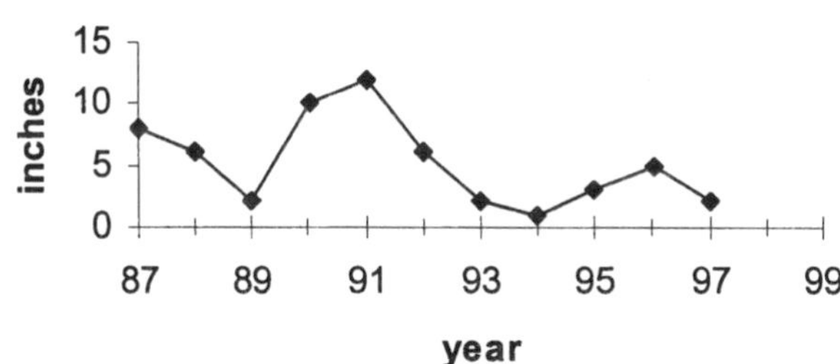

a. How much rainfall was there in 1987?

b. What year or years had 10 inches of rainfall?

c. What year had the most rainfall?

d. When did the greatest increase in annual rainfall occur?

2. Solve the following inequalities.

a. $11 - 3x \leq 53$

b. $2 \leq 7 + 2x \leq 15$

3. The Windless Surfing Company has determined its cost for making custom sails to be

$$C = 380 + 18S,$$

where C is the cost in dollars and S is the number of sails. If the cost can be higher than $4,000 but must be smaller than $11,000, how many sails can they make per week? (You must set up an inequality equation.)

Week Six Review Problems

1. An internet provider, Boundless Web, charges $12 per month plus 25 cents an hour.

   a. Complete the table below.

Hours	Calculation	Cost
20		
50		
100		
h		

   b. What is the equation that relates cost and hours?

   c. Use the results in Part a. to graph the equation in Part b. Choose an appropriate scale and only graph the portion that makes sense to the problem. Label the axes.

Hours	**Cost**	**Point (h, c)**
20		
50		
100		

2. Use the table to answer the following questions.

Year	**Number of Computers Sold**
1995	8.2 million
2000	13.5 million

   a. Find the average rate of change.

   b. Find the percent increase.

3. Find the x and y intercepts and graph the lines. Label your axis and choose an appropriate scale.

a. $y = 3x - 21$

b. $.04x - 18y = 7$

Week Seven Review Problems

1. You are trying to decide which phone company to chose for your business. Company Static will charge you \$170 per month while Company Ringer will charge you \$89 per month plus 18¢ per minute.

   a. Write an equation for the cost of making phone calls for each company.

   b. Use the equations to find when the two companies will cost you the same amount. Label this point on the graph you create below.

   c. Graph both equations on the same set of axis. Label your axis and choose an appropriate scale. Only graph the portion that is relevant to the problem.

   d. Use the graph to find when Static costs more than Ringer.

   e. Use the graph to find when Ringer costs more than Static.

   f. What does the y intercepts for both equations mean in terms of the problem?

   g. Find the slope of each line and explain what they mean in terms of the problem.

Week Eight Review Problems

1. There are 1400 bacteria initially present in a culture. The culture grows at a rate of 4% a day.

   a. Complete the table below.

Time	Calculation	Number of Bacteria
Initial Day		
1 Day Later		
2 Days Later		
3 Days Later		
n Days Later		

   b. Use the equation to find how many bacteria there will be in 30 days.

2. Assuming that the interest is compounded monthly, the formula below computes how much money will be in your account at sometime in the future.

$$FV = P(1 + i)^n$$

where FV is Future Value
P is amount invested
i is interest rate per month
n is the number of months

   a. A couple invests $2500 at an annual interest rate of 6%. How much money will they have after 10 years? (Hint: i = 0.06/12)

   b. How much money should you invest at an annual interest rate of 3% if you want $20,000 in 30 years? (Hint: i = 0.03/12)

Week Nine Review Problems

1. Use the following formula to answer the question below.

$$P = A\left[\frac{i}{1-(1+i)^{-n}}\right]$$

P is the monthly payment
A is the amount of the loan
n is the number of payments
i is the interest rate per month

Tom Ridge is borrowing $35,000 to buy a car. He takes out a 48 month car loan at an annual interest rate of 3%. Find Tom's monthly payments. (Hint: i= .03/12)

2. Simplify. Write with positive exponents only.

a. $x \cdot x^3$ b. $(5x^2)^4$ c. $\frac{16x}{4x^5}$

d. x^{-3} e. $8x^{-3}$

3. Write the number in Scientific Notation.

620,000,000

4. Write the number in Decimal Notation.

2.6×10^{-3}

Week Ten Review Problems

1. Perform the indicated operations.

a. $\frac{3x}{7y^2} \cdot \frac{49y^3}{6x^2}$

b. $\frac{5x}{3x^3} \div \frac{9x^2}{25}$

c. $\frac{4}{3x} + \frac{5}{15}$

d. $\frac{1}{2} - \frac{7}{x}$

2. Solve each equation.

a. $\frac{x}{3} + \frac{1}{2} = \frac{5}{6}$

b. $\frac{x-1}{3} - \frac{x-2}{2} = \frac{x+1}{6}$

3. Two students pool their money to buy raffle tickets from the MCCC Math Club. One student puts in \$10 and the other student puts in \$7, if they win \$210, how should they divide their winnings?

Week Eleven Review Problems

1. Simplify the following:

   a. $x^2 + 2x + 3 - 2x^2 + 1$

   b. $2(x^2 - x + 1) - 2(x^2 - x - 1)$

2. Multiply:

   a. $(x - 3)(x + 5)$

   c. $(x + 4)^2$

3. A rocket is launched from the top of a cliff with an initial velocity of 320 feet per second. The height (in feet) of the rocket is given by the equation:

$$h = -16t^2 + 320t + 4800,$$

where t is the number of seconds the rocket is in the air.
Find the height of the rocket for

a. $t = 0$

b. $t = 5$

c. $t = 8$

d. $t = 10$

e. $t = 15$

f. $t = 30$

g. According to the calculations above, when will the rocket reach its maximum height?

h. According to the calculations above, estimate when the rocket hits the ground?

i. Graph the points a through f.

Week Twelve Review Problems

1. State the quadratic formula.

2. If the revenue function is given by: $R = 5x^2 - 20x$

   and the Cost function is given by: $C = 7x^2 - 50x + 100.$

   a. Find the profit equation.

   b. Find the break even points.

   c. Find the values for x that will give a profit of 150.

Week Thirteen Review Problems

1. State the formula for the x coordinate of the vertex

2. Deadly Toy Company makes BB guns. The cost of making *x* hundred BB guns per month is

$$C = .3x^2 - 65x + 150$$

and the revenue from selling *x* BB guns per month is

$$R = -.7x^2 + 25x.$$

C and R are in thousands of dollars.

a. Find the equation for profit. (Profit = Revenue - Cost)

b. Graph the profit equation. Explain what the vertex, x intercepts, p intercept mean in terms of making rocking chairs. Make sure you label the axis and use an appropriate scale.

c. Suppose the company needs to make $1,000 in profit (P = 1,000). Graph this line on the graph above and find where the line intersects the graph of the quadratic. Explain what the answers mean.

3. Factor

a. $3x^2 + 6x$

b. $x^2 + 12x + 20$

c. $x^2 - 49$

How to Use the TI-30X IIS Calculator

e following pages contain Power Point slides that accompany the CD that comes with the book. Learning w to use a calculator effectively is an important skill for MAT 011 students.

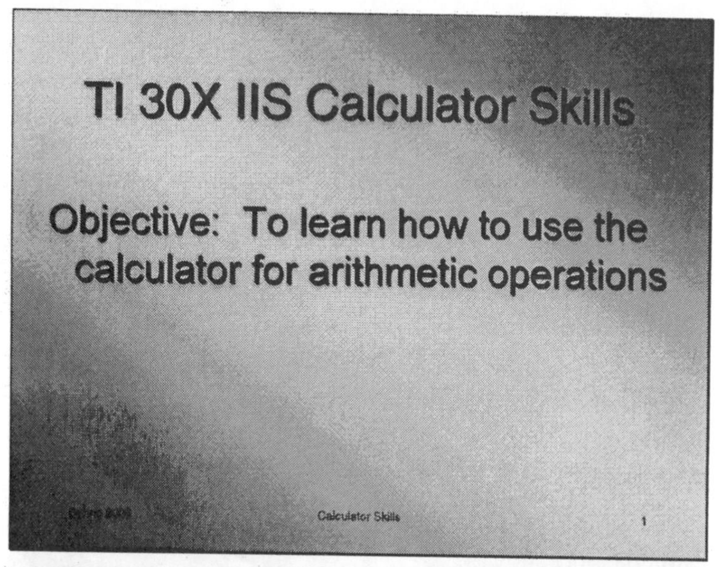

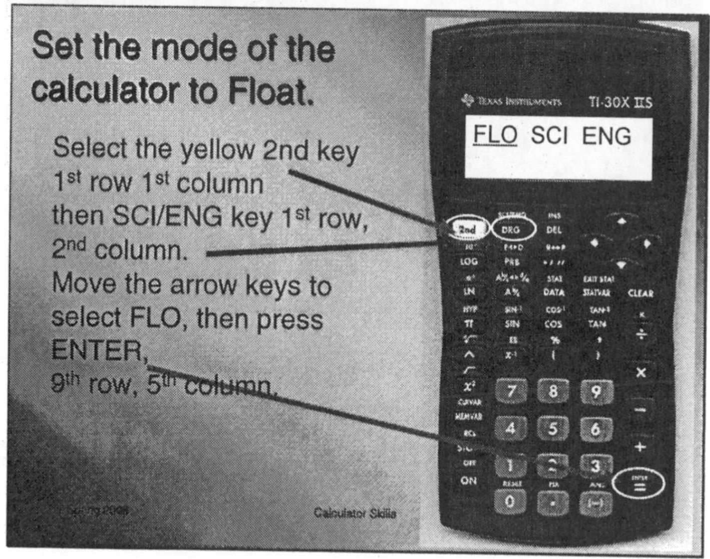

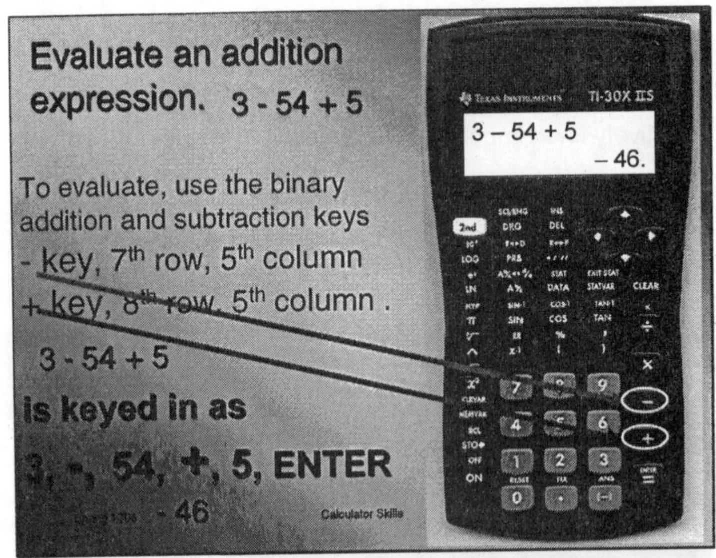

Evaluate an addition expression. 3 - 54 + 5
To evaluate, use the binary addition and subtraction keys
- key, 7th row, 5th column
+ key, 8th row, 5th column .
3 - 54 + 5
is keyed in as
3, -, 54, +, 5, ENTER
- 46
Calculator Skills
TEXAS INSTRUMENTS TI-30X IIS
3 – 54 + 5
– 46.

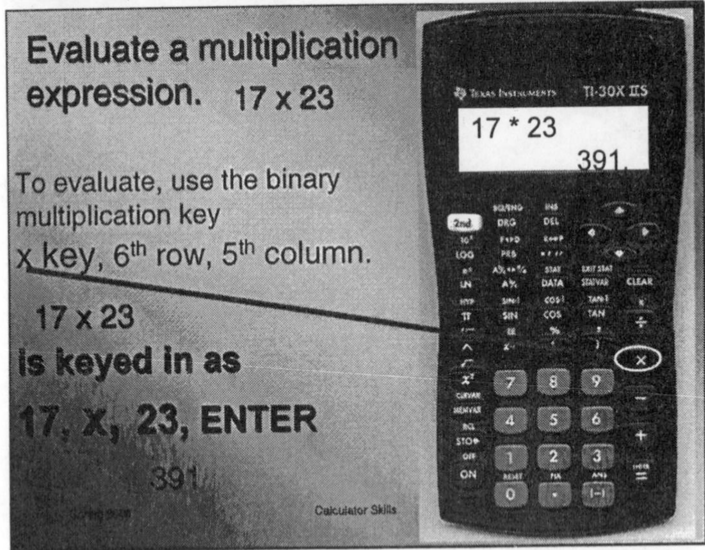

Evaluate a multiplication expression. 17 x 23
To evaluate, use the binary multiplication key
x key, 6th row, 5th column.
17 x 23
is keyed in as
17, X, 23, ENTER
391
Calculator Skills
TEXAS INSTRUMENTS TI-30X IIS
17 * 23
391.

Note that the key symbol is marked x, but * symbol shows in the display.

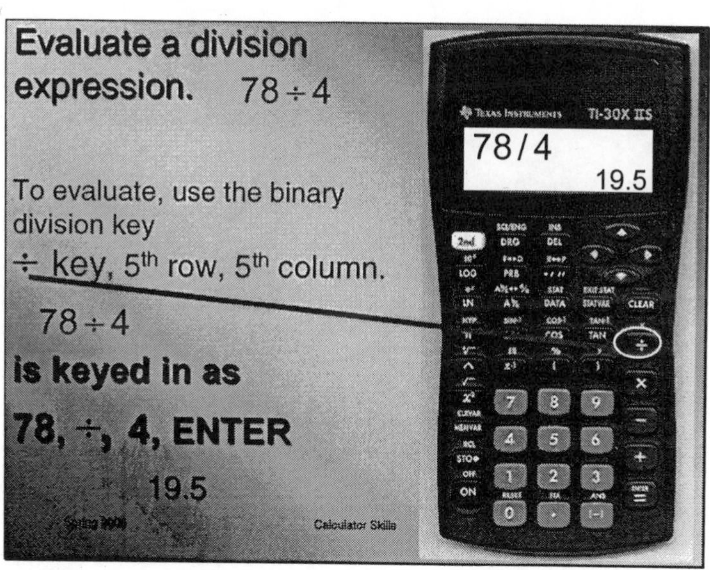

Evaluate a division expression. 78 ÷ 4
To evaluate, use the binary division key
÷ key, 5th row, 5th column.
78 ÷ 4
is keyed in as
78, ÷, 4, ENTER
19.5
Calculator Skills
TEXAS INSTRUMENTS TI-30X IIS
78/4
19.5

Note that the key symbol is marked ÷, but / symbol shows in the display.

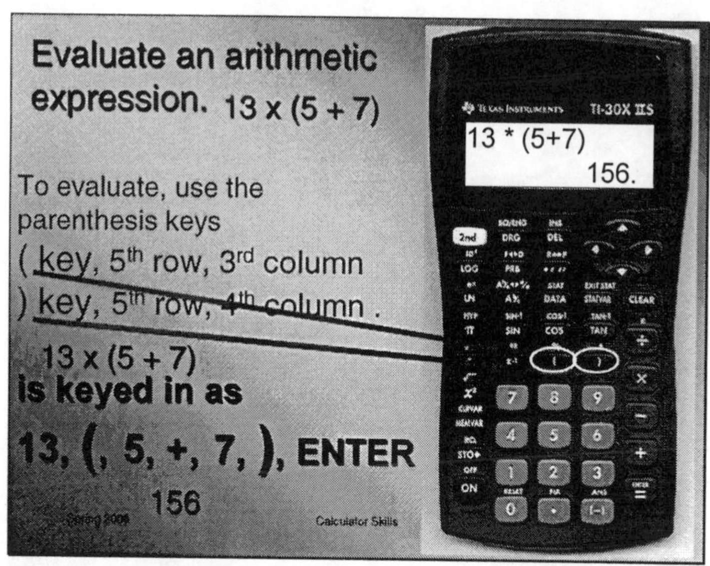

Evaluate an arithmetic expression. 13 x (5 + 7)
To evaluate, use the parenthesis keys
(key, 5th row, 3rd column
) key, 5th row, 4th column .
13 x (5 + 7)
is keyed in as
13, (, 5, +, 7,), ENTER
156
Calculator Skills
TEXAS INSTRUMENTS TI-30X IIS
13 * (5+7)
156.

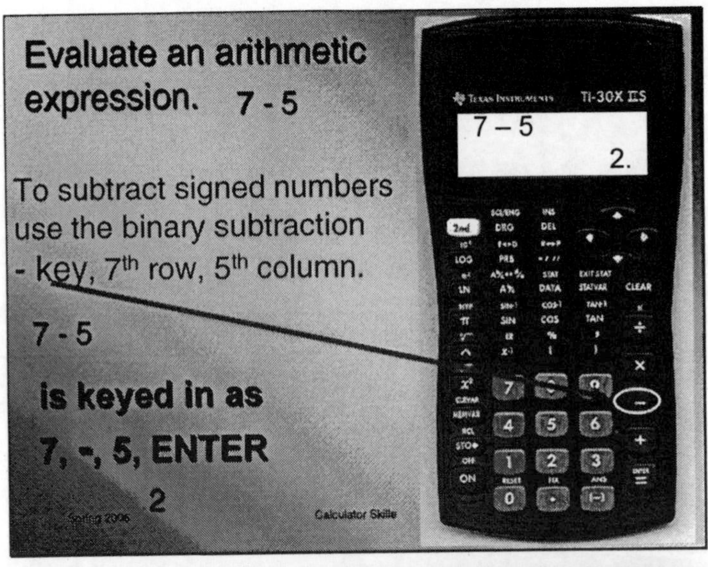
Evaluate an arithmetic expression. 7 - 5
To subtract signed numbers use the binary subtraction - key, 7th row, 5th column.
7 - 5
is keyed in as
7, -, 5, ENTER
2
Spring 2006
Calculator Skills
TI-30X IIS
7 – 5
2.

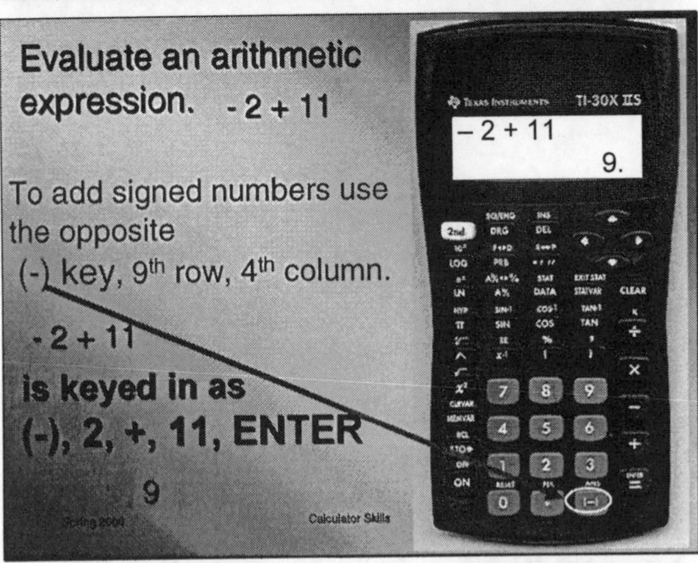
Evaluate an arithmetic expression. - 2 + 11
To add signed numbers use the opposite (-) key, 9th row, 4th column.
- 2 + 11
is keyed in as
(-), 2, +, 11, ENTER
9
Spring 2006
Calculator Skills
TI-30X IIS
– 2 + 11
9.

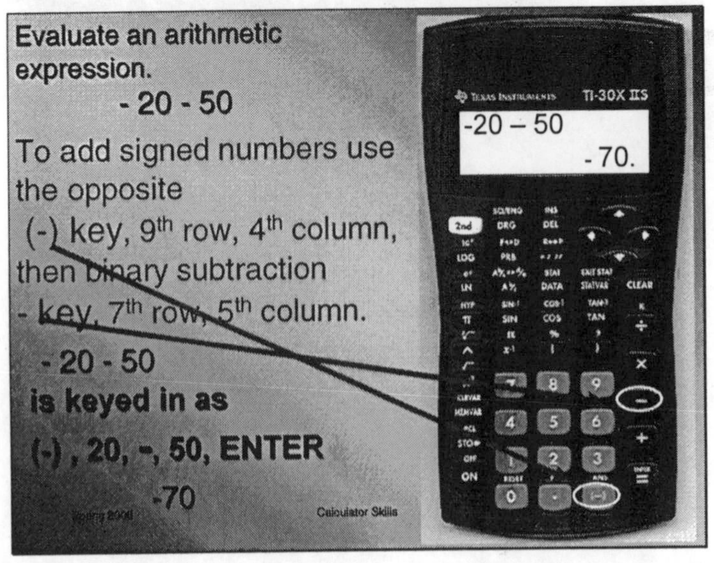
Evaluate an arithmetic expression.
- 20 - 50
To add signed numbers use the opposite (-) key, 9th row, 4th column, then binary subtraction - key, 7th row, 5th column.
- 20 - 50
is keyed in as
(-) , 20, -, 50, ENTER
-70
Spring 2006
Calculator Skills
TI-30X IIS
-20 – 50
- 70.

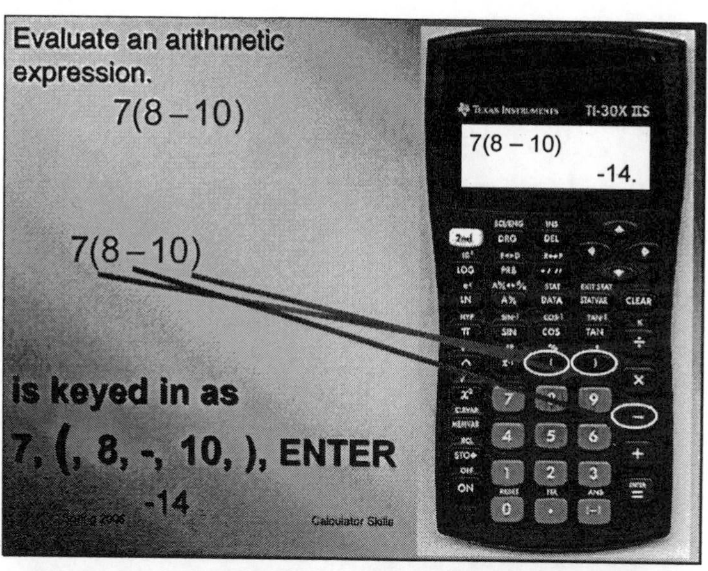
Evaluate an arithmetic expression.
7(8 – 10)
TEXAS INSTRUMENTS TI-30X IIS
7(8 – 10)
-14.
7(8 – 10)
is keyed in as
7, (, 8, -, 10,), ENTER
-14
Calculator Skills

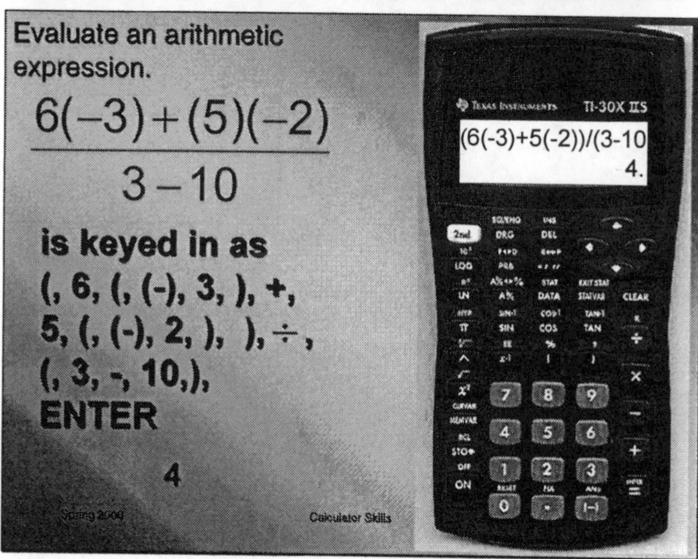
Evaluate an arithmetic expression.
6(–3) + (5)(–2) / 3 – 10
TEXAS INSTRUMENTS TI-30X IIS
(6(-3)+5(-2))/(3-10
4.
is keyed in as
(, 6, (, (-), 3,), +,
5, (, (-), 2,),), ÷,
(, 3, -, 10,),
ENTER
4
Calculator Skills

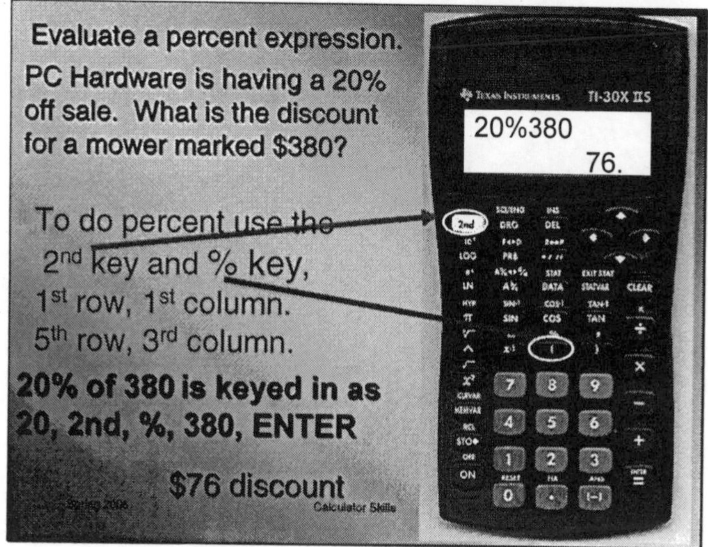
Evaluate a percent expression.
PC Hardware is having a 20% off sale. What is the discount for a mower marked $380?
TEXAS INSTRUMENTS TI-30X IIS
20%380
76.
To do percent use the 2nd key and % key,
1st row, 1st column.
5th row, 3rd column.
20% of 380 is keyed in as
20, 2nd, %, 380, ENTER
$76 discount
Calculator Skills

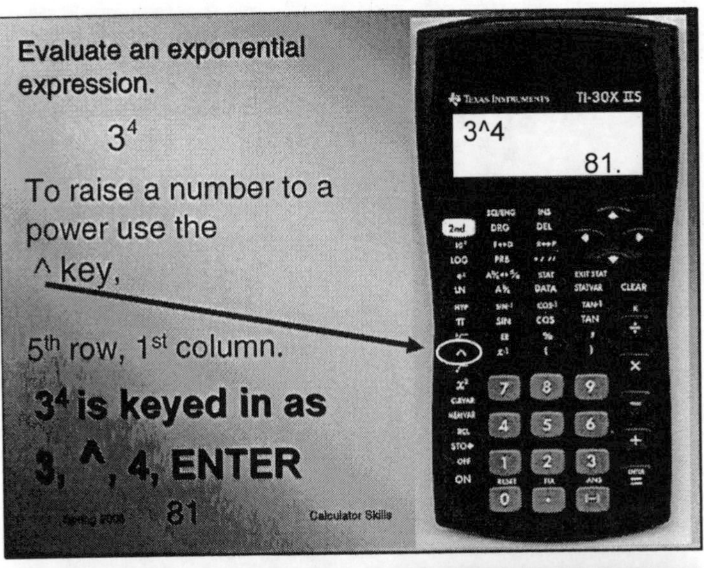
Evaluate an exponential expression.
3^4
To raise a number to a power use the
^ key,
5th row, 1st column.
3^4 is keyed in as
3, ^, 4, ENTER
81
Calculator Skills
TEXAS INSTRUMENTS
TI-30X IIS
3^4
81.

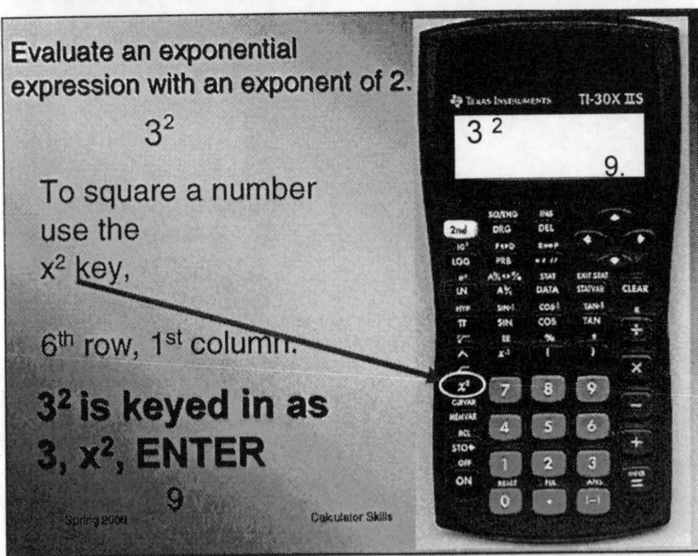
Evaluate an exponential expression with an exponent of 2.
3^2
To square a number use the
x^2 key,
6th row, 1st column.
3^2 is keyed in as
3, x^2, ENTER
9
Spring 2006
Calculator Skills
TEXAS INSTRUMENTS
TI-30X IIS
3 2
9.

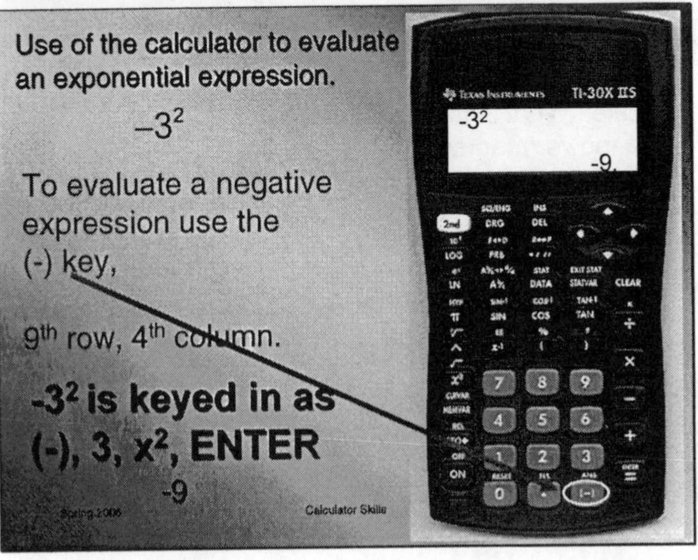
Use of the calculator to evaluate an exponential expression.
−3^2
To evaluate a negative expression use the
(-) key,
9th row, 4th column.
-3^2 is keyed in as
(-), 3, x^2, ENTER
-9
Spring 2006
Calculator Skills
TEXAS INSTRUMENTS
TI-30X IIS
-3^2
-9.

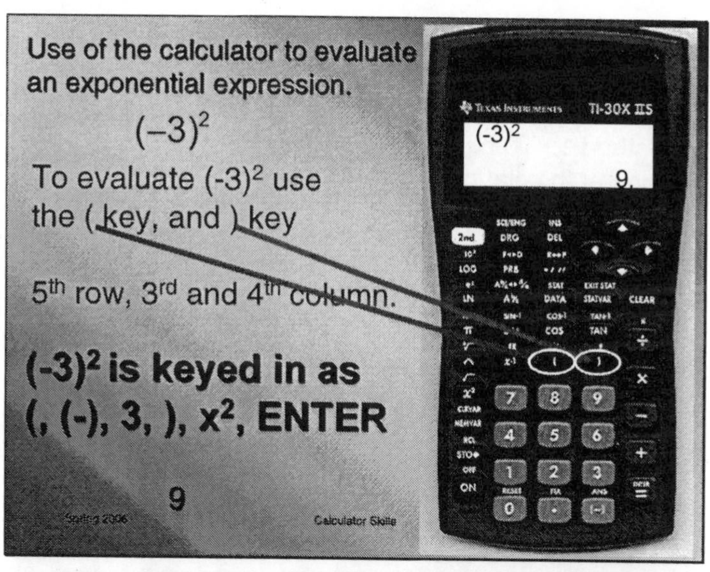
Use of the calculator to evaluate
an exponential expression.
(-3)2
To evaluate (-3)2 use
the (key, and) key
5th row, 3rd and 4th column.
(-3)2 is keyed in as
(, (-), 3,), x2, ENTER
9
Calculator Skills
TEXAS INSTRUMENTS TI-30X IIS
(-3)2
9.

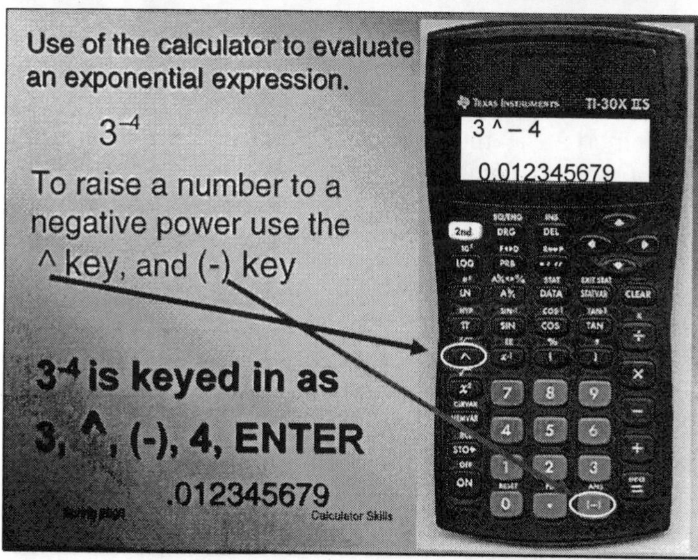
Use of the calculator to evaluate
an exponential expression.
3-4
To raise a number to a
negative power use the
^ key, and (-) key
3-4 is keyed in as
3, ^, (-), 4, ENTER
.012345679
Calculator Skills
TEXAS INSTRUMENTS TI-30X IIS
3 ^ - 4
0.012345679

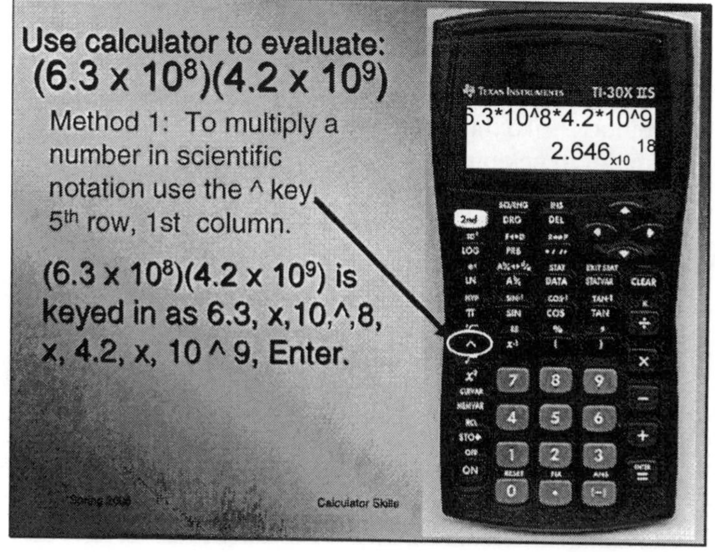
Use calculator to evaluate:
(6.3 x 108)(4.2 x 109)
Method 1: To multiply a
number in scientific
notation use the ^ key
5th row, 1st column.
(6.3 x 108)(4.2 x 109) is
keyed in as 6.3, x,10,^,8,
x, 4.2, x, 10 ^ 9, Enter.
Calculator Skills
TEXAS INSTRUMENTS TI-30X IIS
6.3*10^8*4.2*10^9
2.646x10 18

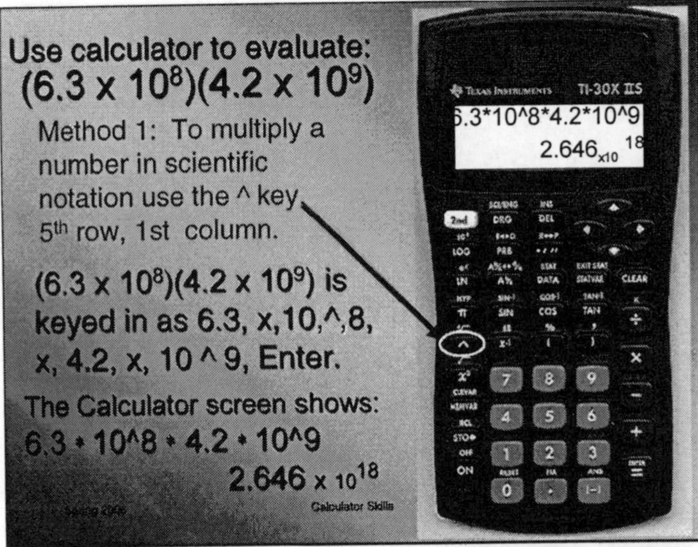
Use calculator to evaluate:
(6.3 x 10^8)(4.2 x 10^9)
Method 1: To multiply a number in scientific notation use the ^ key, 5th row, 1st column.
(6.3 x 10^8)(4.2 x 10^9) is keyed in as 6.3, x,10,^,8, x, 4.2, x, 10 ^ 9, Enter.
The Calculator screen shows:
6.3 * 10^8 * 4.2 * 10^9
2.646 x 10^18
Calculator Skills
TEXAS INSTRUMENTS TI-30X IIS
.3*10^8*4.2*10^9
2.646x10 18

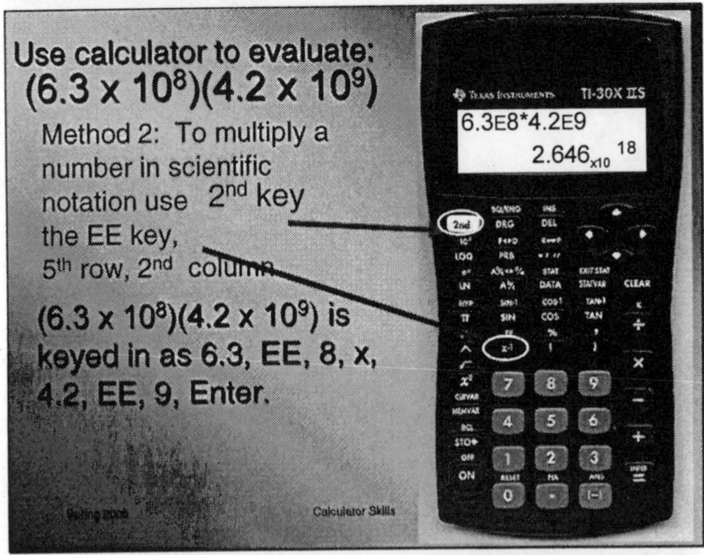
Use calculator to evaluate:
(6.3 x 10^8)(4.2 x 10^9)
Method 2: To multiply a number in scientific notation use 2nd key the EE key, 5th row, 2nd column
(6.3 x 10^8)(4.2 x 10^9) is keyed in as 6.3, EE, 8, x, 4.2, EE, 9, Enter.
Calculator Skills
TEXAS INSTRUMENTS TI-30X IIS
6.3E8*4.2E9
2.646x10 18

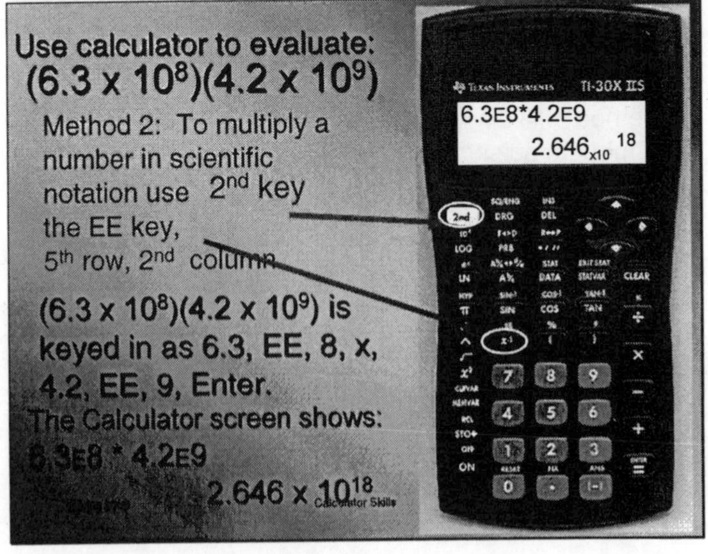
Use calculator to evaluate:
(6.3 x 10^8)(4.2 x 10^9)
Method 2: To multiply a number in scientific notation use 2nd key the EE key, 5th row, 2nd column
(6.3 x 10^8)(4.2 x 10^9) is keyed in as 6.3, EE, 8, x, 4.2, EE, 9, Enter.
The Calculator screen shows:
6.3E8 * 4.2E9
2.646 x 10^18
TEXAS INSTRUMENTS TI-30X IIS
6.3E8*4.2E9
2.646x10 18

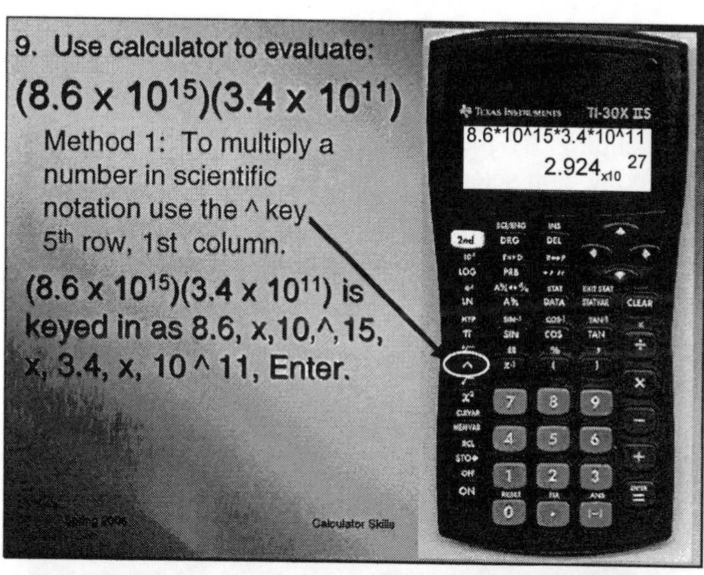
9. Use calculator to evaluate:
(8.6 x 10^15)(3.4 x 10^11)
Method 1: To multiply a number in scientific notation use the ^ key, 5th row, 1st column.
(8.6 x 10^15)(3.4 x 10^11) is keyed in as 8.6, x,10,^,15, x, 3.4, x, 10 ^ 11, Enter.
8.6*10^15*3.4*10^11
2.924x10 27
TI-30X IIS
Calculator Skills

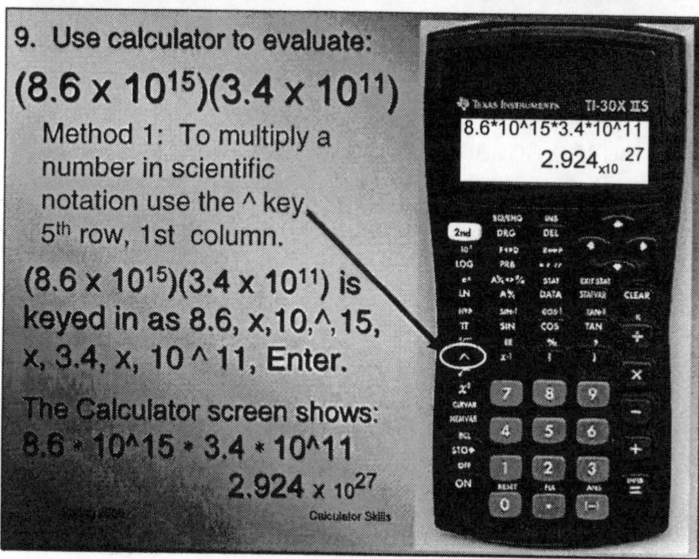
9. Use calculator to evaluate:
(8.6 x 10^15)(3.4 x 10^11)
Method 1: To multiply a number in scientific notation use the ^ key, 5th row, 1st column.
(8.6 x 10^15)(3.4 x 10^11) is keyed in as 8.6, x,10,^,15, x, 3.4, x, 10 ^ 11, Enter.
The Calculator screen shows:
8.6 * 10^15 * 3.4 * 10^11
2.924 x 10^27
8.6*10^15*3.4*10^11
2.924x10 27
TI-30X IIS
Calculator Skills

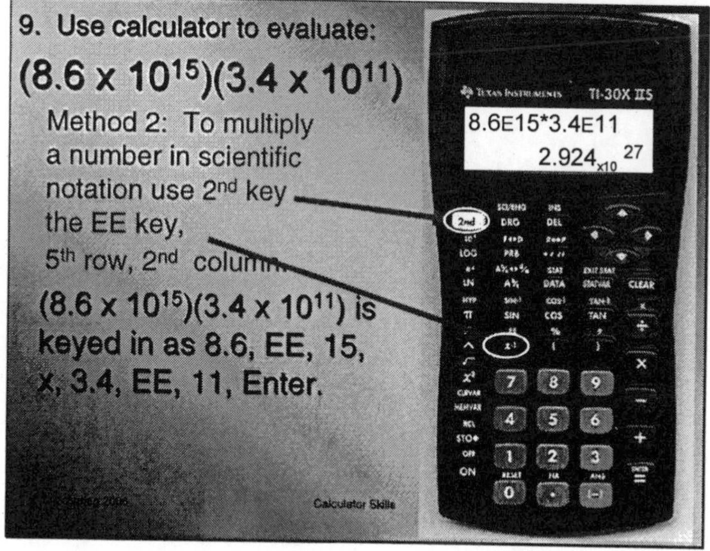
9. Use calculator to evaluate:
(8.6 x 10^15)(3.4 x 10^11)
Method 2: To multiply a number in scientific notation use 2nd key the EE key, 5th row, 2nd column.
(8.6 x 10^15)(3.4 x 10^11) is keyed in as 8.6, EE, 15, x, 3.4, EE, 11, Enter.
8.6E15*3.4E11
2.924x10 27
TI-30X IIS
Calculator Skills

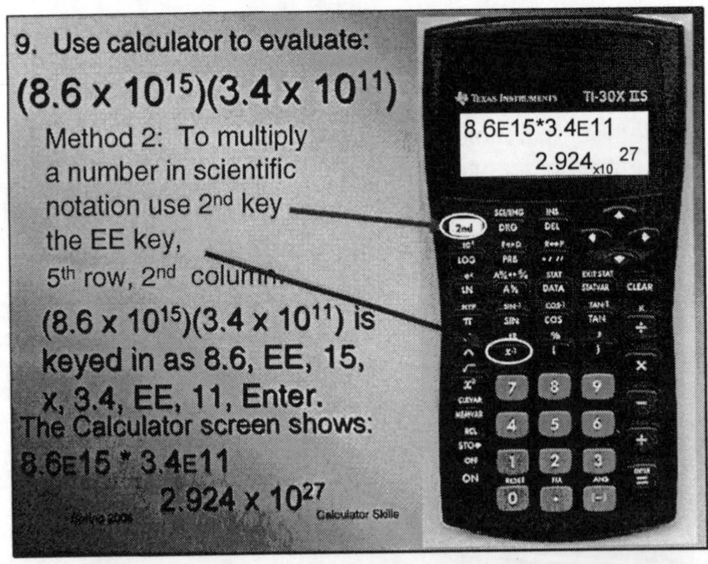
9. Use calculator to evaluate:
(8.6 x 10^15)(3.4 x 10^11)
Method 2: To multiply a number in scientific notation use 2nd key the EE key, 5th row, 2nd column.
(8.6 x 10^15)(3.4 x 10^11) is keyed in as 8.6, EE, 15, x, 3.4, EE, 11, Enter.
The Calculator screen shows:
8.6E15 * 3.4E11
2.924 x 10^27
Calculator Skills
8.6E15*3.4E11
2.924x10 27
TEXAS INSTRUMENTS
TI-30X IIS

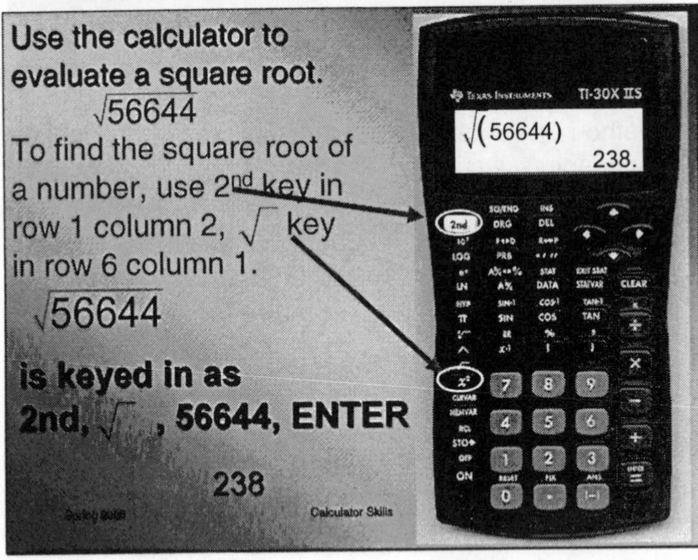
Use the calculator to evaluate a square root.
√56644
To find the square root of a number, use 2nd key in row 1 column 2, √ key in row 6 column 1.
√56644
is keyed in as
2nd, √ , 56644, ENTER
238
Calculator Skills
√(56644)
238.
TEXAS INSTRUMENTS
TI-30X IIS

TI 30X IIS Calculator Skills, Part 2

Objective: To learn how to use the calculator for operations with fractions.

Spring, 2006 Calculator Skills 1

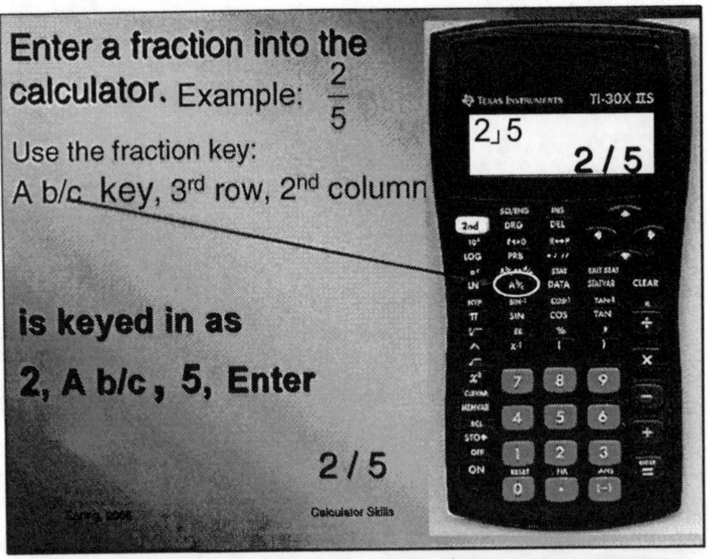
Enter a fraction into the calculator. Example: 2/5
Use the fraction key:
A b/c key, 3rd row, 2nd column
is keyed in as
2, A b/c , 5, Enter
2 / 5
Calculator Skills
TEXAS INSTRUMENTS
TI-30X IIS
2⌋5
2 / 5

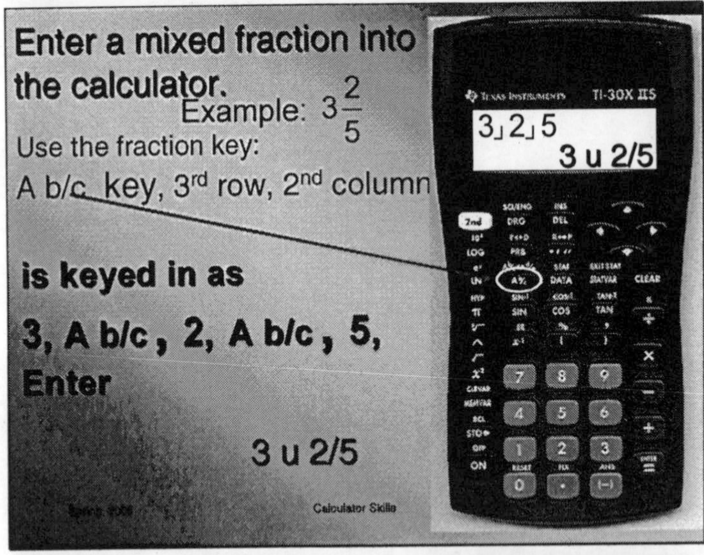
Enter a mixed fraction into the calculator.
Example: 3 2/5
Use the fraction key:
A b/c key, 3rd row, 2nd column
is keyed in as
3, A b/c , 2, A b/c , 5, Enter
3 u 2/5
Calculator Skills
TEXAS INSTRUMENTS
TI-30X IIS
3⌋2⌋5
3 u 2/5

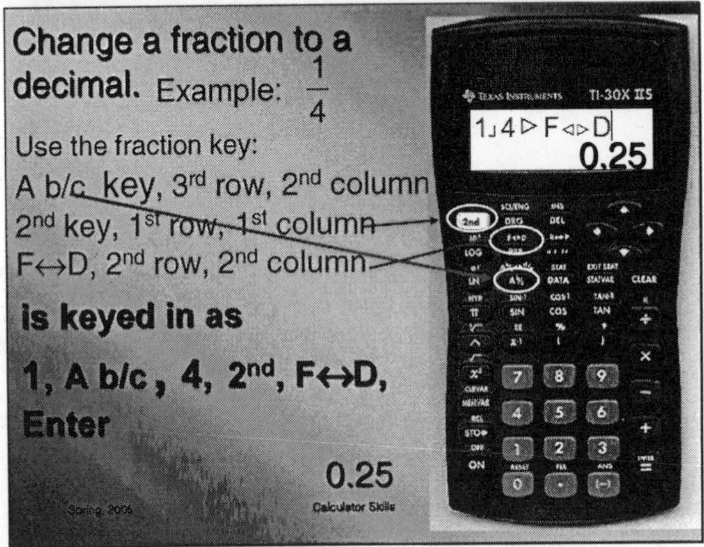
Change a fraction to a decimal. Example: 1/4
Use the fraction key:
A b/c key, 3rd row, 2nd column
2nd key, 1st row, 1st column
F↔D, 2nd row, 2nd column
is keyed in as
1, A b/c , 4, 2nd, F↔D, Enter
0.25
Spring, 2005
Calculator Skills
TEXAS INSTRUMENTS
TI-30X IIS
1⌋4 ▷ F◁▷D
0.25

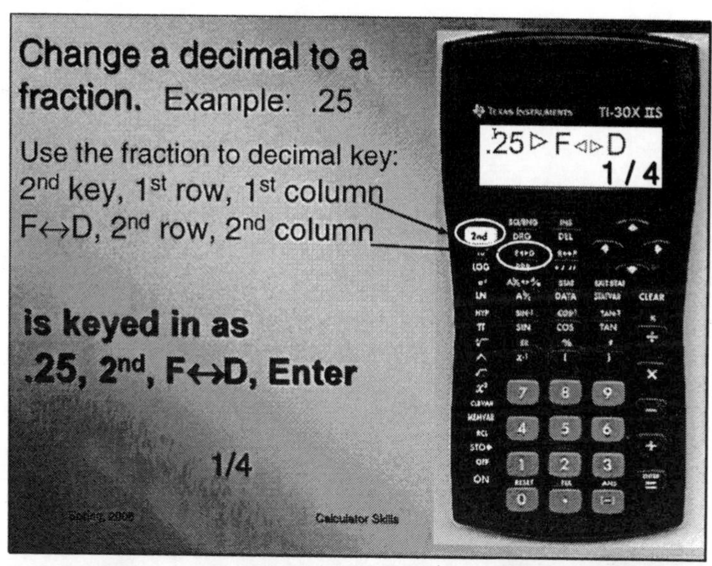
Change a decimal to a fraction. Example: .25
Use the fraction to decimal key:
2nd key, 1st row, 1st column
F↔D, 2nd row, 2nd column
is keyed in as
.25, 2nd, F↔D, Enter
1/4
Calculator Skills
TEXAS INSTRUMENTS TI-30X IIS
.25 ▷ F◁▷D
1 / 4

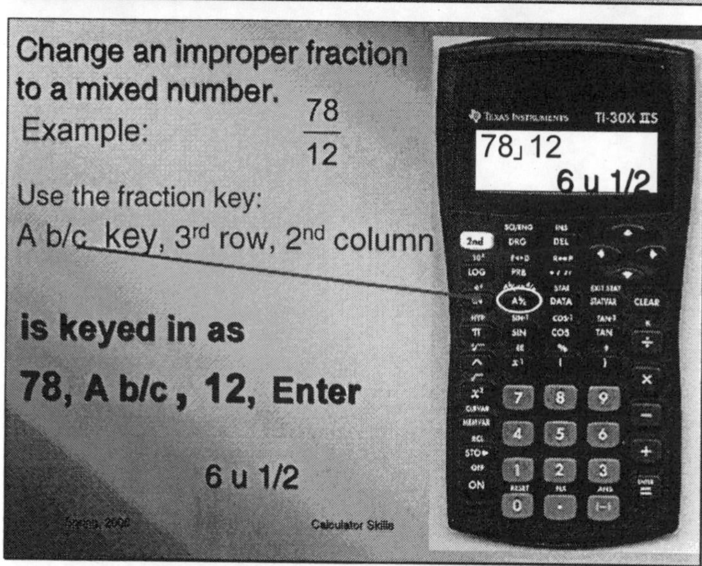
Change an improper fraction to a mixed number.
Example: 78/12
Use the fraction key:
A b/c key, 3rd row, 2nd column
is keyed in as
78, A b/c , 12, Enter
6 u 1/2
Calculator Skills
TEXAS INSTRUMENTS TI-30X IIS
78⌋12
6 u 1/2

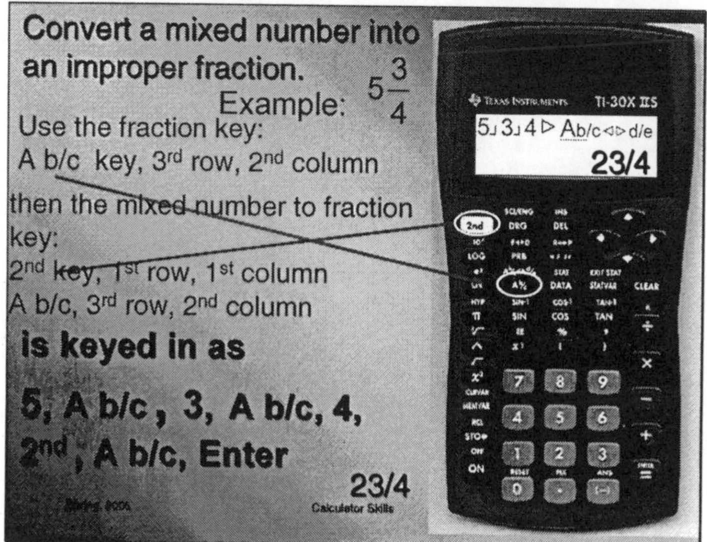
Convert a mixed number into an improper fraction.
Example: 5 3/4
Use the fraction key:
A b/c key, 3rd row, 2nd column
then the mixed number to fraction key:
2nd key, 1st row, 1st column
A b/c, 3rd row, 2nd column
is keyed in as
5, A b/c , 3, A b/c, 4,
2nd, A b/c, Enter
23/4
Calculator Skills
TEXAS INSTRUMENTS TI-30X IIS
5⌋3⌋4 ▷ Ab/c◁▷d/e
23/4

The following material taken from:

Introductory Algebra, **Tenth Edition**

By

Marvin L. Bittinger

The following material taken from:

Introductory Algebra, **Tenth Edition**

By

Marvin L. Bittinger

Contents

1 INTRODUCTION TO REAL NUMBERS AND ALGEBRAIC EXPRESSIONS

SOLVING EQUATIONS AND INEQUALITIES

3 GRAPHS OF LINEAR EQUATIONS

4 POLYNOMIALS: OPERATIONS

5 POLYNOMIALS: FACTORING

6 RATIONAL EXPRESSIONS AND EQUATIONS

RADICAL EXPRESSIONS AND EQUATIONS

9 QUADRATIC EQUATIONS

ntroduction to Real Numbers and Algebraic Expressions

eal-World Application

rface temperatures on Mars vary from $-128°C$ ring polar night to $27°C$ at the equator during dday at the closest point in orbit to the sun. Find difference between the highest value and the vest value in this temperature range.

rce: Mars Institute

is problem appears Example 13 in ction 1.4.

1.1 INTRODUCTION TO ALGEBRA

Objectives

a Evaluate algebraic expressions by substitution.

b Translate phrases to algebraic expressions.

1. Translate this problem to an equation. Use the graph below.

Mountain Peaks. There are 92 mountain peaks in the United States higher than 14,000 ft. The bar graph below shows data for six of these. How much higher is Mt. Fairweather than Mt. Rainer?

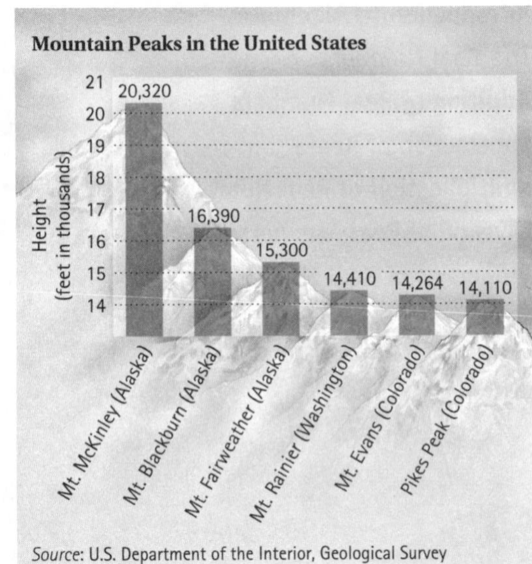

Source: U.S. Department of the Interior, Geological Survey

Answer on page A-3

The study of algebra involves the use of equations to solve problems. Equations are constructed from algebraic expressions. The purpose of this section is to introduce you to the types of expressions encountered in algebra.

a Evaluating Algebraic Expressions

In arithmetic, you have worked with expressions such as

$$49 + 75, \quad 8 \times 6.07, \quad 29 - 14, \quad \text{and} \quad \frac{5}{6}.$$

In algebra, we use certain letters for numbers and work with *algebraic expressions* such as

$$x + 75, \quad 8 \times y, \quad 29 - t, \quad \text{and} \quad \frac{a}{b}.$$

Sometimes a letter can represent various numbers. In that case, we call the letter a **variable.** Let a = your age. Then a is a variable since it changes from year to year. Sometimes a letter can stand for just one number. In that case, we call the letter a **constant.** Let b = your date of birth. Then b is a constant.

Where do algebraic expressions occur? Most often we encounter them when we are solving applied problems. For example, consider the bar graph shown at left, one that we might find in a book or magazine. Suppose we want to know how much higher Mt. McKinley is than Mt. Evans. Using arithmetic, we might simply subtract. But let's see how we can find this out using algebra. We translate the problem into a statement of equality, an equation. It could be done as follows:

Height of Mt. Evans	plus	How much more	is	Height of Mt. McKinley
↓	↓	↓	↓	↓
14,264	+	x	=	20,320.

Note that we have an algebraic expression, $14{,}264 + x$, on the left of the equals sign. To find the number x, we can subtract 14,264 on both sides of the equation:

$$14{,}264 + x = 20{,}320$$
$$14{,}264 + x - 14{,}264 = 20{,}320 - 14{,}264$$
$$x = 6056.$$

This value of x gives the answer, 6056 ft.

We call $14{,}264 + x$ an *algebraic expression* and $14{,}264 + x = 20{,}320$ an *algebraic equation*. Note that there is no equals sign, =, in an algebraic expression.

In arithmetic, you probably would do this subtraction without ever considering an equation. *In algebra, more complex problems are difficult to solve without first writing an equation.*

Do Exercise 1.

An **algebraic expression** consists of variables, constants, numerals, and operation signs. When we replace a variable with a number, we say that we are **substituting** for the variable. This process is called **evaluating the expression.**

EXAMPLE 1 Evaluate $x + y$ when $x = 37$ and $y = 29$.

We substitute 37 for x and 29 for y and carry out the addition:

$$x + y = 37 + 29 = 66.$$

The number 66 is called the **value** of the expression.

Algebraic expressions involving multiplication can be written in several ways. For example, "8 times a" can be written as

$$8 \times a, \quad 8 \cdot a, \quad (8a), \quad \text{or simply} \quad 8a.$$

Two letters written together without an operation symbol, such as ab, also indicate a multiplication.

EXAMPLE 2 Evaluate $3y$ when $y = 14$.

$$3y = 3(14) = 42$$

Do Exercises 2–4.

EXAMPLE 3 *Area of a Rectangle.* The area A of a rectangle of length l and width w is given by the formula $A = lw$. Find the area when l is 24.5 in. and w is 16 in.

We substitute 24.5 in. for l and 16 in. for w and carry out the multiplication:

$$\begin{aligned} A = lw &= (24.5 \text{ in.})(16 \text{ in.}) \\ &= (24.5)(16)(\text{in.})(\text{in.}) \\ &= 392 \text{ in}^2, \text{ or } 392 \text{ square inches.} \end{aligned}$$

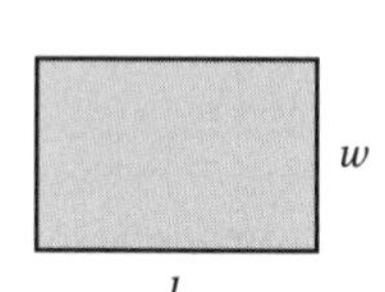

Do Exercise 5.

Algebraic expressions involving division can also be written in several ways. For example, "8 divided by t" can be written as

$$8 \div t, \quad \frac{8}{t}, \quad 8/t, \quad \text{or} \quad 8 \cdot \frac{1}{t},$$

where the fraction bar is a division symbol.

EXAMPLE 4 Evaluate $\frac{a}{b}$ when $a = 63$ and $b = 9$.

We substitute 63 for a and 9 for b and carry out the division:

$$\frac{a}{b} = \frac{63}{9} = 7.$$

2. Evaluate $a + b$ when $a = 38$ and $b = 26$.

3. Evaluate $x - y$ when $x = 57$ and $y = 29$.

4. Evaluate $4t$ when $t = 15$.

5. Find the area of a rectangle when l is 24 ft and w is 8 ft.

6. Evaluate a/b when $a = 200$ and $b = 8$.

7. Evaluate $10p/q$ when $p = 40$ and $q = 25$.

Answers on page A-3

8. Motorcycle Travel. Find the time it takes to travel 660 mi if the speed is 55 mph.

EXAMPLE 5 Evaluate $\frac{12m}{n}$ when $m = 8$ and $n = 16$.

$$\frac{12m}{n} = \frac{12 \cdot 8}{16} = \frac{96}{16} = 6$$

Do Exercises 6 and 7 on the preceding page.

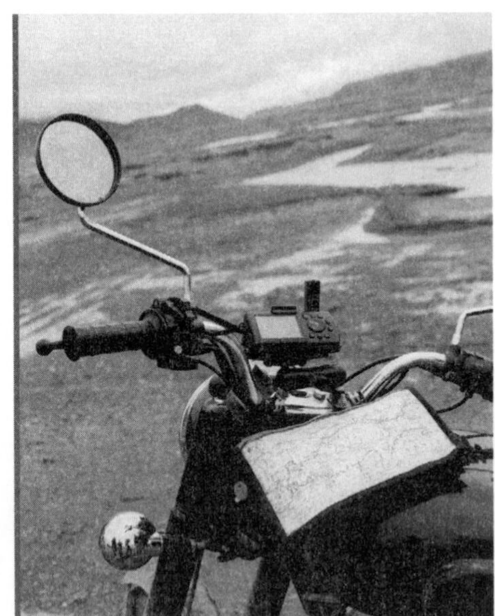

EXAMPLE 6 *Motorcycle Travel.* Ed takes a trip on his motorcycle. He wants to travel 660 mi on a particular day. The time t, in hours, that it takes to travel 660 mi is given by

$$t = \frac{660}{r},$$

where r is the speed of Ed's motorcycle. Find the time of travel if the speed r is 60 mph.

We substitute 60 for r and carry out the division:

$$t = \frac{660}{r} = \frac{660}{60} = 11 \text{ hr}.$$

Do Exercise 8.

CALCULATOR CORNER

Evaluating Algebraic Expressions *To the student and the instructor:* This book contains a series of *optional* discussions on using a calculator. A calculator is *not* a requirement for this textbook. There are many kinds of calculators and different instructions for their usage. We have included instructions here for the scientific keys on a graphing calculator such as a TI-84 Plus. Be sure to consult your user's manual as well. Also, check with your instructor about whether you are allowed to use a calculator in the course.

We can evaluate algebraic expressions on a calculator by making the appropriate substitutions, keeping in mind the rules for order of operations, and then carrying out the resulting calculations. To evaluate $12m/n$ when $m = 8$ and $n = 16$, as in Example 5, we enter $12 \cdot 8/16$ by pressing 1 2 × 8 ÷ 1 6 ENTER . The result is 6.

Exercises: Evaluate.

1. $\frac{12m}{n}$, when $m = 42$ and $n = 9$
2. $a + b$, when $a = 8.2$ and $b = 3.7$
3. $b - a$, when $a = 7.6$ and $b = 9.4$
4. $27xy$, when $x = 12.7$ and $y = 100.4$
5. $3a + 2b$, when $a = 2.9$ and $b = 5.7$
6. $2a + 3b$, when $a = 7.3$ and $b = 5.1$

Answer on page A-3

b Translating to Algebraic Expressions

In algebra, we translate problems to equations. The different parts of an equation are translations of word phrases to algebraic expressions. It is easier to translate if we know that certain words often translate to certain operation symbols.

WORDS, PHRASES, AND CONCEPTS

DDITION (+)	SUBTRACTION (−)	MULTIPLICATION (·)	DIVISION (÷)
d	subtract	multiply	divide
ded to	subtracted from	multiplied by	divided by
m	difference	product	quotient
tal	minus	times	
us	less than	of	
ore than	decreased by		
creased by	take away		

To the student:

In the preface, at the front of the text, you will find a Student Organizer card. This pullout card will help you keep track of important dates and useful contact information. You can also use it to plan time for class, study, work, and relaxation. By managing your time wisely, you will provide yourself the best possible opportunity to be successful in this course.

EXAMPLE 7 Translate to an algebraic expression:

Twice (or two times) some number.

Think of some number, say, 8. We can write 2 times 8 as 2×8, or $2 \cdot 8$. We multiplied by 2. Do the same thing using a variable. We can use any variable we wish, such as x, y, m, or n. Let's use y to stand for some number. If we multiply by 2, we get an expression

$y \times 2$, $\quad 2 \times y$, $\quad 2 \cdot y$, or $2y$.

In algebra, $2y$ is the expression generally used.

EXAMPLE 8 Translate to an algebraic expression:

Thirty-eight percent of some number.

Let $n =$ the number. The word "of" translates to a multiplication symbol, so we get the following expressions as a translation:

$38\% \cdot n$, $\quad 0.38 \times n$, or $0.38n$.

EXAMPLE 9 Translate to an algebraic expression:

Seven less than some number.

We let

x represent the number.

Now if the number were 23, then 7 less than 23 is 16, that is, $(23 - 7)$, not $(7 - 23)$. If we knew the number to be 345, then the translation would be $345 - 7$. If the number is x, then the translation is

$x - 7$.

Caution!

Note that $7 - x$ is *not* a correct translation of the expression in Example 9. The expression $7 - x$ is a translation of "seven minus some number" or "some number less than seven."

Translate to an algebraic expression.

9. Eight less than some number

10. Eight more than some number

11. Four less than some number

12. Half of a number

13. Six more than eight times some number

14. The difference of two numbers

15. Fifty-nine percent of some number

16. Two hundred less than the product of two numbers

17. The sum of two numbers

Answers on page A-3

EXAMPLE 10 Translate to an algebraic expression:

Eighteen more than a number.

We let

$t =$ the number.

Now if the number were 26, then the translation would be $26 + 18$, or $18 + 26$. If we knew the number to be 174, then the translation would be $174 + 18$, or $18 + 174$. If the number is t, then the translation is

$$t + 18, \quad \text{or} \quad 18 + t.$$

EXAMPLE 11 Translate to an algebraic expression:

A number divided by 5.

We let

$m =$ the number.

Now if the number were 76, then the translation would be $76 \div 5$, or $76/5$, or $\frac{76}{5}$. If the number were 213, then the translation would be $213 \div 5$, or $213/5$, or $\frac{213}{5}$. If the number is m, then the translation is

$$m \div 5, \quad m/5, \quad \text{or} \quad \frac{m}{5}.$$

EXAMPLE 12 Translate each phrase to an algebraic expression.

PHRASE	ALGEBRAIC EXPRESSION
Five more than some number	$n + 5$, or $5 + n$
Half of a number	$\frac{1}{2}t, \frac{t}{2}$, or $t/2$
Five more than three times some number	$3p + 5$, or $5 + 3p$
The difference of two numbers	$x - y$
Six less than the product of two numbers	$mn - 6$
Seventy-six percent of some number	$76\%z$, or $0.76z$
Four less than twice some number	$2x - 4$

Do Exercises 9–17.

1.1 EXERCISE SET

For Extra Help

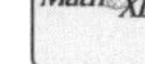

MathXL | MyMathLab | InterAct Math | Math Tutor Center | Digital Video Tutor CD 1 Videotape 2 | Student's Solutions Manual

a Substitute to find values of the expressions in each of the following applied problems.

1. *Commuting Time.* It takes Erin 24 min less time to commute to work than it does George. Suppose that the variable x stands for the time it takes George to get to work. Then $x - 24$ stands for the time it takes Erin to get to work. How long does it take Erin to get to work if it takes George 56 min? 93 min? 105 min?

2. *Enrollment Costs.* At Emmett Community College, it costs \$600 to enroll in the 8 A.M. section of Elementary Algebra. Suppose that the variable n stands for the number of students who enroll. Then $600n$ stands for the total amount of money collected for this course. How much is collected if 34 students enroll? 78 students? 250 students?

3. *Area of a Triangle.* The area A of a triangle with base b and height h is given by $A = \frac{1}{2}bh$. Find the area when $b = 45$ m (meters) and $h = 86$ m.

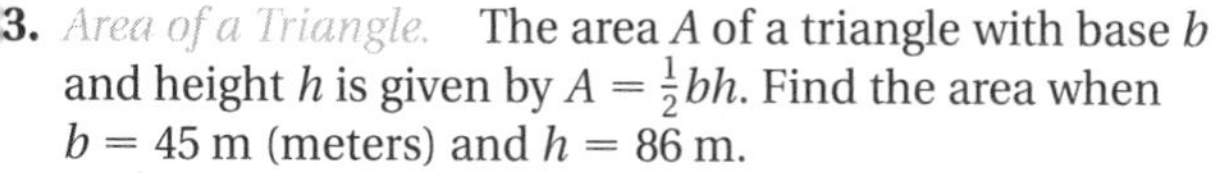

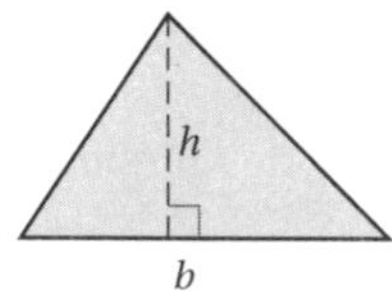

4. *Area of a Parallelogram.* The area A of a parallelogram with base b and height h is given by $A = bh$. Find the area of the parallelogram when the height is 15.4 cm (centimeters) and the base is 6.5 cm.

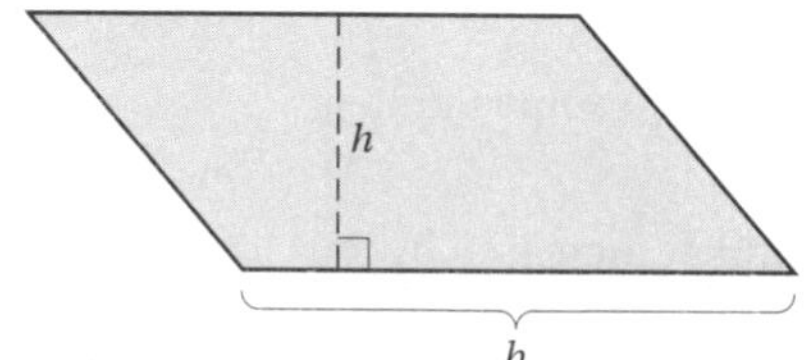

5. *Distance Traveled.* A driver who drives at a constant speed of r mph for t hr will travel a distance d mi given by $d = rt$ mi. How far will a driver travel at a speed of 65 mph for 4 hr?

6. *Simple Interest.* The simple interest I on a principal of P dollars at interest rate r for time t, in years, is given by $I = Prt$. Find the simple interest on a principal of \$4800 at 9% for 2 yr. (*Hint*: 9% = 0.09.)

7. *Hockey Goal.* The front of a regulation hockey goal is a rectangle that is 6 ft wide and 4 ft high. Find its area.

Source: National Hockey League

8. *Zoology.* A great white shark has triangular teeth. Each tooth measures about 5 cm across the base and has a height of 6 cm. Find the surface area of one side of one tooth. (See Exercise 3.)

Evaluate.

9. $8x$, when $x = 7$

10. $6y$, when $y = 7$

11. $\frac{c}{d}$, when $c = 24$ and $d = 3$

12. $\frac{p}{q}$, when $p = 16$ and $q = 2$

13. $\frac{3p}{q}$, when $p = 2$ and $q = 6$

14. $\frac{5y}{z}$, when $y = 15$ and $z = 25$

15. $\frac{x + y}{5}$, when $x = 10$ and $y = 20$

16. $\frac{p + q}{2}$, when $p = 2$ and $q = 16$

17. $\frac{x - y}{8}$, when $x = 20$ and $y = 4$

18. $\frac{m - n}{5}$, when $m = 16$ and $n = 6$

b Translate each phrase to an algebraic expression. Use any letter for the variable unless directed otherwise.

19. Seven more than some number

20. Nine more than some number

21. Twelve less than some number

22. Fourteen less than some number

23. Some number increased by four

24. Some number increased by thirteen

25. b more than a

26. c more than d

27. x divided by y

28. c divided by h

29. x plus w

30. s added to t

31. m subtracted from n

32. p subtracted from q

33. The sum of two numbers

34. The sum of nine and some number

35. Twice some number

36. Three times some number

37. Three multiplied by some number

38. The product of eight and some number

39. Six more than four times some number

40. Two more than six times some number

41. Eight less than the product of two numbers

42. The product of two numbers minus seven

43. Five less than twice some number

44. Six less than seven times some number

45. Three times some number plus eleven

46. Some number times 8 plus 5

47. The sum of four times a number plus three times another number

48. Five times a number minus eight times another numbe

49. The product of 89% and your salary

50. 67% of the women attending

51. Your salary after a 5% salary increase if your salary before the increase was s

52. The price of a blouse after a 30% reduction if the price before the reduction was P

53. Danielle drove at a speed of 65 mph for t hours. How far did Danielle travel?

54. Juan has d dollars before spending $29.95 on a DVD of the movie *Chicago*. How much did Juan have after the purchase?

55. Lisa had $50 before spending x dollars on pizza. How much money remains?

56. Dino drove his pickup truck at 55 mph for t hours. How far did he travel?

To the student and the instructor: The Discussion and Writing exercises are meant to be answered with one or more sentences. They can be discussed and answered collaboratively by the entire class or by small groups. Because of their open-ended nature, the answers to these exercises do not appear at the back of the book. They are denoted by the symbol DW.

57. DW If the length of a rectangle is doubled, does the area double? Why or why not?

58. DW If the height and the base of a triangle are doubled, what happens to the area? Explain.

SKILL MAINTENANCE

This heading indicates that the exercises that follow are Skill Maintenance exercises, which review any skill previously studied in the text. You can expect such exercises in every exercise set. Answers to *all* skill maintenance exercises are found at the back of the book. If you miss an exercise, restudy the objective shown in red.

Find the prime factorization. [R.1a]

59. 54
60. 32
61. 108
62. 192
63. 1023

Find the LCM. [R.1b]

64. 6, 18
65. 6, 24, 32
66. 10, 20, 30
67. 16, 24, 32
68. 18, 36, 44

SYNTHESIS

To the student and the instructor: The Synthesis exercises found at the end of most exercise sets challenge students to combine concepts or skills studied in that section or in preceding parts of the text.

Evaluate.

69. $\frac{a - 2b + c}{4b - a}$, when $a = 20$, $b = 10$, and $c = 5$

70. $\frac{x}{y} - \frac{5}{x} + \frac{2}{y}$, when $x = 30$ and $y = 6$

71. $\frac{12 - c}{c + 12b}$, when $b = 1$ and $c = 12$

72. $\frac{2w - 3z}{7y}$, when $w = 5$, $y = 6$, and $z = 1$

Objectives

a State the integer that corresponds to a real-world situation.

b Graph rational numbers on a number line.

c Convert from fraction notation to decimal notation for a rational number.

d Determine which of two real numbers is greater and indicate which, using < or >; given an inequality like $a > b$, write another inequality with the same meaning. Determine whether an inequality like $-3 \leq 5$ is true or false.

e Find the absolute value of a real number.

Study Tips

THE AW MATH TUTOR CENTER

www.aw-bc.com/tutorcenter

The AW Math Tutor Center is staffed by highly qualified mathematics instructors who provide students with tutoring on text examples and odd-numbered exercises. Tutoring is provided free to students who have bought a new text-book with a special access card bound with the book. Tutoring is available by toll-free telephone, toll-free fax, e-mail, and the Internet. White-board technology allows tutors and students to actually see problems worked while they "talk" live in real time during the tutoring sessions. If you purchased a book without this card, you can purchase an access code through your bookstore using ISBN 0-201-72170-8. (This is also discussed in the Preface.)

1.2 THE REAL NUMBERS

A **set** is a collection of objects. (See Appendix D for more on sets.) For our purposes, we will most often be considering sets of numbers. One way to name a set uses what is called **roster notation.** For example, roster notation for the set containing the numbers 0, 2, and 5 is $\{0, 2, 5\}$.

Sets that are part of other sets are called **subsets.** In this section, we become acquainted with the set of *real numbers* and its various subsets.

Two important subsets of the real numbers are listed below using roster notation.

NATURAL NUMBERS

The set of **natural numbers** $= \{1, 2, 3, \ldots\}$. These are the numbers used for counting.

WHOLE NUMBERS

The set of **whole numbers** $= \{0, 1, 2, 3, \ldots\}$. This is the set of natural numbers with 0 included.

We can represent these sets on a number line. The natural numbers are those to the right of zero. The whole numbers are the natural numbers and zero.

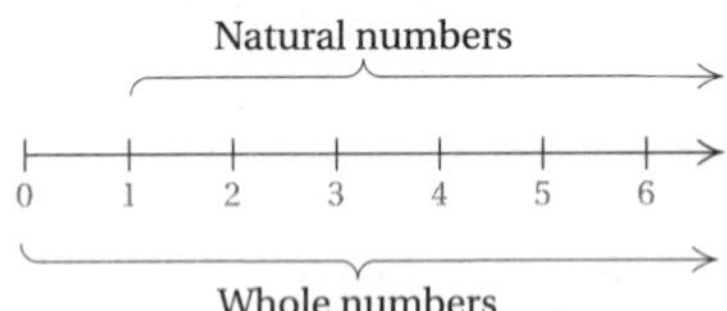

We create a new set, called the *integers,* by starting with the whole numbers, 0, 1, 2, 3, and so on. For each natural number 1, 2, 3, and so on, we obtain a new number to the left of zero on the number line:

For the number 1, there will be an *opposite* number -1 (negative 1).

For the number 2, there will be an *opposite* number -2 (negative 2).

For the number 3, there will be an *opposite* number -3 (negative 3), and so on.

The **integers** consist of the whole numbers and these new numbers.

INTEGERS

The set of **integers** $= \{\ldots, -5, -4, -3, -2, -1, 0, 1, 2, 3, 4, 5, \ldots\}$.

We picture the integers on a number line as follows.

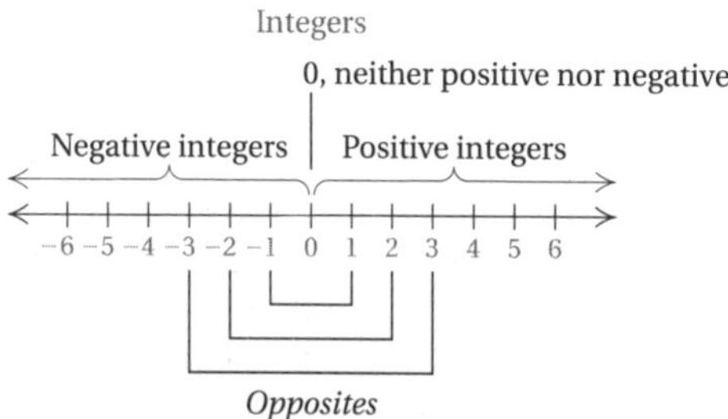

We call these new numbers to the left of 0 **negative integers.** The natural numbers are also called **positive integers.** Zero is neither positive nor negative. We call -1 and 1 **opposites** of each other. Similarly, -2 and 2 are opposites, -3 and 3 are opposites, -100 and 100 are opposites, and 0 is its own opposite. Pairs of opposite numbers like -3 and 3 are the same distance from 0. The integers extend infinitely on the number line to the left and right of zero.

a Integers and the Real World

Integers correspond to many real-world problems and situations. The following examples will help you get ready to translate problem situations that involve integers to mathematical language.

EXAMPLE 1 Tell which integer corresponds to this situation: The temperature is 4 degrees below zero.

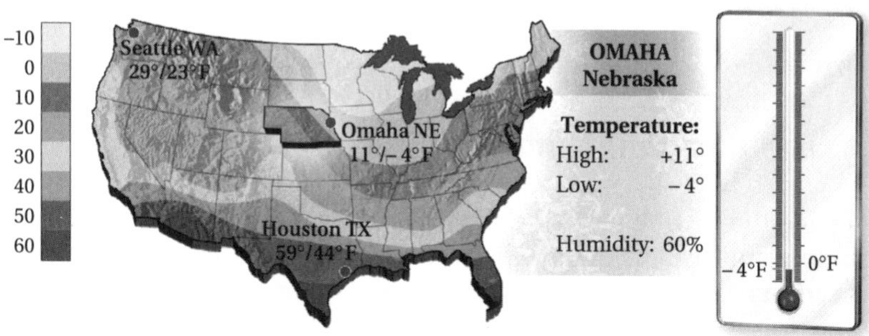

The integer -4 corresponds to the situation. The temperature is $-4°$.

EXAMPLE 2 *"Jeopardy."* Tell which integer corresponds to this situation: A contestant missed a \$600 question on the television game show "Jeopardy."

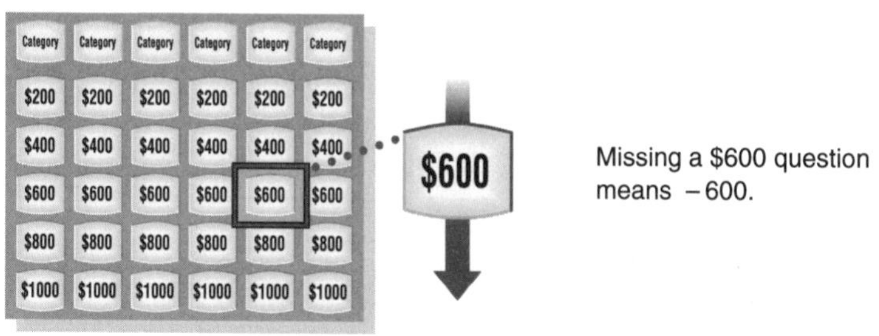

Missing a \$600 question causes a \$600 loss on the score—that is, the contestant earns -600 dollars.

State the integers that correspond to the given situation.

1. The halfback gained 8 yd on the first down. The quarterback was sacked for a 5-yd loss on the second down.

2. **Temperature High and Low.** The highest recorded temperature in Nevada is 125°F on June 29, 1994, in Laughlin. The lowest recorded temperature in Nevada is 50°F below zero on June 8, 1937, in San Jacinto.

   Sources: National Climatic Data Center, Asheville, NC, and Storm Phillips, STORMFAX, INC.

3. **Stock Decrease.** The price of Wendy's stock decreased from \$41 per share to \$38 per share over a recent time period.

   Source: The New York Stock Exchange

4. At 10 sec before liftoff, ignition occurs. At 156 sec after liftoff, the first stage is detached from the rocket.

5. A submarine dove 120 ft, rose 50 ft, and then dove 80 ft.

Answers on page A-4

EXAMPLE 3 *Elevation.* Tell which integer corresponds to this situation: The shores of California's largest lake, the Salton Sea, are 227 ft below sea level.

Source: *National Geographic*, February 2005, p. 88. Salton Sea, by Joel K. Bourne, Jr., Senior Writer.

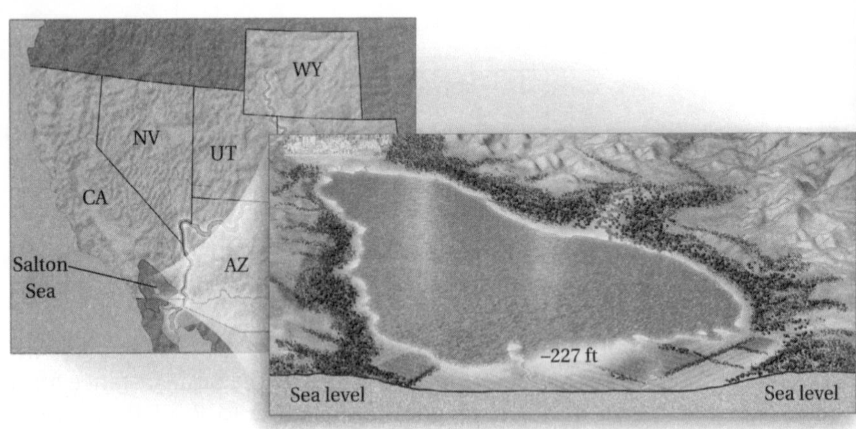

The integer -227 corresponds to the situation. The elevation is -227 ft.

EXAMPLE 4 *Stock Price Change.* Tell which integers correspond to this situation: The price of Pearson Education stock decreased from \$27 per share to \$11 per share over a recent time period. The price of Safeway stock increased from \$20 per share to \$22 per share over a recent time period.

Source: The New York Stock Exchange

The integer -16 corresponds to the decrease in the stock value. The integer 2 represents the increase in stock value.

Do Exercises 1–5.

b The Rational Numbers

We created the set of integers by obtaining a negative number for each natural number and also including 0. To create a larger number system, called the set of **rational numbers,** we consider quotients of integers with nonzero divisors. The following are some examples of rational numbers:

$$\frac{2}{3},\quad -\frac{2}{3},\quad \frac{7}{1},\quad 4,\quad -3,\quad 0,\quad \frac{23}{-8},\quad 2.4,\quad -0.17,\quad 10\frac{1}{2}.$$

The number $-\frac{2}{3}$ (read "negative two-thirds") can also be named $\frac{-2}{3}$ or $\frac{2}{-3}$; that is,

$$-\frac{a}{b} = \frac{-a}{b} = \frac{a}{-b}.$$

The number 2.4 can be named $\frac{24}{10}$ or $\frac{12}{5}$, and -0.17 can be named $-\frac{17}{100}$. We can describe the set of rational numbers as follows.

RATIONAL NUMBERS

The set of **rational numbers** = the set of numbers $\frac{a}{b}$, where a and b are integers and b is not equal to 0 ($b \neq 0$).

Note that this new set of numbers, the rational numbers, contains the whole numbers, the integers, the arithmetic numbers (also called the nonnegative rational numbers), and the negative rational numbers.

We picture the rational numbers on a number line as follows.

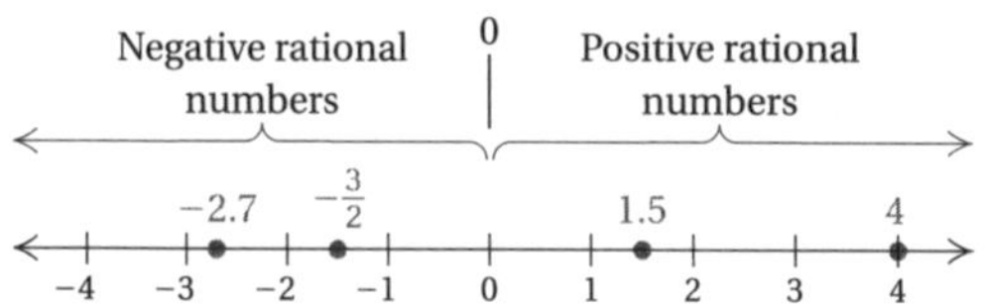

To **graph** a number means to find and mark its point on the number line. Some rational numbers are graphed in the preceding figure.

EXAMPLE 5 Graph: $\frac{5}{2}$.

The number $\frac{5}{2}$ can be named $2\frac{1}{2}$, or 2.5. Its graph is halfway between 2 and 3.

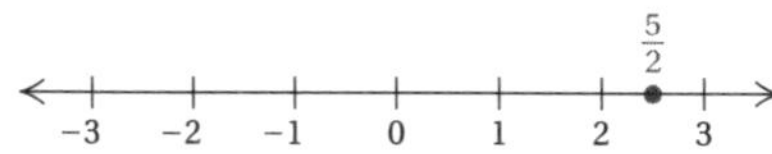

EXAMPLE 6 Graph: −3.2.

The graph of −3.2 is $\frac{2}{10}$ of the way from −3 to −4.

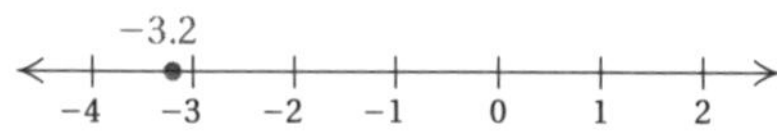

EXAMPLE 7 Graph: $\frac{13}{8}$.

The number $\frac{13}{8}$ can be named $1\frac{5}{8}$, or 1.625. The graph is $\frac{5}{8}$ of the way from 1 to 2.

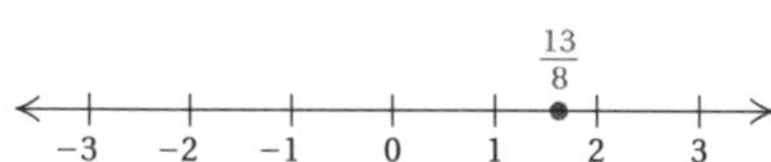

Do Exercises 6–8.

C Notation for Rational Numbers

Each rational number can be named using fraction or decimal notation.

EXAMPLE 8 Convert to decimal notation: $-\frac{5}{8}$.

We first find decimal notation for $\frac{5}{8}$. Since $\frac{5}{8}$ means 5 ÷ 8, we divide.

```
    0.6 2 5
8 ) 5.0 0 0
    4 8
    ---
      2 0
      1 6
      ---
        4 0
        4 0
        ---
          0
```

Thus, $\frac{5}{8} = 0.625$, so $-\frac{5}{8} = -0.625$.

Graph on a number line.

6. $-\frac{7}{2}$

−6 −5 −4 −3 −2 −1 0 1 2 3 4 5 6

7. −1.4

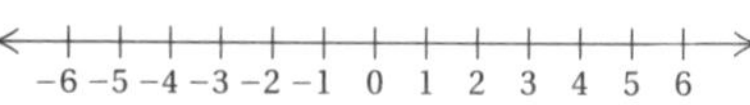

8. $\frac{11}{4}$

Answers on page A-4

CALCULATOR CORNER

Negative Numbers on a Calculator; Converting to Decimal Notation We use the opposite key (−) to enter negative numbers on a graphing calculator. Note that this is different from the − key, which is used for the operation of subtraction. To convert $-\frac{5}{8}$ to decimal notation, as in Example 8, we press (−) 5 ÷ 8 ENTER. The result is −0.625.

Exercises: Convert each of the following negative numbers to decimal notation.

1. $-\frac{3}{4}$
2. $-\frac{9}{20}$
3. $-\frac{1}{8}$
4. $-\frac{9}{5}$
5. $-\frac{27}{40}$
6. $-\frac{11}{16}$
7. $-\frac{7}{2}$
8. $-\frac{19}{25}$

Convert to decimal notation.

9. $-\frac{3}{8}$

10. $-\frac{6}{11}$

11. $\frac{4}{3}$

Answers on page A-4

CALCULATOR CORNER

Approximating Square Roots and π Square roots are found by pressing 2ND $\sqrt{}$. ($\sqrt{}$ is the second operation associated with the x^2 key.)

To find an approximation for $\sqrt{48}$, we press 2ND $\sqrt{}$ 4 8 ENTER. The approximation 6.92820323 is displayed.

To find $8 \cdot \sqrt{13}$, we press

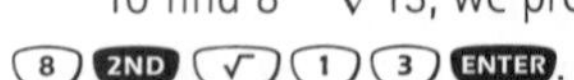

The approximation 28.8444102 is displayed. The number π is used widely enough to have its own key. (π is the second operation associated with the ^ key.)

To approximate π, we press 2ND π ENTER. The approximation 3.141592654 is displayed.

Exercises: Approximate.

1. $\sqrt{76}$
2. $\sqrt{317}$
3. $15 \cdot \sqrt{20}$
4. $29 + \sqrt{42}$
5. π
6. $29 \cdot \pi$
7. $\pi \cdot 13^2$
8. $5 \cdot \pi + 8 \cdot \sqrt{237}$

Decimal notation for $-\frac{5}{8}$ is -0.625. We consider -0.625 to be a **terminating decimal.** Decimal notation for some numbers repeats.

EXAMPLE 9 Convert to decimal notation: $\frac{7}{11}$.

```
        0.6 3 6 3...    Dividing
  1 1 ) 7.0 0 0 0
        6 6
          4 0
          3 3
            7 0
            6 6
              4 0
              3 3
                7
```

We can abbreviate repeating decimal notation by writing a bar over the repeating part—in this case, $0.\overline{63}$. Thus, $\frac{7}{11} = 0.\overline{63}$.

Each rational number can be expressed in either terminating or repeating decimal notation.

The following are other examples to show how each rational number can be named using fraction or decimal notation:

$$0 = \frac{0}{8}, \quad \frac{27}{100} = 0.27, \quad -8\frac{3}{4} = -8.75, \quad -\frac{13}{6} = -2.1\overline{6}.$$

Do Exercises 9–11.

d The Real Numbers and Order

Every rational number has a point on the number line. However, there are some points on the line for which there is no rational number. These points correspond to what are called **irrational numbers.**

What kinds of numbers are irrational? One example is the number π, which is used in finding the area and the circumference of a circle: $A = \pi r^2$ and $C = 2\pi r$.

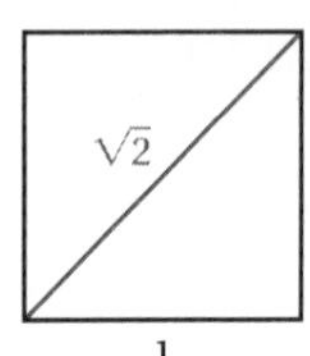

Another example of an irrational number is the square root of 2, named $\sqrt{2}$. It is the length of the diagonal of a square with sides of length 1. It is also the number that when multiplied by itself gives 2—that is, $\sqrt{2} \cdot \sqrt{2} = 2$. There is no rational number that can be multiplied by itself to get 2. But the following are rational *approximations*:

1.4 is an approximation of $\sqrt{2}$ because $(1.4)^2 = 1.96$;

1.41 is a better approximation because $(1.41)^2 = 1.9881$;

1.4142 is an even better approximation because $(1.4142)^2 = 1.99996164$.

We can find rational approximations for square roots using a calculator.

Decimal notation for rational numbers *either* terminates *or* repeats. Decimal notation for irrational numbers *neither* terminates *nor* repeats.

Some other examples of irrational numbers are $\sqrt{3}$, $-\sqrt{8}$, $\sqrt{11}$, and 0.121221222122221.... Whenever we take the square root of a number that is not a perfect square, we will get an irrational number.

The rational numbers and the irrational numbers together correspond to all the points on a number line and make up what is called the **real-number system.**

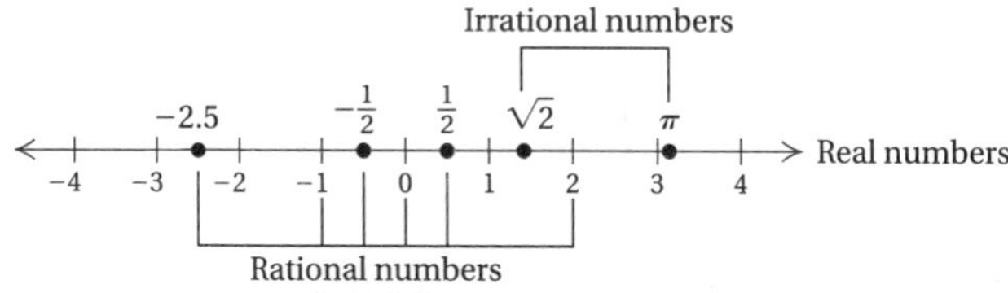

REAL NUMBERS

The set of **real numbers** = The set of all numbers corresponding to points on the number line.

The real numbers consist of the rational numbers and the irrational numbers. The following figure shows the relationships among various kinds of numbers.

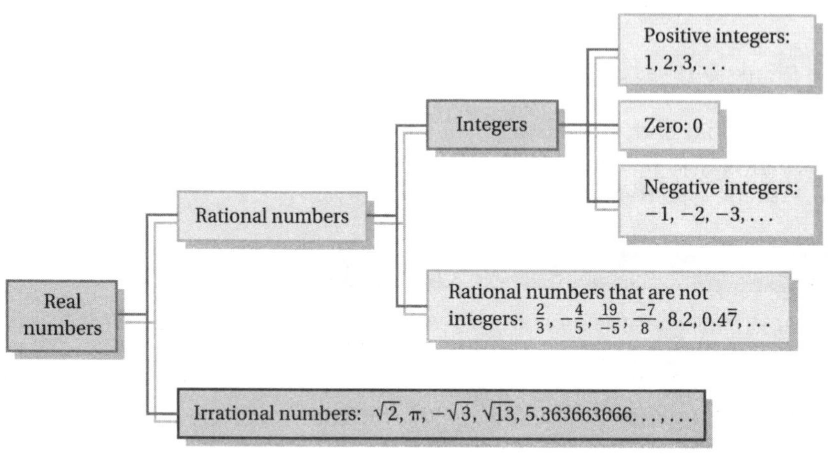

ORDER

Real numbers are named in order on the number line, with larger numbers named farther to the right. For any two numbers on the line, the one to the left is less than the one to the right.

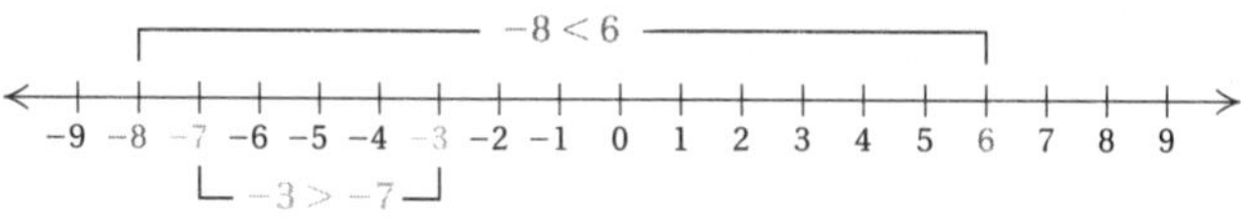

We use the symbol **<** to mean "**is less than.**" The sentence $-8 < 6$ means "-8 is less than 6." The symbol **>** means "**is greater than.**" The sentence $-3 > -7$ means "-3 is greater than -7." The sentences $-8 < 6$ and $-3 > -7$ are **inequalities.**

Use either < or > for □ to write a true sentence.

12. -3 □ 7

13. -8 □ -5

14. 7 □ -10

15. 3.1 □ -9.5

16. $-\frac{2}{3}$ □ -1

17. $-\frac{11}{8}$ □ $\frac{23}{15}$

18. $-\frac{2}{3}$ □ $-\frac{5}{9}$

19. -4.78 □ -5.01

Answers on page A-4

EXAMPLES Use either $<$ or $>$ for $\square$ to write a true sentence.

10. $2 \square 9$	Since 2 is to the left of 9, 2 is less than 9, so $2 < 9$.
11. $-7 \square 3$	Since -7 is to the left of 3, we have $-7 < 3$.
12. $6 \square -12$	Since 6 is to the right of -12, then $6 > -12$.
13. $-18 \square -5$	Since -18 is to the left of -5, we have $-18 < -5$.
14. $-2.7 \square -\frac{3}{2}$	The answer is $-2.7 < -\frac{3}{2}$.

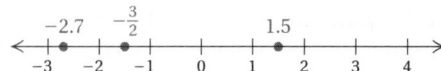

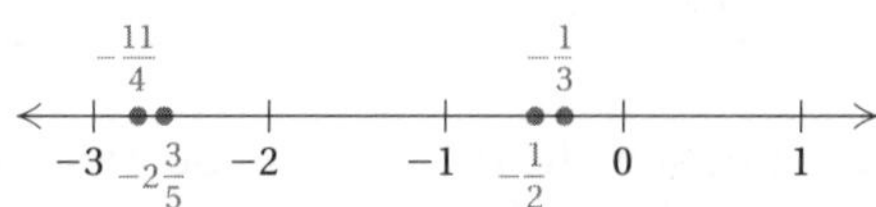

15. $1.5 \square -2.7$	The answer is $1.5 > -2.7$.
16. $1.38 \square 1.83$	The answer is $1.38 < 1.83$.
17. $-3.45 \square 1.32$	The answer is $-3.45 < 1.32$.
18. $-4 \square 0$	The answer is $-4 < 0$.
19. $5.8 \square 0$	The answer is $5.8 > 0$.
20. $\frac{5}{8} \square \frac{7}{11}$	We convert to decimal notation: $\frac{5}{8} = 0.625$ and $\frac{7}{11} = 0.6363\ldots$. Thus, $\frac{5}{8} < \frac{7}{11}$.
21. $-\frac{1}{2} \square -\frac{1}{3}$	The answer is $-\frac{1}{2} < -\frac{1}{3}$.
22. $-2\frac{3}{5} \square -\frac{11}{4}$	The answer is $-2\frac{3}{5} > -\frac{11}{4}$.

Do Exercises 12–19 on the preceding page.

Note that both $-8 < 6$ and $6 > -8$ are true. Every true inequality yields another true inequality when we interchange the numbers or variables and reverse the direction of the inequality sign.

ORDER; $>$, $<$

$a < b$ also has the meaning $b > a$.

EXAMPLES Write another inequality with the same meaning.

23. $-3 > -8$ The inequality $-8 < -3$ has the same meaning.

24. $a < -5$ The inequality $-5 > a$ has the same meaning.

A helpful mental device is to think of an inequality sign as an "arrow" with the arrow pointing to the smaller number.

Do Exercises 20 and 21.

Write another inequality with the same meaning.

20. $-5 < 7$

21. $x > 4$

Write true or false.

22. $-4 \leq -6$

23. $7.8 \geq 7.8$

24. $-2 \leq \frac{3}{8}$

Answers on page A-4

Note that all positive real numbers are greater than zero and all negative real numbers are less than zero.

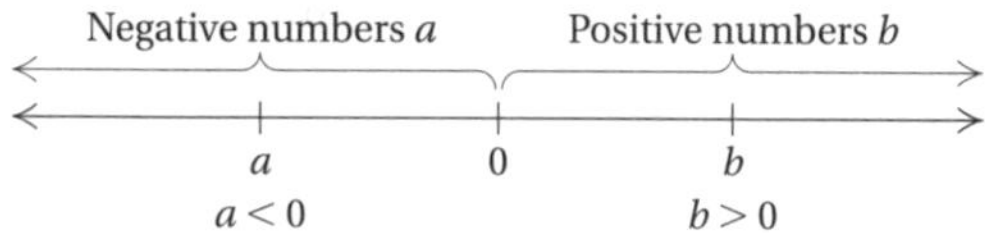

If b is a positive real number, then $b > 0$.
If a is a negative real number, then $a < 0$.

Expressions like $a \le b$ and $b \ge a$ are also inequalities. We read $\boldsymbol{a \le b}$ as **"a is less than or equal to b."** We read $\boldsymbol{a \ge b}$ as **"a is greater than or equal to b."**

EXAMPLES Write true or false for the statement.

25. $-3 \le 5.4$ True since $-3 < 5.4$ is true

26. $-3 \le -3$ True since $-3 = -3$ is true

27. $-5 \ge 1\frac{2}{3}$ False since neither $-5 > 1\frac{2}{3}$ nor $-5 = 1\frac{2}{3}$ is true

Do Exercises 22–24 on the preceding page.

e Absolute Value

From the number line, we see that numbers like 4 and -4 are the same distance from zero. Distance is always a nonnegative number. We call the distance of a number from zero on a number line the **absolute value** of the number.

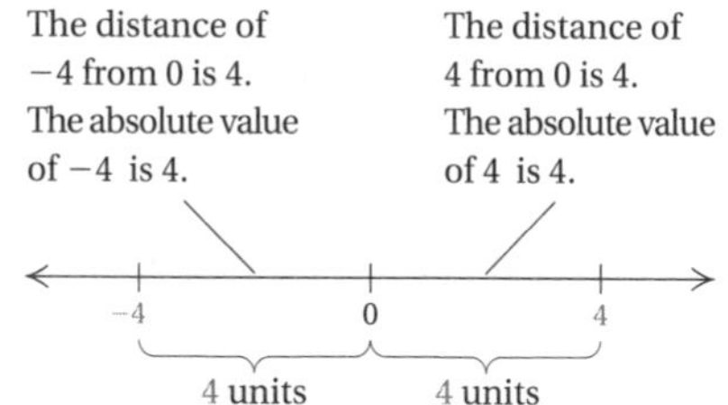

ABSOLUTE VALUE

The **absolute value** of a number is its distance from zero on a number line. We use the symbol $|x|$ to represent the absolute value of a number x.

CALCULATOR CORNER

Absolute Value The absolute-value operation is the first item in the Catalog on the TI-84 Plus graphing calculator. To find $|-7|$, as in Example 28, we first press 2ND CATALOG ENTER to copy "abs(" to the home screen. (CATALOG is the second operation associated with the 0 numeric key.) Then we press (-) 7) ENTER. The result is 7. To find $\left|-\frac{1}{2}\right|$ and express the result as a fraction, we press 2ND CATALOG ENTER (-) 1 ÷ 2) MATH 1 ENTER. The result is $\frac{1}{2}$.

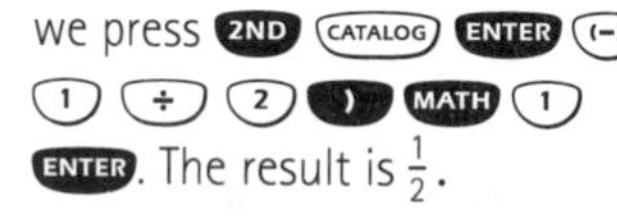

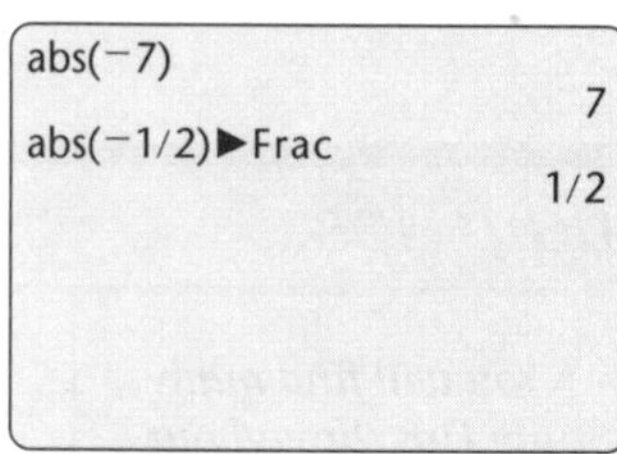

Exercises: Find the absolute value.

1. $|-5|$
2. $|17|$
3. $|0|$
4. $|6.48|$
5. $|-12.7|$
6. $|-0.9|$
7. $\left|-\frac{5}{7}\right|$
8. $\left|\frac{4}{3}\right|$

Find the absolute value.

25. $|8|$

26. $|-9|$

27. $\left|-\frac{2}{3}\right|$

28. $|5.6|$

Answers on page A-4

FINDING ABSOLUTE VALUE

a) If a number is negative, its absolute value is positive.
b) If a number is positive or zero, its absolute value is the same as the number.

EXAMPLES Find the absolute value.

28. $|-7|$ The distance of -7 from 0 is 7, so $|-7| = 7$.

29. $|12|$ The distance of 12 from 0 is 12, so $|12| = 12$.

30. $|0|$ The distance of 0 from 0 is 0, so $|0| = 0$.

31. $\left|\frac{3}{2}\right| = \frac{3}{2}$

32. $|-2.73| = 2.73$

Do Exercises 25–28.

Study Tips

USING THIS TEXTBOOK

You will find many Study Tips throughout the book. An index of all Study Tips can be found at the front of the book. One of the most important ways to improve your math study skills is to learn the proper use of the textbook. Here we highlight a few points that we consider most helpful.

- **Be sure to note the special symbols a, b, c, and so on, that correspond to the objectives you are to be able to perform.** The first time you see them is in the margin at the beginning of each section; the second time is in the subheadings of each section; and the third time is in the exercise set for the section. You will also find them next to the skill maintenance exercises in each exercise set and in the review exercises at the end of the chapter, as well as in the answers to the chapter tests and the cumulative reviews. These objective symbols allow you to refer to the appropriate place in the text whenever you need to review a topic.
- **Read and study each step of each example.** The examples include important side comments that explain each step. These carefully chosen examples and notes prepare you for success in the exercise set.
- **Stop and do the margin exercises as you study a section.** Doing the margin exercises is one of the most effective ways to enhance your ability to learn mathematics from this text. Don't deprive yourself of its benefits!
- **Note the icons listed at the top of each exercise set.** These refer to the many distinctive multimedia study aids that accompany the book.
- **Odd-numbered exercises.** Usually an instructor assigns some odd-numbered exercises. When you complete these, you can check your answers at the back of the book. If you miss any, check your work in the *Student's Solutions Manual* or ask your instructor for guidance.
- **Even-numbered exercises.** Whether or not your instructor assigns the even-numbered exercises, always do some on your own. Remember, there are no answers given for the class tests, so you need to practice doing exercises without answers. Check your answers later with a friend or your instructor.

1.2 EXERCISE SET

For Extra Help

MathXL MyMathLab InterAct Math Math Tutor Center Digital Video Tutor CD 1 Videotape 2 Student's Solutions Manual

a State the integers that correspond to the situation.

1. *Pollution Fine.* In 2003, The Colonial Pipeline Company was fined a record $34 million for pollution.
Source: greenconsumerguide.com

2. *Lake Powell.* The water level of Lake Powell, a desert reservoir behind Glen Canyon Dam in northern Arizona and southeastern Utah, has dropped 130 ft since 2000.

3. On Wednesday, the temperature was 24° above zero. On Thursday, it was 2° below zero.

4. A student deposited her tax refund of $750 in a savings account. Two weeks later, she withdrew $125 to pay sorority fees.

5. *Temperature Extremes.* The highest temperature ever created on Earth was 950,000,000°F. The lowest temperature ever created was approximately 460°F below zero.
Source: *Guinness Book of World Records*

6. *Extreme Climate.* Verkhoyansk, a river port in northeast Siberia, has the most extreme climate on the planet. Its average monthly winter temperature is 58.5°F below zero, and its average monthly summer temperature is 56.5°F.
Source: *Guinness Book of World Records*

7. In bowling, the Alley Cats are 34 pins behind the Strikers going into the last frame. Describe the situation of each team.

8. During a video game, Maggie intercepted a missile worth 20 points, lost a starship worth 150 points, and captured a landing base worth 300 points.

b Graph the number on the number line.

9. $\frac{10}{3}$

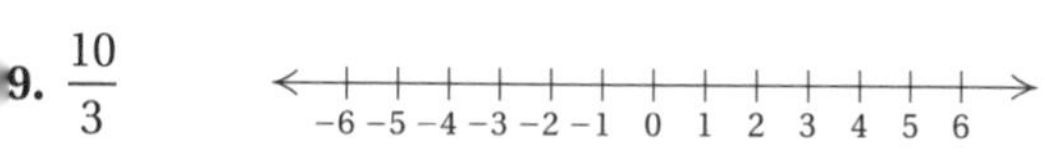

10. $-\frac{17}{4}$

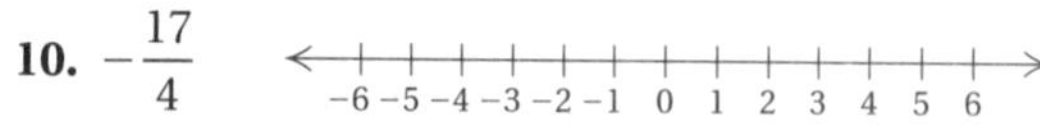

1. -5.2

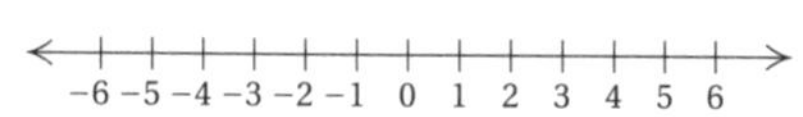

12. 4.78

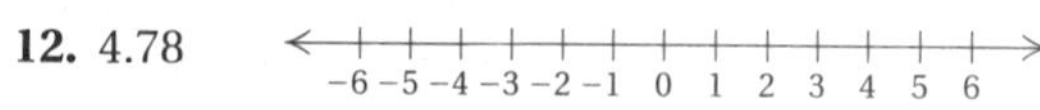

3. $-4\frac{2}{5}$

−6 −5 −4 −3 −2 −1 0 1 2 3 4 5 6

14. $2\frac{6}{11}$

−6 −5 −4 −3 −2 −1 0 1 2 3 4 5 6

c Convert to decimal notation.

15. $-\frac{7}{8}$

16. $-\frac{3}{16}$

17. $\frac{5}{6}$

18. $\frac{5}{3}$

19. $-\frac{7}{6}$

20. $-\frac{5}{12}$

21. $\frac{2}{3}$

22. $-\frac{11}{9}$

23. $\frac{1}{10}$

24. $\frac{1}{4}$

25. $-\frac{1}{2}$

26. $\frac{9}{8}$

27. $\frac{4}{25}$

28. $-\frac{7}{20}$

d Use either $<$ or $>$ for $\square$ to write a true sentence.

29. $8 \square 0$

30. $3 \square 0$

31. $-8 \square 3$

32. $6 \square -6$

33. $-8 \square 8$

34. $0 \square -9$

35. $-8 \square -5$

36. $-4 \square -3$

37. $-5 \square -11$

38. $-3 \square -4$

39. $-6 \square -5$

40. $-10 \square -14$

41. $2.14 \square 1.24$

42. $-3.3 \square -2.2$

43. $-14.5 \square 0.011$

44. $17.2 \square -1.67$

45. $-12.88 \square -6.45$

46. $-14.34 \square -17.88$

47. $-\frac{1}{2} \square -\frac{2}{3}$

48. $-\frac{5}{4} \square -\frac{3}{4}$

49. $-\frac{2}{3} \square \frac{1}{3}$

50. $\frac{3}{4} \square -\frac{5}{4}$

51. $\frac{5}{12} \square \frac{11}{25}$

52. $-\frac{13}{16} \square -\frac{5}{9}$

Vrite true or false.

3. $-3 \geq -11$

54. $5 \leq -5$

55. $0 \geq 8$

56. $-5 \leq 7$

Vrite an inequality with the same meaning.

7. $-6 > x$

58. $x < 8$

59. $-10 \leq y$

60. $12 \geq t$

e Find the absolute value.

1. $|-3|$

62. $|-7|$

63. $|10|$

64. $|11|$

65. $|0|$

6. $|-2.7|$

67. $|-30.4|$

68. $|325|$

69. $\left|-\frac{2}{3}\right|$

70. $\left|-\frac{10}{7}\right|$

1. $\left|\frac{0}{4}\right|$

72. $|14.8|$

73. $\left|-3\frac{5}{8}\right|$

74. $\left|-7\frac{4}{5}\right|$

5. D_W When Jennifer's calculator gives a decimal approximation for $\sqrt{2}$ and that approximation is promptly squared, the result is 2. Yet, when that same approximation is entered by hand and then squared, the result is not exactly 2. Why do you suppose this happens?

76. D_W How many rational numbers are there between 0 and 1? Why?

SKILL MAINTENANCE

onvert to decimal notation. [R.4a]

7. 63%

78. $23\frac{4}{5}\%$

79. 110%

80. 22.76%

onvert to percent notation. [R.4d]

1. $\frac{13}{25}$

82. $\frac{5}{4}$

83. $\frac{5}{6}$

84. $\frac{19}{32}$

SYNTHESIS

ist in order from the least to the greatest.

5. $-\frac{2}{3}, \frac{1}{2}, -\frac{3}{4}, -\frac{5}{6}, \frac{3}{8}, \frac{1}{6}$

86. $\frac{2}{3}, -\frac{1}{7}, \frac{1}{3}, -\frac{2}{7}, -\frac{2}{3}, \frac{2}{5}, -\frac{1}{3}, -\frac{2}{5}, \frac{9}{8}$

7. $-5.16, -4.24, -8.76, 5.23, 1.85, -2.13$

88. $-8\frac{7}{8}, 7^1, -5, |-6|, 4, |3|, -8\frac{5}{8}, -100, 0, 1^7, \frac{14}{4}, -\frac{67}{8}$

iven that $0.\overline{3} = \frac{1}{3}$ and $0.\overline{6} = \frac{2}{3}$, express each of the following as a quotient or ratio of two integers.

). $0.\overline{1}$

90. $0.\overline{9}$

91. $5.\overline{5}$

1.3 ADDITION OF REAL NUMBERS

Objectives

a Add real numbers without using a number line.

b Find the opposite, or additive inverse, of a real number.

c Solve applied problems involving addition of real numbers.

In this section, we consider addition of real numbers. First, to gain a understanding, we add using a number line. Then we consider rules fo addition.

ADDITION ON A NUMBER LINE

To do the addition $a + b$ on a number line, we start at 0. Then we move to a and then move according to b.

a) If b is positive, we move from a to the right.
b) If b is negative, we move from a to the left.
c) If b is 0, we stay at a.

EXAMPLE 1 Add: $3 + (-5)$.

We start at 0 and move to 3. Then we move 5 units left since -5 i negative.

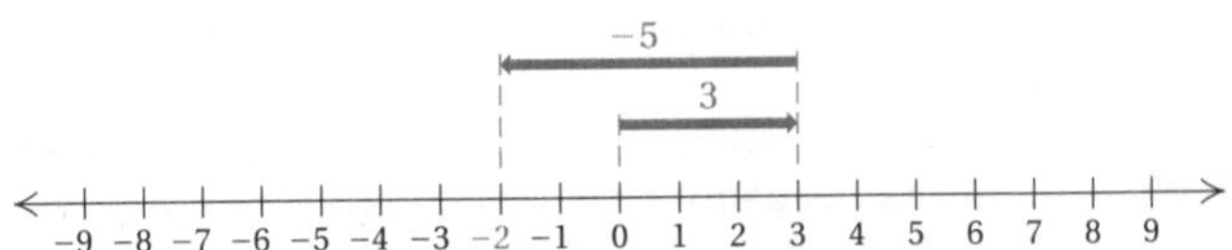

$3 + (-5) = -2$

EXAMPLE 2 Add: $-4 + (-3)$.

We start at 0 and move to -4. Then we move 3 units left since -3 negative.

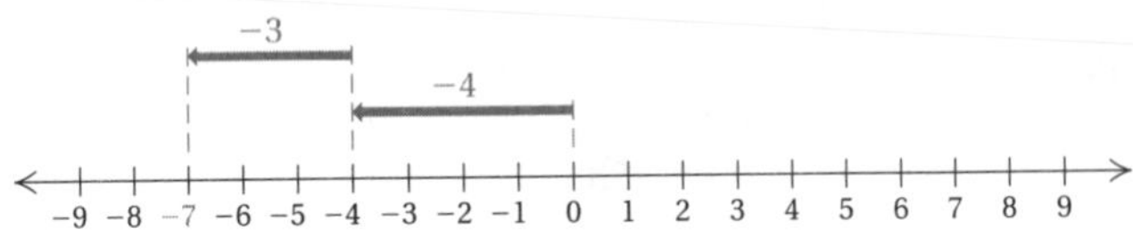

$-4 + (-3) = -7$

EXAMPLE 3 Add: $-4 + 9$.

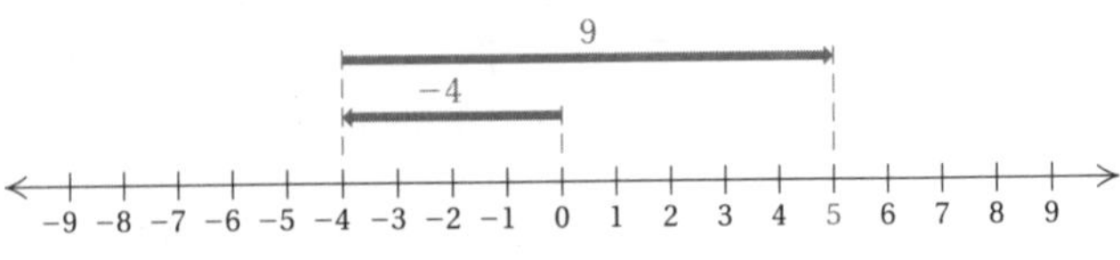

$-4 + 9 = 5$

Add using a number line.

1. $0 + (-3)$

2. $1 + (-4)$

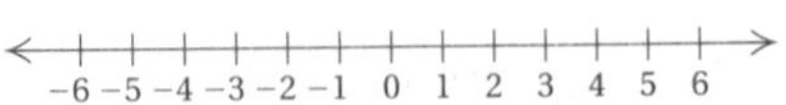

3. $-3 + (-2)$

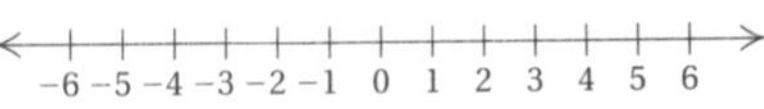

4. $-3 + 7$

5. $-2.4 + 2.4$

6. $-\frac{5}{2} + \frac{1}{2}$

Answers on page A-4

EXAMPLE 4 Add: $-5.2 + 0$.

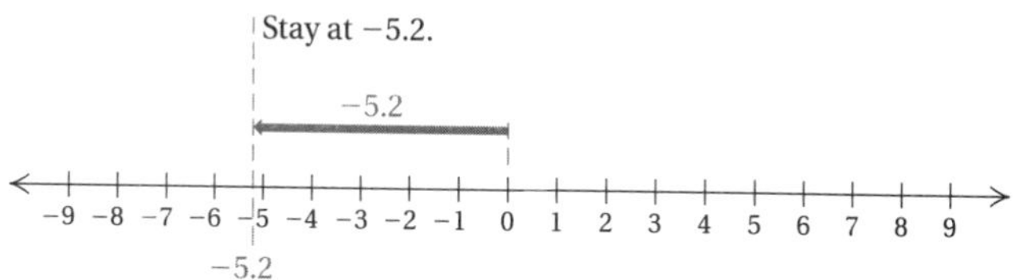

$-5.2 + 0 = -5.2$

Do Exercises 1–6 on the preceding page.

a Adding Without a Number Line

You may have noticed some patterns in the preceding examples. These lead us to rules for adding without using a number line that are more efficient for adding larger numbers.

RULES FOR ADDITION OF REAL NUMBERS

1. *Positive numbers*: Add the same as arithmetic numbers. The answer is positive.
2. *Negative numbers*: Add absolute values. The answer is negative.
3. *A positive and a negative number*: Subtract the smaller absolute value from the larger. Then:
   a) If the positive number has the greater absolute value, the answer is positive.
   b) If the negative number has the greater absolute value, the answer is negative.
   c) If the numbers have the same absolute value, the answer is 0.
4. *One number is zero*: The sum is the other number.

Rule 4 is known as the **identity property of 0.** It says that for any real number a, $a + 0 = a$.

EXAMPLES Add without using a number line.

5. $-12 + (-7) = -19$ Two negatives. Add the absolute values: $|-12| + |-7| = 12 + 7 = 19$. Make the answer *negative*: -19.

6. $-1.4 + 8.5 = 7.1$ One negative, one positive. Find the absolute values: $|-1.4| = 1.4$; $|8.5| = 8.5$. Subtract the smaller absolute value from the larger: $8.5 - 1.4 = 7.1$. The *positive* number, 8.5, has the larger absolute value, so the answer is *positive*: 7.1.

7. $-36 + 21 = -15$ One negative, one positive. Find the absolute values: $|-36| = 36$, $|21| = 21$. Subtract the smaller absolute value from the larger: $36 - 21 = 15$. The *negative* number, -36, has the larger absolute value, so the answer is *negative*: -15.

Add without using a number line.

7. $-5 + (-6)$

8. $-9 + (-3)$

9. $-4 + 6$

10. $-7 + 3$

11. $5 + (-7)$

12. $-20 + 20$

13. $-11 + (-11)$

14. $10 + (-7)$

15. $-0.17 + 0.7$

16. $-6.4 + 8.7$

17. $-4.5 + (-3.2)$

18. $-8.6 + 2.4$

19. $\frac{5}{9} + \left(-\frac{7}{9}\right)$

20. $-\frac{1}{5} + \left(-\frac{3}{4}\right)$

Answers on page A-4

Add.

21. $(-15) + (-37) + 25 + 42 + (-59) + (-14)$

22. $42 + (-81) + (-28) + 24 + 18 + (-31)$

23. $-2.5 + (-10) + 6 + (-7.5)$

24. $-35 + 17 + 14 + (-27) + 31 + (-12)$

Find the opposite, or additive inverse, of each of the following.

25. -4

26. 8.7

27. -7.74

28. $-\frac{8}{9}$

29. 0

30. 12

Answers on page A-4

8. $1.5 + (-1.5) = 0$ — The numbers have the same absolute value. The sum is 0.

9. $-\frac{7}{8} + 0 = -\frac{7}{8}$ — One number is zero. The sum is $-\frac{7}{8}$.

10. $-9.2 + 3.1 = -6.1$

11. $-\frac{3}{2} + \frac{9}{2} = \frac{6}{2} = 3$

12. $-\frac{2}{3} + \frac{5}{8} = -\frac{16}{24} + \frac{15}{24} = -\frac{1}{24}$

Do Exercises 7–20 on the preceding page.

Suppose we want to add several numbers, some positive and some negative, as follows. How can we proceed?

$$15 + (-2) + 7 + 14 + (-5) + (-12)$$

We can change grouping and order as we please when adding. For instance we can group the positive numbers together and the negative numbers together and add them separately. Then we add the two results.

EXAMPLE 13 Add: $15 + (-2) + 7 + 14 + (-5) + (-12)$.

a) $15 + 7 + 14 = 36$ — Adding the positive numbers

b) $-2 + (-5) + (-12) = -19$ — Adding the negative numbers

$36 + (-19) = 17$ — Adding (a) and (b)

We can also add the numbers in any other order we wish, say, from left to right as follows:

$$\begin{aligned} 15 + (-2) + 7 + 14 + (-5) + (-12) &= 13 + 7 + 14 + (-5) + (-12) \\ &= 20 + 14 + (-5) + (-12) \\ &= 34 + (-5) + (-12) \\ &= 29 + (-12) \\ &= 17 \end{aligned}$$

Do Exercises 21–24.

b Opposites, or Additive Inverses

Suppose we add two numbers that are **opposites,** such as 6 and -6. The result is 0. When opposites are added, the result is always 0. Such numbers are also called **additive inverses.** Every real number has an opposite, or additive inverse.

OPPOSITES, OR ADDITIVE INVERSES

Two numbers whose sum is 0 are called **opposites,** or **additive inverses,** of each other.

EXAMPLES Find the opposite, or additive inverse, of each number.

14. 34 — The opposite of 34 is -34 because $34 + (-34) = 0$.

15. -8 — The opposite of -8 is 8 because $-8 + 8 = 0$.

16. 0 — The opposite of 0 is 0 because $0 + 0 = 0$.

17. $-\frac{7}{8}$ — The opposite of $-\frac{7}{8}$ is $\frac{7}{8}$ because $-\frac{7}{8} + \frac{7}{8} = 0$.

Do Exercises 25–30 on the preceding page.

To name the opposite, we use the symbol $-$, as follows.

SYMBOLIZING OPPOSITES

The opposite, or additive inverse, of a number a can be named $-a$ (read "the opposite of a," or "the additive inverse of a").

Note that if we take a number, say, 8, and find its opposite, -8, and then find the opposite of the result, we will have the original number, 8, again.

THE OPPOSITE OF AN OPPOSITE

The **opposite of the opposite** of a number is the number itself. (The additive inverse of the additive inverse of a number is the number itself.) That is, for any number a,

$$-(-a) = a.$$

EXAMPLE 18 Evaluate $-x$ and $-(-x)$ when $x = 16$.

If $x = 16$, then $-x = -16$. — The opposite of 16 is -16.

If $x = 16$, then $-(-x) = -(-16) = 16$. — The opposite of the opposite of 16 is 16.

EXAMPLE 19 Evaluate $-x$ and $-(-x)$ when $x = -3$.

If $x = -3$, then $-x = -(-3) = 3$.

If $x = -3$, then $-(-x) = -(-(-3)) = -(3) = -3$.

Note that in Example 19 we used a second set of parentheses to show that we are substituting the negative number -3 for x. Symbolism like $--x$ is not considered meaningful.

Do Exercises 31–36.

A symbol such as -8 is usually read "negative 8." It could be read "the additive inverse of 8," because the additive inverse of 8 is negative 8. It could also be read "the opposite of 8," because the opposite of 8 is -8. Thus a symbol like -8 can be read in more than one way. It is never correct to read -8 as "minus 8."

Caution!

A symbol like $-x$, which has a variable, should be read "the opposite of x" or "the additive inverse of x" and *not* "negative x," because we do not know whether x represents a positive number, a negative number, or 0. You can check this in Examples 18 and 19.

Evaluate $-x$ and $-(-x)$ when:

31. $x = 14$.

32. $x = 1$.

33. $x = -19$.

34. $x = -1.6$.

35. $x = \frac{2}{3}$.

36. $x = -\frac{9}{8}$.

Answers on page A-4

Find the opposite. (Change the sign.)

37. -4

38. -13.4

39. 0

40. $\frac{1}{4}$

41. Change in Class Size. During the first two weeks of the semester in Jim's algebra class, 4 students withdrew, 8 students enrolled in the class, and 6 students were dropped as "no shows." By how many students had the class size changed at the end of the first two weeks?

Answers on page A-4

Study Tips

SMALL STEPS LEAD TO GREAT SUCCESS (PART 1)

What is your long-term goal for getting an education? How does math help you to attain that goal? As you begin this course, approach each short-term task, such as going to class, asking questions, using your time wisely, and doing your homework, as part of the framework of your long-term goal.

"What man actually needs is not a tensionless state but rather the struggling and striving for a worthwhile goal, a freely chosen task."

Victor Frankl

We can use the symbolism $-a$ to restate the definition of opposite, or additive inverse.

THE SUM OF OPPOSITES

For any real number a, the **opposite,** or **additive inverse,** of a, expressed as $-a$, is such that

$$a + (-a) = (-a) + a = 0.$$

SIGNS OF NUMBERS

A negative number is sometimes said to have a "negative sign." A positive number is said to have a "positive sign." When we replace a number with its opposite, we can say that we have "changed its sign."

EXAMPLES Find the opposite. (Change the sign.)

20. -3 $\quad -(-3) = 3$

21. $-\frac{2}{13}$ $\quad -\left(-\frac{2}{13}\right) = \frac{2}{13}$

22. 0 $\quad -(0) = 0$

23. 14 $\quad -(14) = -14$

Do Exercises 37–40.

C Applications and Problem Solving

Addition of real numbers occurs in many real-world situations.

EXAMPLE 24 *Lake Level.* In the course of one four-month period, the water level of Lake Champlain went down 2 ft, up 1 ft, down 5 ft, and up 3 ft. How much had the lake level changed at the end of the four months?

We let T = the total change in the level of the lake. Then the problem translates to a sum:

Total change	is	1st change	plus	2nd change	plus	3rd change	plus	4th change
↓	↓	↓	↓	↓	↓	↓	↓	↓
T	=	-2	+	1	+	(-5)	+	3

Adding from left to right, we have

$$\begin{aligned} T = -2 + 1 + (-5) + 3 &= -1 + (-5) + 3 \\ &= -6 + 3 \\ &= -3. \end{aligned}$$

The lake level has dropped 3 ft at the end of the four-month period.

Do Exercise 41.

1.3 EXERCISE SET

For Extra Help

MathXL | MyMathLab | InterAct Math | Math Tutor Center | Digital Video Tutor CD 1 Videotape 2 | Student's Solutions Manual

a Add. Do not use a number line except as a check.

1. $2 + (-9)$
2. $-5 + 2$
3. $-11 + 5$
4. $4 + (-3)$
5. $-6 + 6$

6. $8 + (-8)$
7. $-3 + (-5)$
8. $-4 + (-6)$
9. $-7 + 0$
10. $-13 + 0$

11. $0 + (-27)$
12. $0 + (-35)$
13. $17 + (-17)$
14. $-15 + 15$
15. $-17 + (-25)$

16. $-24 + (-17)$
17. $18 + (-18)$
18. $-13 + 13$
19. $-28 + 28$
20. $11 + (-11)$

. $8 + (-5)$
22. $-7 + 8$
23. $-4 + (-5)$
24. $10 + (-12)$
25. $13 + (-6)$

26. $-3 + 14$
27. $-25 + 25$
28. $50 + (-50)$
29. $53 + (-18)$
30. $75 + (-45)$

. $-8.5 + 4.7$
32. $-4.6 + 1.9$
33. $-2.8 + (-5.3)$
34. $-7.9 + (-6.5)$
35. $-\frac{3}{5} + \frac{2}{5}$

. $-\frac{4}{3} + \frac{2}{3}$
37. $-\frac{2}{9} + \left(-\frac{5}{9}\right)$
38. $-\frac{4}{7} + \left(-\frac{6}{7}\right)$
39. $-\frac{5}{8} + \frac{1}{4}$
40. $-\frac{5}{6} + \frac{2}{3}$

. $-\frac{5}{8} + \left(-\frac{1}{6}\right)$
42. $-\frac{5}{6} + \left(-\frac{2}{9}\right)$
43. $-\frac{3}{8} + \frac{5}{12}$
44. $-\frac{7}{16} + \frac{7}{8}$

. $-\frac{1}{6} + \frac{7}{10}$
46. $-\frac{11}{18} + \left(-\frac{3}{4}\right)$
47. $\frac{7}{15} + \left(-\frac{1}{9}\right)$
48. $-\frac{4}{21} + \frac{3}{14}$

49. $76 + (-15) + (-18) + (-6)$

50. $29 + (-45) + 18 + 32 + (-96)$

51. $-44 + \left(-\frac{3}{8}\right) + 95 + \left(-\frac{5}{8}\right)$

52. $24 + 3.1 + (-44) + (-8.2) + 63$

53. $98 + (-54) + 113 + (-998) + 44 + (-612)$

54. $-458 + (-124) + 1025 + (-917) + 218$

Find the opposite, or additive inverse.

55. 24

56. -64

57. -26.9

58. 48.2

Evaluate $-x$ when:

59. $x = 8$.

60. $x = -27$.

61. $x = -\frac{13}{8}$.

62. $x = \frac{1}{236}$.

Evaluate $-(-x)$ when:

63. $x = -43$.

64. $x = 39$.

65. $x = \frac{4}{3}$.

66. $x = -7.1$.

Find the opposite. (Change the sign.)

67. -24

68. -12.3

69. $-\frac{3}{8}$

70. 10

c Solve.

71. *Tallest Mountain.* The tallest mountain in the world, when measured from base to peak, is Mauna Kea (White Mountain) in Hawaii. From its base 19,684 ft below sea level in the Hawaiian Trough, it rises 33,480 ft. What is the elevation of the peak above sea level?

Source: *The Guinness Book of Records*

72. *Telephone Bills.* Erika's cell-phone bill for July was $8[…] She sent a check for $50 and then made $37 worth of calls in August. How much did she then owe on her ce[…] phone bill?

73. *Temperature Changes.* One day the temperature in Lawrence, Kansas, is 32°F at 6:00 A.M. It rises 15° by noon, but falls 50° by midnight when a cold front moves in. What is the final temperature?

74. *Stock Changes.* On a recent day, the price of a stock opened at a value of $61.38. During the day, it rose $4.75, dropped $7.38, and rose $5.13. Find the value o[…] the stock at the end of the day.

5. *Profits and Losses.* A business expresses a profit as a positive number and refers to it as operating "in the black." A loss is expressed as a negative number and is referred to as operating "in the red." The profits and losses of Xponent Corporation over various years are shown in the bar graph below. Find the sum of the profits and losses.

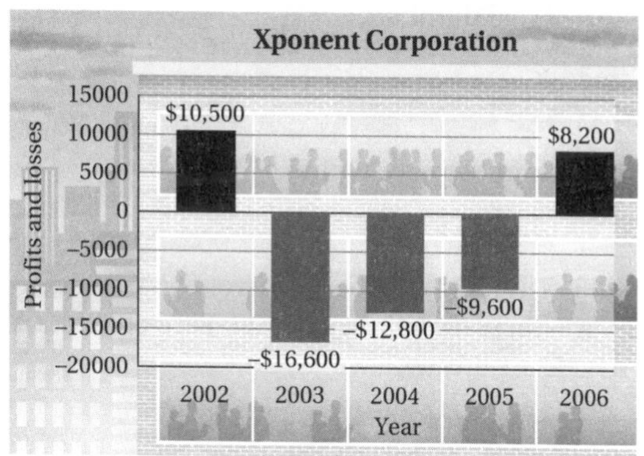

76. *Football Yardage.* In a college football game, the quarterback attempted passes with the following results. Find the total gain or loss.

TRY	GAIN OR LOSS
1st	13-yd gain
2nd	12-yd loss
3rd	21-yd gain

7. *Credit Card Bills.* On August 1, Lyle's credit card bill shows that he owes $470. During the month of August, Lyle sends a check for $45 to the credit card company, charges another $160 in merchandise, and then pays off another $500 of his bill. What is the new balance of Lyle's account at the end of August?

78. *Account Balance.* Leah has $460 in a checking account. She writes a check for $530, makes a deposit of $75, and then writes a check for $90. What is the balance in her account?

9. ^{D}W Without actually performing the addition, explain why the sum of all integers from -50 to 50 is 0.

80. ^{D}W Explain in your own words why the sum of two negative numbers is always negative.

SKILL MAINTENANCE

onvert to decimal notation. [R.4a]

1. 71.3%

82. $92\frac{7}{8}\%$

Convert to percent notation. [R.4d]

83. $\frac{1}{8}$

84. $\frac{13}{32}$

5. Divide and simplify: $\frac{2}{3} \div \frac{5}{12}$. [R.2c]

86. Subtract and simplify: $\frac{2}{3} - \frac{5}{12}$. [R.2c]

SYNTHESIS

7. For what numbers x is $-x$ negative?

88. For what numbers x is $-x$ positive?

or each of Exercises 89 and 90, choose the correct answer from the selections given.

9. If a is positive and b is negative, then $-a + b$ is:

a) Positive.
b) Negative.
c) 0.
d) Cannot be determined without more information

90. If $a = b$ and a and b are negative, then $-a + (-b)$ is:

a) Positive.
b) Negative.
c) 0.
d) Cannot be determined without more information

1.4 SUBTRACTION OF REAL NUMBERS

Objectives

a Subtract real numbers and simplify combinations of additions and subtractions.

b Solve applied problems involving subtraction of real numbers.

Subtract.

1. $-6 - 4$

Think: What number can be added to 4 to get -6:

$$\square + 4 = -6?$$

2. $-7 - (-10)$

Think: What number can be added to -10 to get -7:

$$\square + (-10) = -7?$$

3. $-7 - (-2)$

Think: What number can be added to -2 to get -7:

$$\square + (-2) = -7?$$

Subtract. Use a number line, doing the "opposite" of addition.

4. $-4 - (-3)$

5. $-4 - (-6)$

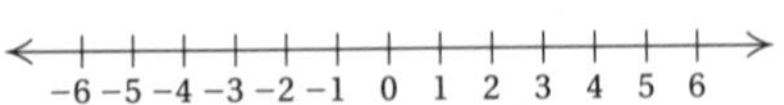

6. $5 - 9$

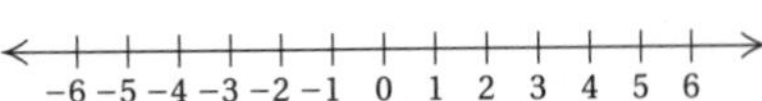

Answers on page A-4

a Subtraction

We now consider subtraction of real numbers.

SUBTRACTION

The difference $a - b$ is the number c for which $a = b + c$.

Consider, for example, $45 - 17$. *Think*: What number can we add to 17 to get 45? Since $45 = 17 + 28$, we know that $45 - 17 = 28$. Let's consider an example whose answer is a negative number.

EXAMPLE 1 Subtract: $3 - 7$.

Think: What number can we add to 7 to get 3? The number must be negative. Since $7 + (-4) = 3$, we know the number is -4: $3 - 7 = -4$. That is, $3 - 7 = -4$ because $7 + (-4) = 3$.

Do Exercises 1–3.

The definition above does not provide the most efficient way to do subtraction. We can develop a faster way to subtract. As a rationale for the faster way, let's compare $3 + 7$ and $3 - 7$ on a number line.

To find $3 + 7$ on a number line, we move 3 units to the right from 0 since 3 is positive. Then we move 7 units farther to the right since 7 is positive.

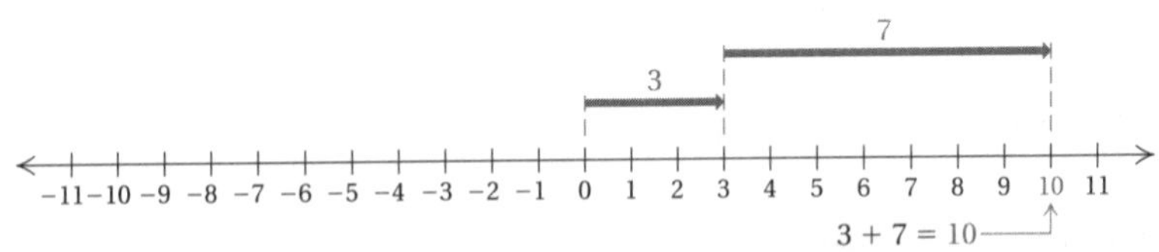

To find $3 - 7$, we do the "opposite" of adding 7: We move 7 units to the *left* to do the subtracting. This is the same as *adding* the opposite of 7, -7, to 3.

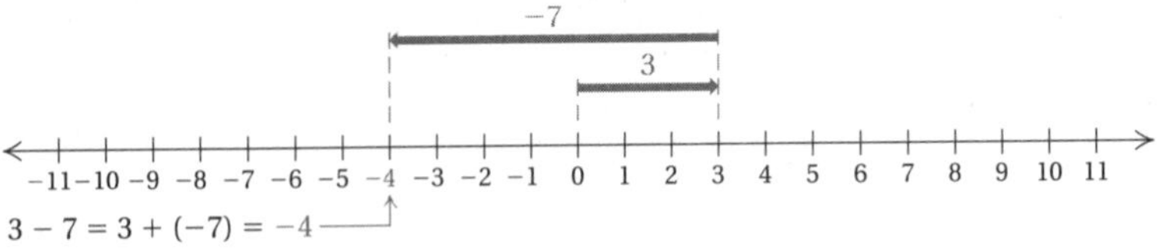

Do Exercises 4–6.

Look for a pattern in the examples shown at right.

SUBTRACTING	ADDING AN OPPOSITE
$5 - 8 = -3$	$5 + (-8) = -3$
$-6 - 4 = -10$	$-6 + (-4) = -10$
$-7 - (-2) = -5$	$-7 + 2 = -5$

Do Exercises 7–10 on the following page.

Perhaps you have noticed that we can subtract by adding the opposite of he number being subtracted. This can always be done.

SUBTRACTING BY ADDING THE OPPOSITE

For any real numbers a and b,

$$a - b = a + (-b).$$

(To subtract, add the opposite, or additive inverse, of the number being subtracted.)

This is the method generally used for quick subtraction of real numbers.

XAMPLES Subtract.

2. $2 - 6 = 2 + (-6) = -4$ — The opposite of 6 is -6. We change the subtraction to addition and add the opposite. *Check*: $-4 + 6 = 2$.

3. $4 - (-9) = 4 + 9 = 13$ — The opposite of -9 is 9. We change the subtraction to addition and add the opposite. *Check*: $13 + (-9) = 4$.

4. $-4.2 - (-3.6) = -4.2 + 3.6 = -0.6$ — Adding the opposite. *Check*: $-0.6 + (-3.6) = -4.2$.

5. $-\frac{1}{2} - \left(-\frac{3}{4}\right) = -\frac{1}{2} + \frac{3}{4}$
$= -\frac{2}{4} + \frac{3}{4} = \frac{1}{4}$ — Adding the opposite. *Check*: $\frac{1}{4} + \left(-\frac{3}{4}\right) = -\frac{1}{2}$.

o Exercises 11–16.

XAMPLES Read each of the following. Then subtract by adding the oppo-te of the number being subtracted.

6. $3 - 5$ — Read "three minus five is three plus the opposite of five"
$3 - 5 = 3 + (-5) = -2$

7. $\frac{1}{8} - \frac{7}{8}$ — Read "one-eighth minus seven-eighths is one-eighth plus the opposite of seven-eighths"
$\frac{1}{8} - \frac{7}{8} = \frac{1}{8} + \left(-\frac{7}{8}\right) = -\frac{6}{8}$, or $-\frac{3}{4}$

8. $-4.6 - (-9.8)$ — Read "negative four point six minus negative nine point eight is negative four point six plus the opposite of negative nine point eight"
$-4.6 - (-9.8) = -4.6 + 9.8 = 5.2$

9. $-\frac{3}{4} - \frac{7}{5}$ — Read "negative three-fourths minus seven-fifths is negative three-fourths plus the opposite of seven-fifths"
$-\frac{3}{4} - \frac{7}{5} = -\frac{3}{4} + \left(-\frac{7}{5}\right) = -\frac{15}{20} + \left(-\frac{28}{20}\right) = -\frac{43}{20}$

o Exercises 17–21 on the following page.

Complete the addition and compare with the subtraction.

7. $4 - 6 = -2;$
$4 + (-6) =$ ______

8. $-3 - 8 = -11;$
$-3 + (-8) =$ ______

9. $-5 - (-9) = 4;$
$-5 + 9 =$ ______

10. $-5 - (-3) = -2;$
$-5 + 3 =$ ______

Subtract.

11. $2 - 8$

12. $-6 - 10$

13. $12.4 - 5.3$

14. $-8 - (-11)$

15. $-8 - (-8)$

16. $\frac{2}{3} - \left(-\frac{5}{6}\right)$

Answers on page A-4

Read each of the following. Then subtract by adding the opposite of the number being subtracted.

17. $3 - 11$

18. $12 - 5$

19. $-12 - (-9)$

20. $-12.4 - 10.9$

21. $-\frac{4}{5} - \left(-\frac{4}{5}\right)$

Simplify.

22. $-6 - (-2) - (-4) - 12 + 3$

23. $\frac{2}{3} - \frac{4}{5} - \left(-\frac{11}{15}\right) + \frac{7}{10} - \frac{5}{2}$

24. $-9.6 + 7.4 - (-3.9) - (-11)$

25. Temperature Extremes. The highest temperature ever recorded in the United States is 134°F in Greenland Ranch, California, on July 10, 1913. The lowest temperature ever recorded is -80°F in Prospect Creek, Alaska, on January 23, 1971. How much higher was the temperature in Greenland Ranch than that in Prospect Creek?

Source: National Oceanographic and Atmospheric Administration

Answers on page A-4

When several additions and subtractions occur together, we can mak[e] them all additions.

EXAMPLES Simplify.

10. $8 - (-4) - 2 - (-4) + 2 = 8 + 4 + (-2) + 4 + 2$ Adding the opposite

$= 16$

11. $8.2 - (-6.1) + 2.3 - (-4) = 8.2 + 6.1 + 2.3 + 4 = 20.6$

12. $\frac{3}{4} - \left(-\frac{1}{12}\right) - \frac{5}{6} - \frac{2}{3} = \frac{9}{12} + \frac{1}{12} + \left(-\frac{10}{12}\right) + \left(-\frac{8}{12}\right)$

$= \frac{9 + 1 + (-10) + (-8)}{12}$

$= \frac{-8}{12} = -\frac{8}{12} = -\frac{2}{3}$

Do Exercises 22–24.

b Applications and Problem Solving

Let's now see how we can use subtraction of real numbers to solve applie[d] problems.

EXAMPLE 13 *Surface Temperatures on Mars.* Surface temperatures o[n] Mars vary from -128°C during polar night to 27°C at the equator during mi[d]day at the closest point in orbit to the sun. Find the difference between th[e] highest value and the lowest value in this temperature range.

Source: Mars Institute

We let $D =$ the difference in the temperatures. Then the problem tran[s]lates to the following subtraction:

Difference in temperature	is	Highest temperature	minus	Lowest temperature
↓	↓	↓	↓	↓
D	$=$	27	$-$	(-128)

$D = 27 + 128 = 155$

The difference in the temperatures is 155°C.

Do Exercise 25.

1.4 EXERCISE SET

For Extra Help

MathXL | MyMathLab | InterAct Math | Math Tutor Center | Digital Video Tutor CD 1 Videotape 2 | Student's Solutions Manual

a Subtract.

1. $2 - 9$

2. $3 - 8$

3. $-8 - (-2)$

4. $-6 - (-8)$

5. $-11 - (-11)$

6. $-6 - (-6)$

7. $12 - 16$

8. $14 - 19$

9. $20 - 27$

10. $30 - 4$

11. $-9 - (-3)$

12. $-7 - (-9)$

13. $-40 - (-40)$

14. $-9 - (-9)$

15. $7 - (-7)$

16. $4 - (-4)$

17. $8 - (-3)$

18. $-7 - 4$

19. $-6 - 8$

20. $6 - (-10)$

21. $-4 - (-9)$

22. $-14 - 2$

23. $-6 - (-5)$

24. $-4 - (-3)$

25. $8 - (-10)$

26. $5 - (-6)$

27. $-5 - (-2)$

28. $-3 - (-1)$

29. $-7 - 14$

30. $-9 - 16$

31. $0 - (-5)$

32. $0 - (-1)$

33. $-8 - 0$

34. $-9 - 0$

35. $7 - (-5)$

36. $7 - (-4)$

37. $2 - 25$

38. $18 - 63$

39. $-42 - 26$

40. $-18 - 63$

41. $-71 - 2$

42. $-49 - 3$

43. $24 - (-92)$

44. $48 - (-73)$

45. $-50 - (-50)$

46. $-70 - (-70)$

47. $-\frac{3}{8} - \frac{5}{8}$

48. $\frac{3}{9} - \frac{9}{9}$

49. $\frac{3}{4} - \frac{2}{3}$

50. $\frac{5}{8} - \frac{3}{4}$

51. $-\frac{3}{4} - \frac{2}{3}$

52. $-\frac{5}{8} - \frac{3}{4}$

53. $-\frac{5}{8} - \left(-\frac{3}{4}\right)$

54. $-\frac{3}{4} - \left(-\frac{2}{3}\right)$

55. $6.1 - (-13.8)$

56. $1.5 - (-3.5)$

57. $-2.7 - 5.9$

58. $-3.2 - 5.8$

59. $0.99 - 1$

60. $0.87 - 1$

61. $-79 - 114$

62. $-197 - 216$

63. $0 - (-500)$

64. $500 - (-1000)$

65. $-2.8 - 0$

66. $6.04 - 1.1$

67. $7 - 10.53$

68. $8 - (-9.3)$

69. $\frac{1}{6} - \frac{2}{3}$

70. $-\frac{3}{8} - \left(-\frac{1}{2}\right)$

71. $-\frac{4}{7} - \left(-\frac{10}{7}\right)$

72. $\frac{12}{5} - \frac{12}{5}$

73. $-\frac{7}{10} - \frac{10}{15}$

74. $-\frac{4}{18} - \left(-\frac{2}{9}\right)$

75. $\frac{1}{5} - \frac{1}{3}$

76. $-\frac{1}{7} - \left(-\frac{1}{6}\right)$

77. $\frac{5}{12} - \frac{7}{16}$

78. $-\frac{1}{35} - \left(-\frac{9}{40}\right)$

79. $-\frac{2}{15} - \frac{7}{12}$

80. $\frac{2}{21} - \frac{9}{14}$

implify.

81. $18 - (-15) - 3 - (-5) + 2$

82. $22 - (-18) + 7 + (-42) - 27$

83. $-31 + (-28) - (-14) - 17$

84. $-43 - (-19) - (-21) + 25$

85. $-34 - 28 + (-33) - 44$

86. $39 + (-88) - 29 - (-83)$

87. $-93 - (-84) - 41 - (-56)$

88. $84 + (-99) + 44 - (-18) - 43$

89. $-5.4 - (-30.9) + 30.8 + 40.2 - (-12)$

90. $14.9 - (-50.7) + 20 - (-32.8)$

91. $-\frac{7}{12} + \frac{3}{4} - \left(-\frac{5}{8}\right) - \frac{13}{24}$

92. $-\frac{11}{16} + \frac{5}{32} - \left(-\frac{1}{4}\right) + \frac{7}{8}$

b Solve.

93. *Ocean Depth.* The deepest point in the Pacific Ocean is the Marianas Trench, with a depth of 10,924 m. The deepest point in the Atlantic Ocean is the Puerto Rico Trench, with a depth of 8605 m. What is the difference in the elevation of the two trenches?

Source: *The World Almanac and Book of Facts*

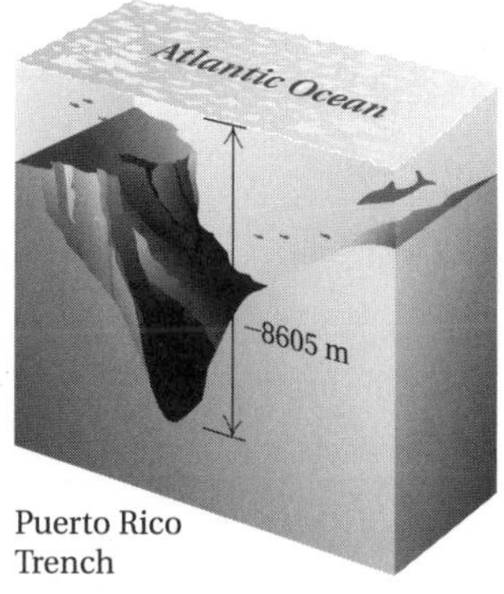

94. *Elevations in Africa.* The elevation of the highest point in Africa, Mt. Kilimanjaro, Tanzania, is 19,340 ft. The lowest elevation, at Lake Assal, Djibouti, is −512 ft. What is the difference in the elevations of the two locations?

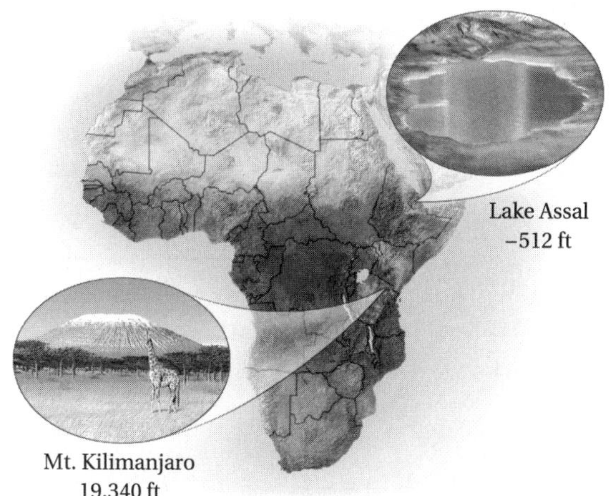

95. Claire has a charge of $476.89 on her credit card, but she then returns a sweater that cost $128.95. How much does she now owe on her credit card?

96. Chris has $720 in a checking account. He writes a check for $970 to pay for a sound system. What is the balance in his checking account?

97. *Home-Run Differential.* In baseball, the difference between the number of home runs hit by a team's players and the number allowed by its pitchers is called the *home-run differential,* that is,

$$\text{Home run differential} = \frac{\text{Number of}}{\text{home runs hit}} - \frac{\text{Number of home}}{\text{runs allowed}}.$$

Teams strive for a positive home-run differential.

a) In a recent year, Atlanta hit 197 home runs and allowed 120. Find its home-run differential.

b) In a recent year, San Francisco hit 153 home runs and allowed 194. Find its home-run differential.

Source: Major League Baseball

98. *Temperature Records.* The greatest recorded temperature change in one 24-hour period occurred between January 23 and January 24, 1916, in Browning, Montana, where the temperature fell from 44°F to −56°F. By how much did the temperature drop?

Source: *The Guinness Book of Records*, 2004

99. *Low Points on Continents.* The lowest point in Africa is Lake Assal, which is 512 ft below sea level. The lowest point in South America is the Valdes Peninsula, which is 131 ft below sea level. How much lower is Lake Assal than the Valdes Peninsula?

Source: National Geographic Society

100. *Elevation Changes.* The lowest elevation in North America, Death Valley, California, is 282 ft below sea level. The highest elevation in North America, Mount McKinley, Alaska, is 20,320 ft. Find the difference in elevation between the highest point and the lowest.

Source: National Geographic Society

101. $\mathbf{D_W}$ If a negative number is subtracted from a positive number, will the result always be positive? Why or why not?

102. $\mathbf{D_W}$ Write a problem for a classmate to solve. Design the problem so that the solution is "The temperature dropped to −9°."

SKILL MAINTENANCE

Simplify. [R.5c]

103. $256 \div 64 \div 2^3 + 100$

104. $5 \cdot 6 + (7 \cdot 2)^2$

105. $2^5 \div 4 + 20 \div 2^2$

106. $65 - 5^2 \div 5 - 5 \cdot 2$

107. Add and simplify: $\frac{1}{8} + \frac{7}{12} + \frac{5}{24}$. [R.2c]

108. Simplify: $\frac{164}{256}$. [R.2b]

SYNTHESIS

Tell whether the statement is true or false for all integers a and b. If false, give an example to show why.

109. $a - 0 = 0 - a$

110. $0 - a = a$

111. If $a \neq b$, then $a - b \neq 0$.

112. If $a = -b$, then $a + b = 0$.

113. If $a + b = 0$, then a and b are opposites.

114. If $a - b = 0$, then $a = -b$.

1.5 MULTIPLICATION OF REAL NUMBERS

a Multiplication

Multiplication of real numbers is very much like multiplication of arithmetic numbers. The only difference is that we must determine whether the answer is positive or negative.

MULTIPLICATION OF A POSITIVE NUMBER AND A NEGATIVE NUMBER

To see how to multiply a positive number and a negative number, consider the pattern of the following.

This number decreases by 1 each time.

$$\begin{aligned} 4 \cdot 5 &= 20 \\ 3 \cdot 5 &= 15 \\ 2 \cdot 5 &= 10 \\ 1 \cdot 5 &= 5 \\ 0 \cdot 5 &= 0 \\ -1 \cdot 5 &= -5 \\ -2 \cdot 5 &= -10 \\ -3 \cdot 5 &= -15 \end{aligned}$$

This number decreases by 5 each time.

Do Exercise 1.

According to this pattern, it looks as though the product of a negative number and a positive number is negative. That is the case, and we have the first part of the rule for multiplying numbers.

THE PRODUCT OF A POSITIVE AND A NEGATIVE NUMBER

To multiply a positive number and a negative number, multiply their absolute values. The answer is negative.

EXAMPLES Multiply.

1. $8(-5) = -40$

2. $-\frac{1}{3} \cdot \frac{5}{7} = -\frac{5}{21}$

3. $(-7.2)5 = -36$

Do Exercises 2–7.

MULTIPLICATION OF TWO NEGATIVE NUMBERS

How do we multiply two negative numbers? Again, we look for a pattern.

This number decreases by 1 each time.

$$\begin{aligned} 4 \cdot (-5) &= -20 \\ 3 \cdot (-5) &= -15 \\ 2 \cdot (-5) &= -10 \\ 1 \cdot (-5) &= -5 \\ 0 \cdot (-5) &= 0 \\ -1 \cdot (-5) &= 5 \\ -2 \cdot (-5) &= 10 \\ -3 \cdot (-5) &= 15 \end{aligned}$$

This number increases by 5 each time.

Objectives

a Multiply real numbers.

b Solve applied problems involving multiplication of real numbers.

1. Complete, as in the example.

$$\begin{aligned} 4 \cdot 10 &= 40 \\ 3 \cdot 10 &= 30 \\ 2 \cdot 10 &= \\ 1 \cdot 10 &= \\ 0 \cdot 10 &= \\ -1 \cdot 10 &= \\ -2 \cdot 10 &= \\ -3 \cdot 10 &= \end{aligned}$$

Multiply.

2. $-3 \cdot 6$

3. $20 \cdot (-5)$

4. $4 \cdot (-20)$

5. $-\frac{2}{3} \cdot \frac{5}{6}$

6. $-4.23(7.1)$

7. $\frac{7}{8}\left(-\frac{4}{5}\right)$

8. Complete, as in the example.

$$\begin{aligned} 3 \cdot (-10) &= -30 \\ 2 \cdot (-10) &= -20 \\ 1 \cdot (-10) &= \\ 0 \cdot (-10) &= \\ -1 \cdot (-10) &= \\ -2 \cdot (-10) &= \\ -3 \cdot (-10) &= \end{aligned}$$

Answers on page A-5

Multiply.

9. $-9 \cdot (-3)$

10. $-16 \cdot (-2)$

11. $-7 \cdot (-5)$

12. $-\frac{4}{7}\left(-\frac{5}{9}\right)$

13. $-\frac{3}{2}\left(-\frac{4}{9}\right)$

14. $-3.25(-4.14)$

Multiply.

15. $5(-6)$

16. $(-5)(-6)$

17. $(-3.2) \cdot 0$

18. $\left(-\frac{4}{5}\right)\left(\frac{10}{3}\right)$

19. $0 \cdot (-34.2)$

20. $23 \cdot 0 \cdot \left(-4\frac{2}{3}\right)$

Answers on page A-5

Do Exercise 8 on the preceding page.

According to the pattern, it appears that the product of two negativ numbers is positive. That is actually so, and we have the second part of th rule for multiplying real numbers.

THE PRODUCT OF TWO NEGATIVE NUMBERS

To multiply two negative numbers, multiply their absolute values. The answer is positive.

Do Exercises 9–14.

The following is another way to consider the rules we have fo multiplication.

To multiply two nonzero real numbers:

a) Multiply the absolute values.
b) If the signs are the same, the answer is positive.
c) If the signs are different, the answer is negative.

MULTIPLICATION BY ZERO

The only case that we have not considered is multiplying by zero. As wit other numbers, the product of any real number and 0 is 0.

THE MULTIPLICATION PROPERTY OF ZERO

For any real number a,

$$a \cdot 0 = 0 \cdot a = 0.$$

(The product of 0 and any real number is 0.)

EXAMPLES Multiply.

4. $(-3)(-4) = 12$
5. $-1.6(2) = -3.2$
6. $-19 \cdot 0 = 0$
7. $\left(-\frac{5}{6}\right)\left(-\frac{1}{9}\right) = \frac{5}{54}$
8. $0 \cdot (-452) = 0$
9. $23 \cdot 0 \cdot \left(-8\frac{2}{3}\right) = 0$

Do Exercises 15–20.

ɪULTIPLYING MORE THAN TWO NUMBERS

ʋhen multiplying more than two real numbers, we can choose order and rouping as we please.

XAMPLES Multiply.

0. $-8 \cdot 2(-3) = -16(-3)$ Multiplying the first two numbers
$= 48$

1. $-8 \cdot 2(-3) = 24 \cdot 2$ Multiplying the negatives. Every pair of negative numbers gives a positive product.
$= 48$

2. $-3(-2)(-5)(4) = 6(-5)(4)$ Multiplying the first two numbers
$= (-30)4$
$= -120$

3. $\left(-\frac{1}{2}\right)(8)\left(-\frac{2}{3}\right)(-6) = (-4)4$ Multiplying the first two numbers and the last two numbers
$= -16$

4. $-5 \cdot (-2) \cdot (-3) \cdot (-6) = 10 \cdot 18 = 180$

5. $(-3)(-5)(-2)(-3)(-6) = (-30)(18) = -540$

Considering that the product of a pair of negative numbers is positive, we ɘe the following pattern.

> The product of an even number of negative numbers is positive.
> The product of an odd number of negative numbers is negative.

o Exercises 21–26.

XAMPLE 16 Evaluate $2x^2$ when $x = 3$ and when $x = -3$.

$2x^2 = 2(3)^2 = 2(9) = 18;$
$2x^2 = 2(-3)^2 = 2(9) = 18$

Let's compare the expressions $(-x)^2$ and $-x^2$.

XAMPLE 17 Evaluate $(-x)^2$ and $-x^2$ when $x = 5$.

$(-x)^2 = (-5)^2 = (-5)(-5) = 25;$ Substitute 5 for x. Then evaluate the power.

$-x^2 = -(5)^2 = -25$ Substitute 5 for x. Evaluate the power. Then find the opposite.

XAMPLE 18 Evaluate $(-a)^2$ and $-a^2$ when $a = -4$.

To make sense of the substitutions and computations, we introduce extra ɾackets into the expressions.

$(-a)^2 = [-(-4)]^2 = [4]^2 = 16;$
$-a^2 = -(-4)^2 = -(16) = -16$

Multiply.

21. $5 \cdot (-3) \cdot 2$

22. $-3 \times (-4.1) \times (-2.5)$

23. $-\frac{1}{2} \cdot \left(-\frac{4}{3}\right) \cdot \left(-\frac{5}{2}\right)$

24. $-2 \cdot (-5) \cdot (-4) \cdot (-3)$

25. $(-4)(-5)(-2)(-3)(-1)$

26. $(-1)(-1)(-2)(-3)(-1)(-1)$

27. Evaluate $(-x)^2$ and $-x^2$ when $x = 2$.

28. Evaluate $(-x)^2$ and $-x^2$ when $x = -3$.

29. Evaluate $3x^2$ when $x = 4$ and when $x = -4$.

Answers on page A-5

30. Chemical Reaction. During a chemical reaction, the temperature in the beaker increased by 3°C every minute until 1:34 P.M. If the temperature was −17°C at 1:10 P.M., when the reaction began, what was the temperature at 1:34 P.M.?

Answer on page A-5

The expressions $(-x)^2$ and $-x^2$ are *not* equivalent. That is, they do no have the same value for every allowable replacement of the variable by a rea number. To find $(-x)^2$, we take the opposite and then square. To find $-x^2$, w find the square and then take the opposite.

Do Exercises 27–29 on the preceding page.

b Applications and Problem Solving

We now consider multiplication of real numbers in real-world applications.

EXAMPLE 19 *Chemical Reaction.* During a chemical reaction, the tem perature in the beaker decreased by 2°C every minute until 10:23 A.M. If th temperature was 17°C at 10:00 A.M., when the reaction began, what was th temperature at 10:23 A.M.?

This is a multistep problem. We first find the total number of degrees tha the temperature dropped, using −2° for each minute. Since it dropped 2° fo each of the 23 minutes, we know that the total drop d is given by

$$d = 23 \cdot (-2) = -46.$$

To determine the temperature after this time period, we find the sum of 1 and −46, or

$$T = 17 + (-46) = -29.$$

Thus the temperature at 10:23 A.M. was −29°C.

Do Exercise 30.

Study Tips

ATTITUDE AND THE POWER OF YOUR CHOICES

Making the right choices can give you the power to succeed in learning mathematics.

You can choose to improve your attitude and raise the academic goals that you have set for yourself. Projecting a positive attitude toward your study of mathematics and expecting a positive outcome can make it easier for you to learn and to perform well in this course.

Here are some positive choices you can make:

- Choose to allocate the proper amount of time to learn.
- Choose to place the primary responsibility for learning on yourself.
- Choose to make a strong commitment to learning.

Well-known American psychologist William James once said, "The one thing that will guarantee the successful conclusion of a doubtful undertaking is faith in the beginning that you can do it."

1.5 EXERCISE SET

For Extra Help

MathXL | MyMathLab | InterAct Math | Math Tutor Center | Digital Video Tutor CD 1 Videotape 2 | Student's Solutions Manual

a Multiply.

1. $-4 \cdot 2$ **2.** $-3 \cdot 5$ **3.** $-8 \cdot 6$ **4.** $-5 \cdot 2$ **5.** $8 \cdot (-3)$

6. $9 \cdot (-5)$ **7.** $-9 \cdot 8$ **8.** $-10 \cdot 3$ **9.** $-8 \cdot (-2)$ **10.** $-2 \cdot (-5)$

1. $-7 \cdot (-6)$ **12.** $-9 \cdot (-2)$ **13.** $15 \cdot (-8)$ **14.** $-12 \cdot (-10)$ **15.** $-14 \cdot 17$

6. $-13 \cdot (-15)$ **17.** $-25 \cdot (-48)$ **18.** $39 \cdot (-43)$ **19.** $-3.5 \cdot (-28)$ **20.** $97 \cdot (-2.1)$

1. $9 \cdot (-8)$ **22.** $7 \cdot (-9)$ **23.** $4 \cdot (-3.1)$ **24.** $3 \cdot (-2.2)$ **25.** $-5 \cdot (-6)$

6. $-6 \cdot (-4)$ **27.** $-7 \cdot (-3.1)$ **28.** $-4 \cdot (-3.2)$ **29.** $\frac{2}{3} \cdot \left(-\frac{3}{5}\right)$ **30.** $\frac{5}{7} \cdot \left(-\frac{2}{3}\right)$

1. $-\frac{3}{8} \cdot \left(-\frac{2}{9}\right)$ **32.** $-\frac{5}{8} \cdot \left(-\frac{2}{5}\right)$ **33.** -6.3×2.7 **34.** -4.1×9.5

5. $-\frac{5}{9} \cdot \frac{3}{4}$ **36.** $-\frac{8}{3} \cdot \frac{9}{4}$ **37.** $7 \cdot (-4) \cdot (-3) \cdot 5$ **38.** $9 \cdot (-2) \cdot (-6) \cdot 7$

9. $-\frac{2}{3} \cdot \frac{1}{2} \cdot \left(-\frac{6}{7}\right)$ **40.** $-\frac{1}{8} \cdot \left(-\frac{1}{4}\right) \cdot \left(-\frac{3}{5}\right)$ **41.** $-3 \cdot (-4) \cdot (-5)$ **42.** $-2 \cdot (-5) \cdot (-7)$

3. $-2 \cdot (-5) \cdot (-3) \cdot (-5)$ **44.** $-3 \cdot (-5) \cdot (-2) \cdot (-1)$ **45.** $\frac{1}{5}\left(-\frac{2}{9}\right)$

6. $-\frac{3}{5}\left(-\frac{2}{7}\right)$ **47.** $-7 \cdot (-21) \cdot 13$ **48.** $-14 \cdot (34) \cdot 12$

49. $-4 \cdot (-1.8) \cdot 7$

50. $-8 \cdot (-1.3) \cdot (-5)$

51. $-\frac{1}{9}\left(-\frac{2}{3}\right)\left(\frac{5}{7}\right)$

52. $-\frac{7}{2}\left(-\frac{5}{7}\right)\left(-\frac{2}{5}\right)$

53. $4 \cdot (-4) \cdot (-5) \cdot (-12)$

54. $-2 \cdot (-3) \cdot (-4) \cdot (-5)$

55. $0.07 \cdot (-7) \cdot 6 \cdot (-6)$

56. $80 \cdot (-0.8) \cdot (-90) \cdot (-0.09)$

57. $\left(-\frac{5}{6}\right)\left(\frac{1}{8}\right)\left(-\frac{3}{7}\right)\left(-\frac{1}{7}\right)$

58. $\left(\frac{4}{5}\right)\left(-\frac{2}{3}\right)\left(-\frac{15}{7}\right)\left(\frac{1}{2}\right)$

59. $(-14) \cdot (-27) \cdot 0$

60. $7 \cdot (-6) \cdot 5 \cdot (-4) \cdot 3 \cdot (-2) \cdot 1 \cdot$

61. $(-8)(-9)(-10)$

62. $(-7)(-8)(-9)(-10)$

63. $(-6)(-7)(-8)(-9)(-10)$

64. $(-5)(-6)(-7)(-8)(-9)(-10)$

65. $(-1)^{12}$

66. $(-1)^9$

67. Evaluate $(-x)^2$ and $-x^2$ when $x = 4$ and when $x = -4$.

68. Evaluate $(-x)^2$ and $-x^2$ when $x = 10$ and when $x = -10$.

69. Evaluate $(-3x)^2$ and $-3x^2$ when $x = 7$.

70. Evaluate $(-2x)^2$ and $-2x^2$ when $x = 3$.

71. Evaluate $5x^2$ when $x = 2$ and when $x = -2$.

72. Evaluate $2x^2$ when $x = 5$ and when $x = -5$.

73. Evaluate $-2x^3$ when $x = 1$ and when $x = -1$.

74. Evaluate $-3x^3$ when $x = 2$ and when $x = -2$.

b Solve.

75. *Lost Weight.* Dave lost 2 lb each week for a period of 10 weeks. Express his total weight change as an integer.

76. *Stock Loss.* Emma lost $3 each day for a period of 5 days in the value of a stock she owned. Express her total loss as an integer.

77. *Chemical Reaction.* The temperature of a chemical compound was 0°C at 11:00 A.M. During a reaction, it dropped 3°C per minute until 11:18 A.M. What was the temperature at 11:18 A.M.?

78. *Chemical Reaction.* The temperature in a chemical compound was −5°C at 3:20 P.M. During a reaction, it increased 2°C per minute until 3:52 P.M. What was the temperature at 3:52 P.M.?

79. *Stock Price.* The price of ePDQ.com began the day at \$23.75 per share and dropped \$1.38 per hour for 8 hr. What was the price of the stock after 8 hr?

80. *Population Decrease.* The population of a rural town was 12,500. It decreased 380 each year for 4 yr. What was the population of the town after 4 yr?

81. *Diver's Position.* After diving 95 m below the sea level, a diver rises at a rate of 7 meters per minute for 9 min. Where is the diver in relation to the surface?

82. *Checking Account Balance.* Karen had \$68 in her checking account. After she had written checks to make seven purchases at \$13 each, what was the balance in her checking account?

83. **D**W Multiplication can be thought of as repeated addition. Using this concept and a number line, explain why $3 \cdot (-5) = -15$.

84. **D**W What rule have we developed that would tell you the sign of $(-7)^8$ and $(-7)^{11}$ without doing the computations? Explain.

SKILL MAINTENANCE

85. Find the LCM of 36 and 60. [R.1b]

86. Find the prime factorization of 4608. [R.1a]

Simplify. [R.2b]

87. $\frac{26}{39}$

88. $\frac{48}{54}$

89. $\frac{264}{484}$

90. $\frac{1025}{6625}$

91. $\frac{275}{800}$

92. $\frac{111}{201}$

93. $\frac{11}{264}$

94. $\frac{78}{13}$

SYNTHESIS

For each of Exercises 95 and 96, choose the correct answer from the selections given.

95. If a is positive and b is negative, then $-ab$ is:

a) Positive.
b) Negative.
c) 0.
d) Cannot be determined without more information

96. If a is positive and b is negative, then $(-a)(-b)$ is:

a) Positive.
b) Negative.
c) 0.
d) Cannot be determined without more information

97. Below is a number line showing 0 and two positive numbers x and y. Use a compass or ruler to locate as best you can the following:

$2x,\quad 3x,\quad 2y,\quad -x,\quad -y,\quad x + y,\quad x - y,\quad x - 2y.$

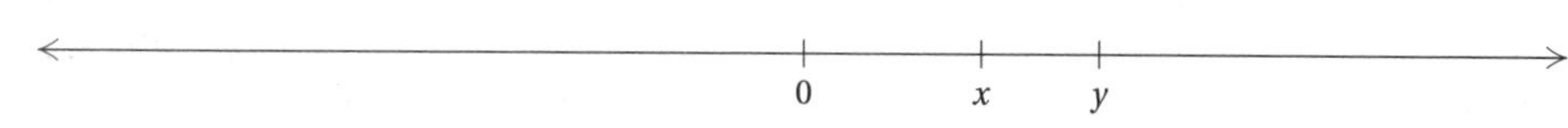

98. Of all possible quotients of the numbers 10, $-\frac{1}{2}$, -5, and $\frac{1}{5}$, which two produce the largest quotient? Which two produce the smallest quotient?

1.6 DIVISION OF REAL NUMBERS

Objectives

a Divide integers.

b Find the reciprocal of a real number.

c Divide real numbers.

d Solve applied problems involving division of real numbers.

Divide.

1. $6 \div (-3)$

   Think: What number multiplied by -3 gives 6?

2. $\dfrac{-15}{-3}$

   Think: What number multiplied by -3 gives -15?

3. $-24 \div 8$

   Think: What number multiplied by 8 gives -24?

4. $\dfrac{-48}{-6}$

5. $\dfrac{30}{-5}$

6. $\dfrac{30}{-7}$

Answers on page A-5

We now consider division of real numbers. The definition of division results in rules for division that are the same as those for multiplication.

a Division of Integers

DIVISION

The quotient $a \div b$, or $\dfrac{a}{b}$, where $b \neq 0$, is that unique real number c for which $a = b \cdot c$.

Let's use the definition to divide integers.

EXAMPLES Divide, if possible. Check your answer.

1. $14 \div (-7) = -2$ — *Think*: What number multiplied by -7 gives 14? That number is -2. *Check*: $(-2)(-7) = 14$.

2. $\dfrac{-32}{-4} = 8$ — *Think*: What number multiplied by -4 gives -32? That number is 8. *Check*: $8(-4) = -32$.

3. $\dfrac{-10}{7} = -\dfrac{10}{7}$ — *Think*: What number multiplied by 7 gives -10? That number is $-\frac{10}{7}$. *Check*: $-\frac{10}{7} \cdot 7 = -10$.

4. $\dfrac{-17}{0}$ **is not defined.** — *Think*: What number multiplied by 0 gives -17? There is no such number because the product of 0 and *any* number is 0.

The rules for division are the same as those for multiplication.

To multiply or divide two real numbers (where the divisor is nonzero):

a) Multiply or divide the absolute values.
b) If the signs are the same, the answer is positive.
c) If the signs are different, the answer is negative.

Do Exercises 1–6.

EXCLUDING DIVISION BY 0

Example 4 shows why we cannot divide -17 by 0. We can use the same argument to show why we cannot divide any nonzero number b by 0. Consider $b \div 0$. We look for a number that when multiplied by 0 gives b. There is no such number because the product of 0 and any number is 0. Thus we cannot divide a nonzero number b by 0.

On the other hand, if we divide 0 by 0, we look for a number c such that $0 \cdot c = 0$. But $0 \cdot c = 0$ for any number c. Thus it appears that $0 \div 0$ could be any number we choose. Getting any answer we want when we divide 0 by 0 would be very confusing. Thus we agree that division by zero is not defined.

EXCLUDING DIVISION BY 0

Division by 0 is not defined.

$a \div 0$, or $\frac{a}{0}$, is not defined for all real numbers a.

DIVIDING 0 BY OTHER NUMBERS

Note that

$$0 \div 8 = 0 \text{ because } 0 = 0 \cdot 8; \qquad \frac{0}{-5} = 0 \text{ because } 0 = 0 \cdot (-5).$$

DIVIDENDS OF 0

Zero divided by any nonzero real number is 0:

$$\frac{0}{a} = 0; \qquad a \neq 0.$$

EXAMPLES Divide.

5. $0 \div (-6) = 0$ **6.** $\frac{0}{12} = 0$ **7.** $\frac{-3}{0}$ is not defined.

Do Exercises 7 and 8.

b Reciprocals

When two numbers like $\frac{1}{2}$ and 2 are multiplied, the result is 1. Such numbers are called **reciprocals** of each other. Every nonzero real number has a reciprocal, also called a **multiplicative inverse.**

RECIPROCALS

Two numbers whose product is 1 are called **reciprocals,** or **multiplicative inverses,** of each other.

EXAMPLES Find the reciprocal.

8. $\frac{7}{8}$ The reciprocal of $\frac{7}{8}$ is $\frac{8}{7}$ because $\frac{7}{8} \cdot \frac{8}{7} = 1$.

9. -5 The reciprocal of -5 is $-\frac{1}{5}$ because $-5\left(-\frac{1}{5}\right) = 1$.

10. 3.9 The reciprocal of 3.9 is $\frac{1}{3.9}$ because $3.9\left(\frac{1}{3.9}\right) = 1$.

11. $-\frac{1}{2}$ The reciprocal of $-\frac{1}{2}$ is -2 because $\left(-\frac{1}{2}\right)(-2) = 1$.

12. $-\frac{2}{3}$ The reciprocal of $-\frac{2}{3}$ is $-\frac{3}{2}$ because $\left(-\frac{2}{3}\right)\left(-\frac{3}{2}\right) = 1$.

13. $\frac{1}{3/4}$ The reciprocal of $\frac{1}{3/4}$ is $\frac{3}{4}$ because $\left(\frac{1}{3/4}\right)\left(\frac{3}{4}\right) = 1$.

Divide, if possible.

7. $\frac{-5}{0}$

8. $\frac{0}{-3}$

Find the reciprocal.

9. $\frac{2}{3}$

10. $-\frac{5}{4}$

11. -3

12. $-\frac{1}{5}$

13. 1.6

14. $\frac{1}{2/3}$

Answers on page A-5

15. Complete the following table.

NUMBER	OPPOSITE	RECIPROCAL
$\frac{2}{3}$		
$-\frac{5}{4}$		
0		
1		
−8		
−4.5		

Answers on page A-5

Study Tips

TAKE THE TIME!

The foundation of all your study skills is *time*! If you invest your time, we will help you achieve success.

"Nine-tenths of wisdom is being wise in time."

Theodore Roosevelt

RECIPROCAL PROPERTIES

For $a \neq 0$, the reciprocal of a can be named $\frac{1}{a}$ and the reciprocal of $\frac{1}{a}$ is a.

The reciprocal of a nonzero number $\frac{a}{b}$ can be named $\frac{b}{a}$.

The number 0 has no reciprocal.

Do Exercises 9–14 on the preceding page.

The reciprocal of a positive number is also a positive number, because their product must be the positive number 1. The reciprocal of a negative number is also a negative number, because their product must be the positive number 1.

THE SIGN OF A RECIPROCAL

The reciprocal of a number has the same sign as the number itself.

Caution!

It is important *not* to confuse *opposite* with *reciprocal.* Keep in mind that the opposite, or additive inverse, of a number is what we add to the number to get 0. The reciprocal, or multiplicative inverse, is what we multiply the number by to get 1.

Compare the following.

NUMBER	OPPOSITE (Change the sign.)	RECIPROCAL (Invert but do not change the sign.)
$-\frac{3}{8}$	$\frac{3}{8}$	$-\frac{8}{3}$
19	−19	$\frac{1}{19}$
$\frac{18}{7}$	$-\frac{18}{7}$	$\frac{7}{18}$
−7.9	7.9	$-\frac{1}{7.9}$, or $-\frac{10}{79}$
0	0	Not defined

$\left(-\frac{3}{8}\right)\left(-\frac{8}{3}\right) =$

$-\frac{3}{8} + \frac{3}{8} = 0$

Do Exercise 15.

C Division of Real Numbers

We know that we can subtract by adding an opposite. Similarly, we can divide by multiplying by a reciprocal.

RECIPROCALS AND DIVISION

For any real numbers a and b, $b \neq 0$,

$$a \div b = \frac{a}{b} = a \cdot \frac{1}{b}.$$

(To divide, multiply by the reciprocal of the divisor.)

EXAMPLES Rewrite the division as a multiplication.

14. $-4 \div 3$ $-4 \div 3$ is the same as $-4 \cdot \frac{1}{3}$

15. $\frac{6}{-7}$ $\frac{6}{-7} = 6\left(-\frac{1}{7}\right)$

16. $\frac{x+2}{5}$ $\frac{x+2}{5} = (x+2)\frac{1}{5}$ Parentheses are necessary here.

17. $\frac{-17}{1/b}$ $\frac{-17}{1/b} = -17 \cdot b$

18. $\frac{3}{5} \div \left(-\frac{9}{7}\right)$ $\frac{3}{5} \div \left(-\frac{9}{7}\right) = \frac{3}{5}\left(-\frac{7}{9}\right)$

Do Exercises 16–20.

When actually doing division calculations, we sometimes multiply by a reciprocal and we sometimes divide directly. With fraction notation, it is usually better to multiply by a reciprocal. With decimal notation, it is usually better to divide directly.

EXAMPLES Divide by multiplying by the reciprocal of the divisor.

19. $\frac{2}{3} \div \left(-\frac{5}{4}\right) = \frac{2}{3} \cdot \left(-\frac{4}{5}\right) = -\frac{8}{15}$

20. $-\frac{5}{6} \div \left(-\frac{3}{4}\right) = -\frac{5}{6} \cdot \left(-\frac{4}{3}\right) = \frac{20}{18} = \frac{10 \cdot 2}{9 \cdot 2} = \frac{10}{9} \cdot \frac{2}{2} = \frac{10}{9}$

Caution!

Be careful not to change the sign when taking a reciprocal!

21. $-\frac{3}{4} \div \frac{3}{10} = -\frac{3}{4} \cdot \left(\frac{10}{3}\right) = -\frac{30}{12} = -\frac{5}{2} \cdot \frac{6}{6} = -\frac{5}{2}$

Rewrite the division as a multiplication.

16. $\frac{4}{7} \div \left(-\frac{3}{5}\right)$

17. $\frac{5}{-8}$

18. $\frac{a-b}{7}$

19. $\frac{-23}{1/a}$

20. $-5 \div 7$

Divide by multiplying by the reciprocal of the divisor.

21. $\frac{4}{7} \div \left(-\frac{3}{5}\right)$

22. $-\frac{8}{5} \div \frac{2}{3}$

23. $-\frac{12}{7} \div \left(-\frac{3}{4}\right)$

24. Divide: $21.7 \div (-3.1)$.

Answers on page A-5

Find two equal expressions for the number with negative signs in different places.

25. $\frac{-5}{6}$

26. $-\frac{8}{7}$

27. $\frac{10}{-3}$

Answers on page A-5

Study Tips

VIDEOTAPES

(ISBN 0-321-30608-2)
Developed and produced especially for this text, the videotapes feature an engaging team of instructors, who present material and concepts by using examples and exercises from every section of the text.

DIGITAL VIDEO TUTOR

(ISBN 0-321-30606-6)
The videotapes for this text are also available on CD-ROM, making it easy and convenient for you to watch video segments from a computer at home or on campus. The complete digitized video set, both affordable and portable, is ideal for distance learning or supplemental instruction.

With decimal notation, it is easier to carry out long division than to multiply by the reciprocal.

EXAMPLES Divide.

22. $-27.9 \div (-3) = \frac{-27.9}{-3} = 9.3$ Do the long division $3\overline{)27.9}$ (quotient 9.3). The answer is positive.

23. $-6.3 \div 2.1 = -3$ Do the long division $2.1\overline{)6.3}$ (quotient 3.). The answer is negative.

Do Exercises 21–24 on the preceding page.

Consider the following:

1. $\frac{2}{3} = \frac{2}{3} \cdot 1 = \frac{2}{3} \cdot \frac{-1}{-1} = \frac{2(-1)}{3(-1)} = \frac{-2}{-3}$. Thus, $\frac{2}{3} = \frac{-2}{-3}$.

   (A negative number divided by a negative number is positive.)

2. $-\frac{2}{3} = -1 \cdot \frac{2}{3} = \frac{-1}{1} \cdot \frac{2}{3} = \frac{-1 \cdot 2}{1 \cdot 3} = \frac{-2}{3}$. Thus, $-\frac{2}{3} = \frac{-2}{3}$.

   (A negative number divided by a positive number is negative.)

3. $\frac{-2}{3} = \frac{-2}{3} \cdot 1 = \frac{-2}{3} \cdot \frac{-1}{-1} = \frac{-2(-1)}{3(-1)} = \frac{2}{-3}$. Thus, $-\frac{2}{3} = \frac{2}{-3}$.

   (A positive number divided by a negative number is negative.)

We can use the following properties to make sign changes in fraction notation.

SIGN CHANGES IN FRACTION NOTATION

For any numbers a and b, $b \neq 0$:

1. $\frac{-a}{-b} = \frac{a}{b}$

   (The opposite of a number a divided by the opposite of another number b is the same as the quotient of the two numbers a and b.)

2. $\frac{-a}{b} = \frac{a}{-b} = -\frac{a}{b}$

   (The opposite of a number a divided by another number b is the same as the number a divided by the opposite of the number b, and both are the same as the opposite of *a divided by b*.)

Do Exercises 25–27.

d Applications and Problem Solving

EXAMPLE 24 *Chemical Reaction.* During a chemical reaction, the temperature in the beaker decreased every minute by the same number of degrees. The temperature was 56°F at 10:10 A.M. By 10:42 A.M., the temperature had dropped to −12°F. By how many degrees did it change each minute?

We first determine by how many degrees d the temperature changed altogether. We subtract −12 from 56:

$$d = 56 - (-12) = 56 + 12 = 68.$$

The temperature changed a total of 68°. We can express this as −68° since the temperature dropped.

The amount of time t that passed was 42 − 10, or 32 min. Thus the number of degrees T that the temperature dropped each minute is given by

$$T = \frac{d}{t} = \frac{-68}{32} = -2.125.$$

The change was −2.125°F per minute.

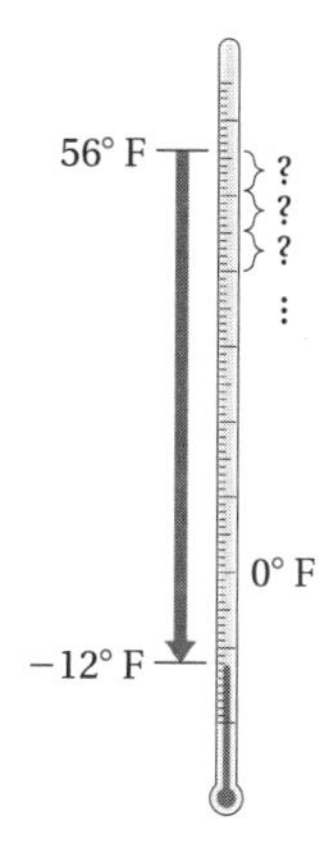

Do Exercise 28.

28. Chemical Reaction. During a chemical reaction, the temperature in the beaker decreased every minute by the same number of degrees. The temperature was 71°F at 2:12 P.M. By 2:37 P.M., the temperature had changed to −14°F. By how many degrees did it change each minute?

Answer on page A-5

CALCULATOR CORNER

Operations on the Real Numbers We can perform operations on the real numbers on a graphing calculator. Recall that negative numbers are entered using the opposite key, (−), rather than the subtraction operation key, −. Consider the sum −5 + (−3.8). We use parentheses when we write this sum in order to separate the addition symbol and the "opposite of" symbol and thus make the expression more easily read. When we enter this calculation on a graphing calculator, however, the parentheses are not necessary. We can press (−) 5 + (−) 3 . 8 ENTER. The result is −8.8. Note that it is not incorrect to enter the parentheses. The result will be the same if this is done.

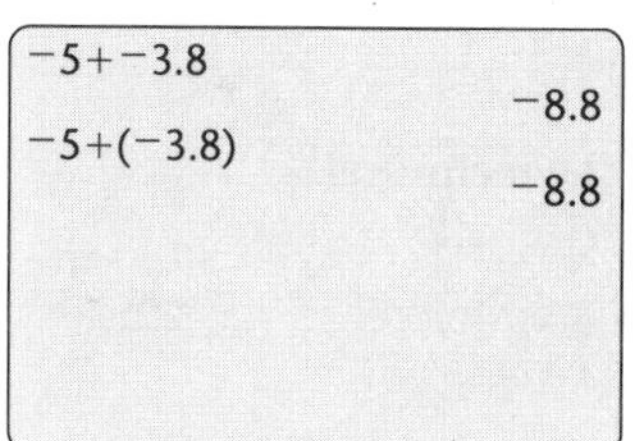

To find the difference 10 − (−17), we press 1 0 − (−) 1 7 ENTER. The result is 27. We can also multiply and divide real numbers. To find −5 · (−7), we press (−) 5 × (−) 7 ENTER, and to find 45 ÷ (−9), we press 4 5 ÷ (−) 9 ENTER. Note that it is not necessary to use parentheses in any of these calculations.

```
10−−17
                27
−5*−7
                35
45/−9
                −5
```

Exercises: Use a calculator to perform the operation.

1. −8 + 4
2. 1.2 + (−1.5)
3. −7 + (−5)
4. −7.6 + (−1.9)
5. −8 − 4
6. 1.2 − (−1.5)
7. −7 − (−5)
8. −7.6 − (−1.9)
9. −8 · 4
10. 1.2 · (−1.5)
11. −7 · (−5)
12. −7.6 · (−1.9)
13. −8 ÷ 4
14. 1.2 ÷ (−1.5)
15. −7 ÷ (−5)
16. −7.6 ÷ (−1.9)

1.6 EXERCISE SET

For Extra Help

MathXL | MyMathLab | InterAct Math | Math Tutor Center | Digital Video Tutor CD 1 Videotape 2 | Student's Solutions Manual

a Divide, if possible. Check each answer.

1. $48 \div (-6)$

2. $\frac{42}{-7}$

3. $\frac{28}{-2}$

4. $24 \div (-12)$

5. $\frac{-24}{8}$

6. $-18 \div (-2)$

7. $\frac{-36}{-12}$

8. $-72 \div (-9)$

9. $\frac{-72}{9}$

10. $\frac{-50}{25}$

11. $-100 \div (-50)$

12. $\frac{-200}{8}$

13. $-108 \div 9$

14. $\frac{-63}{-7}$

15. $\frac{200}{-25}$

16. $-300 \div (-16)$

17. $\frac{75}{0}$

18. $\frac{0}{-5}$

19. $\frac{0}{-2.6}$

20. $\frac{-23}{0}$

b Find the reciprocal.

21. $\frac{15}{7}$

22. $\frac{3}{8}$

23. $-\frac{47}{13}$

24. $-\frac{31}{12}$

25. 13

26. -10

27. 4.3

28. -8.5

29. $\frac{1}{-7.1}$

30. $\frac{1}{-4.9}$

31. $\frac{p}{q}$

32. $\frac{s}{t}$

33. $\frac{1}{4y}$

34. $\frac{-1}{8a}$

35. $\frac{2a}{3b}$

36. $\frac{-4y}{3x}$

C Rewrite the division as a multiplication.

37. $4 \div 17$

38. $5 \div (-8)$

39. $\frac{8}{-13}$

40. $-\frac{13}{47}$

41. $\frac{13.9}{-1.5}$

42. $-\frac{47.3}{21.4}$

43. $\frac{x}{\frac{1}{y}}$

44. $\frac{13}{x}$

45. $\frac{3x + 4}{5}$

46. $\frac{4y - 8}{-7}$

47. $\frac{5a - b}{5a + b}$

48. $\frac{2x + x^2}{x - 5}$

Divide.

49. $\frac{3}{4} \div \left(-\frac{2}{3}\right)$

50. $\frac{7}{8} \div \left(-\frac{1}{2}\right)$

51. $-\frac{5}{4} \div \left(-\frac{3}{4}\right)$

52. $-\frac{5}{9} \div \left(-\frac{5}{6}\right)$

53. $-\frac{2}{7} \div \left(-\frac{4}{9}\right)$

54. $-\frac{3}{5} \div \left(-\frac{5}{8}\right)$

55. $-\frac{3}{8} \div \left(-\frac{8}{3}\right)$

56. $-\frac{5}{8} \div \left(-\frac{6}{5}\right)$

57. $-6.6 \div 3.3$

58. $-44.1 \div (-6.3)$

59. $\frac{-11}{-13}$

60. $\frac{-1.9}{20}$

61. $\frac{48.6}{-3}$

62. $\frac{-17.8}{3.2}$

63. $\frac{-9}{17 - 17}$

64. $\frac{-8}{-5 + 5}$

d *Percent of Increase or Decrease in Employment.* A percent of increase is generally positive and a percent of decrease is generally negative. The following table lists estimates of the number of job opportunities for various occupations in 2002 and 2012. In Exercises 65–68, find the missing numbers.

	OCCUPATION	NUMBER OF JOBS IN 2002 (in thousands)	NUMBER OF JOBS IN 2012 (in thousands)	CHANGE	PERCENT OF INCREASE OR DECREASE
	Electrician	659	814	155	23.5%
	Travel agent	118	102	−16	−13.6%
65.	Fitness trainer/ aerobic instructor	183	264	81	
66.	Child-care worker	1211	1353	142	
67.	Telemarketer	428	406	−22	
68.	Aerospace engineer	78	74	−4	

Source: U.S. Bureau of Labor Statistics

69. D$_W$ Explain how multiplication can be used to justify why a negative number divided by a positive number is negative.

70. D$_W$ Explain how multiplication can be used to justify why a negative number divided by a negative number is positive.

SKILL MAINTENANCE

Simplify. [R.5c]

71. $2^3 - 5 \cdot 3 + 8 \cdot 10 \div 2$

72. $16 \cdot 2^3 - 5 \cdot 3 + 80 \div 10 \cdot 2$

73. $1000 \div 100 \div 10$

74. $216 \cdot 6^3 \div 6^2$

75. Simplify: $\frac{264}{468}$. [R.2b]

76. Convert to decimal notation: 47.7%. [R.4a]

77. Convert to percent notation: $\frac{7}{8}$. [R.4d]

78. Simplify: $\frac{40}{60}$. [R.2b]

79. Divide and simplify: $\frac{12}{25} \div \frac{32}{75}$. [R.2c]

80. Multiply and simplify: $\frac{12}{25} \cdot \frac{32}{75}$. [R.2c]

SYNTHESIS

81. Find the reciprocal of −10.5. What happens if you take the reciprocal of the result?

82. Determine those real numbers a for which the opposite of a is the same as the reciprocal of a.

Tell whether the expression represents a positive number or a negative number when a and b are negative.

83. $\frac{-a}{b}$

84. $\frac{-a}{-b}$

85. $-\left(\frac{a}{-b}\right)$

86. $-\left(\frac{-a}{b}\right)$

87. $-\left(\frac{-a}{-b}\right)$

1.7 PROPERTIES OF REAL NUMBERS

Objectives

a Find equivalent fraction expressions and simplify fraction expressions.

b Use the commutative and associative laws to find equivalent expressions.

c Use the distributive laws to multiply expressions like 8 and $x - y$.

d Use the distributive laws to factor expressions like $4x - 12 + 24y$.

e Collect like terms.

a Equivalent Expressions

n solving equations and doing other kinds of work in algebra, we manipulate xpressions in various ways. For example, instead of $x + x$, we might write $2x$, nowing that the two expressions represent the same number for any allowble replacement of x. In that sense, the expressions $x + x$ and $2x$ are **equivaent,** as are $\frac{3}{x}$ and $\frac{3x}{x^2}$, even though 0 is not an allowable replacement because ivision by 0 is not defined.

EQUIVALENT EXPRESSIONS

Two expressions that have the same value for all allowable replacements are called **equivalent.**

The expressions $x + 3x$ and $5x$ are *not* equivalent.

o Exercises 1 and 2.

Complete the table by evaluating each expression for the given values.

1.

Value	$x + x$	$2x$
$x = 3$		
$x = -6$		
$x = 4.8$		

2.

Value	$x + 3x$	$5x$
$x = 2$		
$x = -6$		
$x = 4.8$		

In this section, we will consider several laws of real numbers that will llow us to find equivalent expressions. The first two laws are the *identity roperties of 0 and 1.*

THE IDENTITY PROPERTY OF 0

For any real number a,

$$a + 0 = 0 + a = a.$$

(The number 0 is the *additive identity.*)

THE IDENTITY PROPERTY OF 1

For any real number a,

$$a \cdot 1 = 1 \cdot a = a.$$

(The number 1 is the *multiplicative identity.*)

We often refer to the use of the identity property of 1 as "multiplying by ." We can use this method to find equivalent fraction expressions. Recall om arithmetic that to multiply with fraction notation, we multiply numerars and denominators. (See also Section R.2.)

XAMPLE 1 Write a fraction expression equivalent to $\frac{2}{3}$ with a denominar of $3x$:

$$\frac{2}{3} = \frac{\square}{3x}.$$

Answers on page A-6

3. Write a fraction expression equivalent to $\frac{3}{4}$ with a denominator of 8:

$$\frac{3}{4} = \frac{\square}{8}.$$

4. Write a fraction expression equivalent to $\frac{3}{4}$ with a denominator of $4t$:

$$\frac{3}{4} = \frac{\square}{4t}.$$

Simplify.

5. $\frac{3y}{4y}$

6. $-\frac{16m}{12m}$

7. $\frac{5xy}{40y}$

8. $\frac{18p}{24pq}$

9. Evaluate $x + y$ and $y + x$ when $x = -2$ and $y = 3$.

10. Evaluate xy and yx when $x = -2$ and $y = 5$.

Answers on page A-6

Note that $3x = 3 \cdot x$. We want fraction notation for $\frac{2}{3}$ that has a denominator of $3x$, but the denominator 3 is missing a factor of x. Thus we multiply by 1, using x/x as an equivalent expression for 1:

$$\frac{2}{3} = \frac{2}{3} \cdot 1 = \frac{2}{3} \cdot \frac{x}{x} = \frac{2x}{3x}.$$

The expressions $2/3$ and $2x/3x$ are equivalent. They have the same value for any allowable replacement. Note that $2x/3x$ is not defined for a replacement of 0, but for all nonzero real numbers, the expressions $2/3$ and $2x/3x$ have the same value.

Do Exercises 3 and 4.

In algebra, we consider an expression like $2/3$ to be "simplified" from $2x/3x$. To find such simplified expressions, we use the identity property of 1 to remove a factor of 1. (See also Section R.2.)

EXAMPLE 2 Simplify: $-\frac{20x}{12x}$.

$$-\frac{20x}{12x} = -\frac{5 \cdot 4x}{3 \cdot 4x}$$ We look for the largest factor common to both the numerator and the denominator and factor each.

$$= -\frac{5}{3} \cdot \frac{4x}{4x}$$ Factoring the fraction expression

$$= -\frac{5}{3} \cdot 1$$ $\frac{4x}{4x} = 1$

$$= -\frac{5}{3}$$ Removing a factor of 1 using the identity property of 1

EXAMPLE 3 Simplify: $\frac{14ab}{56a}$.

$$\frac{14ab}{56a} = \frac{14a \cdot b}{14a \cdot 4} = \frac{14a}{14a} \cdot \frac{b}{4} = 1 \cdot \frac{b}{4} = \frac{b}{4}$$

Do Exercises 5–8.

b The Commutative and Associative Laws

THE COMMUTATIVE LAWS

Let's examine the expressions $x + y$ and $y + x$, as well as xy and yx.

EXAMPLE 4 Evaluate $x + y$ and $y + x$ when $x = 4$ and $y = 3$.

We substitute 4 for x and 3 for y in both expressions:

$$x + y = 4 + 3 = 7; \qquad y + x = 3 + 4 = 7.$$

EXAMPLE 5 Evaluate xy and yx when $x = 23$ and $y = -12$.

We substitute 23 for x and -12 for y in both expressions:

$$xy = 23 \cdot (-12) = -276; \qquad yx = (-12) \cdot 23 = -276.$$

Do Exercises 9 and 10 on the preceding page.

Note that the expressions $x + y$ and $y + x$ have the same values no matter what the variables stand for. Thus they are equivalent. Therefore, when we add two numbers, the order in which we add does not matter. Similarly, the expressions xy and yx are equivalent. They also have the same values, no matter what the variables stand for. Therefore, when we multiply two numbers, the order in which we multiply does not matter.

The following are examples of general patterns or laws.

THE COMMUTATIVE LAWS

Addition. For any numbers a and b,

$$a + b = b + a.$$

(We can change the order when adding without affecting the answer.)

Multiplication. For any numbers a and b,

$$ab = ba.$$

(We can change the order when multiplying without affecting the answer.)

Using a commutative law, we know that $x + 2$ and $2 + x$ are equivalent. Similarly, $3x$ and $x(3)$ are equivalent. Thus, in an algebraic expression, we can replace one with the other and the result will be equivalent to the original expression.

EXAMPLE 6 Use the commutative laws to write an expression equivalent to $y + 5$, ab, and $7 + xy$.

An expression equivalent to $y + 5$ is $5 + y$ by the commutative law of addition.

An expression equivalent to ab is ba by the commutative law of multiplication.

An expression equivalent to $7 + xy$ is $xy + 7$ by the commutative law of addition. Another expression equivalent to $7 + xy$ is $7 + yx$ by the commutative law of multiplication. Another equivalent expression is $yx + 7$.

Do Exercises 11–13.

Use a commutative law to write an equivalent expression.

11. $x + 9$

12. pq

13. $xy + t$

THE ASSOCIATIVE LAWS

Now let's examine the expressions $a + (b + c)$ and $(a + b) + c$. Note that these expressions involve the use of parentheses as *grouping* symbols, and they also involve three numbers. Calculations within parentheses are to be done first.

EXAMPLE 7 Calculate and compare: $3 + (8 + 5)$ and $(3 + 8) + 5$.

$3 + (8 + 5) = 3 + 13$ Calculating within parentheses first; adding the 8 and 5

$= 16;$

$(3 + 8) + 5 = 11 + 5$ Calculating within parentheses first; adding the 3 and 8

$= 16$

Answers on page A-6

14. Calculate and compare:

$8 + (9 + 2)$ and $(8 + 9) + 2$.

15. Calculate and compare:

$10 \cdot (5 \cdot 3)$ and $(10 \cdot 5) \cdot 3$.

Use an associative law to write an equivalent expression.

16. $r + (s + 7)$

17. $9(ab)$

Answers on page A-6

The two expressions in Example 7 name the same number. Moving the parentheses to group the additions differently does not affect the value of the expression.

EXAMPLE 8 Calculate and compare: $3 \cdot (4 \cdot 2)$ and $(3 \cdot 4) \cdot 2$.

$$3 \cdot (4 \cdot 2) = 3 \cdot 8 = 24; \qquad (3 \cdot 4) \cdot 2 = 12 \cdot 2 = 24$$

Do Exercises 14 and 15.

You may have noted that when only addition is involved, parentheses can be placed any way we please without affecting the answer. When only multiplication is involved, parentheses also can be placed any way we please without affecting the answer.

THE ASSOCIATIVE LAWS

Addition. For any numbers a, b, and c,

$$a + (b + c) = (a + b) + c.$$

(Numbers can be grouped in any manner for addition.)

Multiplication. For any numbers a, b, and c,

$$a \cdot (b \cdot c) = (a \cdot b) \cdot c.$$

(Numbers can be grouped in any manner for multiplication.)

EXAMPLE 9 Use an associative law to write an expression equivalent to $(y + z) + 3$ and $8(xy)$.

An expression equivalent to $(y + z) + 3$ is $y + (z + 3)$ by the associative law of addition.

An expression equivalent to $8(xy)$ is $(8x)y$ by the associative law of multiplication.

Do Exercises 16 and 17.

The associative laws say parentheses can be placed any way we please when only additions or only multiplications are involved. Thus we often omit them. For example,

$x + (y + 2)$ means $x + y + 2$, and $(lw)h$ means lwh.

USING THE COMMUTATIVE AND ASSOCIATIVE LAWS TOGETHER

EXAMPLE 10 Use the commutative and associative laws to write at least three expressions equivalent to $(x + 5) + y$.

a) $(x + 5) + y = x + (5 + y)$
$= x + (y + 5)$
Using the associative law first and then using the commutative law

b) $(x + 5) + y = y + (x + 5)$
$= y + (5 + x)$
Using the commutative law first and then the commutative law again

c) $(x + 5) + y = (5 + x) + y$
$= 5 + (x + y)$
Using the commutative law first and then the associative law

XAMPLE 11 Use the commutative and associative laws to write at least hree expressions equivalent to $(3x)y$.

) $(3x)y = 3(xy)$ — Using the associative law first and then using the commutative law

$= 3(yx)$

) $(3x)y = y(3x)$ — Using the commutative law twice

$= y(x \cdot 3)$

) $(3x)y = (x \cdot 3)y$ — Using the commutative law, and then the associative law, and then the commutative law again

$= x(3y)$

$= x(y \cdot 3)$

o Exercises 18 and 19.

Use the commutative and associative laws to write at least three equivalent expressions.

18. $4(tu)$

19. $r + (2 + s)$

C The Distributive Laws

he *distributive laws* are the basis of many procedures in both arithmetic and gebra. They are probably the most important laws that we use to manipu- te algebraic expressions. The distributive law of multiplication over addition volves two operations: addition and multiplication.

Let's begin by considering a multiplication problem from arithmetic:

$$\begin{array}{r} 4\ 5 \\ \times\ \ \ 7 \\ \hline 3\ 5 \\ 2\ 8\ 0 \\ \hline 3\ 1\ 5 \end{array}$$

3 5 ← This is $7 \cdot 5$.
2 8 0 ← This is $7 \cdot 40$.
3 1 5 ← This is the sum $7 \cdot 40 + 7 \cdot 5$.

carry out the multiplication, we actually added two products. That is,

$$7 \cdot 45 = 7(40 + 5) = 7 \cdot 40 + 7 \cdot 5.$$

Let's examine this further. If we wish to multiply a sum of several numbers a factor, we can either add and then multiply, or multiply and then add.

XAMPLE 12 Compute in two ways: $5 \cdot (4 + 8)$.

$5 \cdot (4 + 8)$ — Adding within parentheses first, and then multiplying

$= 5 \cdot 12$

$= 60$

$(5 \cdot 4) + (5 \cdot 8)$ — Distributing the multiplication to terms within parentheses first and then adding

$= 20 + 40$

$= 60$

Exercises 20–22.

Compute.

20. a) $7 \cdot (3 + 6)$

b) $(7 \cdot 3) + (7 \cdot 6)$

21. a) $2 \cdot (10 + 30)$

b) $(2 \cdot 10) + (2 \cdot 30)$

22. a) $(2 + 5) \cdot 4$

b) $(2 \cdot 4) + (5 \cdot 4)$

THE DISTRIBUTIVE LAW OF MULTIPLICATION OVER ADDITION

For any numbers a, b, and c,

$$a(b + c) = ab + ac.$$

Answers on page A-6

Calculate.

23. a) $4(5 - 3)$

b) $4 \cdot 5 - 4 \cdot 3$

24. a) $-2 \cdot (5 - 3)$

b) $-2 \cdot 5 - (-2) \cdot 3$

25. a) $5 \cdot (2 - 7)$

b) $5 \cdot 2 - 5 \cdot 7$

What are the terms of the expression?

26. $5x - 8y + 3$

27. $-4y - 2x + 3z$

Multiply.

28. $3(x - 5)$

29. $5(x + 1)$

30. $\frac{3}{5}(p + q - t)$

Answers on page A-6

In the statement of the distributive law, we know that in an expressio such as $ab + ac$, the multiplications are to be done first according to the rule for order of operations. (See Section R.5.) So, instead of writing $(4 \cdot 5) +$ $(4 \cdot 7)$, we can write $4 \cdot 5 + 4 \cdot 7$. However, in $a(b + c)$, we cannot omit th parentheses. If we did, we would have $ab + c$, which means $(ab) + c$. For ex ample, $3(4 + 2) = 18$, but $3 \cdot 4 + 2 = 14$.

There is another distributive law that relates multiplication and subtrac tion. This law says that to multiply by a difference, we can either subtract an then multiply, or multiply and then subtract.

THE DISTRIBUTIVE LAW OF MULTIPLICATION OVER SUBTRACTION

For any numbers a, b, and c,

$$a(b - c) = ab - ac.$$

We often refer to "*the* distributive law" when we mean *either* or *both* c these laws.

Do Exercises 23–25.

What do we mean by the *terms* of an expression? **Terms** are separated b addition signs. If there are subtraction signs, we can find an equivalent ex pression that uses addition signs.

EXAMPLE 13 What are the terms of $3x - 4y + 2z$?

We have

$$3x - 4y + 2z = 3x + (-4y) + 2z. \qquad \text{Separating parts with + signs}$$

The terms are $3x$, $-4y$, and $2z$.

Do Exercises 26 and 27.

The distributive laws are a basis for a procedure in algebra called **mult plying.** In an expression like $8(a + 2b - 7)$, we multiply each term inside th parentheses by 8:

$$8(a + 2b - 7) = 8 \cdot a + 8 \cdot 2b - 8 \cdot 7 = 8a + 16b - 56.$$

EXAMPLES Multiply.

14. $9(x - 5) = 9x - 9(5)$ Using the distributive law of multiplication over subtraction

$= 9x - 45$

15. $\frac{2}{3}(w + 1) = \frac{2}{3} \cdot w + \frac{2}{3} \cdot 1$ Using the distributive law of multiplication over addition

$= \frac{2}{3}w + \frac{2}{3}$

16. $\frac{4}{3}(s - t + w) = \frac{4}{3}s - \frac{4}{3}t + \frac{4}{3}w$ Using both distributive laws

Do Exercises 28–30.

XAMPLE 17 Multiply: $-4(x - 2y + 3z)$.

$$-4(x - 2y + 3z) = -4 \cdot x - (-4)(2y) + (-4)(3z)$$ Using both distributive laws

$$= -4x - (-8y) + (-12z)$$ Multiplying

$$= -4x + 8y - 12z$$

We can also do this problem by first finding an equivalent expression with ll plus signs and then multiplying:

$$-4(x - 2y + 3z) = -4[x + (-2y) + 3z]$$
$$= -4 \cdot x + (-4)(-2y) + (-4)(3z)$$
$$= -4x + 8y - 12z.$$

ɔ Exercises 31–33.

Multiply.

31. $-2(x - 3)$

32. $5(x - 2y + 4z)$

33. $-5(x - 2y + 4z)$

XAMPLES Name the property illustrated by the equation.

Equation	Property
3. $5x = x(5)$	Commutative law of multiplication
9. $a + (8.5 + b) = (a + 8.5) + b$	Associative law of addition
0. $0 + 11 = 11$	Identity property of 0
1. $(-5s)t = -5(st)$	Associative law of multiplication
2. $\frac{3}{4} \cdot 1 = \frac{3}{4}$	Identity property of 1
3. $12.5(w - 3) = 12.5w - 12.5(3)$	Distributive law of multiplication over subtraction
4. $y + \frac{1}{2} = \frac{1}{2} + y$	Commutative law of addition

ɔ Exercises 34–40.

Name the property illustrated by the equation.

34. $(-8a)b = -8(ab)$

35. $p \cdot 1 = p$

36. $m + 34 = 34 + m$

37. $2(t + 5) = 2t + 2(5)$

38. $0 + k = k$

39. $-8x = x(-8)$

40. $x + (4.3 + b) = (x + 4.3) + b$

Answers on page A-6

1 Factoring

ctoring is the reverse of multiplying. To factor, we can use the distributive ws in reverse:

$$ab + ac = a(b + c) \quad \text{and} \quad ab - ac = a(b - c).$$

FACTORING

To **factor** an expression is to find an equivalent expression that is a product.

Look at Example 14. To *factor* $9x - 45$, we find an equivalent expression at is a product, $9(x - 5)$. When all the terms of an expression have a factor common, we can "factor it out" using the distributive laws. Note the lowing.

$9x$ has the factors $9, -9, 3, -3, 1, -1, x, -x, 3x, -3x, 9x, -9x$;

-45 has the factors $1, -1, 3, -3, 5, -5, 9, -9, 15, -15, 45, -45$

Factor.

41. $6x - 12$

42. $3x - 6y + 9$

43. $bx + by - bz$

44. $16a - 36b + 42$

45. $\frac{3}{8}x - \frac{5}{8}y + \frac{7}{8}$

46. $-12x + 32y - 16z$

Answers on page A-6

We generally remove the largest common factor. In this case, that factor i 9. Thus,

$$9x - 45 = 9 \cdot x - 9 \cdot 5$$
$$= 9(x - 5).$$

Remember that an expression has been factored when we have found a equivalent expression that is a product. Above, we note that $9x - 45$ an $9(x - 5)$ are equivalent expressions. The expression $9x - 45$ is the differenc of $9x$ and 45; the expression $9(x - 5)$ is the product of 9 and $(x - 5)$.

EXAMPLES Factor.

25. $5x - 10 = 5 \cdot x - 5 \cdot 2$ Try to do this step mentally.
$= 5(x - 2)$ You can check by multiplying.

26. $ax - ay + az = a(x - y + z)$

27. $9x + 27y - 9 = 9 \cdot x + 9 \cdot 3y - 9 \cdot 1 = 9(x + 3y - 1)$

Note in Example 27 that you might, at first, just factor out a 3, as follow

$$9x + 27y - 9 = 3 \cdot 3x + 3 \cdot 9y - 3 \cdot 3$$
$$= 3(3x + 9y - 3).$$

At this point, the mathematics is correct, but the answer is not because the is another factor of 3 that can be factored out, as follows:

$$3 \cdot 3x + 3 \cdot 9y - 3 \cdot 3 = 3(3x + 9y - 3)$$
$$= 3(3 \cdot x + 3 \cdot 3y - 3 \cdot 1)$$
$$= 3 \cdot 3(x + 3y - 1)$$
$$= 9(x + 3y - 1).$$

We now have a correct answer, but it took more work than we did i Example 27. Thus it is better to look for the greatest common factor at th outset.

EXAMPLES Factor. Try to write just the answer, if you can.

28. $5x - 5y = 5(x - y)$

29. $-3x + 6y - 9z = -3(x - 2y + 3z)$

We usually factor out a negative factor when the first term is negative. Th way we factor can depend on the situation in which we are working. W might also factor the expression in Example 29 as follows:

$$-3x + 6y - 9z = 3(-x + 2y - 3z).$$

30. $18z - 12x - 24 = 6(3z - 2x - 4)$

31. $\frac{1}{2}x + \frac{3}{2}y - \frac{1}{2} = \frac{1}{2}(x + 3y - 1)$

Remember that you can always check factoring by multiplying. Keep in mind that an expression is factored when it is written as a product.

Do Exercises 41–46.

e Collecting Like Terms

erms such as $5x$ and $-4x$, whose variable factors are exactly the same, are alled **like terms.** Similarly, numbers, such as -7 and 13, are like terms. Also, y^2 and $9y^2$ are like terms because the variables are raised to the same power. erms such as $4y$ and $5y^2$ are not like terms, and $7x$ and $2y$ are not like terms.

The process of **collecting like terms** is also based on the distributive laws. Ve can apply the distributive law when a factor is on the right because of the ommutative law of multiplication.

Later in this text, terminology like "collecting like terms" and "combining ke terms" will also be referred to as "simplifying."

XAMPLES Collect like terms. Try to write just the answer, if you can.

2. $4x + 2x = (4 + 2)x = 6x$ Factoring out the x using a distributive law

3. $2x + 3y - 5x - 2y = 2x - 5x + 3y - 2y$
$= (2 - 5)x + (3 - 2)y = -3x + y$

4. $3x - x = 3x - 1x = (3 - 1)x = 2x$

5. $x - 0.24x = 1 \cdot x - 0.24x = (1 - 0.24)x = 0.76x$

6. $x - 6x = 1 \cdot x - 6 \cdot x = (1 - 6)x = -5x$

7. $4x - 7y + 9x - 5 + 3y - 8 = 13x - 4y - 13$

8. $\frac{2}{3}a - b + \frac{4}{5}a + \frac{1}{4}b - 10 = \frac{2}{3}a - 1 \cdot b + \frac{4}{5}a + \frac{1}{4}b - 10$
$= \left(\frac{2}{3} + \frac{4}{5}\right)a + \left(-1 + \frac{1}{4}\right)b - 10$
$= \left(\frac{10}{15} + \frac{12}{15}\right)a + \left(-\frac{4}{4} + \frac{1}{4}\right)b - 10$
$= \frac{22}{15}a - \frac{3}{4}b - 10$

o Exercises 47–53.

Collect like terms.

47. $6x - 3x$

48. $7x - x$

49. $x - 9x$

50. $x - 0.41x$

51. $5x + 4y - 2x - y$

52. $3x - 7x - 11 + 8y + 4 - 13y$

53. $-\frac{2}{3} - \frac{3}{5}x + y + \frac{7}{10}x - \frac{2}{9}y$

Answers on page A-6

Study Tips — LEARNING RESOURCES

Are you aware of all the learning resources that exist for this textbook? Many details are given in the Preface.

- The *Student's Solutions Manual* contains fully worked-out solutions to the odd-numbered exercises in the exercise sets, with the exception of the discussion and writing exercises, as well as solutions to all exercises in Chapter Reviews, Chapter Tests, and Cumulative Reviews. You can order this through the bookstore or by calling 1-800-282-0693.
- An extensive set of *videotapes* supplements this text. These are available on CD-ROM by calling 1-800-282-0693.
- *Tutorial software* called InterAct Math also accompanies this text. If it is not available in the campus learning center, you can order it by calling 1-800-282-0693.
- The Addison-Wesley *Math Tutor Center* is available for help with the odd-numbered exercises. You can order this service by calling 1-800-824-7799.
- Extensive help is available online via MyMathLab and/or MathXL. Ask your instructor for information about these or visit MyMathLab.com and MathXL.com.

1.7 EXERCISE SET

For Extra Help

MathXL · MyMathLab · InterAct Math · Math Tutor Center · Digital Video Tutor CD 1 Videotape 2 · Student's Solutions Manual

a Find an equivalent expression with the given denominator.

1. $\frac{3}{5} = \frac{\square}{5y}$ **2.** $\frac{5}{8} = \frac{\square}{8t}$ **3.** $\frac{2}{3} = \frac{\square}{15x}$ **4.** $\frac{6}{7} = \frac{\square}{14y}$ **5.** $\frac{2}{x} = \frac{\square}{x^2}$ **6.** $\frac{4}{9x} = \frac{\square}{9xy}$

Simplify.

7. $-\frac{24a}{16a}$ **8.** $-\frac{42t}{18t}$ **9.** $-\frac{42ab}{36ab}$ **10.** $-\frac{64pq}{48pq}$ **11.** $\frac{20st}{15t}$ **12.** $\frac{21w}{7wz}$

b Write an equivalent expression. Use a commutative law.

13. $y + 8$ **14.** $x + 3$ **15.** mn **16.** ab

17. $9 + xy$ **18.** $11 + ab$ **19.** $ab + c$ **20.** $rs + t$

Write an equivalent expression. Use an associative law.

21. $a + (b + 2)$ **22.** $3(vw)$ **23.** $(8x)y$ **24.** $(y + z) + 7$

25. $(a + b) + 3$ **26.** $(5 + x) + y$ **27.** $3(ab)$ **28.** $(6x)y$

Use the commutative and associative laws to write three equivalent expressions.

29. $(a + b) + 2$ **30.** $(3 + x) + y$ **31.** $5 + (v + w)$ **32.** $6 + (x + y)$

33. $(xy)3$ **34.** $(ab)5$ **35.** $7(ab)$ **36.** $5(xy)$

c Multiply.

37. $2(b + 5)$ **38.** $4(x + 3)$ **39.** $7(1 + t)$ **40.** $4(1 + y)$

41. $6(5x + 2)$ **42.** $9(6m + 7)$ **43.** $7(x + 4 + 6y)$ **44.** $4(5x + 8 + 3p)$

45. $7(x - 3)$

46. $15(y - 6)$

47. $-3(x - 7)$

48. $1.2(x - 2.1)$

49. $\frac{2}{3}(b - 6)$

50. $\frac{5}{8}(y + 16)$

51. $7.3(x - 2)$

52. $5.6(x - 8)$

53. $-\frac{3}{5}(x - y + 10)$

54. $-\frac{2}{3}(a + b - 12)$

55. $-9(-5x - 6y + 8)$

56. $-7(-2x - 5y + 9)$

57. $-4(x - 3y - 2z)$

58. $8(2x - 5y - 8z)$

59. $3.1(-1.2x + 3.2y - 1.1)$

60. $-2.1(-4.2x - 4.3y - 2.2)$

List the terms of the expression.

61. $4x + 3z$

62. $8x - 1.4y$

63. $7x + 8y - 9z$

64. $8a + 10b - 18c$

d Factor. Check by multiplying.

65. $2x + 4$

66. $5y + 20$

67. $30 + 5y$

68. $7x + 28$

69. $14x + 21y$

70. $18a + 24b$

71. $5x + 10 + 15y$

72. $9a + 27b + 81$

73. $8x - 24$

74. $10x - 50$

75. $-4y + 32$

76. $-6m + 24$

77. $8x + 10y - 22$

78. $9a + 6b - 15$

79. $ax - a$

80. $by - 9b$

81. $ax - ay - az$

82. $cx + cy - cz$

83. $-18x + 12y + 6$

84. $-14x + 21y + 7$

85. $\frac{2}{3}x - \frac{5}{3}y + \frac{1}{3}$

86. $\frac{3}{5}a + \frac{4}{5}b - \frac{1}{5}$

e Collect like terms.

87. $9a + 10a$

88. $12x + 2x$

89. $10a - a$

90. $-16x + x$

91. $2x + 9z + 6x$

92. $3a - 5b + 7a$

93. $7x + 6y^2 + 9y^2$

94. $12m^2 + 6q + 9m^2$

95. $41a + 90 - 60a - 2$

96. $42x - 6 - 4x + 2$

97. $23 + 5t + 7y - t - y - 27$

98. $45 - 90d - 87 - 9d + 3 + 7d$

99. $\frac{1}{2}b + \frac{1}{2}b$

100. $\frac{2}{3}x + \frac{1}{3}x$

101. $2y + \frac{1}{4}y + y$

102. $\frac{1}{2}a + a + 5a$

103. $11x - 3x$

104. $9t - 17t$

105. $6n - n$

106. $100t - t$

107. $y - 17y$

108. $3m - 9m + 4$

109. $-8 + 11a - 5b + 6a - 7b + 7$

110. $8x - 5x + 6 + 3y - 2y - 4$

1. $9x + 2y - 5x$

112. $8y - 3z + 4y$

113. $11x + 2y - 4x - y$

4. $13a + 9b - 2a - 4b$

115. $2.7x + 2.3y - 1.9x - 1.8y$

116. $6.7a + 4.3b - 4.1a - 2.9b$

7. $\frac{13}{2}a + \frac{9}{5}b - \frac{2}{3}a - \frac{3}{10}b - 42$

118. $\frac{11}{4}x + \frac{2}{3}y - \frac{4}{5}x - \frac{1}{6}y + 12$

9. **DW** The distributive law was introduced before the discussion on collecting like terms. Why do you think this was done?

120. **DW** Find two algebraic expressions for the total area of this figure. Explain the equivalence of the expressions in terms of the distributive law.

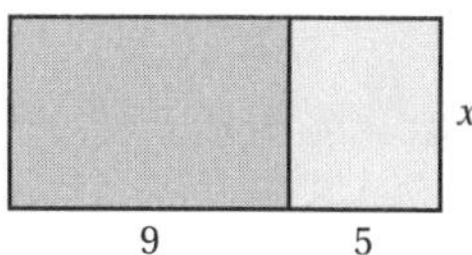

SKILL MAINTENANCE

nd the LCM. [R.1b]

1. 16, 18

122. 18, 24

123. 16, 18, 24

124. 12, 15, 20

5. 16, 32

126. 24, 72

127. 15, 45, 90

128. 18, 54, 108

9. Add and simplify: $\frac{11}{12} + \frac{15}{16}$. [R.2c]

130. Subtract and simplify: $\frac{7}{8} - \frac{2}{3}$. [R.2c]

1. Subtract and simplify: $\frac{1}{8} - \frac{1}{3}$. [R.2c], [1.4a]

132. Convert to percent notation: $\frac{3}{10}$. [R.4d]

SYNTHESIS

ll whether the expressions are equivalent. Give an example if they are not.

3. $3t + 5$ and $3 \cdot 5 + t$

134. $4x$ and $x + 4$

5. $5m + 6$ and $6 + 5m$

136. $(x + y) + z$ and $z + (x + y)$

7. Factor: $q + qr + qrs + qrst$.

138. Collect like terms:

$$21x + 44xy + 15y - 16x - 8y - 38xy + 2y + xy.$$

1.8 SIMPLIFYING EXPRESSIONS; ORDER OF OPERATIONS

Objectives

a. Find an equivalent expression for an opposite without parentheses, where an expression has several terms.

b. Simplify expressions by removing parentheses and collecting like terms.

c. Simplify expressions with parentheses inside parentheses.

d. Simplify expressions using rules for order of operations.

Find an equivalent expression without parentheses.

1. $-(x + 2)$

2. $-(5x + 2y + 8)$

Answers on page A-6

We now expand our ability to manipulate expressions by first consideri[ng] opposites of sums and differences. Then we simplify expressions involvi[ng] parentheses.

a Opposites of Sums

What happens when we multiply a real number by -1? Consider the follo[w]ing products:

$$-1(7) = -7, \qquad -1(-5) = 5, \qquad -1(0) = 0.$$

From these examples, it appears that when we multiply a number by -1, [w]e get the opposite, or additive inverse, of that number.

THE PROPERTY OF −1

For any real number a,

$$-1 \cdot a = -a.$$

(Negative one times a is the opposite, or additive inverse, of a.)

The property of -1 enables us to find certain expressions equivalent [to] opposites of sums.

EXAMPLES Find an equivalent expression without parentheses.

1. $-(3 + x) = -1(3 + x)$ Using the property of -1

$= -1 \cdot 3 + (-1)x$ Using a distributive law, multiplying eac[h] term by -1

$= -3 + (-x)$ Using the property of -1

$= -3 - x$

2. $-(3x + 2y + 4) = -1(3x + 2y + 4)$ Using the property of -1

$= -1(3x) + (-1)(2y) + (-1)4$ Using a distributive l[aw]

$= -3x - 2y - 4$ Using the property of -1

Do Exercises 1 and 2.

Suppose we want to remove parentheses in an expression like

$$-(x - 2y + 5).$$

We can first rewrite any subtractions inside the parentheses as additio[ns]. Then we take the opposite of each term:

$$-(x - 2y + 5) = -[x + (-2y) + 5]$$
$$= -x + 2y - 5.$$

The most efficient method for removing parentheses is to replace each te[rm] in the parentheses with its opposite ("change the sign of every term"). Doi[ng] so for $-(x - 2y + 5)$, we obtain $-x + 2y - 5$ as an equivalent expression.

EXAMPLES Find an equivalent expression without parentheses.

3. $-(5 - y) = -5 + y = y + (-5) = y - 5$ Changing the sign of each term

4. $-(2a - 7b - 6) = -2a + 7b + 6$

5. $-(-3x + 4y + z - 7w - 23) = 3x - 4y - z + 7w + 23$

Do Exercises 3–6.

b Removing Parentheses and Simplifying

When a sum is added, as in $5x + (2x + 3)$, we can simply remove, or drop, the parentheses and collect like terms because of the associative law of addition:

$$5x + (2x + 3) = 5x + 2x + 3 = 7x + 3.$$

On the other hand, when a sum is subtracted, as in $3x - (4x + 2)$, no "associative" law applies. However, we can subtract by adding an opposite. We then remove parentheses by changing the sign of each term inside the parentheses and collecting like terms.

EXAMPLE 6 Remove parentheses and simplify.

$3x - (4x + 2) = 3x + [-(4x + 2)]$ Adding the opposite of $(4x + 2)$

$= 3x + (-4x - 2)$ Changing the sign of each term inside the parentheses

$= 3x - 4x - 2$

$= -x - 2$ Collecting like terms

Caution!

Note that $3x - (4x + 2) \neq 3x - 4x + 2$. That is, $3x - (4x + 2)$ is *not* equivalent to $3x - 4x + 2$. You cannot simply drop the parentheses.

Do Exercises 7 and 8.

In practice, the first three steps of Example 6 are usually combined by changing the sign of each term in parentheses and then collecting like terms.

EXAMPLES Remove parentheses and simplify.

7. $5y - (3y + 4) = 5y - 3y - 4$ Removing parentheses by changing the sign of every term inside the parentheses

$= 2y - 4$ Collecting like terms

8. $3x - 2 - (5x - 8) = 3x - 2 - 5x + 8$

$= -2x + 6$, or $6 - 2x$

9. $(3a + 4b - 5) - (2a - 7b + 4c - 8)$

$= 3a + 4b - 5 - 2a + 7b - 4c + 8$

$= a + 11b - 4c + 3$

Do Exercises 9–11.

Find an equivalent expression without parentheses. Try to do this in one step.

3. $-(6 - t)$

4. $-(x - y)$

5. $-(-4a + 3t - 10)$

6. $-(18 - m - 2n + 4z)$

Remove parentheses and simplify.

7. $5x - (3x + 9)$

8. $5y - 2 - (2y - 4)$

Remove parentheses and simplify.

9. $6x - (4x + 7)$

10. $8y - 3 - (5y - 6)$

11. $(2a + 3b - c) - (4a - 5b + 2c)$

Answers on page A-6

Next, consider subtracting an expression consisting of several terms multiplied by a number other than 1 or -1.

EXAMPLE 10 Remove parentheses and simplify.

$$x - 3(x + y) = x + [-3(x + y)] \quad \text{Adding the opposite of } 3(x+y)$$
$$= x + [-3x - 3y] \quad \text{Multiplying } x + y \text{ by } -3$$
$$= x - 3x - 3y$$
$$= -2x - 3y \quad \text{Collecting like terms}$$

EXAMPLES Remove parentheses and simplify.

11. $3y - 2(4y - 5) = 3y - 8y + 10$ Multiplying each term in parentheses by -2

$= -5y + 10$

12. $(2a + 3b - 7) - 4(-5a - 6b + 12)$

$= 2a + 3b - 7 + 20a + 24b - 48 = 22a + 27b - 55$

13. $2y - \frac{1}{3}(9y - 12) = 2y - 3y + 4 = -y + 4$

14. $6.4(5x - 3y) - 2.5(8x + y) = 32x - 19.2y - 20x - 2.5y = 12x - 21.7y$

Do Exercises 12–16.

C Parentheses Within Parentheses

In addition to parentheses, some expressions contain other grouping symbols such as brackets [ ] and braces { }.

When more than one kind of grouping symbol occurs, do the computations in the innermost ones first. Then work from the inside out.

EXAMPLES Simplify.

15. $[3 - (7 + 3)] = [3 - 10] = -7$

16. $\{8 - [9 - (12 + 5)]\} = \{8 - [9 - 17]\}$ Computing $12 + 5$

$= \{8 - [-8]\}$ Computing $9 - 17$

$= 8 + 8 = 16$

17. $\left[(-4) \div \left(-\frac{1}{4}\right)\right] \div \frac{1}{4} = [(-4) \cdot (-4)] \div \frac{1}{4}$ Working within the brackets; computing $(-4) \div \left(-\frac{1}{4}\right)$

$= 16 \div \frac{1}{4}$

$= 16 \cdot 4 = 64$

18. $4(2 + 3) - \{7 - [4 - (8 + 5)]\}$

$= 4 \cdot 5 - \{7 - [4 - 13]\}$ Working with the innermost parentheses first

$= 20 - \{7 - [-9]\}$ Computing $4 \cdot 5$ and $4 - 13$

$= 20 - 16$ Computing $7 - [-9]$

$= 4$

Do Exercises 17–20.

Remove parentheses and simplify.

12. $y - 9(x + y)$

13. $5a - 3(7a - 6)$

14. $4a - b - 6(5a - 7b + 8c)$

15. $5x - \frac{1}{4}(8x + 28)$

16. $4.6(5x - 3y) - 5.2(8x + y)$

Simplify.

17. $12 - (8 + 2)$

18. $\{9 - [10 - (13 + 6)]\}$

19. $[24 \div (-2)] \div (-2)$

20. $5(3 + 4) - \{8 - [5 - (9 + 6)]\}$

Answers on page A-6

EXAMPLE 19 Simplify.

$[5(x+2)-3x]-[3(y+2)-7(y-3)]$
$= [5x+10-3x]-[3y+6-7y+21]$ Working with the innermost parentheses first
$= [2x+10]-[-4y+27]$ Collecting like terms within brackets
$= 2x+10+4y-27$ Removing brackets
$= 2x+4y-17$ Collecting like terms

Do Exercise 21.

21. Simplify:

$[3(x+2)+2x]-$
$[4(y+2)-3(y-2)].$

d Order of Operations

When several operations are to be done in a calculation or a problem, we apply the same rules that we did in Section R.5. We repeat them here for review. (If you did not study that section earlier, you should do so now.)

RULES FOR ORDER OF OPERATIONS

1. Do all calculations within grouping symbols before operations outside.
2. Evaluate all exponential expressions.
3. Do all multiplications and divisions in order from left to right.
4. Do all additions and subtractions in order from left to right.

These rules are consistent with the way in which most computers and scientific calculators perform calculations.

EXAMPLE 20 Simplify: $-34 \cdot 56 - 17$.

There are no parentheses or powers, so we start with the third step.

$-34 \cdot 56 - 17 = -1904 - 17$ Doing all multiplications and divisions in order from left to right
$= -1921$ Doing all additions and subtractions in order from left to right

EXAMPLE 21 Simplify: $25 \div (-5) + 50 \div (-2)$.

There are no calculations inside parentheses or powers. The parentheses with (-5) and (-2) are used only to represent the negative numbers. We begin by doing all multiplications and divisions.

$\underbrace{25 \div (-5)} + \underbrace{50 \div (-2)}$
$= -5 + (-25)$ Doing all multiplications and divisions in order from left to right
$= -30$ Doing all additions and subtractions in order from left to right.

Do Exercises 22–24.

Simplify.

22. $23 - 42 \cdot 30$

23. $32 \div 8 \cdot 2$

24. $-24 \div 3 - 48 \div (-4)$

Answers on page A-6

EXAMPLE 22 Simplify: $-2^4 + 51 \cdot 4 - (37 + 23 \cdot 2)$.

$-2^4 + 51 \cdot 4 - (37 + 23 \cdot 2)$

$= -2^4 + 51 \cdot 4 - (37 + 46)$	Following the rules for order of operations within the parentheses first
$= -2^4 + 51 \cdot 4 - 83$	Completing the addition inside parentheses
$= -16 + 51 \cdot 4 - 83$	Evaluating exponential expressions. Note that $-2^4 \neq (-2)^4$.
$= -16 + 204 - 83$	Doing all multiplications
$= 188 - 83$	Doing all additions and subtractions in order from left to right
$= 105$	

CALCULATOR CORNER

Order of Operations and Grouping Symbols Parentheses are necessary in some calculations in order to ensure that operations are performed in the desired order. To simplify $-5(3 - 6) - 12$, we press (-) 5 (3 − 6) − 1 2 ENTER. The result is 3. Without parentheses, the computation is $-5 \cdot 3 - 6 - 12$, and the result is -33.

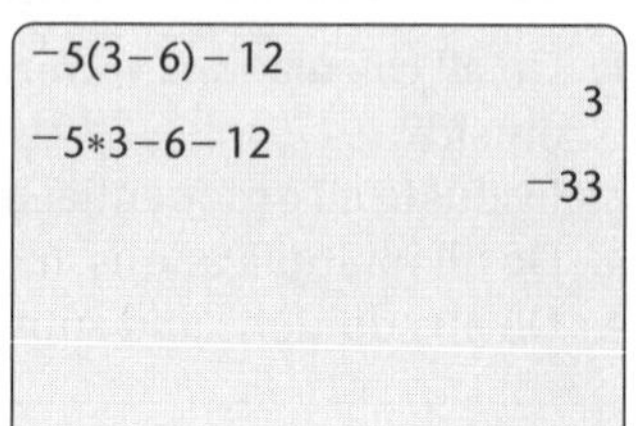

-5(3−6)−12
3
-5*3−6−12
−33

When a negative number is raised to an even power, parentheses must also be used. To find $(-3)^4$, we press ((-) 3) ^ 4 ENTER. The result is 81. Without parentheses, the computation is $-3^4 = -1 \cdot 3^4 = -1 \cdot 81 = -81$.

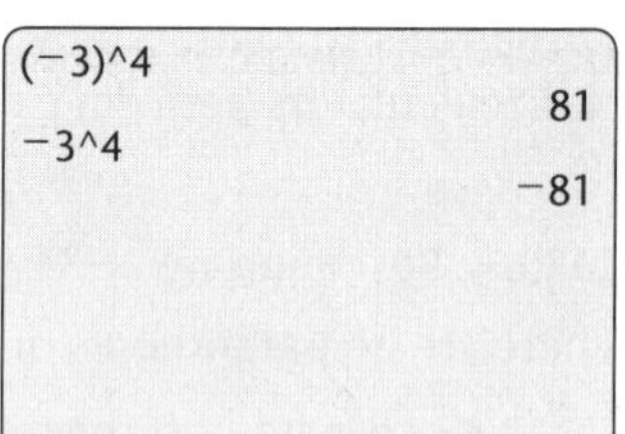

(−3)^4
81
−3^4
−81

To simplify an expression like $\frac{49 - 104}{7 + 4}$, we must enter it as $(49 - 104) \div (7 + 4)$. We press (4 9 − 1 0 4) ÷ (7 + 4) ENTER. The result is -5.

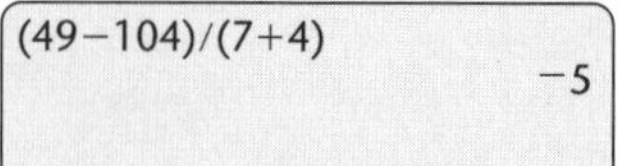

(49−104)/(7+4)
−5

Exercises: Calculate.

1. $-8 + 4(7 - 9) + 5$
2. $-3[2 + (-5)]$
3. $7[4 - (-3)] + 5[3^2 - (-4)]$
4. $(-7)^6$
5. $(-17)^5$
6. $(-104)^3$
7. -7^6
8. -17^5
9. -104^3
10. $\dfrac{38 - 178}{5 + 30}$
11. $\dfrac{311 - 17^2}{2 - 13}$
12. $785 - \dfrac{285 - 5^4}{17 + 3 \cdot 51}$

A fraction bar can play the role of a grouping symbol, although such a mbol is not as evident as the others.

XAMPLE 23 Simplify: $\dfrac{-64 \div (-16) \div (-2)}{2^3 - 3^2}$.

An equivalent expression with brackets as grouping symbols is

$$[-64 \div (-16) \div (-2)] \div [2^3 - 3^2].$$

his shows, in effect, that we do the calculations in the numerator and then in e denominator, and divide the results:

$$\frac{-64 \div (-16) \div (-2)}{2^3 - 3^2} = \frac{4 \div (-2)}{8 - 9} = \frac{-2}{-1} = 2.$$

o Exercises 25 and 26.

Simplify.

25. $-4^3 + 52 \cdot 5 + 5^3 - (4^2 - 48 \div 4)$

26. $\dfrac{5 - 10 - 5 \cdot 23}{2^3 + 3^2 - 7}$

Answers on page A-6

tudy Tips

TEST PREPARATION

You are probably ready to begin preparing for your first test. Here are some test-taking study tips.

- **Make up your own test questions as you study.** After you have done your homework over a particular objective, write one or two questions on your own that you think might be on a test. You will be amazed at the insight this will provide.
- **Do an overall review of the chapter, focusing on the objectives and the examples.** This should be accompanied by a study of any class notes you may have taken.
- **Do the review exercises at the end of the chapter.** Check your answers at the back of the book. If you have trouble with an exercise, use the objective symbol as a guide to go back and do further study of that objective.
- **Call the AW Math Tutor Center if you need extra help at 1-888-777-0463.**
- **Do the chapter test at the end of the chapter.** Check the answers and use the objective symbols at the back of the book as a reference for where to review.
- **Ask former students for old exams.** Working such exams can be very helpful and allows you to see what various professors think is important.
- **When taking a test, read each question carefully and try to do all the questions the first time through, but pace yourself.** Answer all the questions, and mark those to recheck if you have time at the end. Very often, your first hunch will be correct.
- **Try to write your test in a neat and orderly manner.** Very often, your instructor tries to give you partial credit when grading an exam. If your test paper is sloppy and disorderly, it is difficult to verify the partial credit. Doing your work neatly can ease such a task for the instructor.

1.8 EXERCISE SET

For Extra Help

MathXL | MyMathLab | InterAct Math | Math Tutor Center | Digital Video Tutor CD 1 Videotape 2 | Student's Solutions Manual

a Find an equivalent expression without parentheses.

1. $-(2x + 7)$

2. $-(8x + 4)$

3. $-(8 - x)$

4. $-(a - b)$

5. $-(4a - 3b + 7c)$

6. $-(x - 4y - 3z)$

7. $-(6x - 8y + 5)$

8. $-(4x + 9y + 7)$

9. $-(3x - 5y - 6)$

10. $-(6a - 4b - 7)$

11. $-(-8x - 6y - 43)$

12. $-(-2a + 9b - 5c)$

b Remove parentheses and simplify.

13. $9x - (4x + 3)$

14. $4y - (2y + 5)$

15. $2a - (5a - 9)$

16. $12m - (4m - 6)$

17. $2x + 7x - (4x + 6)$

18. $3a + 2a - (4a + 7)$

19. $2x - 4y - 3(7x - 2y)$

20. $3a - 9b - 1(4a - 8b)$

21. $15x - y - 5(3x - 2y + 5z)$

22. $4a - b - 4(5a - 7b + 8c)$

23. $(3x + 2y) - 2(5x - 4y)$

24. $(-6a - b) - 5(2b + a)$

25. $(12a - 3b + 5c) - 5(-5a + 4b - 6c)$

26. $(-8x + 5y - 12) - 6(2x - 4y - 10)$

c Simplify.

27. $[9 - 2(5 - 4)]$

28. $[6 - 5(8 - 4)]$

29. $8[7 - 6(4 - 2)]$

30. $10[7 - 4(7 - 5)]$

31. $[4(9 - 6) + 11] - [14 - (6 + 4)]$

32. $[7(8 - 4) + 16] - [15 - (7 + 8)]$

33. $[10(x + 3) - 4] + [2(x - 1) + 6]$

34. $[9(x + 5) - 7] + [4(x - 12) + 9]$

35. $[7(x + 5) - 19] - [4(x - 6) + 10]$

36. $[6(x + 4) - 12] - [5(x - 8) + 14]$

37. $3\{[7(x - 2) + 4] - [2(2x - 5) + 6]\}$

38. $4\{[8(x - 3) + 9] - [4(3x - 2) + 6]\}$

39. $4\{[5(x - 3) + 2] - 3[2(x + 5) - 9]\}$

40. $3\{[6(x - 4) + 5] - 2[5(x + 8) - 3]\}$

d Simplify.

41. $8 - 2 \cdot 3 - 9$

42. $8 - (2 \cdot 3 - 9)$

43. $(8 - 2 \cdot 3) - 9$

44. $(8 - 2)(3 - 9)$

45. $[(-24) \div (-3)] \div \left(-\frac{1}{2}\right)$

46. $[32 \div (-2)] \div \left(-\frac{1}{4}\right)$

47. $16 \cdot (-24) + 50$

48. $10 \cdot 20 - 15 \cdot 24$

49. $2^4 + 2^3 - 10$

50. $40 - 3^2 - 2^3$

51. $5^3 + 26 \cdot 71 - (16 + 25 \cdot 3)$

52. $4^3 + 10 \cdot 20 + 8^2 - 23$

53. $4 \cdot 5 - 2 \cdot 6 + 4$

54. $4 \cdot (6 + 8)/(4 + 3)$

55. $4^3/8$

56. $5^3 - 7^2$

57. $8(-7) + 6(-5)$

58. $10(-5) + 1(-1)$

59. $19 - 5(-3) + 3$

60. $14 - 2(-6) + 7$

61. $9 \div (-3) + 16 \div 8$

62. $-32 - 8 \div 4 - (-2)$

63. $-4^2 + 6$

64. $-5^2 + 7$

65. $-8^2 - 3$

66. $-9^2 - 11$

67. $12 - 20^3$

68. $20 + 4^3 \div (-8)$

69. $2 \cdot 10^3 - 5000$

70. $-7(3^4) + 18$

71. $6[9 - (3 - 4)]$

72. $8[(6 - 13) - 11]$

73. $-1000 \div (-100) \div 10$

74. $256 \div (-32) \div (-4)$

75. $8 - (7 - 9)$

76. $(8 - 7) - 9$

77. $\dfrac{10 - 6^2}{9^2 + 3^2}$

78. $\dfrac{5^2 - 4^3 - 3}{9^2 - 2^2 - 1^5}$

79. $\dfrac{3(6 - 7) - 5 \cdot 4}{6 \cdot 7 - 8(4 - 1)}$

80. $\dfrac{20(8 - 3) - 4(10 - 3)}{10(2 - 6) - 2(5 + 2)}$

81. $\dfrac{|2^3 - 3^2| + |12 \cdot 5|}{-32 \div (-16) \div (-4)}$

82. $\dfrac{|3 - 5|^2 - |7 - 13|}{|12 - 9| + |11 - 14|}$

83. DW Jake keys in 18/2 · 3 on his calculator and expects the result to be 3. What mistake is he making?

84. DW Determine whether $|-x|$ and $|x|$ are equivalent. Explain.

SKILL MAINTENANCE

VOCABULARY REINFORCEMENT

In each of Exercises 85–92, fill in the blank with the correct term from the given list. Some of the choices may not be used and some may be used more than once.

85. The set of ______________ is $\{\ldots, -5, -4, -3, -2, -1, 0, 1, 2, 3, \ldots\}$. [1.2a]

86. Two numbers whose sum is 0 are called ______________ of each other. [1.3b]

87. The ______________ of addition says that $a + b = b + a$ for any real numbers a and b. [1.7b]

88. The ______________ states that for any real number a, $a \cdot 1 = 1 \cdot a = a$. [1.7a]

89. The ______________ of addition says that $a + (b + c) = (a + b) + c$ for any real numbers a, b, and c. [1.7b]

90. The ______________ of multiplication says that $a(bc) = (ab)c$ for any real numbers a, b, and c. [1.7b]

91. Two numbers whose product is 1 are called ______________ of each other. [1.6b]

92. The equation $y + 0 = y$ illustrates the ______________. [1.7a]

natural numbers
multiplicative inverses
distributive law
associative law
whole numbers
additive inverses
identity property of 0
property of −1
integers
commutative law
identity property of 1
real numbers

SYNTHESIS

Find an equivalent expression by enclosing the last three terms in parentheses preceded by a minus sign.

93. $6y + 2x - 3a + c$

94. $x - y - a - b$

95. $6m + 3n - 5m + 4b$

Simplify.

96. $z - \{2z - [3z - (4z - 5z) - 6z] - 7z\} - 8z$

97. $\{x - [f - (f - x)] + [x - f]\} - 3x$

98. $x - \{x - 1 - [x - 2 - (x - 3 - \{x - 4 - [x - 5 - (x - 6)]\})]\}$

99. Use your calculator to do the following.

a) Evaluate $x^2 + 3$ when $x = 7$, when $x = -7$, and when $x = -5.013$.

b) Evaluate $1 - x^2$ when $x = 5$, when $x = -5$, and when $x = -10.455$.

100. Express $3^3 + 3^3 + 3^3$ as a power of 3.

Find the average.

101. $-15,\ 20,\ 50,\ -82,\ -7,\ -2$

102. $-1,\ 1,\ 2,\ -2,\ 3,\ -8,\ -10$

1 Summary and Review

The review that follows is meant to prepare you for a chapter exam. It consists of three parts. The first part, Concept Reinforcement, is designed to increase understanding of the concepts through true/false exercises. The second part is a list of important properties and formulas. The third part is the Review Exercises. These provide practice exercises for the exam, together with references to section objectives so you can go back and review. Before beginning, stop and look back over the skills you have obtained. What skills in mathematics do you have now that you did not have before studying this chapter?

CONCEPT REINFORCEMENT

Determine whether the statement is true or false. Answers are given at the back of the book.

_______ **1.** The set of whole numbers is a subset of the set of integers.

_______ **2.** All rational numbers can be named using fraction or decimal notation.

_______ **3.** The product of an even number of negative numbers is negative.

_______ **4.** The operation of subtraction is not commutative.

_______ **5.** The product of a number and its multiplicative inverse is -1.

_______ **6.** Decimal notation for irrational numbers neither repeats nor terminates.

_______ **7.** $a < b$ also has the meaning $b \geq a$.

IMPORTANT PROPERTIES AND FORMULAS

Properties of the Real-Number System

The Commutative Laws: $a + b = b + a, \quad ab = ba$

The Associative Laws: $a + (b + c) = (a + b) + c, \quad a(bc) = (ab)c$

The Identity Properties: $a + 0 = 0 + a = a, \quad a \cdot 1 = 1 \cdot a = a$

The Inverse Properties: For any real number a, there is an opposite $-a$ such that $a + (-a) = (-a) + a = 0$.

For any nonzero real number a, there is a reciprocal $\frac{1}{a}$ such that $a \cdot \frac{1}{a} = \frac{1}{a} \cdot a = 1$.

The Distributive Laws: $a(b + c) = ab + ac, \quad a(b - c) = ab - ac$

Review Exercises

The review exercises that follow are for practice. Answers are at the back of the book. If you miss an exercise, restudy the objective indicated in red after the exercise or the direction line that precedes it.

1. Evaluate $\frac{x - y}{3}$ when $x = 17$ and $y = 5$. [1.1a]

2. Translate to an algebraic expression: [1.1b]
Nineteen percent of some number.

3. Tell which integers correspond to this situation: [1.2a]
David has a debt of \$45 and Joe has \$72 in his savings account.

4. Find: $|-38|$. [1.2e]

Graph the number on a number line. [1.2b]

5. -2.5

6. $\frac{8}{9}$

Use either < or > for □ to write a true sentence. [1.2d]

7. -3 □ 10

8. -1 □ -6

9. 0.126 □ -12.6

10. $-\frac{2}{3}$ □ $-\frac{1}{10}$

Find the opposite. [1.3b]

11. 3.8

12. $-\frac{3}{4}$

Find the reciprocal. [1.6b]

13. $\frac{3}{8}$

14. -7

15. Evaluate $-x$ when $x = -34$. [1.3b]

16. Evaluate $-(-x)$ when $x = 5$. [1.3b]

Compute and simplify.

17. $4 + (-7)$ [1.3a]

18. $6 + (-9) + (-8) + 7$ [1.3a]

19. $-3.8 + 5.1 + (-12) + (-4.3) + 10$ [1.3a]

20. $-3 - (-7) + 7 - 10$ [1.4a]

21. $-\frac{9}{10} - \frac{1}{2}$ [1.4a]

22. $-3.8 - 4.1$ [1.4a]

23. $-9 \cdot (-6)$ [1.5a]

24. $-2.7(3.4)$ [1.5a]

25. $\frac{2}{3} \cdot \left(-\frac{3}{7}\right)$ [1.5a]

26. $3 \cdot (-7) \cdot (-2) \cdot (-5)$ [1.5a]

27. $35 \div (-5)$ [1.6a]

28. $-5.1 \div 1.7$ [1.6c]

29. $-\frac{3}{11} \div \left(-\frac{4}{11}\right)$ [1.6c]

Simplify. [1.8d]

30. $(-3.4 - 12.2) - 8(-7)$

31. $\frac{-12(-3) - 2^3 - (-9)(-10)}{3 \cdot 10 + 1}$

32. $-16 \div 4 - 30 \div (-5)$

33. $\frac{9[(7 - 14) - 13]}{|-2(8) - 4|}$

Solve.

34. On the first, second, and third downs, a football team had these gains and losses: 5-yd gain, 12-yd loss, and 15-yd gain, respectively. Find the total gain (or loss). [1.3c]

35. Kaleb's total assets are \$170. He borrows \$300. What are his total assets now? [1.4b]

36. *Stock Price.* The value of EFX Corp. stock began the day at \$17.68 per share and dropped \$1.63 per hour for 8 hr. What was the price of the stock after 8 hr? [1.5b]

37. *Checking Account Balance.* Yuri had \$68 in his checking account. After writing checks to make seven purchases of DVDs at the same price for each, the balance in his account was −\$64.65. What was the price of each DVD? [1.6d]

Multiply. [1.7c]

38. $5(3x - 7)$

39. $-2(4x - 5)$

40. $10(0.4x + 1.5)$

41. $-8(3 - 6x)$

Factor. [1.7d]

42. $2x - 14$

43. $-6x + 6$

44. $5x + 10$

45. $-3x + 12y - 12$

Collect like terms. [1.7e]

46. $11a + 2b - 4a - 5b$

47. $7x - 3y - 9x + 8y$

48. $6x + 3y - x - 4y$

49. $-3a + 9b + 2a - b$

Remove parentheses and simplify.

50. $2a - (5a - 9)$ [1.8b]

51. $3(b + 7) - 5b$ [1.8b]

52. $3[11 - 3(4 - 1)]$ [1.8c]

53. $2[6(y - 4) + 7]$ [1.8c]

54. $[8(x + 4) - 10] - [3(x - 2) + 4]$ [1.8c]

55. $5\{[6(x - 1) + 7] - [3(3x - 4) + 8]\}$ [1.8c]

Answer True or False. [1.2d]

56. $-9 \leq 11$

57. $-11 \geq -3$

58. Write another inequality with the same meaning as $-3 < x$. [1.2d]

59. $\mathbf{D_W}$ Explain the notion of the opposite of a number in as many ways as possible. [1.3b]

60. $\mathbf{D_W}$ Is the absolute value of a number always positive? Why or why not? [1.2e]

SYNTHESIS

Simplify. [1.2e], [1.4a], [1.6a], [1.8d]

61. $-\left|\frac{7}{8} - \left(-\frac{1}{2}\right) - \frac{3}{4}\right|$

62. $(|2.7 - 3| + 3^2 - |-3|) \div (-3)$

63. $2000 - 1990 + 1980 - 1970 + \cdots + 20 - 10$

64. Find a formula for the perimeter of the following figure. [R.6a], [1.7e]

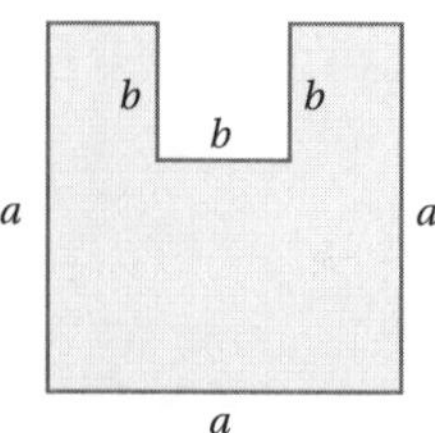

1 Chapter Test

For Extra Help

Work It Out!
Chapter Test Video
on CD

1. Evaluate $\frac{3x}{y}$ when $x = 10$ and $y = 5$.

2. Write an algebraic expression: Nine less than some number.

3. Find the area of a triangle when the height h is 30 ft and the base b is 16 ft.

Jse either $<$ or $>$ for $\square$ to write a true sentence.

4. $-4 \square 0$

5. $-3 \square -8$

6. $-0.78 \square -0.87$

7. $-\frac{1}{8} \square \frac{1}{2}$

ind the absolute value.

8. $|-7|$

9. $\left|\frac{9}{4}\right|$

10. $|-2.7|$

ind the opposite.

1. $\frac{2}{3}$

12. -1.4

3. Evaluate $-x$ when $x = -8$.

ind the reciprocal.

4. -2

15. $\frac{4}{7}$

ompute and simplify.

6. $3.1 - (-4.7)$

17. $-8 + 4 + (-7) + 3$

18. $-\frac{1}{5} + \frac{3}{8}$

9. $2 - (-8)$

20. $3.2 - 5.7$

21. $\frac{1}{8} - \left(-\frac{3}{4}\right)$

2. $4 \cdot (-12)$

23. $-\frac{1}{2} \cdot \left(-\frac{3}{8}\right)$

24. $-45 \div 5$

5. $-\frac{3}{5} \div \left(-\frac{4}{5}\right)$

26. $4.864 \div (-0.5)$

7. $-2(16) - |2(-8) - 5^3|$

28. $-20 \div (-5) + 36 \div (-4)$

29. *Antarctica Highs and Lows.* The continent of Antarctica, which lies in the southern hemisphere, experiences winter in July. The average high temperature is $-67°F$ and the average low temperature is $-81°F$. How much higher is the average high than the average low?

Source: National Climatic Data Center

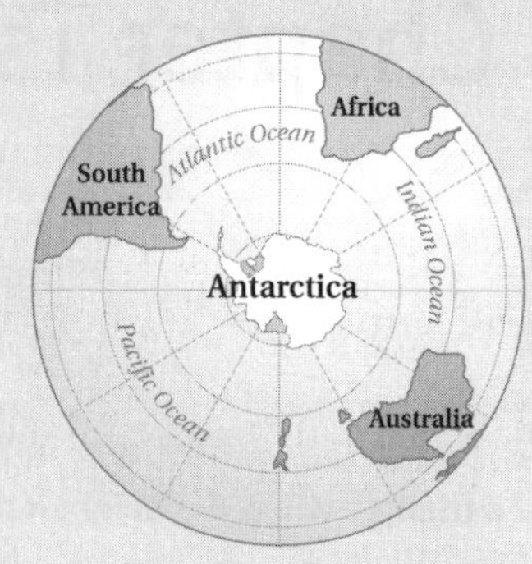

30. Maureen is a stockbroker. She kept track of the changes in the stock market over a period of 5 weeks. By how many points had the market risen or fallen over this time?

WEEK 1	WEEK 2	WEEK 3	WEEK 4	WEEK 5
Down 13 pts	Down 16 pts	Up 36 pts	Down 11 pts	Up 19 pts

31. *Population Decrease.* The population of a city was 18,600. It dropped 420 each year for 6 yr. What was the population of the city after 6 yr?

32. *Chemical Experiment.* During a chemical reaction, the temperature in the beaker decreased every minute by the same number of degrees. The temperature was 16°C at 11:08 A.M. By 11:43 A.M., the temperature had dropped to $-17°C$. By how many degrees did it drop each minute?

Multiply.

33. $3(6 - x)$

34. $-5(y - 1)$

Factor.

35. $12 - 22x$

36. $7x + 21 + 14y$

Simplify.

37. $6 + 7 - 4 - (-3)$

38. $5x - (3x - 7)$

39. $4(2a - 3b) + a - 7$

40. $4\{3[5(y - 3) + 9] + 2(y + 8)\}$

41. $256 \div (-16) \div 4$

42. $2^3 - 10[4 - (-2 + 18)3]$

43. Write an inequality with the same meaning as $x \leq -2$.

SYNTHESIS

Simplify.

44. $|-27 - 3(4)| - |-36| + |-12|$

45. $a - \{3a - [4a - (2a - 4a)]\}$

46. Find a formula for the perimeter of the figure shown here.

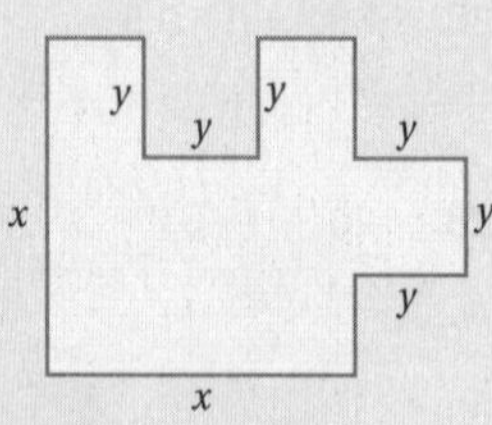

Solving Equations and Inequalities

2

Real-World Application

The average top speed of the three fastest roller coasters in the world is 109 mph. The third fastest roller coaster, Superman the Escape (at Six Flags Magic Mountain, Los Angeles, CA) reaches a top speed of 20 mph less than the fastest roller coaster, Top Thrill Dragster (in Cedar Point, Sandusky, OH). The second fastest roller coaster, Dodonpa (in Fujikyu Highlands, Japan), has a top speed of 107 mph. What is the top speed of the fastest roller coaster?

Source: *Fortune Small Business*, June 2004, p. 48

This problem appears as Example 7 in Section 2.6.

2.1 SOLVING EQUATIONS: THE ADDITION PRINCIPLE

Objectives

a Determine whether a given number is a solution of a given equation.

b Solve equations using the addition principle.

Determine whether the equation is true, false, or neither.

1. $5 - 8 = -4$

2. $12 + 6 = 18$

3. $x + 6 = 7 - x$

Answers on page A-7

a Equations and Solutions

In order to solve problems, we must learn to solve equations.

EQUATION

An **equation** is a number sentence that says that the expressions on either side of the equals sign, =, represent the same number.

Here are some examples:

$$3 + 2 = 5, \quad 14 - 10 = 1 + 3, \quad x + 6 = 13, \quad 3x - 2 = 7 - x.$$

Equations have expressions on each side of the equals sign. The sentence "$14 - 10 = 1 + 3$" asserts that the expressions $14 - 10$ and $1 + 3$ name the same number.

Some equations are true. Some are false. Some are neither true nor false.

EXAMPLES Determine whether the equation is true, false, or neither.

1. $3 + 2 = 5$ The equation is *true*.

2. $7 - 2 = 4$ The equation is *false*.

3. $x + 6 = 13$ The equation is *neither* true nor false, because we do not know what number x represents.

Do Exercises 1–3.

SOLUTION OF AN EQUATION

Any replacement for the variable that makes an equation true is called a **solution** of the equation. To solve an equation means to find *all* of its solutions.

One way to determine whether a number is a solution of an equation is to evaluate the expression on each side of the equals sign by substitution. If the values are the same, then the number is a solution.

EXAMPLE 4 Determine whether 7 is a solution of $x + 6 = 13$.

We have

$x + 6 = 13$	Writing the equation
$7 + 6 \ ? \ 13$	Substituting 7 for x
$13 \mid$	TRUE

Since the left-hand and the right-hand sides are the same, we have a solution. No other number makes the equation true, so the only solution is the number 7.

EXAMPLE 5 Determine whether 19 is a solution of $7x = 141$.

$7x = 141$	Writing the equation
$7(19) \ ? \ 141$	Substituting 19 for x
$133 \mid$	FALSE

Since the left-hand and the right-hand sides are not the same, we do not have a solution.

Do Exercises 4–7.

b Using the Addition Principle

Consider the equation

$$x = 7.$$

We can easily see that the solution of this equation is 7. If we replace x with 7, we get

$$7 = 7, \quad \text{which is true.}$$

Now consider the equation of Example 4:

$$x + 6 = 13.$$

In Example 4, we discovered that the solution of this equation is also 7, but the fact that 7 is the solution is not as obvious. We now begin to consider principles that allow us to start with an equation like $x + 6 = 13$ and end up with an *equivalent equation,* like $x = 7$, in which the variable is alone on one side and for which the solution is easier to find.

EQUIVALENT EQUATIONS

Equations with the same solutions are called **equivalent equations.**

One of the principles that we use in solving equations involves adding. An equation $a = b$ says that a and b stand for the same number. Suppose this is true, and we add a number c to the number a. We get the same answer if we add c to b, because a and b are the same number.

THE ADDITION PRINCIPLE FOR EQUATIONS

For any real numbers a, b, and c,

$$a = b \quad \text{is equivalent to} \quad a + c = b + c.$$

Let's again solve the equation $x + 6 = 13$ using the addition principle. We want to get x alone on one side. To do so, we use the addition principle, choosing to add -6 because $6 + (-6) = 0$:

$x + 6 = 13$	
$x + 6 + (-6) = 13 + (-6)$	Using the addition principle: adding -6 on both sides
$x + 0 = 7$	Simplifying
$x = 7.$	Identity property of 0: $x + 0 = x$

The solution of $x + 6 = 13$ is 7.

Determine whether the given number is a solution of the given equation.

4. 8; $x + 4 = 12$

5. 0; $x + 4 = 12$

6. -3; $7 + x = -4$

7. $-\frac{3}{5}$; $-5x = 3$

Answers on page A-7

8. Solve using the addition principle:

$x + 2 = 11.$

Do Exercise 8.

When we use the addition principle, we sometimes say that we "add th same number on both sides of the equation." This is also true for subtraction since we can express every subtraction as an addition. That is, since

$$a - c = b - c \quad \text{is equivalent to} \quad a + (-c) = b + (-c),$$

the addition principle tells us that we can "subtract the same number on bot sides of the equation."

EXAMPLE 6 Solve: $x + 5 = -7$.

We have

$$x + 5 = -7$$
$$x + 5 - 5 = -7 - 5 \quad \text{Using the addition principle: adding } -5 \text{ on both sides or subtracting 5 on both sides}$$
$$x + 0 = -12 \quad \text{Simplifying}$$
$$x = -12. \quad \text{Identity property of 0}$$

To check the answer, we substitute -12 in the original equation.

Check: $\quad x + 5 = -7$

$-12 + 5 \;?\; -7$

$-7 \quad$ TRUE

The solution of the original equation is -12.

9. Solve using the addition principle, subtracting 5 on both sides:

$x + 5 = -8.$

In Example 6, to get x alone, we used the addition principle and sub tracted 5 on both sides. This eliminated the 5 on the left. We started wit $x + 5 = -7$, and, using the addition principle, we found a simpler equatio $x = -12$ for which it was easy to *"see"* the solution. The equations $x + 5 = -$ and $x = -12$ are *equivalent.*

Do Exercise 9.

Now we use the addition principle to solve an equation that involves subtraction.

10. Solve: $t - 3 = 19$.

EXAMPLE 7 Solve: $a - 4 = 10$.

We have

$$a - 4 = 10$$
$$a - 4 + 4 = 10 + 4 \quad \text{Using the addition principle: adding 4 on both sides}$$
$$a + 0 = 14 \quad \text{Simplifying}$$
$$a = 14. \quad \text{Identity property of 0}$$

Check: $\quad a - 4 = 10$

$14 - 4 \;?\; 10$

$10 \quad$ TRUE

The solution is 14.

Answers on page A-7

Do Exercise 10.

XAMPLE 8 Solve: $-6.5 = y - 8.4$.

We have

$$-6.5 = y - 8.4$$

$$-6.5 + 8.4 = y - 8.4 + 8.4$$ Using the addition principle: adding 8.4 on both sides to eliminate −8.4 on the right

$$1.9 = y.$$

heck:

$-6.5 = y - 8.4$	
-6.5 ?	$1.9 - 8.4$
	-6.5 TRUE

he solution is 1.9.

Note that equations are reversible. That is, if $a = b$ is true, then $b = a$ s true. Thus when we solve $-6.5 = y - 8.4$, we can reverse it and solve $- 8.4 = -6.5$ if we wish.

o Exercises 11 and 12.

Solve.

11. $8.7 = n - 4.5$

12. $y + 17.4 = 10.9$

XAMPLE 9 Solve: $-\frac{2}{3} + x = \frac{5}{2}$.

We have

$$-\frac{2}{3} + x = \frac{5}{2}$$

$$\frac{2}{3} - \frac{2}{3} + x = \frac{2}{3} + \frac{5}{2}$$ Adding $\frac{2}{3}$ on both sides

$$x = \frac{2}{3} + \frac{5}{2}$$

$$x = \frac{2}{3} \cdot \frac{2}{2} + \frac{5}{2} \cdot \frac{3}{3}$$ Multiplying by 1 to obtain equivalent fraction expressions with the least common denominator 6

$$x = \frac{4}{6} + \frac{15}{6}$$

$$x = \frac{19}{6}.$$

heck:

$-\frac{2}{3} + x = \frac{5}{2}$	
$-\frac{2}{3} + \frac{19}{6}$?	$\frac{5}{2}$
$-\frac{4}{6} + \frac{19}{6}$	
$\frac{15}{6}$	
$\frac{5}{2}$	TRUE

he solution is $\frac{19}{6}$.

o Exercises 13 and 14.

Solve.

13. $x + \frac{1}{2} = -\frac{3}{2}$

14. $t - \frac{13}{4} = \frac{5}{8}$

Answers on page A-7

2.1 EXERCISE SET

For Extra Help

MathXL | MyMathLab | InterAct Math | Math Tutor Center | Digital Video Tutor CD 2 Videotape 3 | Student's Solutions Manual

a Determine whether the given number is a solution of the given equation.

1. 15; $x + 17 = 32$

2. 35; $t + 17 = 53$

3. 21; $x - 7 = 12$

4. 36; $a - 19 = 17$

5. -7; $6x = 54$

6. -9; $8y = -72$

7. 30; $\frac{x}{6} = 5$

8. 49; $\frac{y}{8} = 6$

9. 19; $5x + 7 = 107$

10. 9; $9x + 5 = 86$

11. -11; $7(y - 1) = 63$

12. -18; $x + 3 = 3 + x$

b Solve using the addition principle. Don't forget to check!

13. $x + 2 = 6$

Check: $x + 2 = 6$?

14. $y + 4 = 11$

Check: $y + 4 = 11$?

15. $x + 15 = -5$

Check: $x + 15 = -5$?

16. $t + 10 = 44$

Check: $t + 10 = 44$?

17. $x + 6 = -8$

Check: $x + 6 = -8$?

18. $z + 9 = -14$

19. $x + 16 = -2$

20. $m + 18 = -13$

21. $x - 9 = 6$

22. $x - 11 = 12$

23. $x - 7 = -21$

24. $x - 3 = -14$

25. $5 + t = 7$

26. $8 + y = 12$

27. $-7 + y = 13$

28. $-8 + y = 17$

29. $-3 + t = -9$

30. $-8 + t = -24$

31. $x + \frac{1}{2} = 7$

32. $24 = -\frac{7}{10} + r$

33. $12 = a - 7.9$

34. $2.8 + y = 11$

35. $r + \frac{1}{3} = \frac{8}{3}$

36. $t + \frac{3}{8} = \frac{5}{8}$

37. $m + \frac{5}{6} = -\frac{11}{12}$

38. $x + \frac{2}{3} = -\frac{5}{6}$

39. $x - \frac{5}{6} = \frac{7}{8}$

40. $y - \frac{3}{4} = \frac{5}{6}$

41. $-\frac{1}{5} + z = -\frac{1}{4}$

42. $-\frac{1}{8} + y = -\frac{3}{4}$

43. $7.4 = x + 2.3$

44. $8.4 = 5.7 + y$

45. $7.6 = x - 4.8$

46. $8.6 = x - 7.4$

47. $-9.7 = -4.7 + y$

48. $-7.8 = 2.8 + x$

49. $5\frac{1}{6} + x = 7$

50. $5\frac{1}{4} = 4\frac{2}{3} + x$

51. $q + \frac{1}{3} = -\frac{1}{7}$

52. $52\frac{3}{8} = -84 + x$

53. D~W~ Explain the difference between equivalent expressions and equivalent equations.

54. D~W~ When solving an equation using the addition principle, how do you determine which number to add or subtract on both sides of the equation?

SKILL MAINTENANCE

55. Add: $-3 + (-8)$. [1.3a]

56. Subtract: $-3 - (-8)$. [1.4a]

57. Multiply: $-\frac{2}{3} \cdot \frac{5}{8}$. [1.5a]

58. Divide: $-\frac{3}{7} \div \left(-\frac{9}{7}\right)$. [1.6c]

59. Divide: $\frac{2}{3} \div \left(-\frac{4}{9}\right)$. [1.6c]

60. Add: $-8.6 + 3.4$. [1.3a]

61. Subtract: $-\frac{2}{3} - \left(-\frac{5}{8}\right)$. [1.4a]

62. Multiply: $(-25.4)(-6.8)$. [1.5a]

Translate to an algebraic expression. [1.1b]

63. Jane had \$83 before paying x dollars for a pair of tennis shoes. How much does she have left?

64. Justin drove his S-10 pickup truck 65 mph for t hours. How far did he drive?

SYNTHESIS

Solve.

65. $-356.788 = -699.034 + t$

66. $-\frac{4}{5} + \frac{7}{10} = x - \frac{3}{4}$

67. $x + \frac{4}{5} = -\frac{2}{3} - \frac{4}{15}$

68. $8 - 25 = 8 + x - 21$

69. $16 + x - 22 = -16$

70. $x + x = x$

71. $x + 3 = 3 + x$

72. $x + 4 = 5 + x$

73. $-\frac{3}{2} + x = -\frac{5}{17} - \frac{3}{2}$

74. $|x| = 5$

75. $|x| + 6 = 19$

2.2 SOLVING EQUATIONS: THE MULTIPLICATION PRINCIPLE

Objective

a Solve equations using the multiplication principle.

1. Solve. Multiply on both sides.

$6x = 90$

2. Solve. Divide on both sides.

$4x = -7$

Answers on page A-7

a Using the Multiplication Principle

Suppose that $a = b$ is true, and we multiply a by some number c. We get the same number if we multiply b by c, because a and b are the same number.

THE MULTIPLICATION PRINCIPLE FOR EQUATIONS

For any real numbers a, b, and c, $c \neq 0$,

$$a = b \quad \text{is equivalent to} \quad a \cdot c = b \cdot c.$$

When using the multiplication principle, we sometimes say that we "multiply on both sides of the equation by the same number."

EXAMPLE 1 Solve: $5x = 70$.

To get x alone, we multiply by the *multiplicative inverse,* or *reciprocal* of 5. Then we get the *multiplicative identity* 1 times x, or $1 \cdot x$, which simplifies to x. This allows us to eliminate 5 on the left.

$5x = 70$	The reciprocal of 5 is $\frac{1}{5}$.
$\frac{1}{5} \cdot 5x = \frac{1}{5} \cdot 70$	Multiplying by $\frac{1}{5}$ to get $1 \cdot x$ and eliminate 5 on the left
$1 \cdot x = 14$	Simplifying
$x = 14$	Identity property of 1: $1 \cdot x = x$

Check:

$$\begin{array}{c|c} 5x & 70 \\ \hline 5 \cdot 14 \; ? & 70 \\ 70 & \end{array} \quad \text{TRUE}$$

The solution is 14.

The multiplication principle also tells us that we can "divide on both sides of the equation by a nonzero number." This is because division is the same as multiplying by a reciprocal. That is,

$$\frac{a}{c} = \frac{b}{c} \quad \text{is equivalent to} \quad a \cdot \frac{1}{c} = b \cdot \frac{1}{c}, \quad \text{when } c \neq 0.$$

In an expression like $5x$ in Example 1, the number 5 is called the **coefficient.** Example 1 could be done as follows, dividing on both sides by 5, the coefficient of x.

EXAMPLE 2 Solve: $5x = 70$.

$5x = 70$	
$\frac{5x}{5} = \frac{70}{5}$	Dividing by 5 on both sides
$1 \cdot x = 14$	Simplifying
$x = 14$	Identity property of 1

o Exercises 1 and 2 on the preceding page.

XAMPLE 3 Solve: $-4x = 92$.

We have

$$-4x = 92$$

$$\frac{-4x}{-4} = \frac{92}{-4} \quad \text{Using the multiplication principle. Dividing by } -4 \text{ on both sides is the same as multiplying by } -\tfrac{1}{4}.$$

$$1 \cdot x = -23 \quad \text{Simplifying}$$

$$x = -23. \quad \text{Identity property of 1}$$

heck:

$$-4x = 92$$
$$-4(-23) \;?\; 92$$
$$92 \quad \text{TRUE}$$

he solution is -23.

o Exercise 3.

XAMPLE 4 Solve: $-x = 9$.

We have

$$-x = 9$$

$$-1 \cdot x = 9 \quad \text{Using the property of } -1\text{: } -x = -1 \cdot x$$

$$\frac{-1 \cdot x}{-1} = \frac{9}{-1} \quad \text{Dividing by } -1 \text{ on both sides}$$

$$1 \cdot x = -9$$

$$x = -9.$$

eck:

$$-x = 9$$
$$-(-9) \;?\; 9$$
$$9 \quad \text{TRUE}$$

he solution is -9.

o Exercise 4.

We can also solve the equation $-x = 9$ by multiplying as follows.

XAMPLE 5 Solve: $-x = 9$.

We have

$$-x = 9$$

$$-1(-x) = -1 \cdot 9 \quad \text{Multiplying by } -1 \text{ on both sides}$$

$$-1 \cdot (-1) \cdot x = -9$$

$$1 \cdot x = -9$$

$$x = -9.$$

e solution is -9.

Exercise 5.

3. Solve: $-6x = 108$.

4. Solve: $-x = -10$.

5. Solve: $-x = -10$.

Answers on page A-7

6. Solve: $\frac{2}{3} = -\frac{5}{6}y$.

In practice, it is generally more convenient to divide on both sides of th equation if the coefficient of the variable is in decimal notation or is an inte ger. If the coefficient is in fraction notation, it is more convenient to multip by a reciprocal.

EXAMPLE 6 Solve: $\frac{3}{8} = -\frac{5}{4}x$.

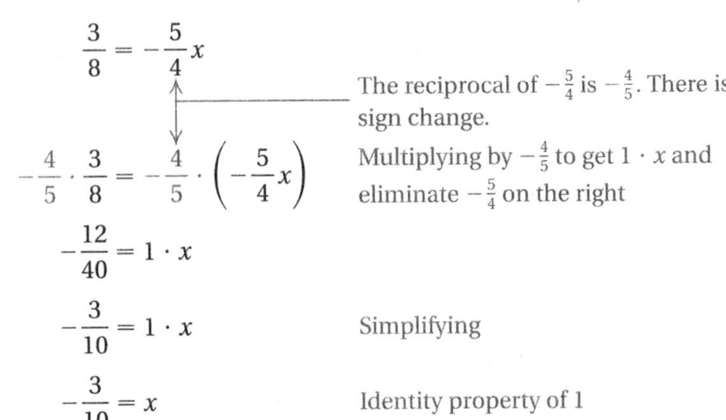

$$\frac{3}{8} = -\frac{5}{4}x$$

The reciprocal of $-\frac{5}{4}$ is $-\frac{4}{5}$. There is no sign change.

$$-\frac{4}{5} \cdot \frac{3}{8} = -\frac{4}{5} \cdot \left(-\frac{5}{4}x\right)$$ Multiplying by $-\frac{4}{5}$ to get $1 \cdot x$ and eliminate $-\frac{5}{4}$ on the right

$$-\frac{12}{40} = 1 \cdot x$$

$$-\frac{3}{10} = 1 \cdot x$$ Simplifying

$$-\frac{3}{10} = x$$ Identity property of 1

Solve.

7. $1.12x = 8736$

Check: $\frac{3}{8} = -\frac{5}{4}x$

$\frac{3}{8} \;?\; -\frac{5}{4}\left(-\frac{3}{10}\right)$

$\frac{3}{8}$ TRUE

The solution is $-\frac{3}{10}$.

Note that equations are reversible. That is, if $a = b$ is true, then $b =$ is true. Thus when we solve $\frac{3}{8} = -\frac{5}{4}x$, we can reverse it and solve $-\frac{5}{4}x = \frac{3}{8}$ we wish.

Do Exercise 6.

8. $6.3 = -2.1y$

EXAMPLE 7 Solve: $1.16y = 9744$.

$$1.16y = 9744$$

$$\frac{1.16y}{1.16} = \frac{9744}{1.16}$$ Dividing by 1.16 on both sides

$$y = \frac{9744}{1.16}$$

$$y = 8400$$ Using a calculator to divide

Check: $1.16y = 9744$

$1.16(8400) \;?\; 9744$

9744 TRUE

The solution is 8400.

Do Exercises 7 and 8.

Answers on page A-7

Now we use the multiplication principle to solve an equation that in-olves division.

9. Solve: $-14 = \frac{-y}{2}$.

XAMPLE 8 Solve: $\frac{-y}{9} = 14$.

$$\frac{-y}{9} = 14$$

$$9 \cdot \frac{-y}{9} = 9 \cdot 14 \qquad \text{Multiplying by 9 on both sides}$$

$$-y = 126$$

$$-1 \cdot (-y) = -1 \cdot 126 \qquad \text{Multiplying by } -1 \text{ on both sides}$$

$$y = -126$$

heck:

$$\frac{-y}{9} = 14$$

$$\frac{-(-126)}{9} \stackrel{?}{=} 14$$

$$\frac{126}{9}$$

$$14 \qquad \text{TRUE}$$

he solution is -126.

There are other ways to solve the equation in Example 8. One is by multi-lying by -9 on both sides as follows:

$$-9 \cdot \frac{-y}{9} = -9 \cdot 14$$

$$\frac{(-9)(-y)}{9} = -126$$

$$\frac{9y}{9} = -126$$

$$y = -126.$$

o *Exercise 9.*

Answer on page A-7

Study Tips

TIME MANAGEMENT (PART 1)

Time is the most critical factor in your success in learning mathematics. Have reasonable expectations about the time you need to study math. (See also the Study Tips on time management in Sections 5.2 and 5.6.)

- **Juggling time.** Working 40 hours per week and taking 12 credit hours is equivalent to working two full-time jobs. Can you handle such a load? Your ratio of number of work hours to number of credit hours should be about 40/3, 30/6, 20/9, 10/12, or 5/14.
- **A rule of thumb on study time.** Budget about 2–3 hours for homework and study per week for every hour of class time.

"You cannot increase the quality or quantity of your achievement or performance except to the degree in which you increase your ability to use time effectively."

Brian Tracy, motivational speaker

2.2 EXERCISE SET

For Extra Help

MathXL | MyMathLab | InterAct Math | Math Tutor Center | Digital Video Tutor CD 2 Videotape 3 | Student's Solutions Manual

a Solve using the multiplication principle. Don't forget to check!

1. $6x = 36$

Check: $6x = 36$?

2. $3x = 51$

Check: $3x = 51$?

3. $5x = 45$

Check: $5x = 45$?

4. $8x = 72$

Check: $8x = 72$?

5. $84 = 7x$

6. $63 = 9x$

7. $-x = 40$

8. $53 = -x$

9. $-x = -1$

10. $-47 = -t$

11. $7x = -49$

12. $8x = -56$

13. $-12x = 72$

14. $-15x = 105$

15. $-21x = -126$

16. $-13x = -104$

17. $\frac{t}{7} = -9$

18. $\frac{y}{-8} = 11$

19. $\frac{3}{4}x = 27$

20. $\frac{4}{5}x = 16$

21. $\frac{-t}{3} = 7$

22. $\frac{-x}{6} = 9$

23. $-\frac{m}{3} = \frac{1}{5}$

24. $\frac{1}{8} = -\frac{y}{5}$

25. $-\frac{3}{5}r = \frac{9}{10}$

26. $\frac{2}{5}y = -\frac{4}{15}$

27. $-\frac{3}{2}r = -\frac{27}{4}$

28. $-\frac{3}{8}x = -\frac{15}{16}$

9. $6.3x = 44.1$

30. $2.7y = 54$

31. $-3.1y = 21.7$

32. $-3.3y = 6.6$

3. $38.7m = 309.6$

34. $29.4m = 235.2$

35. $-\frac{2}{3}y = -10.6$

36. $-\frac{9}{7}y = 12.06$

7. $\frac{-x}{5} = 10$

38. $\frac{-x}{8} = -16$

39. $-\frac{t}{2} = 7$

40. $\frac{m}{-3} = 10$

1. D$_W$ When solving an equation using the multiplication principle, how do you determine by what number to multiply or divide on both sides of the equation?

42. D$_W$ Are the equations $x = 5$ and $x^2 = 25$ equivalent? Why or why not?

SKILL MAINTENANCE

ollect like terms. [1.7e]

3. $3x + 4x$

44. $6x + 5 - 7x$

5. $-4x + 11 - 6x + 18x$

46. $8y - 16y - 24y$

emove parentheses and simplify. [1.8b]

7. $3x - (4 + 2x)$

48. $2 - 5(x + 5)$

. $8y - 6(3y + 7)$

50. $-2a - 4(5a - 1)$

anslate to an algebraic expression. [1.1b]

. Patty drives her van for 8 hr at a speed of r mph. How far does she drive?

52. A triangle has a height of 10 meters and a base of b meters. What is the area of the triangle?

SYNTHESIS

lve.

. $-0.2344m = 2028.732$

54. $0 \cdot x = 0$

55. $0 \cdot x = 9$

. $4|x| = 48$

57. $2|x| = -12$

lve for x.

. $ax = 5a$

59. $3x = \frac{b}{a}$

60. $cx = a^2 + 1$

61. $\frac{a}{b}x = 4$

. A student makes a calculation and gets an answer of 22.5. On the last step, she multiplies by 0.3 when she should have divided by 0.3. What is the correct answer?

2.3 USING THE PRINCIPLES TOGETHER

Objectives

a Solve equations using both the addition and the multiplication principles.

b Solve equations in which like terms may need to be collected.

c Solve equations by first removing parentheses and collecting like terms; solve equations with no solutions and equations with an infinite number of solutions.

1. Solve: $9x + 6 = 51$.

Solve.

2. $8x - 4 = 28$

3. $-\frac{1}{2}x + 3 = 1$

Answers on page A-8

a Applying Both Principles

Consider the equation $3x + 4 = 13$. It is more complicated than those we discussed in the preceding two sections. In order to solve such an equation, we first isolate the x-term, $3x$, using the addition principle. Then we apply the multiplication principle to get x by itself.

EXAMPLE 1 Solve: $3x + 4 = 13$.

$$3x + 4 = 13$$

$$3x + 4 - 4 = 13 - 4 \quad \text{Using the addition principle: subtracting 4 on both sides}$$

First isolate the x-term. → $3x = 9$ Simplifying

$$\frac{3x}{3} = \frac{9}{3} \quad \text{Using the multiplication principle: dividing by 3 on both sides}$$

Then isolate x. → $x = 3$ Simplifying

Check:

$$3x + 4 = 13$$

$$3 \cdot 3 + 4 \ ? \ 13$$

$$9 + 4$$

$$13 \quad \text{TRUE}$$

We use the rules for order of operations to carry out the check. We find the product $3 \cdot 3$. Then we add 4.

The solution is 3.

Do Exercise 1.

EXAMPLE 2 Solve: $-5x - 6 = 16$.

$$-5x - 6 = 16$$

$$-5x - 6 + 6 = 16 + 6 \quad \text{Adding 6 on both sides}$$

$$-5x = 22$$

$$\frac{-5x}{-5} = \frac{22}{-5} \quad \text{Dividing by } -5 \text{ on both sides}$$

$$x = -\frac{22}{5}, \text{ or } -4\frac{2}{5} \quad \text{Simplifying}$$

Check:

$$-5x - 6 = 16$$

$$-5\left(-\frac{22}{5}\right) - 6 \ ? \ 16$$

$$22 - 6$$

$$16 \quad \text{TRUE}$$

The solution is $-\frac{22}{5}$.

Do Exercises 2 and 3.

XAMPLE 3 Solve: $45 - t = 13$.

$$45 - t = 13$$
$$-45 + 45 - t = -45 + 13 \quad \text{Adding } -45 \text{ on both sides}$$
$$-t = -32$$
$$-1(-t) = -1(-32) \quad \text{Multiplying by } -1 \text{ on both sides}$$
$$t = 32$$

he number 32 checks and is the solution.

o Exercise 4.

4. Solve: $-18 - m = -57$.

XAMPLE 4 Solve: $16.3 - 7.2y = -8.18$.

$$16.3 - 7.2y = -8.18$$
$$-16.3 + 16.3 - 7.2y = -16.3 + (-8.18) \quad \text{Adding } -16.3 \text{ on both sides}$$
$$-7.2y = -24.48$$
$$\frac{-7.2y}{-7.2} = \frac{-24.48}{-7.2} \quad \text{Dividing by } -7.2 \text{ on both sides}$$
$$y = 3.4$$

neck:

$$\begin{array}{r|l} 16.3 - 7.2y & = -8.18 \\ \hline 16.3 - 7.2(3.4) & ?\ -8.18 \\ 16.3 - 24.48 & \\ -8.18 & \quad \text{TRUE} \end{array}$$

he solution is 3.4.

Exercises 5 and 6.

Solve.

5. $-4 - 8x = 8$

6. $41.68 = 4.7 - 8.6y$

Collecting Like Terms

there are like terms on one side of the equation, we collect them before ing the addition or the multiplication principle.

XAMPLE 5 Solve: $3x + 4x = -14$.

$$3x + 4x = -14$$
$$7x = -14 \quad \text{Collecting like terms}$$
$$\frac{7x}{7} = \frac{-14}{7} \quad \text{Dividing by 7 on both sides}$$
$$x = -2$$

e number -2 checks, so the solution is -2.

Exercises 7 and 8.

Solve.

7. $4x + 3x = -21$

8. $x - 0.09x = 728$

If there are like terms on opposite sides of the equation, we get them the same side by using the addition principle. Then we collect them. In her words, we get all terms with a variable on one side and all numbers the other.

Answers on page A-8

Solve.

9. $7y + 5 = 2y + 10$

10. $5 - 2y = 3y - 5$

EXAMPLE 6 Solve: $2x - 2 = -3x + 3$.

$$
\begin{aligned}
2x - 2 &= -3x + 3 \\
2x - 2 + 2 &= -3x + 3 + 2 && \text{Adding 2} \\
2x &= -3x + 5 && \text{Collecting like terms} \\
2x + 3x &= -3x + 3x + 5 && \text{Adding } 3x \\
5x &= 5 && \text{Simplifying} \\
\frac{5x}{5} &= \frac{5}{5} && \text{Dividing by 5} \\
x &= 1 && \text{Simplifying}
\end{aligned}
$$

Check:

$$
\begin{array}{r|l}
\multicolumn{2}{c}{2x - 2 = -3x + 3} \\
\hline
2 \cdot 1 - 2 \ ? & -3 \cdot 1 + 3 \\
2 - 2 & -3 + 3 \\
0 & 0
\end{array}
$$

Substituting in the original equation

TRUE

The solution is 1.

Do Exercises 9 and 10.

In Example 6, we used the addition principle to get all terms with a var-
able on one side and all numbers on the other side. Then we collected lik
terms and proceeded as before. If there are like terms on one side at the ou
set, they should be collected before proceeding.

Solve.

11. $7x - 17 + 2x = 2 - 8x + 15$

12. $3x - 15 = 5x + 2 - 4x$

EXAMPLE 7 Solve: $6x + 5 - 7x = 10 - 4x + 3$.

$$
\begin{aligned}
6x + 5 - 7x &= 10 - 4x + 3 \\
-x + 5 &= 13 - 4x && \text{Collecting like terms} \\
4x - x + 5 &= 13 - 4x + 4x && \text{Adding } 4x \text{ to get all terms with a variable on one side} \\
3x + 5 &= 13 && \text{Simplifying; that is, collecting like terms} \\
3x + 5 - 5 &= 13 - 5 && \text{Subtracting 5} \\
3x &= 8 && \text{Simplifying} \\
\frac{3x}{3} &= \frac{8}{3} && \text{Dividing by 3} \\
x &= \frac{8}{3} && \text{Simplifying}
\end{aligned}
$$

The number $\frac{8}{3}$ checks, so it is the solution.

Do Exercises 11 and 12.

CLEARING FRACTIONS AND DECIMALS

In general, equations are easier to solve if they do not contain fractions
decimals. Consider, for example,

$$\frac{1}{2}x + 5 = \frac{3}{4} \quad \text{and} \quad 2.3x + 7 = 5.4.$$

Answers on page A-8

f we multiply by 4 on both sides of the first equation and by 10 on both sides f the second equation, we have

$$4\left(\frac{1}{2}x + 5\right) = 4 \cdot \frac{3}{4} \quad \text{and} \quad 10(2.3x + 7) = 10 \cdot 5.4$$

$$4 \cdot \frac{1}{2}x + 4 \cdot 5 = 4 \cdot \frac{3}{4} \quad \text{and} \quad 10 \cdot 2.3x + 10 \cdot 7 = 10 \cdot 5.4$$

$$2x + 20 = 3 \quad \text{and} \quad 23x + 70 = 54.$$

he first equation has been "cleared of fractions" and the second equation has een "cleared of decimals." Both resulting equations are equivalent to the riginal equations and are easier to solve. *It is your choice* whether to clear actions or decimals, but doing so often eases computations.

The easiest way to clear an equation of fractions is to multiply *every term n both sides* by the **least common multiple of all the denominators.**

XAMPLE 8 Solve: $\frac{2}{3}x - \frac{1}{6} + \frac{1}{2}x = \frac{7}{6} + 2x$.

The number 6 is the least common multiple of all the denominators. We ultiply by 6 on both sides.

$$6\left(\frac{2}{3}x - \frac{1}{6} + \frac{1}{2}x\right) = 6\left(\frac{7}{6} + 2x\right) \qquad \text{Multiplying by 6 on both sides}$$

$$\cdot \frac{2}{3}x - 6 \cdot \frac{1}{6} + 6 \cdot \frac{1}{2}x = 6 \cdot \frac{7}{6} + 6 \cdot 2x \qquad \text{Using the distributive law (\textit{Caution}! Be sure to multiply \textit{all} the terms by 6.)}$$

$$4x - 1 + 3x = 7 + 12x \qquad \text{Simplifying. Note that the fractions are cleared.}$$

$$7x - 1 = 7 + 12x \qquad \text{Collecting like terms}$$

$$7x - 1 - 12x = 7 + 12x - 12x \qquad \text{Subtracting } 12x$$

$$-5x - 1 = 7 \qquad \text{Collecting like terms}$$

$$-5x - 1 + 1 = 7 + 1 \qquad \text{Adding 1}$$

$$-5x = 8 \qquad \text{Collecting like terms}$$

$$\frac{-5x}{-5} = \frac{8}{-5} \qquad \text{Dividing by } -5$$

$$x = -\frac{8}{5}$$

heck: $\frac{2}{3}x - \frac{1}{6} + \frac{1}{2}x = \frac{7}{6} + 2x$

$\frac{2}{3}\left(-\frac{8}{5}\right) - \frac{1}{6} + \frac{1}{2}\left(-\frac{8}{5}\right)$	? $\frac{7}{6} + 2\left(-\frac{8}{5}\right)$
$-\frac{16}{15} - \frac{1}{6} - \frac{8}{10}$	$\frac{7}{6} - \frac{16}{5}$
$-\frac{32}{30} - \frac{5}{30} - \frac{24}{30}$	$\frac{35}{30} - \frac{96}{30}$
$\frac{-32 - 5 - 24}{30}$	$-\frac{61}{30}$
$-\frac{61}{30}$	

TRUE

13. Solve: $\frac{7}{8}x - \frac{1}{4} + \frac{1}{2}x = \frac{3}{4} + x.$

14. Solve: $41.68 = 4.7 - 8.6y.$

Solve.

15. $2(2y + 3) = 14$

16. $5(3x - 2) = 35$

Answers on page A-8

The solution is $-\frac{8}{5}$.

Do Exercise 13.

To illustrate clearing decimals, we repeat Example 4, but this time w clear the equation of decimals first. Compare both methods.

To clear an equation of decimals, we count the greatest number of deci mal places in any one number. If the greatest number of decimal places is 1 we multiply every term on both sides by 10; if it is 2, we multiply by 100; an so on.

EXAMPLE 9 Solve: $16.3 - 7.2y = -8.18.$

The greatest number of decimal places in any one number is *two*. Multi plying by 100, which has *two* 0's, will clear all decimals.

$$100(16.3 - 7.2y) = 100(-8.18) \quad \text{Multiplying by 100 on both sides}$$

$$100(16.3) - 100(7.2y) = 100(-8.18) \quad \text{Using the distributive law}$$

$$1630 - 720y = -818 \quad \text{Simplifying}$$

$$1630 - 720y - 1630 = -818 - 1630 \quad \text{Subtracting 1630}$$

$$-720y = -2448 \quad \text{Collecting like terms}$$

$$\frac{-720y}{-720} = \frac{-2448}{-720} \quad \text{Dividing by } -720$$

$$y = \frac{17}{5}, \text{ or } 3.4$$

The number $\frac{17}{5}$, or 3.4, checks, as shown in Example 4, so it is the solution.

Do Exercise 14.

C Equations Containing Parentheses

To solve certain kinds of equations that contain parentheses, we first use th distributive laws to remove the parentheses. Then we proceed as before.

EXAMPLE 10 Solve: $8x = 2(12 - 2x).$

$$8x = 2(12 - 2x)$$

$$8x = 24 - 4x \quad \text{Using the distributive laws to multiply and remove parentheses}$$

$$8x + 4x = 24 - 4x + 4x \quad \text{Adding } 4x \text{ to get all the } x\text{-terms on one side}$$

$$12x = 24 \quad \text{Collecting like terms}$$

$$\frac{12x}{12} = \frac{24}{12} \quad \text{Dividing by 12}$$

$$x = 2$$

The number 2 checks, so the solution is 2.

Do Exercises 15 and 16.

Here is a procedure for solving the types of equation discussed in this section.

AN EQUATION-SOLVING PROCEDURE

1. Multiply on both sides to clear the equation of fractions or decimals. (This is optional, but it can ease computations.)
2. If parentheses occur, multiply to remove them using the *distributive laws.*
3. Collect like terms on each side, if necessary.
4. Get all terms with variables on one side and all numbers (constant terms) on the other side, using the *addition principle.*
5. Collect like terms again, if necessary.
6. Multiply or divide to solve for the variable, using the *multiplication principle.*
7. Check all possible solutions in the original equation.

EXAMPLE 11 Solve: $2 - 5(x + 5) = 3(x - 2) - 1$.

$2 - 5(x + 5) = 3(x - 2) - 1$	
$2 - 5x - 25 = 3x - 6 - 1$	Using the distributive laws to multiply and remove parentheses
$-5x - 23 = 3x - 7$	Collecting like terms
$-5x - 23 + 5x = 3x - 7 + 5x$	Adding $5x$
$-23 = 8x - 7$	Collecting like terms
$-23 + 7 = 8x - 7 + 7$	Adding 7
$-16 = 8x$	Collecting like terms
$\frac{-16}{8} = \frac{8x}{8}$	Dividing by 8
$-2 = x$	

Check:

$2 - 5(x + 5)$	$= 3(x - 2) - 1$	
$2 - 5(-2 + 5)$	? $3(-2 - 2) - 1$	
$2 - 5(3)$	$3(-4) - 1$	
$2 - 15$	$-12 - 1$	
-13	-13	TRUE

The solution is -2.

Do Exercises 17 and 18.

EQUATIONS WITH INFINITELY MANY SOLUTIONS

The types of equations we have considered thus far in Sections 2.1–2.3 have all had exactly one solution. We now look at two other possibilities.

Consider

$$3 + x = x + 3.$$

Let's explore the solutions in Margin Exercises 19–22.

Do Exercises 19–22.

Solve.

17. $3(7 + 2x) = 30 + 7(x - 1)$

18. $4(3 + 5x) - 4 = 3 + 2(x - 2)$

Determine whether the given number is a solution of the given equation.

19. 10; $3 + x = x + 3$

20. -7; $3 + x = x + 3$

21. $\frac{1}{2}$; $3 + x = x + 3$

22. 0; $3 + x = x + 3$

Answers on page A-8

Determine whether the given number is a solution of the given equation.

23. 10; $3 + x = x + 8$

24. -7; $3 + x = x + 8$

25. $\frac{1}{2}$; $3 + x = x + 8$

26. 0; $3 + x = x + 8$

Solve.

27. $30 + 5(x + 3) = -3 + 5x + 48$

28. $2x + 7(x - 4) = 13 + 9x$

Answers on page A-8

We know by the commutative law of addition that this equation holds fo[r] any replacement of x with a real number. (See Section 1.7.) We have confirme[d] some of these solutions in Margin Exercises 19–22. Suppose we try to solv[e] this equation using the addition principle:

$$3 + x = x + 3$$
$$-x + 3 + x = -x + x + 3 \quad \text{Adding } -x$$
$$3 = 3. \quad \text{TRUE}$$

We end with a true equation. The original equation holds for all real-numbe[r] replacements. Every real number is a solution. Thus the number of solution[s] is **infinite.**

EXAMPLE 12 Solve: $7x - 17 = 4 + 7(x - 3)$.

$$7x - 17 = 4 + 7(x - 3)$$
$$7x - 17 = 4 + 7x - 21 \quad \text{Using the distributive law to multiply and remove parentheses}$$
$$7x - 17 = 7x - 17 \quad \text{Collecting like terms}$$
$$-7x + 7x - 17 = -7x + 7x - 17 \quad \text{Adding } -7x$$
$$-17 = -17 \quad \text{TRUE}$$

Every real number is a solution. There are infinitely many solutions.

EQUATIONS WITH NO SOLUTION

Now consider

$$3 + x = x + 8.$$

Let's explore the solutions in Margin Exercises 23–26.

Do Exercises 23–26.

None of the replacements in Margin Exercises 23–26 is a solution of th[e] given equation. In fact, there are no solutions. Let's try to solve this equatio[n] using the addition principle:

$$3 + x = x + 8$$
$$-x + 3 + x = -x + x + 8 \quad \text{Adding } -x$$
$$3 = 8. \quad \text{FALSE}$$

We end with a false equation. The original equation is false for all real[-]number replacements. Thus it has **no** solutions.

EXAMPLE 13 Solve: $3x + 4(x + 2) = 11 + 7x$.

$$3x + 4(x + 2) = 11 + 7x$$
$$3x + 4x + 8 = 11 + 7x \quad \text{Using the distributive law to multiply and remove parentheses}$$
$$7x + 8 = 11 + 7x \quad \text{Collecting like terms}$$
$$7x + 8 - 7x = 11 + 7x - 7x \quad \text{Subtracting } 7x$$
$$8 = 11 \quad \text{FALSE}$$

There are no solutions.

Do Exercises 27 and 28.

The following is a guideline for solving linear equations of the types that we have considered in Sections 2.1–2.3.

RESULTING EQUATION	NUMBER OF SOLUTIONS	SOLUTION(S)
$x = a$, where a is a real number	One	The number a
A true equation such as $3 = 3$, $-11 = -11$, or $0 = 0$	Infinitely many	Every real number is a solution.
A false equation such as $3 = 8$, $-4 = 5$, or $0 = -5$	Zero	There are no solutions.

CALCULATOR CORNER

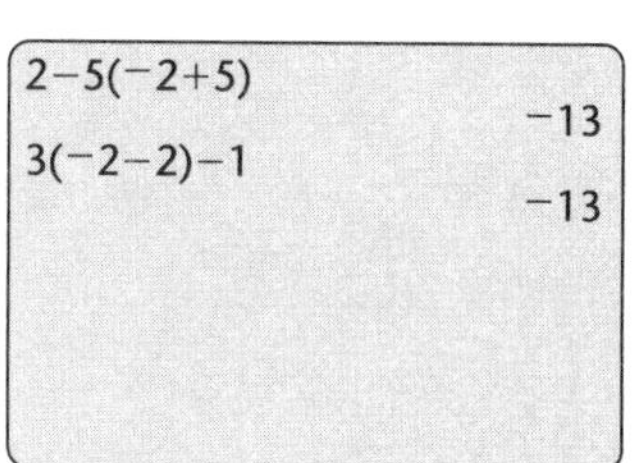

Checking Possible Solutions To check the possible solutions of an equation on a calculator, we can substitute and carry out the calculations on each side of the equation just as we do when we check by hand. To check the possible solution −2 in Example 11, for instance, we first substitute −2 for *x* in the expression on the left side of the equation. We press 2 − 5 ((−) 2 + 5) ENTER. We get −13. Next, we substitute −2 for *x* in the expression on the right side of the equation. We then press 3 ((−) 2 − 2) − 1 ENTER. Again we get −13. Since the two sides of the equation have the same value when *x* is −2, we know that −2 is the solution of the equation.

A table can also be used to check the possible solutions of an equation. First, we enter the left side and the right side of the equation on the Y = or equation editor screen. To do this, we first press Y=. If an expression for Y1 is currently entered, we place the cursor on it and press CLEAR to delete it. We do the same for any other entries that are present.

Next, we position the cursor to the right of Y1 = and enter the left side of the equation by pressing 2 − 5 (X,T,Θ,n + 5). Then we position the cursor beside Y2 = and enter the right side of the equation by pressing 3 (X,T,Θ,n − 2) − 1. Now we press 2ND TBLSET to display the Table Setup screen. (TBLSET is the second operation associated with the WINDOW key.) On the Indpnt line, we position the cursor on "Ask" and press ENTER to set up a table in ASK mode. (The settings for TblStart and ΔTbl are irrelevant in ASK mode.)

Now we press 2ND TABLE to display the table. (TABLE is the second operation associated with the GRAPH key.) We then enter the possible solution, −2, by pressing (−) 2 ENTER. We see that Y1 = −13 = Y2 for this value of *x*. This confirms that the left and right sides of the equation have the same value for *x* = −2, so −2 is the solution of the equation.

```
Plot1  Plot2  Plot3
\Y1 = 2−5(X+5)
\Y2 = 3(X−2)−1
\Y3 =
\Y4 =
\Y5 =
\Y6 =
\Y7 =
```

```
TABLE SETUP
  TblStart=1
  ΔTbl=1
Indpnt: Auto  Ask
Depend: Auto  Ask
```

X	Y1	Y2
−2	−13	−13

X =

Exercises:

1. Use substitution to check the solutions found in Examples 6, 7, and 10.
2. Use a table set in ASK mode to check the solutions found in Examples 6, 7, and 10.

2.3 EXERCISE SET

For Extra Help

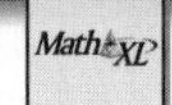

MathXL | MyMathLab | InterAct Math | Math Tutor Center | Digital Video Tutor CD 2 Videotape 3 | Student's Solutions Manual

a Solve. Don't forget to check!

1. $5x + 6 = 31$

Check: $5x + 6 = 31$?

2. $7x + 6 = 13$

Check: $7x + 6 = 13$?

3. $8x + 4 = 68$

Check: $8x + 4 = 68$?

4. $4y + 10 = 46$

Check: $4y + 10 = 46$?

5. $4x - 6 = 34$

6. $5y - 2 = 53$

7. $3x - 9 = 33$

8. $4x - 19 = 5$

9. $7x + 2 = -54$

10. $5x + 4 = -41$

11. $-45 = 3 + 6y$

12. $-91 = 9t + 8$

13. $-4x + 7 = 35$

14. $-5x - 7 = 108$

15. $-8x - 24 = -29\frac{1}{3}$

16. $\frac{3}{2}x - 24 = -36$

b Solve.

17. $5x + 7x = 72$

Check: $5x + 7x = 72$?

18. $8x + 3x = 55$

Check: $8x + 3x = 55$?

19. $8x + 7x = 60$

Check: $8x + 7x = 60$?

20. $8x + 5x = 104$

Check: $8x + 5x = 104$?

21. $4x + 3x = 42$

22. $7x + 18x = 125$

23. $-6y - 3y = 27$

24. $-5y - 7y = 144$

25. $-7y - 8y = -15$

26. $-10y - 3y = -39$

27. $x + \frac{1}{3}x = 8$

28. $x + \frac{1}{4}x = 10$

29. $10.2y - 7.3y = -58$

30. $6.8y - 2.4y = -88$

31. $8y - 35 = 3y$

32. $4x - 6 = 6x$

33. $8x - 1 = 23 - 4x$

34. $5y - 2 = 28 - y$

35. $2x - 1 = 4 + x$

36. $4 - 3x = 6 - 7x$

37. $6x + 3 = 2x + 11$

38. $14 - 6a = -2a + 3$

39. $5 - 2x = 3x - 7x + 25$

40. $-7z + 2z - 3z - 7 = 17$

41. $4 + 3x - 6 = 3x + 2 - x$

42. $5 + 4x - 7 = 4x - 2 - x$

43. $4y - 4 + y + 24 = 6y + 20 - 4y$

44. $5y - 7 + y = 7y + 21 - 5y$

olve. Clear fractions or decimals first.

45. $\frac{7}{2}x + \frac{1}{2}x = 3x + \frac{3}{2} + \frac{5}{2}x$

46. $\frac{7}{8}x - \frac{1}{4} + \frac{3}{4}x = \frac{1}{16} + x$

47. $\frac{2}{3} + \frac{1}{4}t = \frac{1}{3}$

48. $-\frac{3}{2} + x = -\frac{5}{6} - \frac{4}{3}$

49. $\frac{2}{3} + 3y = 5y - \frac{2}{15}$

50. $\frac{1}{2} + 4m = 3m - \frac{5}{2}$

51. $\frac{5}{3} + \frac{2}{3}x = \frac{25}{12} + \frac{5}{4}x + \frac{3}{4}$

52. $1 - \frac{2}{3}y = \frac{9}{5} - \frac{y}{5} + \frac{3}{5}$

53. $2.1x + 45.2 = 3.2 - 8.4x$

54. $0.96y - 0.79 = 0.21y + 0.46$

55. $1.03 - 0.62x = 0.71 - 0.22x$

56. $1.7t + 8 - 1.62t = 0.4t - 0.32 + 8$

57. $\frac{2}{7}x - \frac{1}{2}x = \frac{3}{4}x + 1$

58. $\frac{5}{16}y + \frac{3}{8}y = 2 + \frac{1}{4}y$

C Solve.

59. $3(2y - 3) = 27$

60. $8(3x + 2) = 30$

61. $40 = 5(3x + 2)$

62. $9 = 3(5x - 2)$

63. $-23 + y = y + 25$

64. $17 - t = -t + 68$

65. $-23 + x = x - 23$

66. $y - \frac{2}{3} = -\frac{2}{3} + y$

67. $2(3 + 4m) - 9 = 45$

68. $5x + 5(4x - 1) = 20$

69. $5r - (2r + 8) = 16$

70. $6b - (3b + 8) = 16$

71. $6 - 2(3x - 1) = 2$

72. $10 - 3(2x - 1) = 1$

73. $5x + 5 - 7x = 15 - 12x + 10x - 10$

74. $3 - 7x + 10x - 14 = 9 - 6x + 9x - 20$

75. $22x - 5 - 15x + 3 = 10x - 4 - 3x + 11$

76. $11x - 6 - 4x + 1 = 9x - 8 - 2x + 12$

77. $5(d + 4) = 7(d - 2)$

78. $3(t - 2) = 9(t + 2)$

79. $8(2t + 1) = 4(7t + 7)$

80. $7(5x - 2) = 6(6x - 1)$

81. $3(r - 6) + 2 = 4(r + 2) - 21$

82. $5(t + 3) + 9 = 3(t - 2) + 6$

83. $19 - (2x + 3) = 2(x + 3) + x$

84. $13 - (2c + 2) = 2(c + 2) + 3c$

85. $2[4 - 2(3 - x)] - 1 = 4[2(4x - 3) + 7] - 25$

86. $5[3(7 - t) - 4(8 + 2t)] - 20 = -6[2(6 + 3t) - 4]$

87. $11 - 4(x + 1) - 3 = 11 + 2(4 - 2x) - 16$

88. $6(2x - 1) - 12 = 7 + 12(x - 1)$

89. $22x - 1 - 12x = 5(2x - 1) + 4$

90. $2 + 14x - 9 = 7(2x + 1) - 14$

91. $0.7(3x + 6) = 1.1 - (x + 2)$

92. $0.9(2x + 8) = 20 - (x + 5)$

93. **DW** What procedure would you follow to solve an equation like $0.23x + \frac{17}{3} = -0.8 + \frac{3}{4}x$? Could your procedure be streamlined? If so, how?

94. **DW** You are trying to explain to a classmate how equations can arise with infinitely many solutions and with no solutions. Give such an explanation. Does having no solution mean that 0 is a solution? Explain.

SKILL MAINTENANCE

95. Divide: $-22.1 \div 3.4$. [1.6c]

96. Multiply: $-22.1(3.4)$. [1.5a]

97. Factor: $7x - 21 - 14y$. [1.7d]

98. Factor: $8y - 88x + 8$. [1.7d]

Simplify.

99. $-3 + 2(-5)^2(-3) - 7$ [1.8d]

100. $3x + 2[4 - 5(2x - 1)]$ [1.8c]

101. $23(2x - 4) - 15(10 - 3x)$ [1.8b]

102. $256 \div 64 \div 4^2$ [1.8d]

SYNTHESIS

Solve.

103. $\frac{2}{3}\left(\frac{7}{8} - 4x\right) - \frac{5}{8} = \frac{3}{8}$

104. $\frac{1}{4}(8y + 4) - 17 = -\frac{1}{2}(4y - 8)$

105. $\frac{4 - 3x}{7} = \frac{2 + 5x}{49} - \frac{x}{14}$

106. The width of a rectangle is 5 ft, its length is $(3x + 2)$ ft, and its area is 75 ft^2. Find x.

2.4 FORMULAS

Objectives

a Evaluate a formula.

b Solve a formula for a specified letter.

1. **Storm Distance.** Suppose that it takes the sound of thunder 14 sec to reach you. How far away is the storm?

2. **Socks from Cotton.** Referring to Example 2, find the number of socks that can be made from 65 bales of cotton.

Answers on page A-8

a Evaluating Formulas

A **formula** is a "recipe" for doing a certain type of calculation. Formulas ar often given as equations. When we replace the variables in an equation wit numbers and calculate the result, we are **evaluating** the formula. We di some evaluating in Section 1.1.

Let's consider another example. A formula that has to do with weather $M = \frac{1}{5}t$. You see a flash of lightning. After a few seconds you hear the thund associated with that flash. How far away was the lightning?

Your distance from the storm is M miles. You can find that distance b counting the number of seconds t that it takes the sound of the thunder t reach you and then multiplying by $\frac{1}{5}$.

EXAMPLE 1 *Storm Distance.* Consider the formula $M = \frac{1}{5}t$. It takes 10 se for the sound of thunder to reach you after you have seen a flash of lightnin How far away is the storm?

We substitute 10 for t and calculate M:

$$M = \frac{1}{5}t = \frac{1}{5}(10) = 2.$$

The storm is 2 mi away.

EXAMPLE 2 *Socks from Cotton.* Consider the formula $S = 4321x$, where is the number of socks of normal size that can be produced from x bales cotton. You see a shipment of 300 bales of cotton taken off a ship. How man socks can be made from the cotton?

Source: *Country Woman Magazine*

We substitute 300 for x and calculate S:

$$S = 4321x = 4321(300) = 1{,}296{,}300.$$

Thus, 1,296,300 socks can be made from 300 bales of cotton.

Do Exercises 1 and 2.

EXAMPLE 3 *Distance, Rate, and Time.* The distance d that a car will travel at a rate, or speed, r in time t is given by

$$d = rt.$$

A car travels at 75 miles per hour (mph) for 4.5 hr. How far will it travel?

We substitute 75 for r and 4.5 for t and calculate d:

$$d = rt = (75)(4.5) = 337.5 \text{ mi.}$$

The car will travel 337.5 mi.

Do Exercise 3.

3. Distance, Rate, and Time. A car travels at 55 mph for 6.2 hr. How far will it travel?

b Solving Formulas

Refer to Example 2. Suppose a clothing company wants to produce S socks and needs to know how many bales of cotton to order. If this calculation is to be repeated many times, it might be helpful to first solve the formula for x:

$$S = 4321x$$

$$\frac{S}{4321} = x. \qquad \text{Dividing by 4321}$$

Then we can substitute a number for S and calculate x. For example, if the number of socks S to be produced is 432,100, then

$$x = \frac{S}{4321} = \frac{432{,}100}{4321} = 100.$$

The company would need to order 100 bales of cotton.

EXAMPLE 4 Solve for t: $M = \frac{1}{5}t$.

$$M = \frac{1}{5}t \qquad \text{We want this letter alone.}$$

$$5 \cdot M = 5 \cdot \frac{1}{5}t \qquad \text{Multiplying by 5 on both sides}$$

$$5M = t$$

For $M = 2$ in Example 4, $t = 5M = 5(2)$, or 10.

EXAMPLE 5 *Distance, Rate, and Time.* Solve for t: $d = rt$.

$$d = rt \qquad \text{We want this letter alone.}$$

$$\frac{d}{r} = \frac{rt}{r} \qquad \text{Dividing by } r$$

$$\frac{d}{r} = \frac{r}{r} \cdot t$$

$$\frac{d}{r} = t \qquad \text{Simplifying}$$

Do Exercises 4–6.

4. Solve for q: $B = \frac{1}{3}q$.

5. Distance, Rate, and Time. Solve for r: $d = rt$.

6. Electricity. Solve for I: $E = IR$. (This formula relates voltage E, current I, and resistance R.)

Answers on page A-8

Solve for x.

7. $y = x + 5$

8. $y = x - 7$

9. $y = x - b$

10. Solve for y: $9y = 5x$.

11. Solve for p: $ap = bq$.

12. Solve for x: $y = mx + b$.

13. Solve for Q: $tQ - p = a$.

Answers on page A-8

EXAMPLE 6 Solve for x: $y = x + 3$.

$y = x + 3$	We want this letter alone.
$y - 3 = x + 3 - 3$	Subtracting 3
$y - 3 = x$	Simplifying

EXAMPLE 7 Solve for x: $y = x - a$.

$y = x - a$	We want this letter alone.
$y + a = x - a + a$	Adding a
$y + a = x$	Simplifying

Do Exercises 7–9.

EXAMPLE 8 Solve for y: $6y = 3x$.

$6y = 3x$	We want this letter alone.
$\frac{6y}{6} = \frac{3x}{6}$	Dividing by 6
$y = \frac{1}{2}x$	Simplifying

EXAMPLE 9 Solve for y: $by = ax$.

$by = ax$	We want this letter alone.
$\frac{by}{b} = \frac{ax}{b}$	Dividing by b
$y = \frac{ax}{b}$	Simplifying

Do Exercises 10 and 11.

EXAMPLE 10 Solve for x: $ax + b = c$.

$ax + b = c$	We want this letter alone.
$ax + b - b = c - b$	Subtracting b
$ax = c - b$	Simplifying
$\frac{ax}{a} = \frac{c - b}{a}$	Dividing by a
$x = \frac{c - b}{a}$	Simplifying

Do Exercises 12 and 13.

To solve a formula for a given letter, identify the letter and:

1. Multiply on both sides to clear fractions or decimals, if that is needed.
2. Collect like terms on each side, if necessary.
3. Get all terms with the letter to be solved for on one side of the equation and all other terms on the other side.
4. Collect like terms again, if necessary.
5. Solve for the letter in question.

EXAMPLE 11 *Circumference.* Solve for r: $C = 2\pi r$. This is a formula for the circumference C of a circle of radius r.

$C = 2\pi r$ We want this letter alone.

$\dfrac{C}{2\pi} = \dfrac{2\pi r}{2\pi}$ Dividing by 2π

$\dfrac{C}{2\pi} = r$

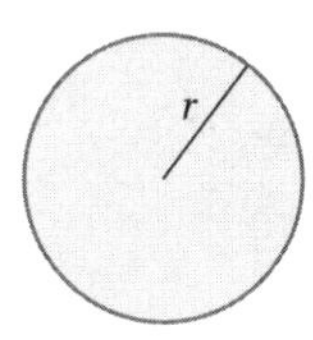

EXAMPLE 12 *Averages.* Solve for a: $A = \dfrac{a + b + c}{3}$. This is a formula for the average A of three numbers a, b, and c.

$A = \dfrac{a + b + c}{3}$ We want the letter a alone.

$3 \cdot A = 3 \cdot \dfrac{a + b + c}{3}$ Multiplying by 3 on both sides

$3A = a + b + c$ Simplifying

$3A - b - c = a$ Subtracting b and c

Do Exercises 14 and 15.

14. Circumference. Solve for D:

$$C = \pi D.$$

(This is a formula for the circumference C of a circle of diameter D.)

15. Averages. Solve for c:

$$A = \frac{a + b + c + d}{4}.$$

Answers on page A-8

Study Tips

HIGHLIGHTING

Reading and highlighting a section before your instructor lectures on it allows you to maximize your learning and understanding during the lecture.

- **Try to keep one section ahead of your syllabus.** If you study ahead of your lectures, you can concentrate on what is being explained in them, rather than trying to write everything down. You can then take notes only of special points or of questions related to what is happening in class.
- **Highlight important points.** You are probably used to highlighting key points as you study. If that works for you, continue to do so. But you will notice many design features throughout this book that already highlight important points. Thus you may not need to highlight as much as you generally do.
- **Highlight points that you do not understand.** Use a unique mark to indicate trouble spots that can lead to questions to be asked during class, in a tutoring session, or when calling or contacting the AW Math Tutor Center.

2.4 EXERCISE SET

For Extra Help

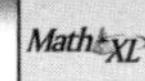

MathXL | MyMathLab | InterAct Math | Math Tutor Center | Digital Video Tutor CD 2 Videotape 3 | Student's Solutions Manual

a, **b** Solve.

1. *Furnace Output.* The formula

$$B = 30a$$

is used in New England to estimate the minimum furnace output B, in Btu's, for a modern house with a square feet of flooring.

Source: U.S. Department of Energy

a) Determine the minimum furnace output for a 1900-ft^2 modern house.
b) Solve for a. That is, solve $B = 30a$ for a.

2. *Furnace Output.* The formula

$$B = 50a$$

is used in New England to estimate the minimum furnace output B, in Btu's, for an old, poorly insulated house with a square feet of flooring.

Source: U.S. Department of Energy

a) Determine the minimum furnace output for a 3200-ft^2 old, poorly insulated house.
b) Solve for a. That is, solve $B = 50a$ for a.

3. *Distance from a Storm.* The formula

$$M = \tfrac{1}{5}t$$

can be used to determine how far M, in miles, you are from lightning when its thunder takes t seconds to reach your ears.

a) It takes 8 sec for the sound of thunder to reach you after you have seen the lightning. How far away is the storm?
b) Solve for t.

4. *Electrical Power.* The power rating P, in watts, of an electrical appliance is determined by

$$P = I \cdot V,$$

where I is the current, in amperes, and V is measured in volts.

a) A kitchen requires 30 amps of current and the voltage in the house is 115 volts. What is the wattage of the kitchen?
b) Solve for I; for V.

5. *College Enrollment.* At many colleges, the number of "full-time-equivalent" students f is given by

$$f = \frac{n}{15},$$

where n is the total number of credits for which students have enrolled in a given semester.

a) Determine the number of full-time-equivalent students on a campus in which students registered for a total of 21,345 credits.
b) Solve for n.

6. *Surface Area of a Cube.* The surface area A of a cube with side s is given by

$$A = 6s^2.$$

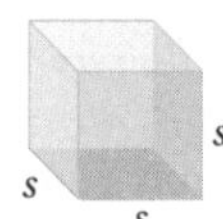

a) Find the surface area of a cube with sides of 3 in.
b) Solve for s^2.

7. *Calorie Density.* The calorie density D, in calories per ounce, of a food that contains c calories and weighs w ounces is given by

$$D = \frac{c}{w}.$$

Eight ounces of fat-free milk contains 84 calories. Find the calorie density of fat-free milk.

Source: *Nutrition Action Healthletter*, March 2000, p. 9. Center for Science in the Public Interest, Suite 300; 1875 Connecticut Ave NW, Washington, D.C. 20008.

8. *Wavelength of a Musical Note.* The wavelength w, in meters per cycle, of a musical note is given by

$$w = \frac{r}{f},$$

where r is the speed of the sound, in meters per second, and f is the frequency, in cycles per second. The speed of sound in air is 344 m/sec. What is the wavelength of a note whose frequency in air is 24 cycles per second?

9. *Size of a League Schedule.* When all n teams in a league play every other team twice, a total of N games are played, where

$$N = n^2 - n.$$

A soccer league has 7 teams and all teams play each other twice. How many games are played?

10. *Size of a League Schedule.* When all n teams in a league play every other team twice, a total of N games are played, where

$$N = n^2 - n.$$

A basketball league has 11 teams and all teams play each other twice. How many games are played?

b Solve for the indicated letter.

1. $y = 5x$, for x

12. $d = 55t$, for t

13. $a = bc$, for c

4. $y = mx$, for x

15. $y = 13 + x$, for x

16. $y = x - \frac{2}{3}$, for x

7. $y = x + b$, for x

18. $y = x - A$, for x

19. $y = 5 - x$, for x

0. $y = 10 - x$, for x

21. $y = a - x$, for x

22. $y = q - x$, for x

3. $8y = 5x$, for y

24. $10y = -5x$, for y

25. $By = Ax$, for x

26. $By = Ax$, for y

27. $W = mt + b$, for t

28. $W = mt - b$, for t

29. $y = bx + c$, for x

30. $y = bx - c$, for x

31. $A = \dfrac{a + b + c}{3}$, for b

32. $A = \dfrac{a + b + c}{3}$, for c

33. $A = at + b$, for t

34. $S = rx + s$, for x

35. *Area of a Parallelogram:*

$A = bh$, for h

(Area A, base b, height h)

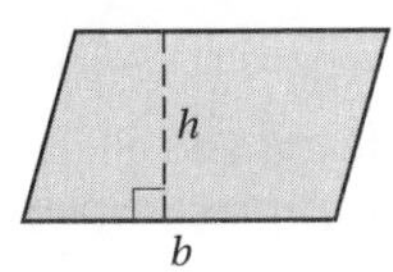

36. *Distance, Rate, Time:*

$d = rt$, for r

(Distance d, speed r, time t)

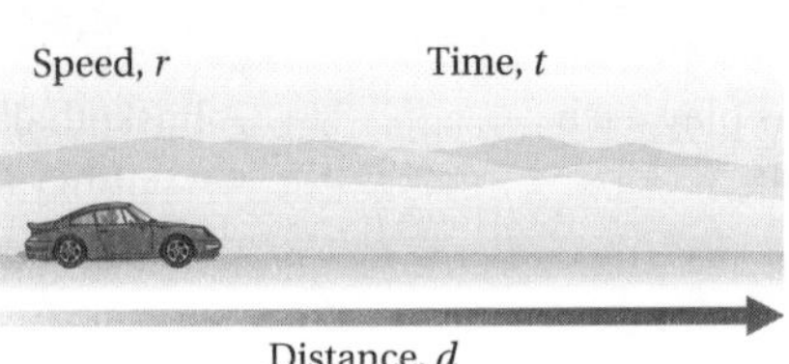

37. *Perimeter of a Rectangle:*

$P = 2l + 2w$, for w

(Perimeter P, length l, width w)

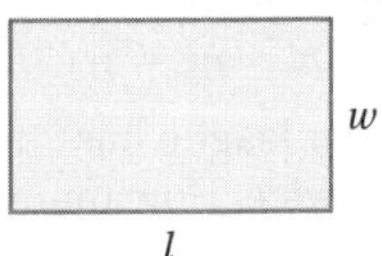

38. *Area of a Circle:*

$A = \pi r^2$, for r^2

(Area A, radius r)

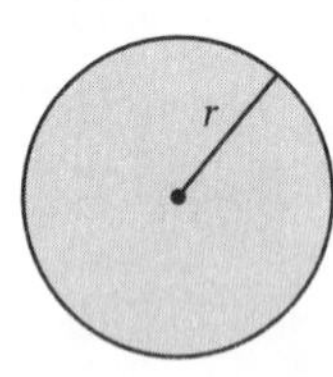

39. *Average of Two Numbers:*

$A = \dfrac{a + b}{2}$, for a

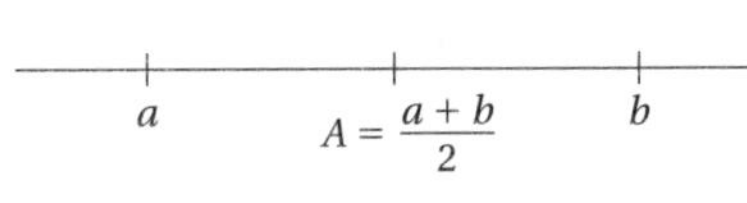

40. *Area of a Triangle:*

$A = \dfrac{1}{2}bh$, for b

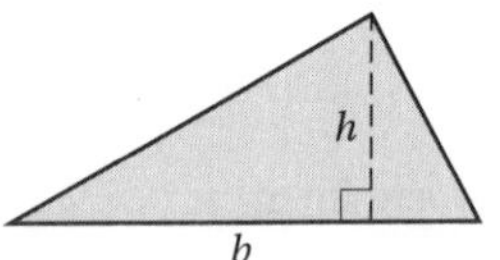

41. *Force:*

$F = ma$, for a

(Force F, mass m, acceleration a)

42. *Simple Interest:*

$I = Prt$, for P

(Interest I, principal P, interest rate r, time t)

43. *Relativity:*

$E = mc^2$, for c^2

(Energy E, mass m, speed of light c)

44. $Q = \dfrac{p - q}{2}$, for p

45. $Ax + By = c$, for x

46. $Ax + By = c$, for y

47. $v = \dfrac{3k}{t}$, for t

48. $P = \dfrac{ab}{c}$, for c

9. DW Devise an application in which it would be useful to solve the equation $d = rt$ for r. (See Exercise 36.)

50. DW The equations

$$P = 2l + 2w \quad \text{and} \quad w = \frac{P}{2} - l$$

are equivalent formulas involving the perimeter P, the length l, and the width w of a rectangle. (See Exercise 37.) Devise a problem for which the second of the two formulas would be more useful.

SKILL MAINTENANCE

1. Convert to decimal notation: $\frac{23}{25}$. [R.3a]

52. Add: $-23 + (-67)$. [1.3a]

3. Add: $0.082 + (-9.407)$. [1.3a]

54. Subtract: $-23 - (-67)$. [1.4a]

5. Subtract: $-45.8 - (-32.6)$. [1.4a]

56. Remove parentheses and simplify: [1.8b]

$$4a - 8b - 5(5a - 4b).$$

onvert to decimal notation. [R.4a]

7. 3.1%

58. 67.1%

9. Add: $-\frac{2}{3} + \frac{5}{6}$. [1.3a]

60. Subtract: $-\frac{2}{3} - \frac{5}{6}$. [1.4a]

SYNTHESIS

1. *Female Caloric Needs.* The number of calories K needed each day by a moderately active woman who weighs w pounds, is h inches tall, and is a years old can be estimated by the formula

$$K = 917 + 6(w + h - a).$$

Source: Parker, M., *She Does Math.* Mathematical Association of America, p. 96

a) Elaine is moderately active, weighs 120 lb, is 67 in. tall, and is 23 yr old. What are her caloric needs?
b) Solve the formula for a; for h; for w.

62. *Male Caloric Needs.* The number of calories K needed each day by a moderately active man who weighs w kilograms, is h centimeters tall, and is a years old can be estimated by the formula

$$K = 19.18w + 7h - 9.52a + 92.4.$$

Source: Parker, M., *She Does Math.* Mathematical Association of America, p. 96

a) Marv is moderately active, weighs 97 kg, is 185 cm tall, and is 55 yr old. What are his caloric needs?
b) Solve the formula for a; for h; for w.

olve.

3. $H = \frac{2}{a - b}$, for b; for a

64. $P = 4m + 7mn$, for m

5. In $A = lw$, l and w both double. What is the effect on A?

66. In $P = 2a + 2b$, P doubles. Do a and b necessarily both double?

7. In $A = \frac{1}{2}bh$, b increases by 4 units and h does not change. What happens to A?

68. Solve for F: $D = \frac{1}{E + F}$.

2.5 APPLICATIONS OF PERCENT

Objective

a Solve applied problems involving percent.

Translate to an equation. Do not solve.

1. 13% of 80 is what number?

2. What number is 60% of 70?

3. 43 is 20% of what number?

4. 110% of what number is 30?

5. 16 is what percent of 80?

6. What percent of 94 is 10.5?

Answers on page A-8

a Translating and Solving

Many applied problems involve percent. Here we begin to see how equation solving can enhance our problem-solving skills. For background on the manipulative skills of percent notation, see Section R.4.

In solving percent problems, we first *translate* the problem to an equation. Then we *solve* the equation using the techniques discussed in Sections 2.1–2.3. The key words in the translation are as follows.

KEY WORDS IN PERCENT TRANSLATIONS

"**Of**" translates to "·" or "×".

"**Is**" translates to "=".

"**What number**" translates to any letter.

% translates to "$\times \frac{1}{100}$" or "× 0.01".

EXAMPLE 1 Translate:

28% of 5 is what number?
↓ ↓ ↓ ↓ ↓
$28\% \cdot 5 = a$ — This is a percent equation.

EXAMPLE 2 Translate:

45% of what number is 28?
↓ ↓ ↓ ↓ ↓
$45\% \times b = 28$

EXAMPLE 3 Translate:

What percent of 90 is 7?
↓ ↓ ↓ ↓ ↓
$n \cdot 90 = 7$

Do Exercises 1–6.

Percent problems are actually of three different types. Although the method we present does *not* require that you be able to identify which type we are studying, it is helpful to know them.

We know that

15 is 25% of 60, or

$15 = 25\% \times 60.$

We can think of this as:

Amount = Percent number × Base.

Each of the three types of percent problems depends on which of the ree pieces of information is missing.

. Finding the ***amount*** (the result of taking the percent)

Example: What number is 25% of 60?

Translation: $y = 25\% \cdot 60$

. Finding the ***base*** (the number you are taking the percent of)

Example: 15 is 25% of what number?

Translation: $15 = 25\% \cdot y$

. Finding the ***percent number*** (the percent itself)

Example: 15 is what percent of 60?

Translation: $15 = y \cdot 60$

NDING THE AMOUNT

KAMPLE 4 What number is 11% of 49?

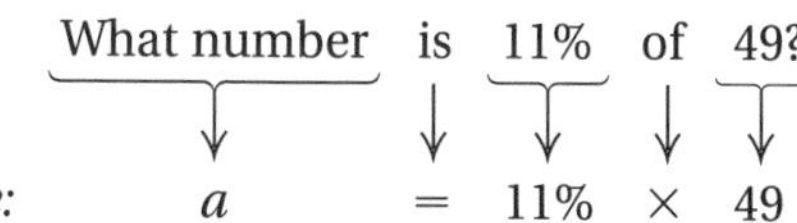

Translate: $a = 11\% \times 49$

lve: The letter is by itself. To solve the equation, we need only convert 11% decimal notation and multiply:

$$a = 11\% \times 49 = 0.11 \times 49 = 5.39.$$

ius, 5.39 is 11% of 49. The answer is 5.39.

Exercise 7.

NDING THE BASE

KAMPLE 5 3 is 16% of what number?

3 is 16% of what number?

Translate: $3 = 16\% \times b$

$3 = 0.16 \times b$ Converting 16% to decimal notation

lve: In this case, the letter is not by itself. To solve the equation, we divide 0.16 on both sides:

$$3 = 0.16 \times b$$

$$\frac{3}{0.16} = \frac{0.16 \times b}{0.16} \quad \text{Dividing by 0.16}$$

$$18.75 = b. \quad \text{Simplifying}$$

e answer is 18.75.

Exercise 8.

7. What number is 2.4% of 80?

8. 25.3 is 22% of what number?

Answers on page A-8

Study Tips

USING THE SUPPLEMENTS

The new mathematical skills and concepts presented in the lectures will be of increased value to you if you begin the homework assignment as soon as possible after the lecture. Then if you still have difficulty with any of the exercises, you have time to access supplementary resources such as:

- *Student's Solutions Manual*
- Videotapes
- Digital Video Tutor
- MathXL Tutorials on CD
- AW Math Tutor Center
- MyMathLab
- MathXL
- Work It Out! Chapter Test Video on CD

9. What percent of $50 is $18?

10. **Areas of Alaska and Arizona.** The area of Arizona is 19% of the area of Alaska. The area of Alaska is 586,400 mi^2. What is the area of Arizona?

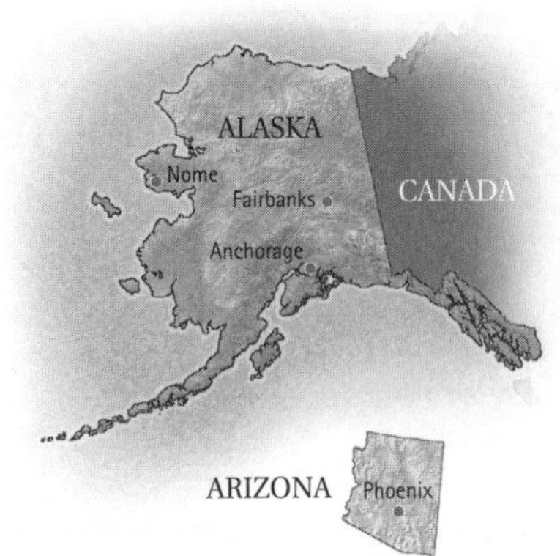

BEST PRICE
PowerShot
4.0
MEGA PIXELS
NOW ONLY!
$349 99

Answers on page A-8

FINDING THE PERCENT NUMBER

In solving these problems, you *must* remember to convert to percent notatic after you have solved the equation.

EXAMPLE 6 $32 is what percent of $50?

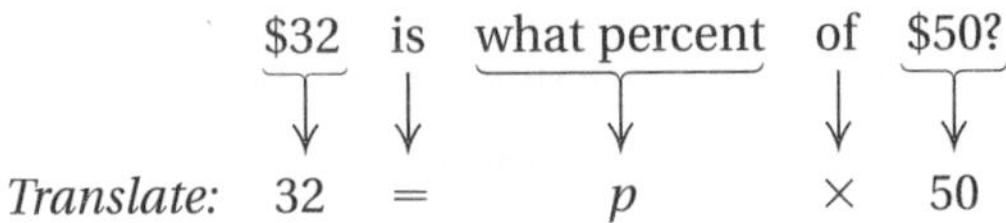

Translate: $32 = p \times 50$

Solve: To solve the equation, we divide by 50 on both sides and convert tl answer to percent notation:

$$32 = p \times 50$$

$$\frac{32}{50} = \frac{p \times 50}{50} \quad \text{Dividing by 50}$$

$$0.64 = p$$

$$64\% = p. \quad \text{Converting to percent notation}$$

Thus, $32 is 64% of $50. The answer is 64%.

Do Exercise 9.

EXAMPLE 7 *Coronary Heart Disease.* In 2001, there were about 206 m lion people age 20 or older in the United States. About 6.4% of them had cor nary heart disease. How many had coronary heart disease?

Source: American Heart Association

To solve the problem, we first reword and then translate. We let a = tl number of people age 20 or older in the United States with coronary hea disease.

Rewording: What number is 6.4% of 206?

Translate: $a = 6.4\% \times 206$

Solve: The letter is by itself. To solve the equation, we need only convert 6.4 to decimal notation and multiply:

$$a = 6.4\% \times 206 = 0.064 \times 206 = 13.184.$$

Thus, 13.184 million is 6.4% of 206 million, so in 2001 about 13.184 millic people age 20 or older in the United States had coronary heart disease.

Do Exercise 10.

EXAMPLE 8 *Digital Camera.* At one time, Best Buy had a Canon Powe Shot digital camera on sale for $349.99. This was 87.5% of the list price. Wh was the list price?

To solve the problem, we first reword and then translate. We l L = the list price.

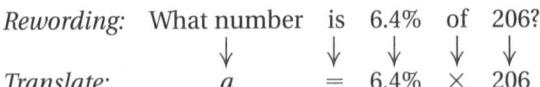

Rewording: $349.99 is 87.5% of what number?

Translate: $349.99 = 87.5\% \times L$

olve: To solve the equation, we convert 87.5% to decimal notation and di-
ide by 0.875 on both sides:

$$349.99 = 87.5\% \times L$$

$$349.99 = 0.875 \times L \qquad \text{Converting to decimal notation}$$

$$\frac{349.99}{0.875} = \frac{0.875 \times L}{0.875} \qquad \text{Dividing by 0.875}$$

$$399.99 \approx L. \qquad \text{Simplifying using a calculator and rounding to the nearest cent}$$

he list price was about $399.99.

o Exercise 11.

XAMPLE 9 *Apple iPod.* An Apple iPod 20.0 GB digital audio player was
n sale at Best Buy for $249.99, decreased from a normal list price of $299.99.
hat was the percent of decrease?

To solve the problem, we must first determine the amount of de-
ease from the original price:

$$\underbrace{\text{Original price}} \;\text{minus}\; \underbrace{\text{Sale price}} = \underbrace{\text{Decrease}}$$

$$\$299.99 \quad - \quad \$249.99 \quad = \quad \$50.00.$$

sing the $50 decrease, we reword and translate. We let $p =$ the per-
nt of decrease. We want to know, "What percent of the *original* price
$50?"

Rewording: $50 is what percent of $299.99?

Translate: $50 = p \times 299.99$

lve: To solve the equation, we divide by 299.99 on both sides and
nvert the answer to percent notation:

$$50 = p \times 299.99$$

$$\frac{50}{299.99} = \frac{p \times 299.99}{299.99} \qquad \text{Dividing by 299.99}$$

$$0.167 \approx p \qquad \text{Simplifying and converting to percent notation}$$

$$16.7\% = p.$$

us the percent of decrease was about 16.7%.

Exercise 12.

11. Population of Nevada. The population of Nevada was 2.2 million in 2002. This was 183.3% of its population in 1990. What was the population in 1990?

Source: U.S. Bureau of the Census

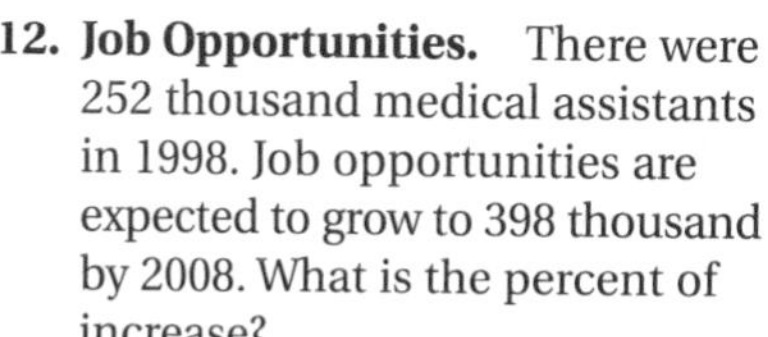

12. Job Opportunities. There were 252 thousand medical assistants in 1998. Job opportunities are expected to grow to 398 thousand by 2008. What is the percent of increase?

Source: *Handbook of U.S. Labor Statistics*

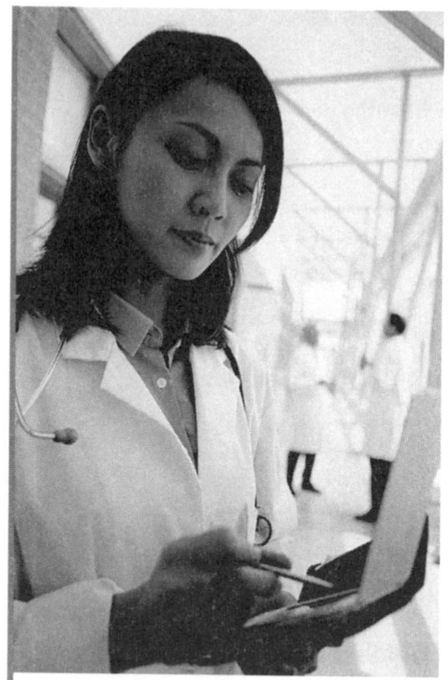

Answers on page A-8

2.5 EXERCISE SET

For Extra Help

MathXL | MyMathLab | InterAct Math | Math Tutor Center | Digital Video Tutor CD 2 Videotape 3 | Student's Solutions Manual

a Solve.

1. What percent of 180 is 36?

2. What percent of 76 is 19?

3. 45 is 30% of what number?

4. 20.4 is 24% of what number?

5. What number is 65% of 840?

6. What number is 50% of 50? (This was a $500.00 question on the "Who Wants To Be a Millionaire?" television quiz show.)

7. 30 is what percent of 125?

8. 57 is what percent of 300?

9. 12% of what number is 0.3?

10. 7 is 175% of what number?

11. 2 is what percent of 40?

12. 40 is 2% of what number?

13. What percent of 68 is 17?

14. What percent of 150 is 39?

15. What number is 35% of 240?

16. What number is 1% of one million?

17. What percent of 125 is 30?

18. What percent of 60 is 75?

19. What percent of 300 is 48?

20. What percent of 70 is 70?

21. 14 is 30% of what number?

22. 54 is 24% of what number?

23. What number is 2% of 40?

24. What number is 40% of 2?

25. 0.8 is 16% of what number?

26. 25 is what percent of 50?

27. 54 is 135% of what number?

28. 8 is 2% of what number?

Costs of Owning a Dog. The American Pet Products Manufacturers Association estimates that the total cost of owning a dog for its lifetime is $6600. The following circle graph shows the relative costs of raising a dog from birth to death.

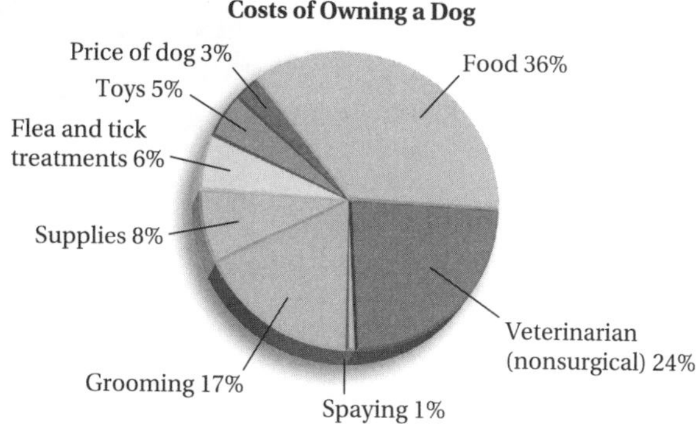

Source: The American Pet Products Manufacturers Association

Complete the following table of costs of owning a dog for its lifetime.

	EXPENSE ITEM	COST		EXPENSE ITEM	COST
29.	Price of dog		**30.**	Food	
31.	Veterinarian		**32.**	Grooming	
33.	Supplies		**34.**	Flea and tick treatments	

35. *Car Sales.* In 2002, there were 8,317,954 retail sales of cars in the United States. Of that total, 2,268,093 were imported. Japan manufactured 1,003,745 of those imports, and Germany manufactured 564,910 of them. What percent of the imported cars were manufactured in Japan? in Germany?

Source: Ward's Communications, *World Almanac and Book of Facts* 2004

36. *Truck Sales.* In 2002, 17,118,000 new motor vehicles were sold in the United States. Of these, 9,036,000 were trucks. Imported trucks made up 1,061,000 of those sales. What percent of the motor vehicles sold were trucks? What percent of the truck sales were imported trucks?

Source: U.S. Bureau of Economic Analysis

37. *Batting Average.* At one point in a recent season, Sammy Sosa of the Chicago Cubs had 193 hits. His batting average was 0.320, or 32%. That is, of the total number of at-bats, 32% were hits. How many at-bats did he have?

Source: Major League Baseball

38. *Pass Completions.* At one point in a recent season, Peyton Manning of the Indianapolis Colts had completed 357 passes. This was 62.5% of his attempts. How many attempts did he make?

Source: National Football League

39. *Student Loans.* To finance her community college education, Sarah takes out a Stafford loan for $6500. After a year, Sarah decides to pay off the interest, which is 3% of $6500. How much will she pay?

40. *Student Loans.* Paul takes out a federal Stafford loan for $5400. After a year, Paul decides to pay off the interest, which is 4.5% of $5400. How much will he pay?

41. *Tipping.* Leon left a $4 tip for a meal that cost $25.

a) What percent of the cost of the meal was the tip?
b) What was the total cost of the meal including the tip?

42. *Tipping.* Selena left a $12.76 tip for a meal that cost $58.

a) What percent of the cost of the meal was the tip?
b) What was the total cost of the meal including the tip?

43. *Tipping.* Leon left a 15% tip for a meal that cost $25.

a) How much was the tip?
b) What was the total cost of the meal including the tip?

44. *Tipping.* Sam, Selena, Rachel, and Clement left a 15% tip for a meal that cost $58.

a) How much was the tip?
b) What was the total cost of the meal including the tip?

45. *Tipping.* Leon left a 15% tip of $4.32 for a meal.

a) What was the cost of the meal before the tip?
b) What was the total cost of the meal including the tip?

46. *Tipping.* Selena left a 15% tip of $8.40 for a meal.

a) What was the cost of the meal before the tip?
b) What was the total cost of the meal including the tip

47. In a medical study of a group of pregnant women with "poor" diets, 16 of the women, or 8%, had babies who were in good or excellent health. How many women were in the original study?

48. In a medical study of a group of pregnant women with "good-to-excellent" diets, 285 of the women, or 95%, had babies who were in good or excellent health. How many women were in the original study?

49. *Body Fat.* The author of this text exercises regularly at a local YMCA that recently offered a body-fat percentage test to its members. The device used measures the passage of a very low voltage of electricity through the body. The author's body-fat percentage was found to be 16.5% and he weighs 191 lb. What part, in pounds, of his body weight is fat?

50. *Junk Mail.* The U.S. Postal Service reports that we open and read 78% of the junk mail that we receive. A sports instructional videotape company sends out 10,500 advertising brochures.

Source: U.S. Postal Service

a) How many of the brochures can it expect to be opened and read?
b) The company sells videos to 189 of the people who receive the brochure. What percent of the 10,500 people who receive the brochure buy the video?

ife Insurance Rates for Smokers and Nonsmokers. The data in the following table illustrate how yearly rates (premiums) for a 500,000 term life insurance policy are increased for smokers. Complete the table by finding the missing numbers. Round to he nearest percent and dollar.

YPICAL INSURANCE PREMIUMS (IN DOLLARS)

	AGE	RATE FOR NONSMOKER	RATE FOR SMOKER	RATE INCREASE	PERCENT OF INCREASE FOR SMOKER
	35	\$255	\$680	\$425	167%
51.	40	\$335	\$990		
52.	45	\$485			208%
53.	50	\$735			198%
54.	55	\$945	\$3330		
55.	60	\$1510	\$5445		
56.	65	\$2545			242%

ource: Faith Financial Planners, Inc.

7. D$_W$ The 80/20 rule is commonly quoted in the field of business. It asserts that 80% of your results will come from 20% of your activities. Discuss how this might affect you as a student and as an employee.

58. D$_W$ Comment on the following quote by Yogi Berra, a famous Major League Hall of Fame baseball player: "Ninety percent of hitting is mental. The other half is physical."

SKILL MAINTENANCE

ompute. [R.3b]

9. $9.076 \div 0.05$

60. 9.076×0.05

61. $1.089 + 10.89 + 0.1089$

62. $1000.23 - 156.0893$

emove parentheses and simplify. [1.8b]

3. $-5a + 3c - 2(c - 3a)$

64. $4(x - 2y) - (y - 3x)$

dd. [1.3a]

5. $-6.5 + 2.6$

66. $-\frac{3}{8} + (-5) + \frac{1}{4} + (-1)$

ll in the blank with a word that makes the statement true.

7. To simplify the calculation $18 - 24 \div 3 - 48 \div (-4)$, do all the ________ calculations first, and then the ________ calculations.

68. To simplify the calculation $18 - 24^3 \div 48 \div (-4)^2$, do all the ________ calculations first, and then the ________ calculations, and finally the ________ calculation.

SYNTHESIS

. It has been determined that at the age of 15, a boy has reached 96.1% of his final adult height. Jaraan is 6 ft 4 in. at the age of 15. What will his final adult height be?

70. It has been determined that at the age of 10, a girl has reached 84.4% of her final adult height. Dana is 4 ft 8 in. at the age of 10. What will her final adult height be?

2.6 APPLICATIONS AND PROBLEM SOLVING

Objective

a Solve applied problems by translating to equations.

a Five Steps for Solving Problems

We have discussed many new equation-solving tools in this chapter and use them for applications and problem solving. Here we consider a five-step strategy that can be very helpful in solving problems.

FIVE STEPS FOR PROBLEM SOLVING IN ALGEBRA

1. *Familiarize* yourself with the problem situation.
2. *Translate* the problem to an equation.
3. *Solve* the equation.
4. *Check* the answer in the original problem.
5. *State* the answer to the problem clearly.

Of the five steps, the most important is probably the first one: becomin familiar with the problem situation. The table below lists some hints fo familiarization.

TO FAMILIARIZE YOURSELF WITH A PROBLEM

- If a problem is given in words, read it carefully. Reread the problem, perhaps aloud. Try to verbalize the problem as if you were explaining it to someone else.
- Choose a variable (or variables) to represent the unknown and clearly state what the variable represents. Be descriptive! For example, let L = the length, d = the distance, and so on.
- Make a drawing and label it with known information, using specific units if given. Also, indicate unknown information.
- Find further information. Look up formulas or definitions with which you are not familiar. (Geometric formulas appear on the inside back cover of this text.) Consult a reference librarian or the Internet.
- Create a table that lists all the information you have available. Look for patterns that may help in the translation to an equation.
- Think of a possible answer and check the guess. Note the manner in which the guess is checked.

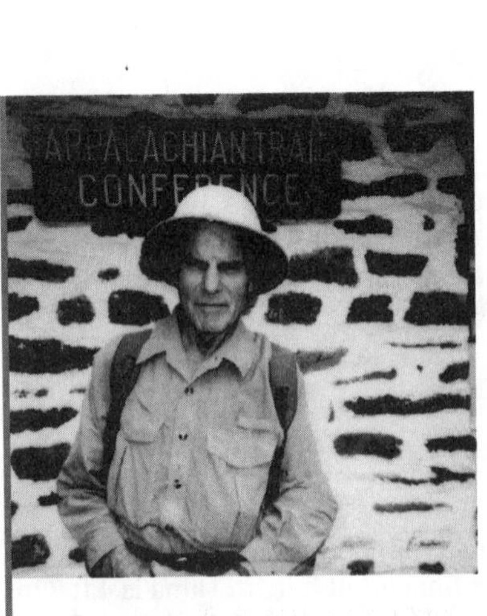

EXAMPLE 1 *Hiking.* In 1998, at age 79, Earl Shaffer became the olde person to through-hike all 2100 miles of the Appalachian Trail—fro Springer Mountain, Georgia, to Mount Katahdin, Maine. Shaffer throug hiked the trail three times, in 1948 (Georgia to Maine), in 1965 (Maine to Geo gia), and in 1998 (Georgia to Maine) near the 50th anniversary of his first hik At one point in 1998, Shaffer stood atop Big Walker Mountain, Virginia, whi is three times as far from the northern end as from the southern end. How f was Shaffer from each end of the trail?

Source: Appalachian Trail Conference; Earl Shaffer Foundation

1. **Familiarize.** Let's consider a drawing.

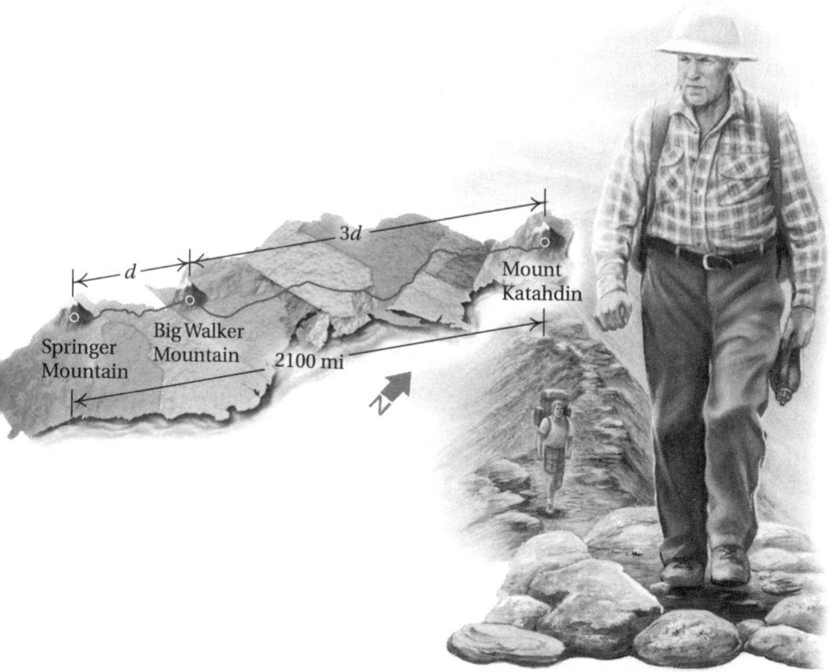

To become familiar with the problem, let's guess a possible distance that Shaffer stood from Springer Mountain—say, 600 mi. Three times 600 mi is 1800 mi. Since 600 mi + 1800 mi = 2400 mi and 2400 mi is greater than 2100 mi, we see that our guess is too large. Rather than guess again, let's use the skills we have obtained in the ability to solve equations. We let

$d =$ the distance, in miles, to the southern end, and

$3d =$ the distance, in miles, to the northern end.

(We could also let $x =$ the distance to the northern end and $\frac{1}{3}x =$ the distance to the southern end.)

2. **Translate.** From the drawing, we see that the lengths of the two parts of the trail must add up to 2100 mi. This leads to our translation.

Distance to southern end	plus	Distance to northern end	is	2100 mi
↓	↓	↓	↓	↓
d	$+$	$3d$	$=$	2100

3. **Solve.** We solve the equation:

$$d + 3d = 2100$$

$$4d = 2100 \quad \text{Collecting like terms}$$

$$\frac{4d}{4} = \frac{2100}{4} \quad \text{Dividing by 4}$$

$$d = 525.$$

4. **Check.** As expected, d is less than 600 mi. If $d = 525$ mi, then $3d =$ 1575 mi. Since 525 mi + 1575 mi = 2100 mi, we have a check.

5. **State.** Atop Big Walker Mountain, Shaffer stood 525 mi from Springer Mountain and 1575 mi from Mount Katahdin.

Do Exercise 1.

1. **Running.** In 1997, Yiannis Kouros of Australia set the record for the greatest distance run in 24 hr by running 188 mi. After 8 hr, he was approximately twice as far from the finish line as he was from the start. How far had he run?

Source: *Guinness World Records*, 2004

Answer on page A-8

EXAMPLE 2 *Rocket Sections.* A rocket is divided into three sections: the payload and navigation section in the top, the fuel section in the middle, and the rocket engine section in the bottom. The top section is one-sixth the length of the bottom section. The middle section is one-half the length of the bottom section. The total length of the rocket is 240 ft. Find the length of each section.

1. Familiarize. We first make a drawing.

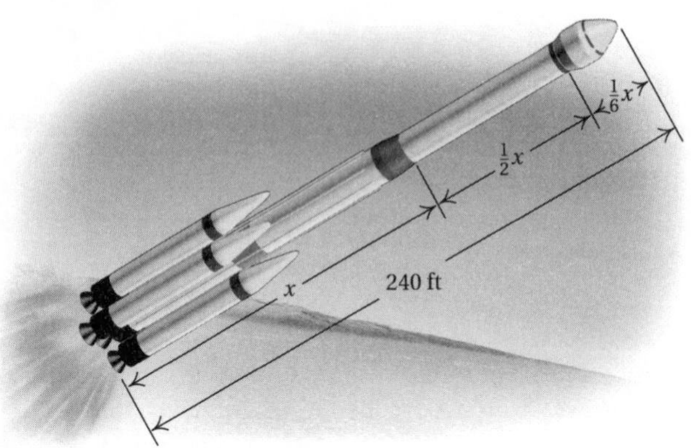

Because the lengths of the top and the middle sections are expressed in terms of the length of the bottom section, we let

$$x = \text{the length of the bottom section.}$$

Then $\frac{1}{6}x$ = the length of the top section

and $\frac{1}{2}x$ = the length of the middle section.

2. Translate. From the statement of the problem and the drawing, we see that the lengths add up to 240 ft. That gives us our translation:

Length of bottom section	plus	Length of middle section	plus	Length of top section	is	Total length
↓	↓	↓	↓	↓	↓	↓
x	$+$	$\frac{1}{2}x$	$+$	$\frac{1}{6}x$	$=$	240.

3. Solve. We begin by clearing fractions and then solving as follows:

$$x + \frac{1}{2}x + \frac{1}{6}x = 240 \qquad \text{The LCM of all the denominators is 6.}$$

$$6\left(x + \frac{1}{2}x + \frac{1}{6}x\right) = 6 \cdot 240 \qquad \text{Multiplying by the LCM, 6}$$

$$6 \cdot x + 6 \cdot \frac{1}{2}x + 6 \cdot \frac{1}{6}x = 6 \cdot 240 \qquad \text{Using the distributive law}$$

$$6x + 3x + x = 1440 \qquad \text{Simplifying}$$

$$10x = 1440 \qquad \text{Collecting like terms}$$

$$\frac{10x}{10} = \frac{1440}{10} \qquad \text{Dividing by 10}$$

$$x = 144.$$

4. **Check.** Do we have an answer to the *problem*? If the length of the bottom section is 144 ft, then the length of the middle section is $\frac{1}{2} \cdot 144$ ft, or 72 ft, and the length of the top section is $\frac{1}{6} \cdot 144$ ft, or 24 ft. These lengths add up to 240 ft. Our answer checks.

5. **State.** The length of the bottom section is 144 ft, the length of the middle section is 72 ft, and the length of the top section is 24 ft. (Note the importance of including the unit, feet, in the answer.)

o Exercise 2.

Recall that the set of integers = $\{\ldots, -5, -4, -3, -2, -1, 0, 1, 2, 3, 4, 5, \ldots\}$. efore we solve the next problem, we need to learn some additional termiology regarding integers.

The following are examples of **consecutive integers:** 16, 17, 18, 19, 20; and 31, -30, -29, -28. Note that consecutive integers can be represented in the rm x, $x + 1$, $x + 2$, and so on.

The following are examples of **consecutive even integers:** 16, 18, 20, 22, 4; and -52, -50, -48, -46. Note that consecutive even integers can be repsented in the form x, $x + 2$, $x + 4$, and so on.

The following are examples of **consecutive odd integers:** 21, 23, 25, 27, 29; nd -71, -69, -67, -65. Note that consecutive odd integers can be repreented in the form x, $x + 2$, $x + 4$, and so on.

KAMPLE 3 *Interstate Mile Markers.* U.S. interstate highways post numered markers every mile to indicate location in case of an accident or breakown. In many states, the numbers on the markers increase from west to east. he sum of two consecutive mile markers on I-70 in Kansas is 559. Find the umbers on the markers.

urce: Federal Highway Administration, Ed Rotalewski

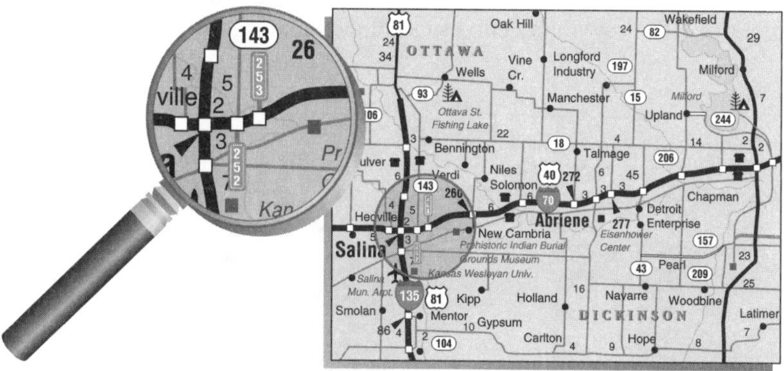

1. **Familiarize.** The numbers on the mile markers are consecutive positive integers. Thus if we let x = the smaller number, then $x + 1$ = the larger number.

To become familiar with the problem, we can make a table. First, we guess a value for x; then we find $x + 1$. Finally, we add the two numbers and check the sum.

x	$x + 1$	Sum of x and $x + 1$
114	115	229
252	253	505
302	303	605

2. **Gourmet Sandwiches.** A gourmet sandwich shop located near a college campus specializes in sandwiches prepared in buns of length 18 in. Suppose Jenny, Emma, and Sarah buy one of these sandwiches and take it back to their apartment. Since they have different appetites, Jenny cuts the sandwich in such a way that Emma gets half of what Jenny gets and Sarah gets three-fourths of what Jenny gets. Find the length of each person's sandwich.

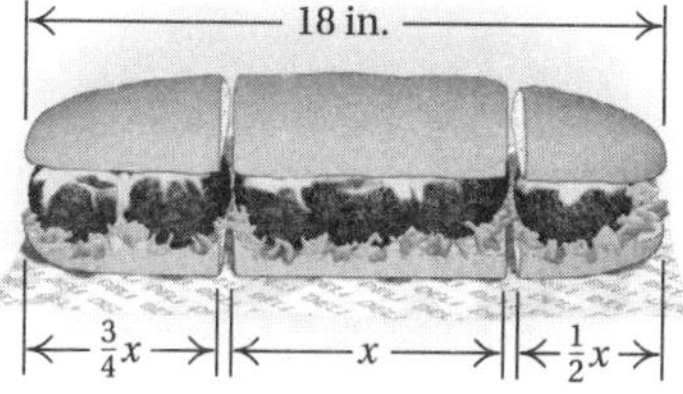

Answer on page A-8

3. **Interstate Mile Markers.** The sum of two consecutive mile markers on I-90 in upstate New York is 627. (On I-90 in New York, the marker numbers increase from east to west.) Find the numbers on the markers.

Source: New York State Department of Transportation

Answer on page A-8

From the table, we see that the first marker will be between 252 and 30
We could continue guessing and solve the problem this way, but let's wo
on developing our algebra skills.

2. **Translate.** We reword the problem and translate as follows.

First integer	plus	Second integer	is	559	Rewording
x	$+$	$(x + 1)$	$=$	559	Translating

3. **Solve.** We solve the equation:

$$
\begin{aligned}
x + (x + 1) &= 559 \\
2x + 1 &= 559 && \text{Collecting like terms} \\
2x + 1 - 1 &= 559 - 1 && \text{Subtracting 1} \\
2x &= 558 \\
\frac{2x}{2} &= \frac{558}{2} && \text{Dividing by 2} \\
x &= 279.
\end{aligned}
$$

If x is 279, then $x + 1$ is 280.

4. **Check.** Our possible answers are 279 and 280. These are consecuti positive integers and $279 + 280 = 559$, so the answers check.

5. **State.** The mile markers are 279 and 280.

Do Exercise 3.

EXAMPLE 4 *Copy Machine Rental.* It costs \$225 per month plus 1.2¢ p copy to rent a copy machine. A law firm needs to lease a copy machine for u during a special case that they anticipate will take 3 months. If they allot budget of \$1100, how many copies can they make?

1. **Familiarize.** Suppose that the law firm makes 20,000 copies. Then t cost is monthly charges plus copy charges, or

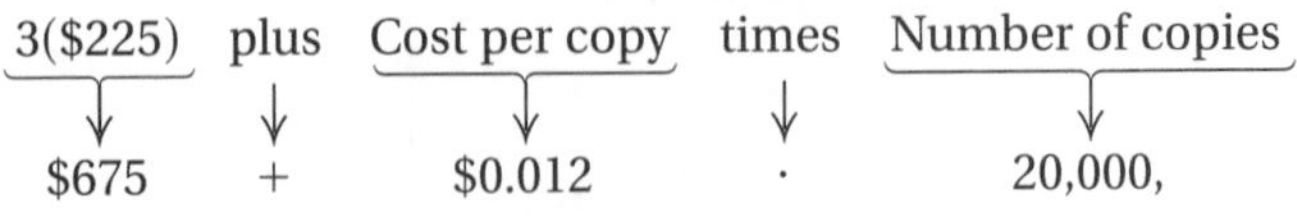

3(\$225)	plus	Cost per copy	times	Number of copies
\$675	+	\$0.012	·	20,000,

which is $915. This process familiarizes us with the way in which a calculation is made. Note that we convert 1.2¢ to $0.012 so that all information is in the same unit, dollars. Otherwise, we will not get the correct answer.

We let c = the number of copies that can be made for the budget of $1100.

2. **Translate.** We reword the problem and translate as follows.

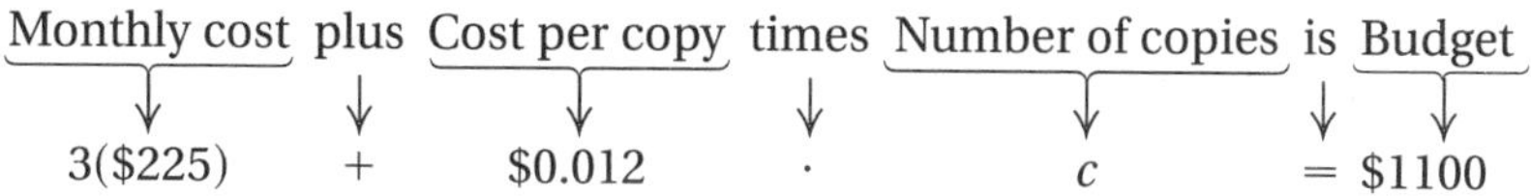

Monthly cost plus Cost per copy times Number of copies is Budget
3($225) + $0.012 · c = $1100

3. **Solve.** We solve the equation:

$$3(225) + 0.012c = 1100$$
$$675 + 0.012c = 1100$$
$$0.012c = 425 \quad \text{Subtracting 675}$$
$$\frac{0.012c}{0.012} = \frac{425}{0.012} \quad \text{Dividing by 0.012}$$
$$c \approx 35{,}417. \quad \text{Rounding to the nearest one}$$

4. **Check.** We check in the original problem. The cost for 35,417 pages is 35,417($0.012) = $425.004. The rental for 3 months is 3($225) = $675. The total cost is then $425.004 + $675 ≈ $1100, which is the $1100 that was allotted.

5. **State.** The law firm can make 35,417 copies on the copy rental allotment of $1100.

o Exercise 4.

XAMPLE 5 *Perimeter of NBA Court.* The perimeter of an NBA basketball ourt is 288 ft. The length is 44 ft longer than the width. Find the dimensions f the court.

urce: National Basketball Association

1. **Familiarize.** We first make a drawing.

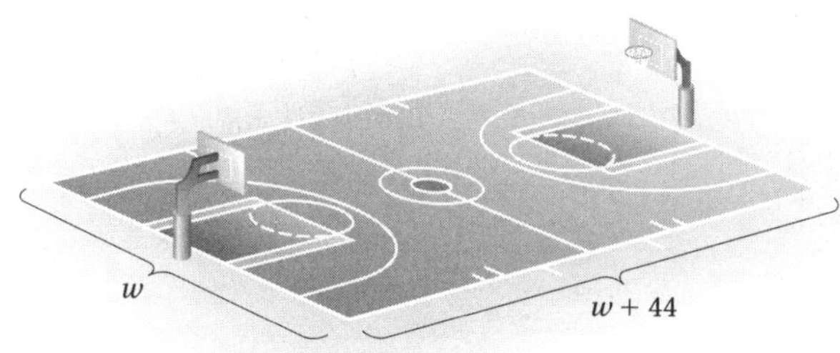

We let w = the width of the rectangle. Then $w + 44$ = the length. The perimeter P of a rectangle is the distance around the rectangle and is given by the formula $2l + 2w = P$, where

l = the length and w = the width.

4. **Copy Machine Rental.** The law firm in Example 4 decides to increase its budget to $1400 for the 3-month period. How many copies can they make for $1400?

Answer on page A-8

2. **Translate.** To translate the problem, we substitute $w + 44$ fo
and 288 for P:

$$2l + 2w = P$$

$$2(w + 44) + 2w = 288.$$

Caution!

Parentheses are important here.

3. **Solve.** We solve the equation:

$$2(w + 44) + 2w = 288$$

$$2 \cdot w + 2 \cdot 44 + 2w = 288 \quad \text{Using the distributive law}$$

$$4w + 88 = 288 \quad \text{Collecting like terms}$$

$$4w + 88 - 88 = 288 - 88 \quad \text{Subtracting 88}$$

$$4w = 200$$

$$\frac{4w}{4} = \frac{200}{4} \quad \text{Dividing by 4}$$

$$w = 50.$$

Thus possible dimensions are

$w = 50$ ft and $l = w + 44 = 50 + 44$, or 94 ft.

4. **Check.** If the width is 50 ft and the length is 94 ft, then t
perimeter is $2(50 \text{ ft}) + 2(94 \text{ ft})$, or 288 ft. This checks.

5. **State.** The width is 50 ft and the length is 94 ft.

5. **Perimeter of High School Basketball Court.** The perimeter of a standard high school basketball court is 268 ft. The length is 34 ft longer than the width. Find the dimensions of the court.

Source: Indiana High School Athletic Association

Do Exercise 5.

EXAMPLE 6 *Roof Gable.* In a triangular gable end of a roof, the angle
the peak is twice as large as the angle of the back side of the house. The me
sure of the angle on the front side is 20° greater than the angle on the ba
side. How large are the angles?

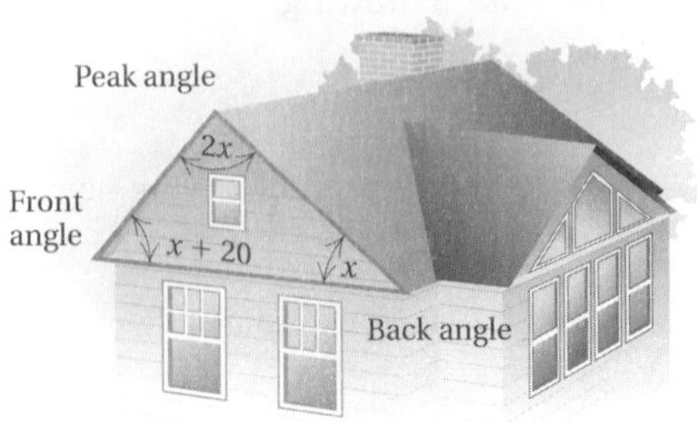

1. **Familiarize.** We first make a drawing as shown above. We let

measure of back angle $= x$.

Then measure of peak angle $= 2x$

and measure of front angle $= x + 20$.

Answer on page A-8

2. **Translate.** To translate, we need to recall a geometric fact. (You might, as part of step 1, look it up in a geometry book or in the list of formulas on the inside back cover.) Remember, the measures of the angles of a triangle total 180°.

Measure of back angle	plus	Measure of peak angle	plus	Measure of front angle	is	180°
↓	↓	↓	↓	↓	↓	↓
x	$+$	$2x$	$+$	$(x + 20)$	$=$	180°

3. **Solve.** We solve the equation:

$$x + 2x + (x + 20) = 180$$
$$4x + 20 = 180$$
$$4x + 20 - 20 = 180 - 20$$
$$4x = 160$$
$$\frac{4x}{4} = \frac{160}{4}$$
$$x = 40.$$

Possible measures for the angles are as follows:

Back angle: $x = 40°$;
Peak angle: $2x = 2(40) = 80°$;
Front angle: $x + 20 = 40 + 20 = 60°$.

4. **Check.** Consider our answers: 40°, 80°, and 60°. The peak is twice the back and the front is 20° greater than the back. The sum is 180°. The angles check.

5. **State.** The measures of the angles are 40°, 80°, and 60°.

Caution!

Units are important in answers. Remember to include them, where appropriate.

o Exercise 6.

Caution!

Always be sure to answer the original problem completely. For instance, in Example 1, we need to find *two* numbers: the distances from *each* end of the trail to the hiker. Similarly, in Example 3, we need to find two mile markers, and in Example 5, we need to find two dimensions, not just the width.

XAMPLE 7 *Top Speeds of Roller Coasters.* The average top speed of the ree fastest roller coasters in the world is 109 mph. The third fastest roller aster, Superman the Escape (at Six Flags Magic Mountain, Los Angeles, CA) aches a top speed of 20 mph less than the fastest roller coaster, Top Thrill ragster (in Cedar Point, Sandusky, OH). The second fastest roller coaster, odonpa (in Fujikyu Highlands, Japan) has a top speed of 107 mph. What is e top speed of the fastest roller coaster?

urce: *Fortune Small Business*, June 2004, p. 48

6. The second angle of a triangle is three times as large as the first. The third angle measures 30° more than the first angle. Find the measures of the angles.

Answer on page A-8

7. Average Test Score. Sam's average score on his first three math tests is 77. He scored 62 on the first test. On the third test, he scored 9 more than he scored on his second test. What did he score on the second and third tests?

1. **Familiarize.** The **average** of a set of numbers is the sum of the numbers divided by the number of addends. (For more on average, see Appendix E

   We are given that the second fastest speed is 107 mph. Suppose the three top speeds are 90, 107, and 112. The average is then

   $$\frac{90 + 107 + 112}{3} = \frac{309}{3} = 103,$$

   which is too low. Instead of continuing to guess, let's use the equation-solving skills we have learned in this chapter. We let x represent the top speed of the fastest roller coaster. Then $x - 20$ is the top speed of the third fastest roller coaster.

2. **Translate.** We reword the problem and translate as follows:

   $$\frac{\text{Speed of fastest coaster} + \text{Speed of second fastest coaster} + \text{Speed of third fastest coaster}}{\text{Number of roller coasters}} = \text{Average speed of three fastest roller coasters}$$

   $$\frac{x + 107 + (x - 20)}{3} = 109.$$

3. **Solve.** We solve as follows:

   $$\frac{x + 107 + (x - 20)}{3} = 109$$

   $$3 \cdot \frac{x + 107 + (x - 20)}{3} = 3 \cdot 109 \qquad \text{Multiplying by 3 on both sides to clear the fraction}$$

   $$x + 107 + (x - 20) = 327$$

   $$2x + 87 = 327 \qquad \text{Collecting like terms}$$

   $$2x = 240 \qquad \text{Subtracting 87}$$

   $$x = 120. \qquad \text{Dividing by 2}$$

4. **Check.** If the top speed of the fastest roller coaster is 120 mph, the the top speed of the third fastest is $120 - 20$, or 100 mph. The average of the top speeds of the three fastest is $(120 + 107 + 100) \div 3 = 327 \div 3$, or 109 mph. The answer checks.

5. **State.** The speed of the fastest roller coaster in the world is 120 mph.

Do Exercise 7.

Answer on page A-8

XAMPLE 8 *Simple Interest.* An investment is made at 6% simple inter-st for 1 year. It grows to \$768.50. How much was originally invested (the rincipal)?

1. **Familiarize.** Suppose that \$100 was invested. Recalling the formula for simple interest, $I = Prt$, we know that the interest for 1 year on \$100 at 6% simple interest is given by $I = \$100 \cdot 0.06 \cdot 1 = \$6$. Then, at the end of the year, the amount in the account is found by adding the principal and the interest:

$$\begin{array}{ccccc} \text{Principal} & + & \text{Interest} & = & \text{Amount} \\ \downarrow & & \downarrow & & \downarrow \\ \$100 & + & \$6 & = & \$106. \end{array}$$

In this problem, we are working backward. We are trying to find the principal, which is the original investment. We let x = the principal. Then the interest earned is $6\%x$.

2. **Translate.** We reword the problem and then translate.

$$\begin{array}{ccccc} \text{Principal} & + & \text{Interest} & = & \text{Amount} \\ \downarrow & & \downarrow & & \downarrow \\ x & + & 6\%x & = & 768.50 \end{array}$$ Interest is 6% of the principal.

3. **Solve.** We solve the equation:

$x + 6\%x = 768.50$

$x + 0.06x = 768.50$ Converting to decimal notation

$1x + 0.06x = 768.50$ Identity property of 1

$1.06x = 768.50$ Collecting like terms

$\frac{1.06x}{1.06} = \frac{768.50}{1.06}$ Dividing by 1.06

$x = 725.$

4. **Check.** We check by taking 6% of \$725 and adding it to \$725:

$6\% \times \$725 = 0.06 \times 725 = \$43.50.$

Then $\$725 + \$43.50 = \$768.50$, so \$725 checks.

5. **State.** The original investment was \$725.

Do Exercise 8.

8. **Simple Interest.** An investment is made at 7% simple interest for 1 year. It grows to \$8988. How much was originally invested (the principal)?

XAMPLE 9 *Selling a Home.* The Landers are planning to sell their home. If they want to be left with \$117,500 after paying 6% of the selling price to a realtor as a commission, for how much must they sell the house?

1. **Familiarize.** Suppose the Landers sell the house for \$120,000. A 6% commission can be determined by finding 6% of \$120,000:

$6\% \text{ of } \$120{,}000 = 0.06(\$120{,}000) = \$7200.$

Subtracting this commission from \$120,000 would leave the Landers with

$\$120{,}000 - \$7200 = \$112{,}800.$

This shows that in order for the Landers to clear \$117,500, the house must sell for more than \$120,000. To determine what the sale price must be, we could check more guesses. Instead, we let x = the selling price, in dollars. With a 6% commission, the realtor would receive $0.06x$.

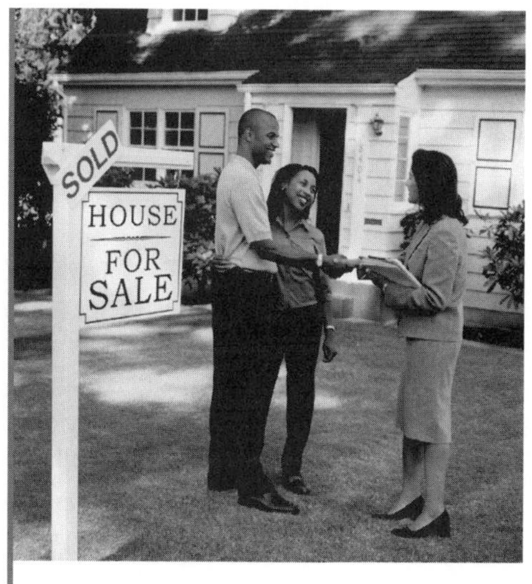

Answer on page A-8

9. Price Before Sale. The price of a suit was decreased to a sale price of \$526.40. This was a 20% reduction. What was the former price?

Answer on page A-8

2. Translate. We reword the problem and translate as follows.

Selling price	less	Commission	is	Amount remaining.
↓	↓	↓	↓	↓
x	$-$	$0.06x$	$=$	117,500

3. Solve. We solve the equation:

$$x - 0.06x = 117{,}500$$

$$1x - 0.06x = 117{,}500$$

$$0.94x = 117{,}500$$ Collecting like terms. Had we noted that afte the commission has been paid, 94% remain we could have begun with this equation.

$$\frac{094x}{0.94} = \frac{117{,}500}{0.94}$$ Dividing by 0.94

$$x = 125{,}000.$$

4. Check. To check, we first find 6% of \$125,000:

6% of \$125,000 = 0.06(\$125,000) = \$7500. This is the commission

Next, we subtract the commission to find the remaining amount:

\$125,000 − \$7500 = \$117,500.

Since, after the commission, the Landers are left with \$117,500, our an swer checks. Note that the \$125,000 selling price is greater tha \$120,000, as predicted in the *Familiarize* step.

5. State. To be left with \$117,500, the Landers must sell the house f \$125,000.

Do Exercise 9.

Caution!

The problem in Example 9 is easy to solve with algebra. Without algebra, it is not. A common error in such a problem is to take 6% of the price after commission and then subtract or add. Note that 6% of the selling price (6% · \$125,000 = \$7500) is not equal to 6% of the amount that the Landers want to be left with (6% · \$117,500 = \$7050).

Study Tips

PROBLEM-SOLVING TIPS

The more problems you solve, the more your skills will improve.

1. Look for patterns when solving problems. Each time you study an example in a text, you may observe a pattern for problems that you will encounter later in the exercise sets or in other practical situations.
2. When translating in mathematics, consider the dimensions of the variables and constants in the equation. The variables that represent length should all be in the same unit, those that represent money should all be in dollars or all in cents, and so on.
3. Make sure that units appear in the answer whenever appropriate and that you have completely answered the original problem.

Translating for Success

ngle Measures. The measure f the second angle of a triangle 51° more than that of the first ngle. The measure of the third ngle is 3° less than twice the rst angle. Find the measures of e angles.

ales Tax. Tina paid $3976 for a sed car. This amount included % for sales tax. How much did e car cost before tax?

erimeter. The perimeter of a ctangle is 2347 ft. The length 28 ft greater than the width. nd the length and the idth.

raternity or Sorority lembership. At Arches Tech niversity, 3976 students belong a fraternity or a sorority. This 35% of the total enrollment. hat is the total enrollment at rches Tech?

raternity or Sorority lembership. At Moab Tech niversity, thirty-five percent of e students belong to a aternity or a sorority. The total nrollment of the university is 1,360 students. How many udents belong to either a aternity or a sorority?

The goal of these matching questions is to practice step (2), *Translate,* of the five-step problem-solving process. Translate each word problem to an equation and select a correct translation from equations A–O.

A. $x + (x - 3) + \frac{4}{5}x = 384$

B. $x + (x + 51) + (2x - 3) = 180$

C. $x + (x + 96) = 180$

D. $2 \cdot 96 + 2x = 3976$

E. $x + (x + 1) + (x + 2) = 384$

F. $3976 = x \cdot 11{,}360$

G. $2x + 2(x + 28) = 2347$

H. $3976 = x + 5\%x$

I. $x + (x + 28) = 2347$

J. $x = 35\% \cdot 11{,}360$

K. $x + 96 = 3976$

L. $x + (x + 3) + \frac{4}{5}x = 384$

M. $x + (x + 2) + (x + 4) = 384$

N. $35\% \cdot x = 3976$

O. $x + (x + 28) = 2347$

Answers on page A-8

6. *Island Population.* There are 180 thousand people living on a small Caribbean island. The women outnumber the men by 96 thousand. How many men live on the island?

7. *Wire Cutting.* A 384-m wire is cut into three pieces. The second piece is 3 m longer than the first. The third is four-fifths as long as the first. How long is each piece?

8. *Locker Numbers.* The numbers on three adjoining lockers are consecutive integers whose sum is 384. Find the integers.

9. *Fraternity or Sorority Membership.* The total enrollment at Canyonlands Tech University is 11,360 students. Of these, 3976 students belong to a fraternity or a sorority. What percent of the students belong to a fraternity or sorority?

10. *Width of a Rectangle.* The length of a rectangle is 96 ft. The perimeter of the rectangle is 3976 ft. Find the width.

2.6 EXERCISE SET

For Extra Help

MathXL

MyMathLab

InterAct Math

Math Tutor Center
Digital Video Tutor CD 2 Videotape 3

Student's Solutions Manual

a Solve. *Even though you might find the answer quickly in some other way, practice using the five-step problem-solving strategy.*

1. *Pipe Cutting.* A 240-in. pipe is cut into two pieces. One piece is three times the length of the other. Find the lengths of the pieces.

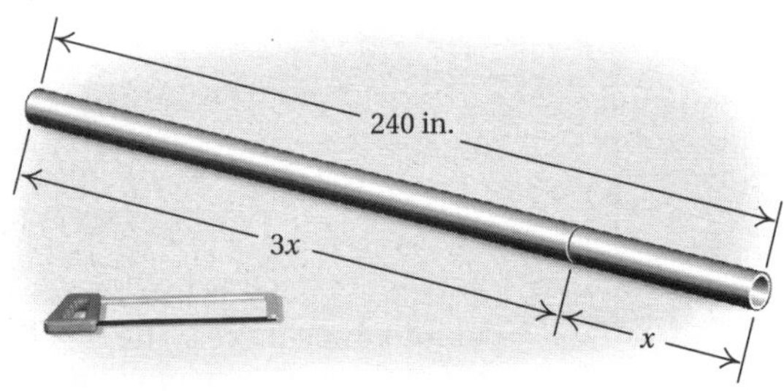

2. *Board Cutting.* A 72-in. board is cut into two pieces. One piece is 2 in. longer than the other. Find the lengths of the pieces.

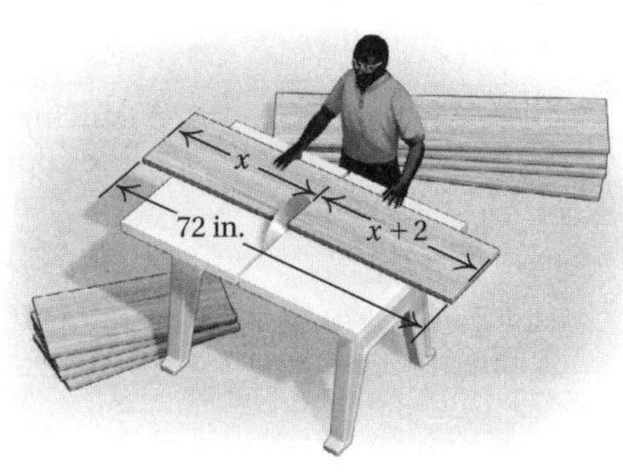

3. *Cinnamon Life.* Recently, the cost of four 21-oz boxes of Cinnamon Life cereal was $17.16. What was the cost of one box?

4. *Area of Lake Ontario.* The area of Lake Superior is about four times the area of Lake Ontario. The area of Lake Superior is 30,172 mi^2. What is the area of Lake Ontario?

5. *Women's Dresses.* In a recent year, the total amount spent on women's blouses was $6.5 billion. This was $0.2 billion more than what was spent on women's dresses. How much was spent on women's dresses?

6. *Statue of Liberty.* The height of the Eiffel Tower is 974 ft, which is about 669 ft higher than the Statue of Liberty. What is the height of the Statue of Liberty?

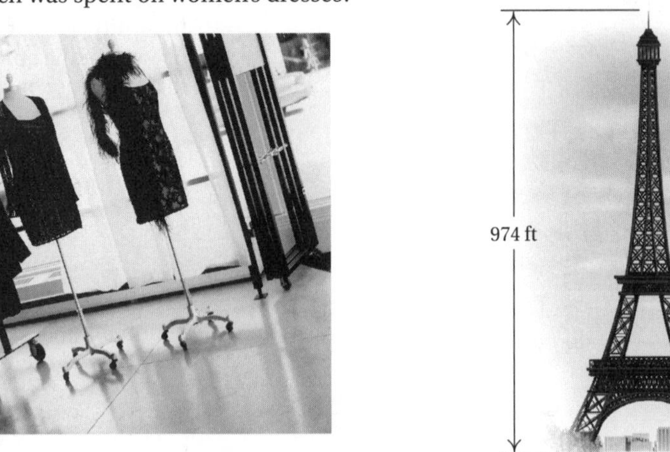
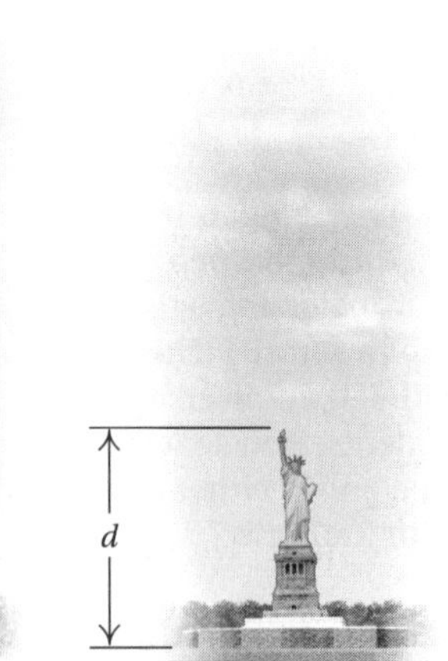

7. *Iditarod Race.* The Iditarod sled dog race extends for 1049 mi from Anchorage to Nome. If a musher is twice as far from Anchorage as from Nome, how many miles of the race has the musher completed?

Source: Iditarod Trail Commission

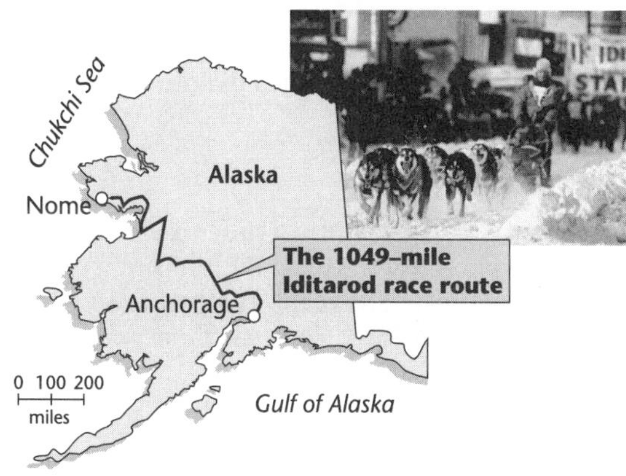

8. *Home Remodeling.* In a recent year, Americans spent a total of $35 billion to remodel bathrooms and kitchens. Twice as much was spent on kitchens as bathrooms. How much was spent on each?

9. *Consecutive Apartment Numbers.* The apartments in Vincent's apartment house are numbered consecutively on each floor. The sum of his number and his next-door neighbor's number is 2409. What are the two numbers?

10. *Consecutive Post Office Box Numbers.* The sum of the numbers on two consecutive post office boxes is 547. What are the numbers?

1. *Consecutive Ticket Numbers.* The numbers on Sam's three raffle tickets are consecutive integers. The sum of the numbers is 126. What are the numbers?

12. *Consecutive Ages.* The ages of Whitney, Wesley, and Wanda are consecutive integers. The sum of their ages is 108. What are their ages?

3. *Consecutive Odd Integers.* The sum of three consecutive odd integers is 189. What are the integers?

14. *Consecutive Integers.* Three consecutive integers are such that the first plus one-half the second plus seven less than twice the third is 2101. What are the integers?

5. *Standard Billboard Sign.* A standard rectangular highway billboard sign has a perimeter of 124 ft. The length is 6 ft more than three times the width. Find the dimensions of the sign.

16. *Two-by-Four.* The perimeter of a cross section or end of a "two-by-four" piece of lumber is 10 in. The length is 2 in. more than the width. Find the actual dimensions of the cross section of a two-by-four.

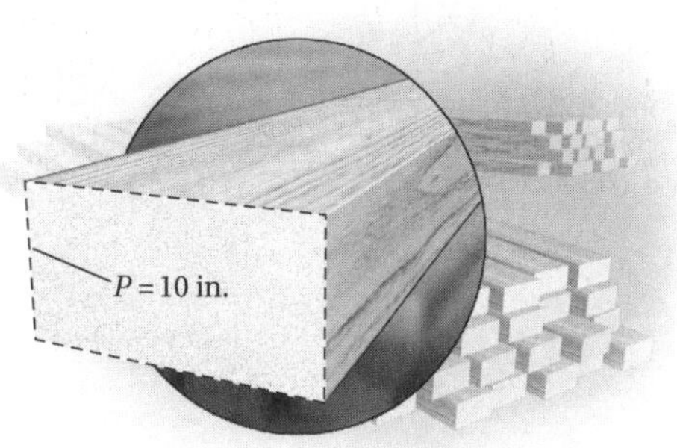

17. *Price of Sneakers.* Amy paid \$63.75 for a pair of New Balance 903 running shoes during a 15%-off sale. What was the regular price?

18. *Price of a CD Player.* Doug paid \$72 for a shockproof portable CD player during a 20%-off sale. What was the regular price?

19. *Price of a Textbook.* Evelyn paid \$89.25, including 5% tax, for her biology textbook. How much did the book itself cost?

20. *Price of a Printer.* Jake paid \$100.70, including 6% tax, for a color printer. How much did the printer itself cost?

21. *Parking Costs.* A hospital parking lot charges \$1.50 for the first hour or part thereof, and \$1.00 for each additional hour or part thereof. A weekly pass costs \$27.00 and allows unlimited parking for 7 days. Suppose that each visit Ed makes to the hospital lasts $1\frac{1}{2}$ hr. What is the minimum number of times that Ed would have to visit per week to make it worthwhile for him to buy the pass?

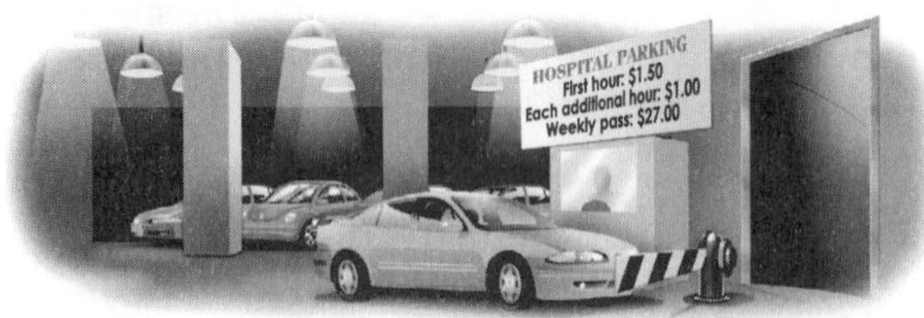

22. *Van Rental.* Value Rent-A-Car rents vans at a daily rate of \$84.95 plus 60 cents per mile. Molly rents a van to deliver electrical parts to her customers. She is allotted a daily budget of \$320. How many miles can she drive for \$320? (*Hint*: 60¢ = \$0.60.)

23. *Triangular Field.* The second angle of a triangular field is three times as large as the first angle. The third angle is 40° greater than the first angle. How large are the angles?

24. *Triangular Parking Lot.* The second angle of a triangular parking lot is four times as large as the first angle. The third angle is 45° less than the sum of the other two angles. How large are the angles?

25. *Triangular Backyard.* A home has a triangular backyard. The second angle of the triangle is 5° more than the first angle. The third angle is 10° more than three times the first angle. Find the angles of the triangular yard.

26. *Boarding Stable.* A rancher needs to form a triangular horse pen using ropes next to a stable. The second angle is three times the first angle. The third angle is 15° less than the first angle. Find the angles of the triangular pen.

7. *Stock Prices.* Sarah's investment in AOL/Time Warner stock grew 28% to $448. How much did she invest?

28. *Savings Interest.* Sharon invested money in a savings account at a rate of 6% simple interest. After 1 yr, she has $6996 in the account. How much did Sharon originally invest?

9. *Credit Cards.* The balance in Will's Mastercard® account grew 2%, to $870, in one month. What was his balance at the beginning of the month?

30. *Loan Interest.* Alvin borrowed money from a cousin at a rate of 10% simple interest. After 1 yr, $7194 paid off the loan. How much did Alvin borrow?

1. *Taxi Fares.* In Beniford, taxis charge $3 plus 75¢ per mile for an airport pickup. How far from the airport can Courtney travel for $12?

32. *Taxi Fares.* In Cranston, taxis charge $4 plus 90¢ per mile for an airport pickup. How far from the airport can Ralph travel for $17.50?

3. *Tipping.* Leon left a 15% tip for a meal. The total cost of the meal, including the tip, was $41.40. What was the cost of the meal before the tip was added?

34. *Tipping.* Selena left an 18% tip for a meal. The total cost of the meal, including the tip, was $40.71. What was the cost of the meal before the tip was added?

5. *Average Price.* Tom paid an average of $34 per tie for a recent purchase of three ties. The price of one tie was twice as much as another, and the remaining tie cost $27. What were the prices of the other two ties?

36. *Average Test Score.* Jaci averaged 84 on her first three history exams. The first score was 67. The second score was 7 less than the third score. What did she score on the second and third exams?

37. $\mathbf{D_W}$ Write a problem for a classmate to solve so that it can be translated to the equation

$$\tfrac{2}{3}x + (x + 5) + x = 375.$$

38. $\mathbf{D_W}$ Erin returns a tent that she bought during a storewide 35%-off sale that has ended. She is offered store credit for 125% of what she paid (not to be used on sale items). Is this fair to Erin? Why or why not?

SKILL MAINTENANCE

Calculate.

39. $-\frac{4}{5} - \frac{3}{8}$ [1.4a]

40. $-\frac{4}{5} + \frac{3}{8}$ [1.3a]

41. $-\frac{4}{5} \cdot \frac{3}{8}$ [1.5a]

42. $-\frac{4}{5} \div \frac{3}{8}$ [1.6c]

43. $\frac{1}{10} \div \left(-\frac{1}{100}\right)$ [1.6c]

44. $-25.6 \div (-16)$ [1.6c]

45. $-25.6(-16)$ [1.5a]

46. $-25.6 - (-16)$ [1.4a]

47. $-25.6 + (-16)$ [1.3a]

48. $(-0.02) \div (-0.2)$ [1.6c]

SYNTHESIS

49. Apples are collected in a basket for six people. One-third, one-fourth, one-eighth, and one-fifth are given to four people, respectively. The fifth person gets ten apples with one apple remaining for the sixth person. Find the original number of apples in the basket.

50. *Test Questions.* A student scored 78 on a test that had 4 seven-point fill-ins and 24 three-point multiple-choice questions. The student had one fill-in wrong. How many multiple-choice questions did the student answer correctly?

51. The area of this triangle is 2.9047 in^2. Find x.

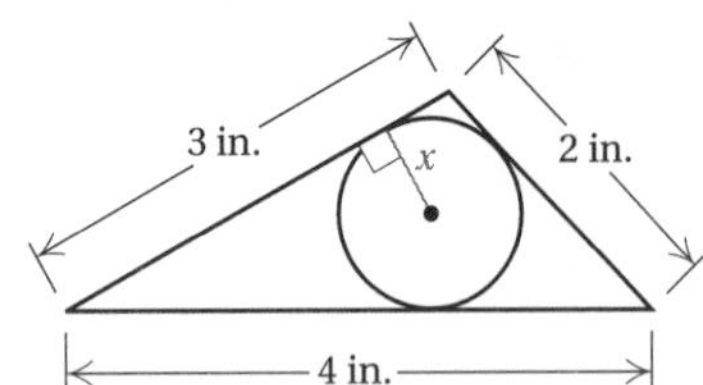

52. A storekeeper goes to the bank to get $10 worth of change. She requests twice as many quarters as half dollars, twice as many dimes as quarters, three times as many nickels as dimes, and no pennies or dollars. How many of each coin did the storekeeper get?

53. In one city, a sales tax of 9% was added to the price of gasoline as registered on the pump. Suppose a driver asked for $10 worth of gas. The attendant filled the tank until the pump read $9.10 and charged the driver $10. Something was wrong. Use algebra to correct the error.

2.7 SOLVING INEQUALITIES

Objectives

- **a** Determine whether a given number is a solution of an inequality.
- **b** Graph an inequality on a number line.
- **c** Solve inequalities using the addition principle.
- **d** Solve inequalities using the multiplication principle.
- **e** Solve inequalities using the addition and multiplication principles together.

We now extend our equation-solving principles to the solving of ıequalities.

a Solutions of Inequalities

n Section 1.2, we defined the symbols $>$ (is greater than), $<$ (is less than), $\geq$ ıs greater than or equal to), and $\leq$ (is less than or equal to). For example, ≤ 4 and $3 \leq 3$ are both true, but $-3 \leq -4$ and $0 \geq 2$ are both false.

An **inequality** is a number sentence with $>, <, \geq$, or $\leq$ as its verb—for xample,

$$-4 > t, \quad x < 3, \quad 2x + 5 \geq 0, \quad \text{and} \quad -3y + 7 \leq -8.$$

ome replacements for a variable in an inequality make it true and some ıake it false.

SOLUTION

A replacement that makes an inequality true is called a **solution.** The set of all solutions is called the **solution set.** When we have found the set of all solutions of an inequality, we say that we have **solved** the inequality.

XAMPLES Determine whether the number is a solution of $x < 2$.

1. -2.7 Since $-2.7 < 2$ is true, -2.7 is a solution.
2. 2 Since $2 < 2$ is false, 2 is not a solution.

XAMPLES Determine whether the number is a solution of $y \geq 6$.

3. 6 Since $6 \geq 6$ is true, 6 is a solution.
4. $-\frac{4}{3}$ Since $-\frac{4}{3} \geq 6$ is false, $-\frac{4}{3}$ is not a solution.

o Exercises 1 and 2.

Determine whether each number is a solution of the inequality.

1. $x > 3$

a) 2 b) 0

c) -5 d) 15.4

e) 3 f) $-\frac{2}{5}$

2. $x \leq 6$

a) 6 b) 0

c) -4.3 d) 25

e) -6 f) $\frac{5}{8}$

Answers on page A-9

b Graphs of Inequalities

ome solutions of $x < 2$ are $-3, 0, 1, 0.45, -8.9, -\pi, \frac{5}{8}$, and so on. In fact, there re infinitely many real numbers that are solutions. Because we cannot list ıem all individually, it is helpful to make a drawing that represents all the olutions.

A **graph** of an inequality is a drawing that represents its solutions. An inquality in one variable can be graphed on a number line. An inequality in wo variables can be graphed on a coordinate plane; we will study such raphs in Chapter 3.

Graph.

3. $x \leq 4$

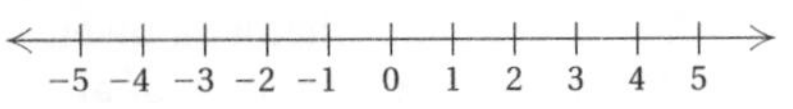

4. $x > -2$

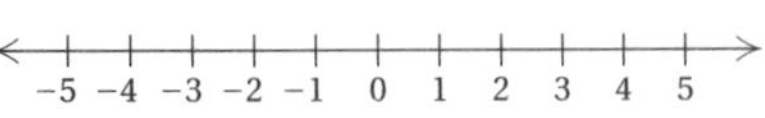

5. $-2 < x \leq 4$

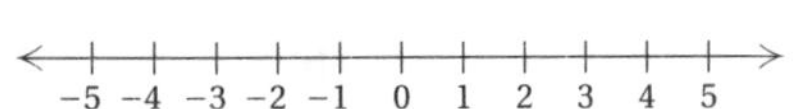

Answers on page A-9

EXAMPLE 5 Graph: $x < 2$.

The solutions of $x < 2$ are all those numbers less than 2. They are show on the graph by shading all points to the left of 2. The open circle at 2 indicate that 2 is *not* part of the graph.

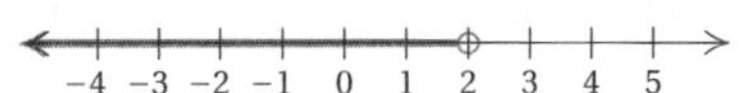

EXAMPLE 6 Graph: $x \geq -3$.

The solutions of $x \geq -3$ are shown on the number line by shading th point for -3 and all points to the right of -3. The closed circle at -3 indicate that -3 *is* part of the graph.

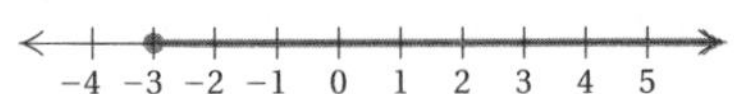

EXAMPLE 7 Graph: $-3 \leq x < 2$.

The inequality $-3 \leq x < 2$ is read "-3 is less than or equal to x *and* x i less than 2," or "x is greater than or equal to -3 *and* x is less than 2." In orde to be a solution of this inequality, a number must be a solution of both $-3 \leq$ and $x < 2$. The number 1 is a solution, as are -1.7, 0, 1.5, and $\frac{3}{8}$. We can se from the graphs below that the solution set consists of the numbers that over lap in the two solution sets in Examples 5 and 6:

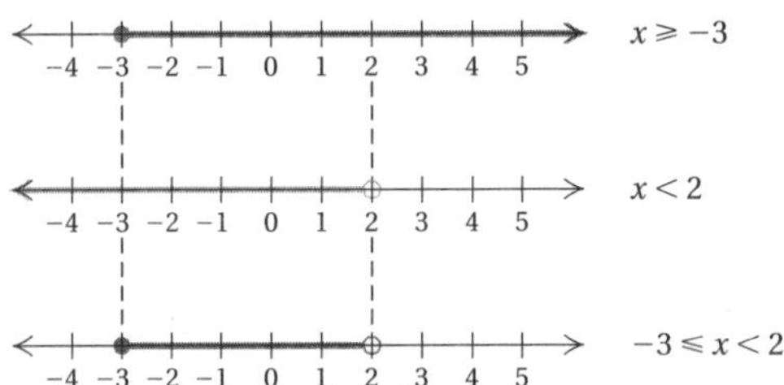

The open circle at 2 means that 2 is *not* part of the graph. The closed circle a -3 means that -3 *is* part of the graph. The other solutions are shaded.

Do Exercises 3–5.

C Solving Inequalities Using the Addition Principle

Consider the true inequality $3 < 7$. If we add 2 on both sides, we get anothe true inequality:

$$3 + 2 < 7 + 2, \quad \text{or} \quad 5 < 9.$$

Similarly, if we add -4 on both sides of $x + 4 < 10$, we get an *equivaler* inequality:

$$x + 4 + (-4) < 10 + (-4),$$

or

$$x < 6.$$

To say that $x + 4 < 10$ and $x < 6$ are **equivalent** is to say that they have th same solution set. For example, the number 3 is a solution of $x + 4 < 10$. It i also a solution of $x < 6$. The number -2 is a solution of $x < 6$. It is also solution of $x + 4 < 10$. Any solution of one is a solution of the other—the are equivalent.

THE ADDITION PRINCIPLE FOR INEQUALITIES

For any real numbers a, b, and c:

$a < b$ is equivalent to $a + c < b + c$;
$a > b$ is equivalent to $a + c > b + c$;
$a \le b$ is equivalent to $a + c \le b + c$;
$a \ge b$ is equivalent to $a + c \ge b + c$.

In other words, when we add or subtract the same number on both sides of an inequality, the direction of the inequality symbol is not changed.

As with equation solving, when solving inequalities, our goal is to isolate the variable on one side. Then it is easier to determine the solution set.

EXAMPLE 8 Solve: $x + 2 > 8$. Then graph.

We use the addition principle, subtracting 2 on both sides:

$$x + 2 - 2 > 8 - 2$$
$$x > 6.$$

From the inequality $x > 6$, we can determine the solutions directly. Any number greater than 6 makes the last sentence true and is a solution of that sentence. Any such number is also a solution of the original sentence. Thus the inequality is solved. The graph is as follows:

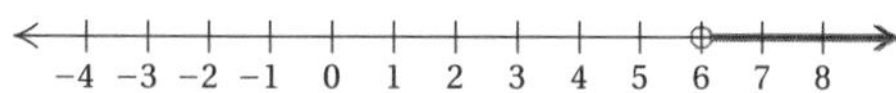

We cannot check all the solutions of an inequality by substitution, as we can check solutions of equations, because there are too many of them. A partial check can be done by substituting a number greater than 6—say, 7—into the original inequality:

$x + 2 > 8$	
$7 + 2$	8
9	TRUE

Since $9 > 8$ is true, 7 is a solution. Any number greater than 6 is a solution.

EXAMPLE 9 Solve: $3x + 1 \le 2x - 3$. Then graph.

We have

$$3x + 1 \le 2x - 3$$
$$3x + 1 - 1 \le 2x - 3 - 1 \quad \text{Subtracting 1}$$
$$3x \le 2x - 4 \quad \text{Simplifying}$$
$$3x - 2x \le 2x - 4 - 2x \quad \text{Subtracting } 2x$$
$$x \le -4. \quad \text{Simplifying}$$

The graph is as follows:

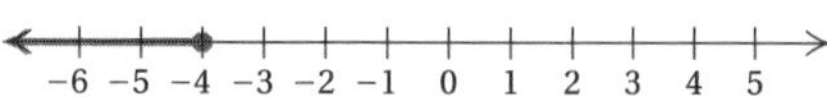

Remember that the graph is a drawing that represents the solutions of the original inequality.

Solve. Then graph.

6. $x + 3 > 5$

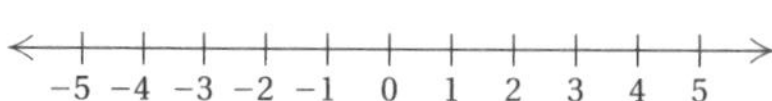

7. $x - 1 \le 2$

8. $5x + 1 < 4x - 2$

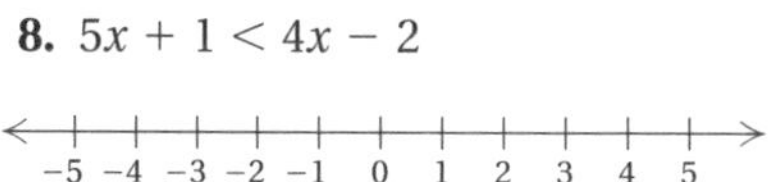

Answers on page A-9

Solve.

9. $x + \frac{2}{3} \geq \frac{4}{5}$

10. $5y + 2 \leq -1 + 4y$

Answers on page A-9

In Example 9, any number less than or equal to -4 is a solution. The following are some solutions:

$$-4, \quad -5, \quad -6, \quad -\frac{13}{3}, \quad -204.5, \quad \text{and} \quad -18\pi.$$

Besides drawing a graph, we can also describe all the solutions of an inequality using **set notation.** We could just begin to list them in a set using roster notation (see p. 66), as follows:

$$\left\{-4, -5, -6, -\frac{13}{3}, -204.5, -18\pi, \ldots\right\}.$$

We can never list them all this way, however. Seeing this set without knowing the inequality makes it difficult for us to know what real numbers we are considering. There is, however, another kind of notation that we can use. It is

$$\{x \mid x \leq -4\},$$

which is read

"The set of all x such that x is less than or equal to -4."

This shorter notation for sets is called **set-builder notation.**

From now on, we will use this notation when solving inequalities.

Do Exercises 6–8 on the preceding page.

EXAMPLE 10 Solve: $x + \frac{1}{3} > \frac{5}{4}$.

We have

$$x + \tfrac{1}{3} > \tfrac{5}{4}$$

$$x + \tfrac{1}{3} - \tfrac{1}{3} > \tfrac{5}{4} - \tfrac{1}{3} \qquad \text{Subtracting } \tfrac{1}{3}$$

$$x > \tfrac{5}{4} \cdot \tfrac{3}{3} - \tfrac{1}{3} \cdot \tfrac{4}{4} \qquad \text{Multiplying by 1 to obtain a common denominator}$$

$$x > \tfrac{15}{12} - \tfrac{4}{12}$$

$$x > \tfrac{11}{12}.$$

Any number greater than $\frac{11}{12}$ is a solution. The solution set is

$$\left\{x \mid x > \tfrac{11}{12}\right\},$$

which is read

"The set of all x such that x is greater than $\frac{11}{12}$."

When solving inequalities, you may obtain an answer like $\frac{11}{12} < x$. Recall from Chapter 1 that this has the same meaning as $x > \frac{11}{12}$. Thus the solution set in Example 10 can be described as $\left\{x \mid \frac{11}{12} < x\right\}$ or as $\left\{x \mid x > \frac{11}{12}\right\}$. The latter is used most often.

Do Exercises 9 and 10.

d Solving Inequalities Using the Multiplication Principle

There is a multiplication principle for inequalities that is similar to that for equations, but it must be modified. When we are multiplying on both sides by a negative number, the direction of the inequality symbol must be changed

Let's see what happens. Consider the true inequality $3 < 7$. If we multiply on both sides by a *positive* number, like 2, we get another true inequality:

$3 \cdot 2 < 7 \cdot 2$, or $6 < 14$. True

If we multiply on both sides by a *negative* number, like -2, and we do not change the direction of the inequality symbol, we get a *false* inequality:

$3 \cdot (-2) < 7 \cdot (-2)$, or $-6 < -14$. False

The fact that $6 < 14$ is true but $-6 < -14$ is false stems from the fact that the negative numbers, in a sense, mirror the positive numbers. That is, whereas 14 is to the *right* of 6 on a number line, the number -14 is to the *left* of -6. Thus, if we reverse (change the direction of) the inequality symbol, we get a *true* inequality: $-6 > -14$.

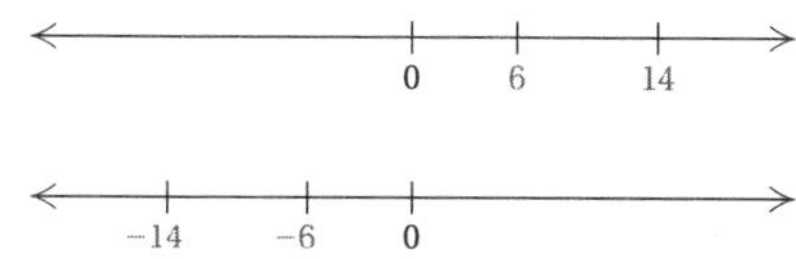

THE MULTIPLICATION PRINCIPLE FOR INEQUALITIES

For any real numbers a and b, and any *positive* number c:

$a < b$ is equivalent to $ac < bc$;
$a > b$ is equivalent to $ac > bc$.

For any real numbers a and b, and any *negative* number c:

$a < b$ is equivalent to $ac > bc$;
$a > b$ is equivalent to $ac < bc$.

Similar statements hold for $\le$ and $\ge$.

In other words, when we multiply or divide by a positive number on both sides of an inequality, the direction of the inequality symbol stays the same. When we multiply or divide by a negative number on both sides of an inequality, the direction of the inequality symbol is reversed.

EXAMPLE 11 Solve: $4x < 28$. Then graph.

We have

$4x < 28$

$\frac{4x}{4} < \frac{28}{4}$ Dividing by 4

The symbol stays the same.

$x < 7$. Simplifying

The solution set is $\{x \mid x < 7\}$. The graph is as follows:

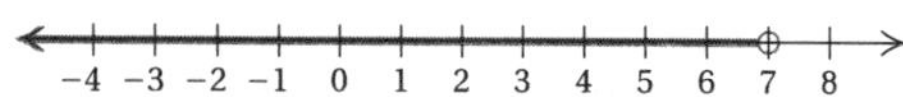

Do Exercises 11 and 12.

Solve. Then graph.

11. $8x < 64$

−12 −8 −4 0 4 8 12

12. $5y \ge 160$

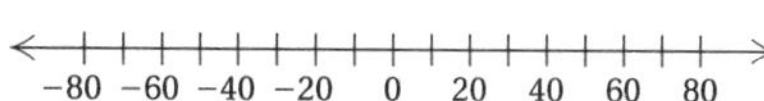

Answers on page A-9

Solve.

13. $-4x \leq 24$

14. $-5y > 13$

15. Solve: $7 - 4x < 8$.

Answers on page A-9

EXAMPLE 12 Solve: $-2y < 18$. Then graph.

$$-2y < 18$$

$$\frac{-2y}{-2} > \frac{18}{-2} \quad \text{Dividing by } -2$$

The symbol must be reversed!

$$y > -9. \quad \text{Simplifying}$$

The solution set is $\{y \mid y > -9\}$. The graph is as follows:

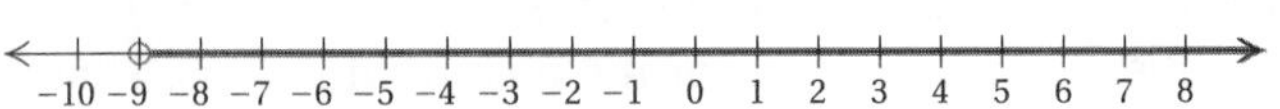

Do Exercises 13 and 14.

e Using the Principles Together

All of the equation-solving techniques used in Sections 2.1–2.3 can be used with inequalities, provided we remember to reverse the inequality symbol when multiplying or dividing on both sides by a negative number.

EXAMPLE 13 Solve: $6 - 5y > 7$.

$$6 - 5y > 7$$

$$-6 + 6 - 5y > -6 + 7 \quad \text{Adding } -6\text{. The symbol stays the same.}$$

$$-5y > 1 \quad \text{Simplifying}$$

$$\frac{-5y}{-5} < \frac{1}{-5} \quad \text{Dividing by } -5$$

The symbol must be reversed because we are dividing by a *negative* number, −5.

$$y < -\frac{1}{5}. \quad \text{Simplifying}$$

The solution set is $\{y \mid y < -\frac{1}{5}\}$.

Do Exercise 15.

EXAMPLE 14 Solve: $8y - 5 > 17 - 5y$.

$$-17 + 8y - 5 > -17 + 17 - 5y \quad \text{Adding } -17\text{. The symbol stays the same.}$$

$$8y - 22 > -5y \quad \text{Simplifying}$$

$$-8y + 8y - 22 > -8y - 5y \quad \text{Adding } -8y$$

$$-22 > -13y \quad \text{Simplifying}$$

$$\frac{-22}{-13} < \frac{-13y}{-13} \quad \text{Dividing by } -13$$

The symbol must be reversed because we are dividing by a *negative* number, −13.

$$\frac{22}{13} < y.$$

The solution set is $\{y \mid \frac{22}{13} < y\}$, or $\{y \mid y > \frac{22}{13}\}$.

Do Exercise 16.

It is typical to try to solve an inequality by isolating the variable on the left side of the inequality. Although this is not necessary, it does prevent having to reverse the inequality symbol at the end. Let's solve the inequality in Example 14 again, but this time we will isolate the variable on the left.

EXAMPLE 15 Solve: $8y - 5 > 17 - 5y$.

Note that if we add $5y$ on both sides, the coefficient of the y-term will be positive after like terms have been collected.

$8y - 5 + 5y > 17 - 5y + 5y$	Adding $5y$
$13y - 5 > 17$	Simplifying
$13y - 5 + 5 > 17 + 5$	Adding 5
$13y > 22$	Simplifying
$\frac{13y}{13} > \frac{22}{13}$	Dividing by 13. We leave the inequality symbol the same because we are dividing by a positive number.
$y > \frac{22}{13}$	

The solution set is $\{y \mid y > \frac{22}{13}\}$.

Do Exercise 17.

EXAMPLE 16 Solve: $3(x - 2) - 1 < 2 - 5(x + 6)$.

We have

$3(x - 2) - 1 < 2 - 5(x + 6)$	
$3x - 6 - 1 < 2 - 5x - 30$	Using the distributive law to multiply and remove parentheses
$3x - 7 < -5x - 28$	Simplifying
$3x + 5x < -28 + 7$	Adding $5x$ and 7 to get all x-terms on one side and all other terms on the other side
$8x < -21$	Simplifying
$x < \frac{-21}{8}$, or $-\frac{21}{8}$.	Dividing by 8

The solution set is $\{x \mid x < -\frac{21}{8}\}$.

Do Exercise 18.

16. Solve. Use a method like the one used in Example 14.

$$24 - 7y \leq 11y - 14$$

17. Solve. Use a method like the one used in Example 15.

$$24 - 7y \leq 11y - 14$$

18. Solve:

$$3(7 + 2x) \leq 30 + 7(x - 1).$$

Answers on page A-9

19. Solve:

$2.1x + 43.2 \geq 1.2 - 8.4x.$

20. Solve:

$\frac{3}{4} + x < \frac{7}{8}x - \frac{1}{4} + \frac{1}{2}x.$

Answers on page A-9

EXAMPLE 17 Solve: $16.3 - 7.2p \leq -8.18$.

The greatest number of decimal places in any one number is *two.* Multiplying by 100, which has two 0's, will clear decimals. Then we proceed as before.

$$\begin{aligned} 16.3 - 7.2p &\leq -8.18 && \\ 100(16.3 - 7.2p) &\leq 100(-8.18) && \text{Multiplying by 100} \\ 100(16.3) - 100(7.2p) &\leq 100(-8.18) && \text{Using the distributive law} \\ 1630 - 720p &\leq -818 && \text{Simplifying} \\ 1630 - 720p - 1630 &\leq -818 - 1630 && \text{Subtracting 1630} \\ -720p &\leq -2448 && \text{Simplifying} \\ \frac{-720p}{-720} &\geq \frac{-2448}{-720} && \text{Dividing by } -720 \text{; The symbol must be reversed.} \\ p &\geq 3.4 && \end{aligned}$$

The solution set is $\{p \mid p \geq 3.4\}$.

Do Exercise 19.

EXAMPLE 18 Solve: $\frac{2}{3}x - \frac{1}{6} + \frac{1}{2}x > \frac{7}{6} + 2x$.

The number 6 is the least common multiple of all the denominators. Thus we multiply by 6 on both sides.

$$\begin{aligned} \frac{2}{3}x - \frac{1}{6} + \frac{1}{2}x &> \frac{7}{6} + 2x && \\ 6\left(\frac{2}{3}x - \frac{1}{6} + \frac{1}{2}x\right) &> 6\left(\frac{7}{6} + 2x\right) && \text{Multiplying by 6 on both sides} \\ 6 \cdot \frac{2}{3}x - 6 \cdot \frac{1}{6} + 6 \cdot \frac{1}{2}x &> 6 \cdot \frac{7}{6} + 6 \cdot 2x && \text{Using the distributive law} \\ 4x - 1 + 3x &> 7 + 12x && \text{Simplifying} \\ 7x - 1 &> 7 + 12x && \text{Collecting like terms} \\ 7x - 1 - 12x &> 7 + 12x - 12x && \text{Subtracting } 12x \\ -5x - 1 &> 7 && \text{Collecting like terms} \\ -5x - 1 + 1 &> 7 + 1 && \text{Adding 1} \\ -5x &> 8 && \text{Simplifying} \\ \frac{-5x}{-5} &< \frac{8}{-5} && \text{Dividing by } -5 \text{; The symbol must be reversed.} \\ x &< -\frac{8}{5} && \end{aligned}$$

The solution set is $\{x \mid x < -\frac{8}{5}\}$.

Do Exercise 20.

2.7 EXERCISE SET

For Extra Help

MathXL | MyMathLab | InterAct Math | Math Tutor Center | Digital Video Tutor CD 2 Videotape 3 | Student's Solutions Manual

a Determine whether each number is a solution of the given inequality.

1. $x > -4$
- **a)** 4
- **b)** 0
- **c)** -4
- **d)** 6
- **e)** 5.6

2. $x \leq 5$
- **a)** 0
- **b)** 5
- **c)** -1
- **d)** -5
- **e)** $7\frac{1}{4}$

3. $x \geq 6.8$
- **a)** -6
- **b)** 0
- **c)** 6
- **d)** 8
- **e)** $-3\frac{1}{2}$

4. $x < 8$
- **a)** 8
- **b)** -10
- **c)** 0
- **d)** 11
- **e)** -4.7

b Graph on a number line.

5. $x > 4$

−5 −4 −3 −2 −1 0 1 2 3 4 5

6. $x < 0$

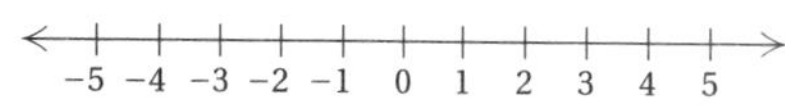

7. $t < -3$

−5 −4 −3 −2 −1 0 1 2 3 4 5

8. $y > 5$

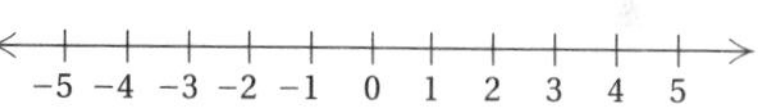

9. $m \geq -1$

−5 −4 −3 −2 −1 0 1 2 3 4 5

10. $x \leq -2$

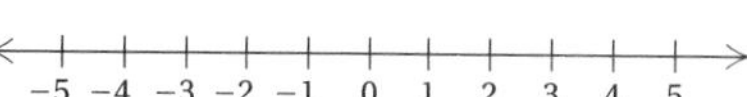

11. $-3 < x \leq 4$

−5 −4 −3 −2 −1 0 1 2 3 4 5

12. $-5 \leq x < 2$

13. $0 < x < 3$

−5 −4 −3 −2 −1 0 1 2 3 4 5

14. $-5 \leq x \leq 0$

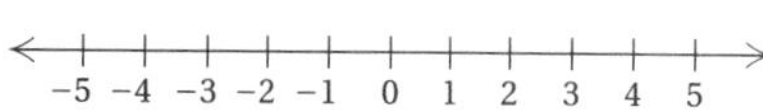

c Solve using the addition principle. Then graph.

15. $x + 7 > 2$

−5 −4 −3 −2 −1 0 1 2 3 4 5

16. $x + 5 > 2$

−5 −4 −3 −2 −1 0 1 2 3 4 5

17. $x + 8 \leq -10$

−40 −30 −20 −10 0 10 20 30 40

18. $x + 8 \leq -11$

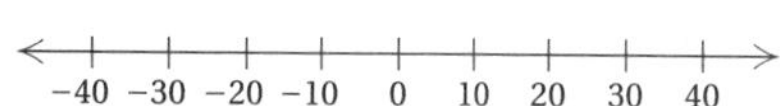

Solve using the addition principle.

19. $y - 7 > -12$

20. $y - 9 > -15$

21. $2x + 3 > x + 5$

22. $2x + 4 > x + 7$

23. $3x + 9 \leq 2x + 6$

24. $3x + 18 \leq 2x + 16$

25. $5x - 6 < 4x - 2$

26. $9x - 8 < 8x - 9$

27. $-9 + t > 5$

28. $-8 + p > 10$

29. $y + \frac{1}{4} \leq \frac{1}{2}$

30. $x - \frac{1}{3} \leq \frac{5}{6}$

31. $x - \frac{1}{3} > \frac{1}{4}$

32. $x + \frac{1}{8} > \frac{1}{2}$

d Solve using the multiplication principle. Then graph.

33. $5x < 35$

−8 −6 −4 −2 0 2 4 6 8

34. $8x \geq 32$

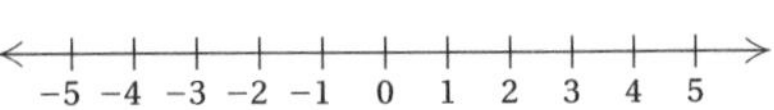

35. $-12x > -36$

−5 −4 −3 −2 −1 0 1 2 3 4 5

36. $-16x > -64$

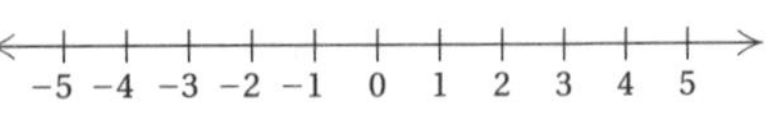

Solve using the multiplication principle.

37. $5y \geq -2$

38. $3x < -4$

39. $-2x \leq 12$

40. $-3x \leq 15$

41. $-4y \geq -16$

42. $-7x < -21$

43. $-3x < -17$

44. $-5y > -23$

45. $-2y > \frac{1}{7}$

46. $-4x \leq \frac{1}{9}$

47. $-\frac{6}{5} \leq -4x$

48. $-\frac{7}{9} > 63x$

e Solve using the addition and multiplication principles.

49. $4 + 3x < 28$

50. $3 + 4y < 35$

51. $3x - 5 \leq 13$

52. $5y - 9 \leq 21$

53. $13x - 7 < -46$

54. $8y - 6 < -54$

55. $30 > 3 - 9x$

56. $48 > 13 - 7y$

57. $4x + 2 - 3x \leq 9$

58. $15x + 5 - 14x \leq 9$

59. $-3 < 8x + 7 - 7x$

60. $-8 < 9x + 8 - 8x - 3$

61. $6 - 4y > 4 - 3y$

62. $9 - 8y > 5 - 7y + 2$

63. $5 - 9y \leq 2 - 8y$

64. $6 - 18x \leq 4 - 12x - 5x$

65. $19 - 7y - 3y < 39$

66. $18 - 6y - 4y < 63 + 5y$

67. $2.1x + 45.2 > 3.2 - 8.4x$

68. $0.96y - 0.79 \leq 0.21y + 0.46$

69. $\frac{x}{3} - 2 \leq 1$

70. $\frac{2}{3} + \frac{x}{5} < \frac{4}{15}$

71. $\frac{y}{5} + 1 \leq \frac{2}{5}$

72. $\frac{3x}{4} - \frac{7}{8} \geq -15$

73. $3(2y - 3) < 27$

74. $4(2y - 3) > 28$

75. $2(3 + 4m) - 9 \geq 45$

76. $3(5 + 3m) - 8 \leq 88$

77. $8(2t + 1) > 4(7t + 7)$

78. $7(5y - 2) > 6(6y - 1)$

79. $3(r - 6) + 2 < 4(r + 2) - 21$

80. $5(x + 3) + 9 \leq 3(x - 2) + 6$

81. $0.8(3x + 6) \geq 1.1 - (x + 2)$

82. $0.4(2x + 8) \geq 20 - (x + 5)$

83. $\frac{5}{3} + \frac{2}{3}x < \frac{25}{12} + \frac{5}{4}x + \frac{3}{4}$

84. $1 - \frac{2}{3}y \geq \frac{9}{5} - \frac{y}{5} + \frac{3}{5}$

85. D$_W$ Are the inequalities $3x - 4 < 10 - 4x$ and $2(x - 5) > 3(2x - 6)$ equivalent? Why or why not?

86. D$_W$ Explain in your own words why it is necessary to reverse the inequality symbol when multiplying on both sides of an inequality by a negative number.

SKILL MAINTENANCE

Add or subtract. [1.3a], [1.4a]

87. $-56 + (-18)$

88. $-2.3 + 7.1$

89. $-\frac{3}{4} + \frac{1}{8}$

90. $8.12 - 9.23$

91. $-56 - (-18)$

92. $-\frac{3}{4} - \frac{1}{8}$

93. $-2.3 - 7.1$

94. $-8.12 + 9.23$

Simplify.

95. $5 - 3^2 + (8 - 2)^2 \cdot 4$ [1.8d]

96. $10 \div 2 \cdot 5 - 3^2 + (-5)^2$ [1.8d]

97. $5(2x - 4) - 3(4x + 1)$ [1.8b]

98. $9(3 + 5x) - 4(7 + 2x)$ [1.8b]

SYNTHESIS

99. Determine whether each number is a solution of the inequality $|x| < 3$.

a) 0
b) -2
c) -3
d) 4
e) 3
f) 1.7
g) -2.8

100. Graph $|x| < 3$ on a number line.

−5 −4 −3 −2 −1 0 1 2 3 4 5

Solve.

101. $x + 3 < 3 + x$

102. $x + 4 > 3 + x$

2.8 APPLICATIONS AND PROBLEM SOLVING WITH INEQUALITIES

Objectives

a Translate number sentences to inequalities.

b Solve applied problems using inequalities.

The five steps for problem solving can be used for problems involving ıequalities.

a Translating to Inequalities

efore solving problems that involve inequalities, we list some important hrases to look for. Sample translations are listed as well.

IMPORTANT WORDS	SAMPLE SENTENCE	TRANSLATION
is at least	Bill is at least 21 years old.	$b \geq 21$
is at most	At most 5 students dropped the course.	$n \leq 5$
cannot exceed	To qualify, earnings cannot exceed \$12,000.	$r \leq 12{,}000$
must exceed	The speed must exceed 15 mph.	$s > 15$
is less than	Tucker's weight is less than 50 lb.	$w < 50$
is more than	Boston is more than 200 miles away.	$d > 200$
is between	The film was between 90 and 100 minutes long.	$90 < t < 100$
no more than	Bing weighs no more than 90 lb.	$w \leq 90$
no less than	Valerie scored no less than 8.3.	$s \geq 8.3$

The following phrases deserve special attention.

TRANSLATING "AT LEAST" AND "AT MOST"

A quantity x is at least some amount q: $x \geq q$.
(If x is at least q, it cannot be less than q.)

A quantity x is at most some amount q: $x \leq q$.
(If x is at most q, it cannot be more than q.)

ɔ *Exercises 1–10.*

Translate.

1. Maggie scored no less than 92 on her English exam.
2. The average credit card holder is at least \$4000 in debt.
3. The price of that PT Cruiser is at most \$21,900.
4. The time of the test was between 45 and 55 min.
5. Normandale Community College is more than 15 mi away.
6. Tania's weight is less than 110 lb.
7. That number is greater than -2.
8. The costs of production of that CD-ROM cannot exceed \$12,500.
9. At most, 11.4% of all deaths in Arizona are from cancer.
10. Yesterday, at least 23 people got tickets for speeding.

Answers on page A-9

ɔ Solving Problems

KAMPLE 1 *Catering Costs.* To cater a party, Curtis' Barbeque charges \$50 setup fee plus \$15 per person. The cost of Hotel Pharmacy's end-of-ason softball party cannot exceed \$450. How many people can attend e party?

urce: Curtis' All American Barbeque, Putney, Vermont

. **Familiarize.** Suppose that 20 people were to attend the party. The cost would then be $\$50 + \$15 \cdot 20$, or \$350. This shows that more than 20 people could attend without exceeding \$450. Instead of making another guess, we let n = the number of people in attendance.

2. **Translate.** The cost of the party will be \$50 for the setup fee plus \$1 times the number of people attending. We can reword and translate to a inequality as follows:

Rewording:	The setup fee	plus	the cost of the meals	cannot exceed	\$450.
Translating:	50	+	$15 \cdot n$	$\leq$	450

3. **Solve.** We solve the inequality for n:

$$50 + 15n \leq 450$$

$$50 + 15n - 50 \leq 450 - 50 \quad \text{Subtracting 50}$$

$$15n \leq 400 \quad \text{Simplifying}$$

$$\frac{15n}{15} \leq \frac{400}{15} \quad \text{Dividing by 15}$$

$$n \leq \frac{400}{15}$$

$$n \leq 26\tfrac{2}{3}. \quad \text{Simplifying}$$

4. **Check.** Although the solution set of the inequality is all numbers le than or equal to $26\frac{2}{3}$, since $n =$ the number of people in attendance, w round *down* to 26. If 26 people attend, the cost will be $\$50 + \$15 \cdot 26$, c \$440, and if 27 attend, the cost will exceed \$450.

5. **State.** At most 26 people can attend the party.

Do Exercise 11.

Caution!

Solutions of problems should always be checked using the original wording of the problem. In some cases, answers might need to be whole numbers or integers or rounded off in a particular direction.

11. **Butter Temperatures.** Butter stays solid at Fahrenheit temperatures below 88°. The formula

$$F = \tfrac{9}{5}C + 32$$

can be used to convert Celsius temperatures C to Fahrenheit temperatures F. Determine (in terms of an inequality) those Celsius temperatures for which butter stays solid.

Answer on page A-9

EXAMPLE 2 *Nutrition.* The U.S. Department of Agriculture recommen that for a typical 2000-calorie daily diet, no more than 20 g of saturated fat b consumed. In the first three days of a four-day vacation, Anthony consume 26 g, 17 g, and 22 g of saturated fat. Determine (in terms of an inequality) ho many grams of saturated fat Anthony can consume on the fourth day if he to average no more than 20 g of saturated fat per day.

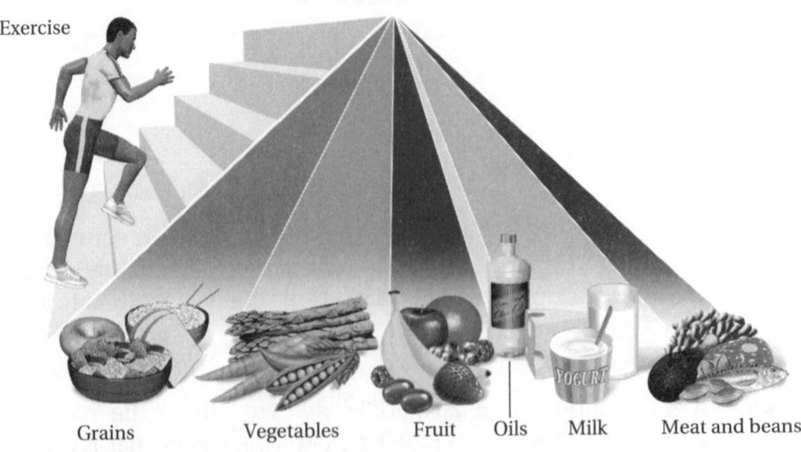

Sources: U.S. Department of Health and Human Services and Department of Agriculture

1. **Familiarize.** Suppose Anthony consumed 19 g of saturated fat on the fourth day. His daily average for the vacation would then be

$$\frac{26\text{ g} + 17\text{ g} + 22\text{ g} + 19\text{ g}}{4} = 21\text{ g}.$$

This shows that Anthony cannot consume 19 g of saturated fat on the fourth day, if he is to average no more than 20 g of fat per day. We let x = the number of grams of fat that Anthony consumes on the fourth day.

2. **Translate.** We reword the problem and translate to an inequality as follows:

Rewording:	The average consumption of saturated fat	should be no more than	20 g.
Translating:	$\frac{26 + 17 + 22 + x}{4}$	$\leq$	20

3. **Solve.** Because of the fraction expression, it is convenient to use the multiplication principle first to solve the inequality:

$$\frac{26 + 17 + 22 + x}{4} \leq 20$$

$$4\left(\frac{26 + 17 + 22 + x}{4}\right) \leq 4 \cdot 20 \quad \text{Multiplying by 4}$$

$$26 + 17 + 22 + x \leq 80$$

$$65 + x \leq 80 \quad \text{Simplifying}$$

$$x \leq 15. \quad \text{Subtracting 65}$$

4. **Check.** As a partial check, we show that Anthony can consume 15 g of saturated fat on the fourth day and not exceed a 20-g average for the four days:

$$\frac{26 + 17 + 22 + 15}{4} = \frac{80}{4} = 20.$$

5. **State.** Anthony's average intake of saturated fat for the vacation will not exceed 20 g per day if he consumes no more than 15 g of saturated fat on the fourth day.

o *Exercise 12.*

Translate to an inequality and solve.

12. **Test Scores.** A pre-med student is taking a chemistry course in which four tests are given. To get an A, she must average at least 90 on the four tests. The student got scores of 91, 86, and 89 on the first three tests. Determine (in terms of an inequality) what scores on the last test will allow her to get an A.

Answer on page A-9

Study Tips

CHECKLIST

The foundation of all your study skills is TIME!

- ☐ Are you approaching your study of mathematics with an assertive, positive attitude?
- ☐ Are you making use of the textbook supplements, such as the AW Math Tutor Center, the *Student's Solutions Manual*, and the videotapes?
- ☐ Have you determined the location of the learning resource centers on your campus, such as a math lab, tutor center, and your instructor's office?
- ☐ Are you stopping to work the margin exercises when directed to do so?
- ☐ Are you keeping one section ahead in your syllabus?

2.8 EXERCISE SET

For Extra Help

MathXL | MyMathLab | InterAct Math | Math Tutor Center | Digital Video Tutor CD 2 Videotape 3 | Student Solutions Manual

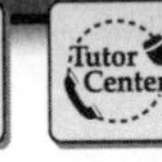

a Translate to an inequality.

1. A number is at least 7.

2. A number is greater than or equal to 5.

3. The baby weighs more than 2 kilograms (kg).

4. Between 75 and 100 people attended the concert.

5. The speed of the train was between 90 and 110 mph.

6. At least 400,000 people attended the Million Man March.

7. At most 1,200,000 people attended the Million Man March.

8. The amount of acid is not to exceed 40 liters (L).

9. The cost of gasoline is no less than \$1.50 per gallon.

10. The temperature is at most $-2°$.

11. A number is greater than 8.

12. A number is less than 5.

13. A number is less than or equal to -4.

14. A number is greater than or equal to 18.

15. The number of people is at least 1300.

16. The cost is at most \$4857.95.

17. The amount of acid is not to exceed 500 liters.

18. The cost of gasoline is no less than 94 cents per gallon.

19. Two more than three times a number is less than 13.

20. Five less than one-half a number is greater than 17.

b Solve.

21. *Test Scores.* A student is taking a literature course in which four tests are given. To get a B, he must average at least 80 on the four tests. The student got scores of 82, 76, and 78 on the first three tests. Determine (in terms of an inequality) what scores on the last test will allow him to get at least a B.

22. *Test Scores.* Your quiz grades are 73, 75, 89, and 91. Determine (in terms of an inequality) what scores on the last quiz will allow you to get an average quiz grad of at least 85.

3. *Gold Temperatures.* Gold stays solid at Fahrenheit temperatures below 1945.4°. Determine (in terms of an inequality) those Celsius temperatures for which gold stays solid. Use the formula given in Margin Exercise 11.

24. *Body Temperatures.* The human body is considered to be fevered when its temperature is higher than 98.6°F. Using the formula given in Margin Exercise 11, determine (in terms of an inequality) those Celsius temperatures for which the body is fevered.

5. *World Records in the 1500-m Run.* The formula

$$R = -0.075t + 3.85$$

can be used to predict the world record in the 1500-m run t years after 1930. Determine (in terms of an inequality) those years for which the world record will be less than 3.5 min.

26. *World Records in the 200-m Dash.* The formula

$$R = -0.028t + 20.8$$

can be used to predict the world record in the 200-m dash t years after 1920. Determine (in terms of an inequality) those years for which the world record will be less than 19.0 sec.

7. *Sizes of Envelopes.* Rhetoric Advertising is a direct-mail company. It determines that for a particular campaign, it can use any envelope with a fixed width of $3\frac{1}{2}$ in. and an area of at least $17\frac{1}{2}$ in^2. Determine (in terms of an inequality) those lengths that will satisfy the company constraints.

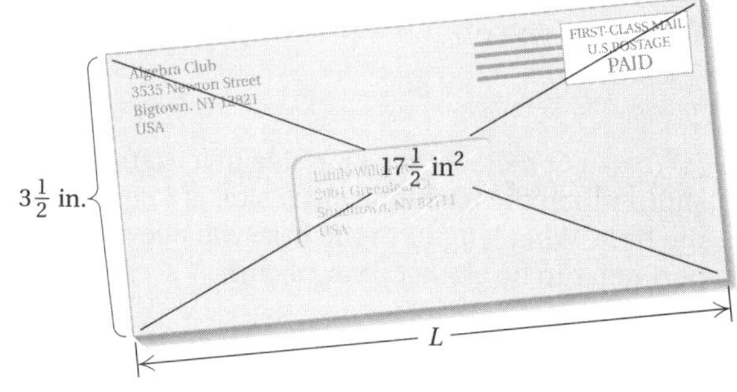

28. *Sizes of Packages.* An overnight delivery service accepts packages of up to 165 in. in length and girth combined. (Girth is the distance around the package.) A package has a fixed girth of 53 in. Determine (in terms of an inequality) those lengths for which a package is acceptable.

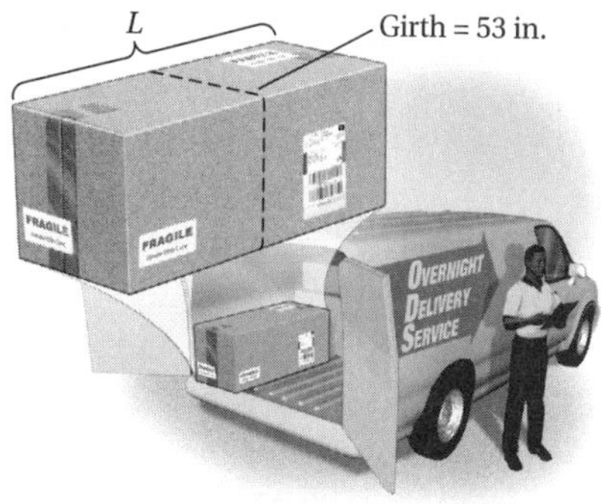

Blueprints. To make copies of blueprints, Vantage Reprographics charges a \$5 setup fee plus \$4 per copy. Myra can spend no more than \$65 for the copying. What numbers of copies will allow her to stay within budget?

30. *Banquet Costs.* The women's volleyball team can spend at most \$450 for its awards banquet at a local restaurant. If the restaurant charges a \$40 setup fee plus \$16 per person, at most how many can attend?

31. *Phone Costs.* Simon claims that it costs him at least \$3.00 every time he calls an overseas customer. If his typical call costs 75¢ plus 45¢ for each minute, how long do his calls typically last? (*Hint*: 75¢ = \$0.75.)

32. *Parking Costs.* Laura is certain that every time she parks in the municipal garage it costs her at least \$2.20. If the garage charges 45¢ plus 25¢ for each half hour, fo how long is Laura's car generally parked?

33. *College Tuition.* Angelica's financial aid stipulates that her tuition not exceed \$1000. If her local community college charges a \$35 registration fee plus \$375 per course, what is the greatest number of courses for which Angelica can register?

34. *Furnace Repairs.* RJ's Plumbing and Heating charges \$25 plus \$30 per hour for emergency service. Gary remembers being billed over \$100 for an emergency call. How long was RJ's there?

35. *Nutrition.* Following the guidelines of the Food and Drug Administration, Dale tries to eat at least 5 servings of fruits or vegetables each day. For the first six days of one week, he had 4, 6, 7, 4, 6, and 4 servings. How many servings of fruits or vegetables should Dale eat on Saturday, in order to average at least 5 servings per day for the week?

36. *College Course Load.* To remain on financial aid, Mill needs to complete an average of at least 7 credits per quarter each year. In the first three quarters of 2005, Millie completed 5, 7, and 8 credits. How many credits of course work must Millie complete in the fourth quarter if she is to remain on financial aid?

37. *Perimeter of a Rectangle.* The width of a rectangle is fixed at 8 ft. What lengths will make the perimeter at least 200 ft? at most 200 ft?

38. *Perimeter of a Triangle.* One side of a triangle is 2 cm shorter than the base. The other side is 3 cm longer th the base. What lengths of the base will allow the perimeter to be greater than 19 cm?

39. *Area of a Rectangle.* The width of a rectangle is fixed at 4 cm. For what lengths will the area be less than 86 cm^2?

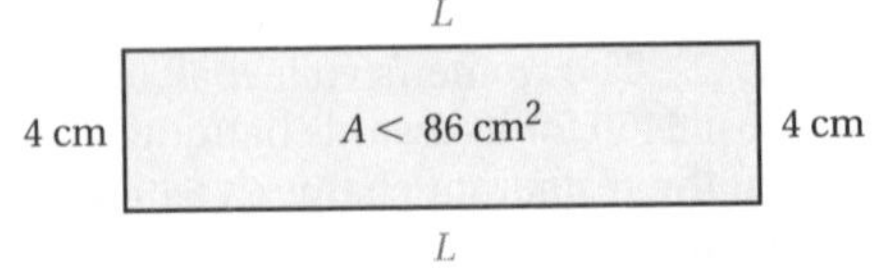

40. *Area of a Rectangle.* The width of a rectangle is fixed 16 yd. For what lengths will the area be at least 264 yd

1. *Insurance-covered Repairs.* Most insurance companies will replace a vehicle if an estimated repair exceeds 80% of the "blue-book" value of the vehicle. Michelle's insurance company paid \$8500 for repairs to her Subaru after an accident. What can be concluded about the blue-book value of the car?

42. *Insurance-covered Repairs.* Following an accident, Jeff's Ford pickup was replaced by his insurance company because the damage was so extensive. Before the damage, the blue-book value of the truck was \$21,000. How much would it have cost to repair the truck? (See Exercise 41.)

3. *Fat Content in Foods.* Reduced Fat Skippy® peanut butter contains 12 g of fat per serving. In order for a food to be labeled "reduced fat," it must have at least 25% less fat than the regular item. What can you conclude about the number of grams of fat in a serving of the regular Skippy peanut butter?
Source: Best Foods

44. *Fat Content in Foods.* Reduced Fat Chips Ahoy!® cookies contain 5 g of fat per serving. What can you conclude about the number of grams of fat in regular Chips Ahoy! cookies (see Exercise 43)?
Source: Nabisco Brands, Inc.

5. *Pond Depth.* On July 1, Garrett's Pond was 25 ft deep. Since that date, the water level has dropped $\frac{2}{3}$ ft per week. For what dates will the water level not exceed 21 ft?

46. *Weight Gain.* A 3-lb puppy is gaining weight at a rate of $\frac{3}{4}$ lb per week. When will the puppy's weight exceed $22\frac{1}{2}$ lb?

7. *Area of a Triangular Flag.* As part of an outdoor education course, Wanda needs to make a bright-colored triangular flag with an area of at least 3 ft^2. What heights can the triangle be if the base is $1\frac{1}{2}$ ft?

48. *Area of a Triangular Sign.* Zoning laws in Harrington prohibit displaying signs with areas exceeding 12 ft^2. If Flo's Marina is ordering a triangular sign with an 8-ft base, how tall can the sign be?

9. *Electrician Visits.* Dot's Electric made 17 customer calls last week and 22 calls this week. How many calls must be made next week in order to maintain an average of at least 20 for the three-week period?

50. *Volunteer Work.* George and Joan do volunteer work at a hospital. Joan worked 3 more hr than George, and together they worked more than 27 hr. What possible numbers of hours did each work?

51. DW If f represents Fran's age and t represents Todd's age, write a sentence that would translate to $t + 3 < f$.

52. DW Explain how the meanings of "Five more than a number" and "Five is more than a number" differ.

SKILL MAINTENANCE

VOCABULARY REINFORCEMENT

In each of Exercises 53–60, fill in the blank with the correct term from the given list. Some of the choices may not be used.

53. The product of a(n) ______________ number of negative numbers is always positive. [1.5a]

54. The product of a(n) ______________ number of negative numbers is always negative. [1.5a]

55. The ______________ inverse of a negative number is always positive. [1.3b]

56. The ______________ inverse of a negative number is always negative. [1.6b]

57. Equations with the same solutions are called ______________ equations. [2.1b]

58. The ______________ for equations asserts that when we add the same number to the expressions on each side of the equation, we get equivalent equations. [2.1b]

59. The ______________ for inequalities asserts that when we multiply or divide by a negative number on both sides of an inequality, the direction of the inequality symbol ______________. [2.7d]

60. Any replacement for the variable that makes an equation true is called a(n) ______________ of the equation. [2.1a]

addition principle
multiplication principle
solution
replacement
variable
is reversed
stays the same
even
odd
multiplicative
additive
equivalent

SYNTHESIS

61. *Ski Wax.* Green ski wax works best between 5° and 15° Fahrenheit. Determine those Celsius temperatures for which green ski wax works best.

62. *Parking Fees.* Mack's Parking Garage charges $4.00 for the first hour and $2.50 for each additional hour. For how long has a car been parked when the charge exceeds $16.50?

63. *Nutritional Standards.* In order for a food to be labeled "lowfat," it must have fewer than 3 g of fat per serving. Reduced fat Tortilla Pops® contain 60% less fat than regular nacho cheese tortilla chips, but still cannot be labeled lowfat. What can you conclude about the fat content of a serving of nacho cheese tortilla chips?

64. *Parking Fees.* When asked how much the parking charge is for a certain car (see Exercise 62), Mack replie "between 14 and 24 dollars." For how long has the car been parked?

2 Summary and Review

The review that follows is meant to prepare you for a chapter exam. It consists of three parts. The first part, Concept Reinforcement, is designed to increase understanding of the concepts through true/false exercises. The second part is a list of important properties and formulas. The third part is the Review Exercises. These provide practice exercises for the exam, together with references to section objectives so you can go back and review. Before beginning, stop and look back over the skills you have obtained. What skills in mathematics do you have now that you did not have before studying this chapter?

CONCEPT REINFORCEMENT

Determine whether the statement is true or false. Answers are given at the back of the book.

_______ **1.** If $x > y$, then $-x < -y$.

_______ **2.** Consecutive odd integers are 2 units apart.

_______ **3.** For any number n, $n \geq n$.

_______ **4.** $3 - x = 4x$ and $5x = -3$ are equivalent equations.

_______ **5.** Some equations have no solution.

_______ **6.** $2x - 7 < 11$ and $x < -9$ are equivalent inequalities.

IMPORTANT PROPERTIES AND FORMULAS

The Addition Principle for Equations: For any real numbers a, b, and c: $a = b$ is equivalent to $a + c = b + c$.

The Multiplication Principle for Equations: For any real numbers a, b, and c, $c \neq 0$: $a = b$ is equivalent to $a \cdot c = b \cdot c$.

The Addition Principle for Inequalities: For any real numbers a, b, and c:
$a < b$ is equivalent to $a + c < b + c$;
$a > b$ is equivalent to $a + c > b + c$;
$a \leq b$ is equivalent to $a + c \leq b + c$;
$a \geq b$ is equivalent to $a + c \geq b + c$.

The Multiplication Principle for Inequalities: For any real numbers a and b, and any *positive* number c:
$a < b$ is equivalent to $ac < bc$; $a > b$ is equivalent to $ac > bc$.
For any real numbers a and b, and any *negative* number c:
$a < b$ is equivalent to $ac > bc$; $a > b$ is equivalent to $ac < bc$.

Review Exercises

Solve. [2.1b]

1. $x + 5 = -17$

2. $n - 7 = -6$

3. $x - 11 = 14$

4. $y - 0.9 = 9.09$

Solve. [2.2a]

5. $-\frac{2}{3}x = -\frac{1}{6}$

6. $-8x = -56$

7. $-\frac{x}{4} = 48$

8. $15x = -35$

9. $\frac{4}{5}y = -\frac{3}{16}$

Solve. [2.3a]

10. $5 - x = 13$

11. $\frac{1}{4}x - \frac{5}{8} = \frac{3}{8}$

Solve. [2.3b, c]

12. $5t + 9 = 3t - 1$

13. $7x - 6 = 25x$

14. $14y = 23y - 17 - 10$

15. $0.22y - 0.6 = 0.12y + 3 - 0.8y$

16. $\frac{1}{4}x - \frac{1}{8}x = 3 - \frac{1}{16}x$

17. $14y + 17 + 7y = 9 + 21y + 8$

Solve. [2.3c]

18. $4(x + 3) = 36$

19. $3(5x - 7) = -66$

20. $8(x - 2) - 5(x + 4) = 20 + x$

21. $-5x + 3(x + 8) = 16$

22. $6(x - 2) - 16 = 3(2x - 5) + 11$

Determine whether the given number is a solution of the inequality $x \leq 4$. [2.7a]

23. -3

24. 7

25. 4

Solve. Write set notation for the answers. [2.7c, d, e]

26. $y + \frac{2}{3} \geq \frac{1}{6}$

27. $9x \geq 63$

28. $2 + 6y > 14$

29. $7 - 3y \geq 27 + 2y$

30. $3x + 5 < 2x - 6$

31. $-4y < 28$

32. $4 - 8x < 13 + 3x$

33. $-4x \leq \frac{1}{3}$

Graph on a number line. [2.7b, e]

34. $4x - 6 < x + 3$

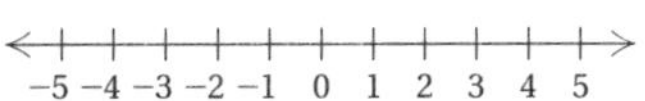

35. $-2 < x \leq 5$

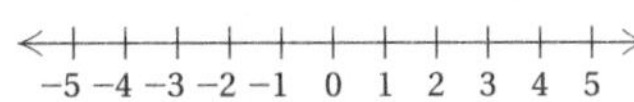

36. $y > 0$

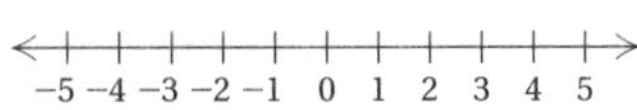

Solve. [2.4b]

37. $C = \pi d$, for d

38. $V = \frac{1}{3}Bh$, for B

39. $A = \frac{a + b}{2}$, for a

40. $y = mx + b$, for x

Solve. [2.6a]

41. *Dimensions of Wyoming.* The state of Wyoming is roughly in the shape of a rectangle whose perimeter is 1280 mi. The length is 90 mi more than the width. Find the dimensions.

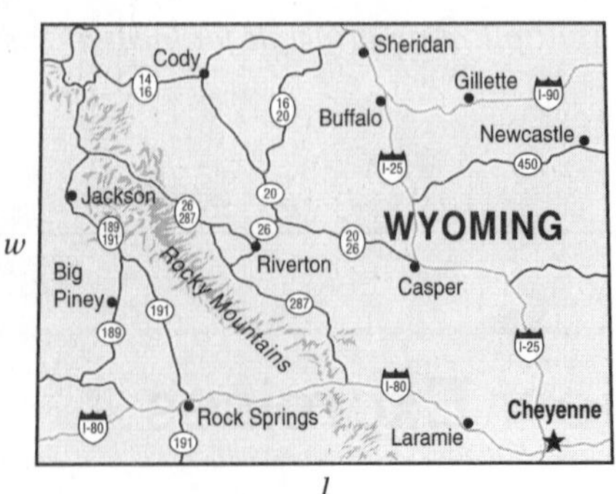

42. *Interstate Mile Markers.* The sum of two consecutive mile markers on I-5 in California is 691. Find the numbers on the markers.

3. An entertainment center sold for $2449 in June. This was $332 more than the cost in February. Find the cost in February.

4. Ty is paid a commission of $4 for each appliance he sells. One week, he received $108 in commissions. How many appliances did he sell?

5. The measure of the second angle of a triangle is 50° more than that of the first angle. The measure of the third angle is 10° less than twice the first angle. Find the measures of the angles.

olve. [2.5a]

6. What number is 20% of 75?

7. Fifteen is what percent of 80?

8. 18 is 3% of what number?

9. *Job Opportunities.* There were 905 thousand child-care workers in 1998. Job opportunities are expected to grow to 1141 thousand by 2008. What is the percent of increase?

Source: *Handbook of U.S. Labor Statistics*

olve. [2.6a]

0. After a 30% reduction, a bread maker is on sale for $154. What was the marked price (the price before the reduction)?

51. A hotel manager's salary is $61,410, which is a 15% increase over the previous year's salary. What was the previous salary?

52. A tax-exempt charity received a bill of $145.90 for a sump pump. The bill incorrectly included sales tax of 5%. How much does the charity actually owe?

Solve. [2.8b]

53. *Test Scores.* Your test grades are 71, 75, 82, and 86. What is the lowest grade that you can get on the next test and still have an average test score of at least 80?

54. The length of a rectangle is 43 cm. What widths will make the perimeter greater than 120 cm?

55. DW Would it be better to receive a 5% raise and then an 8% raise or the other way around? Why? [2.5a]

56. DW Are the inequalities $x > -5$ and $-x < 5$ equivalent? Why or why not? [2.7d]

SYNTHESIS

Solve.

57. $2|x| + 4 = 50$ [1.2e], [2.3a]

58. $|3x| = 60$ [1.2e], [2.2a]

59. $y = 2a - ab + 3$, for a [2.4b]

2 Chapter Test

For Extra Help

Work It Out!
Chapter Test Video
on CD

Solve.

1. $x + 7 = 15$

2. $t - 9 = 17$

3. $3x = -18$

4. $-\frac{4}{7}x = -28$

5. $3t + 7 = 2t - 5$

6. $\frac{1}{2}x - \frac{3}{5} = \frac{2}{5}$

7. $8 - y = 16$

8. $-\frac{2}{5} + x = -\frac{3}{4}$

9. $3(x + 2) = 27$

10. $-3x - 6(x - 4) = 9$

11. $0.4p + 0.2 = 4.2p - 7.8 - 0.6p$

12. $4(3x - 1) + 11 = 2(6x + 5) - 8$

13. $-2 + 7x + 6 = 5x + 4 + 2x$

Solve. Write set notation for the answers.

14. $x + 6 \leq 2$

15. $14x + 9 > 13x - 4$

16. $12x \leq 60$

17. $-2y \geq 26$

18. $-4y \leq -32$

19. $-5x \geq \frac{1}{4}$

20. $4 - 6x > 40$

21. $5 - 9x \geq 19 + 5x$

Graph on a number line.

22. $y \leq 9$

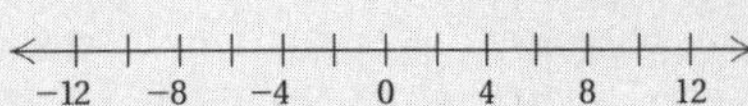

23. $6x - 3 < x + 2$

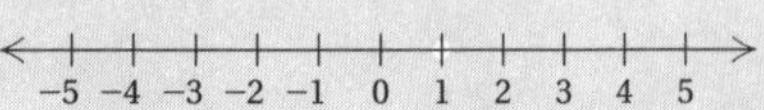

24. $-2 \leq x \leq 2$

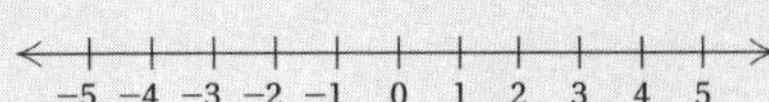

Solve.

25. What number is 24% of 75?

26. 15.84 is what percent of 96?

27. 800 is 2% of what number?

28. *Job Opportunities.* Job opportunities for physician's assistants are expected to increase from 58,000 in 2000 to 89,000 in 2010. What is the percent of increase?
Source: *Monthly Labor Review*, November 2001

9. *Perimeter of a Photograph.* The perimeter of a rectangular photograph is 36 cm. The length is 4 cm greater than the width. Find the width and the length.

30. *Charitable Contributions.* About 35.9% of all charitable contributions are made to religious organizations. In 2003, about \$86.4 billion was given to religious organizations. How much was given to charities in general?

Source: AAFRC Trust for Philanthropy/Giving USA 2004

1. *Raffle Tickets.* The numbers on three raffle tickets are consecutive integers whose sum is 7530. Find the integers.

32. *Savings Account.* Money is invested in a savings account at 5% simple interest. After 1 year, there is \$924 in the account. How much was originally invested?

3. *Board Cutting.* An 8-m board is cut into two pieces. One piece is 2 m longer than the other. How long are the pieces?

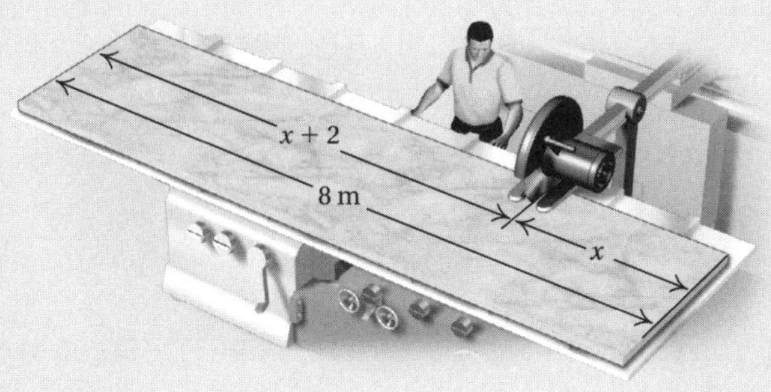

34. *Lengths of a Rectangle.* The width of a rectangle is 96 yd. Find all possible lengths such that the perimeter of the rectangle will be at least 540 yd.

5. *Budgeting.* Jason has budgeted an average of \$95 a month for entertainment. For the first five months of the year, he has spent \$98, \$89, \$110, \$85, and \$83. How much can Jason spend in the sixth month without exceeding his average budget?

36. *Copy Machine Rental.* It costs \$225 per month plus 1.2¢ per copy to rent a copy machine. A catalog publisher needs to lease a copy machine for use during a special project that they anticipate will take 3 months. They decide to rent the copier, but must stay within a budget of \$2400 for copies. Determine (in terms of an inequality) the number of copies they can make and still remain within budget.

7. Solve $A = 2\pi rh$ for r.

38. Solve $y = 8x + b$ for x.

SYNTHESIS

9. Solve $c = \dfrac{1}{a - d}$ for d.

40. Solve: $3|w| - 8 = 37$.

1. A movie theater had a certain number of tickets to give away. Five people got the tickets. The first got one-third of the tickets, the second got one-fourth of the tickets, and the third got one-fifth of the tickets. The fourth person got eight tickets, and there were five tickets left for the fifth person. Find the total number of tickets given away.

CHAPTERS 1–2

Cumulative Review

Evaluate.

1. $\frac{y-x}{4}$, when $y = 12$ and $x = 6$

2. $\frac{3x}{y}$, when $x = 5$ and $y = 4$

3. $x - 3$, when $x = 3$

4. Translate to an algebraic expression: Four less than twice w.

Use $<$ or $>$ for □ to write a true sentence.

5. -4 □ -6

6. 0 □ -5

7. -8 □ 7

8. Find the opposite and the reciprocal of $\frac{2}{5}$.

Find the absolute value.

9. $|3|$

10. $\left|-\frac{3}{4}\right|$

11. $|0|$

Compute and simplify.

12. $-6.7 + 2.3$

13. $-\frac{1}{6} - \frac{7}{3}$

14. $-\frac{5}{8}\left(-\frac{4}{3}\right)$

15. $(-7)(5)(-6)(-0.5)$

16. $81 \div (-9)$

17. $-10.8 \div 3.6$

18. $-\frac{4}{5} \div -\frac{25}{8}$

Multiply.

19. $5(3x + 5y + 2z)$

20. $4(-3x - 2)$

21. $-6(2y - 4x)$

Factor.

22. $64 + 18x + 24y$

23. $16y - 56$

24. $5a - 15b + 25$

Collect like terms.

25. $9b + 18y + 6b + 4y$

26. $3y + 4 + 6z + 6y$

27. $-4d - 6a + 3a - 5d + 1$

28. $3.2x + 2.9y - 5.8x - 8.1y$

Simplify.

29. $7 - 2x - (-5x) - 8$

30. $-3x - (-x + y)$

31. $-3(x - 2) - 4x$

32. $10 - 2(5 - 4x)$

33. $[3(x + 6) - 10] - [5 - 2(x - 8)]$

olve.

4. $x + 1.75 = 6.25$

35. $\frac{5}{2}y = \frac{2}{5}$

36. $-2.6 + x = 8.3$

7. $4\frac{1}{2} + y = 8\frac{1}{3}$

38. $-\frac{3}{4}x = 36$

39. $-2.2y = -26.4$

0. $5.8x = -35.96$

41. $-4x + 3 = 15$

42. $-3x + 5 = -8x - 7$

3. $4y - 4 + y = 6y + 20 - 4y$

44. $-3(x - 2) = -15$

45. $\frac{1}{3}x - \frac{5}{6} = \frac{1}{2} + 2x$

6. $-3.7x + 6.2 = -7.3x - 5.8$

47. $4(x + 2) = 4(x - 2) + 16$

48. $0(x + 3) + 4 = 0$

9. $5(7 + x) = (x + 7)5$

50. $3x - 1 < 2x + 1$

51. $5 - y \leq 2y - 7$

2. $3y + 7 > 5y + 13$

3. $H = 65 - m$, for m
(To determine the number of heating degree days H for a day with m degrees Fahrenheit as the average temperature)

54. $I = Prt$, for P
(Simple-interest formula, where I is interest, P is principal, r is interest rate, and t is time)

olve.

5. What number is 24% of 105?

56. 39.6 is what percent of 88?

7. \$163.60 is 45% of what number?

8. *Overweight Americans.* In 2004, there were 291 million people in the United States. About 60% of them were considered overweight. How many people were overweight?

Source: U.S. Centers for Disease Control

59. *Grade Average.* Nadia is taking a literature course in which four tests are given. To get a B, a student must average at least 80 on the four tests. Nadia scored 82, 76, and 78 on the first three tests. What scores on the last test will earn her at least a B?

0. *Rollerblade Costs.* Susan and Melinda purchased rollerblades for a total of \$107. Susan paid \$17 more for her rollerblades than Melinda did. What did Melinda pay?

61. *Savings Investment.* Money is invested in a savings account at 8% simple interest. After 1 year, there is \$1134 in the account. How much was originally invested?

62. *Wire Cutting.* A 143-m wire is cut into three pieces. The second piece is 3 m longer than the first. The third is four-fifths as long as the first. How long is each piece?

63. *Truck Rentals.* Truck-Rite Rentals rents trucks at a daily rate of \$49.95 plus 39¢ per mile. Concert Productions has budgeted \$100 for renting a truck to haul equipment to an upcoming concert. How far can they travel in one day and stay within their budget?

64. *Price Reduction.* After a 25% reduction, a tie is on sale for \$18.45. What was the price before reduction?

For each of Exercises 65–67, choose the correct answer from the selections given.

65. Simplify: $-125 \div 25 \cdot 625 \div 5$.

a) $-390{,}625$ **b)** -125
c) -625 **d)** 25
e) None of these

66. Remove parentheses and simplify:

$$[5(2x + 6) - 7] - [2(x + 4) + 5].$$

a) $8x + 36$ **b)** $8x - 10$
c) $8x + 8$ **d)** $8x + 10$
e) None of these

67. Solve $V = IR$ for I.

a) $I = V - R$ **b)** $I = \dfrac{V}{R}$

c) $I = \dfrac{R}{V}$ **d)** $I = VR$

e) None of these

SYNTHESIS

68. An engineer's salary at the end of a year is \$48,418.24. This reflects a 4% salary increase and a later 3% cost-of-living adjustment during the year. What was the salary at the beginning of the year?

69. Nadia needs to use a copier to reduce a drawing to fit on a page. The original drawing is 9 in. long and it must fit into a space that is 6.3 in. long. By what percent should she reduce the drawing on the copier?

Solve.

70. $4|x| - 13 = 3$

71. $\dfrac{2 + 5x}{4} = \dfrac{11}{28} + \dfrac{8x + 3}{7}$

72. $p = \dfrac{2}{m + Q}$, for Q

3.1 GRAPHS AND APPLICATIONS OF LINEAR EQUATIONS

Objectives

a Plot points associated with ordered pairs of numbers; determine the quadrant in which a point lies.

b Find the coordinates of a point on a graph.

c Determine whether an ordered pair is a solution of an equation with two variables.

d Graph linear equations of the type $y = mx + b$ and $Ax + By = C$, identifying the y-intercept.

e Solve applied problems involving graphs of linear equations.

You probably have seen bar graphs like the following in newspapers and magazines. Note that a straight line can be drawn along the tops of the bars. Such a line is a *graph of a linear equation.* In this chapter, we study how to graph linear equations and consider properties such as slope and intercepts. Many applications of these topics will also be considered.

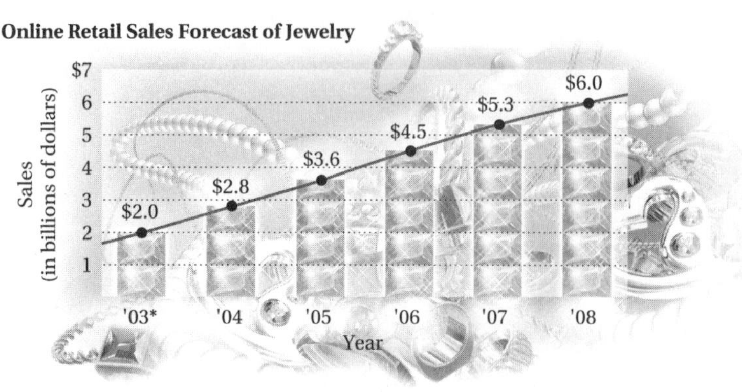

*Actual
Source: Forrester Research

Plot these points on the graph below.

1. $(4, 5)$ **2.** $(5, 4)$

3. $(-2, 5)$ **4.** $(-3, -4)$

5. $(5, -3)$ **6.** $(-2, -1)$

7. $(0, -3)$ **8.** $(2, 0)$

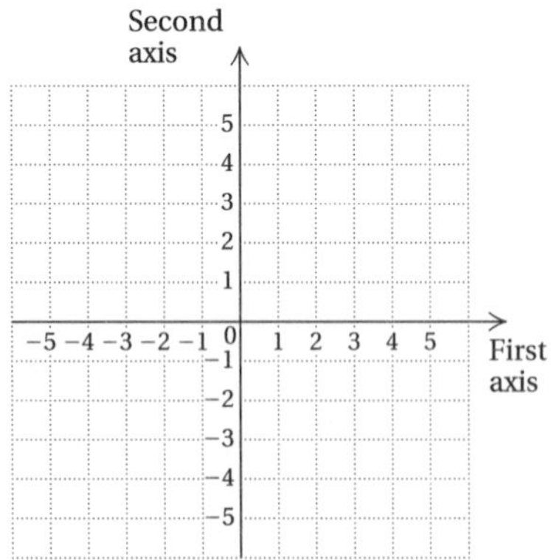

Answers on page A-10

a Plotting Ordered Pairs

In Chapter 2, we graphed numbers and inequalities in one variable on a line. To enable us to graph an equation that contains two variables, we now learn to graph number pairs on a plane.

On a number line, each point is the graph of a number. On a plane, each point is the graph of a number pair. We use two perpendicular number lines called **axes.** They cross at a point called the **origin.** The arrows show the positive directions.

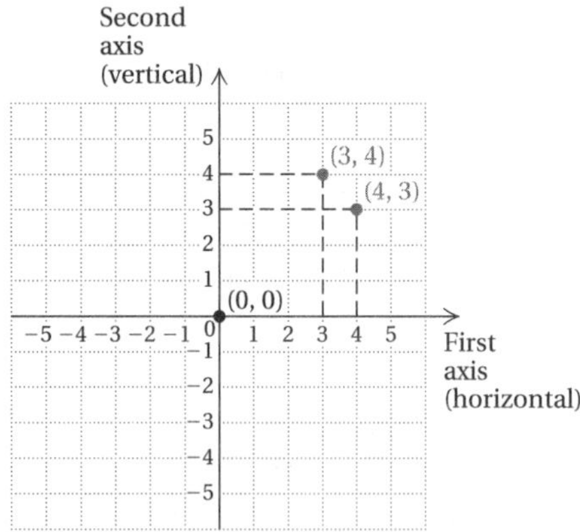

Consider the ordered pair $(3, 4)$. The numbers in an ordered pair are called **coordinates.** In $(3, 4)$, the **first coordinate (abscissa)** is 3 and the **second coordinate (ordinate)** is 4. To plot $(3, 4)$, we start at the origin and move horizontally to the 3. Then we move up vertically 4 units and make a "dot."

The point $(4, 3)$ is also plotted. Note that $(3, 4)$ and $(4, 3)$ give different points. The order of the numbers in the pair is indeed important. They are called **ordered pairs** because it makes a difference which number comes first. The coordinates of the origin are $(0, 0)$.

XAMPLE 1 Plot the point
−5, 2).

The first number, −5, is egative. Starting at the rigin, we move −5 units in he horizontal direction 5 units to the left). The econd number, 2, is positive. Ve move 2 units in the ertical direction (up).

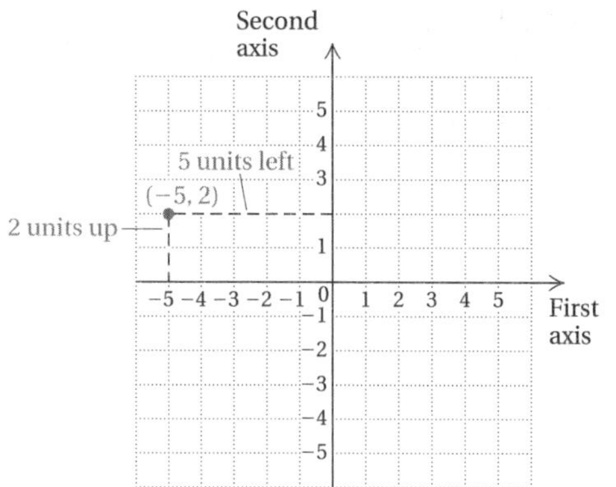

Caution!

The *first* coordinate of an ordered pair is always graphed in a *horizontal* direction and the *second* coordinate is always graphed in a *vertical* direction.

o Exercises 1–8 on the preceding page.

The figure below shows some points and their coordinates. In region I he *first quadrant*), both coordinates of any point are positive. In region II he *second quadrant*), the first coordinate is negative and the second positive. In region III (the *third quadrant*), both coordinates are negative. In region IV (the *fourth quadrant*), the first coordinate is positive and the second negative.

XAMPLE 2 In which quadrant, if any, are the points (−4, 5), (5, −5), (2, 4), −2, −5), and (−5, 0) located?

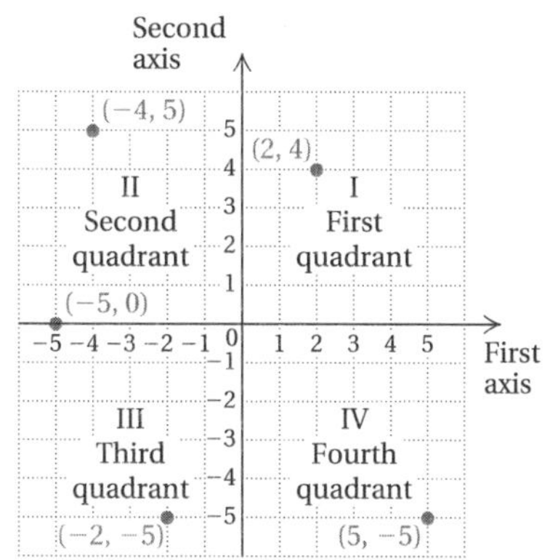

The point (−4, 5) is in the second quadrant. The point (5, −5) is in the ourth quadrant. The point (2, 4) is in the first quadrant. The point (−2, −5) in the third quadrant. The point (−5, 0) is on an axis and is *not* in any uadrant.

o Exercises 9–15.

5 Finding Coordinates

o find the coordinates of a point, we see how far to the right or left of zero it located and how far up or down from zero.

9. What can you say about the coordinates of a point in the third quadrant?

10. What can you say about the coordinates of a point in the fourth quadrant?

In which quadrant, if any, is the point located?

11. (5, 3)

12. (−6, −4)

13. (10, −14)

14. (−13, 9)

15. (0, −3)

16. Find the coordinates of points *A*, *B*, *C*, *D*, *E*, *F*, and *G* on the graph below.

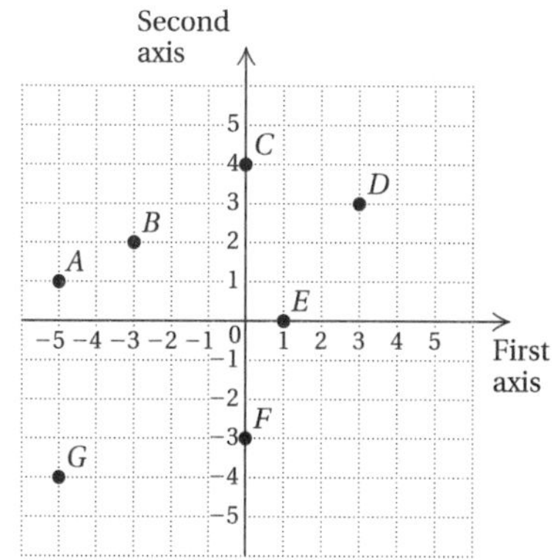

Answers on page A-10

17. Determine whether $(2, -4)$ is a solution of $4q - 3p = 22$.

18. Determine whether $(2, -4)$ is a solution of $7a + 5b = -6$.

Answers on page A-10

EXAMPLE 3 Find the coordinates of points A, B, C, D, E, F, and G.

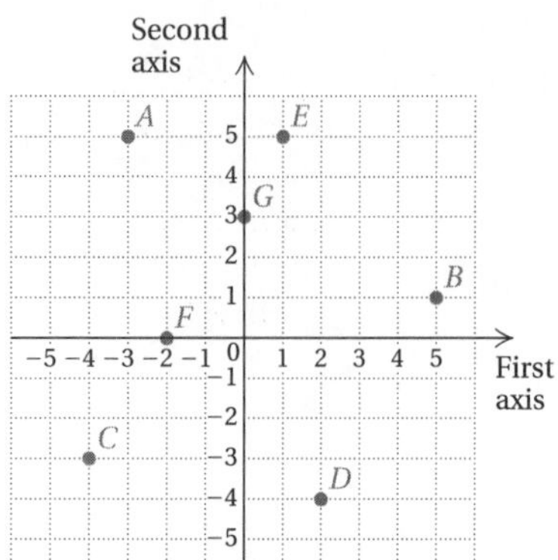

Point A is 3 units to the left (horizontal direction) and 5 units up (vertic direction). Its coordinates are $(-3, 5)$. Point D is 2 units to the right and 4 uni down. Its coordinates are $(2, -4)$. The coordinates of the other points are follows:

B: $(5, 1)$; C: $(-4, -3)$;

E: $(1, 5)$; F: $(-2, 0)$; G: $(0, 3)$.

Do Exercise 16 on the preceding page.

C Solutions of Equations

Now we begin to learn how graphs can be used to represent solutions of equa tions. When an equation contains two variables, the solutions of the equatio are *ordered pairs* in which each number in the pair corresponds to a letter i the equation. Unless stated otherwise, to determine whether a pair is a solu tion, we use the first number in each pair to replace the variable that occu first *alphabetically*.

EXAMPLE 4 Determine whether each of the following pairs is a solution c $4q - 3p = 22$: $(2, 7)$ and $(-1, 6)$.

For $(2, 7)$, we substitute 2 for p and 7 for q (using alphabetical order c variables):

$$\begin{array}{r|l} 4q - 3p & = 22 \\ \hline 4 \cdot 7 - 3 \cdot 2 & ?\ 22 \\ 28 - 6 & \\ 22 & \quad \text{TRUE} \end{array}$$

Thus, $(2, 7)$ is a solution of the equation.

For $(-1, 6)$, we substitute -1 for p and 6 for q:

$$\begin{array}{r|l} 4q - 3p & = 22 \\ \hline 4 \cdot 6 - 3 \cdot (-1) & ?\ 22 \\ 24 + 3 & \\ 27 & \quad \text{FALSE} \end{array}$$

Thus, $(-1, 6)$ is *not* a solution of the equation.

Do Exercises 17 and 18.

EXAMPLE 5 Show that the pairs $(3, 7)$, $(0, 1)$, and $(-3, -5)$ are solutions of $y = 2x + 1$. Then graph the three points and use the graph to determine another pair that is a solution.

To show that a pair is a solution, we substitute, replacing x with the first coordinate and y with the second coordinate of each pair:

$$\begin{array}{c|l} y = 2x + 1 & \\ \hline 7 \ ? & 2 \cdot 3 + 1 \\ & 6 + 1 \\ & 7 \qquad \text{TRUE} \end{array} \qquad \begin{array}{c|l} y = 2x + 1 & \\ \hline 1 \ ? & 2 \cdot 0 + 1 \\ & 0 + 1 \\ & 1 \qquad \text{TRUE} \end{array}$$

$$\begin{array}{c|l} y = 2x + 1 & \\ \hline -5 \ ? & 2(-3) + 1 \\ & -6 + 1 \\ & -5 \qquad \text{TRUE} \end{array}$$

In each of the three cases, the substitution results in a true equation. Thus the pairs are all solutions.

We plot the points as shown at right. The order of the points follows the alphabetical order of the variables. That is, x comes before y, so x-values are first coordinates and y-values are second coordinates. Similarly, we also label the horizontal axis as the x-axis and the vertical axis as the y-axis.

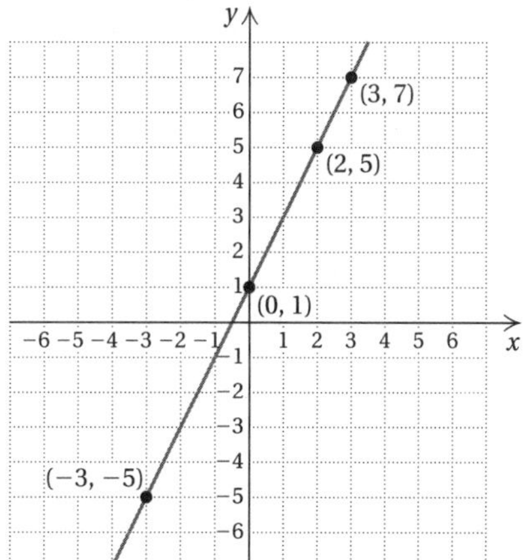

Note that the three points appear to "line up." That is, they appear to be on a straight line. Will other points that line up with these points also represent solutions of $y = 2x + 1$? To find out, we use a straightedge and lightly sketch a line passing through $(3, 7)$, $(0, 1)$, and $(-3, -5)$.

The line appears to pass through $(2, 5)$ as well. Let's see if this pair is a solution of $y = 2x + 1$:

$$\begin{array}{c|l} y = 2x + 1 & \\ \hline 5 \ ? & 2 \cdot 2 + 1 \\ & 4 + 1 \\ & 5 \qquad \text{TRUE} \end{array}$$

Thus, $(2, 5)$ is a solution.

Do Exercise 19.

Example 5 leads us to suspect that any point on the line that passes through $(3, 7)$, $(0, 1)$, and $(-3, -5)$ represents a solution of $y = 2x + 1$. In fact, every solution of $y = 2x + 1$ is represented by a point on that line and every point on that line represents a solution. The line is the *graph* of the equation.

19. Use the graph in Example 5 to find at least two more points that are solutions of $y = 2x + 1$.

Answer on page A-10

Complete the table and graph.

20. $y = -2x$

x	y	(x, y)
-3		
-1		
0		
1		
3		

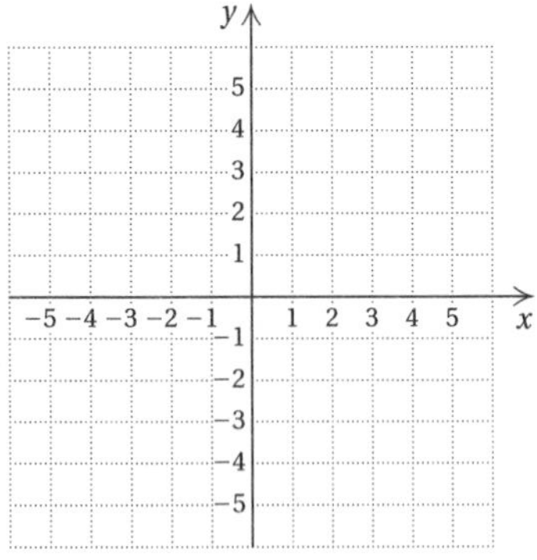

21. $y = \frac{1}{2}x$

x	y	(x, y)
4		
2		
0		
-2		
-4		
-1		

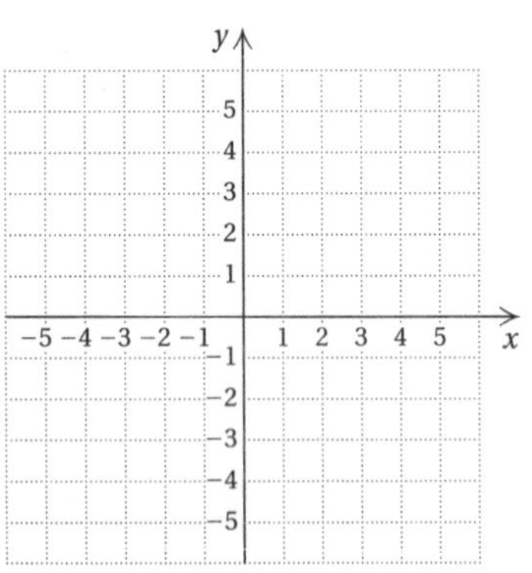

Answers on page A-10

GRAPH OF AN EQUATION

The **graph** of an equation is a drawing that represents all its solutions.

d Graphs of Linear Equations

Equations like $y = 2x + 1$ and $4q - 3p = 22$ are said to be **linear** because the graph of each equation is a straight line. In general, any equation equivalent to one of the form $y = mx + b$ or $Ax + By = C$, where m, b, A, B, and C are constants (not variables) and A and B are not both 0, is linear.

To graph a linear equation:

1. Select a value for one variable and calculate the corresponding value of the other variable. Form an ordered pair using alphabetical order as indicated by the variables.
2. Repeat step (1) to obtain at least two other ordered pairs. Two points are essential to determine a straight line. A third point serves as a check.
3. Plot the ordered pairs and draw a straight line passing through the points.

In general, calculating three (or more) ordered pairs is not difficult for equations of the form $y = mx + b$. We simply substitute values for x and calculate the corresponding values for y.

EXAMPLE 6 Graph: $y = 2x$.

First, we find some ordered pairs that are solutions. We choose *any* number for x and then determine y by substitution. Since $y = 2x$, we find y by doubling x. Suppose that we choose 3 for x. Then

$$y = 2x = 2 \cdot 3 = 6.$$

We get a solution: the ordered pair $(3, 6)$.

Suppose that we choose 0 for x. Then

$$y = 2x = 2 \cdot 0 = 0.$$

We get another solution: the ordered pair $(0, 0)$.

For a third point, we make a negative choice for x. If x is -3, we have

$$y = 2x = 2 \cdot (-3) = -6.$$

We now have enough points to plot the line, but if we wish, we can compute more. If a number takes us off the graph paper, we either do not use it or we use larger paper or rescale the axes. Continuing in this manner, we create a table like the one shown below.

Now we plot these points. We draw the line, or graph, with a straightedge nd label it $y = 2x$.

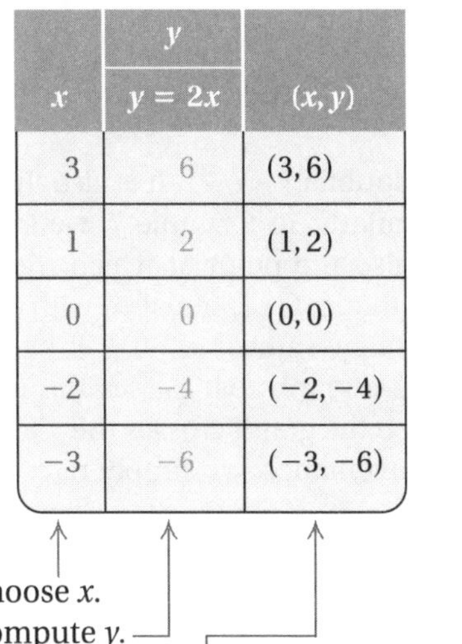

x	y $y = 2x$	(x, y)
3	6	(3, 6)
1	2	(1, 2)
0	0	(0, 0)
−2	−4	(−2, −4)
−3	−6	(−3, −6)

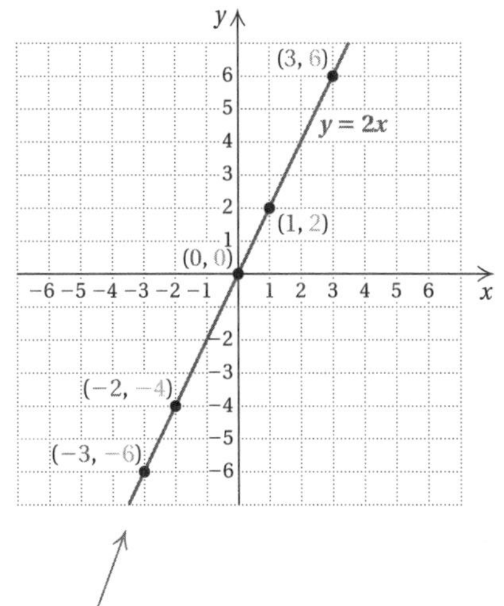

1) Choose x.
2) Compute y.
3) Form the pair (x, y).
4) Plot the points.

Caution!

Keep in mind that you can choose *any* number for x and then compute y. Our choice of certain numbers in the examples does not dictate the ones you can choose.

Do Exercises 20 and 21 on the preceding page.

EXAMPLE 7 Graph: $y = -3x + 1$.

We select a value for x, compute y, and form an ordered pair. Then we repeat the process for other choices of x.

If $x = 2$, then $y = -3 \cdot 2 + 1 = -5$, and $(2, -5)$ is a solution.
If $x = 0$, then $y = -3 \cdot 0 + 1 = 1$, and $(0, 1)$ is a solution.
If $x = -1$, then $y = -3 \cdot (-1) + 1 = 4$, and $(-1, 4)$ is a solution.

Results are often listed in a table, as shown below. The points corresponding to each pair are then plotted.

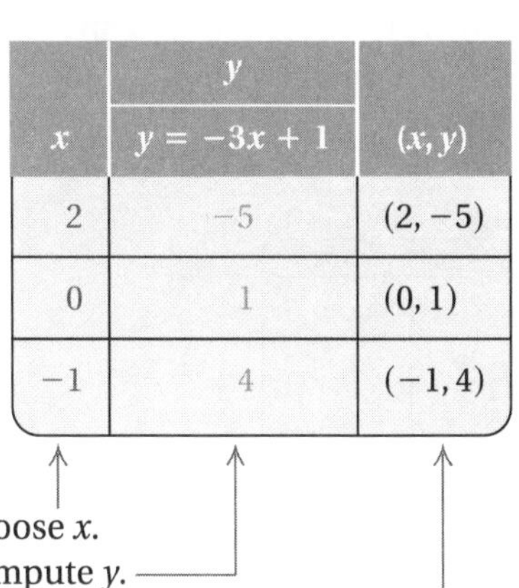

x	y $y = -3x + 1$	(x, y)
2	−5	(2, −5)
0	1	(0, 1)
−1	4	(−1, 4)

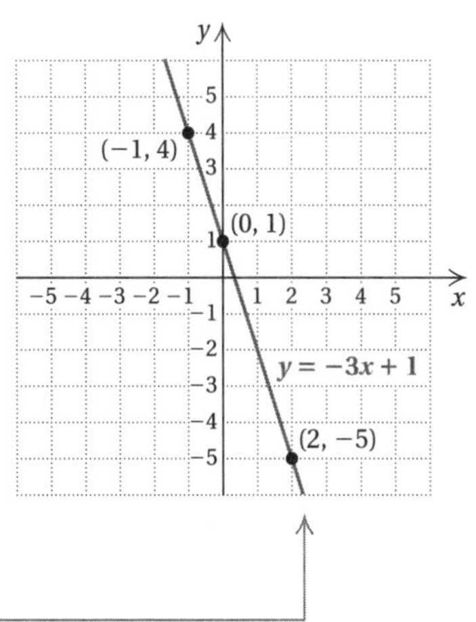

1) Choose x.
2) Compute y.
3) Form the pair (x, y).
4) Plot the points.

Graph.

22. $y = 2x + 3$

x	y	(x, y)

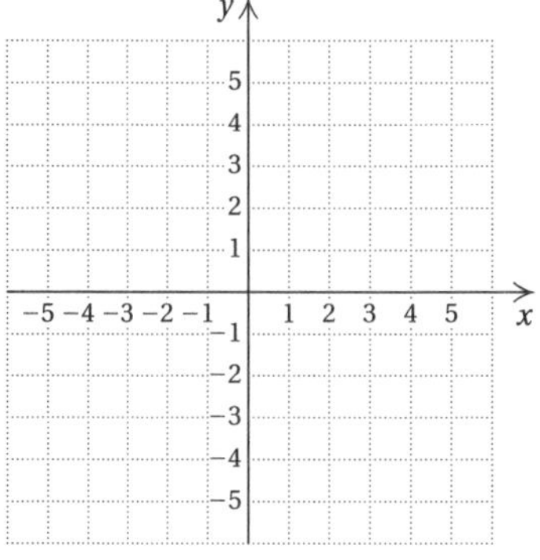

23. $y = -\frac{1}{2}x - 3$

x	y	(x, y)

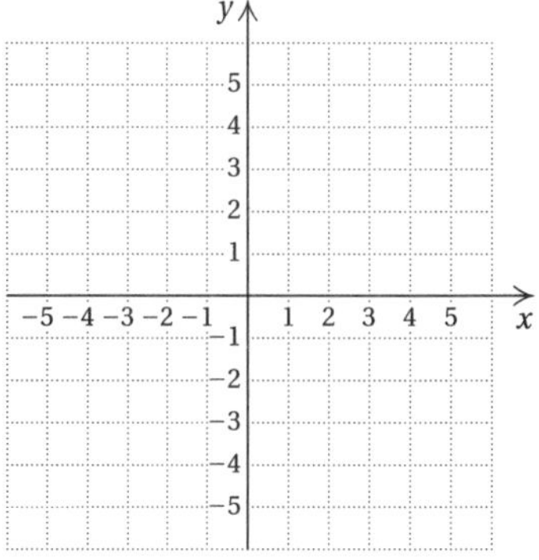

Answers on page A-11

Note that all three points line up. If they did not, we would know that we ha made a mistake. When only two points are plotted, a mistake is harder to de tect. We use a ruler or other straightedge to draw a line through the points Every point on the line represents a solution of $y = -3x + 1$.

Do Exercises 22 and 23 on the preceding page.

In Example 6, we saw that $(0, 0)$ is a solution of $y = 2x$. It is also the poin at which the graph crosses the y-axis. Similarly, in Example 7, we saw tha $(0, 1)$ is a solution of $y = -3x + 1$. It is also the point at which the grapl crosses the y-axis. A generalization can be made: If x is replaced with 0 in th equation $y = mx + b$, then the corresponding y-value is $m \cdot 0 + b$, or b. Thu any equation of the form $y = mx + b$ has a graph that passes through th point $(0, b)$. Since $(0, b)$ is the point at which the graph crosses the y-axis, it i called the ***y*-intercept.** Sometimes, for convenience, we simply refer to b a the y-intercept.

y-INTERCEPT

The graph of the equation $y = mx + b$ passes through the ***y*-intercept** $(0, b)$.

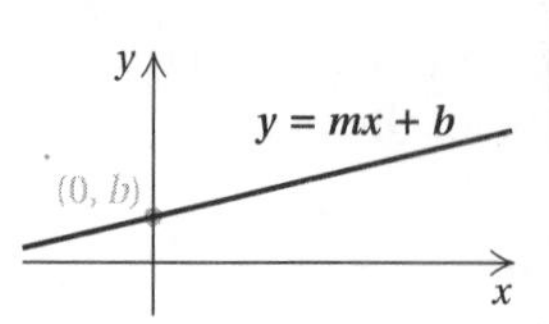

CALCULATOR CORNER

Finding Solutions of Equations A table of values representing ordered pairs that are solutions of an equation can be displayed on a graphing calculator. To do this for the equation in Example 7, $y = -3x + 1$, we first press Y= to access the equation-editor screen. Then we clear any equations that are present. (See the Calculator Corner in Section 2.3 for the procedure for doing this.) Next, we enter the equation by positioning the cursor beside "Y1 =" and pressing (−) 3 X,T,Θ,n + 1. Now we press 2ND TBLSET to display the table set-up screen. (TBLSET is the second function associated with the WINDOW key.) You can choose to supply the x-values yourself or you can set the calculator to supply them. To supply them yourself, follow the procedure for selecting ASK mode on p. 157. To have the calculator supply the x-values, set "Indpnt" to "Auto" by positioning the cursor over "Auto" and pressing ENTER. "Depend" should also be set to "Auto."

When "Indpnt" is set to "Auto," the graphing calculator will supply values of x, beginning with the value specified as TBLSTART and continuing by adding the value of ΔTBL to the preceding value for x. Below, we show a table of values that starts with $x = -2$ and adds 1 to the preceding x-value. We press (−) 2 ▽ 1 or (−) 2 ENTER 1 to select a minimum x-value of -2 and an increment of 1. To display the table, we press 2ND TABLE. (TABLE is the second operation associated with the GRAPH key.) We can use the △ and ▽ keys to scroll up and down through the table to see other solutions of the equation.

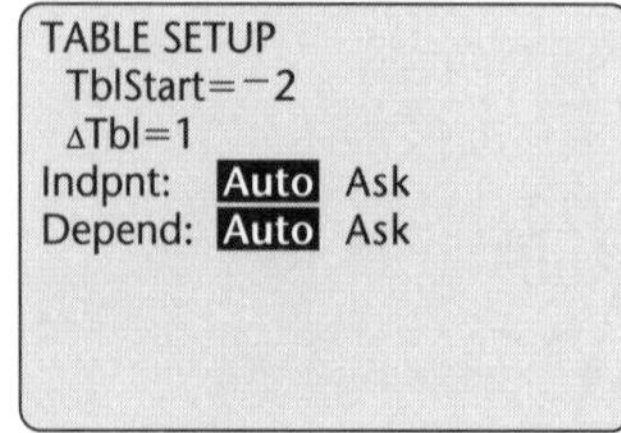

X	Y1
−2	7
−1	4
0	1
1	−2
2	−5
3	−8
4	−11

X = −2

Exercise:

1. Create a table of ordered pairs that are solutions of the equations in Examples 6 and 8.

EXAMPLE 8 Graph $y = \frac{2}{5}x + 4$ and identify the y-intercept.

We select a value for x, compute y, and form an ordered pair. Then we repeat the process for other choices of x. In this case, using multiples of 5 avoids fractions. We try to avoid graphing ordered pairs with fractions because they are difficult to graph accurately.

If $x = 0$, then $y = \frac{2}{5} \cdot 0 + 4 = 4$, and $(0, 4)$ is a solution.

If $x = 5$, then $y = \frac{2}{5} \cdot 5 + 4 = 6$, and $(5, 6)$ is a solution.

If $x = -5$, then $y = \frac{2}{5} \cdot (-5) + 4 = 2$, and $(-5, 2)$ is a solution.

The following table lists these solutions. Next, we plot the points and see that they form a line. Finally, we draw and label the line.

x	y $y = \frac{2}{5}x + 4$	(x, y)
0	4	$(0, 4)$
5	6	$(5, 6)$
-5	2	$(-5, 2)$

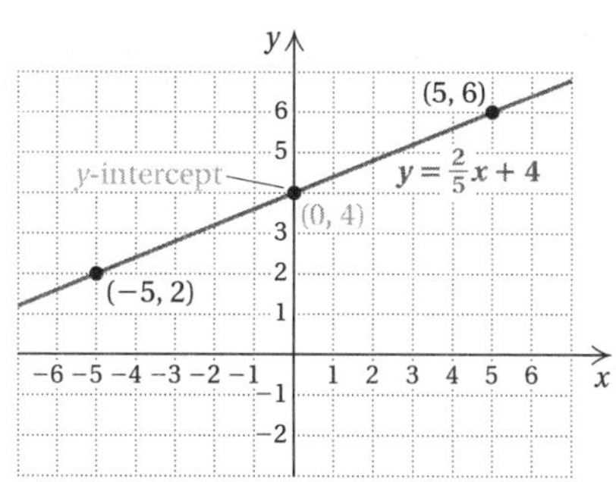

We see that $(0, 4)$ is a solution of $y = \frac{2}{5}x + 4$. It is the y-intercept. Because the equation is in the form $y = mx + b$, we can read the y-intercept directly from the equation as follows:

$$y = \frac{2}{5}x + 4 \qquad (0, 4) \text{ is the } y\text{-intercept.}$$

Do Exercises 24 and 25.

Calculating ordered pairs is generally easiest when y is isolated on one side of the equation, as in $y = mx + b$. To graph an equation in which y is not isolated, we can use the addition and multiplication principles to solve for y (see Section 2.3).

EXAMPLE 9 Graph $3y + 5x = 0$ and identify the y-intercept.

To find an equivalent equation in the form $y = mx + b$, we solve for y:

$$3y + 5x = 0$$

$$3y + 5x - 5x = 0 - 5x \qquad \text{Subtracting } 5x$$

$$3y = -5x \qquad \text{Collecting like terms}$$

$$\frac{3y}{3} = \frac{-5x}{3} \qquad \text{Dividing by 3}$$

$$y = -\frac{5}{3}x.$$

Graph the equation and identify the y-intercept.

24. $y = \frac{3}{5}x + 2$

x	y	(x, y)

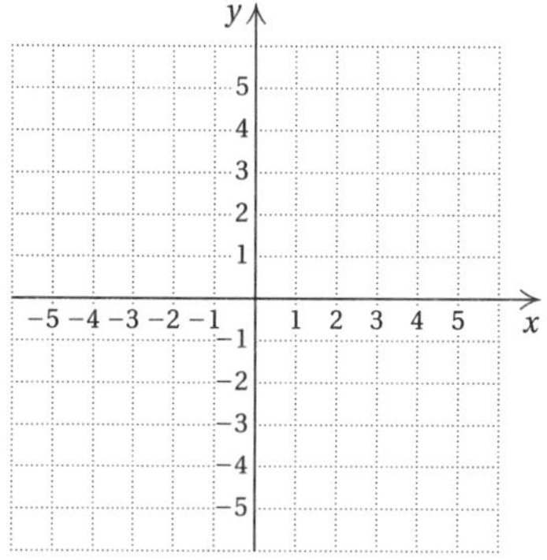

25. $y = -\frac{3}{5}x - 1$

x	y	(x, y)

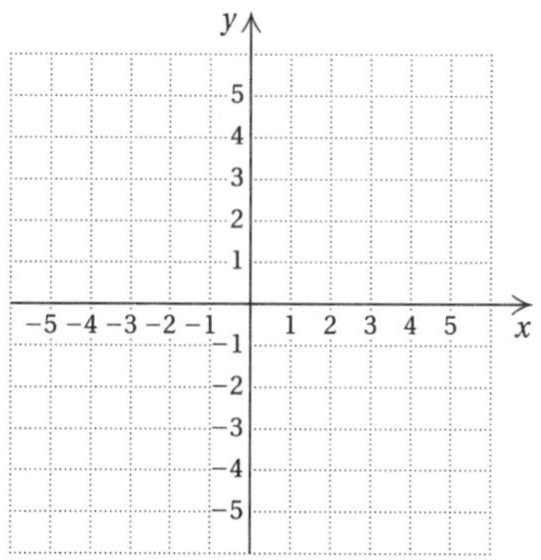

Answers on page A-11

Graph the equation and identify the y-intercept.

26. $5y + 4x = 0$

x	y	
0		← y-intercept

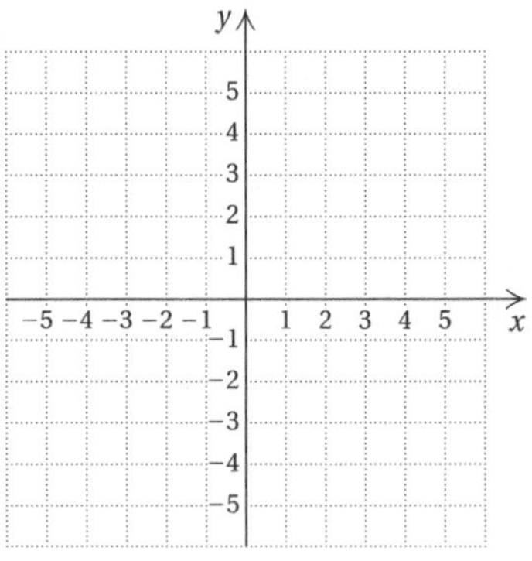

Because all the equations above are equivalent, we can use $y = -\frac{5}{3}x$ to draw the graph of $3y + 5x = 0$. To graph $y = -\frac{5}{3}x$, we select x-values and compute y-values. In this case, if we select multiples of 3, we can avoid fractions.

$$\text{If } x = 0, \quad \text{then } y = -\frac{5}{3} \cdot 0 = 0.$$

$$\text{If } x = 3, \quad \text{then } y = -\frac{5}{3} \cdot 3 = -5.$$

$$\text{If } x = -3, \quad \text{then } y = -\frac{5}{3} \cdot (-3) = 5.$$

We list these solutions in a table. Next, we plot the points and see that they form a line. Finally, we draw and label the line. The y-intercept is $(0, 0)$.

x	y	
0	0	← y-intercept
3	−5	
−3	5	

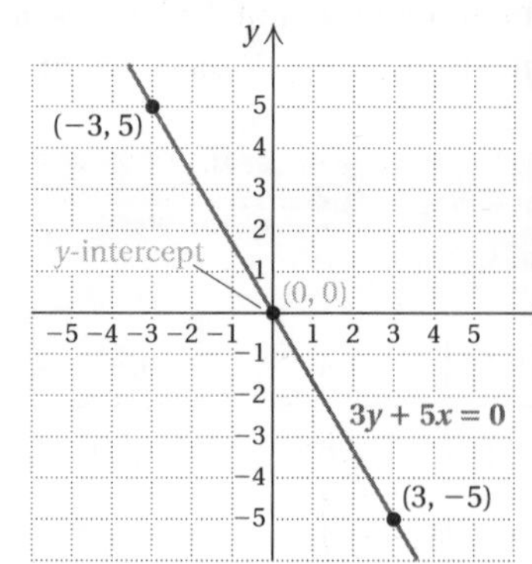

Do Exercises 26 and 27.

27. $4y = 3x$

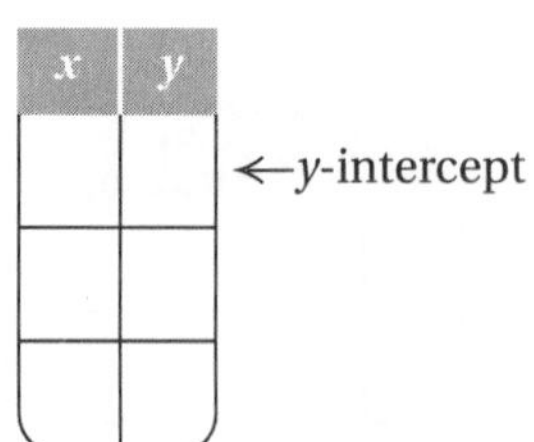

x	y	
		← y-intercept

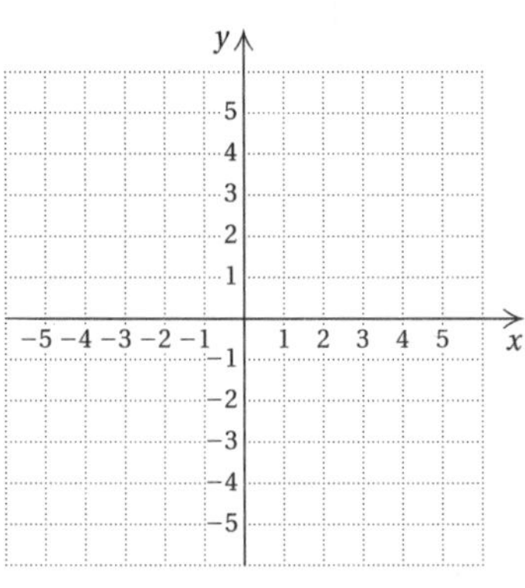

EXAMPLE 10 Graph $4y + 3x = -8$ and identify the y-intercept.

To find an equivalent equation in the form $y = mx + b$, we solve for y:

$$4y + 3x = -8$$

$$4y + 3x - 3x = -8 - 3x \qquad \text{Subtracting } 3x$$

$$4y = -3x - 8 \qquad \text{Simplifying}$$

$$\frac{1}{4} \cdot 4y = \frac{1}{4} \cdot (-3x - 8) \qquad \text{Multiplying by } \tfrac{1}{4} \text{ or dividing by } 4$$

$$y = \frac{1}{4} \cdot (-3x) - \frac{1}{4} \cdot 8 \qquad \text{Using the distributive law}$$

$$y = -\frac{3}{4}x - 2. \qquad \text{Simplifying}$$

Thus, $4y + 3x = -8$ is equivalent to $y = -\frac{3}{4}x - 2$. The y-intercept is $(0, -2)$. We find two other pairs using multiples of 4 for x to avoid fractions. We then complete and label the graph as shown.

x	y	
0	−2	← y-intercept
4	−5	
−4	1	

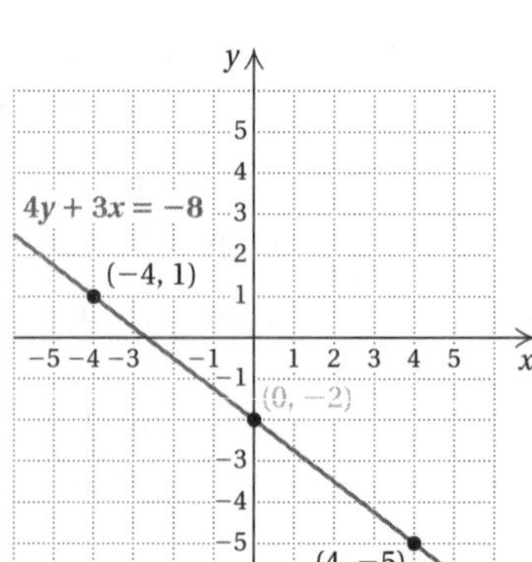

Answers on page A-11

o Exercises 28 and 29.

e Applications of Linear Equations

lathematical concepts become more understandable through visualization. hroughout this text, you will occasionally see the heading AG Algebraic–raphical Connection, as in Example 11, which follows. In this feature, the lgebraic approach is enhanced and expanded with a graphical connection. elating a solution of an equation to a graph can often give added meaning to he algebraic solution.

XAMPLE 11 *Online Retail Sales of Jewelry.* The online retail sales of jewlry y, in billions of dollars, is predicted by

$$y = 0.81x + 2,$$

here x is the number of years since 2003—that is, $x = 0$ corresponds to 003, $x = 5$ corresponds to 2008, and so on.

ource: Forrester Research

) Determine the online retail sales of jewelry in 2003, 2008, and 2015.

) Graph the equation and then use the graph to estimate online retail sales in 2010.

) In what year would online sales be \$9.29 billion?

) The years 2003, 2008, and 2015 correspond to $x = 0$, $x = 5$, and $x = 12$, respectively. We substitute 0, 5, and 12 for x and then calculate y:

$$y = 0.81(0) + 2 = 0 + 2 = 2;$$
$$y = 0.81(5) + 2 = 4.05 + 2 = 6.05;$$
$$y = 0.81(12) + 2 = 9.72 + 2 = 11.72.$$

Online jewelry sales in 2003, 2008, and 2015 are estimated to be \$2.0 billion, \$6.05 billion, and \$11.72 billion, respectively.

LGEBRAIC–GRAPHICAL CONNECTION

) We have three ordered pairs from part (a). We plot these points and see that they line up. Thus our calculations are probably correct. Since we are considering only the year 2003 and the number of years since 2003 ($x \geq 0$) and since the sales, in billions of dollars, for those years will be positive ($y > 0$), we need only the first quadrant for the graph. Then we use these points to draw a straight line through them. See Figure 1 on the following page.

Graph the equation and identify the y-intercept.

28. $5y - 3x = -10$

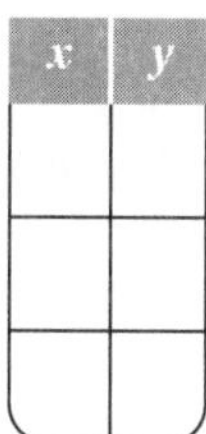

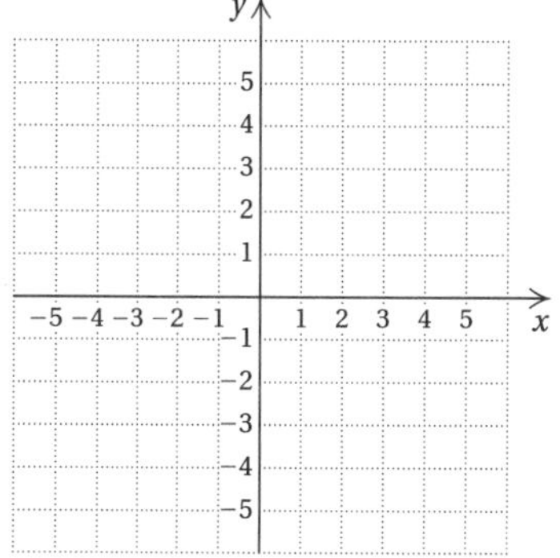

29. $5y + 3x = 20$

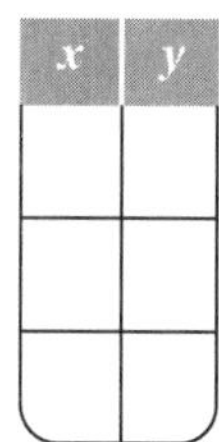

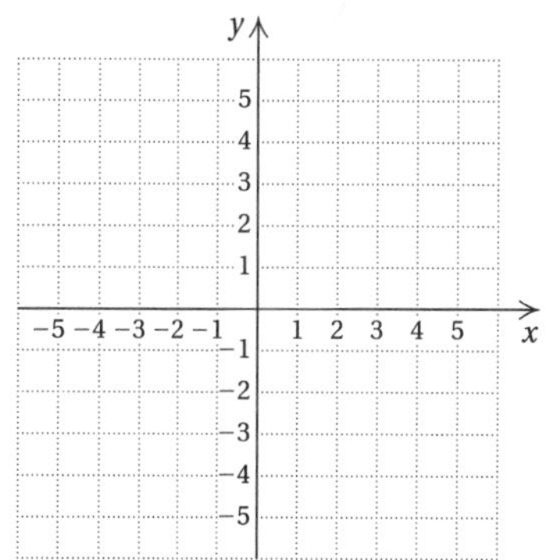

Answers on page A-11

30. Value of a Color Copier. The value of Dupliographic's color copier is given by

$$v = -0.68t + 3.4,$$

where v is the value, in thousands of dollars, t years from the date of purchase.

a) Find the value after 1 yr, 2 yr, 4 yr, and 5 yr.

t	v
1	
2	
4	
5	

b) Graph the equation and use the graph to estimate the value of the copier after $2\frac{1}{2}$ yr.

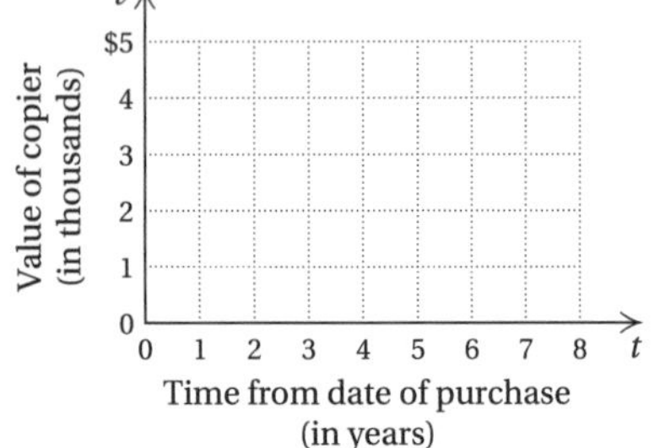

c) After what amount of time is the value of the copier $1500?

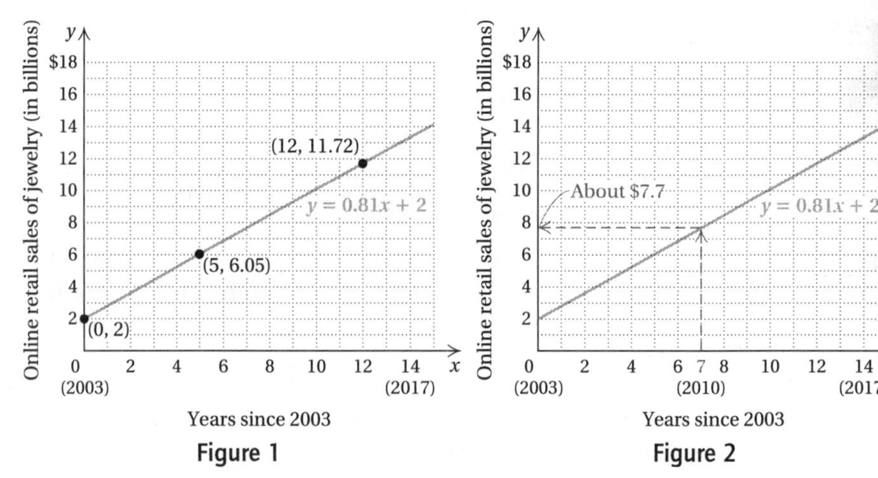

Figure 1

Figure 2

To use the graph to estimate sales in 2010, we first note in Figure 2 that this year corresponds to $x = 7$. We need to determine which y-value is paired with $x = 7$. We locate the point on the graph by moving up vertically from $x = 7$, and then find the value on the y-axis that corresponds to that point. It appears that online jewelry sales in 2010 will be about $7.7 billion.

To find a more accurate value, we can simply substitute into the equation:

$$y = 0.81(7) + 2 = 5.67 + 2 = \$7.67.$$

c) We substitute 9.29 for y and solve for x:

$$y = 0.81x + 2$$

$$9.29 = 0.81x + 2 \quad \text{Substituting}$$

$$7.29 = 0.81x \quad \text{Subtracting 2}$$

$$x = 9. \quad \text{Dividing by 0.81}$$

In 9 years, or in 2012, online jewelry sales will be approximately $9.29 billion.

Do Exercise 30.

Many equations in two variables have graphs that are not straight lines. Three such nonlinear graphs are shown below. We will cover some such graphs in the optional Calculator Corners throughout the text and in Chapter 9.

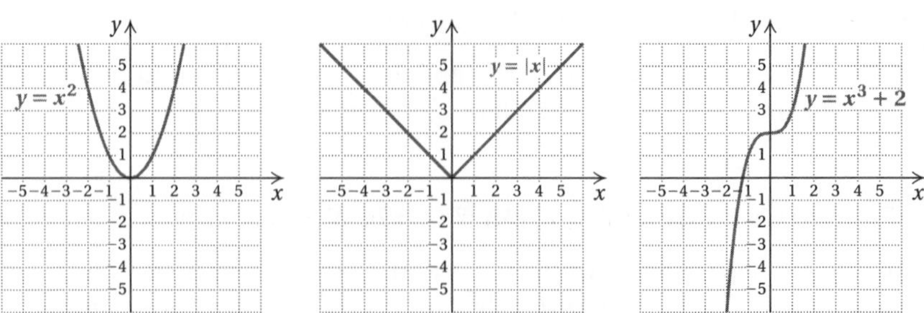

Answers on page A-11

CALCULATOR CORNER

Graphing Equations Graphs of equations are displayed in the **viewing window** of a graphing calculator. The viewing window is the portion of the coordinate plane that appears on the calculator's screen. It is defined by the minimum and maximum values of x and y: Xmin, Xmax, Ymin, and Ymax. The notation [Xmin, Xmax, Ymin, Ymax] is used to represent these window settings or dimensions. For example, $[-12, 12, -8, 8]$ denotes a window that displays the portion of the x-axis from -12 to 12 and the portion of the y-axis from -8 to 8. In addition, the distance between tick marks on the axes is defined by the settings Xscl and Yscl. The Xres setting indicates the pixel resolution. We usually select Xres = 1. The window corresponding to the settings $[-20, 30, -12, 20]$, Xscl = 5, Yscl = 2, Xres = 1, is shown on the left below. Press WINDOW on the top row of the keypad of your calculator to display the current window settings. The settings for the **standard viewing window** are shown on the right below.

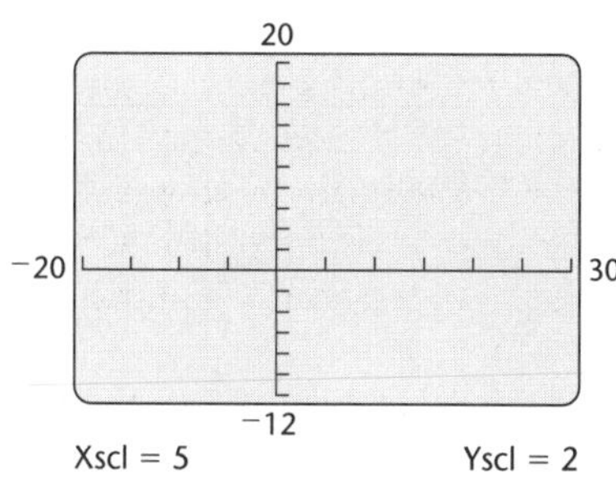

Xscl = 5 Yscl = 2

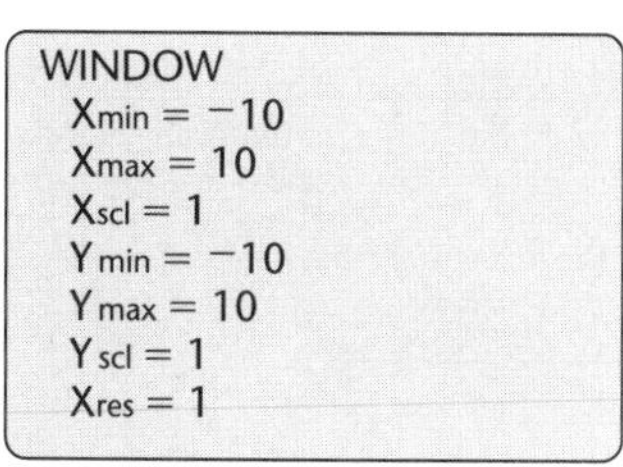

To change a setting, we position the cursor beside the setting we wish to change and enter the new value. For example, to change from the standard settings to $[-20, 30, -12, 20]$, Xscl = 5, Yscl = 2, on the WINDOW screen, we press (−) 2 0 ENTER 3 0 ENTER 5 ENTER (−) 1 2 ENTER 2 0 ENTER 2 ENTER. The ▽ key can be used instead of ENTER after typing each window setting. To see the window, we press GRAPH on the top row of the keypad. To return quickly to the standard window setting $[-10, 10, -10, 10]$, Xscl = 1, Yscl = 1, we press ZOOM 6.

Equations must be solved for y before they can be graphed on the TI-84 Plus. Consider the equation $3x + 2y = 6$. Solving for y, we get $y = \dfrac{6 - 3x}{2}$. We enter this equation as $y_1 = (6 - 3x)/2$ on the equation-editor screen as described in the Calculator Corner in Section 2.3 (see p. 157). Then we press ZOOM 6 to select the standard viewing window and display the graph.

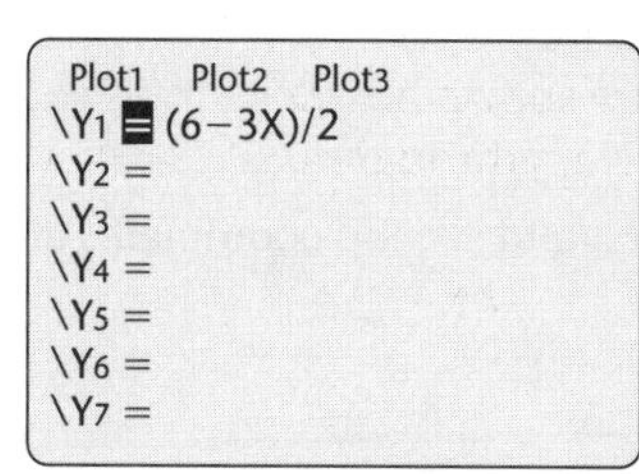

$y = (6 - 3x)/2$

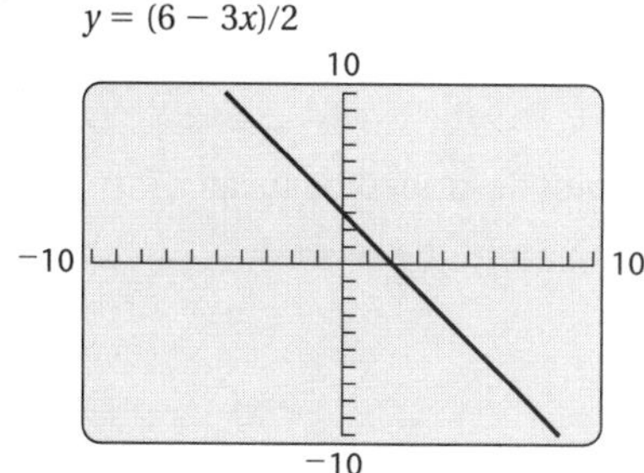

Exercises: Graph each equation in the standard viewing window $[-10, 10, -10, 10]$, Xscl = 1, Yscl = 1.

1. $y = 2x + 1$
2. $y = -3x + 1$
3. $y = -5x + 3$
4. $y = 4x - 5$
5. $4x - 5y = -10$
6. $5y + 5 = -3x$
7. $y = 2.085x + 5.08$
8. $y = -3.45x - 1.68$

3.1 EXERCISE SET

For Extra Help

MathXL

MyMathLab

InterAct Math

Math Tutor Center

Digital Video Tutor CD 2 Videotape 4

Student Solutions Manual

a

1. Plot these points.

$(2, 5)$ $(-1, 3)$ $(3, -2)$ $(-2, -4)$
$(0, 4)$ $(0, -5)$ $(5, 0)$ $(-5, 0)$

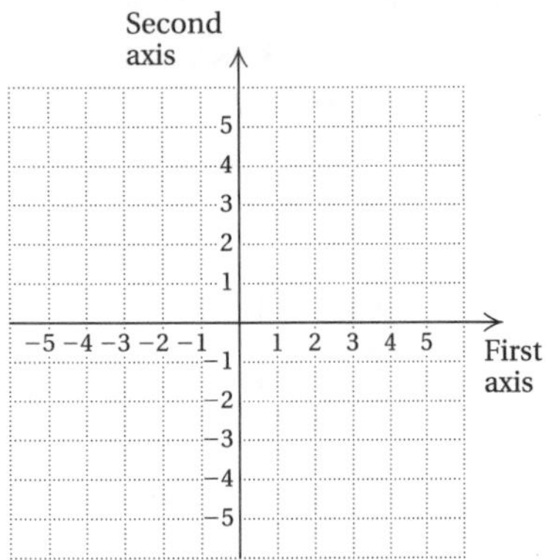

2. Plot these points.

$(4, 4)$ $(-2, 4)$ $(5, -3)$ $(-5, -5)$
$(0, 4)$ $(0, -4)$ $(3, 0)$ $(-4, 0)$

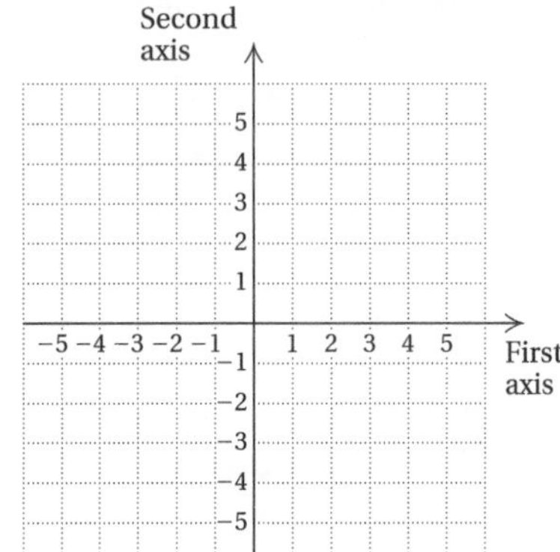

In which quadrant, if any, is the point located?

3. $(-5, 3)$

4. $(1, -12)$

5. $(100, -1)$

6. $(-2.5, 35.6)$

7. $(-6, -29)$

8. $(3.6, 105.9)$

9. $(3.8, 0)$

10. $(0, -492)$

11. $\left(-\frac{1}{3}, \frac{15}{7}\right)$

12. $\left(-\frac{2}{3}, -\frac{9}{8}\right)$

13. $\left(12\frac{7}{8}, -1\frac{1}{2}\right)$

14. $\left(23\frac{5}{8}, 81.74\right)$

In which quadrant(s) can the point described be located?

15. The first coordinate is negative and the second coordinate is positive.

16. The first and second coordinates are positive.

17. The first coordinate is positive.

18. The second coordinate is negative.

19. The first and second coordinates are equal.

20. The first coordinate is the additive inverse of the secon coordinate.

Find the coordinates of points A, B, C, D, and E.

1.

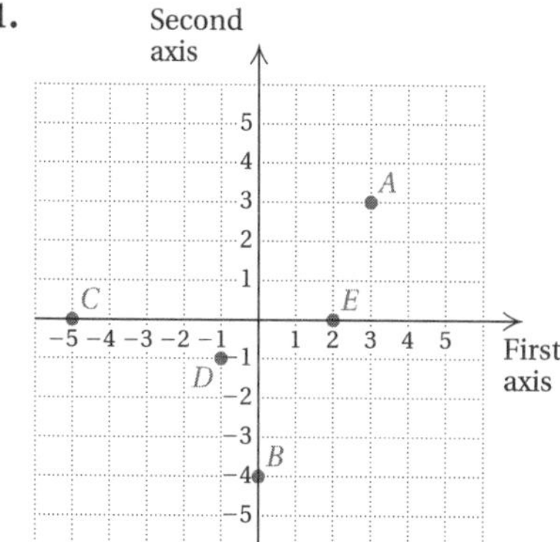

22.

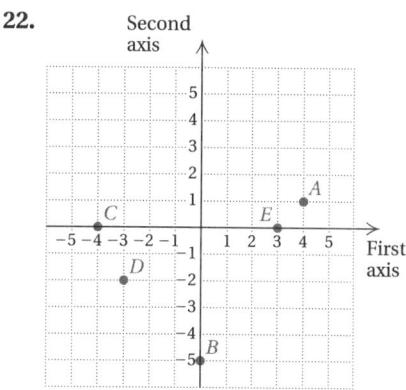

Determine whether the given ordered pair is a solution of the equation.

3. $(2, 9)$; $y = 3x - 1$

24. $(1, 7)$; $y = 2x + 5$

25. $(4, 2)$; $2x + 3y = 12$

5. $(0, 5)$; $5x - 3y = 15$

27. $(3, -1)$; $3a - 4b = 13$

28. $(-5, 1)$; $2p - 3q = -13$

Exercises 29–34, an equation and two ordered pairs are given. Show that each pair is a solution. Then use the graph of the vo points to determine another solution. Answers may vary.

. $y = x - 5$; $(4, -1)$ and $(1, -4)$

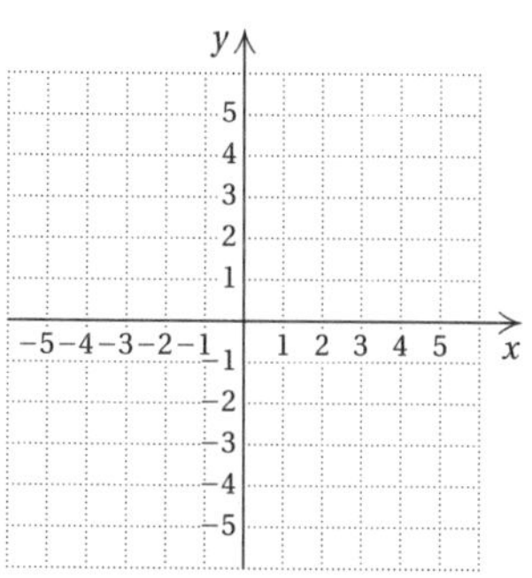

30. $y = x + 3$; $(-1, 2)$ and $(3, 6)$

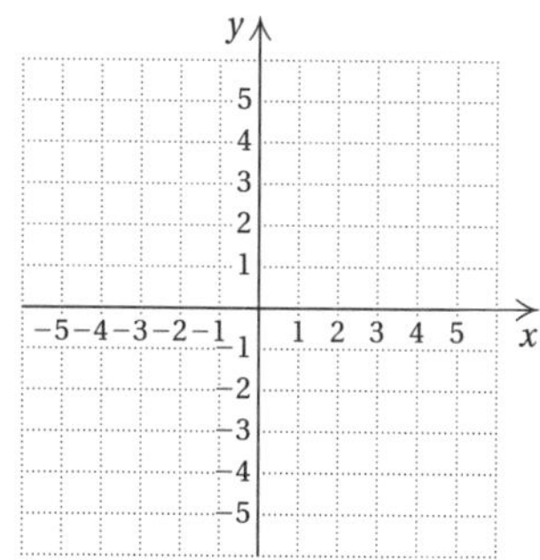

31. $y = \frac{1}{2}x + 3$; $(4, 5)$ and $(-2, 2)$

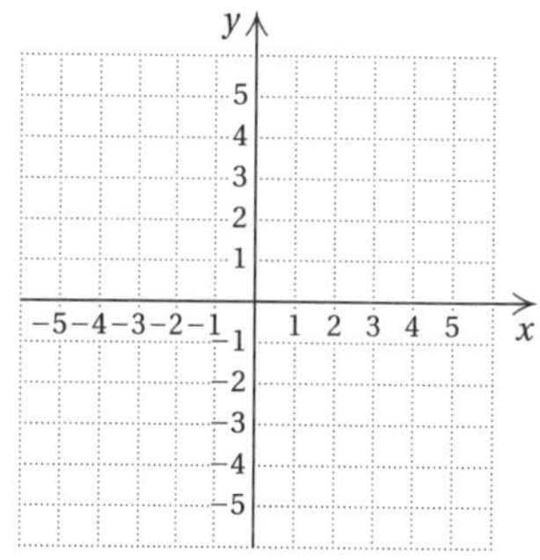

. $3x + y = 7$; $(2, 1)$ and $(4, -5)$

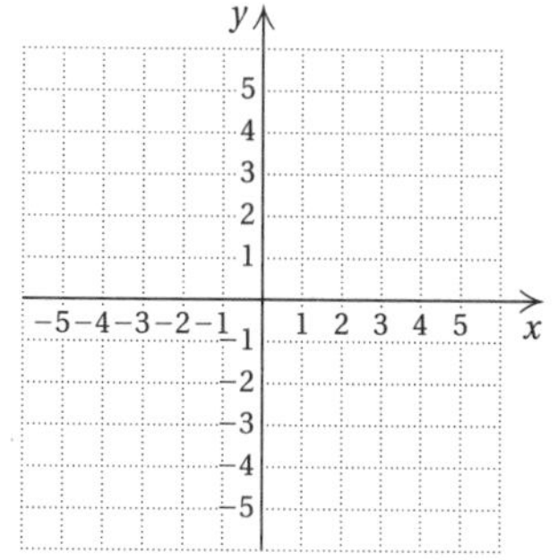

33. $4x - 2y = 10$; $(0, -5)$ and $(4, 3)$

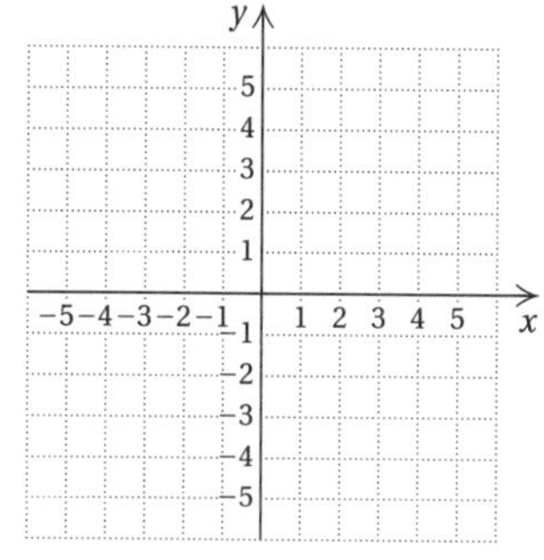

34. $6x - 3y = 3$; $(1, 1)$ and $(-1, -3)$

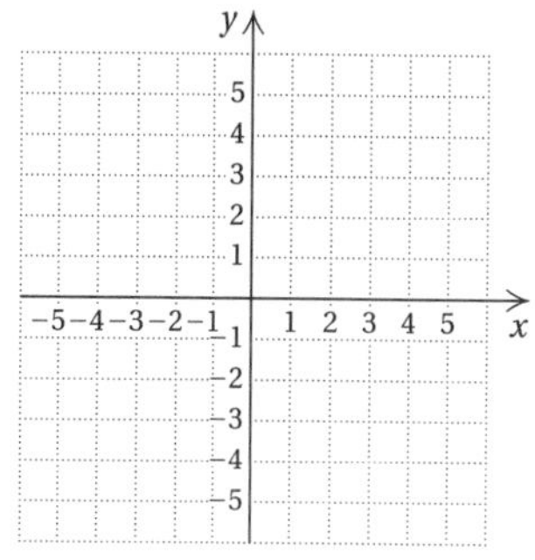

d Graph the equation and identify the y-intercept.

35. $y = x + 1$

x	y
−2	
−1	
0	
1	
2	
3	

36. $y = x - 1$

x	y
−2	
−1	
0	
1	
2	
3	

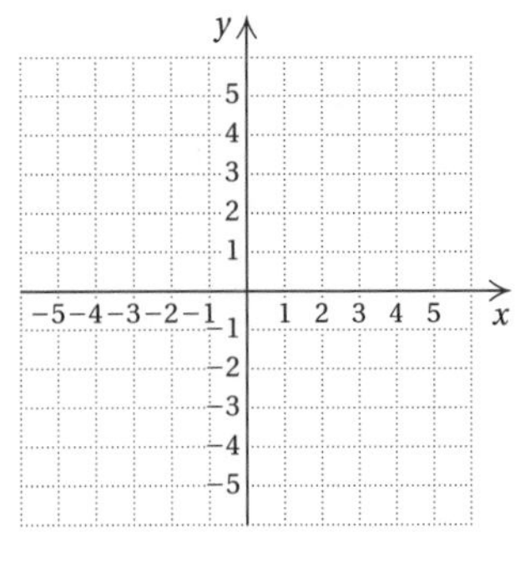

37. $y = x$

x	y
−2	
−1	
0	
1	
2	
3	

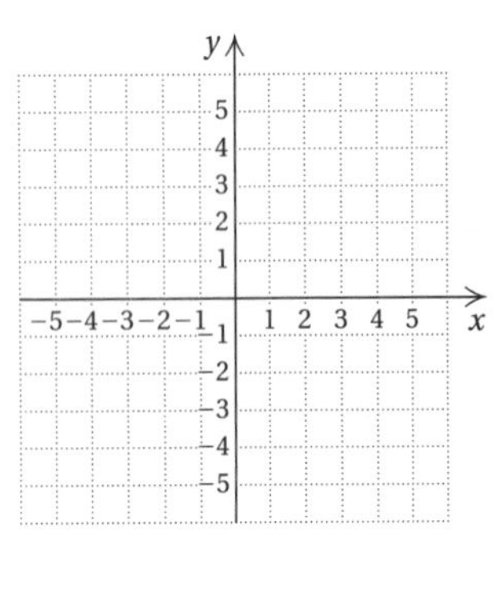

38. $y = -x$

x	y
−2	
−1	
0	
1	
2	
3	

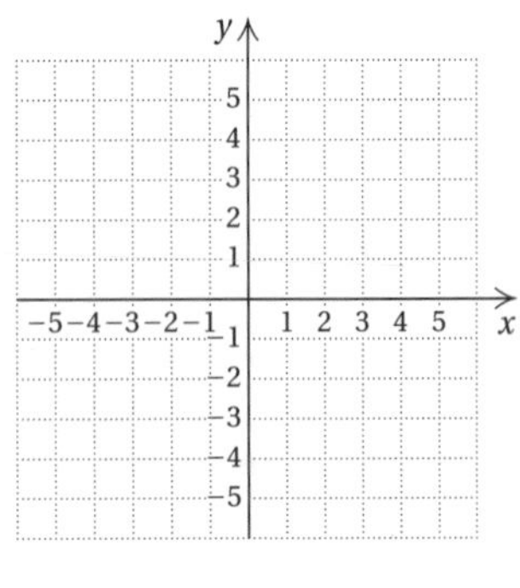

39. $y = \frac{1}{2}x$

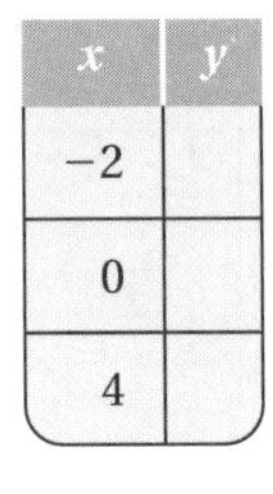

x	y
−2	
0	
4	

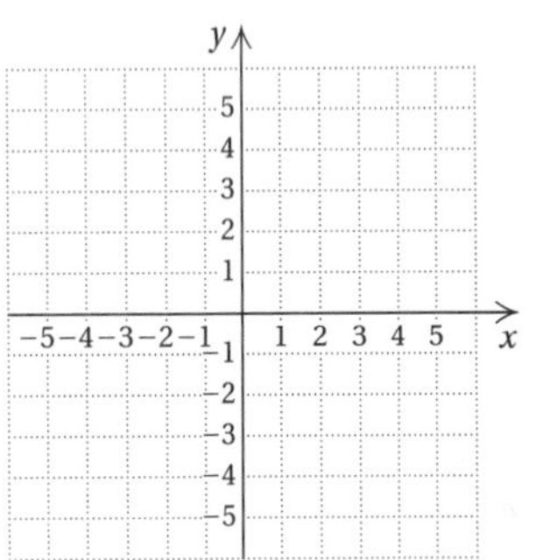

40. $y = \frac{1}{3}x$

x	y
−6	
0	
3	

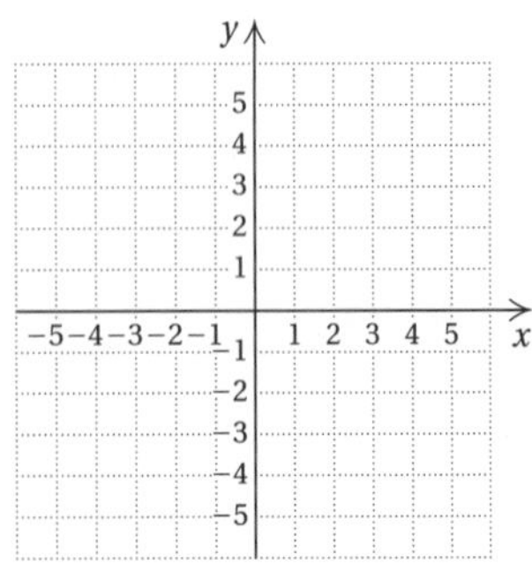

41. $y = x - 3$

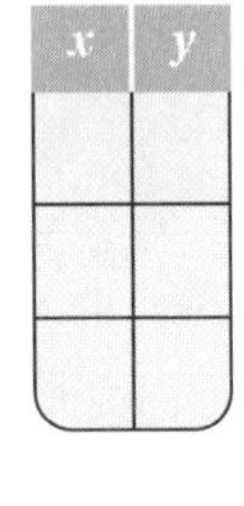

x	y

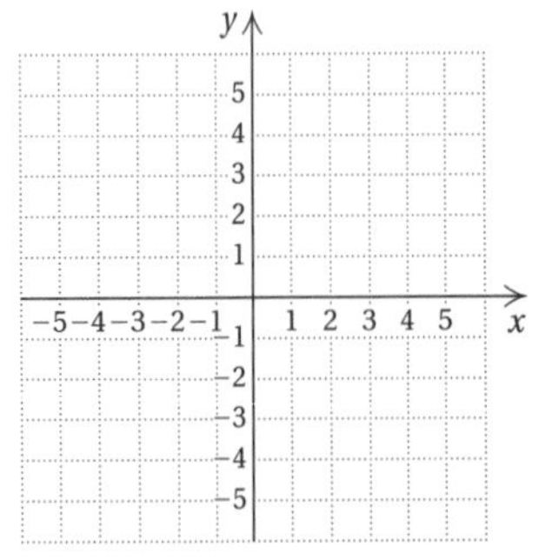

42. $y = x + 3$

x	y

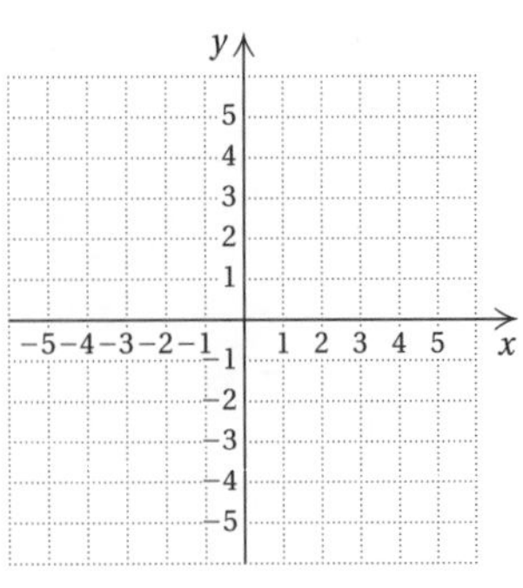

3. $y = 3x - 2$

x	y

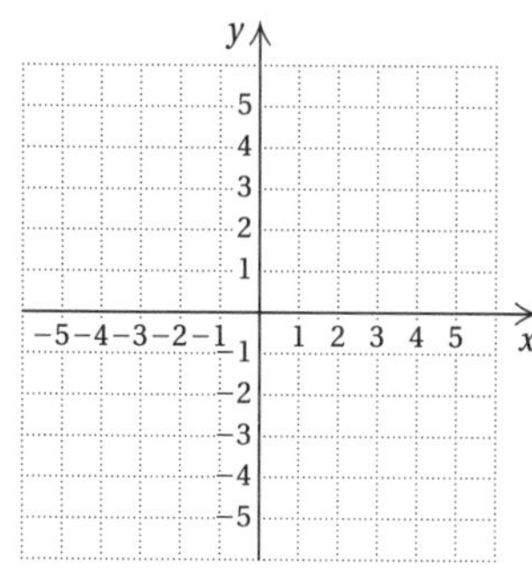

44. $y = 2x + 2$

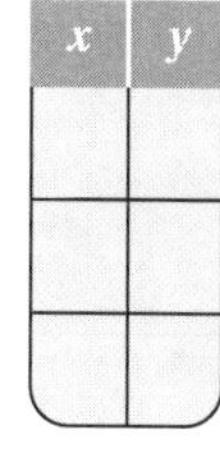

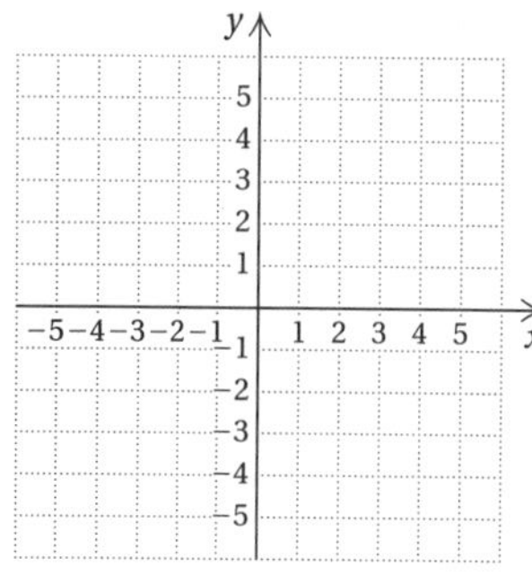

5. $y = \frac{1}{2}x + 1$

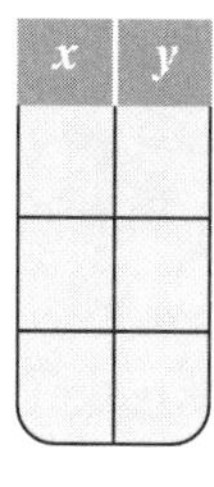

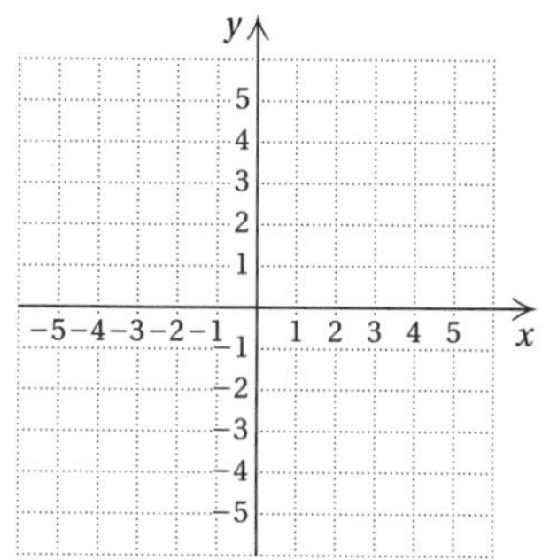

46. $y = \frac{1}{3}x - 4$

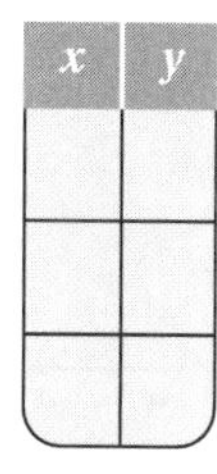

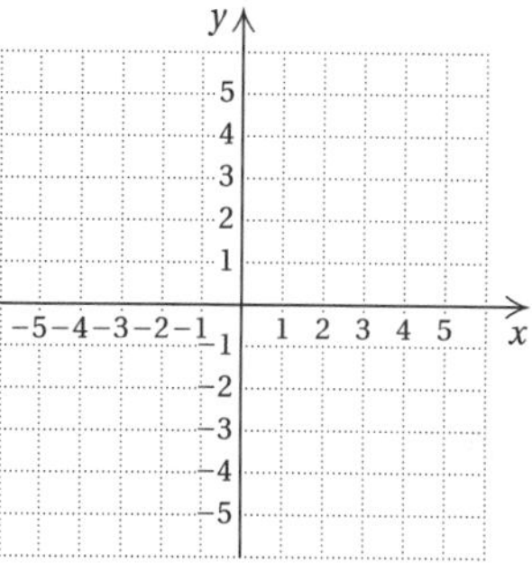

7. $x + y = -5$

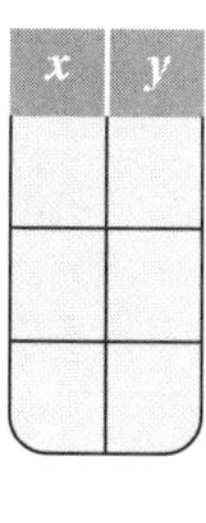

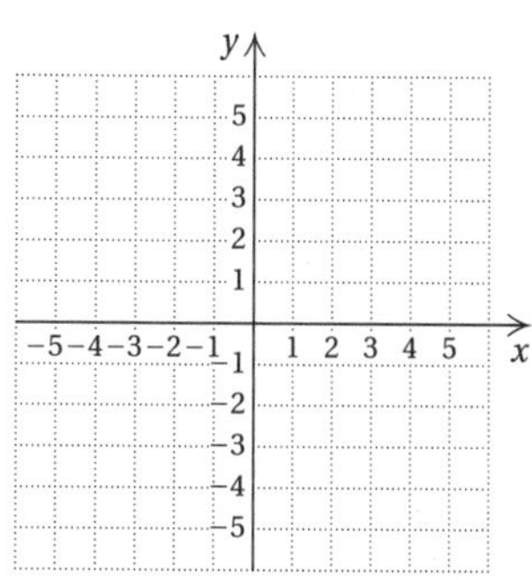

48. $x + y = 4$

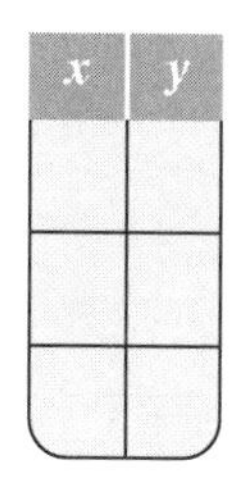

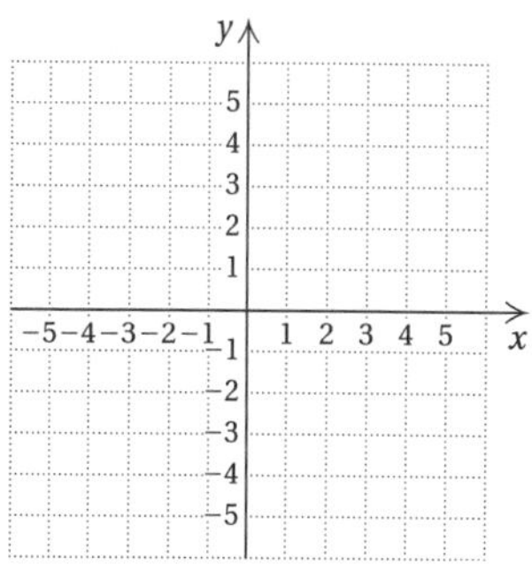

$y = \frac{5}{3}x - 2$

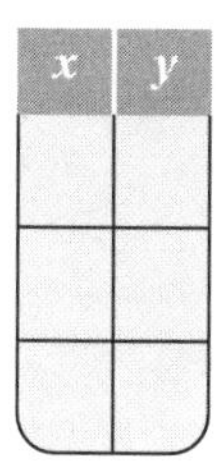

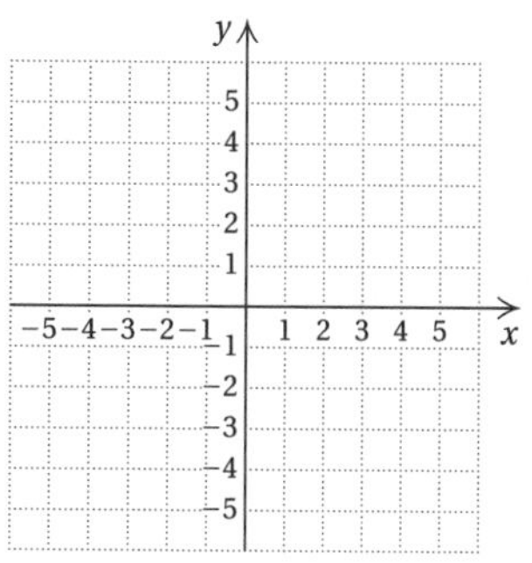

50. $y = \frac{5}{2}x + 3$

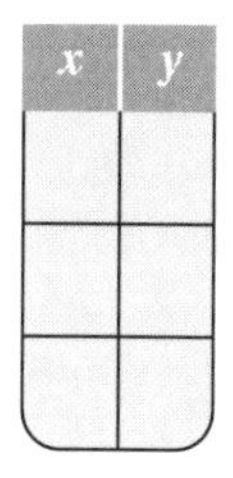

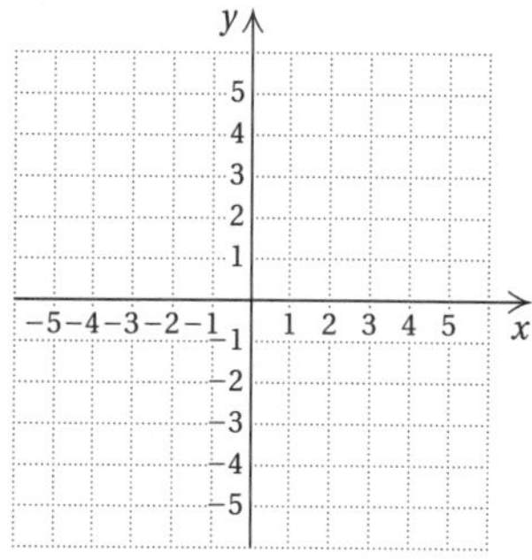

51. $x + 2y = 8$

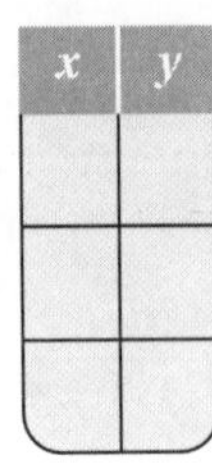

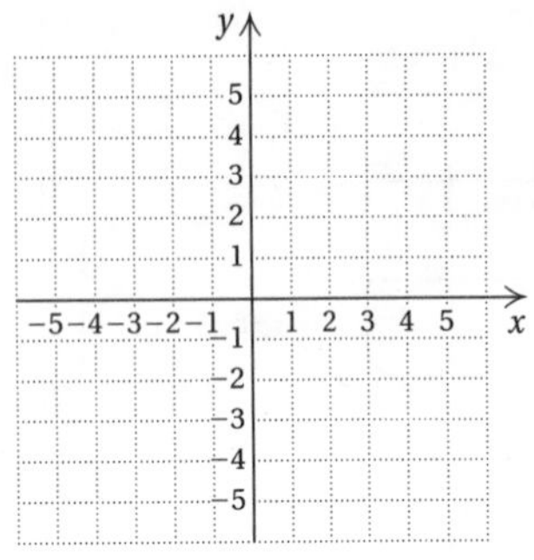

52. $x + 2y = -6$

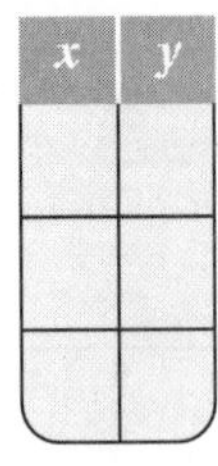

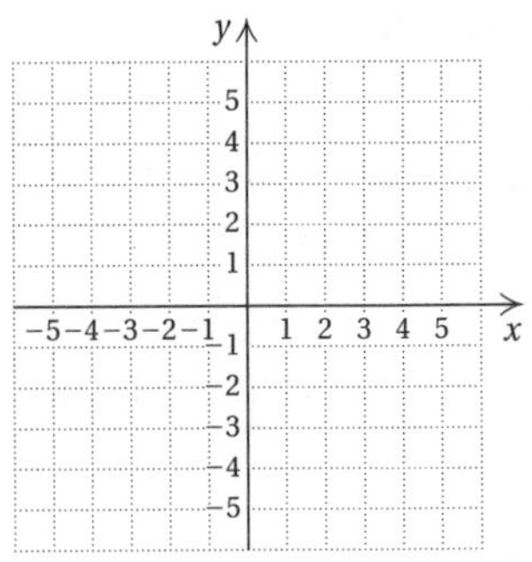

53. $y = \frac{3}{2}x + 1$

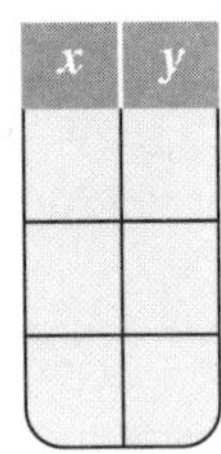

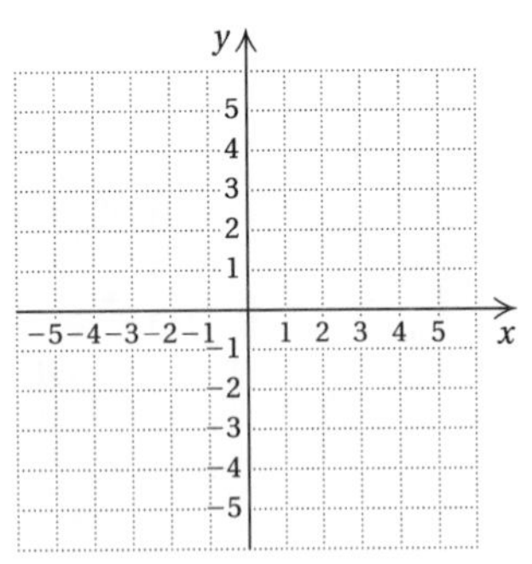

54. $y = -\frac{1}{2}x - 3$

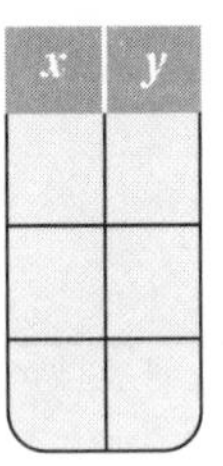

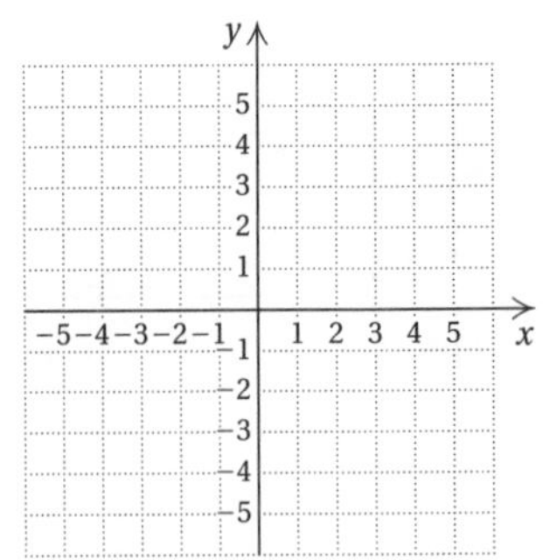

55. $8x - 2y = -10$

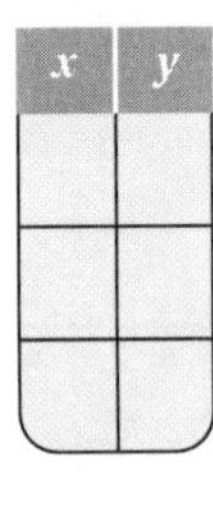

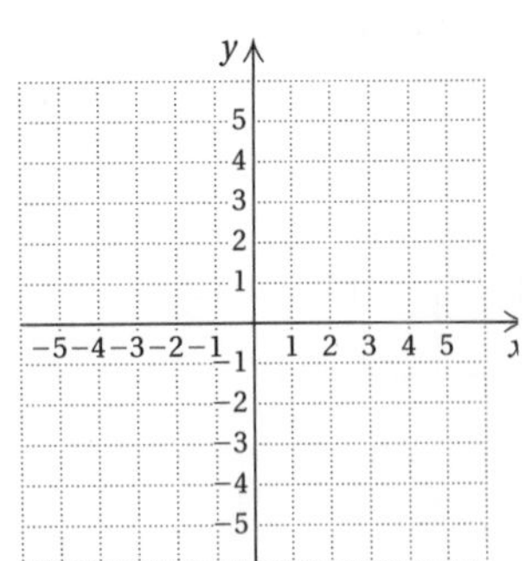

56. $6x - 3y = 9$

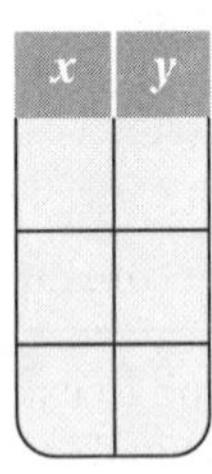

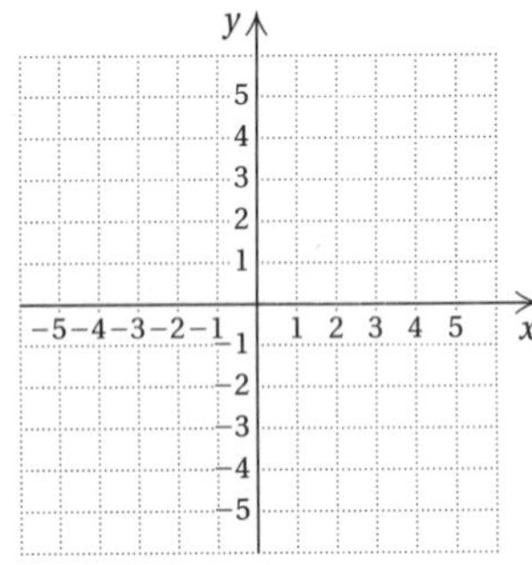

57. $8y + 2x = -4$

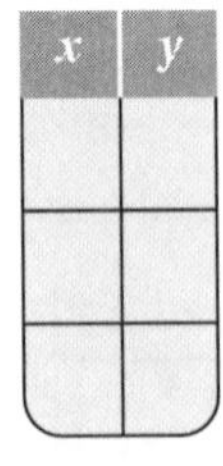

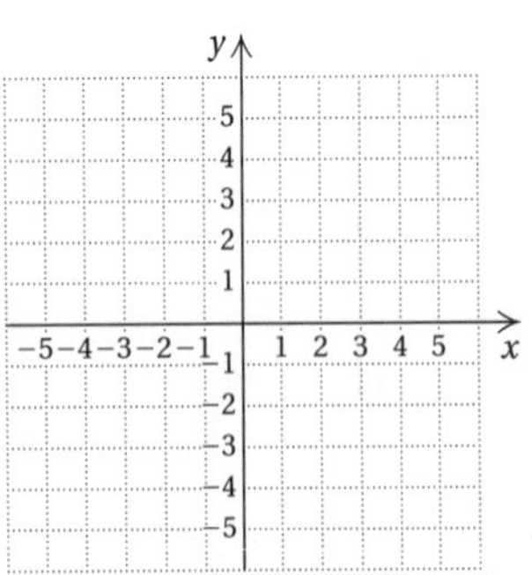

58. $6y + 2x = 8$

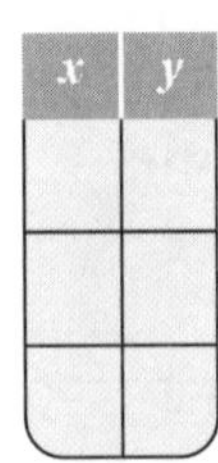

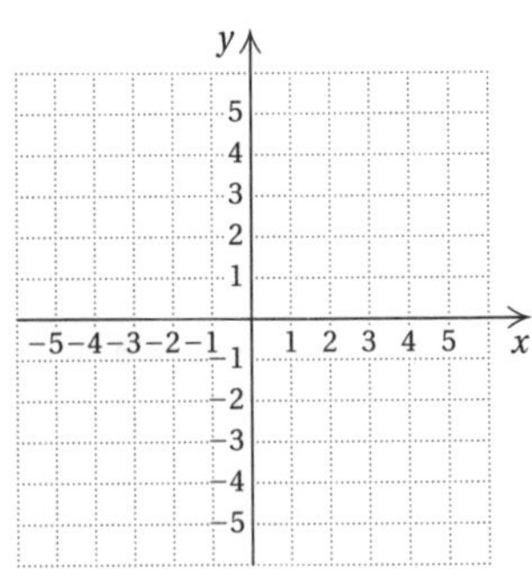

e Solve.

9. *Value of Computer Software.* The value V, in dollars, of a shopkeeper's inventory software program is given by $V = -50t + 300$, where t is the number of years since the shopkeeper first bought the program.

a) Find the value of the software after 0 yr, 4 yr, and 6 yr.
b) Graph the equation and then use the graph to estimate the value of the software after 5 yr.

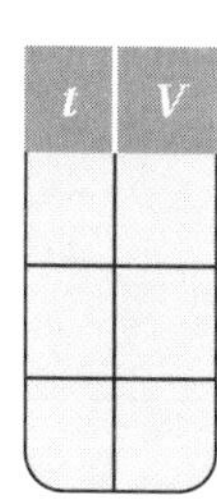

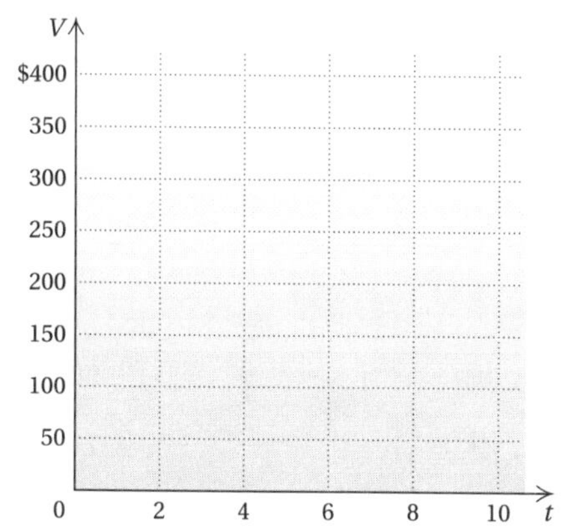

c) After how many years is the value of the software $150?

60. *SAT Math Scores.* The average SAT math scores M of potential college students can be approximated by $M = 1.4t + 518$, where t is the number of years since 2004.

Source: The College Board

a) Find the average SAT math score in 2004 ($t = 0$), 2005 ($t = 1$), and 2010.
b) Graph the equation and then use the graph to estimate the average SAT math score in 2008.

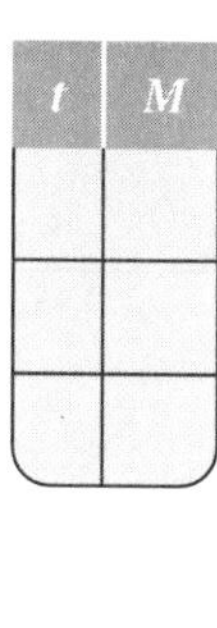

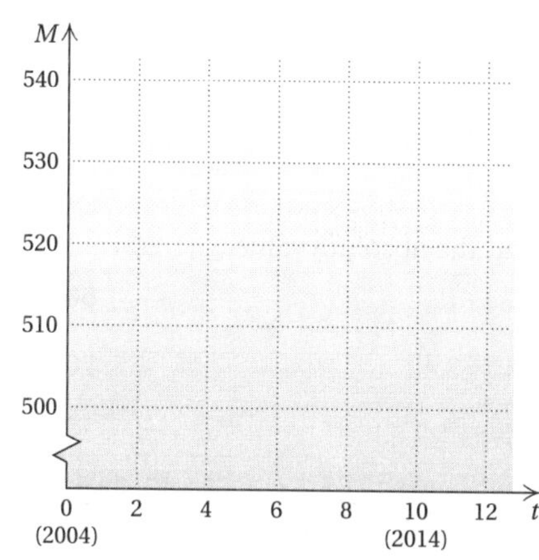

c) In what year will the average SAT math score be 539?

1. *Coffee Consumption.* The number of gallons N of coffee consumed each year by the average U.S. consumer can be approximated by $N = 0.8d + 21.2$, where d is the number of years since 1995.

Source: *Statistical Abstract of the United States*, 2003

a) Find the number of gallons of coffee consumed in 1996 ($d = 1$), 2000, 2006, and 2010.
b) Graph the equation and use the graph to estimate what the coffee consumption was in 2002.

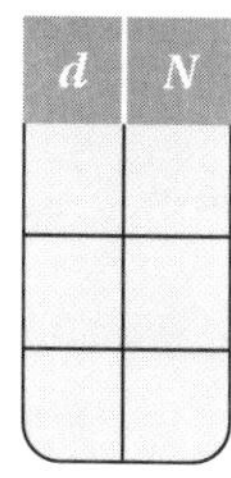

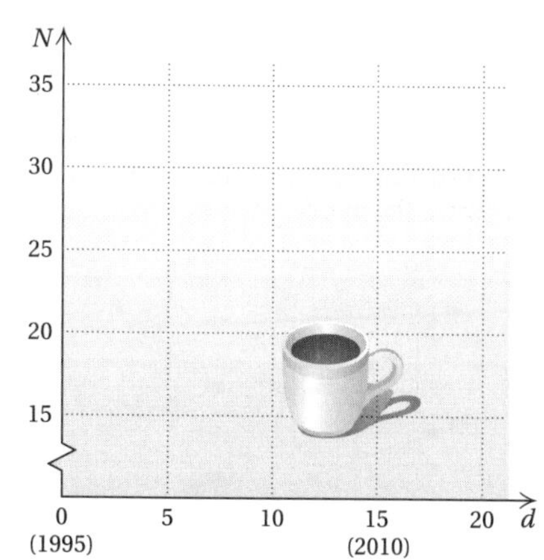

c) In what year will coffee consumption be about 31.6 gal?

62. *Record Temperature Drop.* On 22 January 1943, the temperature T, in degrees Fahrenheit, in Spearfish, South Dakota, could be approximated by $T = -2.15m + 54$, where m is the number of minutes since 9:00 that morning.

Source: *Information Please Almanac*

a) Find the temperature at 9:01 A.M., 9:08 A.M., and 9:20 A.M.
b) Graph the equation and use the graph to estimate the temperature at 9:15 A.M.

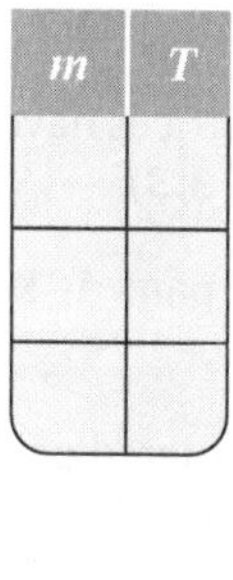

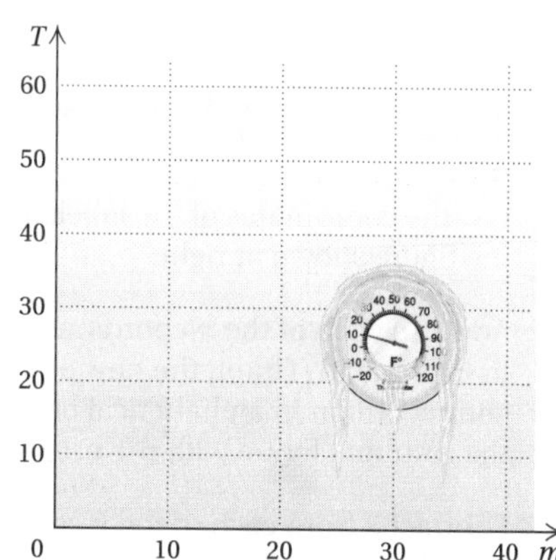

c) The temperature stopped dropping when it reached −4°F. At what time did this occur?

63. DW The equations $3x + 4y = 8$ and $y = -\frac{3}{4}x + 2$ are equivalent. Which equation is easier to graph and why?

64. DW Referring to Exercise 62, discuss why the linear equation no longer described the temperature after the temperature reached $-4°$.

SKILL MAINTENANCE

Find the absolute value. [1.2e]

65. $|-12|$

66. $|4.89|$

67. $|0|$

68. $\left|-\frac{4}{5}\right|$

69. $|-3.4|$

70. $|\sqrt{2}|$

71. $\left|\frac{2}{3}\right|$

72. $\left|-\frac{7}{8}\right|$

Solve. [2.5a]

73. *Baseball Ticket Prices.* In 2004, the average price of a ticket to a major-league baseball game was \$19.82. This price was an increase of 17.9% over the price in 2000. What was the average price in 2000?

Source: Major League Baseball

74. *Tipping.* Erin left a 15% tip for a meal. The total cost of the meal, including the tip, was \$21.16. What was the cost of the meal before the tip was added?

SYNTHESIS

75. The points $(-1, 1)$, $(4, 1)$, and $(4, -5)$ are three vertices of a rectangle. Find the coordinates of the fourth vertex.

76. Three parallelograms share the vertices $(-2, -3)$, $(-1, 2)$, and $(4, -3)$. Find the fourth vertex of each parallelogram.

77. Graph eight points such that the sum of the coordinates in each pair is 6.

78. Graph eight points such that the first coordinate minus the second coordinate is 1.

79. Find the perimeter of a rectangle whose vertices have coordinates $(5, 3)$, $(5, -2)$, $(-3, -2)$, and $(-3, 3)$.

80. Find the area of a triangle whose vertices have coordinates $(0, 9)$, $(0, -4)$, and $(5, -4)$.

81. List the coordinates of the labeled ordered pairs A–K in the figure shown at right.

82. Add 2 to each of the x-coordinates of the ordered pairs in Exercise 81. Graph the new ordered pairs and connect them in alphabetical order with lines. Compare the resulting figure with the original.

83. Subtract 3 from each of the y-coordinates of the ordered pairs in Exercise 81. Graph the new ordered pairs and connect them in alphabetical order with lines. Compare the resulting figure with the original.

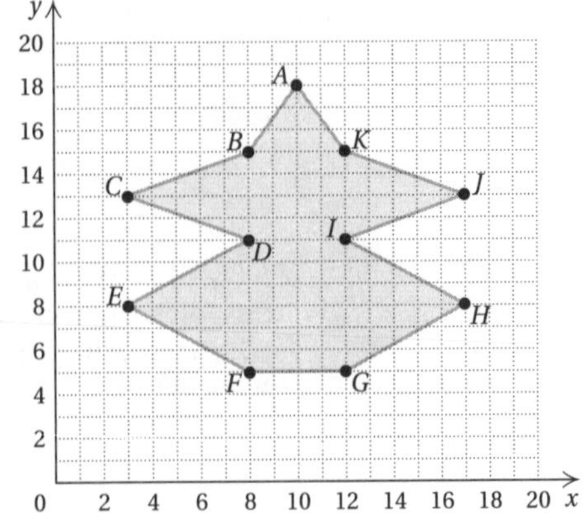

3.2 MORE WITH GRAPHING AND INTERCEPTS

Objectives

a Find the intercepts of a linear equation, and graph using intercepts.

b Graph equations equivalent to those of the type $x = a$ and $y = b$.

a Graphing Using Intercepts

Section 3.1, we graphed linear equations of the form $Ax + By = C$ by first lving for y to find an equivalent equation in the form $y = mx + b$. We did so ecause it is then easier to calculate the y-value that corresponds to a given value. Another convenient way to graph $Ax + By = C$ is to use **intercepts.** ook at the graph of $-2x + y = 4$ shown below.

The y-intercept is $(0, 4)$. It occurs here the line crosses the y-axis and thus ill always have 0 as the first coordinate. e x-intercept is   . It occurs here the line crosses the x-axis and us will always have 0 as the second ordinate.

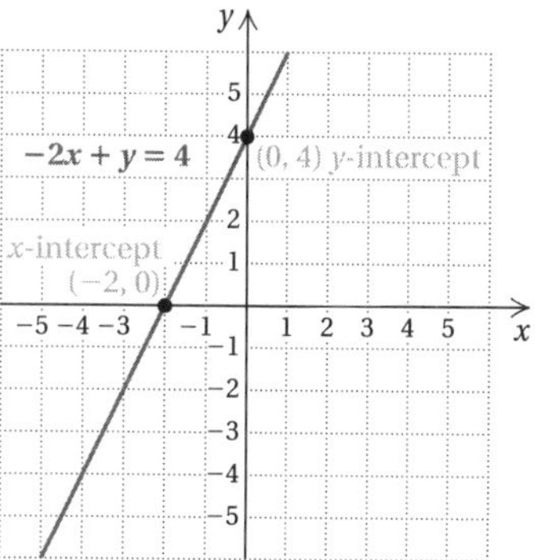

Exercise 1.

We find intercepts as follows.

INTERCEPTS

The **y-intercept** is $(0, b)$. To find b, let $x = 0$ and solve the original equation for y.

The **x-intercept** is $(a, 0)$. To find a, let $y = 0$ and solve the original equation for x.

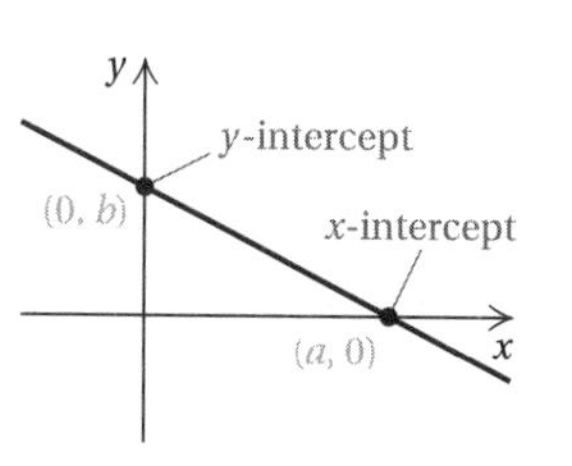

Now let's draw a graph using intercepts.

XAMPLE 1 Consider $4x + 3y = 12$. Find the intercepts. Then graph the uation using the intercepts.

To find the y-intercept, we let $x = 0$. Then we solve for y:

$$4 \cdot 0 + 3y = 12$$
$$3y = 12$$
$$y = 4.$$

us, $(0, 4)$ is the y-intercept. Note that finding this intercept amounts to vering up the x-term and solving the rest of the equation.

To find the x-intercept, we let $y = 0$. Then we solve for x:

$$4x + 3 \cdot 0 = 12$$
$$4x = 12$$
$$x = 3.$$

1. Look at the graph shown below.

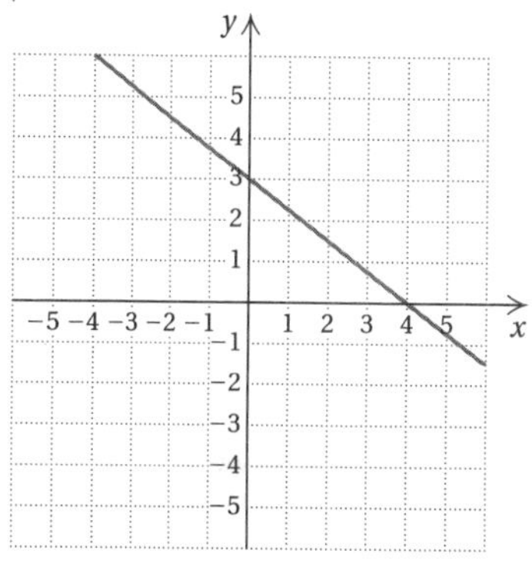

a) Find the coordinates of the y-intercept.

b) Find the coordinates of the x-intercept.

Answers on page A-13

For each equation, find the intercepts. Then graph the equation using the intercepts.

2. $2x + 3y = 6$

x	y	
	0	← x-intercept
0		← y-intercept
		← Check point

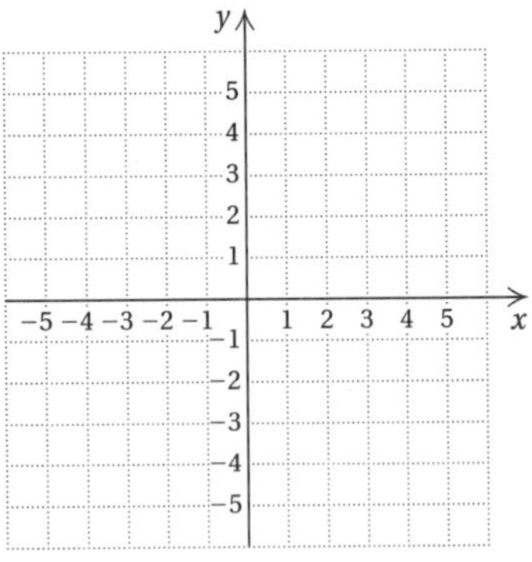

3. $3y - 4x = 12$

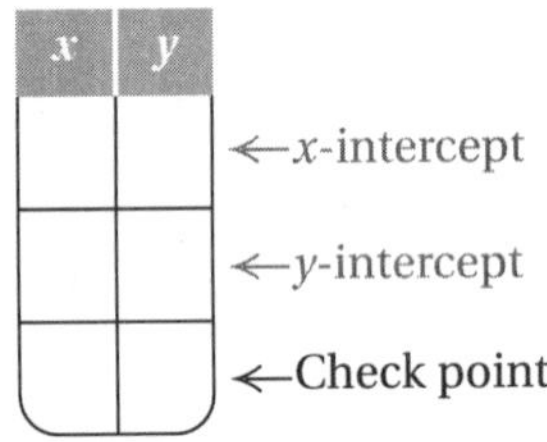

x	y	
		← x-intercept
		← y-intercept
		← Check point

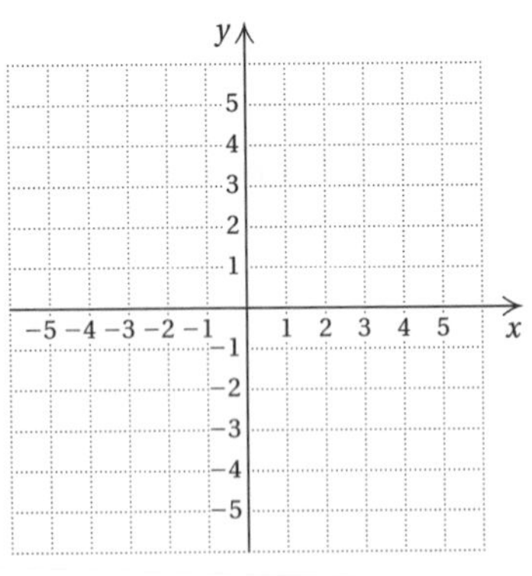

Answers on page A-13

Thus, $(3, 0)$ is the x-intercept. Note that finding this intercept amounts covering up the y-term and solving the rest of the equation.

We plot these points and draw the line, or graph.

x	y	
3	0	← x-intercept
0	4	← y-intercept
-2	$6\frac{2}{3}$	← Check point

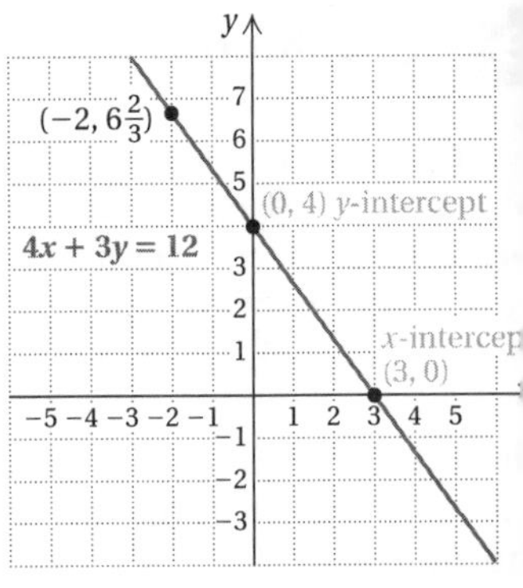

A third point should be used as a check. We substitute any convenie value for x and solve for y. In this case, we choose $x = -2$. Then

$$4(-2) + 3y = 12 \quad \text{Substituting } -2 \text{ for } x$$
$$-8 + 3y = 12$$
$$3y = 12 + 8 = 20$$
$$y = \frac{20}{3}, \text{ or } 6\tfrac{2}{3}. \quad \text{Solving for } y$$

It appears that the point $\left(-2, 6\frac{2}{3}\right)$ is on the graph, though graphing fractic values can be inexact. The graph is probably correct.

Do Exercises 2 and 3.

Graphs of equations of the type $y = mx$ pass through the origin. Thus t x-intercept and the y-intercept are the same, $(0, 0)$. In such cases, we mu calculate another point in order to complete the graph. Another point wou also have to be calculated if a check is desired.

EXAMPLE 2 Graph: $y = 3x$.

We know that $(0, 0)$ is both the x-intercept and the y-intercept. We calc late values at two other points and complete the graph, knowing that it pass through the origin $(0, 0)$.

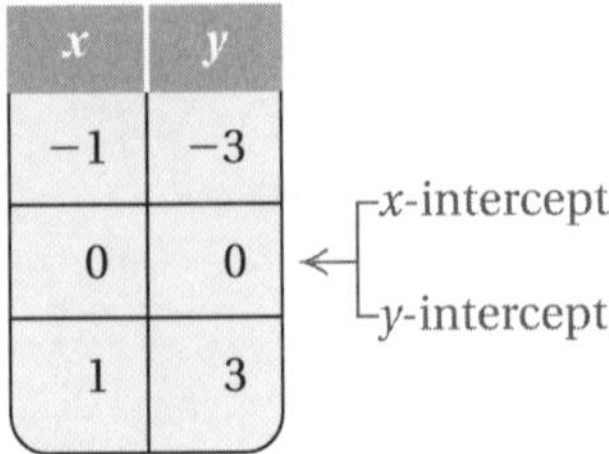

x	y	
-1	-3	
0	0	← x-intercept, y-intercept
1	3	

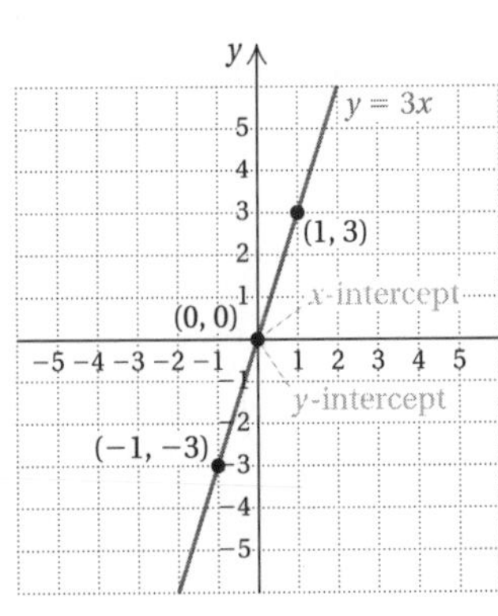

Do Exercises 4 and 5 on the following page.

CALCULATOR CORNER

Viewing the Intercepts Knowing the intercepts of a linear equation helps us to determine a good viewing window for the graph of the equation. For example, when we graph the equation $y = -x + 15$ in the standard window, we see only a small portion of the graph in the upper righthand corner of the screen, as shown on the left below.

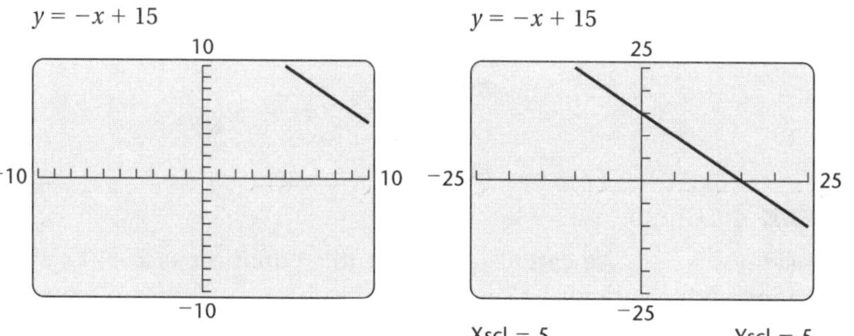

Using algebra, as we did in Example 1, we find that the intercepts of the graph of this equation are (0, 15) and (15, 0). This tells us that, if we are to see more of the graph than is shown on the left above, both Xmax and Ymax should be greater than 15. We can try different window settings until we find one that suits us. One good choice is [−25, 25, −25, 25], Xscl = 5, Yscl = 5, shown on the right above.

Exercises: Find the intercepts of each equation algebraically. Then graph the equation on a graphing calculator, choosing window settings that allow the intercepts to be seen clearly. (Settings may vary.)

1. $y = -7.5x - 15$
2. $y - 2.15x = 43$
3. $6x - 5y = 150$
4. $y = 0.2x - 4$
5. $y = 1.5x - 15$
6. $5x - 4y = 2$

b Equations Whose Graphs Are Horizontal or Vertical Lines

XAMPLE 3 Graph: $y = 3$.

Consider $y = 3$. We can also think of this equation as $0 \cdot x + y = 3$. No atter what number we choose for x, we find that y is 3. We make up a table ith all 3's in the y-column.

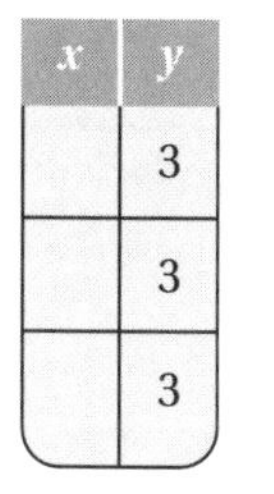

x	y
	3
	3
	3

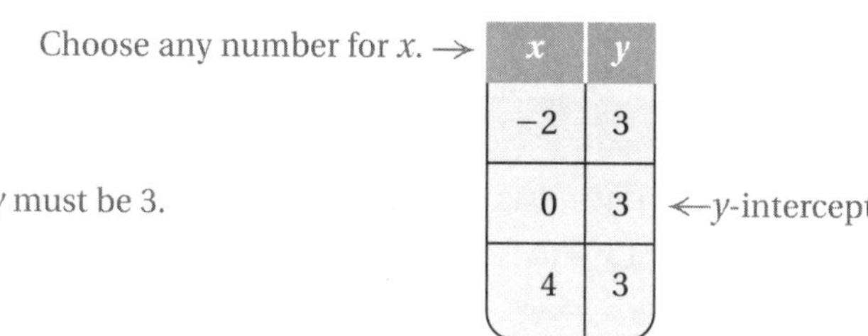

x	y
−2	3
0	3
4	3

Graph.

4. $y = 2x$

x	y
−1	
0	
1	

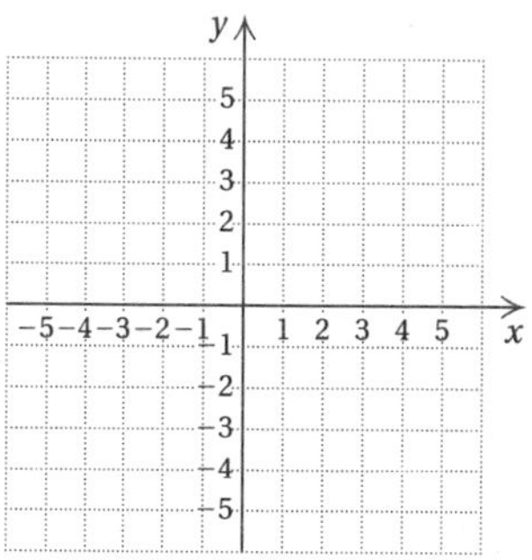

5. $y = -\frac{2}{3}x$

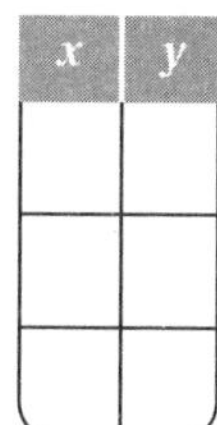

x	y

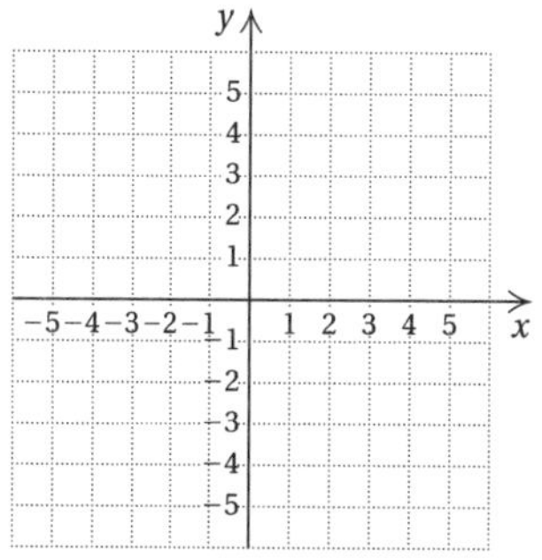

Answers on page A-13

Graph.

6. $x = 5$

x	y
5	
5	
5	

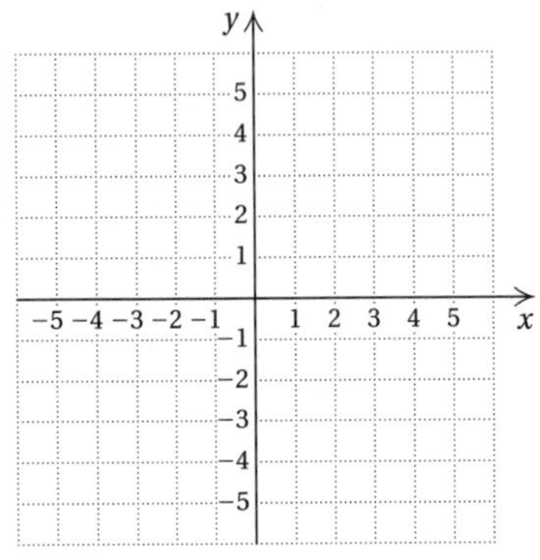

7. $y = -2$

x	y
	−2
	−2
	−2

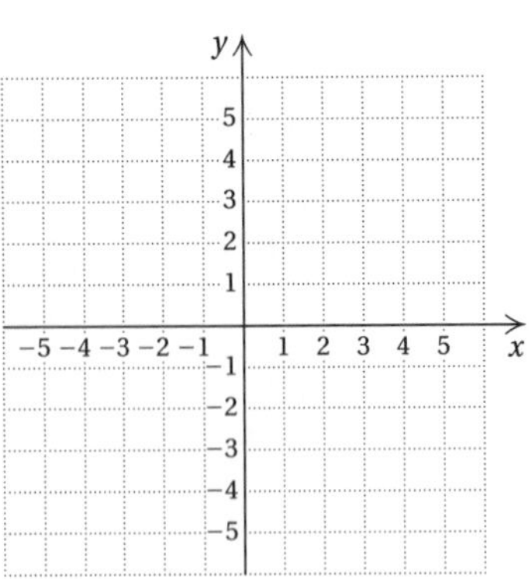

When we plot the ordered pairs $(-2, 3)$, $(0, 3)$, and $(4, 3)$ and connect the points, we obtain a horizontal line. Any ordered pair $(x, 3)$ is a solution. So the line is parallel to the x-axis with y-intercept $(0, 3)$.

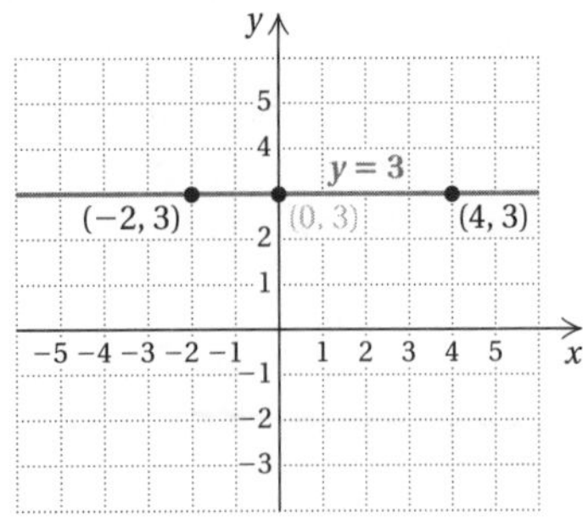

EXAMPLE 4 Graph: $x = -4$.

Consider $x = -4$. We can also think of this equation as $x + 0 \cdot y = -4$. We make up a table with all -4's in the x-column.

x	y
−4	
−4	
−4	
−4	

x must be -4.

Choose any number for y. →

x	y
−4	−5
−4	1
−4	3
−4	0

x-intercept → (row -4, 0)

When we plot the ordered pairs $(-4, -5)$, $(-4, 1)$, $(-4, 3)$, and $(-4, 0)$ and connect the points, we obtain a vertical line. Any ordered pair $(-4, y)$ is a solution. So the line is parallel to the y-axis with x-intercept $(-4, 0)$.

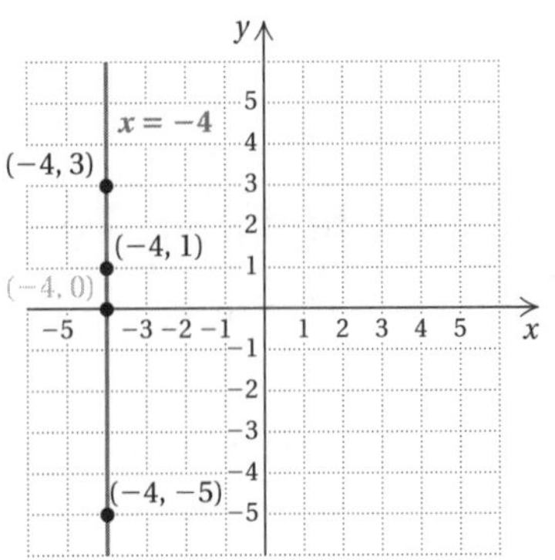

HORIZONTAL AND VERTICAL LINES

The graph of $y = b$ is a **horizontal line.** The y-intercept is $(0, b)$.
The graph of $x = a$ is a **vertical line.** The x-intercept is $(a, 0)$.

Answers on page A-13

Do Exercises 6–9. (Exercises 8 and 9 are on the following page.)

The following is a general procedure for graphing linear equations.

GRAPHING LINEAR EQUATIONS

1. If the equation is of the type $x = a$ or $y = b$, the graph will be a line parallel to an axis; $x = a$ is vertical and $y = b$ is horizontal.

Examples.

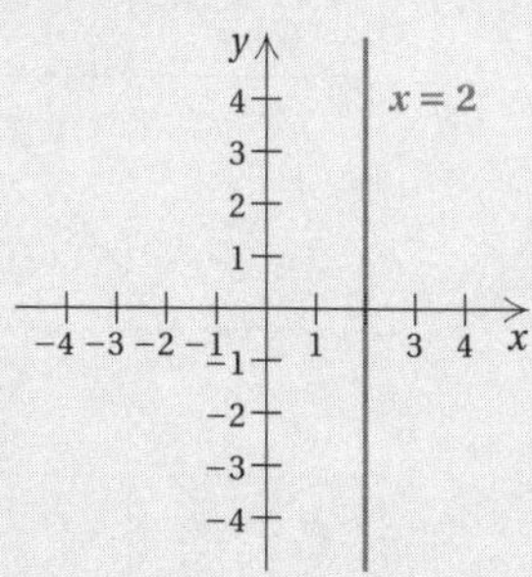

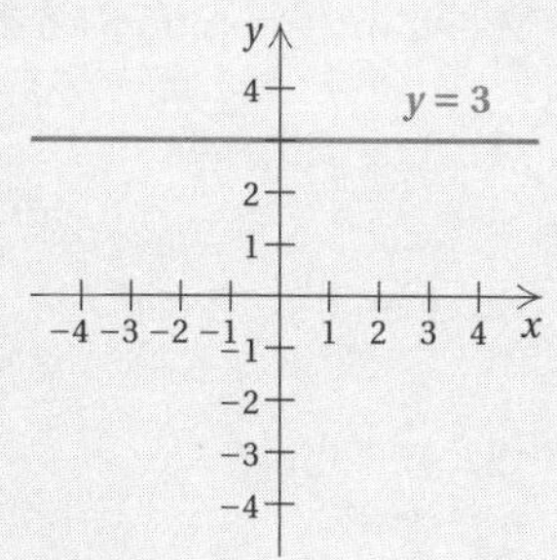

2. If the equation is of the type $y = mx$, both intercepts are the origin, $(0, 0)$. Plot $(0, 0)$ and two other points.

Example.

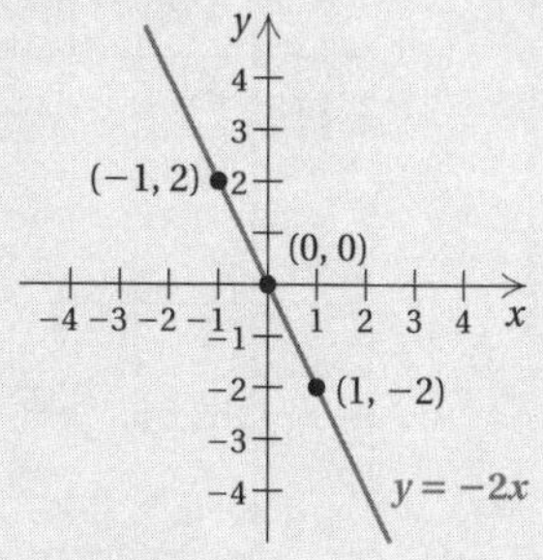

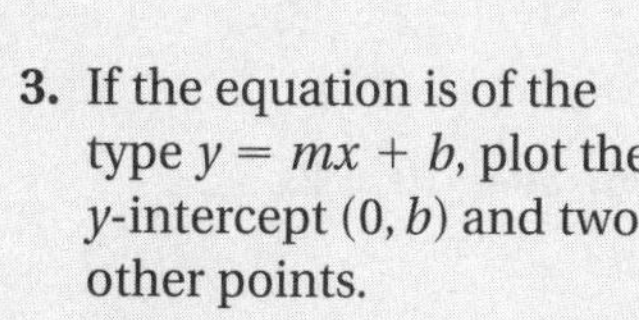
3. If the equation is of the type $y = mx + b$, plot the y-intercept $(0, b)$ and two other points.

Example.

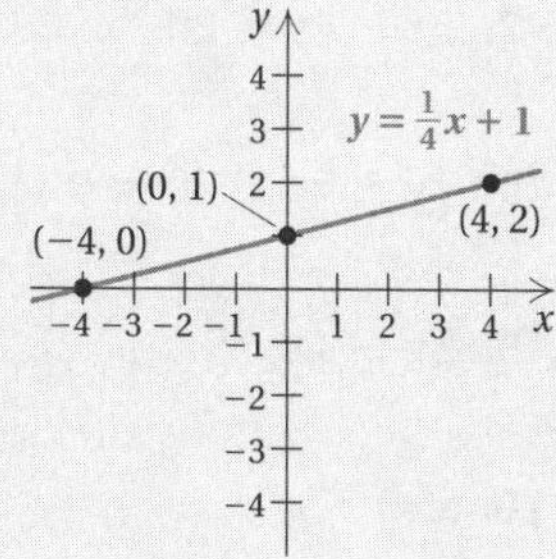

4. If the equation is of the type $Ax + By = C$, but not of the type $x = a$, $y = b$, $y = mx$, or $y = mx + b$, then either solve for y and proceed as with the equation $y = mx + b$, or graph using intercepts. If the intercepts are too close together, choose another point or points farther from the origin.

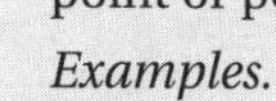
Examples.

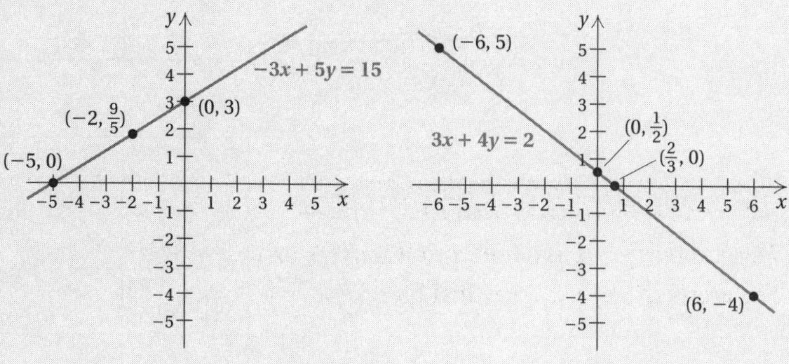

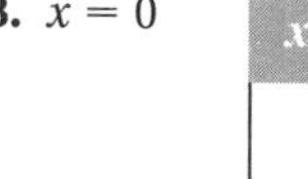
8. $x = 0$

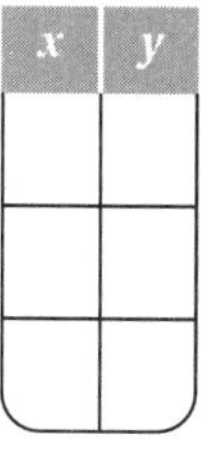

x	y

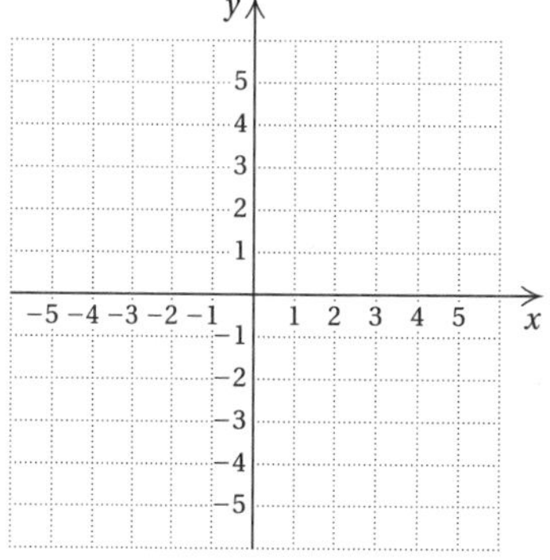

9. $x = -3$

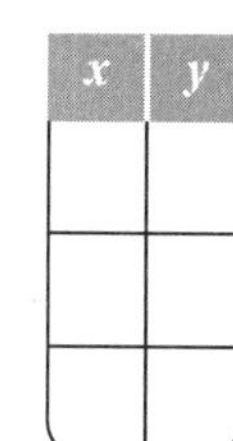

x	y

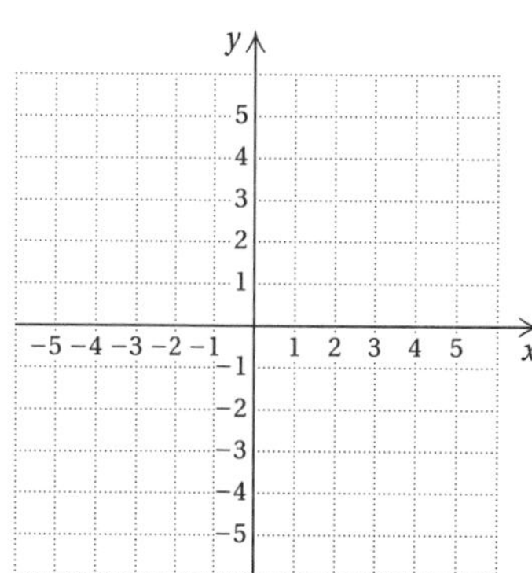

Answers on page A-13

Visualizing for Success

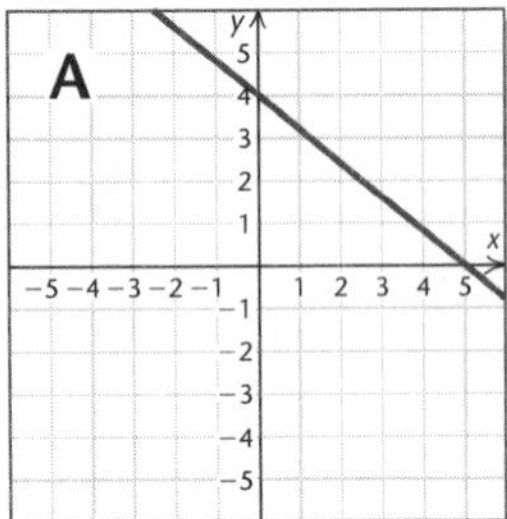
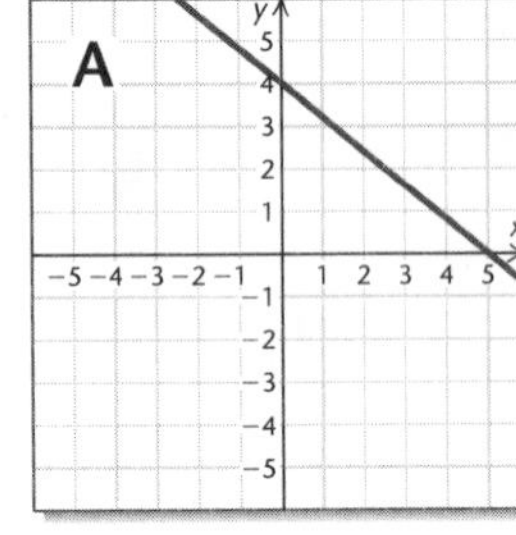

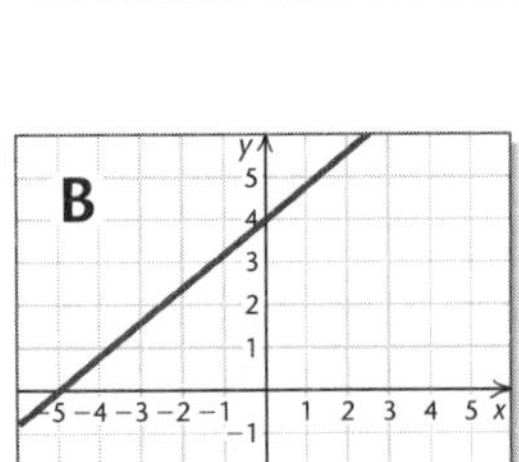

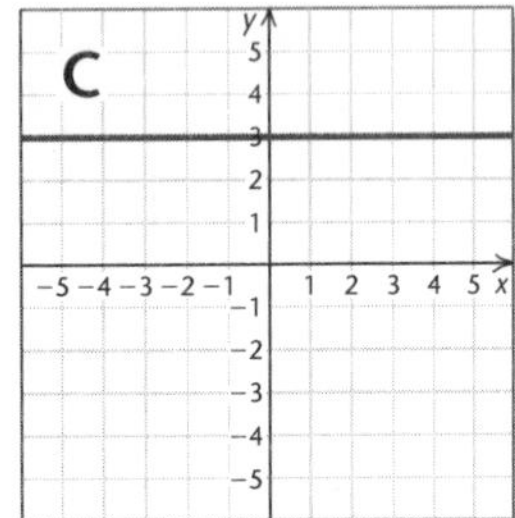

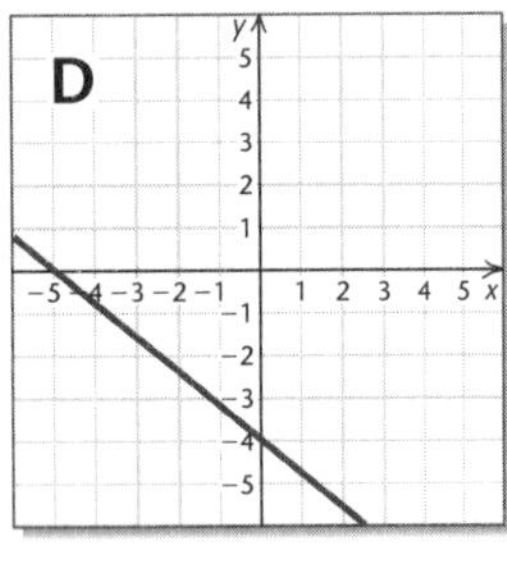

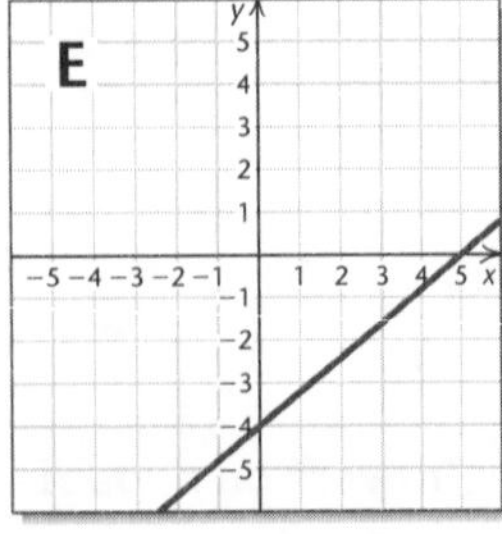

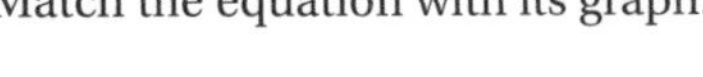
Match the equation with its graph.

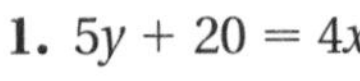
1. $5y + 20 = 4x$

2. $y = 3$

3. $3x + 5y = 15$

4. $5y + 4x = 20$

5. $5y = 10 - 2x$

6. $4x + 5y + 20 = 0$

7. $5x - 4y = 20$

8. $4y + 5x + 20 = 0$

9. $5y - 4x = 20$

10. $x = -3$

Answers on page A-14

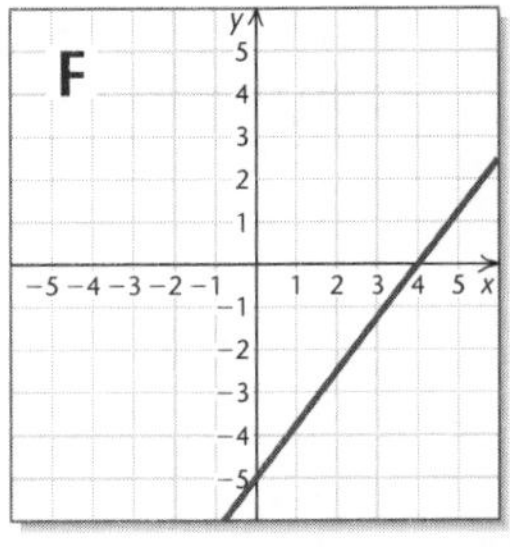

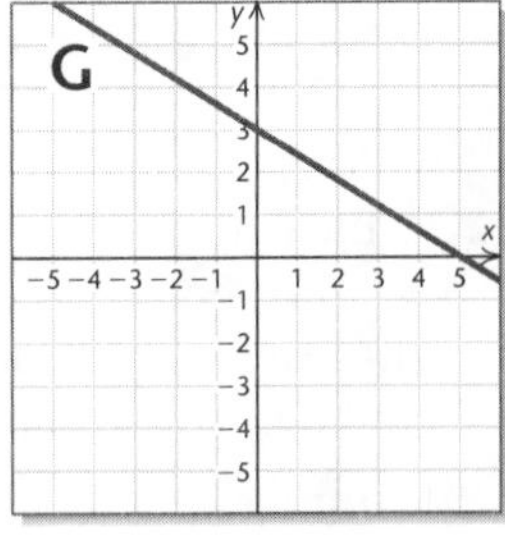

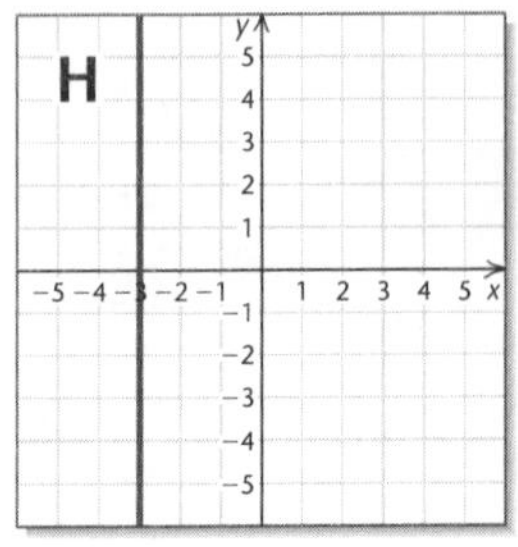

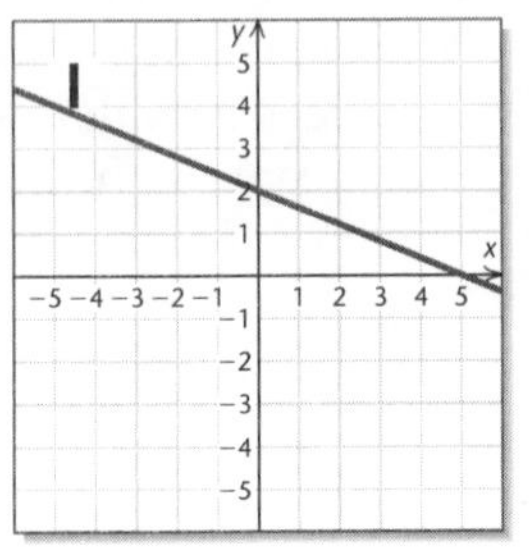

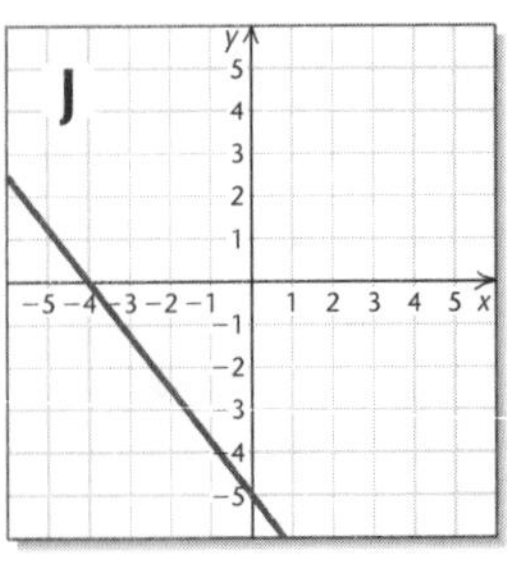

3.2 EXERCISE SET

For Extra Help

MathXL | MyMathLab | InterAct Math | Math Tutor Center | Digital Video Tutor CD 2 Videotape 4 | Student's Solutions Manual

a For Exercises 1–4, find **(a)** the coordinates of the y-intercept and **(b)** the coordinates of the x-intercept.

1.

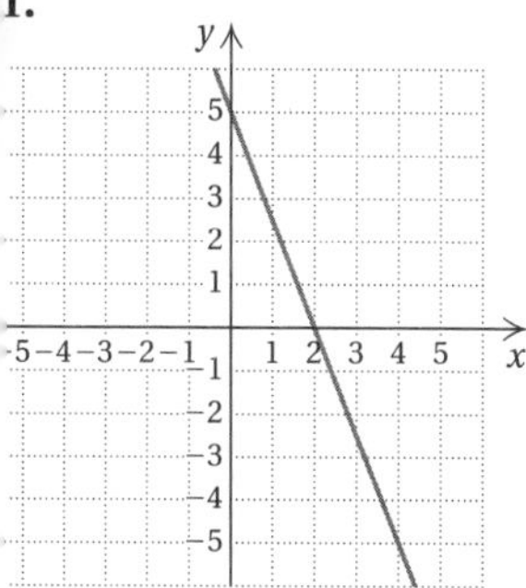

2.

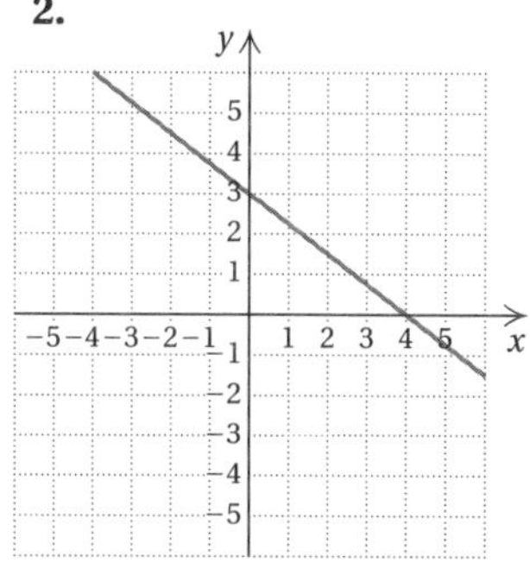

3.

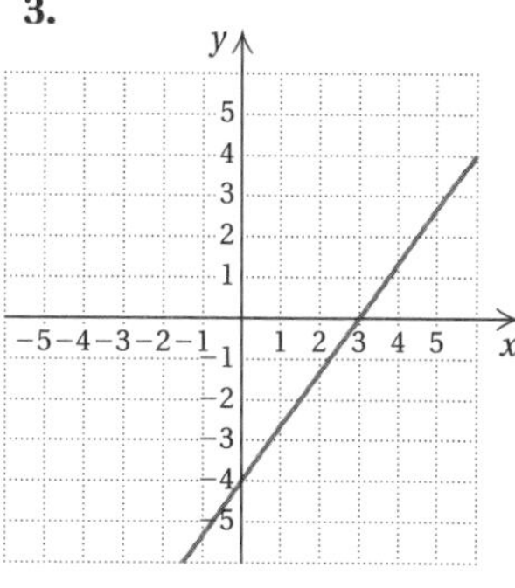

4.

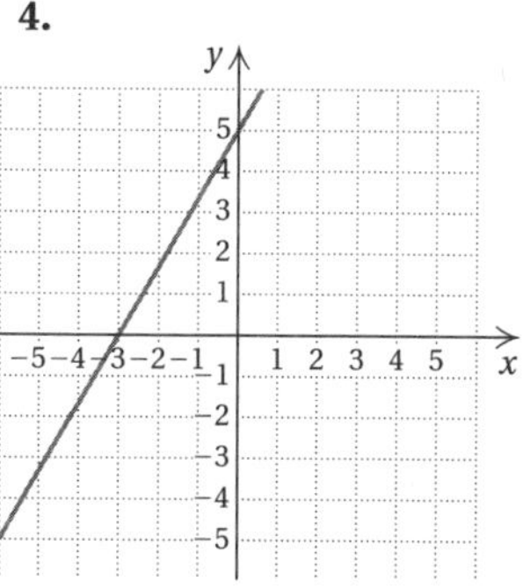

or Exercises 5–12, find **(a)** the coordinates of the y-intercept and **(b)** the coordinates of the x-intercept. Do not graph.

5. $3x + 5y = 15$

6. $5x + 2y = 20$

7. $7x - 2y = 28$

8. $3x - 4y = 24$

9. $-4x + 3y = 10$

10. $-2x + 3y = 7$

11. $6x - 3 = 9y$

12. $4y - 2 = 6x$

or each equation, find the intercepts. Then use the intercepts to graph the equation.

3. $x + 3y = 6$

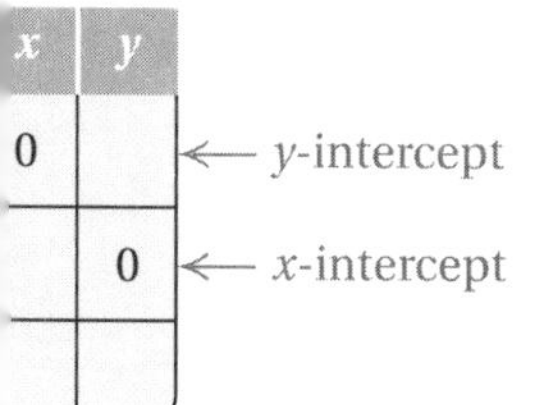

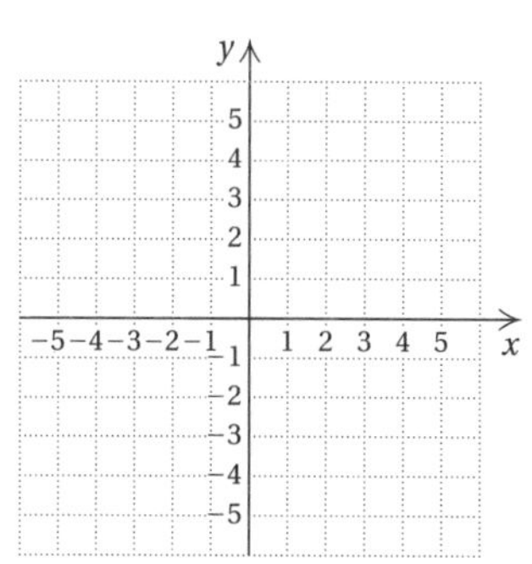

14. $x + 2y = 2$

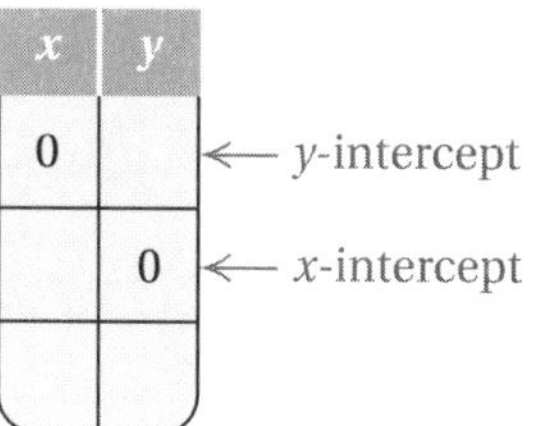

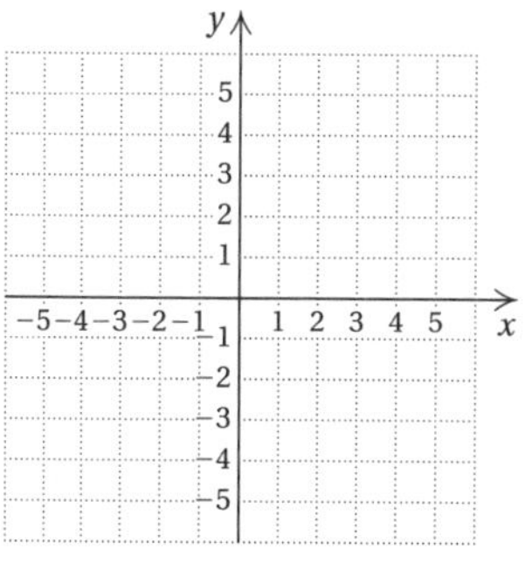

5. $-x + 2y = 4$

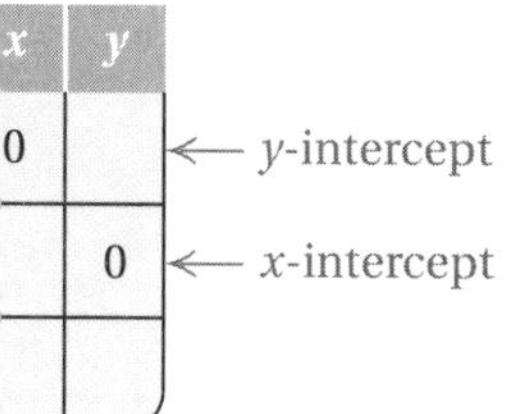

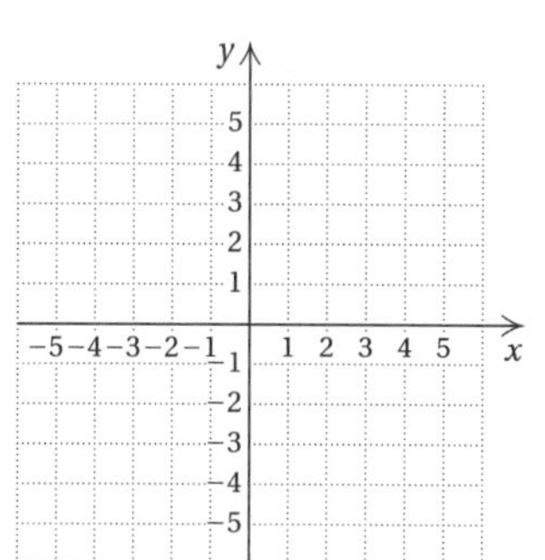

16. $-x + y = 5$

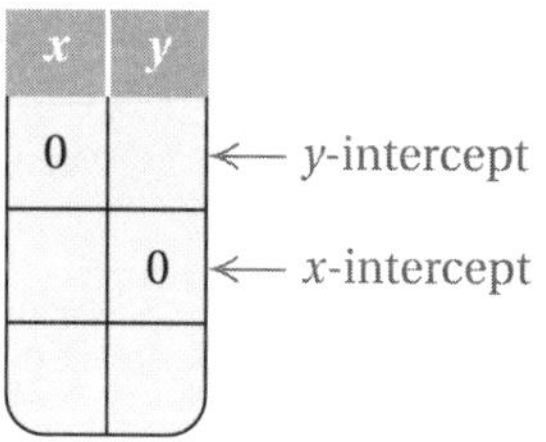

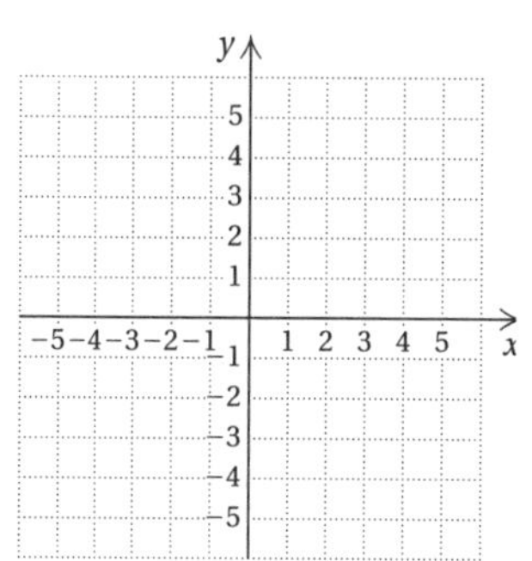

17. $3x + y = 6$

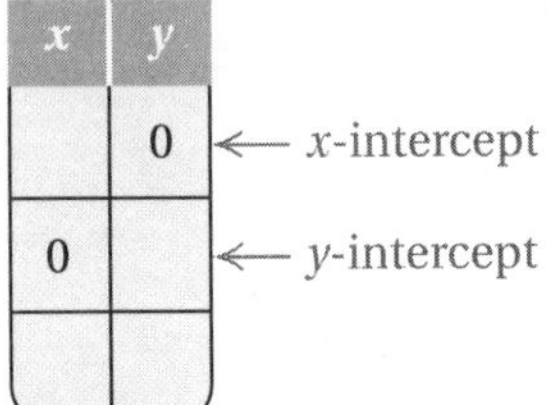

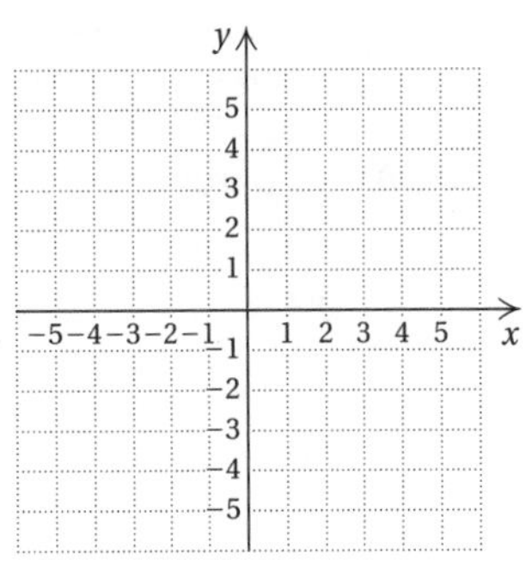

18. $2x + y = 6$

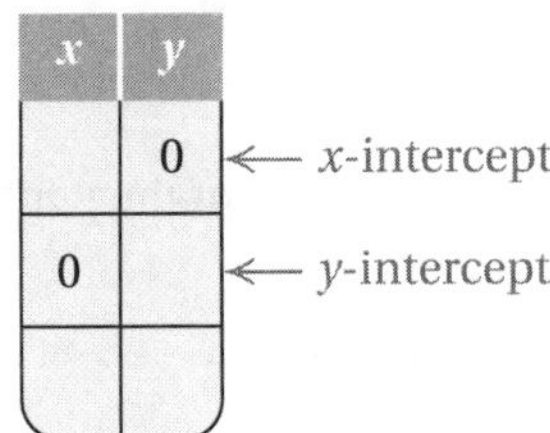

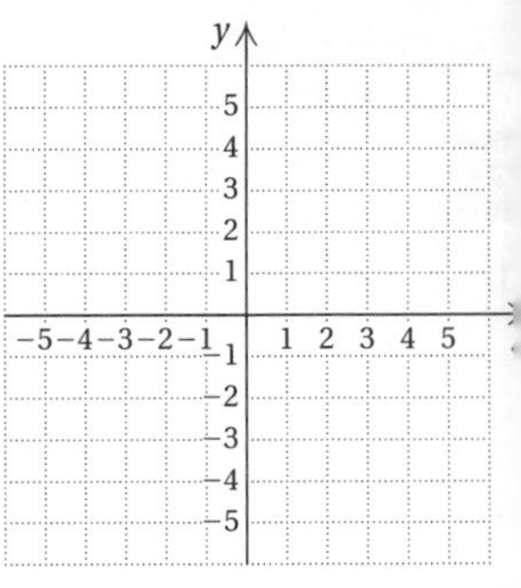

19. $2y - 2 = 6x$

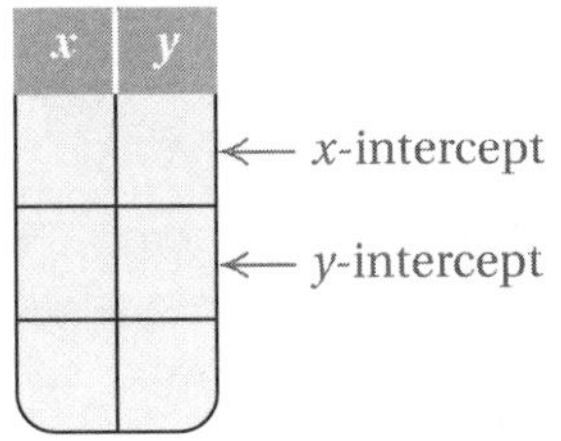

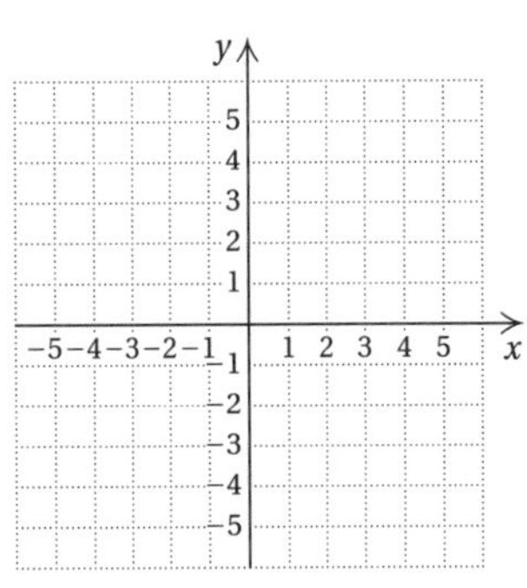

20. $3y - 6 = 9x$

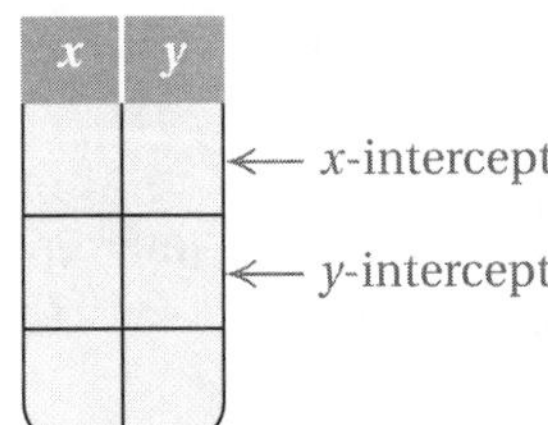

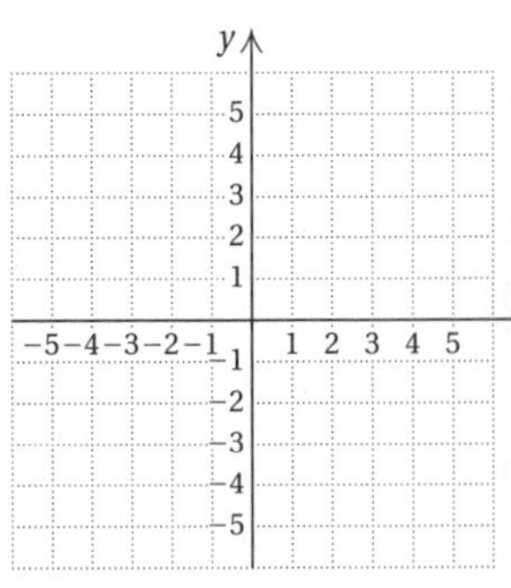

21. $3x - 9 = 3y$

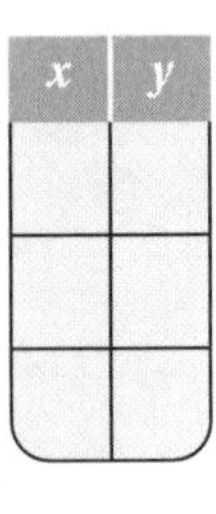

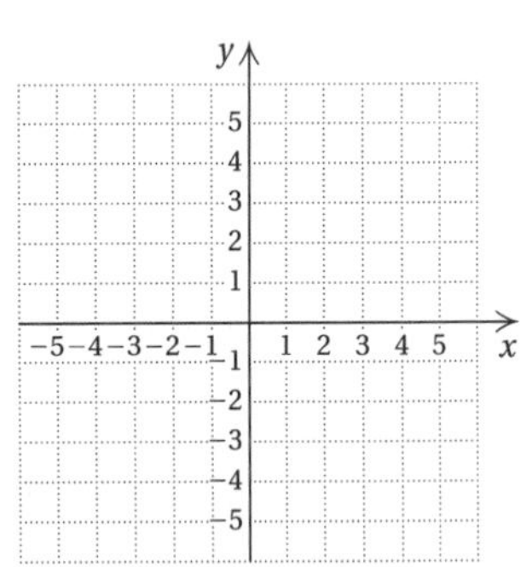

22. $5x - 10 = 5y$

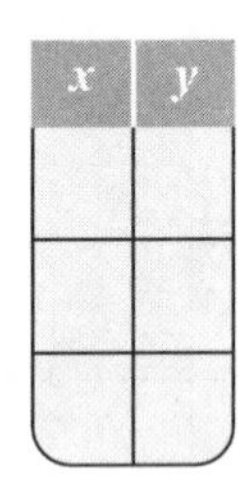

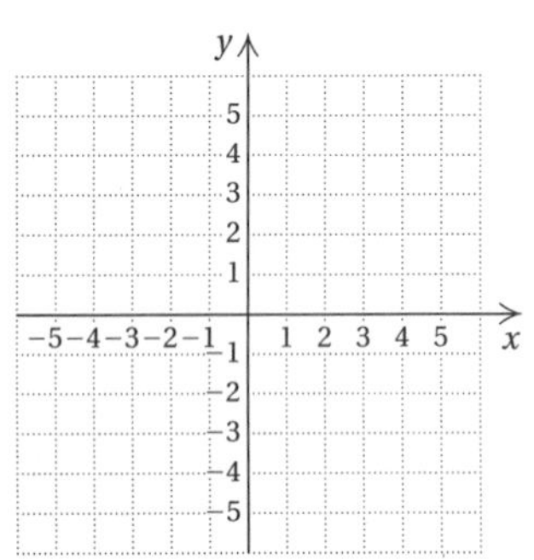

23. $2x - 3y = 6$

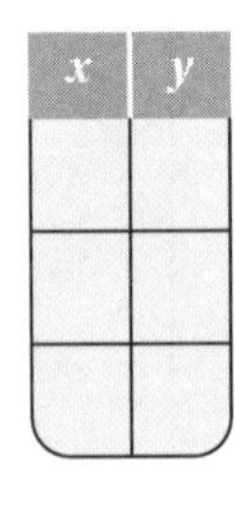

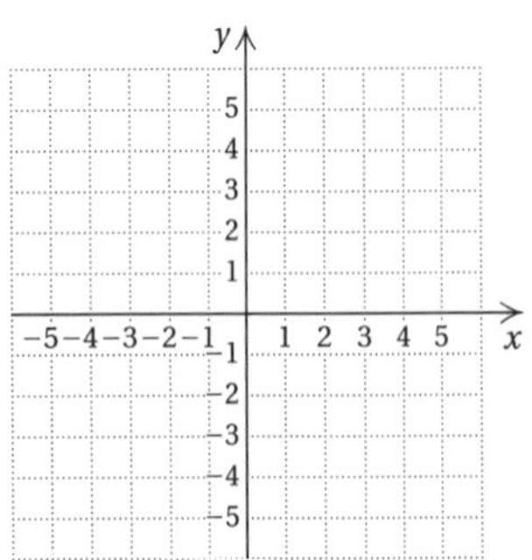

24. $2x - 5y = 10$

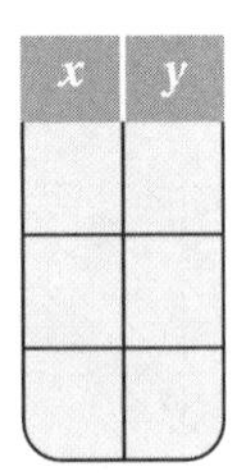

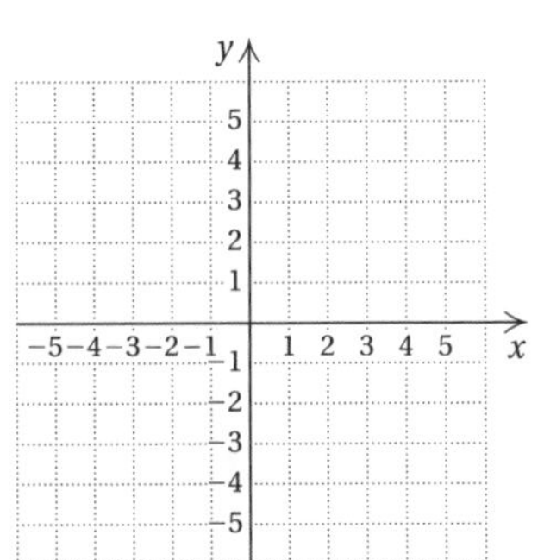

5. $4x + 5y = 20$

x	y

26. $2x + 6y = 12$

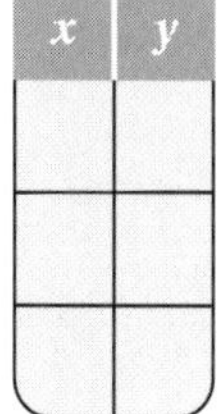

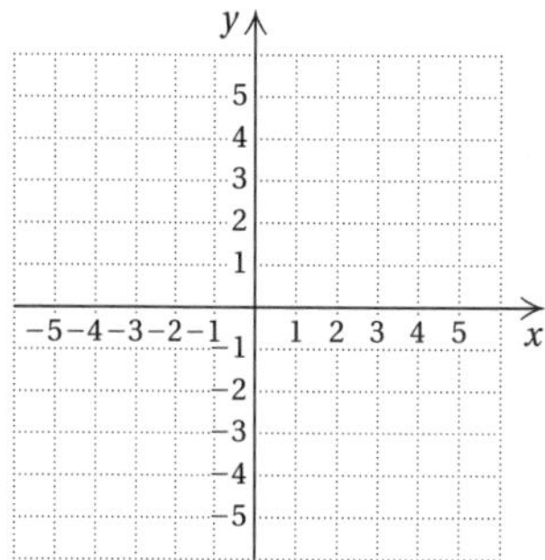

7. $2x + 3y = 8$

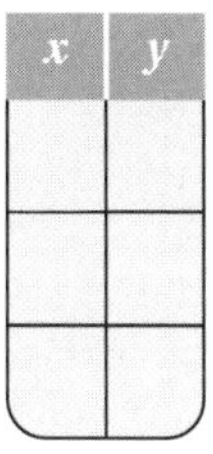

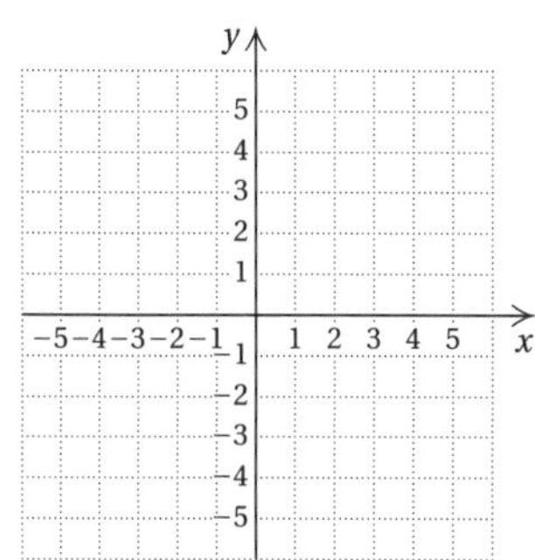

28. $x - 1 = y$

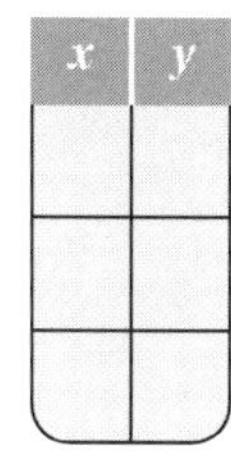

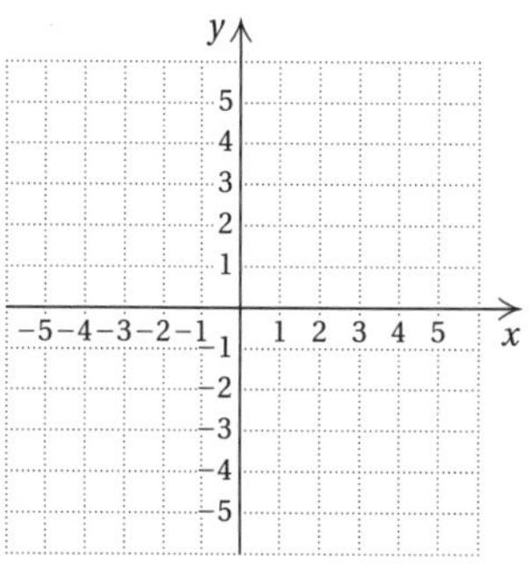

9. $x - 3 = y$

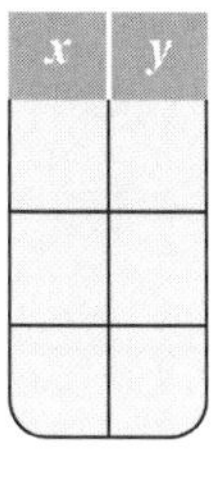

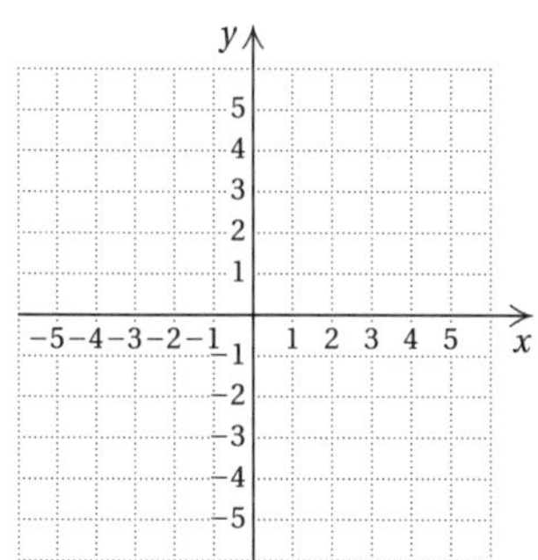

30. $2x - 1 = y$

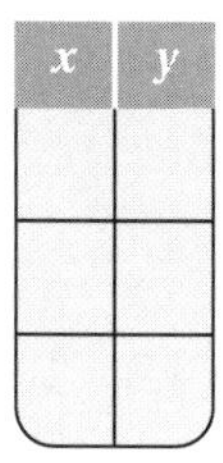

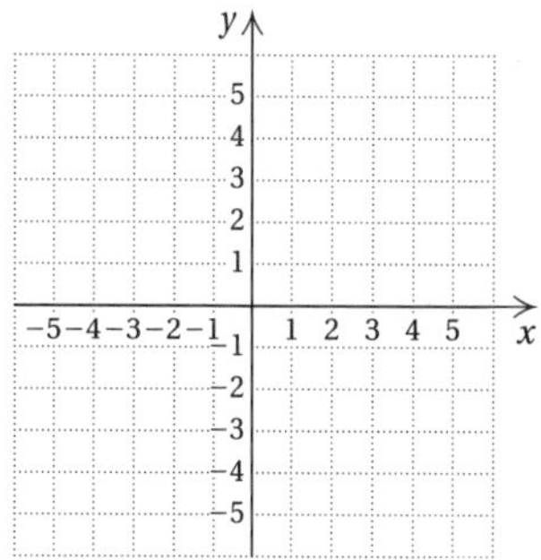

1. $3x - 2 = y$

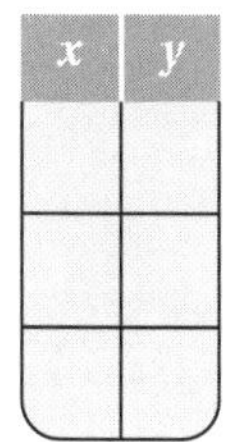

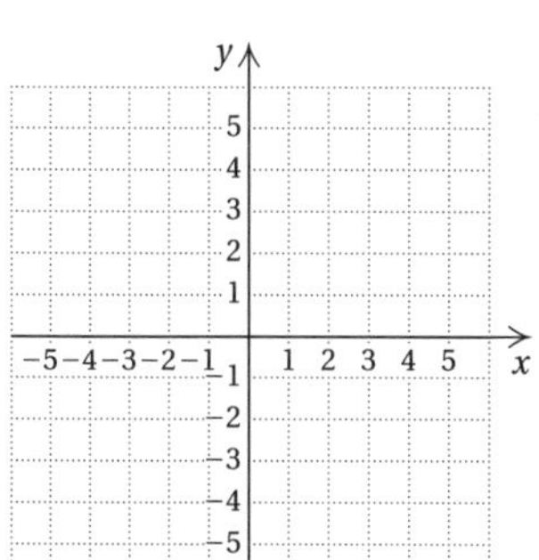

32. $4x - 3y = 12$

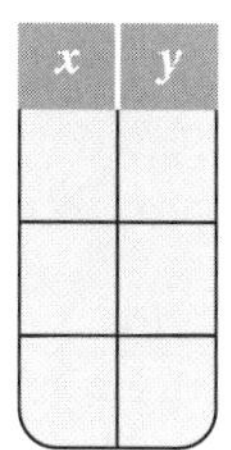

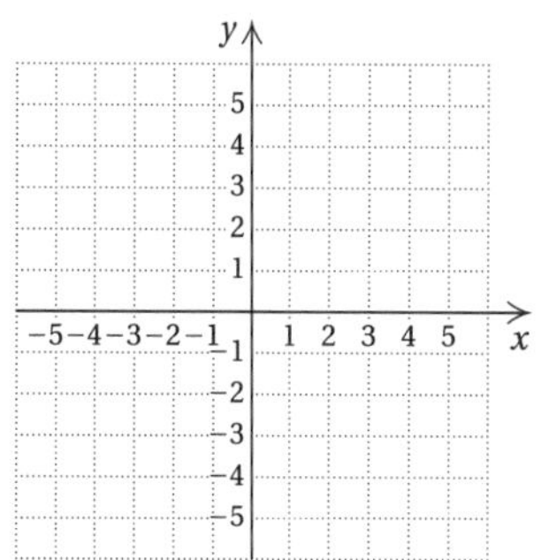

33. $6x - 2y = 12$

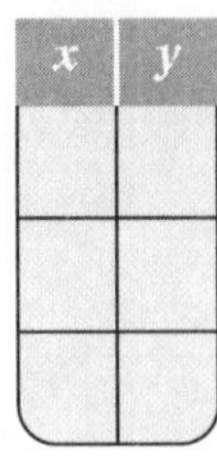

x	y

34. $7x + 2y = 6$

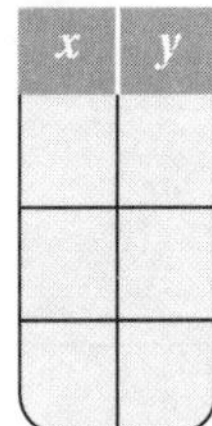

x	y

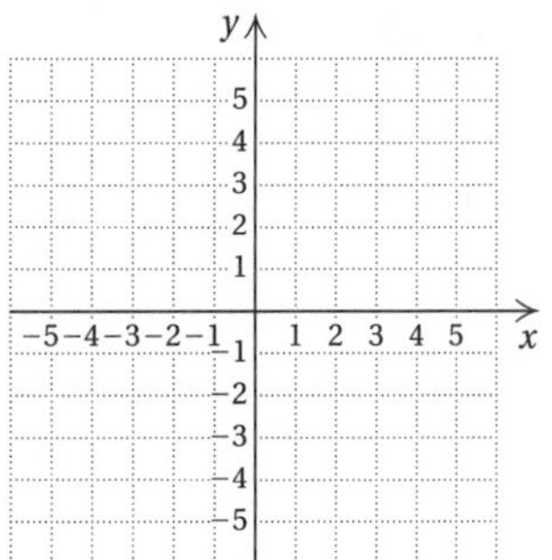

35. $3x + 4y = 5$

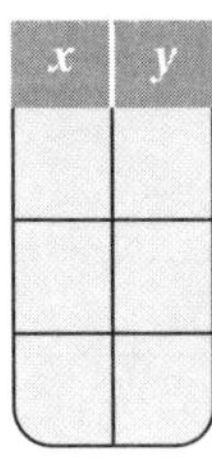

x	y

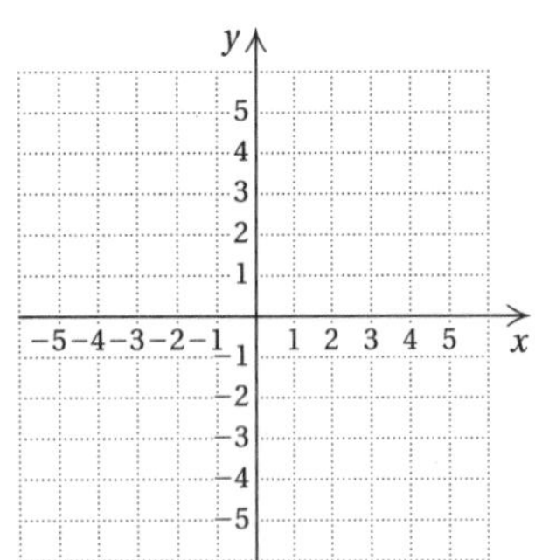

36. $y = -4 - 4x$

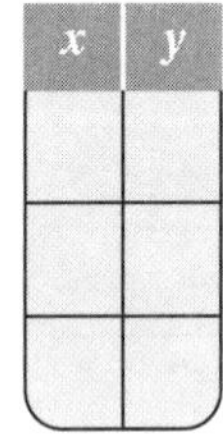

x	y

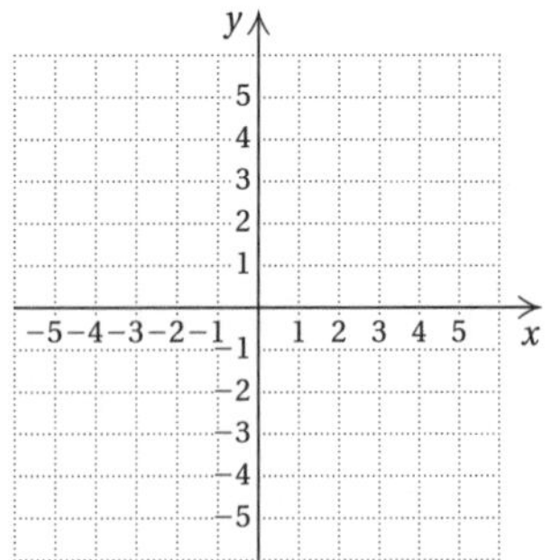

37. $y = -3 - 3x$

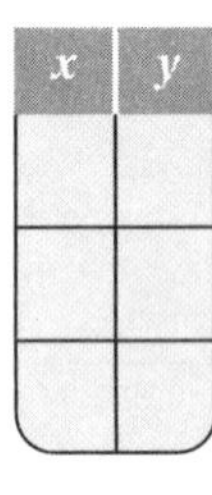

x	y

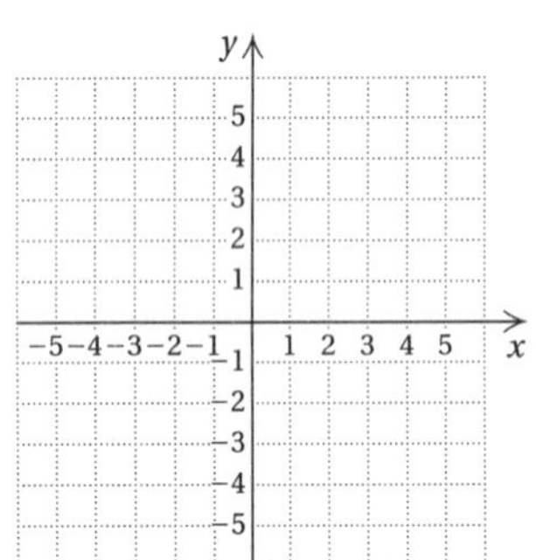

38. $-3x = 6y - 2$

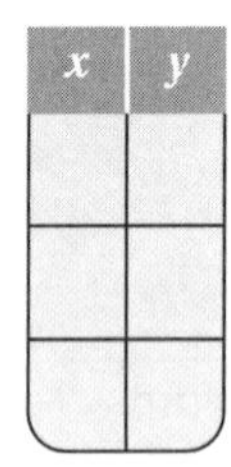

x	y

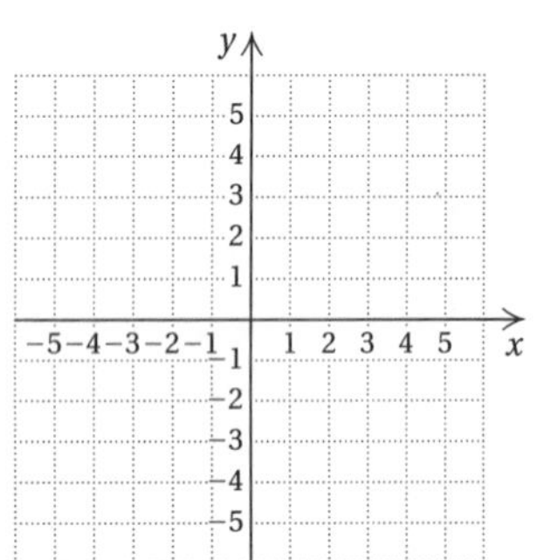

39. $y - 3x = 0$

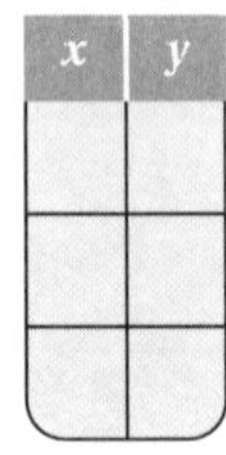

x	y

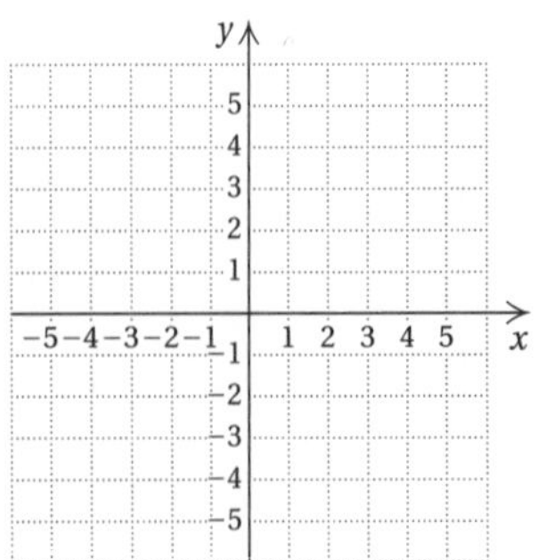

40. $x + 2y = 0$

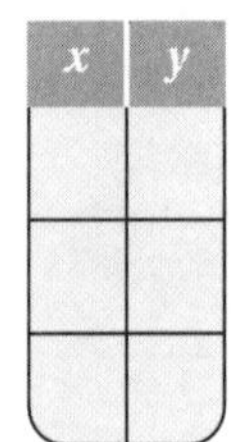

x	y

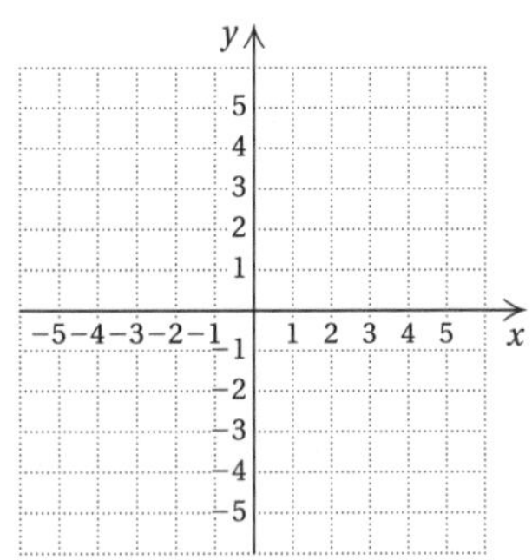

Graph.

1. $x = -2$

x	y
-2	
-2	
-2	

42. $x = 1$

x	y
1	
1	
1	

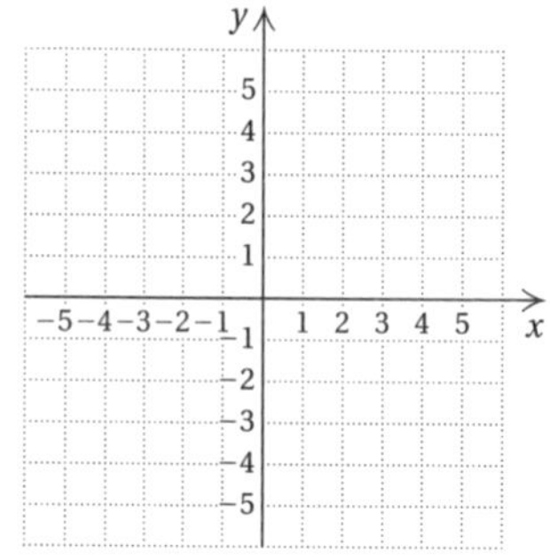

3. $y = 2$

x	y
	2
	2
	2

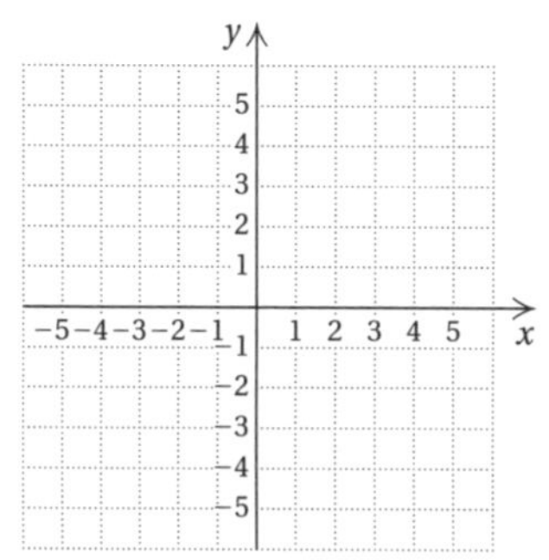

44. $y = -4$

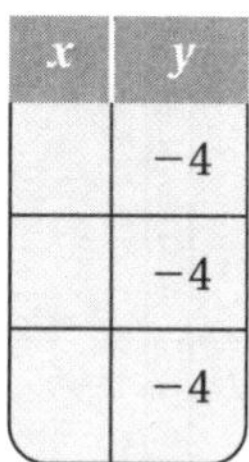

x	y
	-4
	-4
	-4

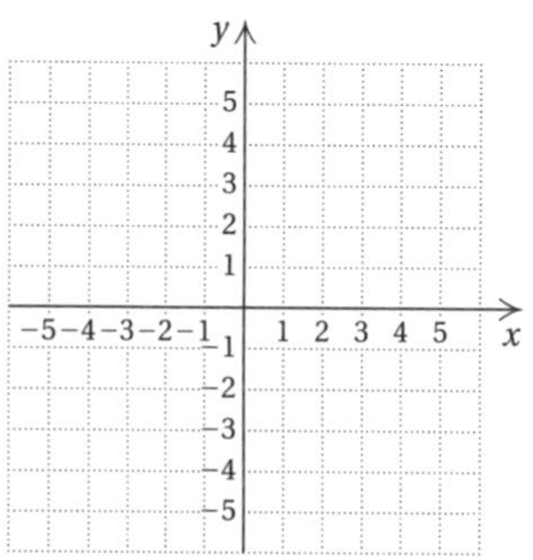

5. $x = 2$

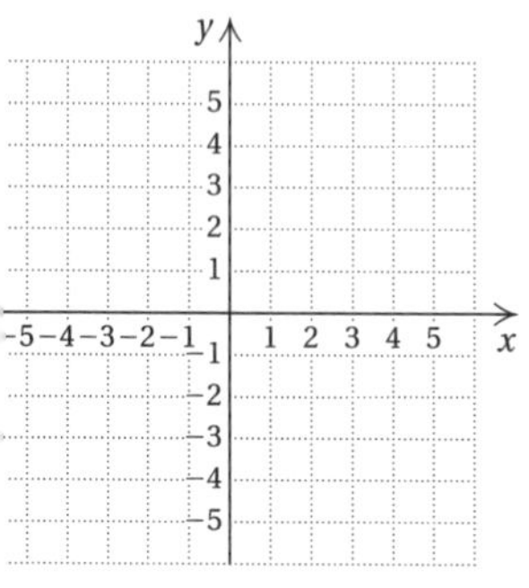

46. $x = 3$

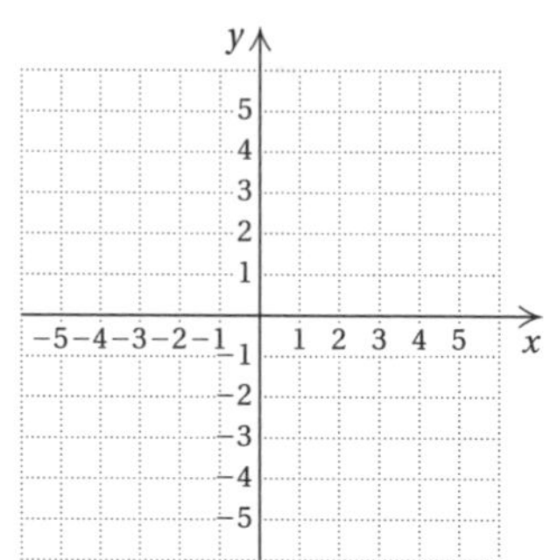

47. $y = 0$

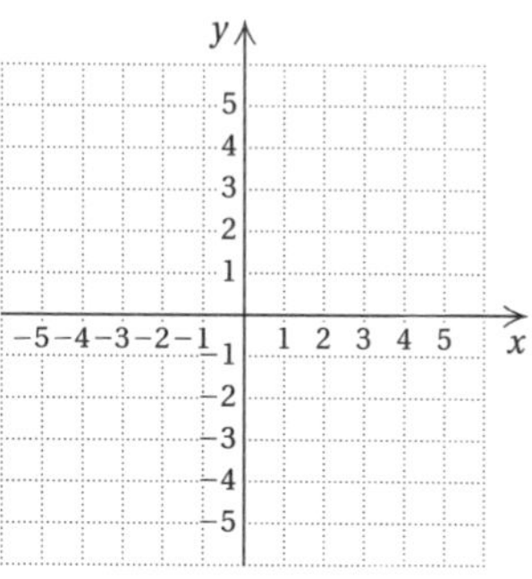

48. $y = -1$

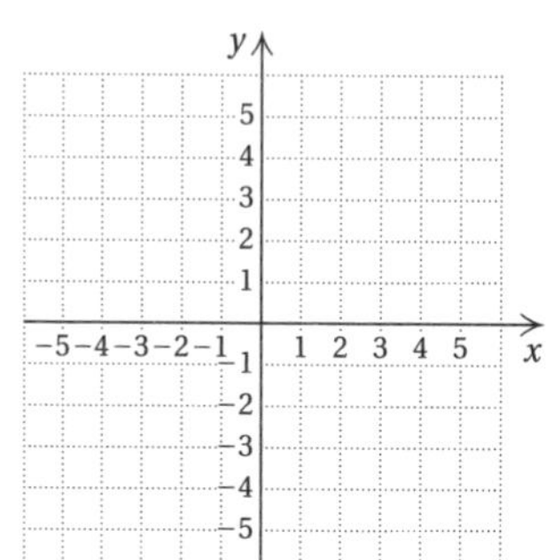

9. $x = \frac{3}{2}$

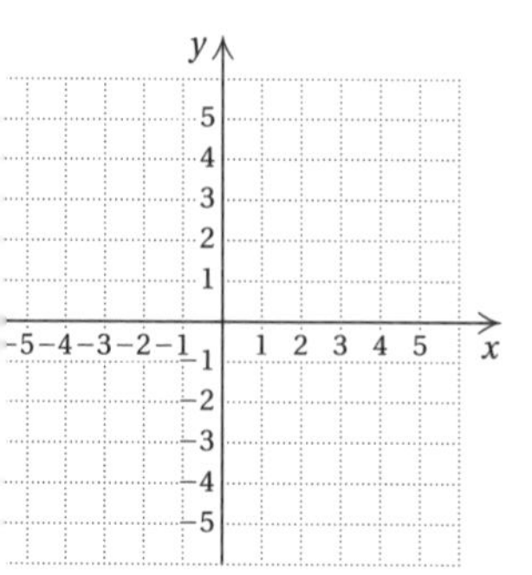

50. $x = -\frac{5}{2}$

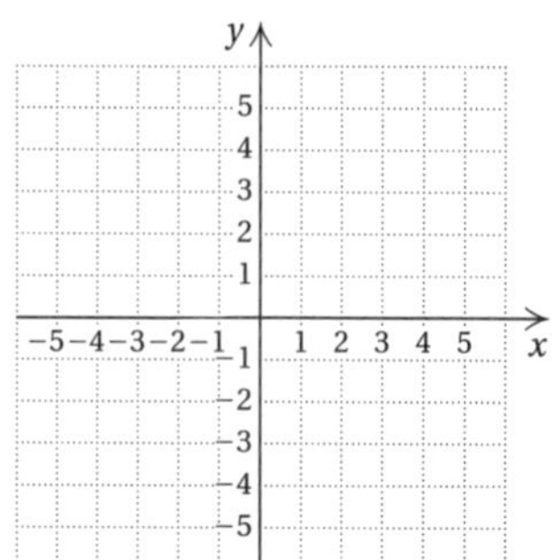

51. $3y = -5$

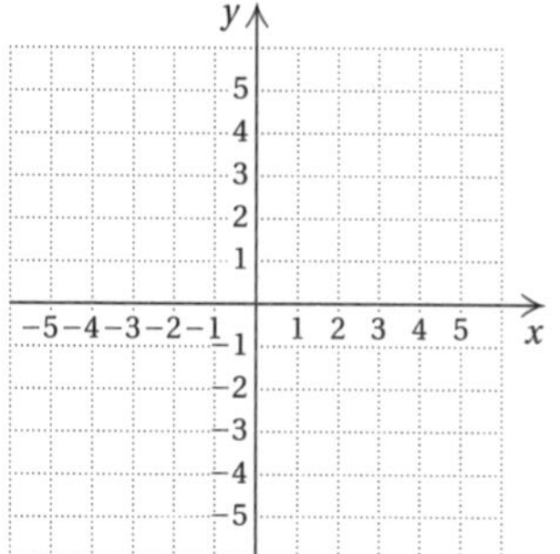

52. $12y = 45$

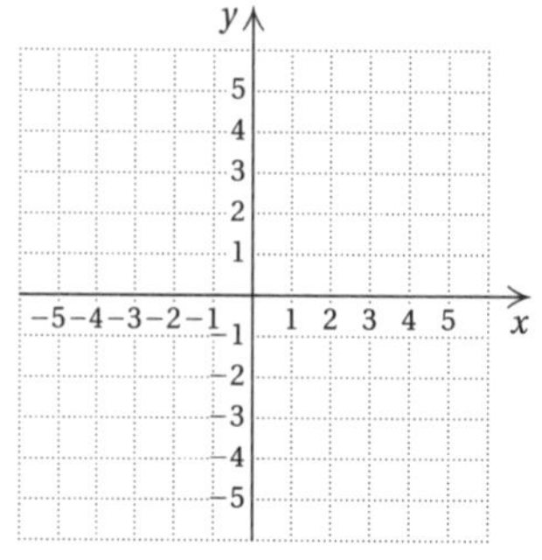

53. $4x + 3 = 0$

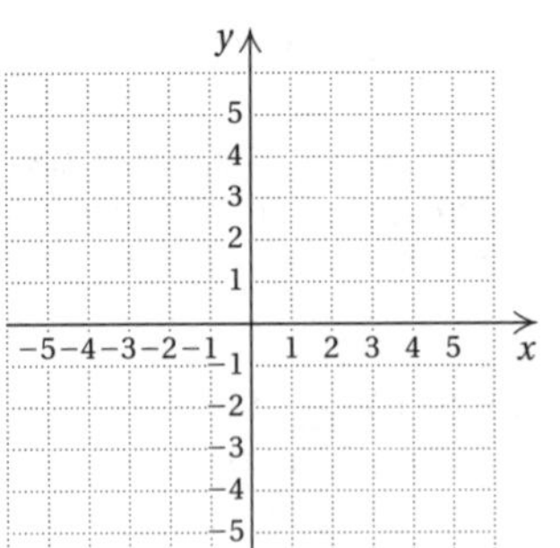

54. $-3x + 12 = 0$

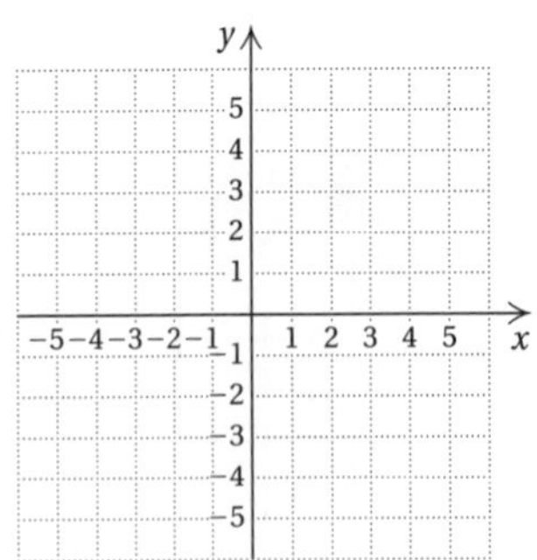

55. $48 - 3y = 0$

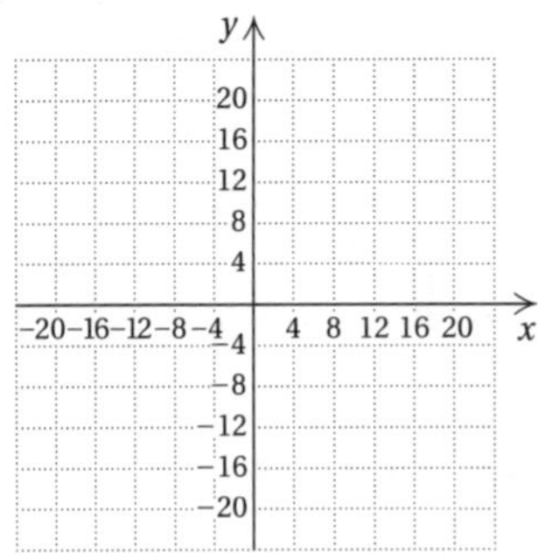

56. $63 + 7y = 0$

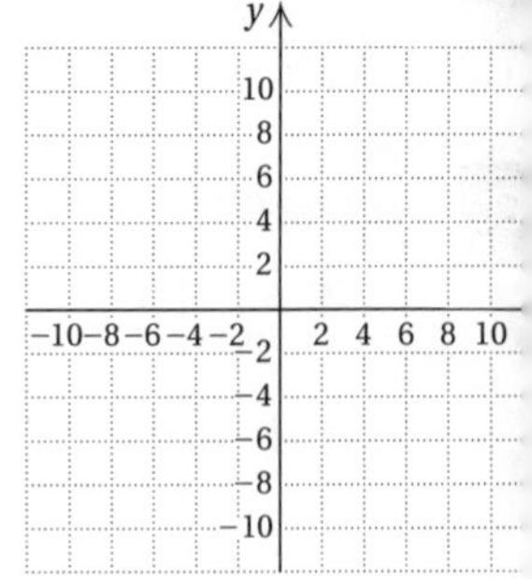

Write an equation for the graph shown.

57.

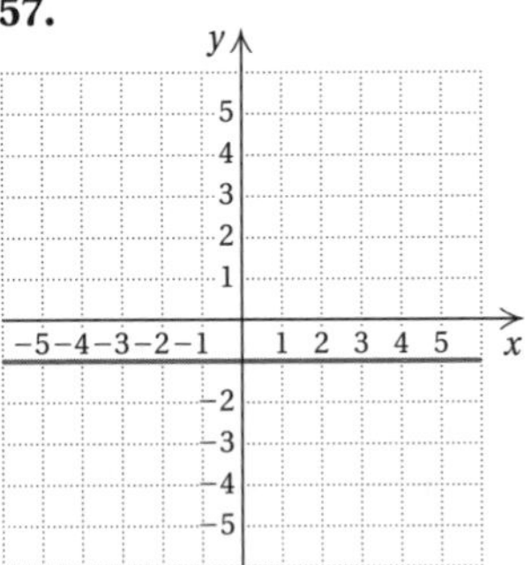

58.

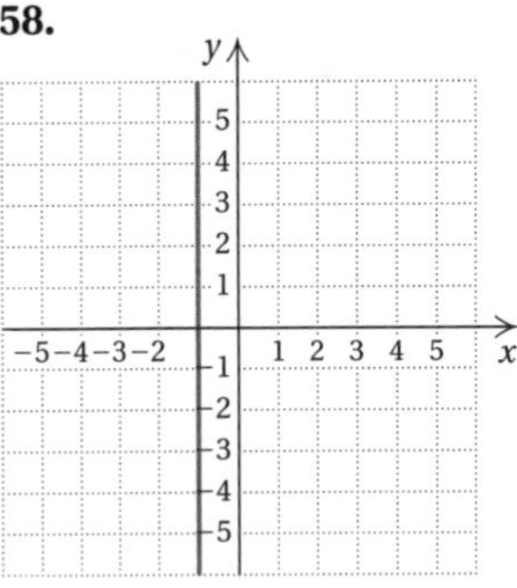

59.

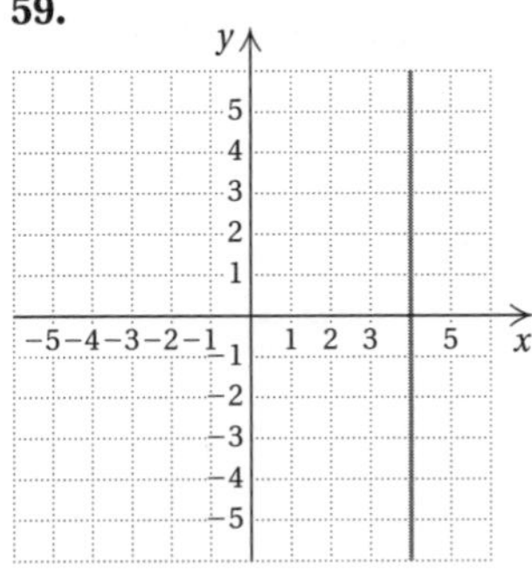

60.

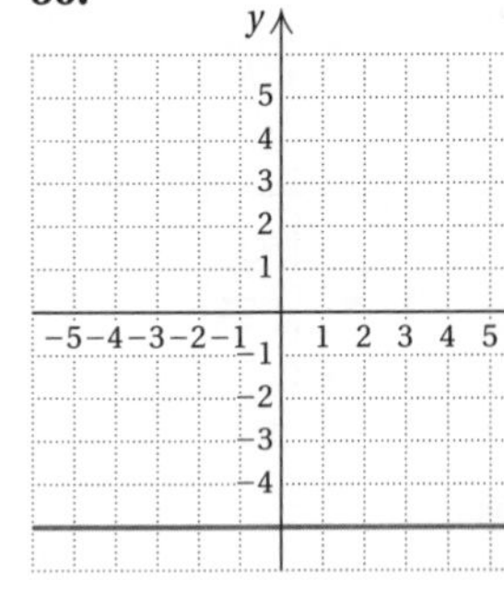

61. **DW** If the graph of the equation $Ax + By = C$ is a horizontal line, what can you conclude about A? Why?

62. **DW** Explain in your own words why the graph of $x = 7$ is a vertical line.

SKILL MAINTENANCE

Solve. [2.5a]

63. *Desserts.* If a restaurant sells 250 desserts in an evening, it is typical that 40 of them will be pie. What percent of the desserts sold will be pie?

64. *Tipping.* Harry left a 20% tip of \$6.50 for a meal. What was the cost of the meal before the tip?

Solve. [2.7e]

65. $-1.6x < 64$

66. $-12x - 71 \geq 13$

67. $x + (x - 1) < (x + 2) - (x + 1)$

68. $6 - 18x \leq 4 - 12x - 5x$

SYNTHESIS

69. Write an equation of a line parallel to the x-axis and passing through $(-3, -4)$.

70. Find the value of m such that the graph of $y = mx + 6$ has an x-intercept of $(2, 0)$.

71. Find the value of k such that the graph of $3x + k = 5y$ has an x-intercept of $(-4, 0)$.

72. Find the value of k such that the graph of $4x = k - 3y$ has a y-intercept of $(0, -8)$.

3.3 SLOPE AND APPLICATIONS

Objectives

a Given the coordinates of two points on a line, find the slope of the line, if it exists.

b Find the slope, or rate of change, in an applied problem involving slope.

c Find the slope of a line from an equation.

a Slope

/e have considered two forms of a linear equation,

$$Ax + By = C \quad \text{and} \quad y = mx + b.$$

/e found that from the form of the equation $y = mx + b$, we know certain ıformation—namely, that the y-intercept of the line is $(0, b)$.

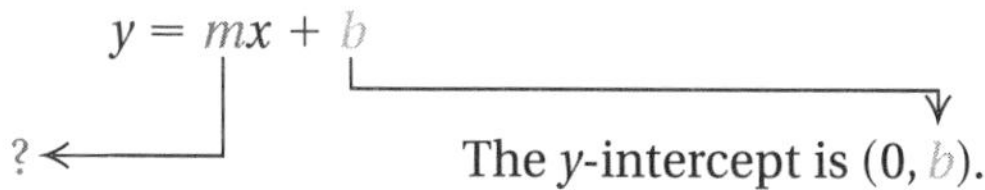

/hat about the constant m? Does it give us certain information about the ne? Look at the following graphs and see if you can make any connection beveen the constant m and the "slant" of the line.

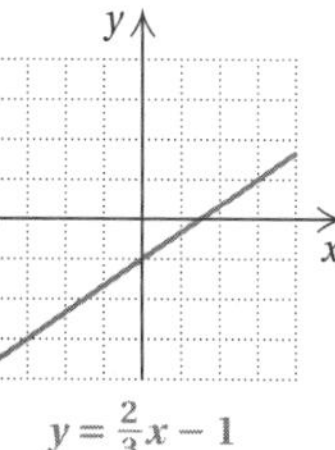

$y = \frac{2}{3}x - 1$

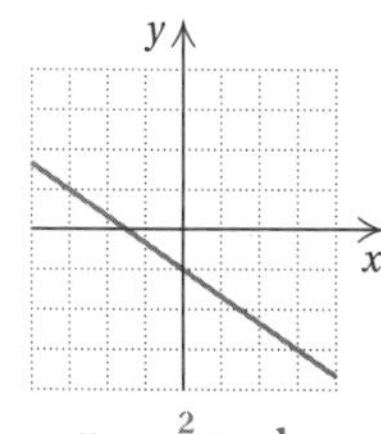

$y = -\frac{2}{3}x - 1$

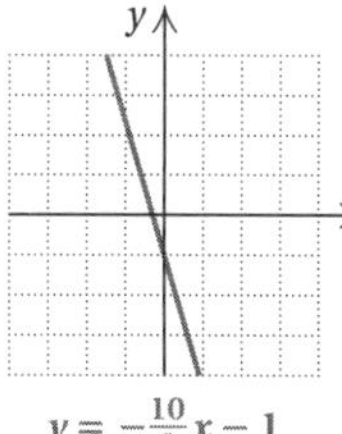

$y = -\frac{10}{3}x - 1$

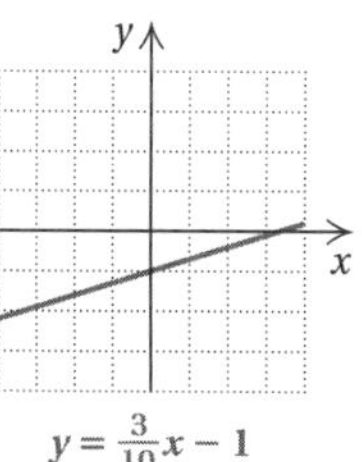

$y = \frac{3}{10}x - 1$

The graphs of some linear equations slant upward from left to right. thers slant downward. Some are vertical and some are horizontal. Some ant more steeply than others. We now look for a way to describe such possiilities with numbers.

Consider a line with two points ıarked P and Q. As we move from to Q, the y-coordinate changes om 1 to 3 and the x-coordinate hanges from 2 to 6. The change in is $3 - 1$, or 2. The change in x is $- 2$, or 4.

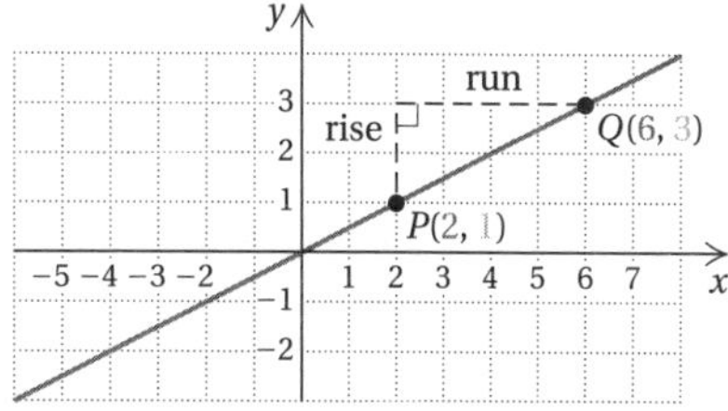

We call the change in y the **rise** and the change in x the **run.** The ratio se/run is the same for any two points on a line. We call this ratio the **slope.** ope describes the slant of a line. The slope of the line in the graph above is iven by

$$\frac{\text{rise}}{\text{run}} = \frac{\text{the change in } y}{\text{the change in } x}, \text{ or } \frac{2}{4}, \text{ or } \frac{1}{2}.$$

SLOPE

The **slope** of a line containing points (x_1, y_1) and (x_2, y_2) is given by

$$m = \frac{\text{rise}}{\text{run}} = \frac{\text{the change in } y}{\text{the change in } x} = \frac{y_2 - y_1}{x_2 - x_1}.$$

Graph the line containing the points and find the slope in two different ways.

1. $(-2, 3)$ and $(3, 5)$

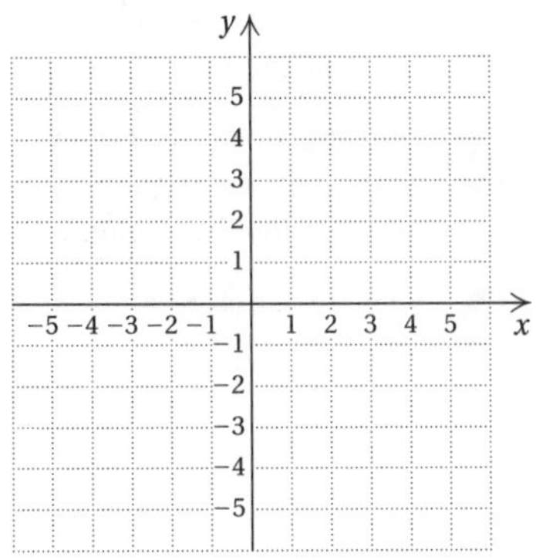

2. $(0, -3)$ and $(-3, 2)$

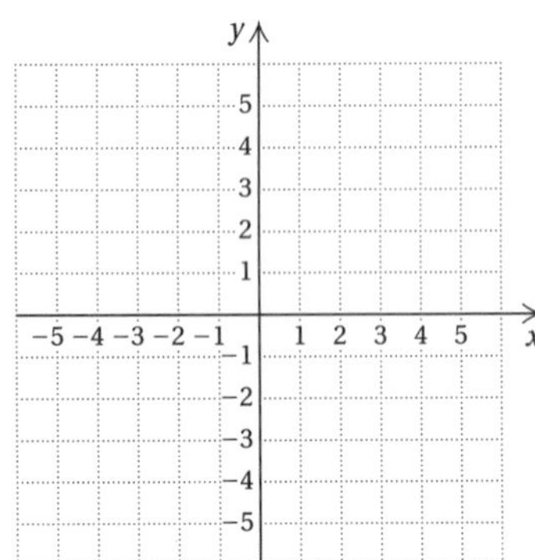

Answers on page A-15

In the preceding definition, (x_1, y_1) and (x_2, y_2)—read "x sub-one, y sub-one and x sub-two, y sub-two"—represent two different points on a line. It does not matter which point is considered (x_1, y_1) and which is considered (x_2, y_2) so long as coordinates are subtracted in the same order in both the numerator and the denominator—for example,

$$\frac{y_2 - y_1}{x_2 - x_1} = \frac{y_1 - y_2}{x_1 - x_2}.$$

EXAMPLE 1 Graph the line containing the points $(-4, 3)$ and $(2, -6)$ and find the slope.

The graph is shown below. We consider (x_1, y_1) to be $(-4, 3)$ and (x_2, y_2) to be $(2, -6)$. From $(-4, 3)$ and $(2, -6)$, we see that the change in y, or the rise, is $-6 - 3$, or -9. The change in x, or the run, is $2 - (-4)$, or 6.

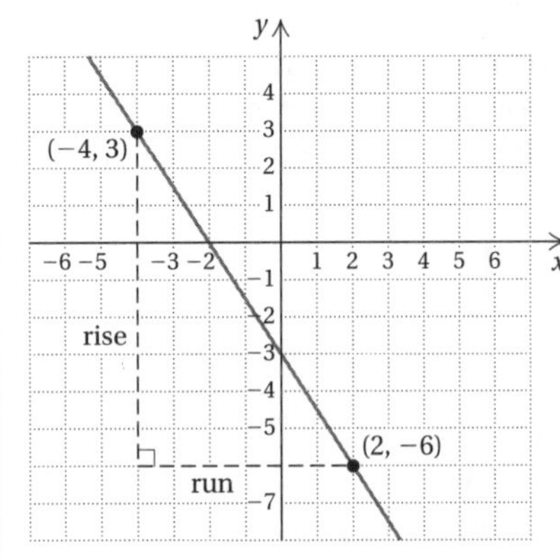

$$\text{Slope} = \frac{\text{rise}}{\text{run}} = \frac{\text{change in } y}{\text{change in } x} = \frac{y_2 - y_1}{x_2 - x_1} = \frac{-6 - 3}{2 - (-4)} = \frac{-9}{6} = -\frac{9}{6}, \text{ or } -\frac{3}{2}$$

When we use the formula

$$m = \frac{y_2 - y_1}{x_2 - x_1},$$

we must remember to subtract the y-coordinates in the same order that we subtract the x-coordinates. Let's redo Example 1, where we consider (x_1, y_1) to be $(2, -6)$ and (x_2, y_2) to be $(-4, 3)$:

$$\text{Slope} = \frac{\text{change in } y}{\text{change in } x} = \frac{3 - (-6)}{-4 - 2} = \frac{9}{-6} = -\frac{3}{2}.$$

Do Exercises 1 and 2.

The slope of a line tells how it slants. A line with positive slope slants up from left to right. The larger the slope, the steeper the slant. A line with negative slope slants downward from left to right.

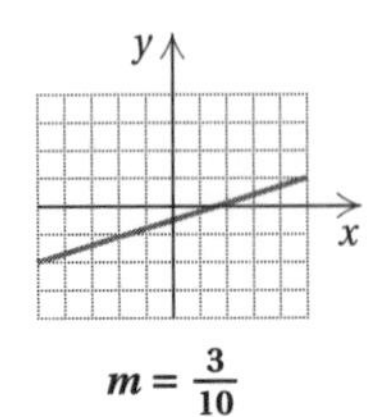

$m = \frac{3}{10}$

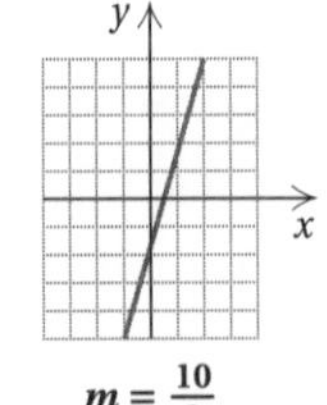

$m = \frac{10}{3}$

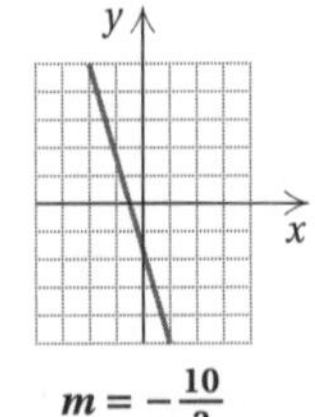

$m = -\frac{10}{3}$

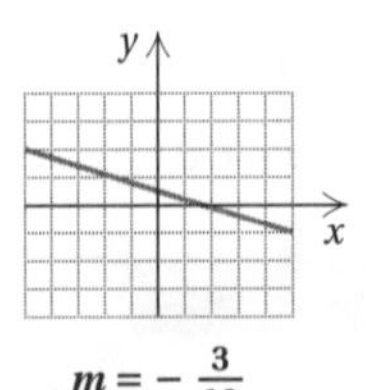

$m = -\frac{3}{10}$

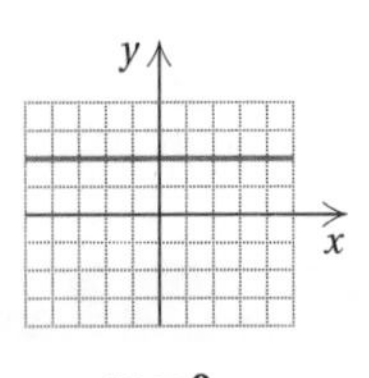

$m = 0$

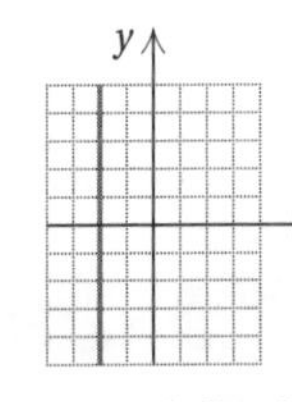

m is not defined.

Later in this section, in Examples 10 and 11, we will discuss the slope of a horizontal line and of a vertical line. The slope of a horizontal line is 0. The slope of a vertical line is not defined.

Applications of Slope; Rates of Change

lope has many real-world applications. For example, numbers like 2%, 3%, nd 6% are often used to represent the *grade* of a road, a measure of how steep road on a hill or mountain is. For example, a 3% grade $\left(3\% = \frac{3}{100}\right)$ means that or every horizontal distance of 100 ft, the road rises 3 ft, and a −3% grade neans that for every horizontal distance of 100 ft, the road drops 3 ft. (Road gns do not include negative signs. It's usually obvious whether you are limbing or descending.) The concept of grade also occurs in skiing or snow-oarding, where a 7% grade is considered very tame, but a 70% grade is con-dered extremely steep. And in cardiology, a physician may change the grade f a treadmill to measure its effect on heartbeat.

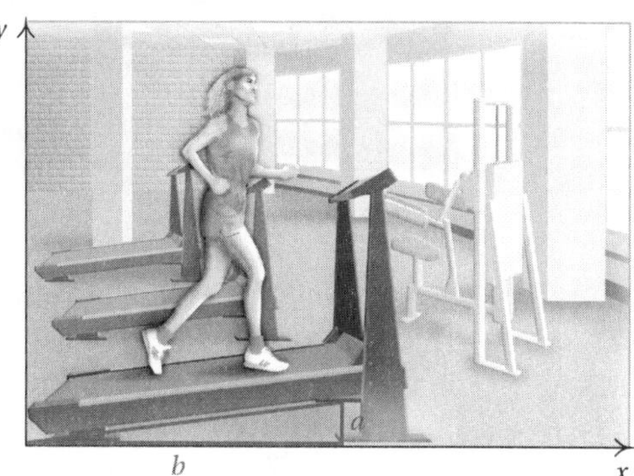

Architects and carpenters use slope when designing and building stairs, amps, or roof pitches. Another application occurs in hydrology. When a river ows, the strength or force of the river depends on how far the river falls ver-cally compared to how far it flows horizontally.

XAMPLE 2 *Skiing.* Among the steepest skiable terrain in North Amer-ca, the Headwall on Mount Washington, in New Hampshire, drops 720 ft over horizontal distance of 900 ft. Find the grade of the Headwall.

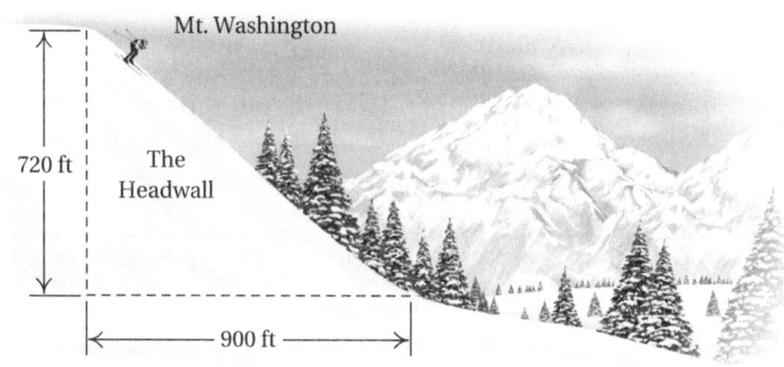

The grade of the Headwall is its slope, expressed as a percent:

$$m = \frac{720}{900} \begin{array}{l} \leftarrow \text{Vertical change} \\ \leftarrow \text{Horizontal change} \end{array}$$

$$= \frac{8}{10} = 80\%.$$

o Exercise 3.

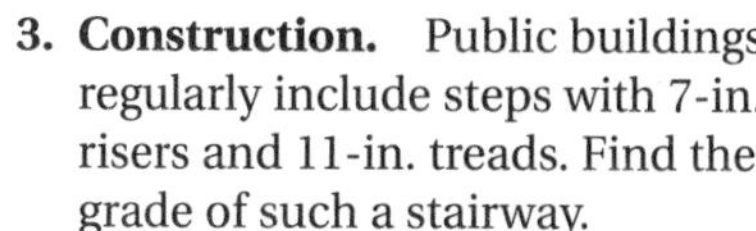

3. **Construction.** Public buildings regularly include steps with 7-in. risers and 11-in. treads. Find the grade of such a stairway.

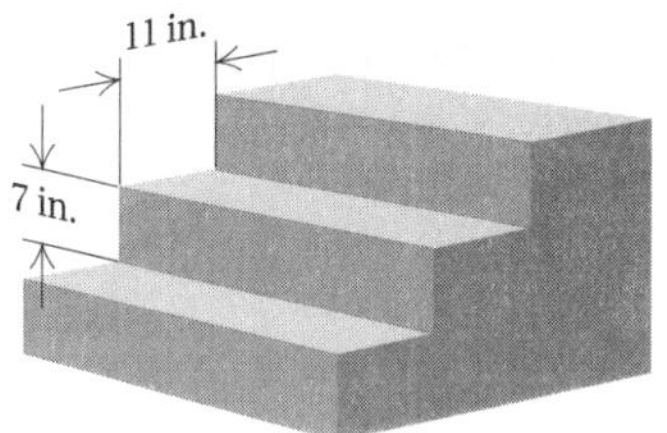

Answer on page A-15

4. **Cost of a Telephone Call.** The following graph shows data of interstate long-distance calling offered by AmeriCom in the Simplicity Plan. At what rate is the customer billed?

Source: AmeriCom

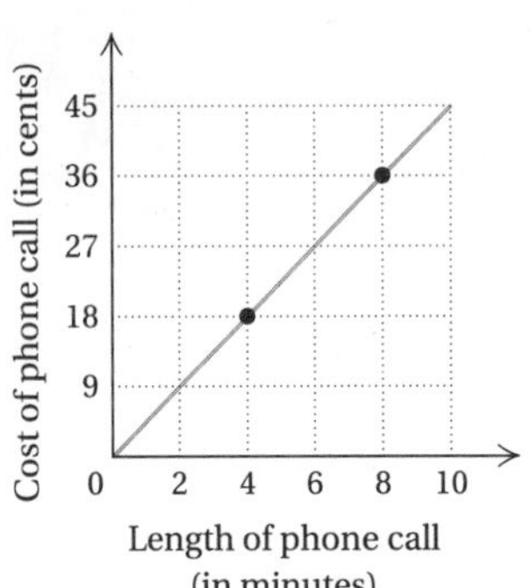

Answer on page A-15

Slope can also be considered as a **rate of change.**

EXAMPLE 3 *Haircutting.* Kiddie Kutters has a graph displaying data fro a recent day's work. Use the graph to determine the slope, or the rate change, of the number of haircuts with respect to time.

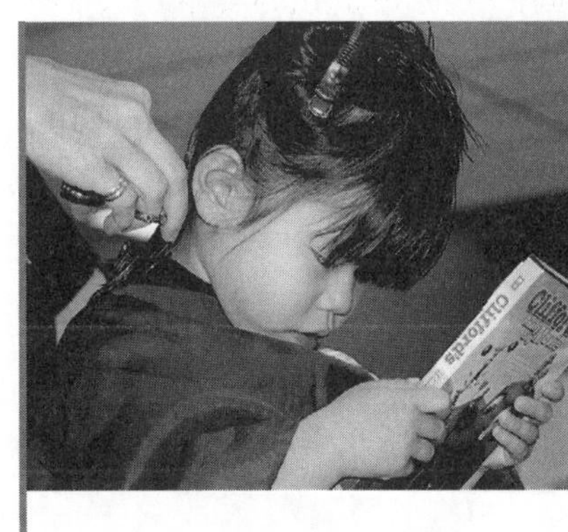

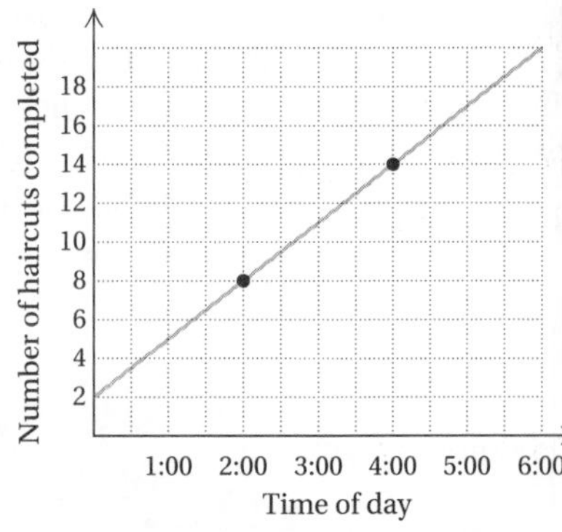

The vertical axis of the graph shows the number of haircuts and the hor zontal axis the time, in units of one hour. We can describe the rate of chang in the number of haircuts with respect to time as

$$\frac{\text{Haircuts}}{\text{Hour}}, \quad \text{or} \quad \textit{number of haircuts per hour.}$$

This value is the slope of the line. We determine two ordered pairs on th graph—in this case,

(2:00, 8 haircuts) and (4:00, 14 haircuts).

This tells us that in the 2 hr between 2:00 and 4:00, 6 haircuts were complete Thus,

$$\text{Rate of change} = \frac{14 \text{ haircuts} - 8 \text{ haircuts}}{4{:}00 - 2{:}00} = \frac{6 \text{ haircuts}}{2 \text{ hours}} = 3 \text{ haircuts per hou}$$

Do Exercise 4.

EXAMPLE 4 *Decreased Smoking.* Each year in the United States, the pe cent of the adult population who smoke declines. Use the following graph t determine the slope, or rate of change of the percent of the adult populatio who smoke with respect to time.

Source: U.S. Centers for Disease Control and Prevention

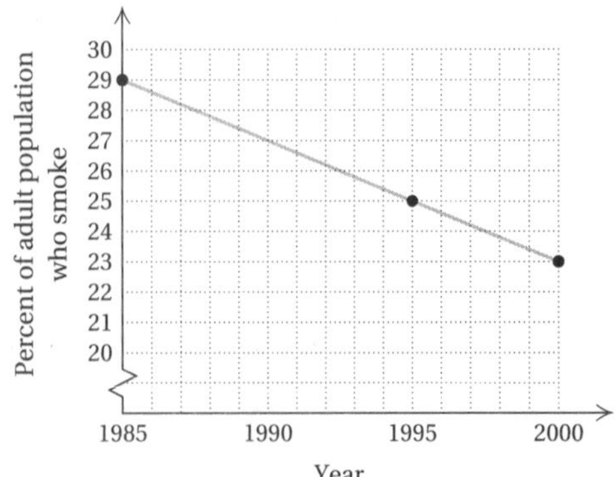

The vertical axis of the graph shows the percent of the adult population who smoke and the horizontal axis shows the years. We can describe the rate of change in the percent who smoke with respect to time as

$$\frac{\text{Percent who smoke}}{\text{Years}}, \quad \text{or} \quad \text{percent who smoke per year.}$$

This value is the slope of the line. We determine two ordered pairs on the graph—in this case,

$$(1995, 25) \quad \text{and} \quad (2000, 23).$$

This tells us that in the 5 yr from 1995 to 2000, the percent dropped from 25% to 23%. Thus

$$\text{Rate of change} = \frac{23\% - 25\%}{2000 - 1995} = \frac{-2\%}{5 \text{ yr}} = -\frac{2}{5}\% \text{ per year.}$$

Do Exercise 5.

5. **Death by Firearms.** Find the rate of change in the number of deaths by firearms.

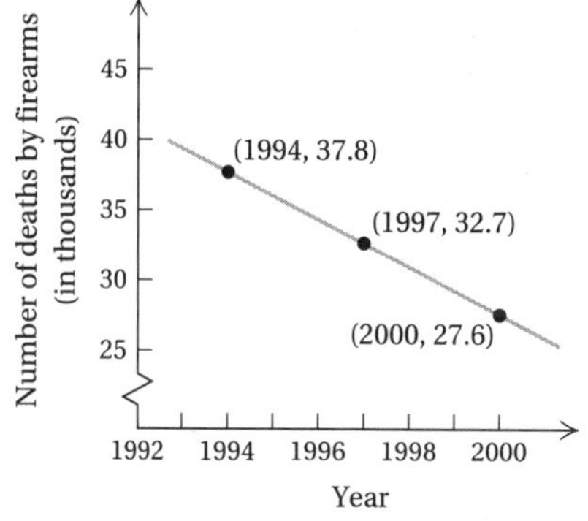

Source: National Vital Statistics Report

Answer on page A-15

Study Tips

SMALL STEPS LEAD TO GREAT SUCCESS (PART 2)

Chris Widener is a popular motivational speaker and writer. In his article "A Little Equation That Creates Big Results," he proposes the following equation: "Your Short-Term Actions Multiplied By Time = Your Long-Term Accomplishments."

Think of the major or career toward which you are working as a long-term accomplishment. We (your authors and instructors) are at a point in life where we realize the long-term benefits of learning mathematics. For you as students, it may be more difficult to see those long-term results. But make an effort to do so.

Widener goes on to say, "We need to take action on our dreams and beliefs every day." Think of the long-term goal as you do the short-term tasks of homework in math, studying for tests, and completing this course so you can move on to what it prepares you for.

Who writes best-selling novels? The person who only dreams of becoming a best-selling author or the one who also spends 4 hours a day doing research and working at a computer?

Who loses weight? The person who thinks about being thin or the one who also plans a healthy diet and runs 3 miles a day?

Who is successful at math? The person who only knows all the benefits of math or the one who also spends at least 2 hours studying outside of class for every hour spent inside class?

"The purpose of man is in action, not thought."

Thomas Carlyle, British historian/essayist

"Prepare for your success in little ways and you will eventually see results in big ways. It's almost magical."

Tom Morris, public philosopher/speaker

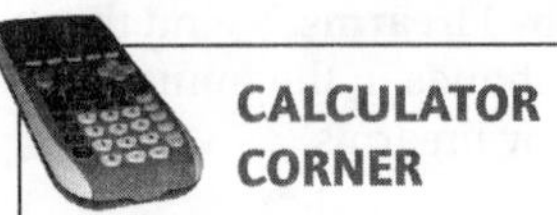

CALCULATOR CORNER

Visualizing Slope

Exercises: Graph each of the following sets of equations using the window settings $[-6, 6, -4, 4]$, Xscl = 1, Yscl = 1.

1. $y = x,\ y = 2x,$
   $y = 5x,\ y = 10x$
   What do you think the graph of $y = 123x$ will look like?
2. $y = x,\ y = \frac{3}{4}x,$
   $y = 0.38x,\ y = \frac{5}{32}x$
   What do you think the graph of $y = 0.000043x$ will look like?

Find the slope of the line.

6. $y = 4x + 11$

7. $y = -17x + 8$

8. $y = -x + \dfrac{1}{2}$

9. $y = \dfrac{2}{3}x - 1$

Find the slope of the line.

10. $4x + 4y = 7$

11. $5x - 4y = 8$

Answers on page A-15

C Finding the Slope from an Equation

It is possible to find the slope of a line from its equation. Let's consider the equation $y = 2x + 3$, which is in the form $y = mx + b$. We can find two points by choosing convenient values for x—say, 0 and 1—and substituting to find the corresponding y-values. We find the two points on the line to be $(0, 3)$ and $(1, 5)$. The slope of the line is found using the definition of slope:

$$m = \frac{\text{change in } y}{\text{change in } x} = \frac{5-3}{1-0} = \frac{2}{1} = 2.$$

The slope is 2. Note that this is also the coefficient of the x-term in the equation $y = 2x + 3$.

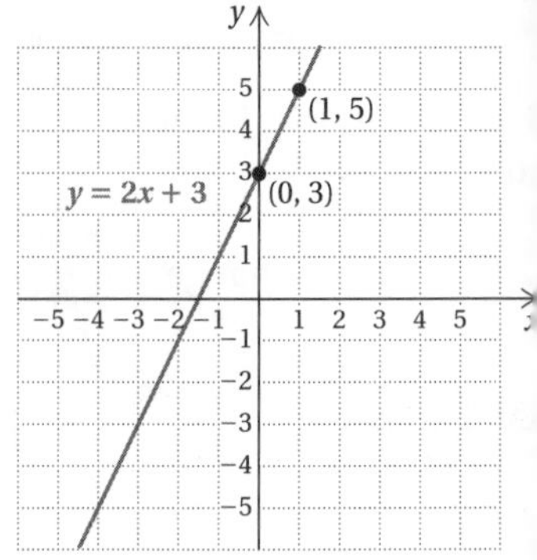

DETERMINING SLOPE FROM THE EQUATION $y = mx + b$

The slope of the line $y = mx + b$ is m. To find the slope of a nonvertical line, solve the linear equation in x and y for y and get the resulting equation in the form $y = mx + b$. The coefficient of the x-term, m, is the slope of the line.

EXAMPLES Find the slope of the line.

5. $y = -3x + \dfrac{2}{9}$

$\quad\rightarrow m = -3 = \text{Slope}$

6. $y = \dfrac{4}{5}x$

$\quad\rightarrow m = \dfrac{4}{5} = \text{Slope}$

7. $y = x + 6$

$\quad\rightarrow m = 1 = \text{Slope}$

8. $y = -0.6x - 3.5$

$\quad\rightarrow m = -0.6 = \text{Slope}$

Do Exercises 6–9.

To find slope from an equation, we may have to first find an equivalent form of the equation.

EXAMPLE 9 Find the slope of the line $2x + 3y = 7$.

We solve for y to get the equation in the form $y = mx + b$:

$$2x + 3y = 7$$
$$3y = -2x + 7$$
$$y = \frac{-2x + 7}{3}$$
$$y = -\frac{2}{3}x + \frac{7}{3}. \qquad \text{This is } y = mx + b.$$

The slope is $-\frac{2}{3}$.

o Exercises 10 and 11 on the preceding page.

What about the slope of a horizontal or a vertical line?

XAMPLE 10 Find the slope of the line $y = 5$.

We can think of $y = 5$ as $y = 0x + 5$. Then from this equation, we see that $= 0$. Consider the points $(-3, 5)$ and $(4, 5)$, which are on the line. The hange in $y = 5 - 5$, or 0. The change in $x = -3 - 4$, or -7. We have

$$m = \frac{5 - 5}{-3 - 4} = \frac{0}{-7} = 0.$$

Any two points on a horizontal line ave the same y-coordinate. The change n y is 0. Thus the slope of a horizontal ne is 0.

XAMPLE 11 Find the slope of the line $x = -4$.

Consider the points $(-4, 3)$ and $(-4, -2)$, which are on the line. The hange in $y = 3 - (-2)$, or 5. The change in $x = -4 - (-4)$, or 0. We have

$$m = \frac{3 - (-2)}{-4 - (-4)} = \frac{5}{0}. \quad \text{Not defined}$$

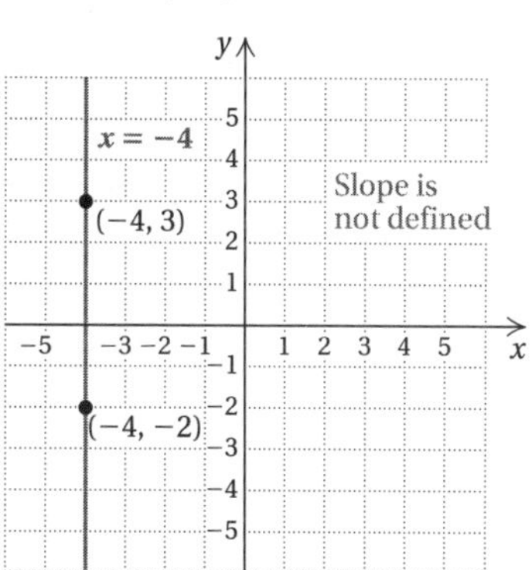

Since division by 0 is not defined, the slope of this line is not defined. The nswer in this example is "The slope of this line is not defined."

SLOPE 0; SLOPE NOT DEFINED

The slope of a horizontal line is 0.

The slope of a vertical line is not defined.

o Exercises 12 and 13.

CALCULATOR CORNER

Visualizing Slope

Exercises: Graph each of the following sets of equations using the window settings $[-6, 6, -4, 4]$, Xscl = 1, Yscl = 1.

1. $y = -x$, $y = -2x$, $y = -5x$, $y = -10x$

   What do you think the graph of $y = -123x$ will look like?

2. $y = -x$, $y = -\frac{3}{4}x$, $y = -0.38x$, $y = -\frac{5}{32}x$

   What do you think the graph of $y = -0.000043x$ will look like?

Find the slope, if it exists, of the line.

12. $x = 7$

13. $y = -5$

Answers on page A-15

3.3 EXERCISE SET

For Extra Help

MathXL | MyMathLab | InterAct Math | Math Tutor Center | Digital Video Tutor CD 2 Videotape 4 | Student Solutions Manual

a Find the slope, if it exists, of the line.

1.

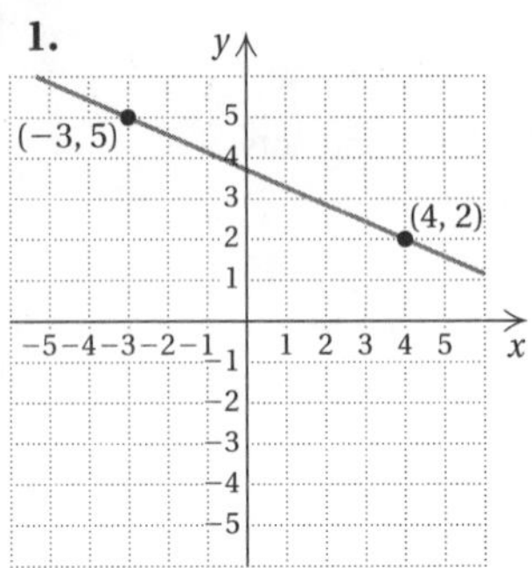

2.

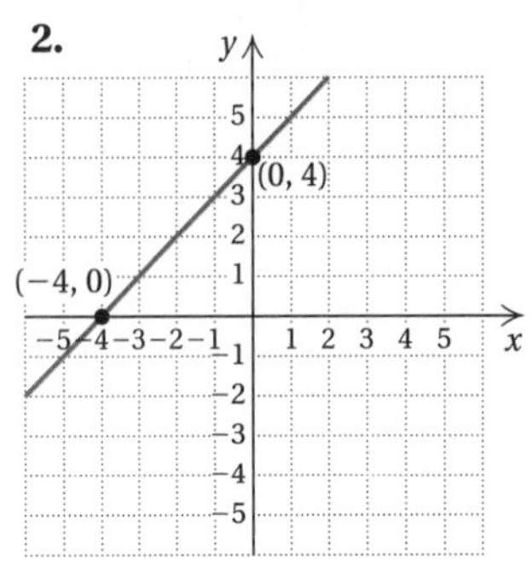

3.

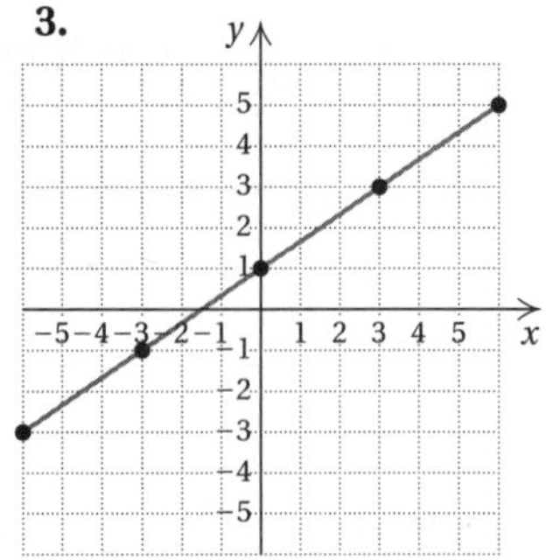

4.

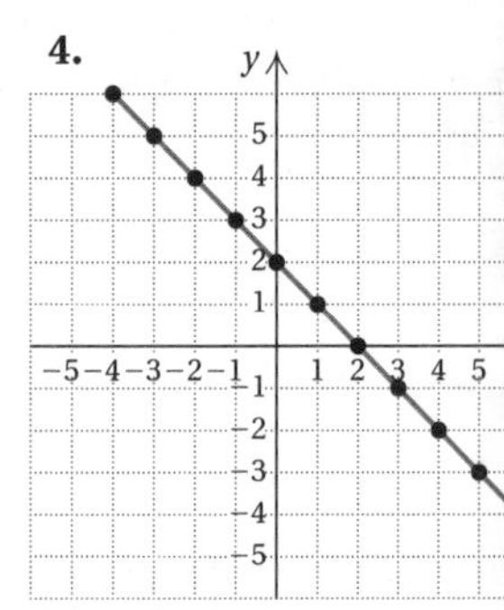

5.

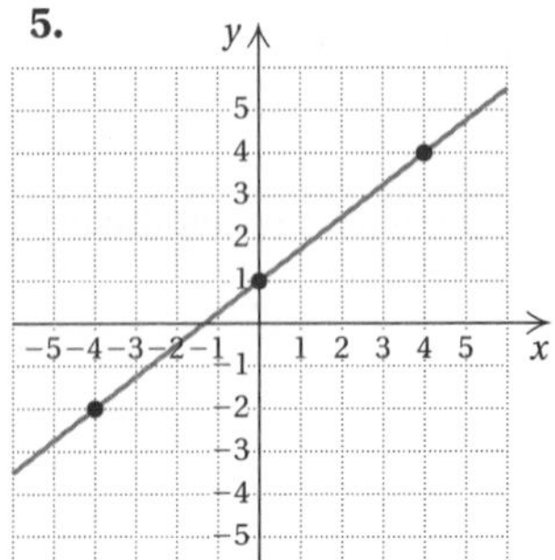

6.

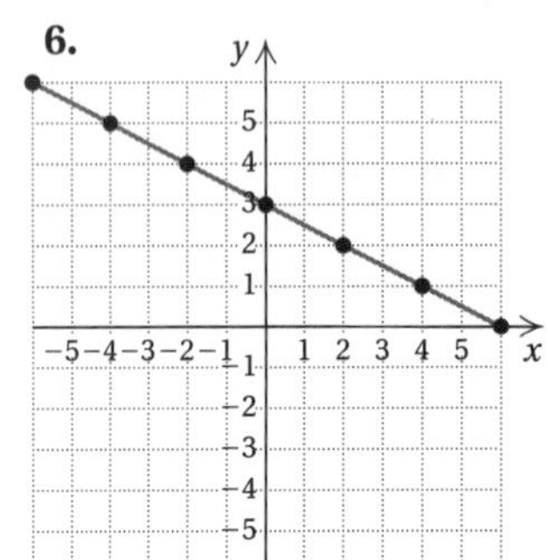

7.

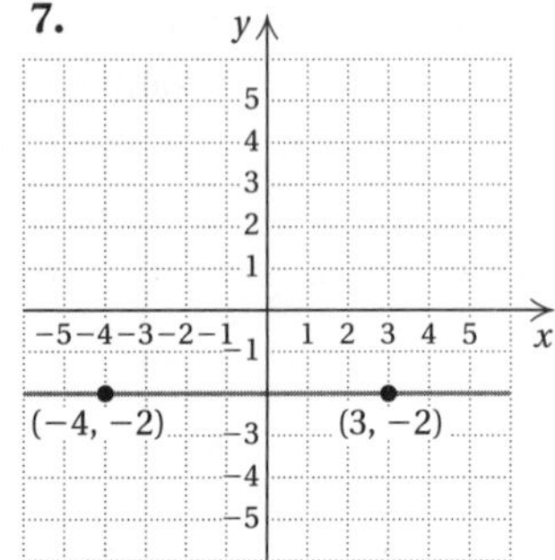

8.

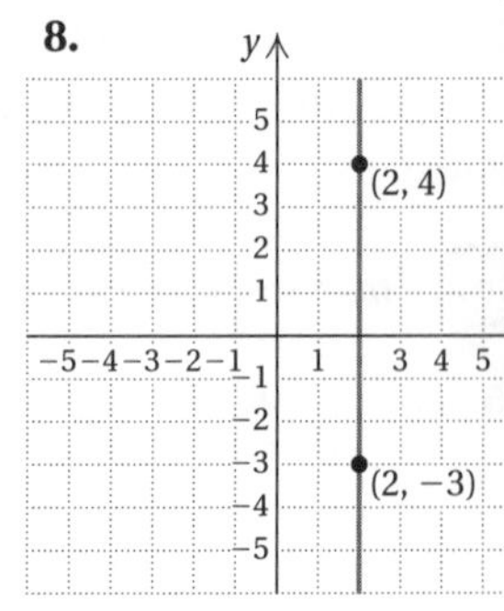

Graph the line containing the given pair of points and find the slope.

9. $(-2, 4), (3, 0)$

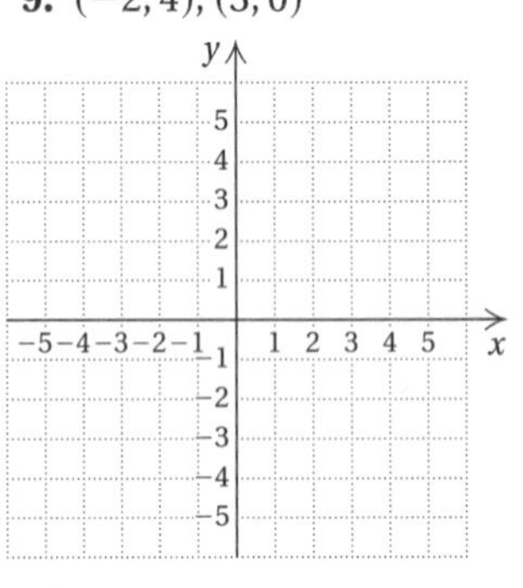

10. $(2, -4), (-3, 2)$

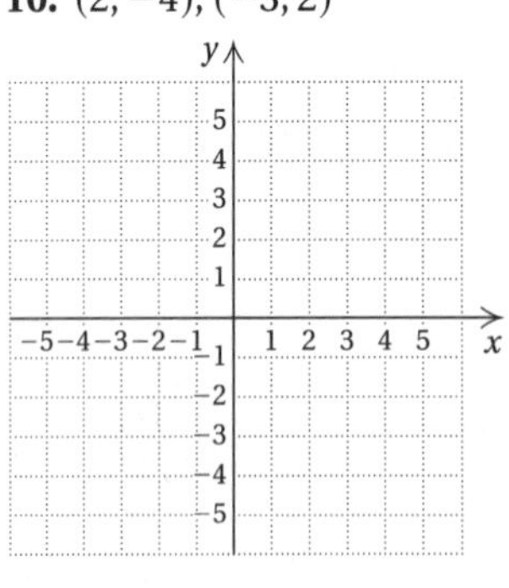

11. $(-4, 0), (-5, -3)$

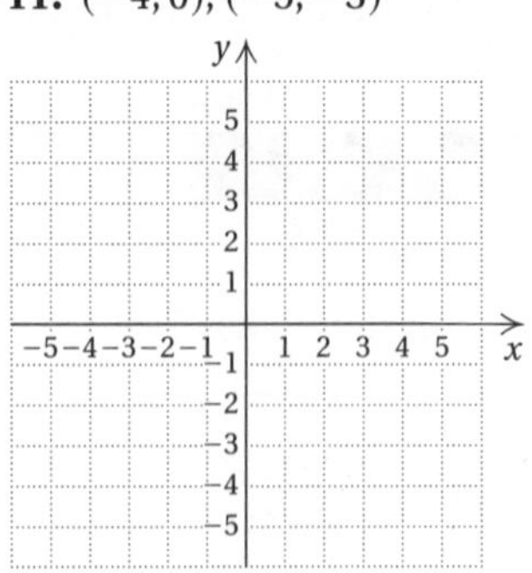

12. $(-3, 0), (-5, -2)$

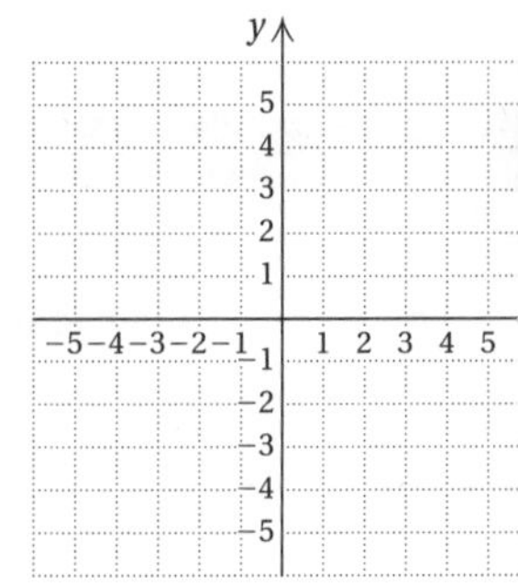

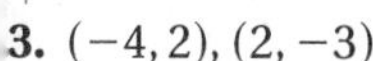

3. $(-4, 2), (2, -3)$

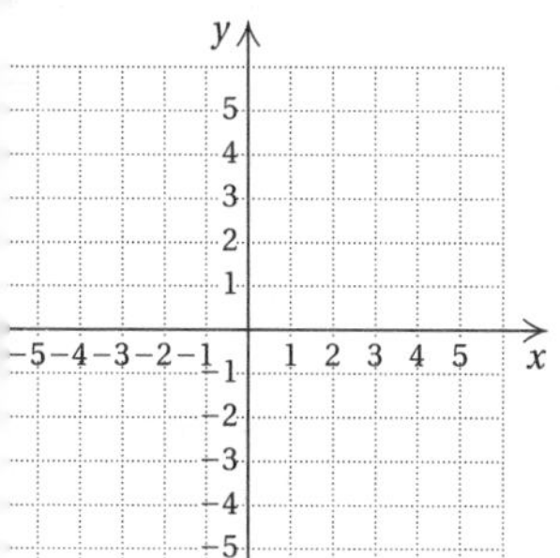

14. $(-3, 5), (4, -3)$

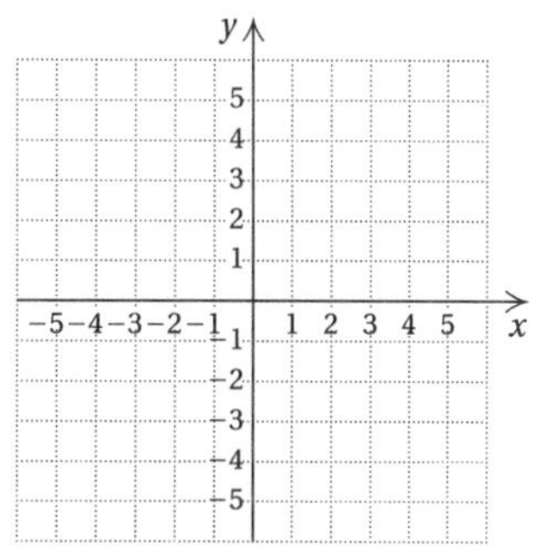

15. $(5, 3), (-3, -4)$

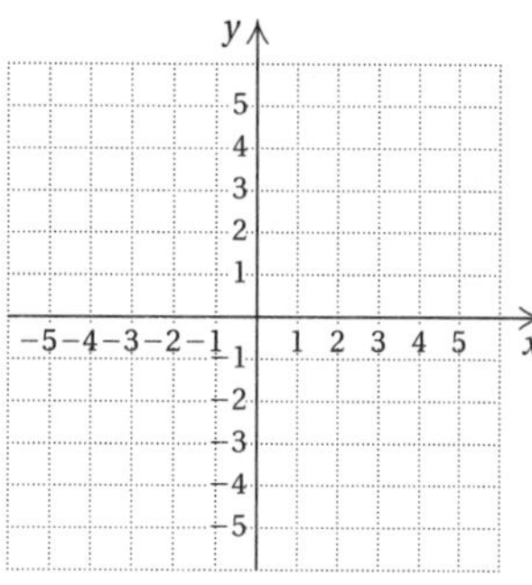

16. $(-4, -3), (2, 5)$

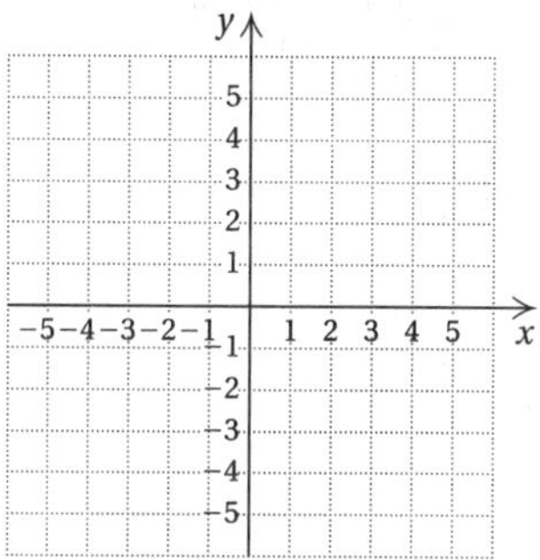

ind the slope, if it exists, of the line containing the given pair of points.

7. $\left(2, -\frac{1}{2}\right), \left(5, \frac{3}{2}\right)$

18. $\left(\frac{2}{3}, -1\right), \left(\frac{5}{3}, 2\right)$

19. $(4, -2), (4, 3)$

20. $(4, -3), (-2, -3)$

1. $(-11, 7), (15, -3)$

22. $(-13, 22), (8, -17)$

23. $\left(-\frac{1}{2}, \frac{3}{11}\right), \left(\frac{5}{4}, \frac{3}{11}\right)$

24. $(0.2, 4), (0.2, -0.04)$

b In Exercises 25–28, find the slope (or rate of change).

5. Find the slope (or pitch) of the roof.

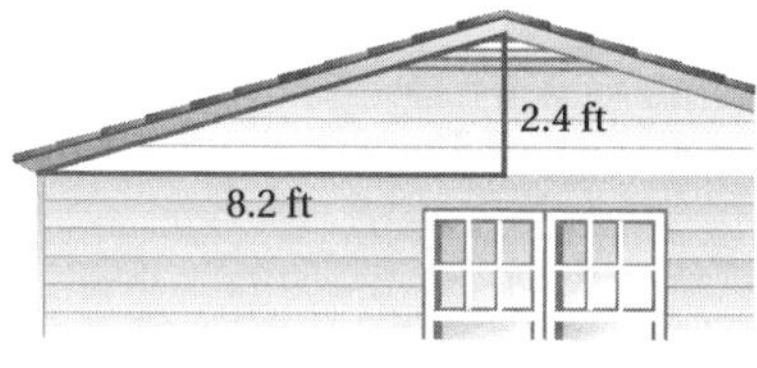

26. Find the slope (or grade) of the road.

7. Find the slope of the river.

28. Find the slope of the treadmill.

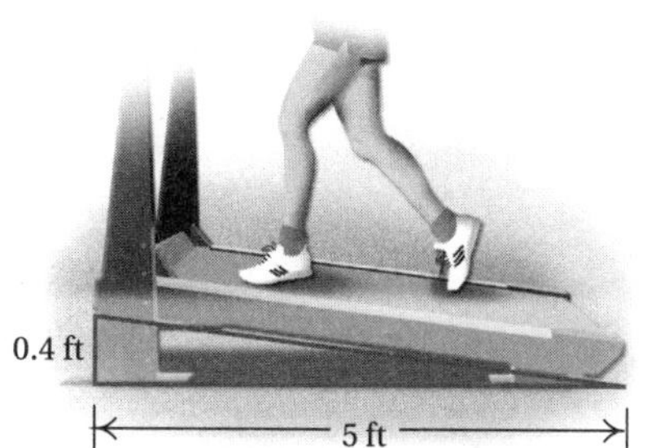

29. *Slope of Long's Peak.* From a base elevation of 9600 ft, Long's Peak in Colorado rises to a summit elevation of 14,255 ft over a horizontal distance of 15,840 ft. Find the grade of Long's Peak.

30. *Ramps for the Disabled.* In order to meet federal standards, a wheelchair ramp must not rise more than 1 ft over a horizontal distance of 12 ft. Express this slope as a grade.

In Exercises 31–34, use the graph to calculate a rate of change in which the units of the horizontal axis are used in the denominator.

31. *Gas Mileage.* The following graph shows data for a Honda Odyssey Minivan driven on interstate highways. Find the rate of change in miles per gallon, that is, the gas mileage.

Source: American Honda Motor Company, Inc.

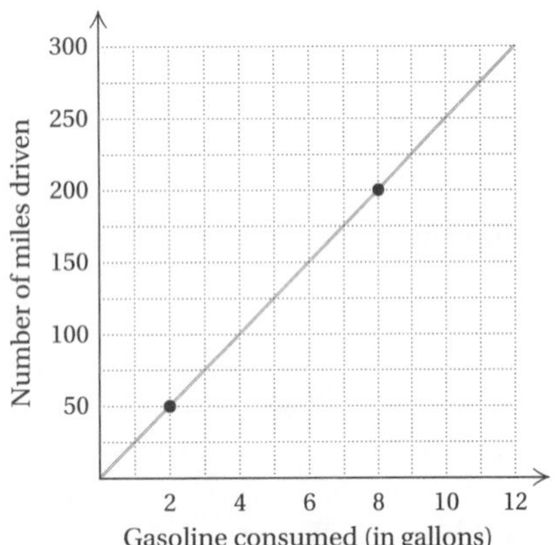

32. *Hairdresser.* Eve's Custom Cuts has a graph displaying data from a recent day of work. Find the rate of change of the number of haircuts with respect to time.

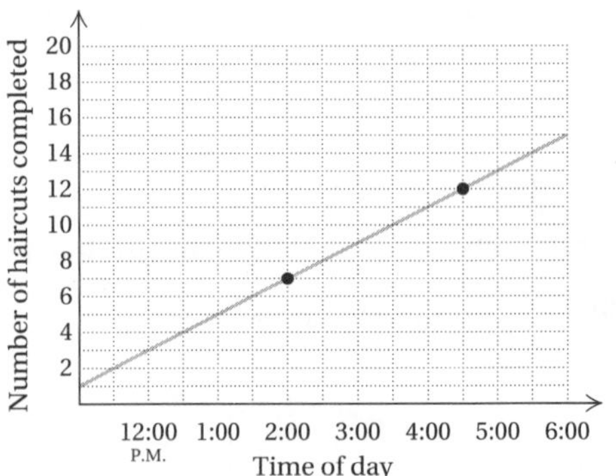

33. *Depreciation of an Office Machine.* The value of a particular color copier is represented in the following graph. Find the rate of change of the value with respect to time, in dollars per year.

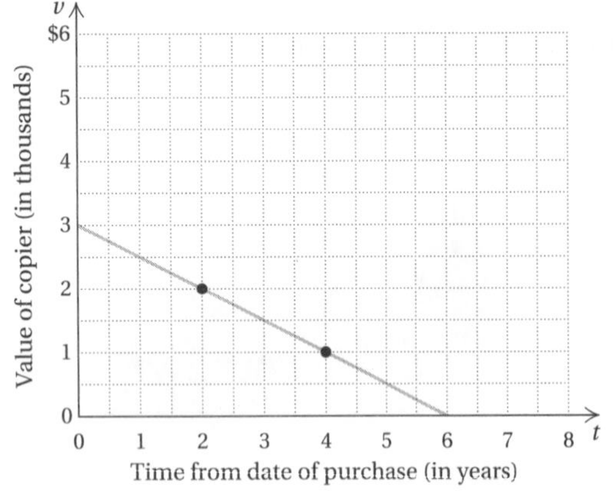

34. *Farmland.* The amount of farmland in the United States, in millions of acres, is represented in the following graph. Find the rate of change, rounded to the nearest hundred thousand, of the number of acres with respect to time, in number of acres per year.

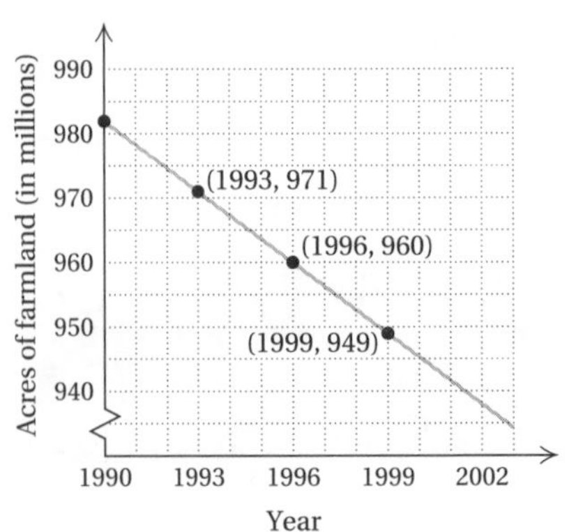

Source: U.S. Department of Agriculture

35. *Population Growth of Alaska.* The population of Alaska is illustrated in the following graph. Find the rate of change, to the nearest hundred, of the population with respect to time, in number of people per year.

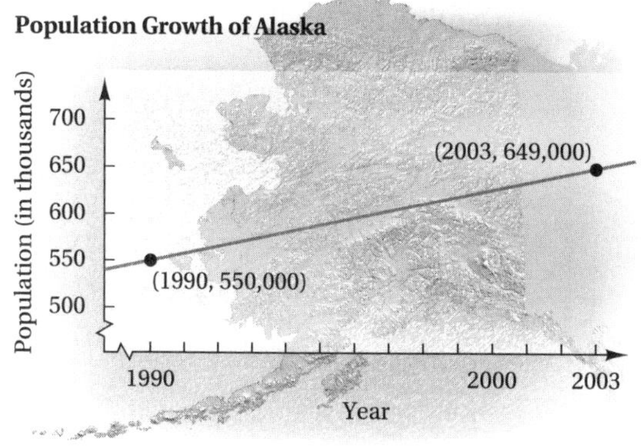

Source: U.S. Bureau of the Census

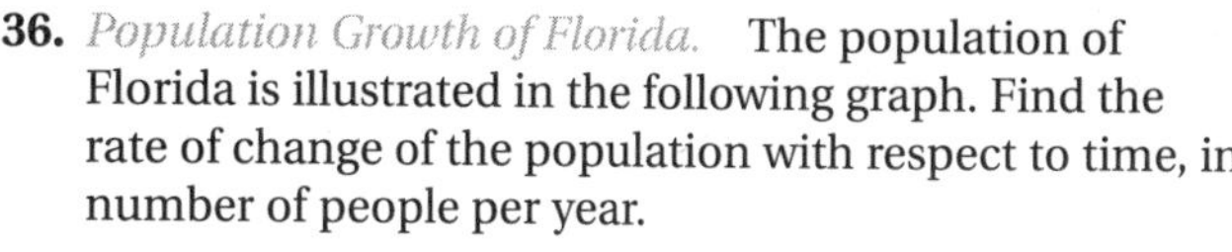

36. *Population Growth of Florida.* The population of Florida is illustrated in the following graph. Find the rate of change of the population with respect to time, in number of people per year.

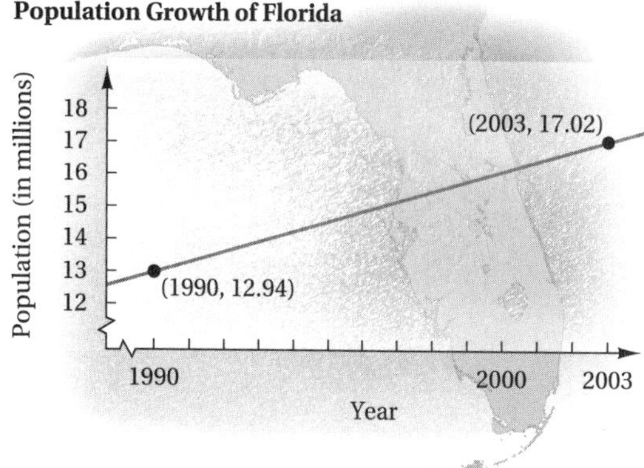

Source: U.S. Bureau of the Census

c Find the slope, if it exists, of the line.

37. $y = -10x + 7$

38. $y = \frac{10}{3}x - \frac{5}{7}$

39. $y = 3.78x - 4$

40. $y = -\frac{3}{5}x + 28$

41. $3x - y = 4$

42. $-2x + y = 8$

43. $x + 5y = 10$

44. $x - 4y = 8$

45. $3x + 2y = 6$

46. $2x - 4y = 8$

47. $x = \frac{2}{15}$

48. $y = -\frac{1}{3}$

49. $y = -2.74x$

50. $y = \frac{219}{298}x - 6.7$

51. $9x = 3y + 5$

52. $4y = 9x - 7$

53. $5x - 4y + 12 = 0$

54. $16 + 2x - 8y = 0$

55. $y = 4$

56. $x = -3$

Assuming that the scales on each axis of each graph are the same, explain how you can estimate the slope of the line that contains segment PQ without knowing the coordinates of the points P and Q.

57. DW

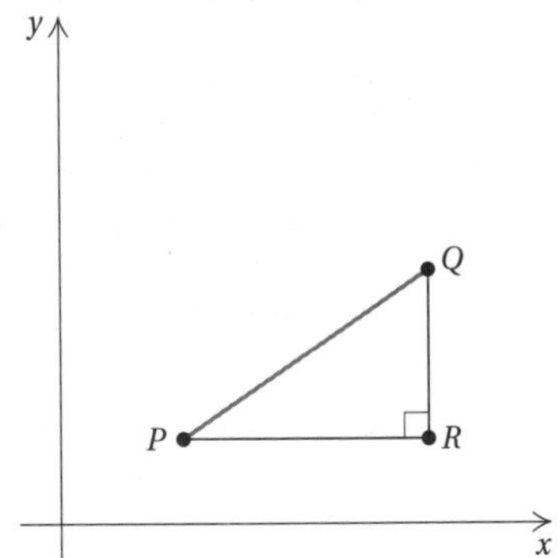

58. DW

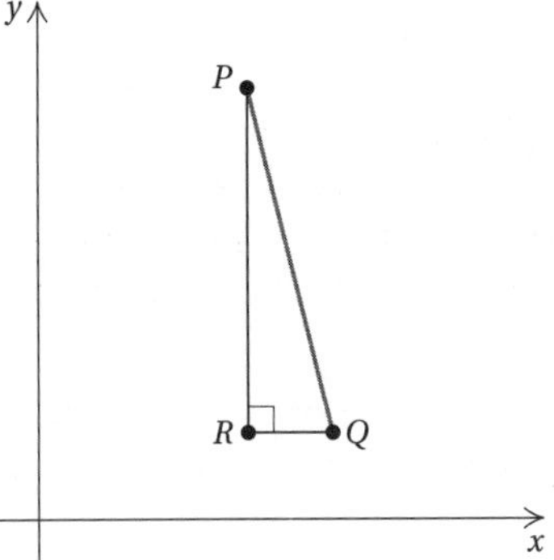

SKILL MAINTENANCE

Convert to fraction notation. [R.4b]

59. 16%

60. $33\frac{1}{3}\%$

61. 37.5%

62. 75%

Solve. [2.5a]

63. What is 15% of $23.80?

64. $7.29 is 15% of what number?

65. Jennifer left an $8.50 tip for a meal that cost $42.50. What percent of the cost of the meal was the tip?

66. Kristen left an 18% tip of $3.24 for a meal. What was the cost of the meal before the tip?

67. Juan left a 15% tip for a meal. The total cost of the meal, including the tip, was $51.92. What was the cost of the meal before the tip was added?

68. After a 25% reduction, a sweater is on sale for $41.25. What was the original price?

SYNTHESIS

In Exercises 69–72, find an equation for the graph shown.

69.

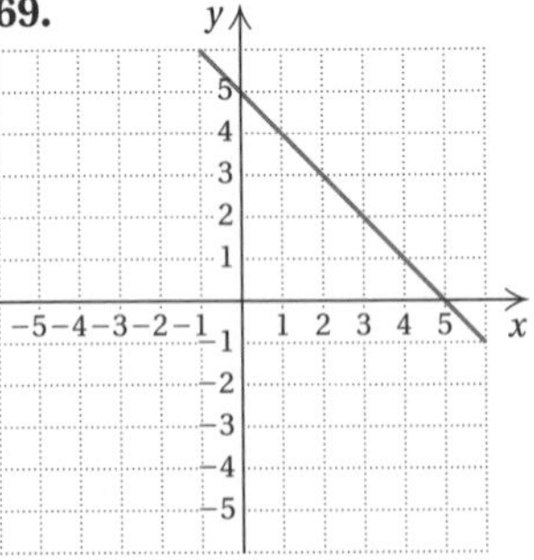

70.

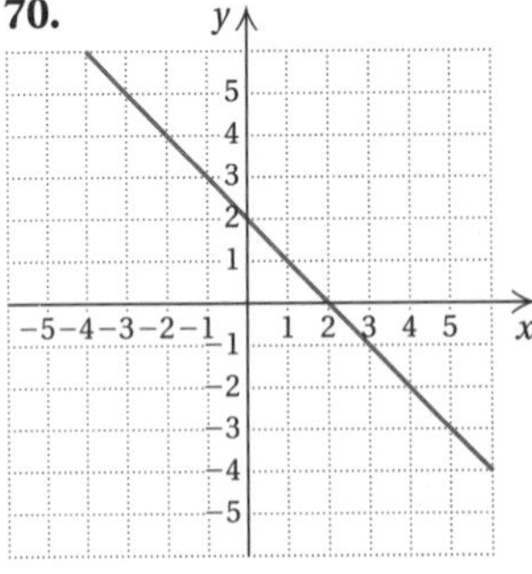

71.

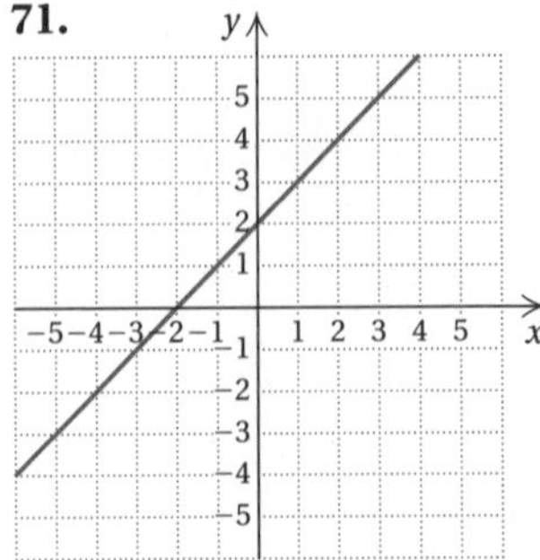

72.

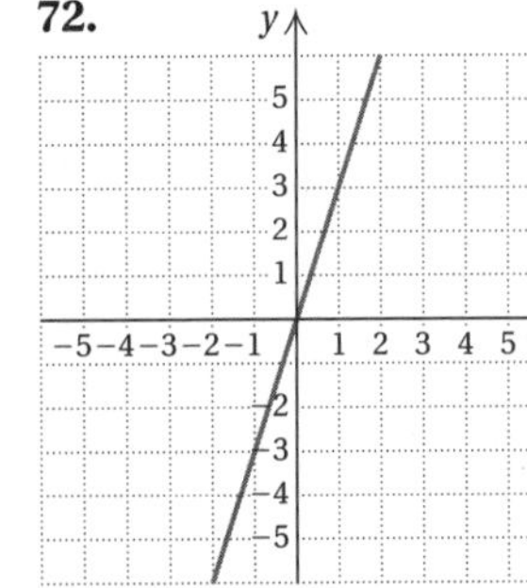

Graph the equation using the standard viewing window. Then construct a table of y-values for x-values starting at $x = -10$ with $\Delta\text{Tbl} = 0.1$.

73. $y = 0.35x - 7$

74. $y = 5.6 - x^2$

75. $y = x^3 - 5$

76. $y = 4 + 3x - x^2$

3.4 EQUATIONS OF LINES

Objectives

a Given an equation in the form $y = mx + b$, find the slope and the y-intercept; find an equation of a line when the slope and the y-intercept are given.

b Find an equation of a line when the slope and a point on the line are given.

c Find an equation of a line when two points on the line are given.

We have learned that the slope of a line and the y-intercept of the graph f the line can be read directly from the equation if it is in the form $= mx + b$. The **slope** is m and the **y-intercept** is $(0, b)$. Here we use slope nd y-intercept in order to examine linear equations in more detail.

a Finding an Equation of a Line When the Slope and the y-Intercept Are Given

Ve know from Sections 3.1 and 3.3 that in the equation $y = mx + b$, the slope m and the y-intercept is $(0, b)$. Thus we call the equation $y = mx + b$ the **lope–intercept equation.**

THE SLOPE–INTERCEPT EQUATION:
$y = mx + b$

The equation $y = mx + b$ is called the **slope–intercept equation.** The slope is m and the y-intercept is $(0, b)$.

XAMPLE 1 Find the slope and the y-intercept of $2x - 3y = 8$.

We first solve for y:

$$2x - 3y = 8$$

$$-3y = -2x + 8 \qquad \text{Subtracting } 2x$$

$$\frac{-3y}{-3} = \frac{-2x + 8}{-3} \qquad \text{Dividing by } -3$$

$$y = \frac{-2x}{-3} + \frac{8}{-3}$$

$$y = \frac{2}{3}x - \frac{8}{3}$$

The slope is $\frac{2}{3}$. The y-intercept is $\left(0, -\frac{8}{3}\right)$.

$2x - 3y = 8$

o Exercises 1–5.

XAMPLE 2 A line has slope -2.4 and y-intercept $(0, 11)$. Find an equation f the line.

We use the slope–intercept equation and substitute -2.4 for m and 11 r b:

$$y = mx + b$$

$$y = -2.4x + 11. \qquad \text{Substituting}$$

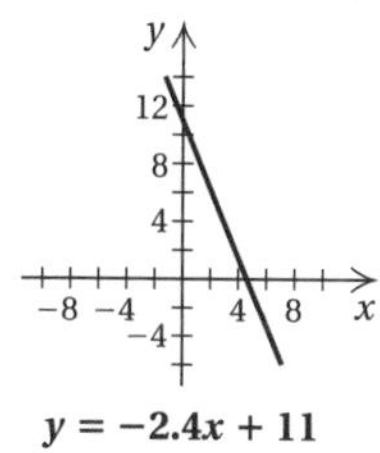

$y = -2.4x + 11$

Find the slope and the y-intercept.

1. $y = 5x$

2. $y = -\frac{3}{2}x - 6$

3. $3x + 4y = 15$

4. $2y = 4x - 17$

5. $-7x - 5y = 22$

Answers on page A-15

6. A line has slope 3.5 and y-intercept $(0, -23)$. Find an equation of the line.

7. A line has slope 0 and y-intercept $(0, 13)$. Find an equation of the line.

8. A line has slope -7.29 and y-intercept $(0, 0)$. Find an equation of the line.

Answers on page A-16

EXAMPLE 3 A line has slope 0 and y-intercept $(0, -6)$. Find an equation of the line.

We use the slope–intercept equation and substitute 0 for m and -6 for b:

$$y = mx + b$$
$$y = 0x + (-6) \quad \text{Substituting}$$
$$y = -6.$$

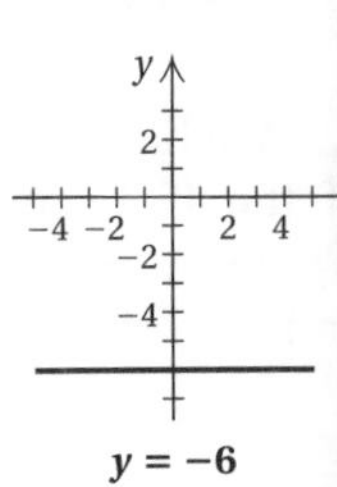

EXAMPLE 4 A line has slope $-\frac{5}{3}$ and y-intercept $(0, 0)$. Find an equation of the line.

We use the slope–intercept equation and substitute $-\frac{5}{3}$ for m and 0 for b:

$$y = mx + b$$
$$y = -\tfrac{5}{3}x + 0 \quad \text{Substituting}$$
$$y = -\tfrac{5}{3}x.$$

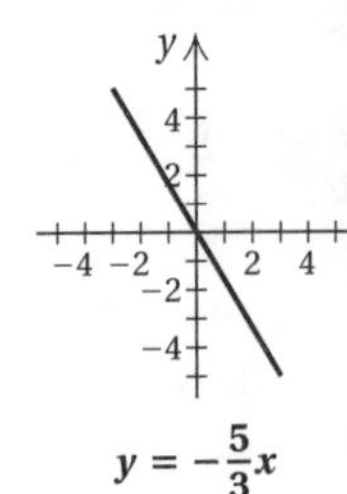

Do Exercises 6–8.

b Finding an Equation of a Line When the Slope and a Point Are Given

Suppose we know the slope of a line and a certain point on that line. We can use the slope–intercept equation $y = mx + b$ to find an equation of the line. To write an equation in this form, we need to know the slope m and the y-intercept $(0, b)$.

EXAMPLE 5 Find an equation of the line with slope 3 that contains the point $(4, 1)$.

We know that the slope is 3, so the equation is $y = 3x + b$. This equation is true for $(4, 1)$. Using the point $(4, 1)$, we substitute 4 for x and 1 for y in $y = 3x + b$. Then we solve for b:

$$y = 3x + b \quad \text{Substituting 3 for } m \text{ in } y = mx + b$$
$$1 = 3(4) + b \quad \text{Substituting 4 for } x \text{ and 1 for } y$$
$$1 = 12 + b$$
$$-11 = b. \quad \text{Solving for } b \text{, we find that the } y\text{-intercept is } (0, -11).$$

We use the equation $y = mx + b$ and substitute 3 for m and -11 for b:

$$y = 3x - 11.$$

his is the equation of the line with slope 3 and y-intercept $(0, -11)$.

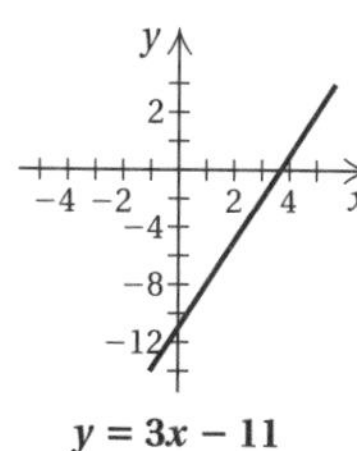

$y = 3x - 11$

XAMPLE 6 Find an equation of the line with slope -5 that contains the oint $(-2, 3)$.

We know that the slope is -5, so the equation is $y = -5x + b$. Using the oint $(-2, 3)$, we substitute -2 for x and 3 for y in $y = -5x + b$. Then we olve for b:

$$y = -5x + b \qquad \text{Substituting } -5 \text{ for } m \text{ in } y = mx + b$$
$$3 = -5(-2) + b \qquad \text{Substituting } -2 \text{ for } x \text{ and 3 for } y$$
$$3 = 10 + b$$
$$-7 = b. \qquad \text{Solving for } b$$

'e use the equation $y = mx + b$ and substitute -5 for m and -7 for b:

$$y = -5x - 7.$$

his is the equation of the line with slope -5 and y-intercept $(0, -7)$.

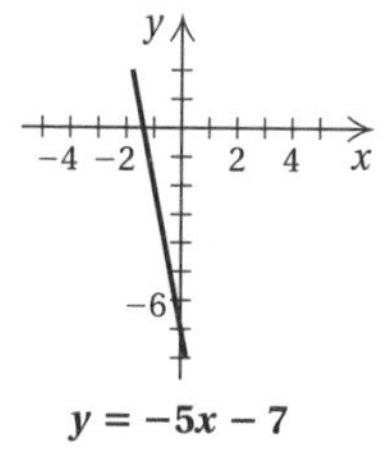

$y = -5x - 7$

› *Exercises 9–12.*

Finding an Equation of a Line When Two Points Are Given

e can also use the slope–intercept equation to find an equation of a line ıen two points are given.

XAMPLE 7 Find an equation of the line containing the points $(2, 3)$ and $6, 1)$.

First, we find the slope:

$$m = \frac{3 - 1}{2 - (-6)} = \frac{2}{8}, \text{ or } \frac{1}{4}.$$

ıus, $y = \frac{1}{4}x + b$. We then proceed as we did in Example 6, using either point find b.

Find an equation of the line that contains the given point and has the given slope.

9. $(4, 2)$, $m = 5$

10. $(-2, 1)$, $m = -3$

11. $(3, 5)$, $m = 6$

12. $(1, 4)$, $m = -\frac{2}{3}$

Answers on page A-16

Find an equation of the line containing the given points.

13. (2, 4) and (3, 5)

14. $(-1, 2)$ and $(-3, -2)$

Answers on page A-16

We choose (2, 3) and substitute 2 for x and 3 for y:

$$y = \frac{1}{4}x + b \qquad \text{Substituting } \frac{1}{4} \text{ for } m \text{ in } y = mx + b$$

$$3 = \frac{1}{4} \cdot 2 + b \qquad \text{Substituting 2 for } x \text{ and 3 for } y$$

$$3 = \frac{1}{2} + b$$

$$\frac{5}{2} = b. \qquad \text{Solving for } b$$

We use the equation $y = mx + b$ and substitute $\frac{1}{4}$ for m and $\frac{5}{2}$ for b:

$$y = \frac{1}{4}x + \frac{5}{2}.$$

This is the equation of the line with slope $\frac{1}{4}$ and y-intercept $\left(0, \frac{5}{2}\right)$.

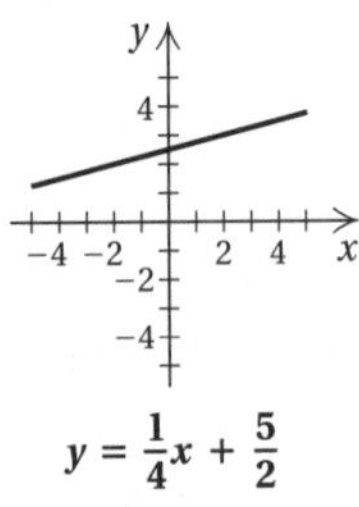

$y = \frac{1}{4}x + \frac{5}{2}$

Do Exercises 13 and 14.

Study Tips

BETTER TEST TAKING

How often do you make the following statement after taking a test: "I was able to do the homework, but I froze during the test"? Here are two tips to help you with this difficulty. Both are intended to make test taking less stressful by getting you to practice good test-taking habits on a daily basis.

- **Treat every homework exercise as if it were a test question.** If you had to work a problem at your job with no backup answer provided, what would you do? You would probably work it very deliberately, checking and rechecking every step. You might work it more than one time, or you might try to work it another way to check the result. Try to use this approach when doing your homework. Treat every exercise as though it were a test question with no answer at the back of the book.
- **Be sure that you do questions without answers as part of every homework assignment whether or not the instructor has assigned them!** One reason a test may seem such a different task is that questions on a test lack answers. That is the reason for taking a test: to see if you can do the questions without assistance. As part of your test preparation, be sure you do some exercises for which you do not have the answers. Thus when you take a test, you are doing a more familiar task.

The purpose of doing your homework using these approaches is to give you more test-taking practice beforehand. Let's use a sports analogy: At a basketball game, the players take lots of practice shots before the game. They play the first half, go to the locker room, and come out for the second half. What do they do before the second half, even though they have just played 20 minutes of basketball? They shoot baskets again! We suggest the same approach here. Create more and more situations in which you practice taking test questions by treating each homework exercise like a test question and by doing exercises for which you have no answers. Good luck!

"He who does not venture has no luck."

3.4 EXERCISE SET

For Extra Help

MathXL | MyMathLab | InterAct Math | Math Tutor Center | Digital Video Tutor CD 2 Videotape 4 | Student's Solutions Manual

a Find the slope and the y-intercept.

1. $y = -4x - 9$

2. $y = -2x + 3$

3. $y = 1.8x$

4. $y = -27.4x$

5. $-8x - 7y = 21$

6. $-2x - 8y = 16$

7. $4x = 9y + 7$

8. $5x + 4y = 12$

9. $-6x = 4y + 2$

10. $4.8x - 1.2y = 36$

11. $y = -17$

12. $y = 28$

nd an equation of the line with the given slope and y-intercept.

3. Slope $= -7$, y-intercept $= (0, -13)$

14. Slope $= 73$, y-intercept $= (0, 54)$

15. Slope $= 1.01$, y-intercept $= (0, -2.6)$

16. Slope $= -\frac{3}{8}$, y-intercept $= \left(0, \frac{7}{11}\right)$

b Find an equation of the line containing the given point and having the given slope.

7. $(-3, 0)$, $m = -2$

18. $(2, 5)$, $m = 5$

19. $(2, 4)$, $m = \frac{3}{4}$

20. $\left(\frac{1}{2}, 2\right)$, $m = -1$

. $(2, -6)$, $m = 1$

22. $(4, -2)$, $m = 6$

23. $(0, 3)$, $m = -3$

24. $(-2, -4)$, $m = 0$

c Find an equation of the line that contains the given pair of points.

. $(12, 16)$ and $(1, 5)$

26. $(-6, 1)$ and $(2, 3)$

27. $(0, 4)$ and $(4, 2)$

28. $(0, 0)$ and $(4, 2)$

29. (3, 2) and (1, 5)

30. (−4, 1) and (−1, 4)

31. (−4, 5) and (−2, −3)

32. (−2, −4) and (2, −1)

33. *Aerobic Exercise.* The line graph below describes the *target heart rate T,* in beats per minute, of a person of age *a,* who is exercising. The goal is to get the number of beats per minute to this target level.

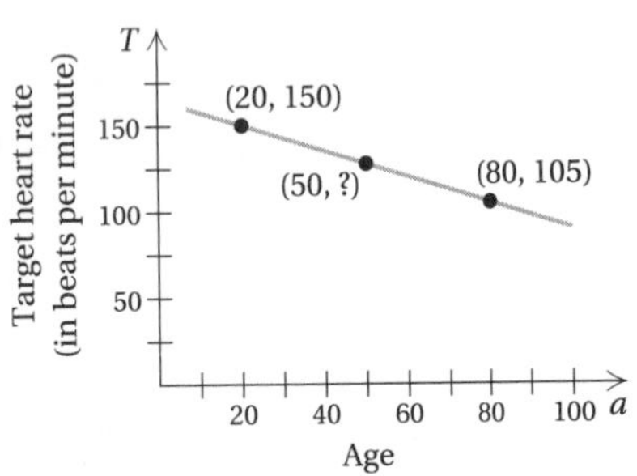

a) Find an equation of the line.
b) What is the rate of change of target heart rate with respect to time?
c) Use the equation to calculate the target heart rate of a person of age 50.

34. *Diabetes Cases.* The line graph below describes the number *N,* in millions, of persons diagnosed with diabetes in the United States in years *x* since 1992.

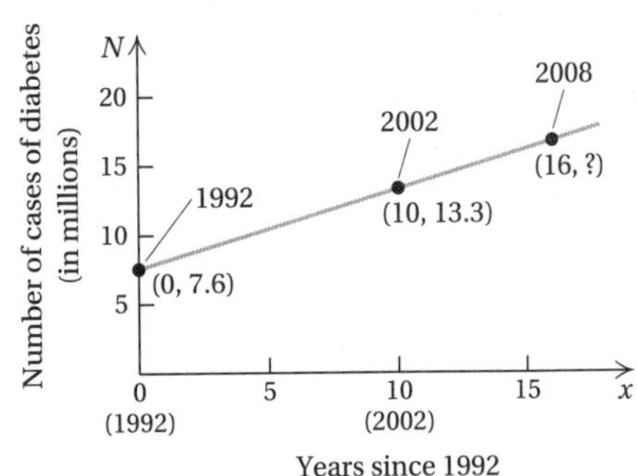

Source: U.S. National Center for Health Statistics

a) Find an equation of the line.
b) What is the rate of change of the number of cases of diabetes with respect to time?
c) Use the equation to predict the number of cases of diabetes in 2008.

35. **DW** Do all graphs of linear equations have *y*-intercepts? Why or why not?

36. **DW** Do all graphs of linear equations have *x*-intercept Why or why not?

SKILL MAINTENANCE

Solve. [2.3b, c]

37. $3x - 4(9 - x) = 17$

38. $2(5 + 2y) + 4y = 13$

39. $40(2x - 7) = 50(4 - 6x)$

40. $\frac{2}{3}(x - 5) = \frac{3}{8}(x + 5)$

41. $3x - 9x + 21x - 15x = 6x - 12 - 24x + 18$

42. $3x - (9x + 21x) - 15x = 6x - (12 - 24x) + 18$

43. $3(x - 9x) + 21(x - 15x) = 6(x - 12) - 24(x + 18)$

44. $3x - (9x + 21x - 15x) = 6x - (12 - 24x + 18)$

SYNTHESIS

45. Find an equation of the line that contains the point (2, −3) and has the same slope as the line $3x - y + 4 = 0$.

46. Find an equation of the line that has the same *y*-intercept as the line $x - 3y = 6$ and contains the point (5, −1).

47. Find an equation of the line with the same slope as the line $3x - 2y = 8$ and the same *y*-intercept as the line $2y + 3x = -$

3.5 GRAPHING USING THE SLOPE AND THE y-INTERCEPT

Objective

a Use the slope and the y-intercept to graph a line.

a Graphs Using the Slope and the y-Intercept

We can graph a line if we know the coordinates of two points on that line. We can also graph a line if we know the slope and the y-intercept.

EXAMPLE 1 Draw a line that has slope $\frac{1}{4}$ and y-intercept $(0, 2)$.

We plot $(0, 2)$ and from there move *up* 1 unit (since the numerator is *positive* and corresponds to the change in y) and *to the right* 4 units (since the denominator is *positive* and corresponds to the change in x). This locates the point $(4, 3)$. We plot $(4, 3)$ and draw a line passing through $(0, 2)$ and $(4, 3)$, as shown on the right below.

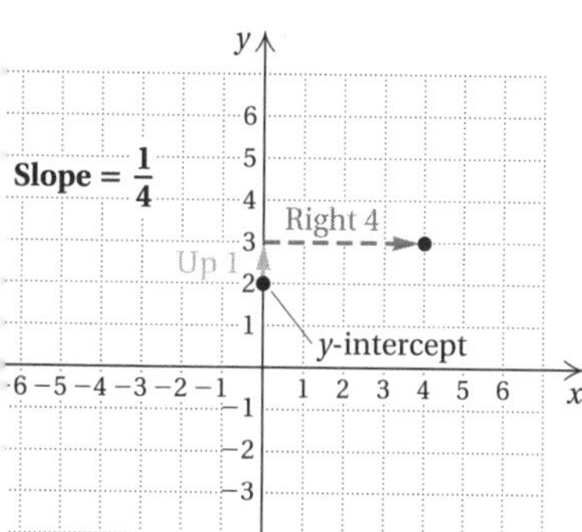

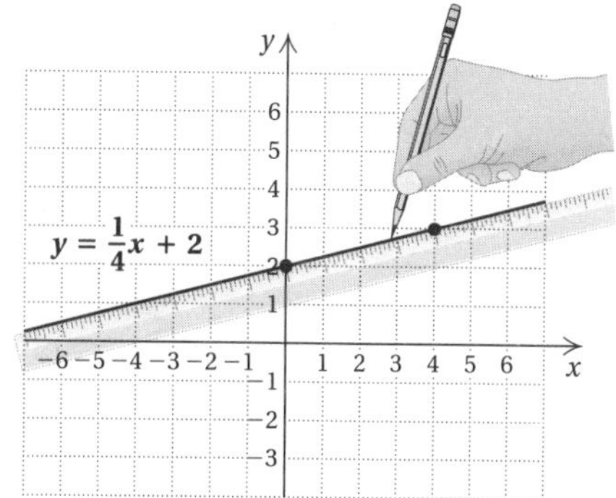

We are actually graphing the equation $y = \frac{1}{4}x + 2$.

EXAMPLE 2 Draw a line that has slope $-\frac{2}{3}$ and y-intercept $(0, 4)$.

We can think of $-\frac{2}{3}$ as $\frac{-2}{3}$. We plot $(0, 4)$ and from there move *down* 2 units (since the numerator is *negative*) and *to the right* 3 units (since the denominator is *positive*). We plot the point $(3, 2)$ and draw a line passing through $(0, 4)$ and $(3, 2)$.

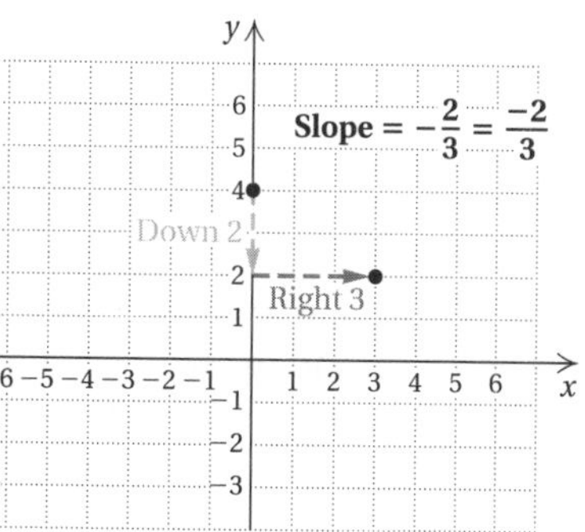

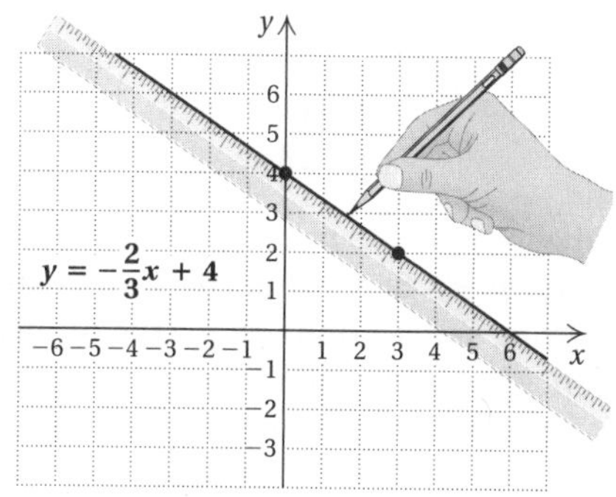

We are actually graphing the equation $y = -\frac{2}{3}x + 4$.

Do Exercises 1–3.

1. Draw a line that has slope $\frac{2}{5}$ and y-intercept $(0, -3)$. What equation is graphed?

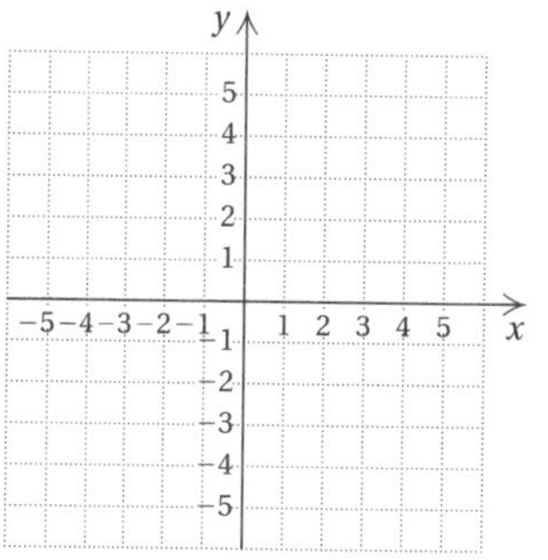

2. Draw a line that has slope $-\frac{2}{5}$ and y-intercept $(0, -3)$. What equation is graphed?

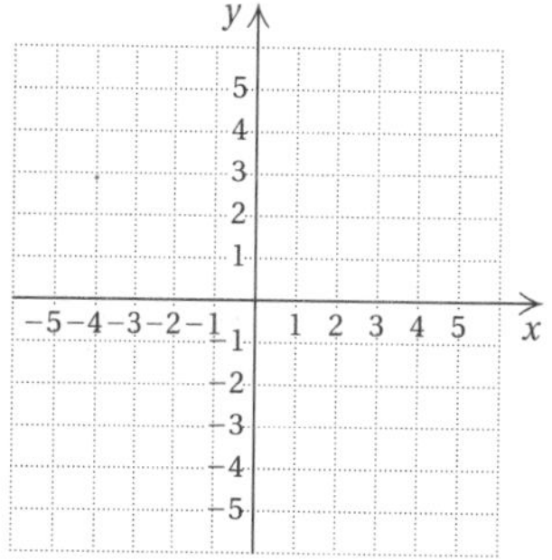

3. Draw a line that has slope 6 and y-intercept $(0, -3)$. Think of 6 as $\frac{6}{1}$. What equation is graphed?

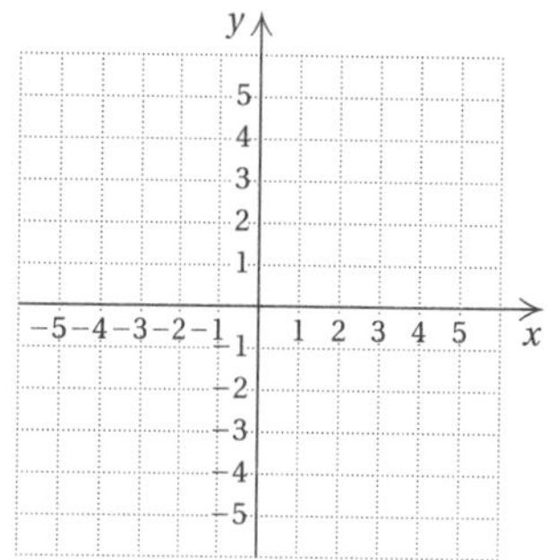

Answers on page A-16

4. Graph $y = \frac{3}{5}x - 4$ using the slope and the y-intercept.

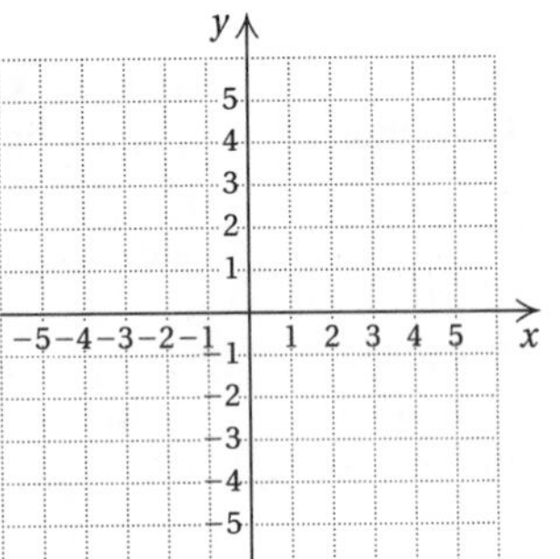

Answer on page A-16

We now use our knowledge of the slope–intercept equation to grap[h] linear equations.

EXAMPLE 3 Graph $y = \frac{3}{4}x + 5$ using the slope and the y-intercept.

From the equation $y = \frac{3}{4}x + 5$, we see that the slope of the graph is $\frac{3}{4}$ an[d] the y-intercept is $(0, 5)$. We plot $(0, 5)$ and then consider the slope, $\frac{3}{4}$. Startin[g] at $(0, 5)$, we plot a second point by moving *up* 3 units (since the numerator i[s] *positive*) and *to the right* 4 units (since the denominator is *positive*). We reac[h] a new point, $(4, 8)$.

We can also rewrite the slope as $\frac{-3}{-4}$. We again start at the y-intercept, $(0, 5)$, but move *down* 3 units (since the numerator is *negative* and corresponds t[o] the change in y) and *to the left* 4 units (since the denominator is *negative* an[d] corresponds to the change in x). We reach another point, $(-4, 2)$. Once two o[r] three points have been plotted, the line representing all solutions o[f] $y = \frac{3}{4}x + 5$ can be drawn.

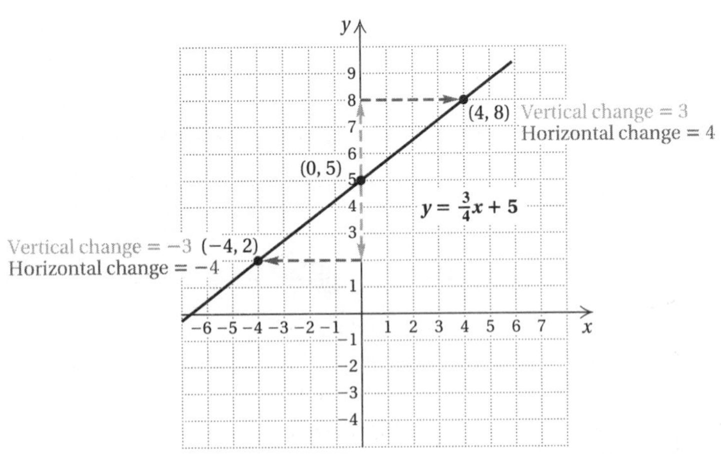

Do Exercise 4.

EXAMPLE 4 Graph $2x + 3y = 3$ using the slope and the y-intercept.

To graph $2x + 3y = 3$, we first rewrite the equation in slope–interce[pt] form:

$$\begin{aligned} 2x + 3y &= 3 & \\ 3y &= -2x + 3 & \text{Adding } -2x \\ \frac{1}{3} \cdot 3y &= \frac{1}{3}(-2x + 3) & \text{Multiplying by } \tfrac{1}{3} \\ y &= -\frac{2}{3}x + 1. & \text{Simplifying} \end{aligned}$$

To graph $y = -\frac{2}{3}x + 1$, we first plot the y-intercept, $(0, 1)$. We can think of th[e] slope as $\frac{-2}{3}$. Starting at $(0, 1)$ and using the slope, we find a second point b[y] moving *down* 2 units (since the numerator is *negative*) and *to the right* 3 uni[ts] (since the denominator is *positive*). We plot the new point, $(3, -1)$. In a sim[i]lar manner, we can move from the point $(3, -1)$ to locate a third point, $(6, -3)$. The line can then be drawn.

Since $-\frac{2}{3} = \frac{2}{-3}$, an alternative approach is to again plot (0, 1), but this time ove *up* 2 units (since the numerator is *positive*) and *to the left* 3 units (since e denominator is *negative*). This leads to another point on the graph, (−3, 3).

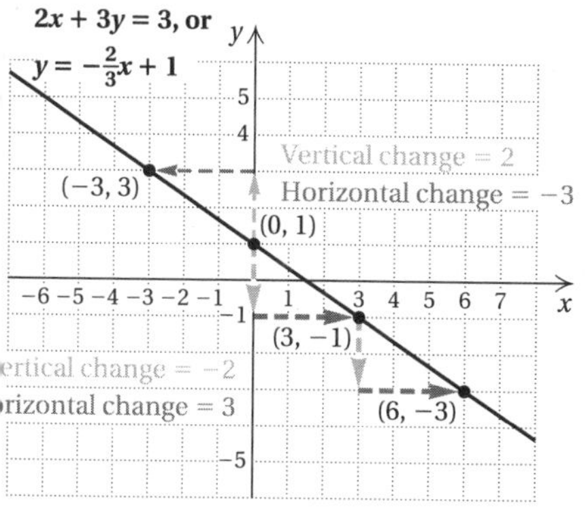

It helps to use both $\frac{2}{-3}$ and $\frac{-2}{3}$ to draw the graph.

Exercise 5.

5. Graph: $3x + 4y = 12$.

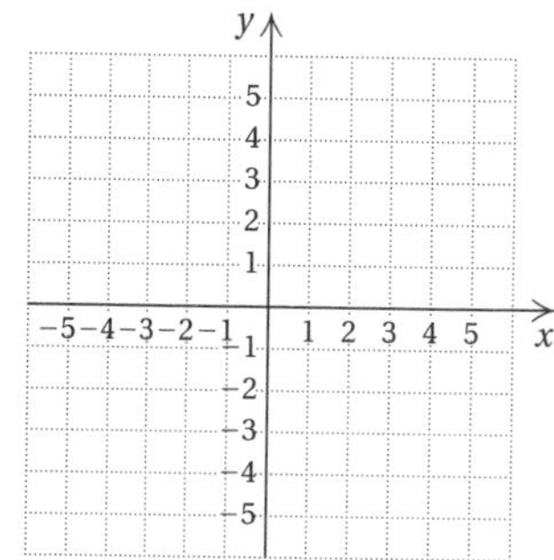

Answer on page A-16

tudy Tips

TURNING NEGATIVES INTO POSITIVES

B. C. Forbes said, "History has demonstrated that notable winners usually encountered heartbreaking obstacles before they triumphed. They won because they refused to become discouraged by their defeats."

Here are some anecdotes about well-known people who turned what could have been a negative experience into a positive outcome.

- *Richard Bach* sold more than 7 million copies of his story about a "soaring" seagull, Jonathan Livingston Seagull. His work was turned down by 18 publishers before Macmillan finally published it in 1970.
- *Walt Disney* was once fired by a newspaper for what they said was his "lack of ideas." He went bankrupt several times before he built an entertainment empire that now includes Disneyland and Disney World.
- *Erik Weihenmayer*, a blind man, has climbed the tallest mountains in Africa and North and South America and recently climbed the tallest mountain in the world, Mt. Everest.
- *Hank Aaron* holds the all-time Major League home run record with a total of 755, topping the former record holder, Babe Ruth, who had 714. But Aaron also held the all-time record for many years for striking out 1383 times, also topping Babe Ruth, who struck out 1330 times!
- At the age of 15, *Michael Jordan* was cut from his school basketball team. He was told he was too small to play. Yet in 2000, he was selected by ESPN as the top athlete of the 20th century.
- *Albert Einstein* didn't speak until he was 4 years old and was not able to read until he was 7. He is now recognized as one of the greatest physicists of all time, having developed the famous theory of relativity.

In an article entitled "*Mistakes–Important Teacher,*" Josh Hinds writes, "Another approach (to negative experiences) is to remind ourselves that failures are not always failures, rather they are lessons. I would challenge you to find one occurrence in your own life where you have learned from a past mistake. While it can be true that we don't gain direct rewards from them, we still gain something of great importance. Therefore we need to explore our failures and take the time to use them as our teachers ..."

"Whoever makes no mistakes is doing nothing."

Dutch proverb

3.5 EXERCISE SET

For Extra Help

a Draw a line that has the given slope and y-intercept.

1. Slope $\frac{2}{5}$; y-intercept $(0, 1)$

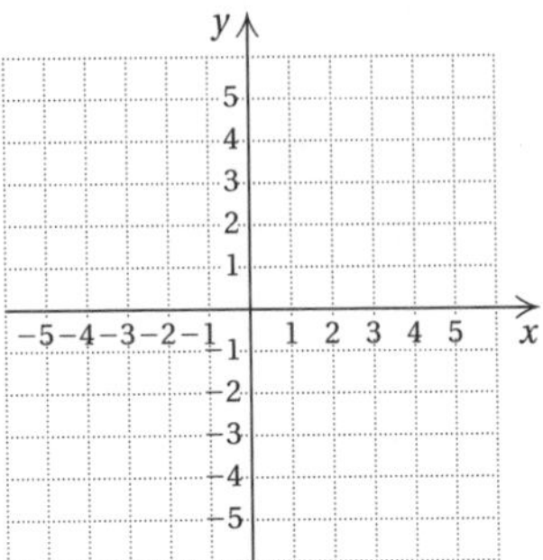

2. Slope $\frac{3}{5}$; y-intercept $(0, -1)$

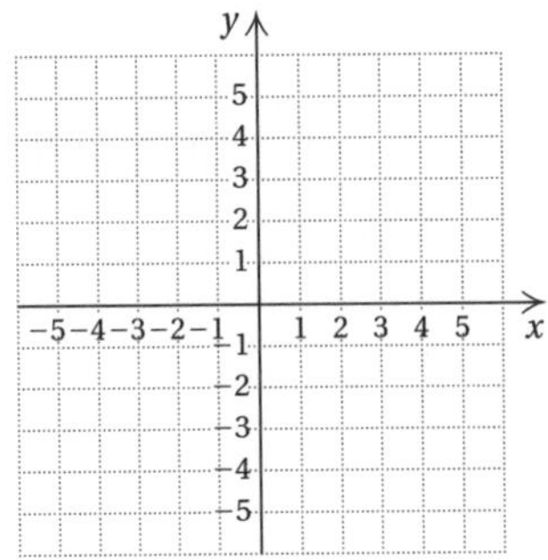

3. Slope $\frac{5}{3}$; y-intercept $(0, -2)$

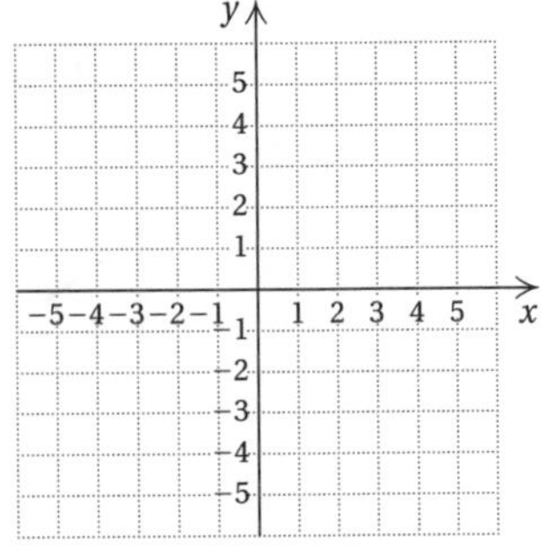

4. Slope $\frac{5}{2}$; y-intercept $(0, 1)$

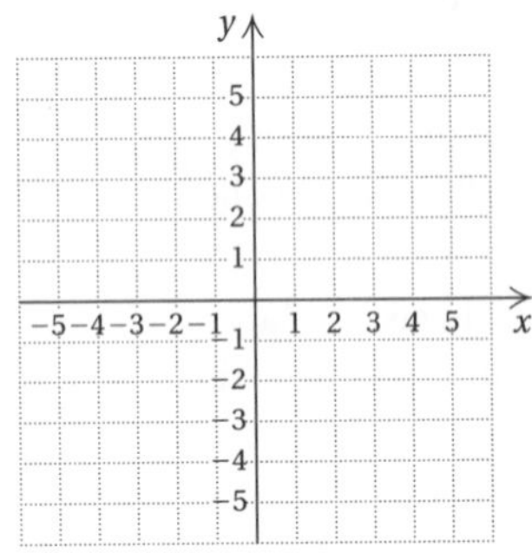

5. Slope $-\frac{3}{4}$; y-intercept $(0, 5)$

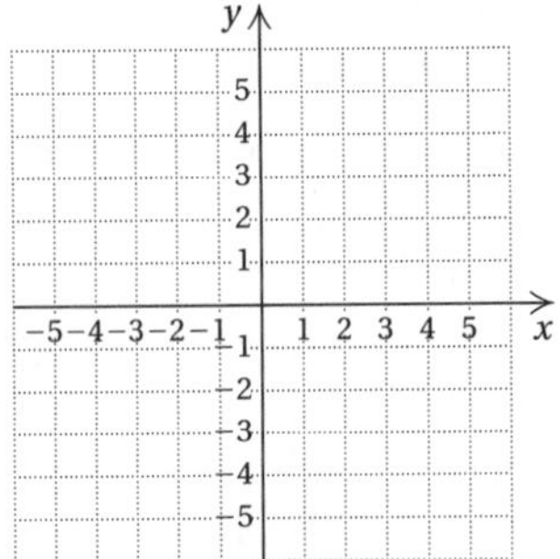

6. Slope $-\frac{4}{5}$; y-intercept $(0, 6)$

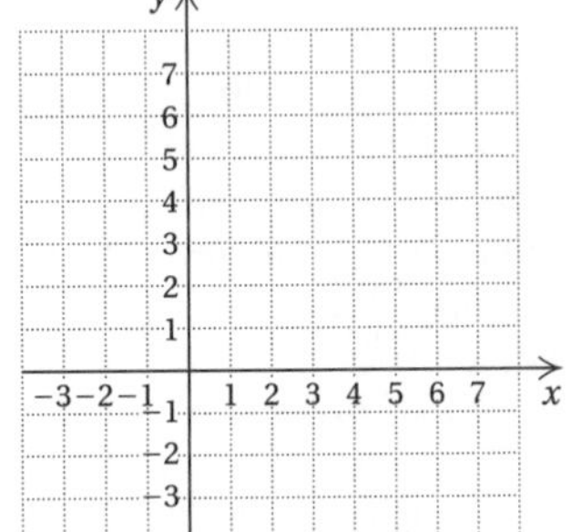

7. Slope $-\frac{1}{2}$; y-intercept $(0, 3)$

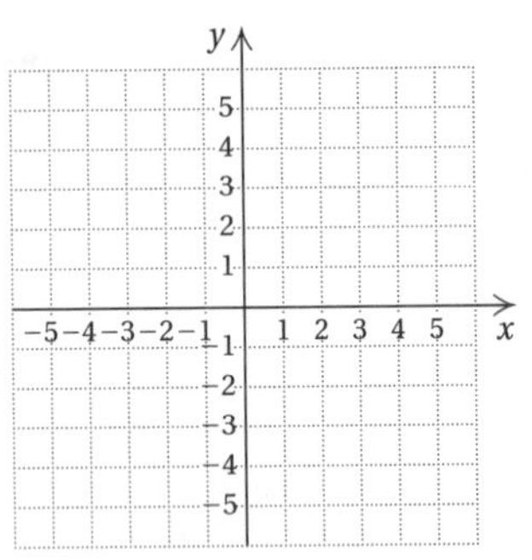

8. Slope $\frac{1}{3}$; y-intercept $(0, -4)$

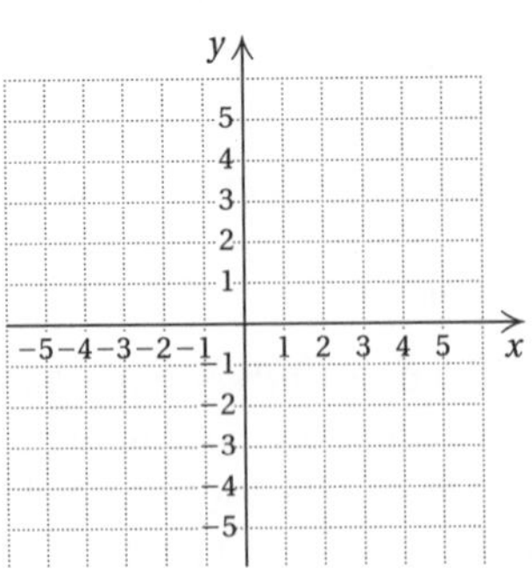

9. Slope 2; y-intercept $(0, -4)$

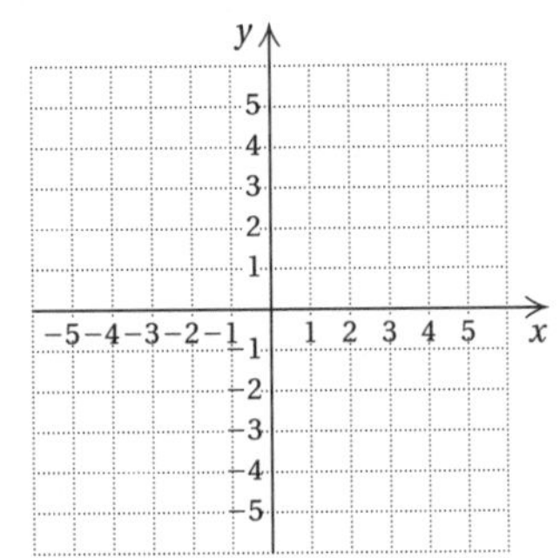

0. Slope -2; y-intercept $(0, -3)$

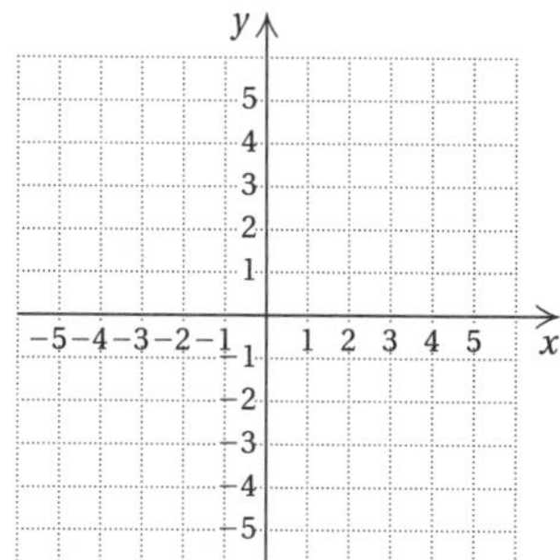

11. Slope -3; y-intercept $(0, 2)$

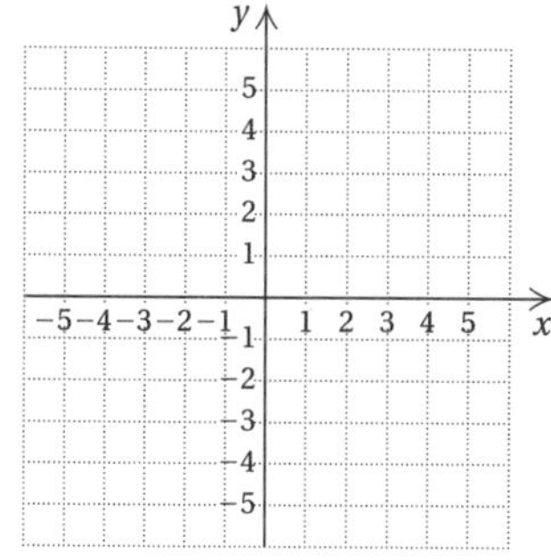

12. Slope 3; y-intercept $(0, 4)$

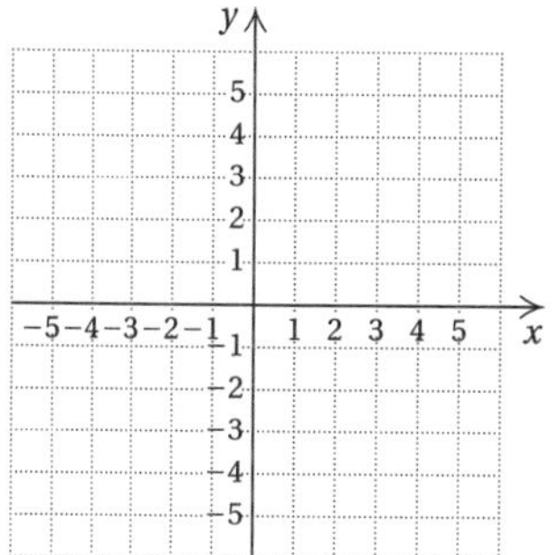

raph using the slope and the y-intercept.

3. $y = \frac{3}{5}x + 2$

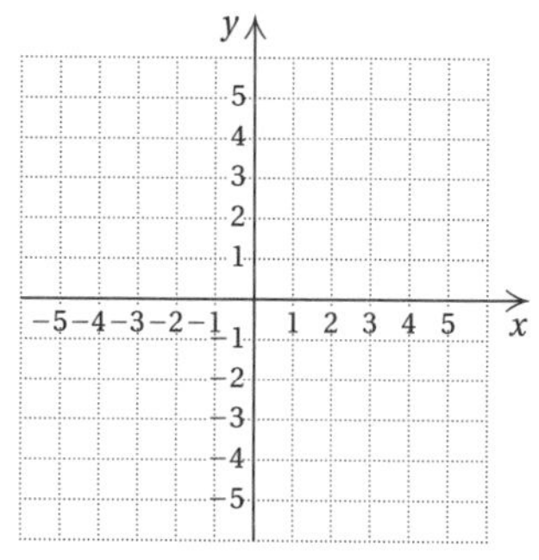

14. $y = -\frac{3}{5}x - 1$

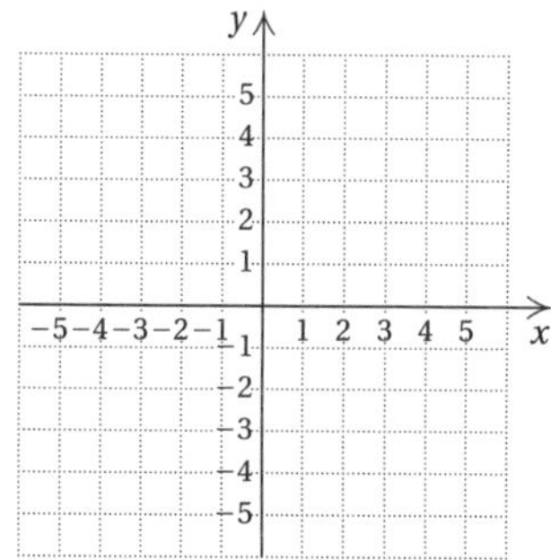

15. $y = -\frac{3}{5}x + 1$

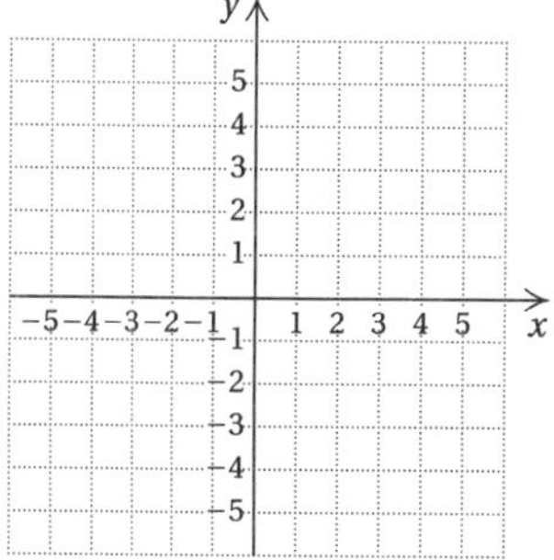

6. $y = \frac{3}{5}x - 2$

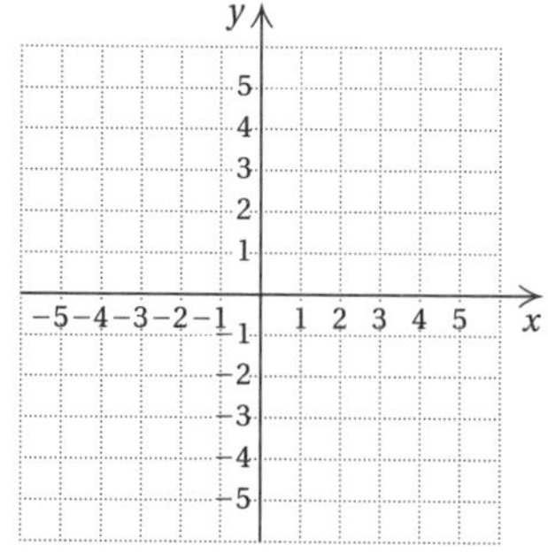

17. $y = \frac{5}{3}x + 3$

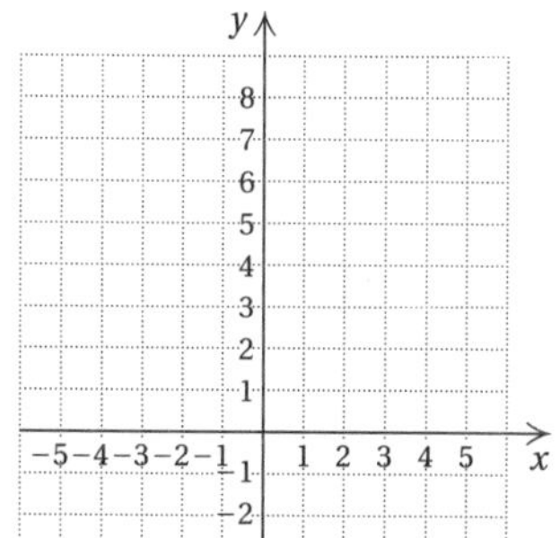

18. $y = \frac{5}{3}x - 2$

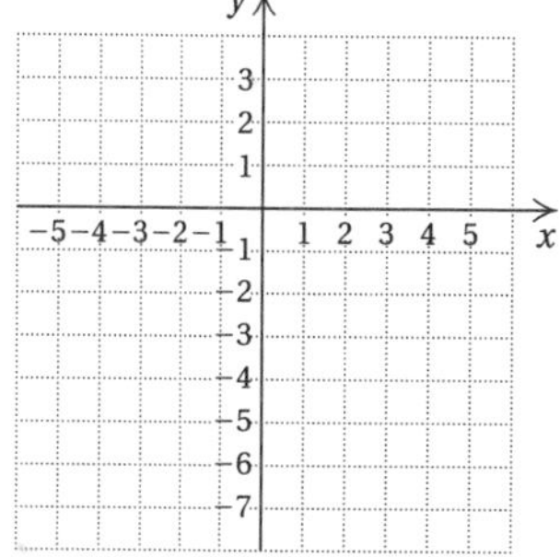

9. $y = -\frac{3}{2}x - 2$

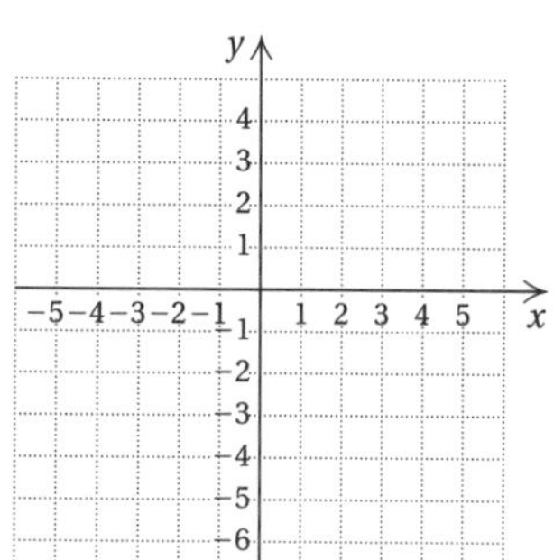

20. $y = -\frac{4}{3}x + 3$

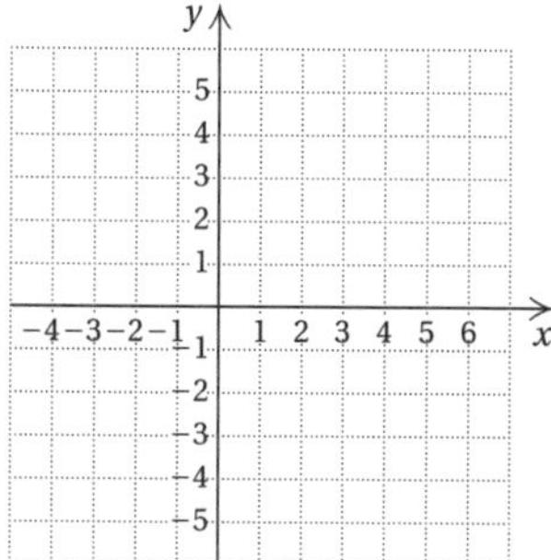

21. $2x + y = 1$

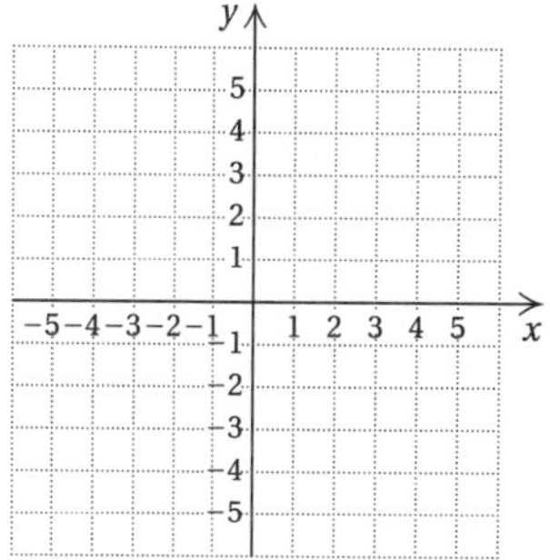

22. $3x + y = 2$

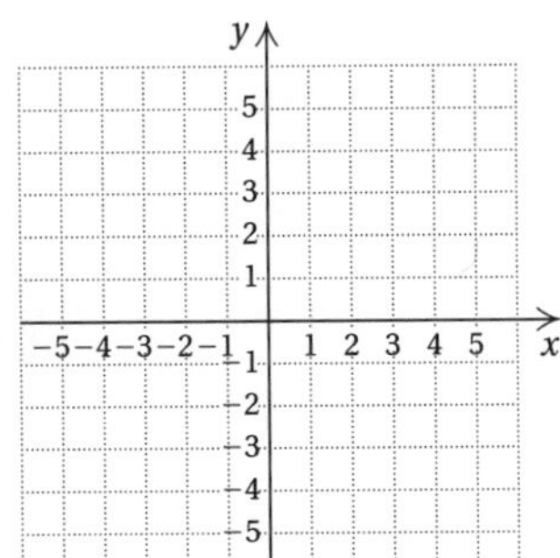

23. $3x - y = 4$

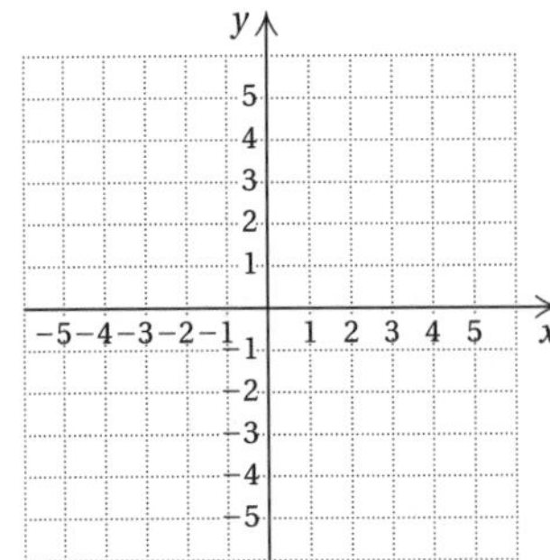

24. $2x - y = 5$

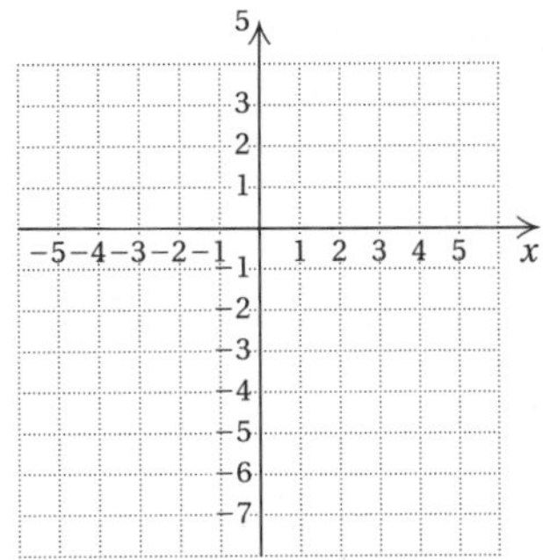

25. $2x + 3y = 9$

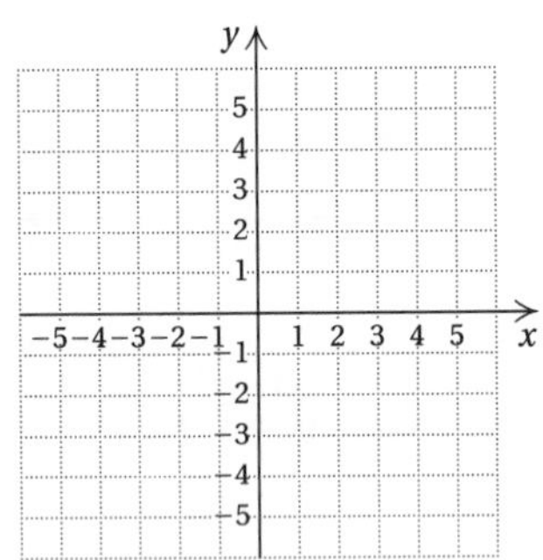

26. $4x + 5y = 15$

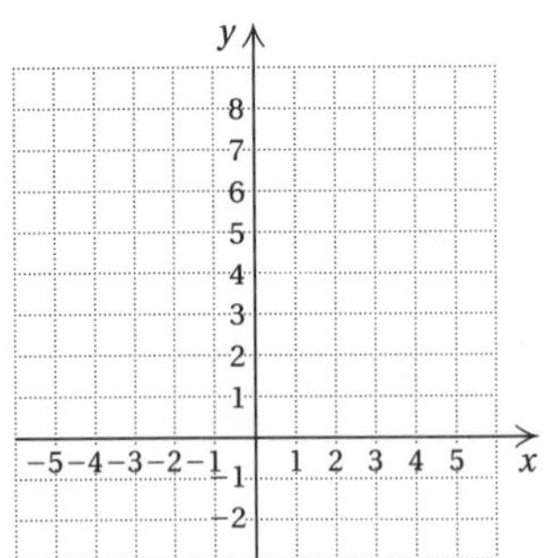

27. $x - 4y = 12$

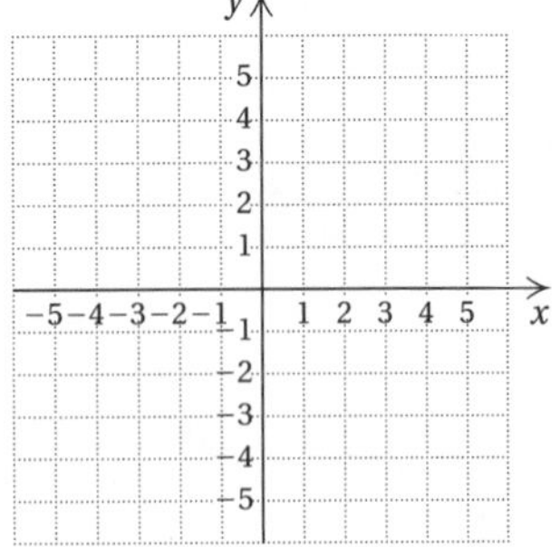

28. $x + 5y = 20$

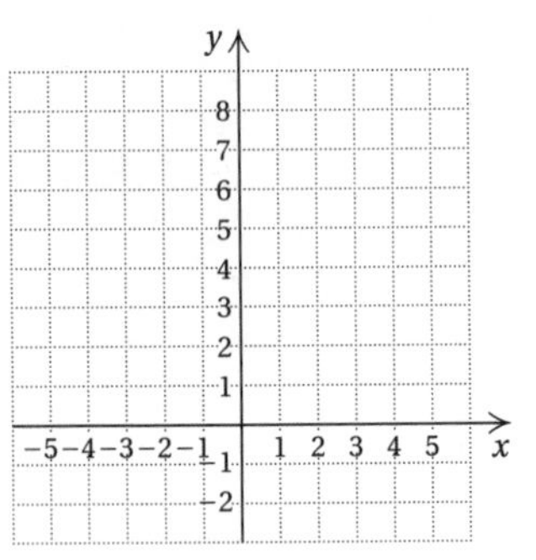

29. $x + 2y = 6$

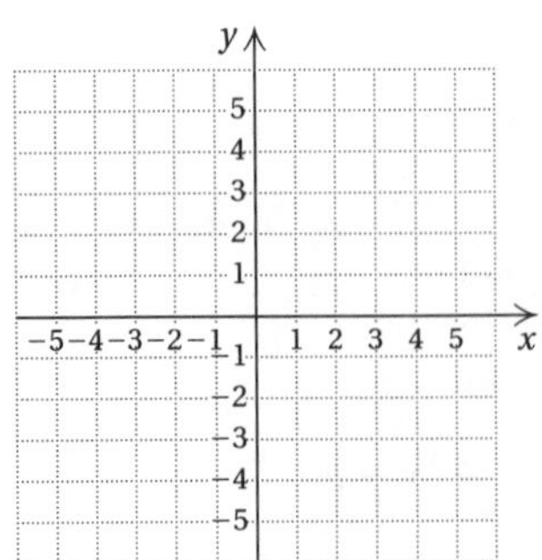

30. $x - 3y = 9$

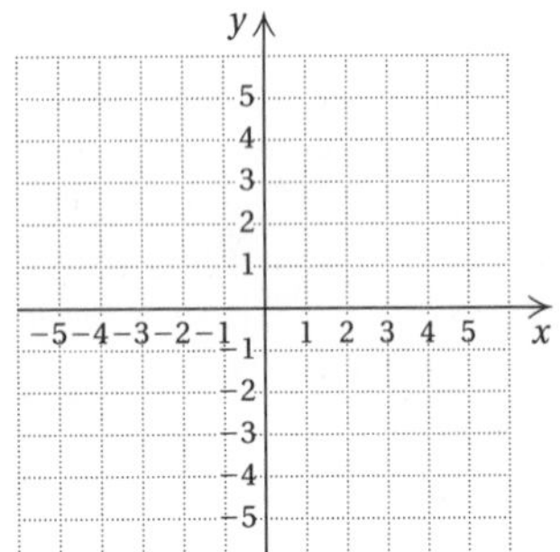

31. $\mathbf{D_W}$ Can a horizontal line be graphed using the method of Examples 3 and 4? Why or why not?

32. $\mathbf{D_W}$ Can a vertical line be graphed using the method of Examples 3 and 4? Why or why not?

SKILL MAINTENANCE

nd the slope of the line containing the given pair of points. [3.3a]

$(-2, -6), (8, 7)$

34. $(2, -6), (8, -7)$

$(4.5, -2.3), (14.5, 4.6)$

36. $(-0.8, -2.3), (-4.8, 0.1)$

$(-2, -6), (8, -6)$

38. $(-2, -6), (-2, 7)$

$(11, -1), (11, -4)$

40. $(-3, 5), (8, 5)$

Kidney Transplants. The number of kidney transplants in the United States has increased in recent years, as shown in the following graph. Find the rate of change in the number of kidney transplants with respect to time. Find the slope of the graph. [3.3b]

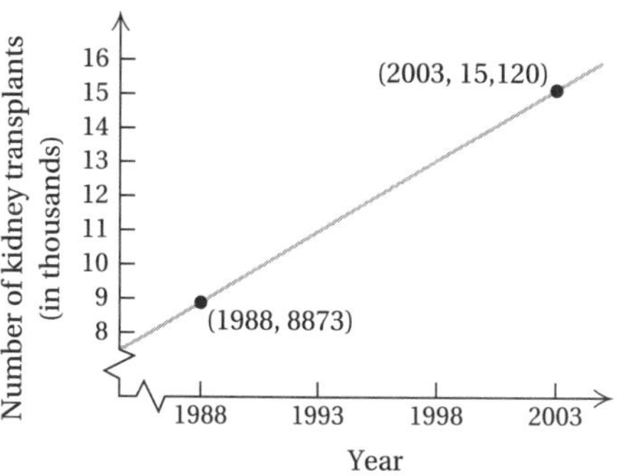

Source: National Organ Procurement and Transplantation Network

42. *Liver Transplants.* The number of liver transplants in the United States has increased in recent years, as shown in the following graph. Find the rate of change in the number of liver transplants with respect to time. Find the slope of the graph. [3.3b]

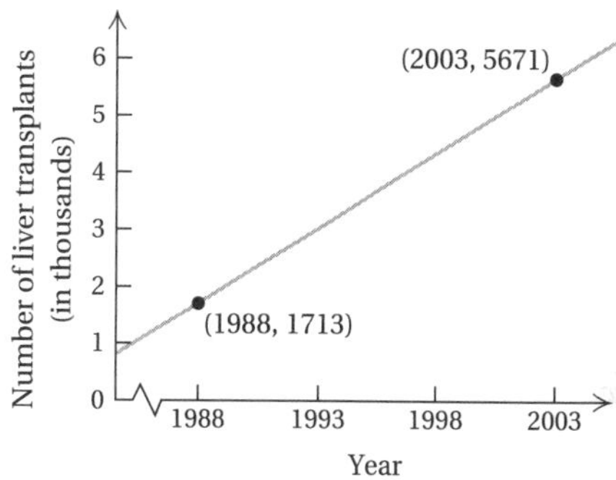

Source: National Organ Procurement and Transplantation Network

SYNTHESIS

Refrigerator Size. Kitchen designers recommend that a refrigerator be selected on the basis of the number of people in the household. For 1–2 people, a 16 ft^3 model is suggested. For each additional person, an additional 1.5 ft^3 is recommended. If x is the number of residents in excess of 2, find the slope–intercept equation for the recommended size of a refrigerator.

Graph the line with slope 2 that passes through the point $(-3, 1)$.

44. *Telephone Service.* In a recent promotion, AT&T charged a monthly fee of \$3.95 plus 7¢ for each minute of long-distance phone calls. If x is the number of minutes of long-distance calls, find the slope–intercept equation for the monthly bill.

4.1 INTEGERS AS EXPONENTS

Objectives

a Tell the meaning of exponential notation.

b Evaluate exponential expressions with exponents of 0 and 1.

c Evaluate algebraic expressions containing exponents.

d Use the product rule to multiply exponential expressions with like bases.

e Use the quotient rule to divide exponential expressions with like bases.

f Express an exponential expression involving negative exponents with positive exponents.

What is the meaning of each of the following?

1. 5^4

2. x^5

3. $(3t)^2$

4. $3t^2$

5. $(-x)^4$

6. $-y^3$

Answers on page A-21

We introduced integer exponents of 2 or higher in Section R.5. Here we consider 0 and 1, as well as negative integers, as exponents.

a Exponential Notation

An exponent of 2 or greater tells how many times the base is used as a factor. For example,

$$a \cdot a \cdot a \cdot a = a^4.$$

In this case, the **exponent** is 4 and the **base** is a. An expression for a power is called **exponential notation.**

a^n ← This is the exponent.
↑
This is the base.

EXAMPLE 1 What is the meaning of 3^5? of n^4? of $(2n)^3$? of $50x^2$? of $(-n)^3$? of $-n^3$?

3^5 means $3 \cdot 3 \cdot 3 \cdot 3 \cdot 3$; n^4 means $n \cdot n \cdot n \cdot n$;

$(2n)^3$ means $2n \cdot 2n \cdot 2n$; $50x^2$ means $50 \cdot x \cdot x$;

$(-n)^3$ means $(-n) \cdot (-n) \cdot (-n)$; $-n^3$ means $-1 \cdot n \cdot n \cdot n$

Do Exercises 1–6.

We read exponential notation as follows: a^n is read the ***n*th power of *a*,** or simply ***a* to the *n*th,** or ***a* to the *n*.** We often read x^2 as "***x*-squared.**" The reason for this is that the area of a square of side x is $x \cdot x$, or x^2. We often read x^3 as "***x*-cubed.**" The reason for this is that the volume of a cube with length, width, and height x is $x \cdot x \cdot x$, or x^3.

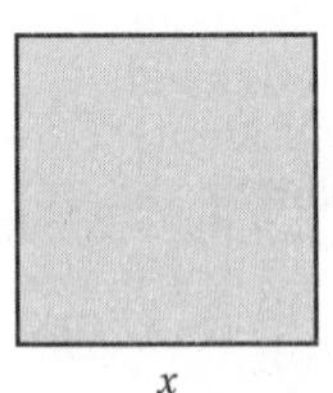

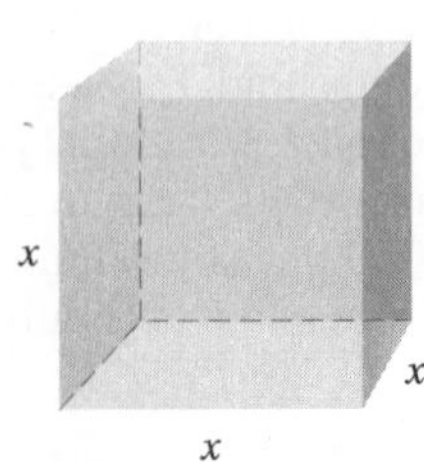

b One and Zero as Exponents

Look for a pattern in the following:

On each side, we **divide** by 8 at each step.

$$8 \cdot 8 \cdot 8 \cdot 8 = 8^4$$
$$8 \cdot 8 \cdot 8 = 8^3$$
$$8 \cdot 8 = 8^2$$
$$8 = 8^?$$
$$1 = 8^?.$$

On this side, the exponents **decrease** by 1.

To continue the pattern, we would say that

$$8 = 8^1 \quad \text{and} \quad 1 = 8^0.$$

We make the following definition.

EXPONENTS OF 0 AND 1

$a^1 = a$, for any number a;
$a^0 = 1$, for any nonzero number a

Ve consider 0^0 to be not defined. We will explain why later in this section.

XAMPLE 2 Evaluate 5^1, $(-8)^1$, 3^0, $(-7.3)^0$, and $(186{,}892{,}046)^0$.

$5^1 = 5$; $(-8)^1 = -8$; $3^0 = 1$;
$(-7.3)^0 = 1$; $(186{,}892{,}046)^0 = 1$

o Exercises 7–12.

Evaluate.

7. 6^1 **8.** 7^0

9. $(8.4)^1$ **10.** 8654^0

11. $(-1.4)^1$ **12.** 0^1

Answers on page A-21

C Evaluating Algebraic Expressions

lgebraic expressions can involve exponential notation. For example, the following are algebraic expressions:

x^4, $(3x)^3 - 2$, $a^2 + 2ab + b^2$.

Ve evaluate algebraic expressions by replacing variables with numbers and ollowing the rules for order of operations.

XAMPLE 3 Evaluate $1000 - x^4$ when $x = 5$.

$1000 - x^4 = 1000 - 5^4$ Substituting
$= 1000 - 5 \cdot 5 \cdot 5 \cdot 5$
$= 1000 - 625$
$= 375$

XAMPLE 4 *Area of a Compact Disc.* The standard compact disc used for oftware and music has a radius of 6 cm. Find the area of such a CD (ignoring ne hole in the middle).

$A = \pi r^2$
$= \pi \cdot (6 \text{ cm})^2$
$= \pi \cdot 6 \text{ cm} \cdot 6 \text{ cm}$
$\approx 3.14 \times 36 \text{ cm}^2$
$= 113.04 \text{ cm}^2$

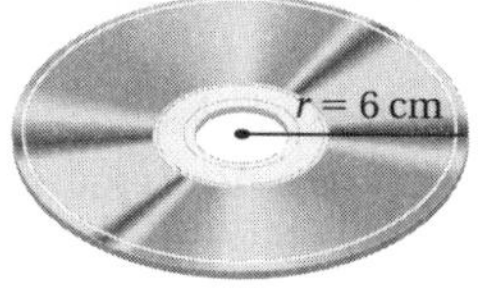

In Example 4, "cm^2" means "square centimeters" and "$\approx$" means "is approximately equal to."

XAMPLE 5 Evaluate $(5x)^3$ when $x = -2$.

When we evaluate with a negative number, we often use extra parentheses to show the substitution.

$(5x)^3 = [5 \cdot (-2)]^3$ Substituting
$= [-10]^3$ Multiplying within brackets first
$= [-10] \cdot [-10] \cdot [-10]$
$= -1000$ Evaluating the power

Study Tips

AUDIO RECORDINGS

Your instructor can request a complete set of audio recordings designed to help lead you through each section of this textbook. If you have difficulty reading or if you want extra review, these recordings explain solution steps for examples, caution you about errors, give instructions to work margin exercises, and then review the solutions to the margin exercises. These recordings are ideal for use outside of class. To obtain these audio recordings, consult with your instructor and refer to the Preface of this text. Recordings are available as MP3 files within MyMathLab.

13. Evaluate t^3 when $t = 5$.

14. Evaluate $-5x^5$ when $x = -2$.

15. Find the area of a circle when $r = 32$ cm. Use 3.14 for π.

16. Evaluate $200 - a^4$ when $a = 3$.

17. Evaluate $t^1 - 4$ and $t^0 - 4$ when $t = 7$.

18. a) Evaluate $(4t)^2$ when $t = -3$.

b) Evaluate $4t^2$ when $t = -3$.

c) Determine whether $(4t)^2$ and $4t^2$ are equivalent.

Multiply and simplify.

19. $3^5 \cdot 3^5$

20. $x^4 \cdot x^6$

21. $p^4p^{12}p^8$

22. $x \cdot x^4$

23. $(a^2b^3)(a^7b^5)$

Answers on page A-21

EXAMPLE 6 Evaluate $5x^3$ when $x = -2$.

$$5x^3 = 5 \cdot (-2)^3 \quad \text{Substituting}$$
$$= 5 \cdot (-2) \cdot (-2) \cdot (-2) \quad \text{Evaluating the power first}$$
$$= 5(-8) \quad (-2)(-2)(-2) = -8$$
$$= -40$$

Recall that two expressions are equivalent if they have the same value for all meaningful replacements. Note that Examples 5 and 6 show that $(5x)^3$ and $5x^3$ are *not* equivalent—that is, $(5x)^3 \neq 5x^3$.

Do Exercises 13–18.

d Multiplying Powers with Like Bases

There are several rules for manipulating exponential notation to obtain equivalent expressions. We first consider multiplying powers with like bases:

$$a^3 \cdot a^2 = (a \cdot a \cdot a)(a \cdot a) = a \cdot a \cdot a \cdot a \cdot a = a^5.$$

3 factors 2 factors 5 factors

Since an integer exponent greater than 1 tells how many times we use a base as a factor, then $(a \cdot a \cdot a)(a \cdot a) = a \cdot a \cdot a \cdot a \cdot a = a^5$ by the associative law. Note that the exponent in a^5 is the sum of those in $a^3 \cdot a^2$, that is, $3 + 2 = 5$. Likewise,

$$b^4 \cdot b^3 = (b \cdot b \cdot b \cdot b)(b \cdot b \cdot b) = b^7, \quad \text{where} \quad 4 + 3 = 7.$$

Adding the exponents gives the correct result.

THE PRODUCT RULE

For any number a and any positive integers m and n,

$$a^m \cdot a^n = a^{m+n}.$$

(When multiplying with exponential notation, if the bases are the same, keep the base and add the exponents.)

EXAMPLES Multiply and simplify. By simplify, we mean write the expression as one number to a nonnegative power.

7. $5^6 \cdot 5^2 = 5^{6+2}$ Adding exponents: $a^m \cdot a^n = a^{m+n}$
$= 5^8$

8. $x^3 \cdot x^9 = x^{3+9} = x^{12}$

9. $m^5m^{10}m^3 = m^{5+10+3} = m^{18}$

10. $x \cdot x^8 = x^1 \cdot x^8$ Writing x as x^1
$= x^{1+8}$
$= x^9$

11. $(a^3b^2)(a^3b^5) = (a^3a^3)(b^2b^5)$
$= a^6b^7$

Do Exercises 19–23.

e Dividing Powers with Like Bases

The following suggests a rule for dividing powers with like bases, such as a^5/a^2:

$$\frac{a^5}{a^2} = \frac{a \cdot a \cdot a \cdot a \cdot a}{a \cdot a} = \frac{a \cdot a \cdot a \cdot a \cdot a}{1 \cdot a \cdot a} = \frac{a \cdot a \cdot a}{1} \cdot \frac{a \cdot a}{a \cdot a} = \frac{a \cdot a \cdot a}{1} \cdot 1$$

$$= a \cdot a \cdot a = a^3.$$

Note that the exponent in a^3 is the difference of those in $a^5 \div a^2$, that is, $5 - 2 = 3$. In a similar way, we have

$$\frac{t^9}{t^4} = \frac{t \cdot t \cdot t \cdot t \cdot t \cdot t \cdot t \cdot t \cdot t}{t \cdot t \cdot t \cdot t} = t^5, \quad \text{where } 9 - 4 = 5.$$

Subtracting exponents gives the correct answer.

THE QUOTIENT RULE

For any nonzero number a and any positive integers m and n,

$$\frac{a^m}{a^n} = a^{m-n}.$$

(When dividing with exponential notation, if the bases are the same, keep the base and subtract the exponent of the denominator from the exponent of the numerator.)

EXAMPLES Divide and simplify. By simplify, we mean write the expression as one number to a nonnegative power.

12. $\frac{6^5}{6^3} = 6^{5-3}$ Subtracting exponents

$= 6^2$

13. $\frac{x^8}{x^2} = x^{8-2}$

$= x^6$

14. $\frac{t^{12}}{t} = \frac{t^{12}}{t^1} = t^{12-1}$

$= t^{11}$

15. $\frac{p^5q^7}{p^2q^5} = \frac{p^5}{p^2} \cdot \frac{q^7}{q^5} = p^{5-2}q^{7-5}$

$= p^3q^2$

The quotient rule can also be used to explain the definition of 0 as an exponent. Consider the expression a^4/a^4, where a is nonzero:

$$\frac{a^4}{a^4} = \frac{a \cdot a \cdot a \cdot a}{a \cdot a \cdot a \cdot a} = 1.$$

This is true because the numerator and the denominator are the same. Now suppose we apply the rule for dividing powers with the same base:

$$\frac{a^4}{a^4} = a^{4-4} = a^0.$$

Since $a^4/a^4 = 1$ and $a^4/a^4 = a^0$, it follows that $a^0 = 1$, when $a \neq 0$.

We can explain why we do not define 0^0 using the quotient rule. We know that 0^0 is 0^{1-1}. But 0^{1-1} is also equal to $0^1/0^1$, or $0/0$. We have already seen that division by 0 is not defined, so 0^0 is also not defined.

Do Exercises 24–27.

Divide and simplify.

24. $\frac{4^5}{4^2}$

25. $\frac{y^6}{y^2}$

26. $\frac{p^{10}}{p}$

27. $\frac{a^7b^6}{a^3b^4}$

Answers on page A-21

Express with positive exponents. Then simplify.

28. 4^{-3}

29. 5^{-2}

30. 2^{-4}

31. $(-2)^{-3}$

32. $4p^{-3}$

33. $\frac{1}{x^{-2}}$

Answers on page A-21

f Negative Integers as Exponents

We can use the rule for dividing powers with like bases to lead us to a definition of exponential notation when the exponent is a negative integer. Consider $5^3/5^7$ and first simplify it using procedures we have learned for working with fractions:

$$\frac{5^3}{5^7} = \frac{5 \cdot 5 \cdot 5}{5 \cdot 5 \cdot 5 \cdot 5 \cdot 5 \cdot 5 \cdot 5} = \frac{5 \cdot 5 \cdot 5 \cdot 1}{5 \cdot 5 \cdot 5 \cdot 5 \cdot 5 \cdot 5 \cdot 5}$$
$$= \frac{5 \cdot 5 \cdot 5}{5 \cdot 5 \cdot 5} \cdot \frac{1}{5 \cdot 5 \cdot 5 \cdot 5} = \frac{1}{5^4}.$$

Now we apply the rule for dividing exponential expressions with the same bases. Then

$$\frac{5^3}{5^7} = 5^{3-7} = 5^{-4}.$$

From these two expressions for $5^3/5^7$, it follows that

$$5^{-4} = \frac{1}{5^4}.$$

This leads to our definition of negative exponents.

NEGATIVE EXPONENT

For any real number a that is nonzero and any integer n,

$$a^{-n} = \frac{1}{a^n}.$$

In fact, the numbers a^n and a^{-n} are reciprocals of each other because

$$a^n \cdot a^{-n} = a^n \cdot \frac{1}{a^n} = \frac{a^n}{a^n} = 1.$$

The following is another way to arrive at the definition of negative exponents.

On each side, we **divide** by 5 at each step.

$$5 \cdot 5 \cdot 5 \cdot 5 = 5^4$$
$$5 \cdot 5 \cdot 5 = 5^3$$
$$5 \cdot 5 = 5^2$$
$$5 = 5^1$$
$$1 = 5^0$$
$$\frac{1}{5} = 5^?$$
$$\frac{1}{25} = 5^?$$

On this side, the exponents **decrease** by 1.

To continue the pattern, it should follow that

$$\frac{1}{5} = \frac{1}{5^1} = 5^{-1} \quad \text{and} \quad \frac{1}{25} = \frac{1}{5^2} = 5^{-2}.$$

EXAMPLES Express using positive exponents. Then simplify.

16. $4^{-2} = \frac{1}{4^2} = \frac{1}{16}$

17. $(-3)^{-2} = \frac{1}{(-3)^2} = \frac{1}{(-3)(-3)} = \frac{1}{9}$

18. $m^{-3} = \frac{1}{m^3}$

19. $ab^{-1} = a\left(\frac{1}{b^1}\right) = a\left(\frac{1}{b}\right) = \frac{a}{b}$

20. $\frac{1}{x^{-3}} = x^{-(-3)} = x^3$

21. $3c^{-5} = 3\left(\frac{1}{c^5}\right) = \frac{3}{c^5}$

Example 20 might also be done as follows:

$$\frac{1}{x^{-3}} = \frac{1}{\frac{1}{x^3}} = 1 \cdot \frac{x^3}{1} = x^3.$$

Caution!

As shown in Examples 16 and 17, a negative exponent does not necessarily mean that an expression is negative.

Do Exercises 28–33 on the preceding page.

The rules for multiplying and dividing powers with like bases still hold when exponents are 0 or negative. We state them in a summary below.

EXAMPLES Simplify. By simplify, we generally mean write the expression as one number or variable to a nonnegative power.

22. $7^{-3} \cdot 7^6 = 7^{-3+6}$ Adding exponents
$= 7^3$

23. $x^4 \cdot x^{-3} = x^{4+(-3)} = x^1 = x$

24. $\frac{5^4}{5^{-2}} = 5^{4-(-2)}$ Subtracting exponents
$= 5^{4+2} = 5^6$

25. $\frac{x}{x^7} = x^{1-7} = x^{-6} = \frac{1}{x^6}$

26. $\frac{b^{-4}}{b^{-5}} = b^{-4-(-5)}$
$= b^{-4+5} = b^1 = b$

27. $y^{-4} \cdot y^{-8} = y^{-4+(-8)}$
$= y^{-12} = \frac{1}{y^{12}}$

Do Exercises 34–38.

The following is a summary of the definitions and rules for exponents that we have considered in this section.

DEFINITIONS AND RULES FOR EXPONENTS

1 as an exponent:	$a^1 = a$
0 as an exponent:	$a^0 = 1, a \neq 0$
Negative integers as exponents:	$a^{-n} = \frac{1}{a^n}, \frac{1}{a^{-n}} = a^n; a \neq 0$
Product Rule:	$a^m \cdot a^n = a^{m+n}$
Quotient Rule:	$\frac{a^m}{a^n} = a^{m-n}, a \neq 0$

Simplify.

34. $5^{-2} \cdot 5^4$

35. $x^{-3} \cdot x^{-4}$

36. $\frac{7^{-2}}{7^3}$

37. $\frac{b^{-2}}{b^{-3}}$

38. $\frac{t}{t^{-5}}$

Answers on page A-21

4.1 EXERCISE SET

For Extra Help

MathXL | MyMathLab | InterAct Math | Math Tutor Center | Digital Video Tutor CD 3 Videotape 5 | Student's Solutions Manual

a What is the meaning of each of the following?

1. 3^4

2. 4^3

3. $(-1.1)^5$

4. $(87.2)^6$

5. $\left(\frac{2}{3}\right)^4$

6. $\left(-\frac{5}{8}\right)^3$

7. $(7p)^2$

8. $(11c)^3$

9. $8k^3$

10. $17x^2$

11. $-6y^4$

12. $-q^5$

b Evaluate.

13. $a^0, a \neq 0$

14. $t^0, t \neq 0$

15. b^1

16. c^1

17. $\left(\frac{2}{3}\right)^0$

18. $\left(-\frac{5}{8}\right)^0$

19. $(-7.03)^1$

20. $\left(\frac{4}{5}\right)^1$

21. 8.38^0

22. 8.38^1

23. $(ab)^1$

24. $(ab)^0, a, b \neq 0$

25. ab^0

26. ab^1

c Evaluate.

27. m^3, when $m = 3$

28. x^6, when $x = 2$

29. p^1, when $p = 19$

30. x^{19}, when $x = 0$

31. $-x^4$, when $x = -3$

32. $-2y^7$, when $x = 2$

33. x^4, when $x = 4$

34. y^{15}, when $y = 1$

35. $y^2 - 7$, when $y = -10$

36. $z^5 + 5$, when $z = -2$

37. $161 - b^2$, when $b = 5$

38. $325 - v^3$, when $v = -3$

39. $x^1 + 3$ and $x^0 + 3$, when $x = 7$

40. $y^0 - 8$ and $y^1 - 8$, when $y = -3$

41. Find the area of a circle when $r = 34$ ft. Use 3.14 for π.

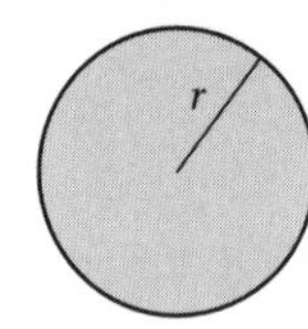

42. The area A of a square with sides of length s is given by $A = s^2$. Find the area of a square with sides of length 24 m.

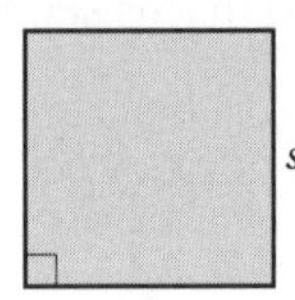

f Express using positive exponents. Then simplify.

43. 3^{-2}

44. 2^{-3}

45. 10^{-3}

46. 5^{-4}

47. 7^{-3}

48. 5^{-2}

49. a^{-3}

50. x^{-2}

51. $\frac{1}{8^{-2}}$

52. $\frac{1}{2^{-5}}$

53. $\frac{1}{y^{-4}}$

54. $\frac{1}{t^{-7}}$

55. $\frac{1}{z^{-n}}$

56. $\frac{1}{h^{-n}}$

xpress using negative exponents.

57. $\frac{1}{4^3}$

58. $\frac{1}{5^2}$

59. $\frac{1}{x^3}$

60. $\frac{1}{y^2}$

61. $\frac{1}{a^5}$

62. $\frac{1}{b^7}$

d, **f** Multiply and simplify.

63. $2^4 \cdot 2^3$

64. $3^5 \cdot 3^2$

65. $8^5 \cdot 8^9$

66. $n^3 \cdot n^{20}$

67. $x^4 \cdot x^3$

68. $y^7 \cdot y^9$

69. $9^{17} \cdot 9^{21}$

70. $t^0 \cdot t^{16}$

71. $(3y)^4(3y)^8$

72. $(2t)^8(2t)^{17}$

73. $(7y)^1(7y)^{16}$

74. $(8x)^0(8x)^1$

75. $3^{-5} \cdot 3^8$

76. $5^{-8} \cdot 5^9$

77. $x^{-2} \cdot x$

78. $x \cdot x^{-1}$

79. $x^{14} \cdot x^3$

80. $x^9 \cdot x^4$

81. $x^{-7} \cdot x^{-6}$

82. $y^{-5} \cdot y^{-8}$

83. $a^{11} \cdot a^{-3} \cdot a^{-18}$

84. $a^{-11} \cdot a^{-3} \cdot a^{-7}$

85. $t^8 \cdot t^{-8}$

86. $m^{10} \cdot m^{-10}$

e, **f** Divide and simplify.

87. $\frac{7^5}{7^2}$

88. $\frac{5^8}{5^6}$

89. $\frac{8^{12}}{8^6}$

90. $\frac{8^{13}}{8^2}$

91. $\frac{y^9}{y^5}$

92. $\frac{x^{11}}{x^9}$

93. $\frac{16^2}{16^8}$

94. $\frac{7^2}{7^9}$

95. $\frac{m^6}{m^{12}}$

96. $\frac{a^3}{a^4}$

97. $\frac{(8x)^6}{(8x)^{10}}$

98. $\frac{(8t)^4}{(8t)^{11}}$

99. $\frac{(2y)^9}{(2y)^9}$

100. $\frac{(6y)^7}{(6y)^7}$

101. $\frac{x}{x^{-1}}$

102. $\frac{y^8}{y}$

103. $\frac{x^7}{x^{-2}}$

104. $\frac{t^8}{t^{-3}}$

105. $\frac{z^{-6}}{z^{-2}}$

106. $\frac{x^{-9}}{x^{-3}}$

107. $\frac{x^{-5}}{x^{-8}}$

108. $\frac{y^{-2}}{y^{-9}}$

109. $\frac{m^{-9}}{m^{-9}}$

110. $\frac{x^{-7}}{x^{-7}}$

Matching. In Exercises 111 and 112, match each item in the first column with the appropriate item in the second column by drawing connecting lines.

111.

5^2	$-\frac{1}{10}$
5^{-2}	$\frac{1}{10}$
$\left(\frac{1}{5}\right)^2$	$-\frac{1}{25}$
$\left(\frac{1}{5}\right)^{-2}$	10
-5^2	25
$(-5)^2$	-25
$-\left(-\frac{1}{5}\right)^2$	$\frac{1}{25}$
$\left(-\frac{1}{5}\right)^{-2}$	-10

112.

$-\left(\frac{1}{8}\right)^2$	16
$\left(\frac{1}{8}\right)^{-2}$	-16
8^{-2}	64
8^2	-64
-8^2	$\frac{1}{64}$
$(-8)^2$	$-\frac{1}{64}$
$\left(-\frac{1}{8}\right)^{-2}$	$-\frac{1}{16}$
$\left(-\frac{1}{8}\right)^2$	$\frac{1}{16}$

13. DW Suppose that the width of a square is three times the width of a second square. How do the areas of the squares compare? Why?

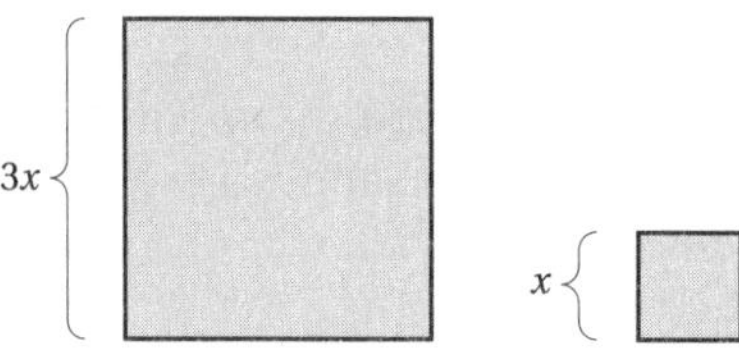

114. DW Suppose that the width of a cube is twice the width of a second cube. How do the volumes of the cubes compare? Why?

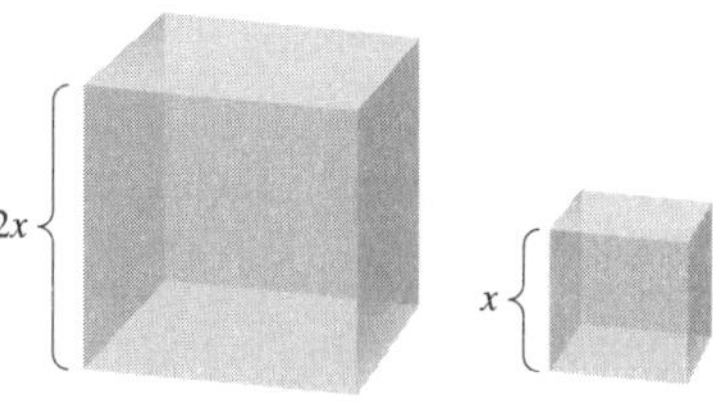

SKILL MAINTENANCE

olve. [2.6a]

15. *Cutting a Submarine Sandwich.* A 12-in. submarine sandwich is cut into two pieces. One piece is twice as long as the other. How long are the pieces?

116. *Book Pages.* A book is opened. The sum of the page numbers on the facing pages is 457. Find the page numbers.

17. The perimeter of a rectangle is 640 ft. The length is 15 ft more than the width. Find the area of the rectangle.

118. The first angle of a triangle is 24° more than the second. The third angle is twice the first. Find the measures of the angles of the triangle.

olve. [2.3c]

19. $-6(2 - x) + 10(5x - 7) = 10$

120. $-10(x - 4) = 5(2x + 5) - 7$

actor. [1.7d]

21. $4x - 12 + 24y$

122. $256 - 2a - 4b$

SYNTHESIS

Determine whether each of the following is correct.

23. $(x + 1)^2 = x^2 + 1$

124. $(x - 1)^2 = x^2 - 2x + 1$

125. $(5x)^0 = 5x^0$

126. $\dfrac{x^3}{x^5} = x^2$

mplify.

27. $(y^{2x})(y^{3x})$

128. $a^{5k} \div a^{3k}$

129. $\dfrac{a^{6t}(a^{7t})}{a^{9t}}$

30. $\dfrac{\left(\frac{1}{2}\right)^4}{\left(\frac{1}{2}\right)^5}$

131. $\dfrac{(0.8)^5}{(0.8)^3(0.8)^2}$

32. Determine whether $(a + b)^2$ and $a^2 + b^2$ are equivalent. (*Hint*: Choose values for a and b and evaluate.)

se >, <, or = for □ to write a true sentence.

33. 3^5 □ 3^4

134. 4^2 □ 4^3

135. 4^3 □ 5^3

136. 4^3 □ 3^4

valuate.

37. $\dfrac{1}{-z^4}$, when $z = -10$

138. $\dfrac{1}{-z^5}$, when $z = -0.1$

4.2 EXPONENTS AND SCIENTIFIC NOTATION

Objectives

a Use the power rule to raise powers to powers.

b Raise a product to a power and a quotient to a power.

c Convert between scientific notation and decimal notation.

d Multiply and divide using scientific notation.

e Solve applied problems using scientific notation.

We now enhance our ability to manipulate exponential expressions by considering three more rules. The rules are also applied to a new way to name numbers called *scientific notation*.

a Raising Powers to Powers

Consider an expression like $(3^2)^4$. We are raising 3^2 to the fourth power:

$$\begin{aligned}(3^2)^4 &= (3^2)(3^2)(3^2)(3^2)\\ &= (3\cdot 3)(3\cdot 3)(3\cdot 3)(3\cdot 3)\\ &= 3\cdot 3\cdot 3\cdot 3\cdot 3\cdot 3\cdot 3\cdot 3\\ &= 3^8.\end{aligned}$$

Note that in this case we could have multiplied the exponents:

$$(3^2)^4 = 3^{2\cdot 4} = 3^8.$$

Likewise, $(y^8)^3 = (y^8)(y^8)(y^8) = y^{24}$. Once again, we get the same result if we multiply the exponents:

$$(y^8)^3 = y^{8\cdot 3} = y^{24}.$$

THE POWER RULE

For any real number a and any integers m and n,

$$(a^m)^n = a^{mn}.$$

(To raise a power to a power, multiply the exponents.)

EXAMPLES Simplify. Express the answers using positive exponents.

1. $(3^5)^4 = 3^{5\cdot 4}$ Multiplying exponents
$= 3^{20}$

2. $(2^2)^5 = 2^{2\cdot 5} = 2^{10}$

3. $(y^{-5})^7 = y^{-5\cdot 7} = y^{-35} = \dfrac{1}{y^{35}}$

4. $(x^4)^{-2} = x^{4(-2)} = x^{-8} = \dfrac{1}{x^8}$

5. $(a^{-4})^{-6} = a^{(-4)(-6)} = a^{24}$

Do Exercises 1–4.

Simplify. Express the answers using positive exponents.

1. $(3^4)^5$

2. $(x^{-3})^4$

3. $(y^{-5})^{-3}$

4. $(x^4)^{-8}$

Answers on page A-21

b Raising a Product or a Quotient to a Power

When an expression inside parentheses is raised to a power, the inside expression is the base. Let's compare $2a^3$ and $(2a)^3$:

$2a^3 = 2\cdot a\cdot a\cdot a;$ The base is a.

$(2a)^3 = (2a)(2a)(2a)$ The base is $2a$.

$= (2\cdot 2\cdot 2)(a\cdot a\cdot a)$ Using the associative and commutative laws of multiplication to regroup the factors

$= 2^3a^3$

$= 8a^3.$

We see that $2a^3$ and $(2a)^3$ are *not* equivalent. We also see that we can evaluate the power $(2a)^3$ by raising each factor to the power 3. This leads us to the following rule for raising a product to a power.

RAISING A PRODUCT TO A POWER

For any real numbers a and b and any integer n,

$$(ab)^n = a^n b^n.$$

(To raise a product to the nth power, raise each factor to the nth power.)

EXAMPLES Simplify.

6. $(4x^2)^3 = (4^1x^2)^3$ Since $4 = 4^1$

$= (4^1)^3 \cdot (x^2)^3$ Raising *each* factor to the third power

$= 4^3 \cdot x^6 = 64x^6$

7. $(5x^3y^5z^2)^4 = 5^4(x^3)^4(y^5)^4(z^2)^4$ Raising *each* factor to the fourth power

$= 625x^{12}y^{20}z^8$

8. $(-5x^4y^3)^3 = (-5)^3(x^4)^3(y^3)^3$

$= -125x^{12}y^9$

9. $[(-x)^{25}]^2 = (-x)^{50}$ Using the power rule

$= (-1 \cdot x)^{50}$ Using the property of -1 (Section 1.8)

$= (-1)^{50}x^{50}$

$= 1 \cdot x^{50}$ The product of an even number of negative factors is positive.

$= x^{50}$

10. $(5x^2y^{-2})^3 = 5^3(x^2)^3(y^{-2})^3 = 125x^6y^{-6}$ Be sure to raise *each* factor to the third power.

$$= \frac{125x^6}{y^6}$$

11. $(3x^3y^{-5}z^2)^4 = 3^4(x^3)^4(y^{-5})^4(z^2)^4 = 81x^{12}y^{-20}z^8 = \dfrac{81x^{12}z^8}{y^{20}}$

12. $(-x^4)^{-3} = (-1 \cdot x^4)^{-3} = (-1)^{-3} \cdot x^{4(-3)} = (-1)^{-3} \cdot x^{-12}$

$$= \frac{1}{(-1)^3} \cdot \frac{1}{x^{12}} = \frac{1}{-1} \cdot \frac{1}{x^{12}} = -\frac{1}{x^{12}}$$

13. $(-2x^{-5}y^4)^{-3} = (-2)^{-3}(x^{-5})^{-3}(y^4)^{-3} = \dfrac{1}{(-2)^3} \cdot x^{15} \cdot y^{-12}$

$$= \frac{1}{-8} \cdot x^{15} \cdot \frac{1}{y^{12}} = -\frac{x^{15}}{8y^{12}}$$

Do Exercises 5–11.

Simplify.

5. $(2x^5y^{-3})^4$

6. $(5x^5y^{-6}z^{-3})^2$

7. $[(-x)^{37}]^2$

8. $(3y^{-2}x^{-5}z^8)^3$

9. $(-y^8)^{-3}$

10. $(-2x^4)^{-3}$

11. $(-3x^2y^{-5})^{-3}$

Answers on page A-21

Simplify.

12. $\left(\frac{x^6}{5}\right)^2$

13. $\left(\frac{2t^5}{w^4}\right)^3$

14. $\left(\frac{x^4}{3}\right)^{-2}$

Do this two ways.

Answers on page A-21

There is a similar rule for raising a quotient to a power.

RAISING A QUOTIENT TO A POWER

For any real numbers a and b, $b \neq 0$, and any integer n,

$$\left(\frac{a}{b}\right)^n = \frac{a^n}{b^n}.$$

(To raise a quotient to the nth power, raise both the numerator and the denominator to the nth power.) Also,

$$\left(\frac{a}{b}\right)^{-n} = \left(\frac{b}{a}\right)^n = \frac{b^n}{a^n}, \quad a \neq 0.$$

EXAMPLES Simplify.

14. $\left(\frac{x^2}{4}\right)^3 = \frac{(x^2)^3}{4^3} = \frac{x^6}{64}$

15. $\left(\frac{3a^4}{b^3}\right)^2 = \frac{(3a^4)^2}{(b^3)^2} = \frac{3^2(a^4)^2}{b^{3\cdot 2}} = \frac{9a^8}{b^6}$

16. $\left(\frac{y^3}{5}\right)^{-2} = \frac{(y^3)^{-2}}{5^{-2}} = \frac{y^{-6}}{5^{-2}} = \frac{\frac{1}{y^6}}{\frac{1}{5^2}} = \frac{1}{y^6} \div \frac{1}{5^2} = \frac{1}{y^6} \cdot \frac{5^2}{1} = \frac{25}{y^6}$

Example 16 might also be done as follows:

$$\left(\frac{y^3}{5}\right)^{-2} = \left(\frac{5}{y^3}\right)^2 \qquad \left(\frac{a}{b}\right)^{-n} = \left(\frac{b}{a}\right)^n$$

$$= \frac{5^2}{(y^3)^2} = \frac{25}{y^6}.$$

Do Exercises 12–14.

C Scientific Notation

There are many kinds of symbols, or notation, for numbers. You are already familiar with fraction notation, decimal notation, and percent notation. Now we study another, **scientific notation,** which makes use of exponential notation. Scientific notation is especially useful when calculations involve very large or very small numbers. The following are examples of scientific notation:

①

②

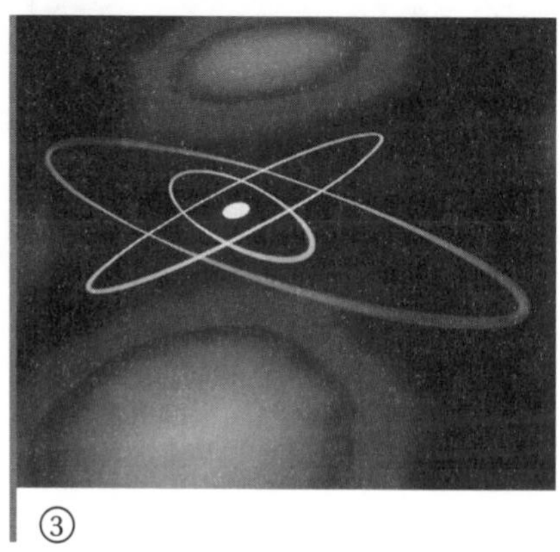
③

①) *Niagara Falls*: On the Canadian side, during the summer the amount of water that spills over the falls in 1 day is about

4.9793×10^{10} gal = 49,793,000,000 gal.

②) *The mass of the earth*: 6.615×10^{21} = 6,615,000,000,000,000,000,000 tons.

③) *The mass of a hydrogen atom*:

1.7×10^{-24} g = 0.0000000000000000000000017 g.

SCIENTIFIC NOTATION

Scientific notation for a number is an expression of the type

$M \times 10^n$,

where n is an integer, M is greater than or equal to 1 and less than 10 ($1 \le M < 10$), and M is expressed in decimal notation. 10^n is also considered to be scientific notation when $M = 1$.

You should try to make conversions to scientific notation mentally as much as possible. Here is a handy mental device.

A positive exponent in scientific notation indicates a large number (greater than or equal to 10) and a negative exponent indicates a small number (between 0 and 1).

EXAMPLES Convert to scientific notation.

7. $78{,}000 = 7.8 \times 10^4$

7.8,000.
4 places

Large number, so the exponent is positive.

8. $0.0000057 = 5.7 \times 10^{-6}$

0.000005.7
6 places

Small number, so the exponent is negative.

Do Exercises 15 and 16 on the following page.

Caution!

Each of the following is *not* scientific notation.

12.46×10^7

This number is greater than 10.

0.347×10^{-5}

This number is less than 1.

Convert to scientific notation.

15. 0.000517

16. 523,000,000

EXAMPLES Convert mentally to decimal notation.

19. $7.893 \times 10^5 = 789{,}300$

7.89300. (5 places)

Positive exponent, so the answer is a large number.

20. $4.7 \times 10^{-8} = 0.000000047$

.00000004.7 (8 places)

Negative exponent, so the answer is a small number.

Do Exercises 17 and 18.

Convert to decimal notation.

17. 6.893×10^{11}

18. 5.67×10^{-5}

d Multiplying and Dividing Using Scientific Notation

MULTIPLYING

Consider the product

$$400 \cdot 2000 = 800{,}000.$$

In scientific notation, this is

$$(4 \times 10^2) \cdot (2 \times 10^3) = (4 \cdot 2)(10^2 \cdot 10^3) = 8 \times 10^5.$$

By applying the commutative and associative laws, we can find this produc by multiplying $4 \cdot 2$, to get 8, and $10^2 \cdot 10^3$, to get 10^5 (we do this by addin the exponents).

EXAMPLE 21 Multiply: $(1.8 \times 10^6) \cdot (2.3 \times 10^{-4})$.

We apply the commutative and associative laws to get

$$\begin{aligned}(1.8 \times 10^6) \cdot (2.3 \times 10^{-4}) &= (1.8 \cdot 2.3) \times (10^6 \cdot 10^{-4}) \\ &= 4.14 \times 10^{6+(-4)} \\ &= 4.14 \times 10^2.\end{aligned}$$

We get 4.14 by multiplying 1.8 and 2.3. We get 10^2 by adding the exponents and -4.

Multiply and write scientific notation for the result.

19. $(1.12 \times 10^{-8})(5 \times 10^{-7})$

20. $(9.1 \times 10^{-17})(8.2 \times 10^3)$

EXAMPLE 22 Multiply: $(3.1 \times 10^5) \cdot (4.5 \times 10^{-3})$.

We have

$$\begin{aligned}(3.1 \times 10^5) \cdot (4.5 \times 10^{-3}) &= (3.1 \times 4.5)(10^5 \cdot 10^{-3}) \\ &= 13.95 \times 10^2 && \text{Not scientific notation. 13.95 is greater than 10.} \\ &= (1.395 \times 10^1) \times 10^2 && \text{Substituting } 1.395 \times 10 \text{ for 13.95} \\ &= 1.395 \times (10^1 \times 10^2) && \text{Associative law} \\ &= 1.395 \times 10^3. && \text{Adding exponents. The answer is now in scientific notation.}\end{aligned}$$

Do Exercises 19 and 20.

Answers on page A-21

DIVIDING

Consider the quotient

$$800{,}000 \div 400 = 2000.$$

In scientific notation, this is

$$(8 \times 10^5) \div (4 \times 10^2) = \frac{8 \times 10^5}{4 \times 10^2} = \frac{8}{4} \times \frac{10^5}{10^2} = 2 \times 10^3.$$

We can find this product by dividing 8 by 4, to get 2, and 10^5 by 10^2, to get 10^3 (we do this by subtracting the exponents.)

EXAMPLE 23 Divide: $(3.41 \times 10^5) \div (1.1 \times 10^{-3})$.

We have

$$\begin{aligned}(3.41 \times 10^5) \div (1.1 \times 10^{-3}) &= \frac{3.41 \times 10^5}{1.1 \times 10^{-3}} = \frac{3.41}{1.1} \times \frac{10^5}{10^{-3}} \\ &= 3.1 \times 10^{5-(-3)} \\ &= 3.1 \times 10^8.\end{aligned}$$

Divide and write scientific notation for the result.

21. $\dfrac{4.2 \times 10^5}{2.1 \times 10^2}$

22. $\dfrac{1.1 \times 10^{-4}}{2.0 \times 10^{-7}}$

Answers on page A-21

CALCULATOR CORNER

1.789E−11
1.789E−11

Scientific Notation To enter a number in scientific notation on a graphing calculator, we first type the decimal portion of the number and then press 2ND EE. (EE is the second operation associated with the , key.) Finally, we type the exponent, which can be at most two digits. For example, to enter 1.789×10^{-11} in scientific notation, we press 1 . 7 8 9 2ND EE (−) 1 1 ENTER. The decimal portion of the number appears before a small E and the exponent follows the E.

NORMAL SCI ENG
FLOAT 0123456789
RADIAN DEGREE
FUNC PAR POL SEQ
CONNECTED DOT
SEQUENTIAL SIMUL
REAL a+bi re^θi
FULL HORIZ G−T

The graphing calculator can be used to perform computations using scientific notation. To find the product in Example 21 and express the result in scientific notation, we first set the calculator in Scientific mode by pressing MODE, positioning the cursor over Sci on the first line, and pressing ENTER. Then we press 2ND QUIT to go to the home screen and enter the computation by pressing 1 . 8 2ND EE 6 × 2 . 3 2ND EE (−) 4 ENTER.

1.8E6*2.3E−4
4.14E2

On a scientific calculator, the answer may appear as follows.

4.14 02

Exercises: Multiply or divide and express the answer in scientific notation.

1. $(3.15 \times 10^7)(4.3 \times 10^{-12})$
2. $(4.76 \times 10^{-5})(1.9 \times 10^{10})$
3. $(8 \times 10^9)(4 \times 10^{-5})$
4. $(4 \times 10^4)(9 \times 10^7)$
5. $\dfrac{4.5 \times 10^6}{1.5 \times 10^{12}}$
6. $\dfrac{6.4 \times 10^{-5}}{1.6 \times 10^{-10}}$
7. $\dfrac{4 \times 10^{-9}}{5 \times 10^{16}}$
8. $\dfrac{9 \times 10^{11}}{3 \times 10^{-2}}$

23. Niagara Falls Water Flow. On the Canadian side, during the summer the amount of water that spills over the falls in 1 min is about

$$1.3088 \times 10^8 \text{ L.}$$

How much water spills over the falls in one day? Express the answer in scientific notation.

Answer on page A-21

Study Tips

WRITING ALL THE STEPS

Take the time to include all the steps when working your homework problems. Doing so will help you organize your thinking and avoid computational errors. If you find a wrong answer, having all the steps allows easier checking of your work. It will also give you complete, step-by-step solutions of the exercises that can be used to study for an exam.

Writing down all the steps and keeping your work organized may also give you a better chance of getting partial credit.

"Success comes before work only in the dictionary."

Anonymous

EXAMPLE 24 Divide: $(6.4 \times 10^{-7}) \div (8.0 \times 10^6)$.

We have

$$\begin{aligned}
(6.4 \times 10^{-7}) \div (8.0 \times 10^6) &= \frac{6.4 \times 10^{-7}}{8.0 \times 10^6} \\
&= \frac{6.4}{8.0} \times \frac{10^{-7}}{10^6} \\
&= 0.8 \times 10^{-7-6} \\
&= 0.8 \times 10^{-13} && \text{Not scientific notation. 0.8 is less than 1.} \\
&= (8.0 \times 10^{-1}) \times 10^{-13} && \text{Substituting } 8.0 \times 10^{-1} \text{ for } 0.8 \\
&= 8.0 \times (10^{-1} \times 10^{-13}) && \text{Associative law} \\
&= 8.0 \times 10^{-14}. && \text{Adding exponents}
\end{aligned}$$

Do Exercises 21 and 22 on the preceding page.

e Applications with Scientific Notation

EXAMPLE 25 *Distance from the Sun to Earth.* Light from the sun traveling at a rate of 300,000 kilometers per second (km/s) reaches Earth in 499 sec. Find the distance, expressed in scientific notation, from the sun to Earth.

The time t that it takes for light to reach Earth from the sun is 4.99×10^2 sec (s). The speed is 3.0×10^5 km/s. Recall that distance can be expressed in terms of speed and time as

$$\text{Distance} = \text{Speed} \cdot \text{Time}$$
$$d = rt.$$

We substitute 3.0×10^5 for r and 4.99×10^2 for t:

$$\begin{aligned}
d &= rt \\
&= (3.0 \times 10^5)(4.99 \times 10^2) && \text{Substituting} \\
&= 14.97 \times 10^7 \\
&= (1.497 \times 10^1) \times 10^7 \\
&= 1.497 \times (10^1 \times 10^7) \\
&= 1.497 \times 10^8 \text{ km.} && \text{Converting to scientific notation}
\end{aligned}$$

Thus the distance from the sun to Earth is 1.497×10^8 km.

Do Exercise 23.

XAMPLE 26 *DNA.* A strand f DNA (deoxyribonucleic acid) about 150 cm long and .3 × 10^{-10} cm wide. How many mes longer is DNA than it is ide?

ource: Human Genome Project Information

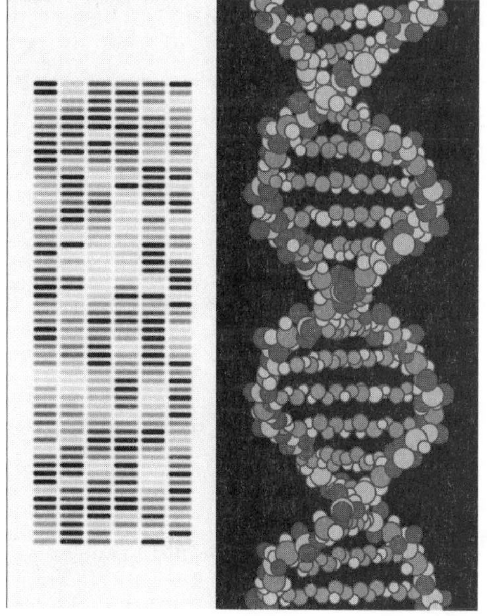

To determine how many times longer (N) DNA is than it is wide, we ivide the length by the width:

$$N = \frac{150}{1.3 \times 10^{-10}} = \frac{150}{1.3} \times \frac{1}{10^{-10}}$$
$$\approx 115.385 \times 10^{10}$$
$$= (1.15385 \times 10^{2}) \times 10^{10}$$
$$= 1.15385 \times 10^{12}.$$

hus the length of DNA is about 1.15385×10^{12} times its width.

o Exercise 24.

The following is a summary of the definitions and rules for exponents at we have considered in this section and the preceding one.

DEFINITIONS AND RULES FOR EXPONENTS

Exponent of 1:	$a^1 = a$
Exponent of 0:	$a^0 = 1, a \neq 0$
Negative exponents:	$a^{-n} = \frac{1}{a^n}, \frac{1}{a^{-n}} = a^n, a \neq 0$
Product Rule:	$a^m \cdot a^n = a^{m+n}$
Quotient Rule:	$\frac{a^m}{a^n} = a^{m-n}, a \neq 0$
Power Rule:	$(a^m)^n = a^{mn}$
Raising a product to a power:	$(ab)^n = a^n b^n$
Raising a quotient to a power:	$\left(\frac{a}{b}\right)^n = \frac{a^n}{b^n}, b \neq 0;$
	$\left(\frac{a}{b}\right)^{-n} = \frac{b^n}{a^n}, b \neq 0, a \neq 0$
Scientific notation:	$M \times 10^n$, or 10^n, where $1 \leq M < 10$

24. **Earth vs. Saturn.** The mass of Earth is about 6×10^{21} metric tons. The mass of Saturn is about 5.7×10^{23} metric tons. About how many times the mass of Earth is the mass of Saturn? Express the answer in scientific notation.

Answer on page A-21

4.2 EXERCISE SET

For Extra Help

MathXL | MyMathLab | InterAct Math | Math Tutor Center | Digital Video Tutor CD 3 Videotape 5 | Student Solutions Manual

a, **b** Simplify.

1. $(2^3)^2$

2. $(5^2)^4$

3. $(5^2)^{-3}$

4. $(7^{-3})^5$

5. $(x^{-3})^{-4}$

6. $(a^{-5})^{-6}$

7. $(a^{-2})^9$

8. $(x^{-5})^6$

9. $(t^{-3})^{-6}$

10. $(a^{-4})^{-7}$

11. $(t^4)^{-3}$

12. $(t^5)^{-2}$

13. $(x^{-2})^{-4}$

14. $(t^{-6})^{-5}$

15. $(ab)^3$

16. $(xy)^2$

17. $(ab)^{-3}$

18. $(xy)^{-6}$

19. $(mn^2)^{-3}$

20. $(x^3y)^{-2}$

21. $(4x^3)^2$

22. $4(x^3)^2$

23. $(3x^{-4})^2$

24. $(2a^{-5})^3$

25. $(x^4y^5)^{-3}$

26. $(t^5x^3)^{-4}$

27. $(x^{-6}y^{-2})^{-4}$

28. $(x^{-2}y^{-7})^{-5}$

29. $(a^{-2}b^7)^{-5}$

30. $(q^5r^{-1})^{-3}$

31. $(5r^{-4}t^3)^2$

32. $(4x^5y^{-6})^3$

33. $(a^{-5}b^7c^{-2})^3$

34. $(x^{-4}y^{-2}z^9)^2$

35. $(3x^3y^{-8}z^{-3})^2$

36. $(2a^2y^{-4}z^{-5})^3$

37. $(-4x^3y^{-2})^2$

38. $(-8x^3y^{-2})^3$

39. $(-a^{-3}b^{-2})^{-4}$

40. $(-p^{-4}q^{-3})^{-2}$

41. $\left(\frac{y^3}{2}\right)^2$

42. $\left(\frac{a^5}{3}\right)^3$

43. $\left(\frac{a^2}{b^3}\right)^4$

44. $\left(\frac{x^3}{y^4}\right)^5$

45. $\left(\frac{y^2}{2}\right)^{-3}$

46. $\left(\frac{a^4}{3}\right)^{-2}$

47. $\left(\frac{7}{x^{-3}}\right)^2$

48. $\left(\frac{3}{a^{-2}}\right)^3$

49. $\left(\frac{x^2y}{z}\right)^3$

50. $\left(\frac{m}{n^4p}\right)^3$

51. $\left(\frac{a^2b}{cd^3}\right)^{-2}$

52. $\left(\frac{2a^2}{3b^4}\right)^{-3}$

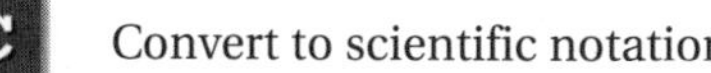

Convert to scientific notation.

3. 28,000,000,000

54. 4,900,000,000,000

55. 907,000,000,000,000,000

56. 168,000,000,000,000

7. 0.00000304

58. 0.000000000865

59. 0.000000018

60. 0.00000000002

1. 100,000,000,000

62. 0.0000001

nvert the number in the sentence to scientific notation.

3. *Population of the United States.* As of July 2005, the population of the United States was about 296 million (1 million $= 10^6$).

Source: U.S. Bureau of the Census

64. *NASCAR.* Total revenue of NASCAR (National Association of Stock Car Automobile Racing) is expected to be $3423 million by 2006.

Source: NASCAR

5. *State Lottery.* Typically, the probability of winning a state lottery is about 1/10,000,000.

66. *Cancer Death Rate.* In Michigan, the death rate due to cancer is about 127.1/1000.

Source: AARP

nvert to decimal notation.

7. 8.74×10^7

68. 1.85×10^8

69. 5.704×10^{-8}

70. 8.043×10^{-4}

1. 10^7

72. 10^6

73. 10^{-5}

74. 10^{-8}

Multiply or divide and write scientific notation for the result.

5. $(3 \times 10^4)(2 \times 10^5)$

76. $(3.9 \times 10^8)(8.4 \times 10^{-3})$

77. $(5.2 \times 10^5)(6.5 \times 10^{-2})$

8. $(7.1 \times 10^{-7})(8.6 \times 10^{-5})$

79. $(9.9 \times 10^{-6})(8.23 \times 10^{-8})$

80. $(1.123 \times 10^4) \times 10^{-9}$

81. $\dfrac{8.5 \times 10^{8}}{3.4 \times 10^{-5}}$

82. $\dfrac{5.6 \times 10^{-2}}{2.5 \times 10^{5}}$

83. $(3.0 \times 10^{6}) \div (6.0 \times 10^{9})$

84. $(1.5 \times 10^{-3}) \div (1.6 \times 10^{-6})$

85. $\dfrac{7.5 \times 10^{-9}}{2.5 \times 10^{12}}$

86. $\dfrac{4.0 \times 10^{-3}}{8.0 \times 10^{20}}$

Solve.

87. *River Discharge.* The average discharge at the mouths of the Amazon River is 4,200,000 cubic feet per second. How much water is discharged from the Amazon River in 1 yr? Express the answer in scientific notation.

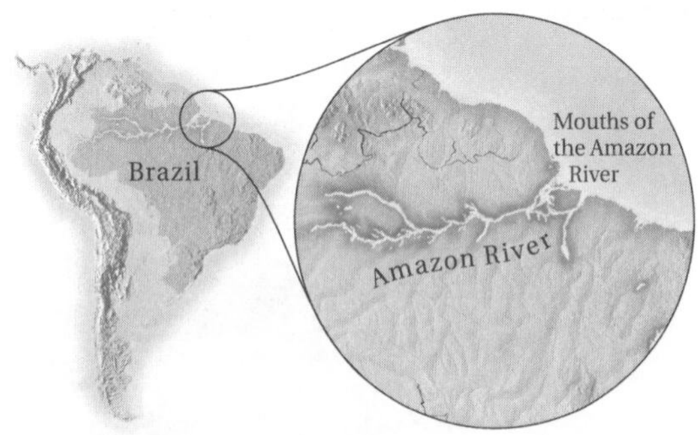

88. *Computers.* A gigabyte is a measure of a computer's storage capacity. One gigabyte holds about one billion bytes of information. If a firm's computer network contains 2500 gigabytes of memory, how many bytes are in the network? Express the answer in scientific notation.

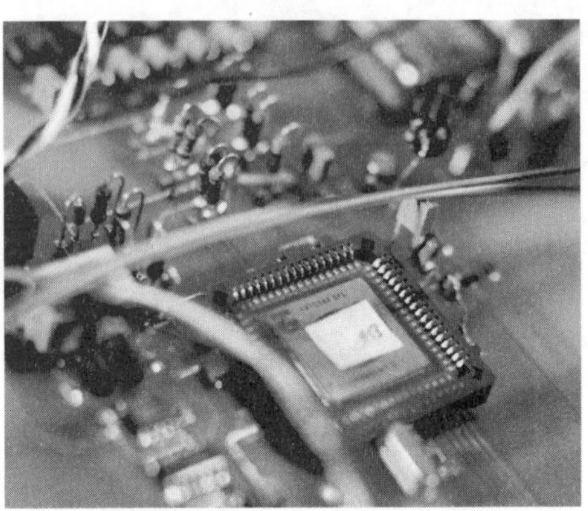

89. *Earth vs. Jupiter.* The mass of Earth is about 6×10^{21} metric tons. The mass of Jupiter is about 1.908×10^{24} metric tons. About how many times the mass of Earth is the mass of Jupiter? Express the answer in scientific notation.

90. *Water Contamination.* In the United States, 200 million gal of used motor oil is improperly disposed of each year. One gallon of used oil can contaminate one million gallons of drinking water. How many gallons of drinking water can 200 million gallons of oil contaminate? Express the answer in scientific notation.

Source: *The Macmillan Visual Almanac*

91. *Stars.* It is estimated that there are 10 billion trillion stars in the known universe. Express the number of stars in scientific notation (1 billion $= 10^9$; 1 trillion $= 10^{12}$).

92. *Closest Star.* Excluding the sun, the closest star to Earth is Proxima Centauri, which is 4.3 light-years away (one light-year $= 5.88 \times 10^{12}$ mi). How far, in miles, is Proxima Centauri from Earth? Express the answer in scientific notation.

93. *Earth vs. Sun.* The mass of Earth is about 6×10^{21} metric tons. The mass of the sun is about 1.998×10^{27} metric tons. About how many times the mass of Earth is the mass of the sun? Express the answer in scientific notation.

94. *Red Light.* The wavelength of light is given by the velocity divided by the frequency. The velocity of red light is 300,000,000 m/sec, and its frequency is 400,000,000,000,000 cycles per second. What is the wavelength of red light? Express the answer in scientific notation.

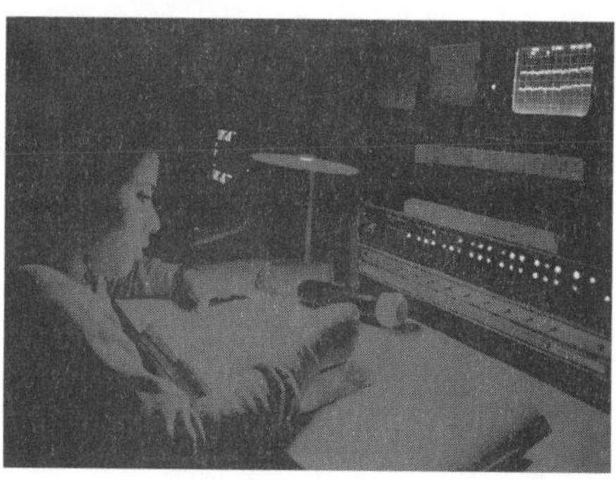

Space Travel. Use the following information for Exercises 95 and 96.

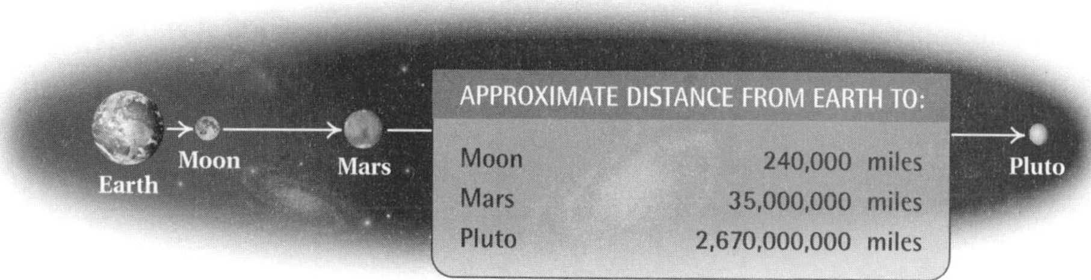

APPROXIMATE DISTANCE FROM EARTH TO:	
Moon	240,000 miles
Mars	35,000,000 miles
Pluto	2,670,000,000 miles

95. *Time to Reach Mars.* Suppose that it takes about 3 days for a space vehicle to travel from Earth to the moon. About how long would it take the same space vehicle traveling at the same speed to reach Mars? Express the answer in scientific notation.

96. *Time to Reach Pluto.* Suppose that it takes about 3 days for a space vehicle to travel from Earth to the moon. About how long would it take the same space vehicle traveling at the same speed to reach Pluto? Express the answer in scientific notation.

97. D_W Explain in your own words when exponents should be added and when they should be multiplied.

98. D_W Without performing actual computations, explain why 3^{-29} is smaller than 2^{-29}.

SKILL MAINTENANCE

Factor. [1.7d]

99. $9x - 36$

100. $4x - 2y + 16$

101. $3s + 3t + 24$

102. $-7x - 14$

Solve. [2.3b]

103. $2x - 4 - 5x + 8 = x - 3$

104. $8x + 7 - 9x = 12 - 6x + 5$

Solve. [2.3c]

105. $8(2x + 3) - 2(x - 5) = 10$

106. $4(x - 3) + 5 = 6(x + 2) - 8$

Graph. [3.1d], [3.2a]

107. $y = x - 5$

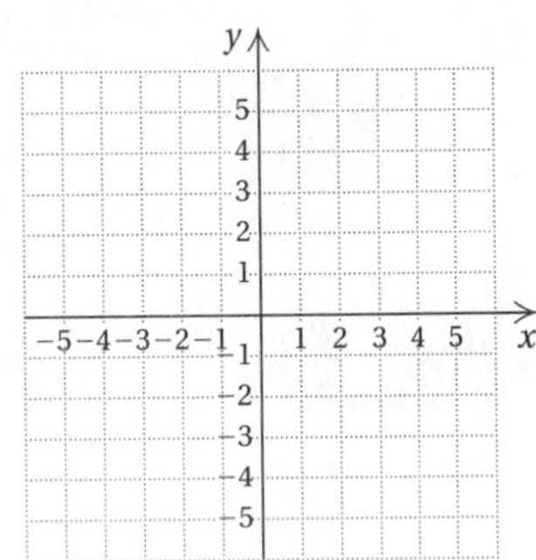

108. $2x + y = 8$

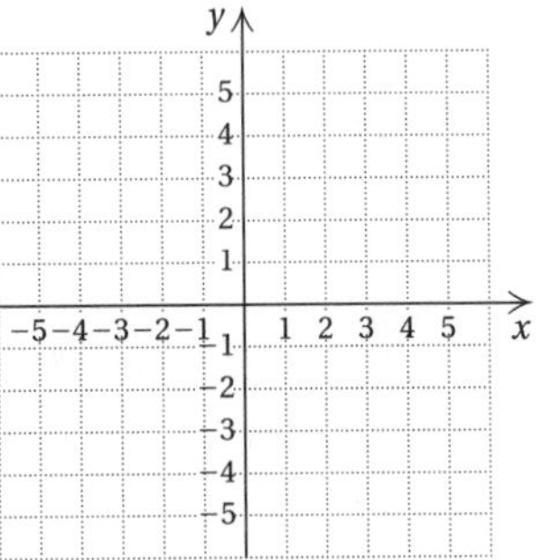

SYNTHESIS

109. Carry out the indicated operations. Express the result in scientific notation.

$$\frac{(5.2 \times 10^6)(6.1 \times 10^{-11})}{1.28 \times 10^{-3}}$$

110. Find the reciprocal and express it in scientific notation.

$$6.25 \times 10^{-3}$$

Simplify.

111. $\dfrac{(5^{12})^2}{5^{25}}$

112. $\dfrac{a^{22}}{(a^2)^{11}}$

113. $\dfrac{(3^5)^4}{3^5 \cdot 3^4}$

114. $\left(\dfrac{5x^{-2}}{3y^{-2}z}\right)^0$

115. $\dfrac{49^{18}}{7^{35}}$

116. $\left(\dfrac{1}{a}\right)^{-n}$

117. $\dfrac{(0.4)^5}{[(0.4^3]^2}$

118. $\left(\dfrac{4a^3b^{-2}}{5c^{-3}}\right)^1$

Determine whether each of the following is true for all pairs of integers m and n and all positive numbers x and y.

119. $x^m \cdot y^n = (xy)^{mn}$

120. $x^m \cdot y^m = (xy)^{2m}$

121. $(x - y)^m = x^m - y^m$

122. $-x^m = (-x)^m$

123. $(-x)^{2m} = x^{2m}$

124. $x^{-m} = \dfrac{-1}{x^m}$

4.3 INTRODUCTION TO POLYNOMIALS

Objectives

- **a** Evaluate a polynomial for a given value of the variable.
- **b** Identify the terms of a polynomial.
- **c** Identify the like terms of a polynomial.
- **d** Identify the coefficients of a polynomial.
- **e** Collect the like terms of a polynomial.
- **f** Arrange a polynomial in descending order, or collect the like terms and then arrange in descending order.
- **g** Identify the degree of each term of a polynomial and the degree of the polynomial.
- **h** Identify the missing terms of a polynomial.
- **i** Classify a polynomial as a monomial, binomial, trinomial, or none of these.

We have already learned to evaluate and to manipulate certain kinds ̈ algebraic expressions. We will now consider algebraic expressions called ›lynomials.

The following are examples of *monomials in one variable*:

$$3x^2, \quad 2x, \quad -5, \quad 37p^4, \quad 0.$$

ıch expression is a constant or a constant times some variable to a nonnega- ›e integer power.

MONOMIAL

A **monomial** is an expression of the type ax^n, where a is a real-number constant and n is a nonnegative integer.

Algebraic expressions like the following are **polynomials:**

$$\tfrac{3}{4}y^5, \quad -2, \quad 5y + 3, \quad 3x^2 + 2x - 5, \quad -7a^3 + \tfrac{1}{2}a, \quad 6x, \quad 37p^4, \quad x, \quad 0.$$

POLYNOMIAL

A **polynomial** is a monomial or a combination of sums and/or differences of monomials.

The following algebraic expressions are *not* polynomials:

$$\textbf{(1)}\ \frac{x+3}{x-4}, \qquad \textbf{(2)}\ 5x^3 - 2x^2 + \frac{1}{x}, \qquad \textbf{(3)}\ \frac{1}{x^3 - 2}.$$

pressions (1) and (3) are not polynomials because they represent quotients, ›t sums or differences. Expression (2) is not a polynomial because

$$\frac{1}{x} = x^{-1},$$

d this is not a monomial because the exponent is negative.

› *Exercise 1.*

1. Write three polynomials.

Evaluating Polynomials and Applications

ıen we replace the variable in a polynomial with a number, the polynomial ən represents a number called a **value** of the polynomial. Finding that num- r, or value, is called **evaluating the polynomial.** We evaluate a polynomial ing the rules for order of operations (Section 1.8).

AMPLE 1 Evaluate the polynomial when $x = 2$.

$$3x + 5 = 3 \cdot 2 + 5 = 6 + 5 = 11$$

b) $$2x^2 - 7x + 3 = 2 \cdot 2^2 - 7 \cdot 2 + 3 = 2 \cdot 4 - 7 \cdot 2 + 3 = 8 - 14 + 3 = -3$$

Answer on page A-22

Evaluate the polynomial when $x = 3$.

2. $-4x - 7$

3. $-5x^3 + 7x + 10$

Evaluate the polynomial when $x = -5$.

4. $5x + 7$

5. $2x^2 + 5x - 4$

6. Use *only* the graph shown in Example 3 to evaluate the polynomial $2x - 2$ when $x = 4$ and when $x = -1$.

7. Referring to Example 4, determine the total number of games to be played in a league of 12 teams.

8. **Perimeter of a Baseball Diamond.** The perimeter P of a square of side x is given by the polynomial equation $P = 4x$.

A baseball diamond is a square 90 ft on a side. Find the perimeter of a baseball diamond.

Answers on page A-22

EXAMPLE 2 Evaluate the polynomial when $x = -4$.

a) $2 - x^3 = 2 - (-4)^3 = 2 - (-64)$
$= 2 + 64$
$= 66$

b) $-x^2 - 3x + 1 = -(-4)^2 - 3(-4) + 1$
$= -16 + 12 + 1$
$= -3$.

Do Exercises 2–5.

AC *ALGEBRAIC–GRAPHICAL CONNECTION*

An equation like $y = 2x - 2$, which has a polynomial on one side and y on the other, is called a **polynomial equation.** Here and in many places throughout the book, we will connect graphs to related concepts.

Recall from Chapter 3 that in order to plot points before graphing an equation, we choose values for x and compute the corresponding y-values. If the equation has y on one side and a polynomial involving x on the other, then determining y is the same as evaluating the polynomial. Once the graph of such an equation has been drawn, we can evaluate the polynomial for a given x-value by finding the y-value that is paired with it on the graph.

EXAMPLE 3 Use *only* the given graph of $y = 2x - 2$ to evaluate the polynomial $2x - 2$ when $x = 3$.

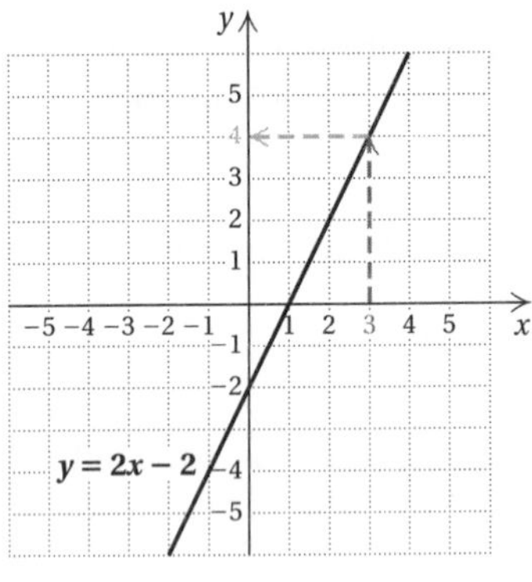

First, we locate 3 on the x-axis. From there we move vertically to the graph of the equation and then horizontally to the y-axis. There we locate the y-value that is paired with 3. Although our drawing may not be precise, it appears that the y-value 4 is paired with 3. Thus the value of $2x - 2$ is 4 when $x = 3$.

Do Exercise 6.

Polynomial equations can be used to model many real-world situatio

EXAMPLE 4 *Games in a Sports League.* In a sports league of x teams which each team plays every other team twice, the total number of gam N to be played is given by the polynomial equation

$$N = x^2 - x.$$

A women's slow-pitch softball league has 10 teams. What is the total numb of games to be played?

We evaluate the polynomial when $x = 10$:

$$N = x^2 - x = 10^2 - 10 = 100 - 10 = 90.$$

The league plays 90 games.

Do Exercises 7 and 8.

XAMPLE 5 *Medical Dosage.* The concentration C, in parts per million, f a certain antibiotic in the bloodstream after t hours is given by the polyomial equation

$$C = -0.05t^2 + 2t + 2.$$

nd the concentration after 2 hr.

To find the concentration after 2 hr, we evaluate the polynomial when $= 2$:

$$\begin{aligned} C &= -0.05t^2 + 2t + 2 \\ &= -0.05(2)^2 + 2(2) + 2 \\ &= -0.05(4) + 2(2) + 2 \\ &= -0.2 + 4 + 2 \\ &= -0.2 + 6 \\ &= 5.8. \end{aligned}$$

Carrying out the calculation using the rules for order of operations

ne concentration after 2 hr is 5.8 parts per million.

9. Medical Dosage.

a) Referring to Example 5, determine the concentration after 3 hr by evaluating the polynomial when $t = 3$.

b) Use *only* the graph showing medical dosage to check the value found in part (a).

LGEBRAIC–GRAPHICAL CONNECTION

ne polynomial equation in Example 5 can be graphed if we evaluate the olynomial for several values of t. We list the values in a table and show e graph below. Note that the concentration peaks at the 20-hr mark and ter slightly more than 40 hr, the concentration is 0. Since neither time or concentration can be negative, our graph uses only the first quadrant.

t	C $C = -0.05t^2 + 2t + 2$
0	2
2	5.8 ← Example 5
10	17
20	22
30	17

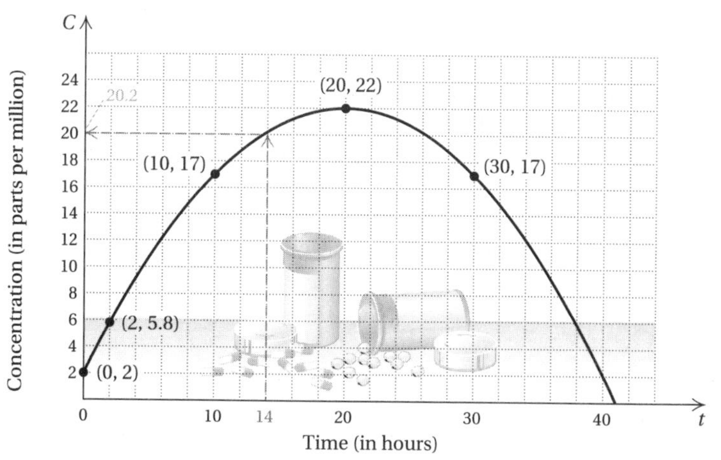

Exercises 9 and 10.

10. Medical Dosage. Referring to Example 5, use *only* the graph showing medical dosage to estimate the value of the polynomial when $t = 26$.

Answers on page A-22

CALCULATOR CORNER

Evaluating Polynomials (*Note*: If you set your graphing calculator in Sci (scientific) mode to do the exercises in Section 4.2, return it to Normal mode now.)

There are several ways to evaluate polynomials on a graphing calculator. One method uses a table. To evaluate the polynomial in Example 2(b), $-x^2 - 3x + 1$, when $x = -4$, we first enter $y_1 = -x^2 - 3x + 1$ on the equation-editor screen. Then we set up a table in ASK mode (see p. 157) and enter the value -4 for x. We see that when $x = -4$, the value of Y1 is -3. This is the value of the polynomial when $x = -4$.

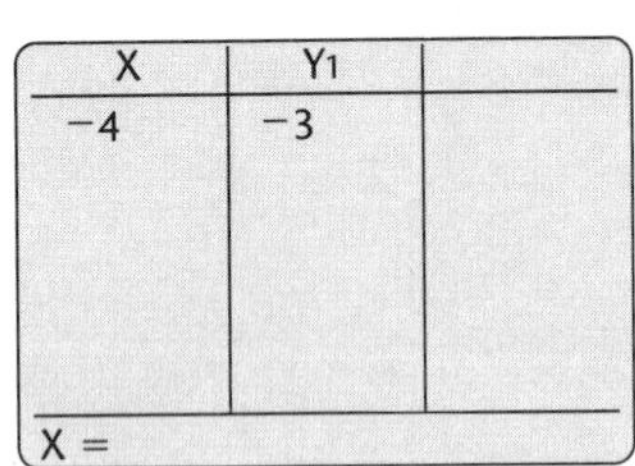

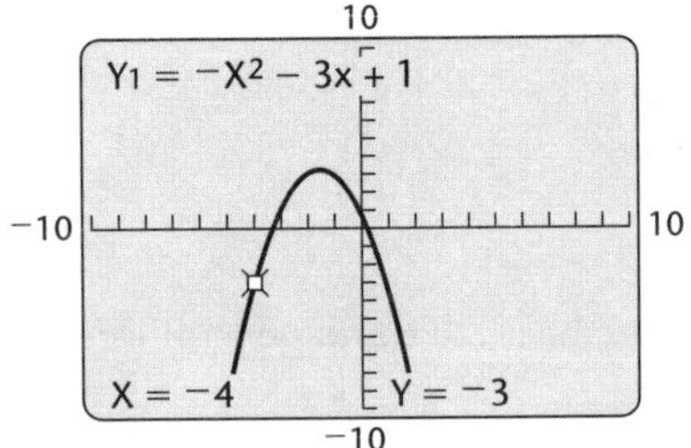

We can also use the Value feature from the CALC menu to evaluate this polynomial. First, we graph $y_1 = -x^2 - 3x + 1$ in a window that includes the x-value -4. We will use the standard window (see p. 235). Then we press 2ND CALC 1 or 2ND CALC ENTER to access the CALC menu and select item 1, Value. Now we supply the desired x-value by pressing (-) 4. We then press ENTER to see X = −4, Y = −3 at the bottom of the screen. Thus, when $x = -4$, the value of $-x^2 - 3x + 1$ is -3.

Exercises: Use the Value feature to evaluate the polynomial for the given values of x.

1. $-x^2 - 3x + 1$, when $x = -2$, $x = -0.5$, and $x = 4$
2. $3x^2 - 5x + 2$, when $x = -3$, $x = 1$, and $x = 2.6$
3. $2x^2 - x - 8$, when $x = -3$, $x = 1.8$, and $x = 3$
4. $-5x^2 + 3x + 7$, when $x = -1$, $x = 2$, and $x = 3.4$

b Identifying Terms

As we saw in Section 1.4, subtractions can be rewritten as additions. For any polynomial that has some subtractions, we can find an equivalent polynomial using only additions.

EXAMPLES Find an equivalent polynomial using only additions.

6. $-5x^2 - x = -5x^2 + (-x)$
7. $4x^5 - 2x^6 + 4x - 7 = 4x^5 + (-2x^6) + 4x + (-7)$

Do Exercises 11 and 12.

When a polynomial has only additions, the monomials being added are called **terms.** In Example 6, the terms are $-5x^2$ and $-x$. In Example 7, the terms are $4x^5$, $-2x^6$, $4x$, and -7.

Find an equivalent polynomial using only additions.

11. $-9x^3 - 4x^5$

12. $-2y^3 + 3y^7 - 7y - 9$

Answers on page A-22

XAMPLE 8 Identify the terms of the polynomial

$$4x^7 + 3x + 12 + 8x^3 + 5x.$$

erms: $4x^7$, $3x$, 12, $8x^3$, and $5x$.

If there are subtractions, you can *think* of them as additions without writing.

XAMPLE 9 Identify the terms of the polynomial

$$3t^4 - 5t^6 - 4t + 2.$$

erms: $3t^4$, $-5t^6$, $-4t$, and 2.

o *Exercises 13 and 14.*

Like Terms

hen terms have the same variable and the variable is raised to the same ower, we say that they are **like terms.**

XAMPLES Identify the like terms in the polynomials.

. $4x^3 + 5x - 4x^2 + 2x^3 + x^2$

Like terms: $4x^3$ and $2x^3$ Same variable and exponent

Like terms: $-4x^2$ and x^2 Same variable and exponent

. $6 - 3a^2 - 8 - a - 5a$

Like terms: 6 and -8 Constant terms are like terms because $6 = 6x^0$ and $-8 = -8x^0$.

Like terms: $-a$ and $-5a$

Exercises 15–17.

Coefficients

e coefficient of the term $5x^3$ is 5. In the following polynomial, the color mbers are the **coefficients,** 3, -2, 5, and 4:

$$3x^5 - 2x^3 + 5x + 4.$$

AMPLE 12 Identify the coefficient of each term in the polynomial

$$3x^4 - 4x^3 + \frac{1}{2}x^2 + x - 8.$$

The coefficient of the first term is 3.

The coefficient of the second term is -4.

The coefficient of the third term is $\frac{1}{2}$.

The coefficient of the fourth term is 1.

The coefficient of the fifth term is -8.

Exercise 18.

Identify the terms of the polynomial.

13. $3x^2 + 6x + \frac{1}{2}$

14. $-4y^5 + 7y^2 - 3y - 2$

Identify the like terms in the polynomial.

15. $4x^3 - x^3 + 2$

16. $4t^4 - 9t^3 - 7t^4 + 10t^3$

17. $5x^2 + 3x - 10 + 7x^2 - 8x + 11$

18. Identify the coefficient of each term in the polynomial

$$2x^4 - 7x^3 - 8.5x^2 + 10x - 4.$$

Answers on page A-22

Collect like terms.

19. $3x^2 + 5x^2$

20. $4x^3 - 2x^3 + 2 + 5$

21. $\frac{1}{2}x^5 - \frac{3}{4}x^5 + 4x^2 - 2x^2$

22. $24 - 4x^3 - 24$

23. $5x^3 - 8x^5 + 8x^5$

24. $-2x^4 + 16 + 2x^4 + 9 - 3x^5$

Collect like terms.

25. $7x - x$

26. $5x^3 - x^3 + 4$

27. $\frac{3}{4}x^3 + 4x^2 - x^3 + 7$

28. $\frac{4}{5}x^4 - x^4 + x^5 - \frac{1}{5} - \frac{1}{4}x^4 + 10$

Answers on page A-22

e Collecting Like Terms

We can often simplify polynomials by **collecting like terms,** or **combini[ng] like terms.** To do this, we use the distributive laws. We factor out the variab[le] expression and add or subtract the coefficients. We try to do this mentally [as] much as possible.

EXAMPLES Collect like terms.

13. $2x^3 - 6x^3 = (2 - 6)x^3$ Using a distributive law

$= -4x^3$

14. $5x^2 + 7 + 4x^4 + 2x^2 - 11 - 2x^4 = (5 + 2)x^2 + (4 - 2)x^4 + (7 - 11)$

$= 7x^2 + 2x^4 - 4$

Note that using the distributive laws in this manner allows us to colle[ct] like terms by adding or subtracting the coefficients. Often the middle step [is] omitted and we add or subtract mentally, writing just the answer. In collec[t]ing like terms, we may get 0.

EXAMPLE 15 Collect like terms: $3x^5 + 2x^2 - 3x^5 + 8$.

$$3x^5 + 2x^2 - 3x^5 + 8 = (3 - 3)x^5 + 2x^2 + 8$$
$$= 0x^5 + 2x^2 + 8$$
$$= 2x^2 + 8$$

Do Exercises 19–24.

Expressing a term like x^2 by showing 1 as a factor, $1 \cdot x^2$, may make [it] easier to understand how to factor or collect like terms.

EXAMPLES Collect like terms.

16. $5x^2 + x^2 = 5x^2 + 1x^2$ Replacing x^2 with $1x^2$

$= (5 + 1)x^2$ Using a distributive law

$= 6x^2$

17. $5x^8 - 6x^5 - x^8 = 5x^8 - 6x^5 - 1x^8$ $x^8 = 1x^8$

$= (5 - 1)x^8 - 6x^5$

$= 4x^8 - 6x^5$

18. $\frac{2}{3}x^4 - x^3 - \frac{1}{6}x^4 + \frac{2}{5}x^3 - \frac{3}{10}x^3 = \left(\frac{2}{3} - \frac{1}{6}\right)x^4 + \left(-1 + \frac{2}{5} - \frac{3}{10}\right)x^3$ $-x^3 = -1$[x^3]

$= \left(\frac{4}{6} - \frac{1}{6}\right)x^4 + \left(-\frac{10}{10} + \frac{4}{10} - \frac{3}{10}\right)x^3$

$= \frac{3}{6}x^4 - \frac{9}{10}x^3$

$= \frac{1}{2}x^4 - \frac{9}{10}x^3$

Do Exercises 25–28.

f Descending and Ascending Order

Note in the following polynomial that the exponents decrease from left [to] right. We say that the polynomial is arranged in **descending order:**

$$2x^4 - 8x^3 + 5x^2 - x + 3.$$

The term with the largest exponent is first. The term with the next largest [ex]ponent is second, and so on. The associative and commutative laws allow [us] to arrange the terms of a polynomial in descending order.

XAMPLES Arrange the polynomial in descending order.

9. $6x^5 + 4x^7 + x^2 + 2x^3 = 4x^7 + 6x^5 + 2x^3 + x^2$

0. $\frac{2}{3} + 4x^5 - 8x^2 + 5x - 3x^3 = 4x^5 - 3x^3 - 8x^2 + 5x + \frac{2}{3}$

o Exercises 29–31.

XAMPLE 21 Collect like terms and then arrange in descending order:

$2x^2 - 4x^3 + 3 - x^2 - 2x^3$.

$2x^2 - 4x^3 + 3 - x^2 - 2x^3 = x^2 - 6x^3 + 3$ Collecting like terms

$= -6x^3 + x^2 + 3$ Arranging in descending order

o Exercises 32 and 33.

We usually arrange polynomials in descending order, but not always. The pposite order is called **ascending order.** Generally, if an exercise is written in certain order, we give the answer in that same order.

g Degrees

he **degree** of a term is the exponent of the variable. The degree of the term $\cdot 5x^3$ is 3.

XAMPLE 22 Identify the degree of each term of $8x^4 - 3x + 7$.

The degree of $8x^4$ is 4.

The degree of $-3x$ is 1. Recall that $x = x^1$.

The degree of 7 is 0. Think of 7 as $7x^0$. Recall that $x^0 = 1$.

The **degree of a polynomial** is the largest of the degrees of the terms, unss it is the polynomial 0. The polynomial 0 is a special case. We agree that it as *no* degree either as a term or as a polynomial. This is because we can exress 0 as $0 = 0x^5 = 0x^7$, and so on, using any exponent we wish.

XAMPLE 23 Identify the degree of the polynomial $5x^3 - 6x^4 + 7$.

$5x^3 - 6x^4 + 7$. The largest exponent is 4.

he degree of the polynomial is 4.

o Exercises 34 and 35.

Let's summarize the terminology that we have learned, using the olynomial $3x^4 - 8x^3 + 5x^2 + 7x - 6$.

TERM	COEFFICIENT	DEGREE OF THE TERM	DEGREE OF THE POLYNOMIAL
$3x^4$	3	4	
$-8x^3$	−8	3	
$5x^2$	5	2	4
$7x$	7	1	
−6	−6	0	

Arrange the polynomial in descending order.

29. $x + 3x^5 + 4x^3 + 5x^2 + 6x^7 - 2x^4$

30. $4x^2 - 3 + 7x^5 + 2x^3 - 5x^4$

31. $-14 + 7t^2 - 10t^5 + 14t^7$

Collect like terms and then arrange in descending order.

32. $3x^2 - 2x + 3 - 5x^2 - 1 - x$

33. $-x + \frac{1}{2} + 14x^4 - 7x - 1 - 4x^4$

Identify the degree of each term and the degree of the polynomial.

34. $-6x^4 + 8x^2 - 2x + 9$

35. $4 - x^3 + \frac{1}{2}x^6 - x^5$

Answers on page A-22

Identify the missing terms in the polynomial.

36. $2x^3 + 4x^2 - 2$

37. $-3x^4$

38. $x^3 + 1$

39. $x^4 - x^2 + 3x + 0.25$

Write the polynomial in two ways: with its missing terms and by leaving space for them.

40. $2x^3 + 4x^2 - 2$

41. $a^4 + 10$

Classify the polynomial as a monomial, binomial, trinomial, or none of these.

42. $5x^4$

43. $4x^3 - 3x^2 + 4x + 2$

44. $3x^2 + x$

45. $3x^2 + 2x - 4$

Answers on page A-22

h Missing Terms

If a coefficient is 0, we generally do not write the term. We say that we have missing term.

EXAMPLE 24 Identify the missing terms in the polynomial

$$8x^5 - 2x^3 + 5x^2 + 7x + 8.$$

There is no term with x^4. We say that the x^4-term is missing.

Do Exercises 36–39.

For certain skills or manipulations, we can write missing terms with zer coefficients or leave space.

EXAMPLE 25 Write the polynomial $x^4 - 6x^3 + 2x - 1$ in two ways: wi its missing terms and by leaving space for them.

a) $x^4 - 6x^3 + 2x - 1 = x^4 - 6x^3 + 0x^2 + 2x - 1$ Writing with the missing x^2-term

b) $x^4 - 6x^3 + 2x - 1 = x^4 - 6x^3 \qquad + 2x - 1$ Leaving space for the missing x^2-term

EXAMPLE 26 Write the polynomial $y^5 - 1$ in two ways: with its missir terms and by leaving space for them.

a) $y^5 - 1 = y^5 + 0y^4 + 0y^3 + 0y^2 + 0y - 1$

b) $y^5 - 1 = y^5 \qquad\qquad - 1$

Do Exercises 40 and 41.

i Classifying Polynomials

Polynomials with just one term are called **monomials.** Polynomials with ju two terms are called **binomials.** Those with just three terms are called **trinomi als.** Those with more than three terms are generally not specified with a nam

EXAMPLE 27

MONOMIALS	BINOMIALS	TRINOMIALS	NONE OF THE
$4x^2$	$2x + 4$	$3x^3 + 4x + 7$	$4x^3 - 5x^2 + x - 8$
9	$3x^5 + 6x$	$6x^7 - 7x^2 + 4$	$z^5 + 2z^4 - z^3 + 7z +$
$-23x^{19}$	$-9x^7 - 6$	$4x^2 - 6x - \frac{1}{2}$	$4x^6 - 3x^5 + x^4 - x^3$

Do Exercises 42–45.

4.3 EXERCISE SET

For Extra Help

MathXL | MyMathLab | InterAct Math | Math Tutor Center | Digital Video Tutor CD 3 Videotape 5 | Student's Solutions Manual

a Evaluate the polynomial when $x = 4$ and when $x = -1$.

1. $-5x + 2$

2. $-8x + 1$

3. $2x^2 - 5x + 7$

4. $3x^2 + x - 7$

5. $x^3 - 5x^2 + x$

6. $7 - x + 3x^2$

Evaluate the polynomial when $x = -2$ and when $x = 0$.

7. $\frac{1}{3}x + 5$

8. $8 - \frac{1}{4}x$

9. $x^2 - 2x + 1$

10. $5x + 6 - x^2$

11. $-3x^3 + 7x^2 - 3x - 2$

12. $-2x^3 + 5x^2 - 4x + 3$

13. *Skydiving.* During the first 13 sec of a jump, the number of feet S that a skydiver falls in t seconds can be approximated by the polynomial equation

$$S = 11.12t^2.$$

Approximately how far has a skydiver fallen 10 sec after having jumped from a plane?

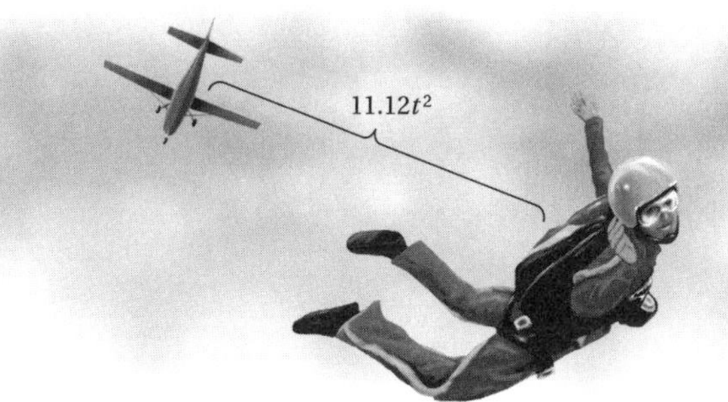

14. *Skydiving.* For jumps that exceed 13 sec, the polynomial equation

$$S = 173t - 369$$

can be used to approximate the distance S, in feet, that a skydiver has fallen in t seconds. Approximately how far has a skydiver fallen 20 sec after having jumped from a plane?

15. *Electricity Consumption.* The net consumption of electricity in China can be approximated by the polynomial equation

$$E = 90.28t + 1138.34,$$

where E is the consumption of electricity, in billions of kilowatt-hours, and t is the number of years since 2001—that is, $t = 0$ corresponds to 2001, $t = 9$ corresponds to 2010, and so on.

Source: Energy Information Administration (EIA), International Energy Outlook 2004

a) Approximate the consumption of electricity, in billions of kilowatt-hours, in 2001, 2005, 2010, 2015, and 2025.

b) Check the results of part (a) using the graph below.

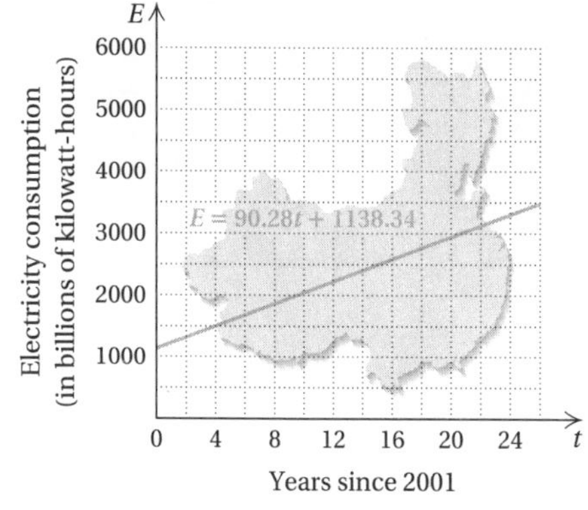

16. *Electricity Consumption.* The net consumption of electricity in the United States can be approximated by the polynomial equation

$$E = 75.72t + 3378.11,$$

where E is the consumption of electricity, in billions of kilowatt-hours, and t is the number of years since 2001—that is, $t = 0$ corresponds to 2001, $t = 9$ corresponds to 2010, and so on.

Source: Energy Information Administration (EIA), International Energy Outlook 2004

a) Approximate the consumption of electricity, in billions of kilowatt-hours, in 2001, 2005, 2010, 2015, and 2025.

b) Check the results of part (a) using the graph below.

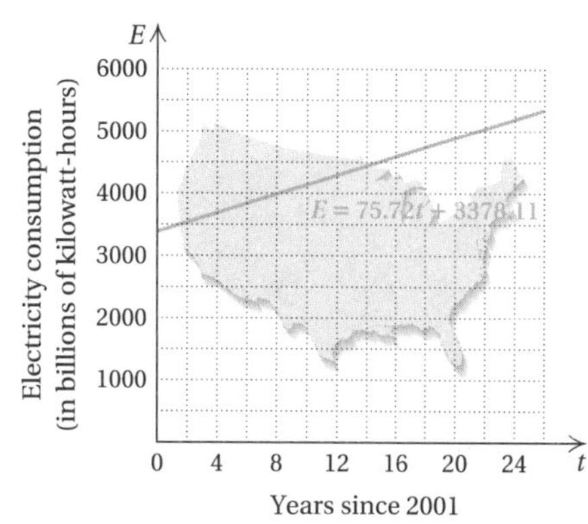

17. *Total Revenue.* Hadley Electronics is marketing a new kind of plasma TV. The firm determines that when it sells x TVs, its total revenue R (the total amount of money taken in) will be

$$R = 280x - 0.4x^2 \text{ dollars.}$$

What is the total revenue from the sale of 75 TVs? 100 TVs?

18. *Total Cost.* Hadley Electronics determines that the total cost C of producing x plasma TVs is given by

$$C = 5000 + 0.6x^2 \text{ dollars.}$$

What is the total cost of producing 500 TVs? 650 TVs?

19. The graph of the polynomial equation $y = 5 - x^2$ is shown below. Use *only* the graph to estimate the value of the polynomial when $x = -3$, $x = -1$, $x = 0$, $x = 1.5$, and $x = 2$.

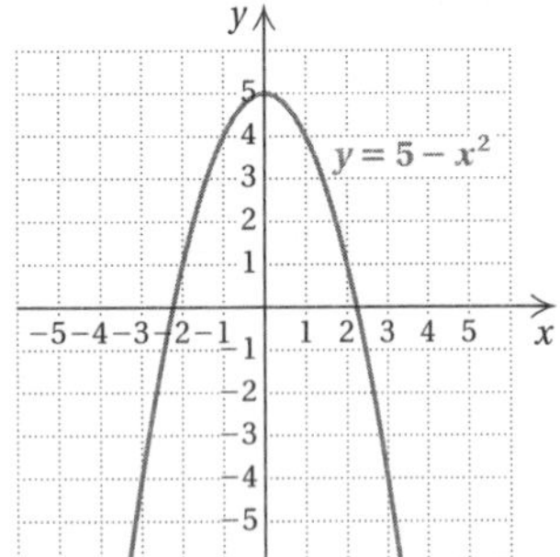

20. The graph of the polynomial equation $y = 6x^3 - 6x$ is shown below. Use *only* the graph to estimate the value of the polynomial when $x = -1$, $x = -0.5$, $x = 0.5$, $x = 1$, and $x = 1.1$.

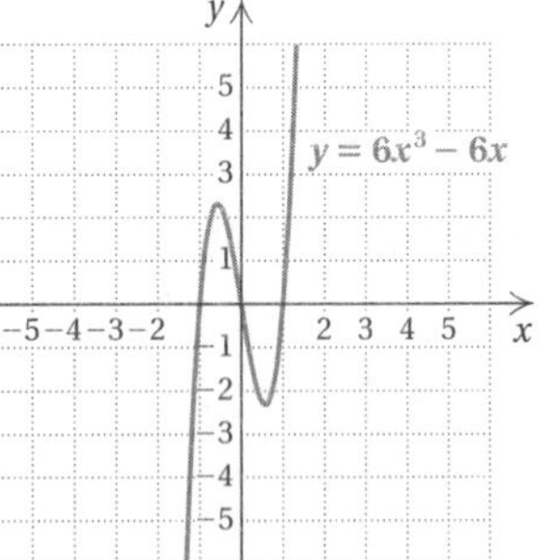

Hearing-Impaired Americans. The number N, in millions, of hearing-impaired Americans of age x can be approximated by the polynomial equation

$$N = -0.00006x^3 + 0.006x^2 - 0.1x + 1.9.$$

The graph of this equation is shown at right. Use either the graph or the polynomial equation for Exercises 21 and 22.

Source: American Speech-Language Hearing Association

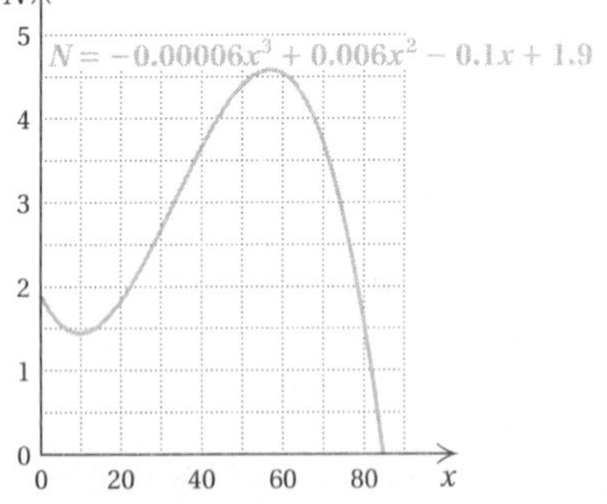

21. Approximate the number of hearing-impaired Americans of ages 20 and 40.

22. Approximate the number of hearing-impaired Americans of ages 50 and 60.

lemorizing words. Participants in a psychology xperiment were able to memorize an average of M words t minutes, where $M = -0.001t^3 + 0.1t^2$. Use the graph elow for Exercises 23–28.

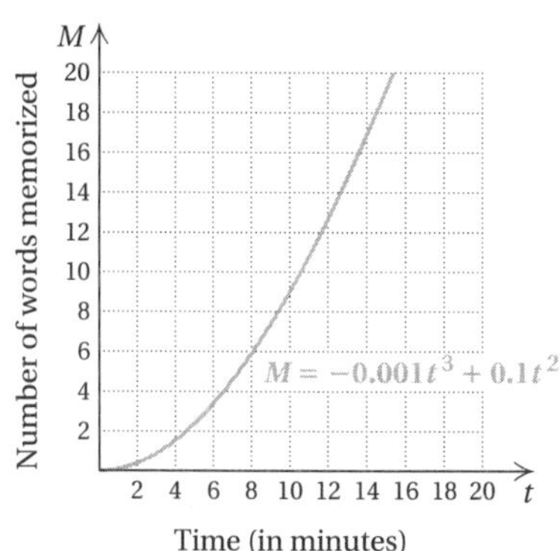

23. Estimate the number of words memorized after 10 min.

24. Estimate the number of words memorized after 14 min.

25. Find the approximate value of M for $t = 8$.

26. Find the approximate value of M for $t = 12$.

27. Estimate the value of M when t is 13.

28. Estimate the value of M when t is 7.

b Identify the terms of the polynomial.

29. $2 - 3x + x^2$

30. $2x^2 + 3x - 4$

31. $-2x^4 + \frac{1}{3}x^3 - x + 3$

32. $-\frac{2}{5}x^5 - x^3 + 6$

c Identify the like terms in the polynomial.

33. $5x^3 + 6x^2 - 3x^2$

34. $3x^2 + 4x^3 - 2x^2$

35. $2x^4 + 5x - 7x - 3x^4$

36. $-3t + t^3 - 2t - 5t^3$

37. $3x^5 - 7x + 8 + 14x^5 - 2x - 9$

38. $8x^3 + 7x^2 - 11 - 4x^3 - 8x^2 - 29$

d Identify the coefficient of each term of the polynomial.

39. $-3x + 6$

40. $2x - 4$

41. $5x^2 + \frac{3}{4}x + 3$

42. $\frac{2}{3}x^2 - 5x + 2$

43. $-5x^4 + 6x^3 - 2.7x^2 + 8x - 2$

44. $7x^3 - 4x^2 - 4.2x + 5$

e Collect like terms.

45. $2x - 5x$

46. $2x^2 + 8x^2$

47. $x - 9x$

48. $x - 5x$

49. $5x^3 + 6x^3 + 4$

50. $6x^4 - 2x^4 + 5$

51. $5x^3 + 6x - 4x^3 - 7x$

52. $3a^4 - 2a + 2a + a^4$

53. $6b^5 + 3b^2 - 2b^5 - 3b^2$

54. $2x^2 - 6x + 3x + 4x^2$

55. $\frac{1}{4}x^5 - 5 + \frac{1}{2}x^5 - 2x - 37$

56. $\frac{1}{3}x^3 + 2x - \frac{1}{6}x^3 + 4 - 16$

57. $6x^2 + 2x^4 - 2x^2 - x^4 - 4x^2$

58. $8x^2 + 2x^3 - 3x^3 - 4x^2 - 4x^2$

59. $\frac{1}{4}x^3 - x^2 - \frac{1}{6}x^2 + \frac{3}{8}x^3 + \frac{5}{16}x^3$

60. $\frac{1}{5}x^4 + \frac{1}{5} - 2x^2 + \frac{1}{10} - \frac{3}{15}x^4 + 2x^2 - \frac{3}{10}$

f Arrange the polynomial in descending order.

61. $x^5 + x + 6x^3 + 1 + 2x^2$

62. $3 + 2x^2 - 5x^6 - 2x^3 + 3x$

63. $5y^3 + 15y^9 + y - y^2 + 7y^8$

64. $9p - 5 + 6p^3 - 5p^4 + p^5$

Collect like terms and then arrange in descending order.

65. $3x^4 - 5x^6 - 2x^4 + 6x^6$

66. $-1 + 5x^3 - 3 - 7x^3 + x^4 + 5$

67. $-2x + 4x^3 - 7x + 9x^3 + 8$

68. $-6x^2 + x - 5x + 7x^2 + 1$

69. $3x + 3x + 3x - x^2 - 4x^2$

70. $-2x - 2x - 2x + x^3 - 5x^3$

71. $-x + \frac{3}{4} + 15x^4 - x - \frac{1}{2} - 3x^4$

72. $2x - \frac{5}{6} + 4x^3 + x + \frac{1}{3} - 2x$

g Identify the degree of each term of the polynomial and the degree of the polynomial.

73. $2x - 4$

74. $6 - 3x$

75. $3x^2 - 5x + 2$

76. $5x^3 - 2x^2 + 3$

77. $-7x^3 + 6x^2 + \frac{3}{5}x + 7$

78. $5x^4 + \frac{1}{4}x^2 - x + 2$

79. $x^2 - 3x + x^6 - 9x^4$

80. $8x - 3x^2 + 9 - 8x^3$

81. Complete the following table for the polynomial $-7x^4 + 6x^3 - 3x^2 + 8x - 2$.

TERM	COEFFICIENT	DEGREE OF THE TERM	DEGREE OF THE POLYNOMIAL
$-7x^4$			
$6x^3$	6		
		2	
$8x$		1	
	-2		

82. Complete the following table for the polynomial $3x^2 + 8x^5 - 46x^3 + 6x - 2.4 - \frac{1}{2}x^4$.

TERM	COEFFICIENT	DEGREE OF THE TERM	DEGREE OF THE POLYNOMIAL
		5	
$-\frac{1}{2}x^4$		4	
	-46		
$3x^2$		2	
	6		
-2.4			

h Identify the missing terms in the polynomial.

83. $x^3 - 27$

84. $x^5 + x$

85. $x^4 - x$

86. $5x^4 - 7x + 2$

87. $2x^3 - 5x^2 + x - 3$

88. $-6x^3$

Write the polynomial in two ways: with its missing terms and by leaving space for them.

89. $x^3 - 27$

90. $x^5 + x$

91. $x^4 - x$

92. $5x^4 - 7x + 2$

93. $2x^3 - 5x^2 + x - 3$

94. $-6x^3$

i Classify the polynomial as a monomial, binomial, trinomial, or none of these.

95. $x^2 - 10x + 25$

96. $-6x^4$

97. $x^3 - 7x^2 + 2x - 4$

98. $x^2 - 9$

99. $4x^2 - 25$

100. $2x^4 - 7x^3 + x^2 + x - 6$

101. $40x$

102. $4x^2 + 12x + 9$

103. $\mathbf{D}_\mathbf{W}$ Is it better to evaluate a polynomial before or after like terms have been collected? Why?

104. $\mathbf{D}_\mathbf{W}$ Explain why an understanding of the rules for order of operations is essential when evaluating polynomials.

SKILL MAINTENANCE

105. Three tired campers stopped for the night. All they had to eat was a bag of apples. During the night, one awoke and ate one-third of the apples. Later, a second camper awoke and ate one-third of the apples that remained. Much later, the third camper awoke and ate one-third of those apples yet remaining after the other two had eaten. When they got up the next morning, 8 apples were left. How many apples did they begin with? [2.6a]

Subtract. [1.4a]

106. $1 - 20$

107. $\frac{1}{8} - \frac{5}{6}$

108. $\frac{3}{8} - \left(-\frac{1}{4}\right)$

109. $5.6 - 8.2$

110. Solve: $3(x + 2) = 5x - 9$. [2.3c]

111. Solve $C = ab - r$ for b. [2.4b]

112. A nut dealer has 1800 lb of peanuts, 1500 lb of cashews, and 700 lb of almonds. What percent of the total is peanuts? cashews? almonds? [2.5a]

113. Factor: $3x - 15y + 63$. [1.7d]

SYNTHESIS

Collect like terms.

114. $6x^3 \cdot 7x^2 - (4x^3)^2 + (-3x^3)^2 - (-4x^2)(5x^3) - 10x^5 + 17x^6$

115. $(3x^2)^3 + 4x^2 \cdot 4x^4 - x^4(2x)^2 + ((2x)^2)^3 - 100x^2(x^2)^2$

116. Construct a polynomial in x (meaning that x is the variable) of degree 5 with four terms and coefficients that are integers.

117. What is the degree of $(5m^5)^2$?

118. A polynomial in x has degree 3. The coefficient of x^2 is 3 less than the coefficient of x^3. The coefficient of x is three times the coefficient of x^2. The remaining coefficient is 2 more than the coefficient of x^3. The sum of the coefficients is -4. Find the polynomial.

Use the CALC feature and choose VALUE on your graphing calculator to find the values in each of the following.

119. Exercise 19

120. Exercise 20

121. Exercise 21

122. Exercise 22

4.4 ADDITION AND SUBTRACTION OF POLYNOMIALS

Objectives

a. Add polynomials.

b. Simplify the opposite of a polynomial.

c. Subtract polynomials.

d. Use polynomials to represent perimeter and area.

a Addition of Polynomials

'o add two polynomials, we can write a plus sign between them and then col-ect like terms. Depending on the situation, you may see polynomials written n descending order, ascending order, or neither. Generally, if an exercise is vritten in a particular order, we write the answer in that same order.

XAMPLE 1 Add: $(-3x^3 + 2x - 4) + (4x^3 + 3x^2 + 2)$.

$$(-3x^3 + 2x - 4) + (4x^3 + 3x^2 + 2)$$
$$= (-3 + 4)x^3 + 3x^2 + 2x + (-4 + 2) \quad \text{Collecting like terms}$$
$$= x^3 + 3x^2 + 2x - 2$$

XAMPLE 2 Add:

$$\left(\tfrac{2}{3}x^4 + 3x^2 - 2x + \tfrac{1}{2}\right) + \left(-\tfrac{1}{3}x^4 + 5x^3 - 3x^2 + 3x - \tfrac{1}{2}\right).$$

We have

$$\tfrac{2}{3}x^4 + 3x^2 - 2x + \tfrac{1}{2}) + \left(-\tfrac{1}{3}x^4 + 5x^3 - 3x^2 + 3x - \tfrac{1}{2}\right)$$
$$= \left(\tfrac{2}{3} - \tfrac{1}{3}\right)x^4 + 5x^3 + (3 - 3)x^2 + (-2 + 3)x + \left(\tfrac{1}{2} - \tfrac{1}{2}\right) \quad \text{Collecting like terms}$$
$$= \tfrac{1}{3}x^4 + 5x^3 + x.$$

We can add polynomials as we do because they represent numbers. After ome practice, you will be able to add mentally.

)o Exercises 1–4.

XAMPLE 3 Add: $(3x^2 - 2x + 2) + (5x^3 - 2x^2 + 3x - 4)$.

$$3x^2 - 2x + 2) + (5x^3 - 2x^2 + 3x - 4)$$
$$= 5x^3 + (3 - 2)x^2 + (-2 + 3)x + (2 - 4) \quad \text{You might do this step mentally.}$$
$$= 5x^3 + x^2 + x - 2 \quad \text{Then you would write only this.}$$

)o Exercises 5 and 6.

We can also add polynomials by writing like terms in columns.

XAMPLE 4 Add: $9x^5 - 2x^3 + 6x^2 + 3$ and $5x^4 - 7x^2 + 6$ and $x^6 - 5x^5 + x^2 + 5$.

We arrange the polynomials with the like terms in columns.

$$\begin{array}{rrrrrr} & 9x^5 & & -\ 2x^3 & +\ 6x^2 & +\ 3 \\ & & 5x^4 & & -\ 7x^2 & +\ 6 \\ x^6 & -\ 5x^5 & & & +\ x^2 & +\ 5 \\ \hline x^6 & +\ 4x^5 & +\ 5x^4 & -\ 2x^3 & & +\ 14 \end{array}$$

We leave spaces for missing terms.

Adding

Ve write the answer as $3x^6 + 4x^5 + 5x^4 - 2x^3 + 14$ without the space.

Add.

1. $(3x^2 + 2x - 2) + (-2x^2 + 5x + 5)$

2. $(-4x^5 + x^3 + 4) + (7x^4 + 2x^2)$

3. $(31x^4 + x^2 + 2x - 1) + (-7x^4 + 5x^3 - 2x + 2)$

4. $(17x^3 - x^2 + 3x + 4) + \left(-15x^3 + x^2 - 3x - \dfrac{2}{3}\right)$

Add mentally. Try to write just the answer.

5. $(4x^2 - 5x + 3) + (-2x^2 + 2x - 4)$

6. $(3x^3 - 4x^2 - 5x + 3) + \left(5x^3 + 2x^2 - 3x - \dfrac{1}{2}\right)$

Answers on page A-22

Add.

7.
$$\begin{array}{r} -2x^3+5x^2-2x+4 \\ x^4 \qquad +6x^2+7x-10 \\ -9x^4+6x^3+x^2 \qquad -2 \\ \hline \end{array}$$

8. $-3x^3+5x+2$ and x^3+x^2+5 and x^3-2x-4

Simplify.

9. $-(4x^3-6x+3)$

10. $-(5x^4+3x^2+7x-5)$

11. $-\left(14x^{10}-\frac{1}{2}x^5+5x^3-x^2+3x\right)$

Subtract.

12. $(7x^3+2x+4)-(5x^3-4)$

13. $(-3x^2+5x-4)-(-4x^2+11x-2)$

Answers on page A-22

Do Exercises 7 and 8.

b Opposites of Polynomials

In Section 1.8, we used the property of -1 to show that we can find the opposite of an expression. For example, the opposite of $x-2y+5$ of can be written as

$$-(x-2y+5)$$

by changing the sign of every term:

$$-(x-2y+5)=-x+2y-5.$$

This applies to polynomials as well.

OPPOSITES OF POLYNOMIALS

To find an equivalent polynomial for the **opposite,** or **additive inverse,** of a polynomial, change the sign of every term. This is the same as multiplying by -1.

EXAMPLE 5 Simplify: $-(x^2-3x+4)$.

$$-(x^2-3x+4)=-x^2+3x-4$$

EXAMPLE 6 Simplify: $-(-t^3-6t^2-t+4)$.

$$-(-t^3-6t^2-t+4)=t^3+6t^2+t-4$$

EXAMPLE 7 Simplify: $-\left(-7x^4-\frac{5}{9}x^3+8x^2-x+67\right)$.

$$-\left(-7x^4-\frac{5}{9}x^3+8x^2-x+67\right)=7x^4+\frac{5}{9}x^3-8x^2+x-67$$

Do Exercises 9–11.

c Subtraction of Polynomials

Recall that we can subtract a real number by adding its opposite, or additive inverse: $a-b=a+(-b)$. This allows us to subtract polynomials.

EXAMPLE 8 Subtract:

$$(9x^5+x^3-2x^2+4)-(2x^5+x^4-4x^3-3x^2).$$

We have

$(9x^5+x^3-2x^2+4)-(2x^5+x^4-4x^3-3x^2)$

$=9x^5+x^3-2x^2+4+[-(2x^5+x^4-4x^3-3x^2)]$ Adding the opposite

$=9x^5+x^3-2x^2+4-2x^5-x^4+4x^3+3x^2$ Finding the opposite by changing the sign of *each* term

$=7x^5-x^4+5x^3+x^2+4.$ Adding (collecting like terms)

Do Exercises 12 and 13.

As with similar work in Section 1.8, we combine steps by changing the sign of each term of the polynomial being subtracted and collecting like terms. Try to do this mentally as much as possible.

EXAMPLE 9 Subtract: $(9x^5 + x^3 - 2x) - (-2x^5 + 5x^3 + 6)$.

$(9x^5 + x^3 - 2x) - (-2x^5 + 5x^3 + 6)$

$= 9x^5 + x^3 - 2x + 2x^5 - 5x^3 - 6$ Finding the opposite by changing the sign of each term

$= 11x^5 - 4x^3 - 2x - 6$ Adding (collecting like terms)

Do Exercises 14 and 15.

We can use columns to subtract. We replace coefficients with their opposites, as shown in Example 8.

EXAMPLE 10 Write in columns and subtract:

$(5x^2 - 3x + 6) - (9x^2 - 5x - 3)$.

a)
$$\begin{array}{r} 5x^2 - 3x + 6 \\ \underline{-(9x^2 - 5x - 3)} \end{array}$$
Writing like terms in columns

b)
$$\begin{array}{r} 5x^2 - 3x + 6 \\ \underline{-9x^2 + 5x + 3} \end{array}$$
Changing signs

c)
$$\begin{array}{r} 5x^2 - 3x + 6 \\ \underline{-9x^2 + 5x + 3} \\ -4x^2 + 2x + 9 \end{array}$$
Adding

If you can do so without error, you can arrange the polynomials in columns and write just the answer, remembering to change the signs and add.

EXAMPLE 11 Write in columns and subtract:

$(x^3 + x^2 + 2x - 12) - (-2x^3 + x^2 - 3x)$.

$$\begin{array}{r} x^3 + x^2 + 2x - 12 \\ \underline{-(-2x^3 + x^2 - 3x \qquad)} \end{array}$$
Leaving space for the missing term

$3x^3 \qquad + 5x - 12.$ Changing the signs and adding

Do Exercises 16 and 17.

d Polynomials and Geometry

EXAMPLE 12 Find a polynomial for the sum of the areas of these rectangles.

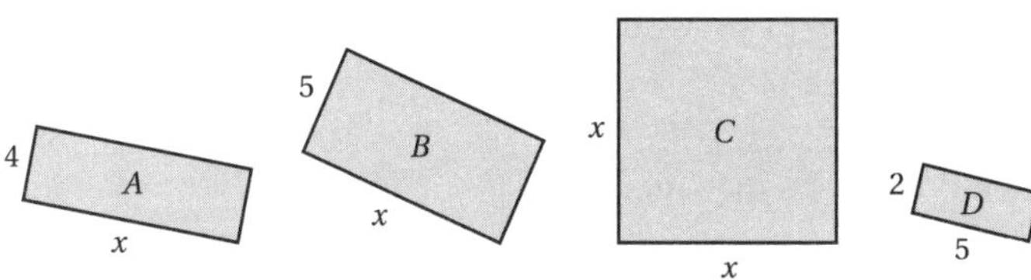

Recall that the area of a rectangle is the product of the length and the width. The sum of the areas is a sum of products. We find these products and then collect like terms.

Subtract.

14. $(-6x^4 + 3x^2 + 6) - (2x^4 + 5x^3 - 5x^2 + 7)$

15. $\left(\frac{3}{2}x^3 - \frac{1}{2}x^2 + 0.3\right) - \left(\frac{1}{2}x^3 + \frac{1}{2}x^2 + \frac{4}{3}x + 1.2\right)$

Write in columns and subtract.

16. $(4x^3 + 2x^2 - 2x - 3) - (2x^3 - 3x^2 + 2)$

17. $(2x^3 + x^2 - 6x + 2) - (x^5 + 4x^3 - 2x^2 - 4x)$

Answers on page A-22

18. Find a polynomial for the sum of the perimeters and the areas of the rectangles.

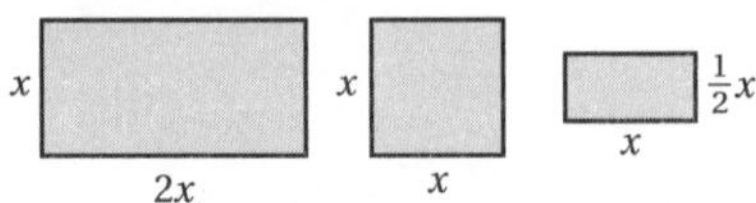

19. Lawn Area. An 8-ft by 8-ft shed is placed on a lawn x ft on a side. Find a polynomial for the remaining area.

Answers on page A-22

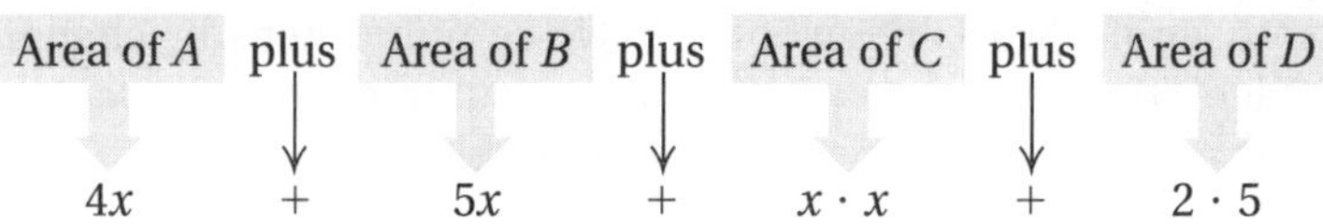

Area of A plus Area of B plus Area of C plus Area of D
4x + 5x + x · x + 2 · 5

We collect like terms:

$$4x + 5x + x^2 + 10 = x^2 + 9x + 10.$$

Do Exercise 18.

EXAMPLE 13 *Lawn Area.* A water fountain with a 4-ft by 4-ft square base is placed on a square grassy park area that is x ft on a side. To determine the amount of grass seed needed for the lawn, find a polynomial for the grassy area.

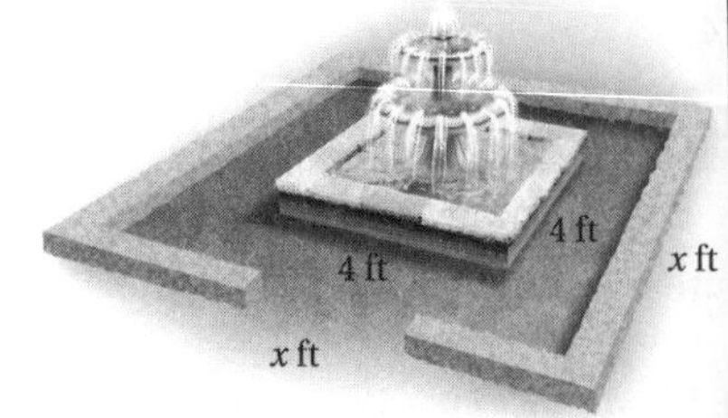

We make a drawing of the situation as shown here. We then reword the problem and write the polynomial as follows.

Area of park	−	Area of base of fountain	=	Area left over
$x \cdot x$	−	$4 \cdot 4$	=	Area left over

Then $(x^2 - 16)\text{ ft}^2$ = Area left over.

Do Exercise 19.

CALCULATOR CORNER

Checking Addition and Subtraction of Polynomials A table set in AUTO mode can be used to perform a partial check that polynomials have been added or subtracted correctly. To check Example 3, we enter $y_1 = (3x^2 - 2x + 2) + (5x^3 - 2x^2 + 3x - 4)$ and $y_2 = 5x^3 + x^2 + x - 2$. If the addition has been done correctly, the values of y_1 and y_2 will be the same regardless of the table settings used.

A graph can also be used to check addition and subtraction. See the Calculator Corner on p. 352 for the procedure.

X	Y1	Y2
−2	−40	−40
−1	−7	−7
0	−2	−2
1	5	5
2	44	44
3	145	145
4	338	338
X = −2		

Exercises: Use a table to determine whether the sum or difference is correct.

1. $(-3x^3 + 2x - 4) + (4x^3 + 3x^2 + 2) = x^3 + 3x^2 + 2x - 2$
2. $(x^3 - 2x^2 + 3x - 7) + (3x^2 - 4x + 5) = x^3 + x^2 - x - 2$
3. $(5x^2 - 7x + 4) + (2x^2 + 3x - 6) = 7x^2 + 4x - 2$
4. $(9x^5 + x^3 - 2x) - (-2x^5 + 5x^3 + 6) = 11x^5 - 4x^3 - 2x - 6$
5. $(3x^4 - 2x^2 - 1) - (2x^4 - 3x^2 - 4) = x^4 + x^2 - 5$
6. $(-2x^3 + 3x^2 - 4x + 5) - (3x^2 + 2x + 8) = -2x^3 - 6x - 3$

4.4 EXERCISE SET

For Extra Help

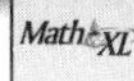 MathXL
MyMathLab
 InterAct Math
 Math Tutor Center
 Digital Video Tutor CD 3 Videotape 5
 Student's Solutions Manual

a Add.

1. $(3x + 2) + (-4x + 3)$

2. $(6x + 1) + (-7x + 2)$

3. $(-6x + 2) + (x^2 + \frac{1}{2}x - 3)$

4. $(x^2 - \frac{5}{3}x + 4) + (8x - 9)$

5. $(x^2 - 9) + (x^2 + 9)$

6. $(x^3 + x^2) + (2x^3 - 5x^2)$

7. $(3x^2 - 5x + 10) + (2x^2 + 8x - 40)$

8. $(6x^4 + 3x^3 - 1) + (4x^2 - 3x + 3)$

9. $(1.2x^3 + 4.5x^2 - 3.8x) + (-3.4x^3 - 4.7x^2 + 23)$

10. $(0.5x^4 - 0.6x^2 + 0.7) + (2.3x^4 + 1.8x - 3.9)$

11. $(1 + 4x + 6x^2 + 7x^3) + (5 - 4x + 6x^2 - 7x^3)$

12. $(3x^4 - 6x - 5x^2 + 5) + (6x^2 - 4x^3 - 1 + 7x)$

13. $\left(\frac{1}{4}x^4 + \frac{2}{3}x^3 + \frac{5}{8}x^2 + 7\right) + \left(-\frac{3}{4}x^4 + \frac{3}{8}x^2 - 7\right)$

14. $\left(\frac{1}{3}x^9 + \frac{1}{5}x^5 - \frac{1}{2}x^2 + 7\right) +$
$\left(-\frac{1}{5}x^9 + \frac{1}{4}x^4 - \frac{3}{5}x^5 + \frac{3}{4}x^2 + \frac{1}{2}\right)$

15. $(0.02x^5 - 0.2x^3 + x + 0.08) +$
$(-0.01x^5 + x^4 - 0.8x - 0.02)$

16. $(0.03x^6 + 0.05x^3 + 0.22x + 0.05) +$
$\left(\frac{7}{100}x^6 - \frac{3}{100}x^3 + 0.5\right)$

17. $(9x^8 - 7x^4 + 2x^2 + 5) + (8x^7 + 4x^4 - 2x) +$
$(-3x^4 + 6x^2 + 2x - 1)$

18. $(4x^5 - 6x^3 - 9x + 1) + (6x^3 + 9x^2 + 9x) +$
$(-4x^3 + 8x^2 + 3x - 2)$

19.
$$\begin{array}{rrrrr}
0.15x^4 & + 0.10x^3 & - 0.9x^2 & & \\
 & - 0.01x^3 & + 0.01x^2 & + x & \\
1.25x^4 & & + 0.11x^2 & & + 0.01 \\
 & 0.27x^3 & & & + 0.99 \\
-0.35x^4 & & + 15x^2 & & - 0.03 \\
\hline
\end{array}$$

20.
$$\begin{array}{rrrrr}
0.05x^4 & + 0.12x^3 & - 0.5x^2 & & \\
 & - 0.02x^3 & + 0.02x^2 & + 2x & \\
1.5x^4 & & + 0.01x^2 & & + 0.15 \\
 & 0.25x^3 & & & + 0.85 \\
-0.25x^4 & & + 10x^2 & & - 0.04 \\
\hline
\end{array}$$

b Simplify.

21. $-(-5x)$

22. $-(x^2 - 3x)$

23. $-(-x^2 + \frac{3}{2}x - 2)$

24. $-(-4x^3 - x^2 - \frac{1}{4}x)$

25. $-(12x^4 - 3x^3 + 3)$

26. $-(4x^3 - 6x^2 - 8x + 1)$

27. $-(3x - 7)$

28. $-(-2x + 4)$

29. $-(4x^2 - 3x + 2)$

30. $-(-6a^3 + 2a^2 - 9a + 1)$

31. $-\left(-4x^4 + 6x^2 + \frac{3}{4}x - 8\right)$

32. $-(-5x^4 + 4x^3 - x^2 + 0.9)$

c Subtract.

33. $(3x + 2) - (-4x + 3)$

34. $(6x + 1) - (-7x + 2)$

35. $(-6x + 2) - (x^2 + x - 3)$

36. $(x^2 - 5x + 4) - (8x - 9)$

37. $(x^2 - 9) - (x^2 + 9)$

38. $(x^3 + x^2) - (2x^3 - 5x^2)$

39. $(6x^4 + 3x^3 - 1) - (4x^2 - 3x + 3)$

40. $(-4x^2 + 2x) - (3x^3 - 5x^2 + 3)$

41. $(1.2x^3 + 4.5x^2 - 3.8x) - (-3.4x^3 - 4.7x^2 + 23)$

42. $(0.5x^4 - 0.6x^2 + 0.7) - (2.3x^4 + 1.8x - 3.9)$

43. $\left(\frac{5}{8}x^3 - \frac{1}{4}x - \frac{1}{3}\right) - \left(-\frac{1}{8}x^3 + \frac{1}{4}x - \frac{1}{3}\right)$

44. $\left(\frac{1}{5}x^3 + 2x^2 - 0.1\right) - \left(-\frac{2}{5}x^3 + 2x^2 + 0.01\right)$

45. $(0.08x^3 - 0.02x^2 + 0.01x) - (0.02x^3 + 0.03x^2 - 1)$

46. $(0.8x^4 + 0.2x - 1) - \left(\frac{7}{10}x^4 + \frac{1}{5}x - 0.1\right)$

ubtract.

7. $\begin{array}{r} x^2 + 5x + 6 \\ -(x^2 + 2x) \\ \hline \end{array}$

48. $\begin{array}{lr} x^3 & + 1 \\ -(x^3 + x^2 &) \\ \hline \end{array}$

49. $\begin{array}{lr} 5x^4 + 6x^3 - 9x^2 & \\ -(-6x^4 - 6x^3 & + 8x + 9) \\ \hline \end{array}$

0. $\begin{array}{l} 5x^4 \quad + 6x^2 - 3x + 6 \\ -(\quad 6x^3 + 7x^2 - 8x - 9) \\ \hline \end{array}$

51. $\begin{array}{lr} x^5 & - 1 \\ -(x^5 - x^4 + x^3 - x^2 + x - 1) & \\ \hline \end{array}$

52. $\begin{array}{r} x^5 + x^4 - x^3 + x^2 - x + 2 \\ -(x^5 - x^4 + x^3 - x^2 - x + 2) \\ \hline \end{array}$

d Solve.

ind a polynomial for the perimeter of the figure.

3.

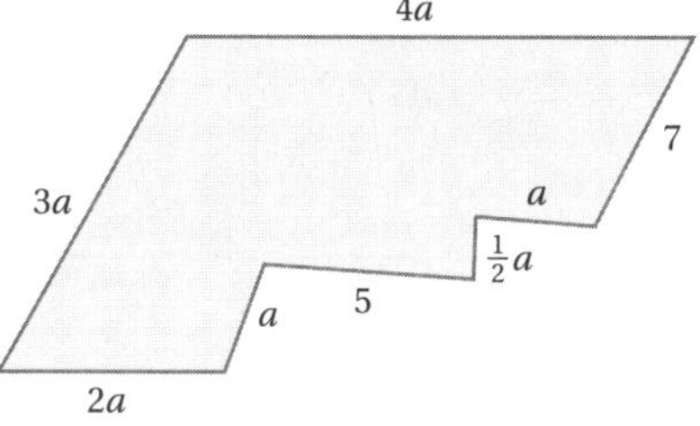

54.

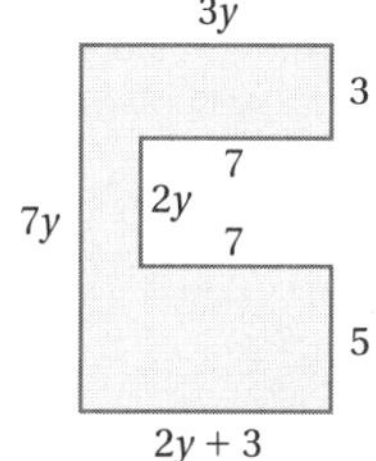

5. Find a polynomial for the sum of the areas of these rectangles.

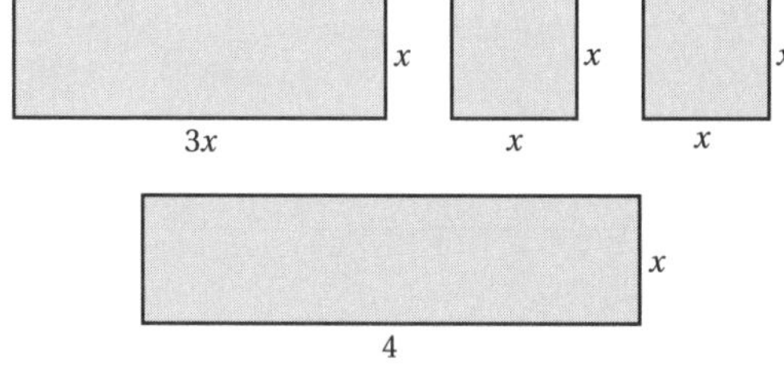

56. Find a polynomial for the sum of the areas of these circles.

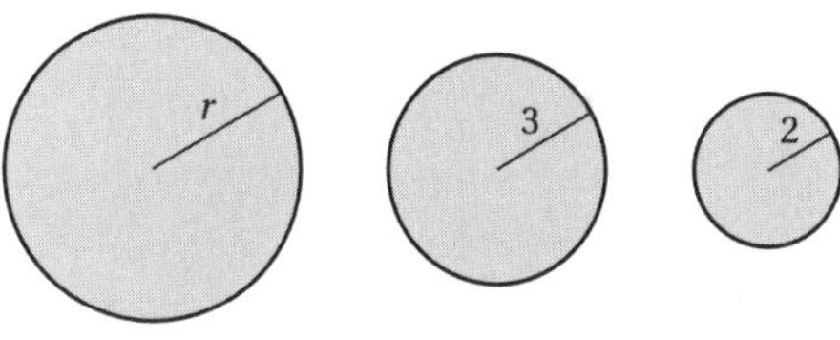

ind two algebraic expressions for the area of each figure. First, regard the figure as one large rectangle, and then regard the gure as a sum of four smaller rectangles.

7.

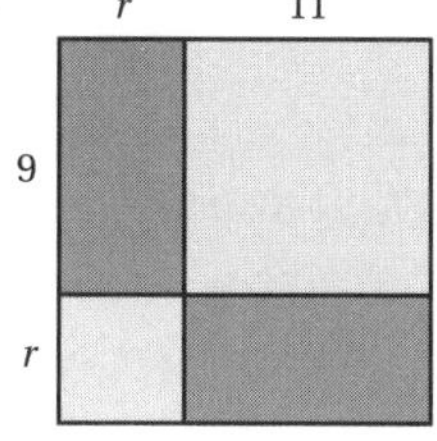

58.

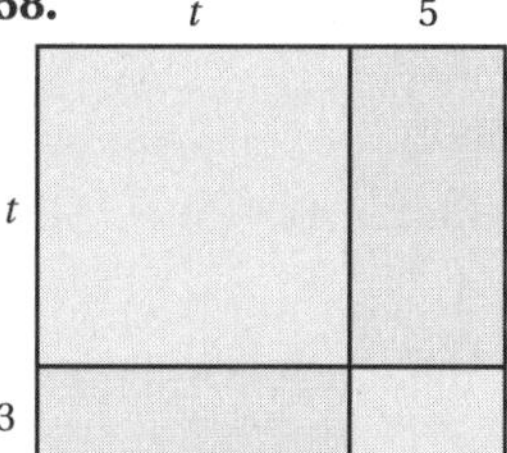

59.

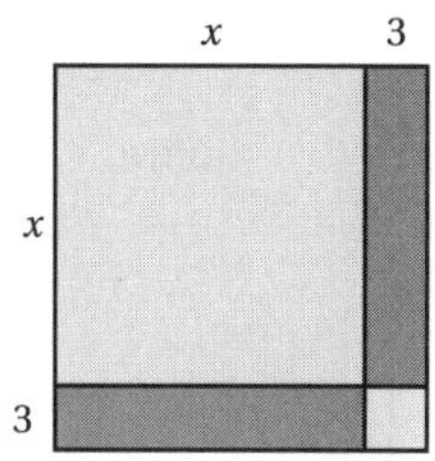

60.

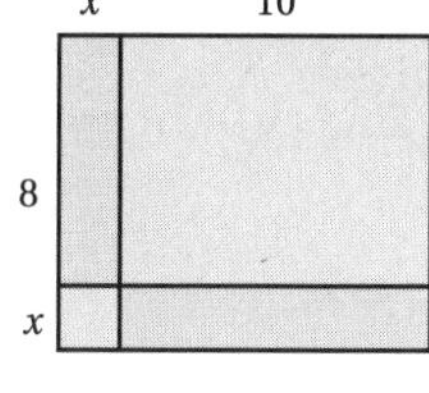

Find a polynomial for the shaded area of the figure.

61.

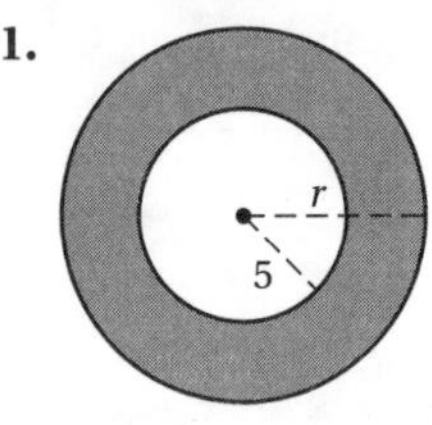

62.

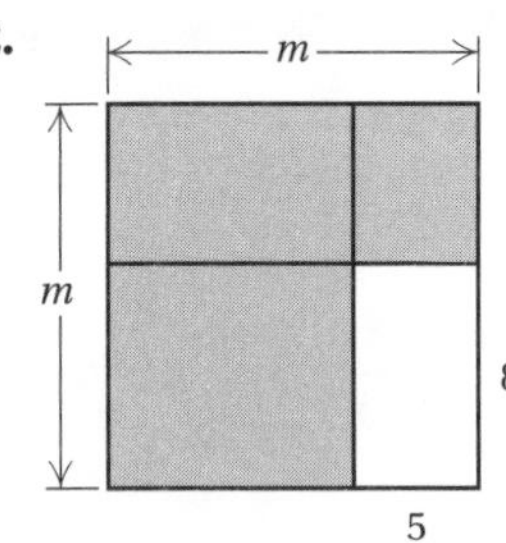

63.

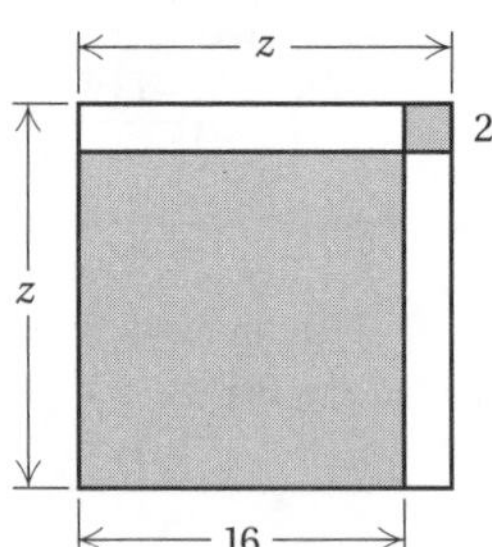

64.

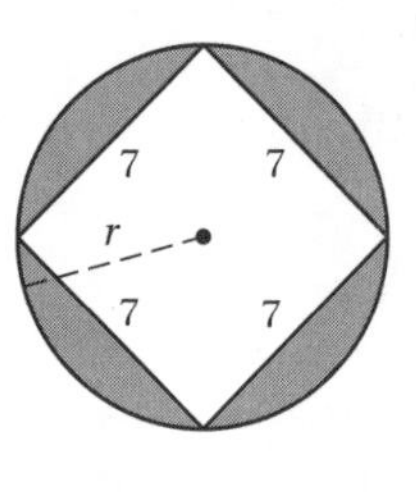

65. D$_W$ Is the sum of two binomials ever a trinomial? Why or why not?

66. D$_W$ Which, if any, of the commutative, associative, and distributive laws are needed for adding polynomials? Why?

SKILL MAINTENANCE

Solve. [2.3b]

67. $8x + 3x = 66$

68. $5x - 7x = 38$

69. $\frac{3}{8}x + \frac{1}{4} - \frac{3}{4}x = \frac{11}{16} + x$

70. $5x - 4 = 26 - x$

71. $1.5x - 2.7x = 22 - 5.6x$

72. $3x - 3 = -4x + 4$

Solve. [2.3c]

73. $6(y - 3) - 8 = 4(y + 2) + 5$

74. $8(5x + 2) = 7(6x - 3)$

Solve. [2.7e]

75. $3x - 7 \leq 5x + 13$

76. $2(x - 4) > 5(x - 3) + 7$

SYNTHESIS

Find a polynomial for the surface area of the right rectangular solid.

77.

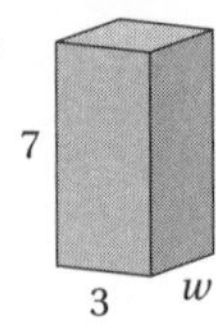

78.

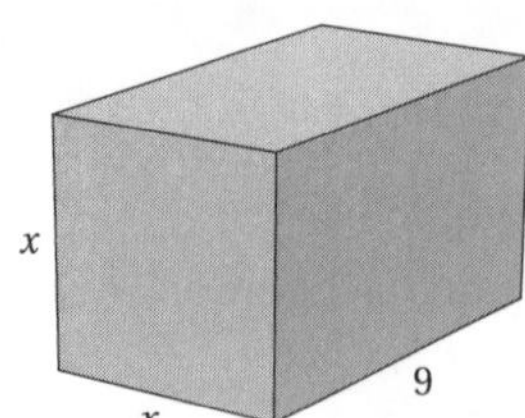

79.

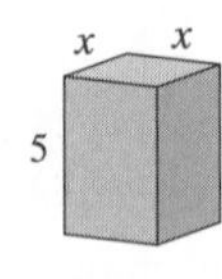

80.

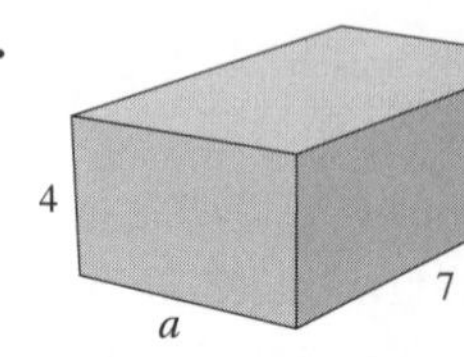

81. Find $(y - 2)^2$ using the four parts of this square.

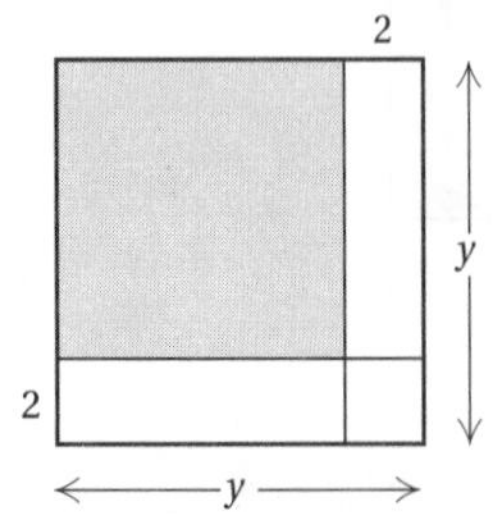

Simplify.

82. $(3x^2 - 4x + 6) - (-2x^2 + 4) + (-5x - 3)$

83. $(7y^2 - 5y + 6) - (3y^2 + 8y - 12) + (8y^2 - 10y + 3)$

84. $(-4 + x^2 + 2x^3) - (-6 - x + 3x^3) - (-x^2 - 5x^3)$

85. $(-y^4 - 7y^3 + y^2) + (-2y^4 + 5y - 2) - (-6y^3 + y^2)$

4.5 MULTIPLICATION OF POLYNOMIALS

We now multiply polynomials using techniques based, for the most part, n the distributive laws, but also on the associative and commutative laws. .s we proceed in this chapter, we will develop special ways to find certain roducts.

a Multiplying Monomials

onsider $(3x)(4x)$. We multiply as follows:

$$\begin{aligned}(3x)(4x) &= 3 \cdot x \cdot 4 \cdot x && \text{By the associative law of multiplication}\\ &= 3 \cdot 4 \cdot x \cdot x && \text{By the commutative law of multiplication}\\ &= (3 \cdot 4)(x \cdot x) && \text{By the associative law}\\ &= 12x^2. && \text{Using the product rule for exponents}\end{aligned}$$

MULTIPLYING MONOMIALS

To find an equivalent expression for the product of two monomials, multiply the coefficients and then multiply the variables using the product rule for exponents.

XAMPLES Multiply.

1. $5x \cdot 6x = (5 \cdot 6)(x \cdot x)$ By the associative and commutative laws
$= 30x^2$ Multiplying the coefficients and multiplying the variables

2. $(3x)(-x) = (3x)(-1x)$
$= (3)(-1)(x \cdot x) = -3x^2$

3. $(-7x^5)(4x^3) = (-7 \cdot 4)(x^5 \cdot x^3)$
$= -28x^{5+3}$ Adding the exponents
$= -28x^8$ Simplifying

After some practice, you can do this mentally. Multiply the coefficients nd then the variables by keeping the base and adding the exponents. Write nly the answer.

o Exercises 1–8.

b Multiplying a Monomial and Any Polynomial

o find an equivalent expression for the product of a monomial, such as $2x$, nd a binomial, such as $5x + 3$, we use a distributive law and multiply each erm of $5x + 3$ by $2x$.

XAMPLE 4 Multiply: $2x(5x + 3)$.

$$\begin{aligned}2x(5x + 3) &= (2x)(5x) + (2x)(3) && \text{Using a distributive law}\\ &= 10x^2 + 6x && \text{Multiplying the monomials}\end{aligned}$$

Objectives

a Multiply monomials.

b Multiply a monomial and any polynomial.

c Multiply two binomials.

d Multiply any two polynomials.

Multiply.

1. $(3x)(-5)$

2. $(-x) \cdot x$

3. $(-x)(-x)$

4. $(-x^2)(x^3)$

5. $3x^5 \cdot 4x^2$

6. $(4y^5)(-2y^6)$

7. $(-7y^4)(-y)$

8. $7x^5 \cdot 0$

Answers on page A-23

Multiply.

9. $4x(2x + 4)$

10. $3t^2(-5t + 2)$

11. $-5x^3(x^3 + 5x^2 - 6x + 8)$

12. Multiply: $(y + 2)(y + 7)$.

a) Fill in the blanks in the steps of the solution below.

$(y + 2)(y + 7)$
$= y \cdot$ ______ $+ 2 \cdot$ ______
$= y \cdot$ ______ $+ y \cdot$ ______
$+ 2 \cdot$ ______ $+ 2 \cdot$ ______
$=$ ______ $+$ ______
$+$ ______ $+$ ______
$= y^2 +$ ______ $+ 14$

b) Write an algebraic expression that represents the total area of the four smaller rectangles in the figure shown here.

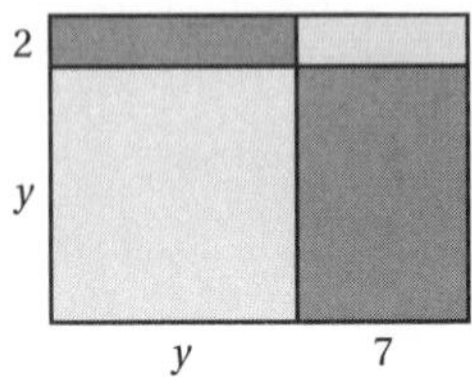

Multiply.

13. $(x + 8)(x + 5)$

14. $(x + 5)(x - 4)$

Answers on page A-23

EXAMPLE 5 Multiply: $5x(2x^2 - 3x + 4)$.

$$5x(2x^2 - 3x + 4) = (5x)(2x^2) - (5x)(3x) + (5x)(4)$$
$$= 10x^3 - 15x^2 + 20x$$

MULTIPLYING A MONOMIAL AND A POLYNOMIAL

To multiply a monomial and a polynomial, multiply each term of the polynomial by the monomial.

EXAMPLE 6 Multiply: $-2x^2(x^3 - 7x^2 + 10x - 4)$.

$$-2x^2(x^3 - 7x^2 + 10x - 4)$$
$$= (-2x^2)(x^3) - (-2x^2)(7x^2) + (-2x^2)(10x) - (-2x^2)(4)$$
$$= -2x^5 + 14x^4 - 20x^3 + 8x^2$$

Do Exercises 9–11.

C Multiplying Two Binomials

To find an equivalent expression for the product of two binomials, we use the distributive laws more than once. In Example 7, we use a distributive law three times.

EXAMPLE 7 Multiply: $(x + 5)(x + 4)$.

$(x + 5)(x + 4) = x(x + 4) + 5(x + 4)$ Using a distributive law

$= x \cdot x + x \cdot 4 + 5 \cdot x + 5 \cdot 4$ Using a distributive law on each part

$= x^2 + 4x + 5x + 20$ Multiplying the monomials

$= x^2 + 9x + 20$ Collecting like terms

To visualize the product in Example 7, consider a rectangle of length $x + 5$ and width $x + 4$.

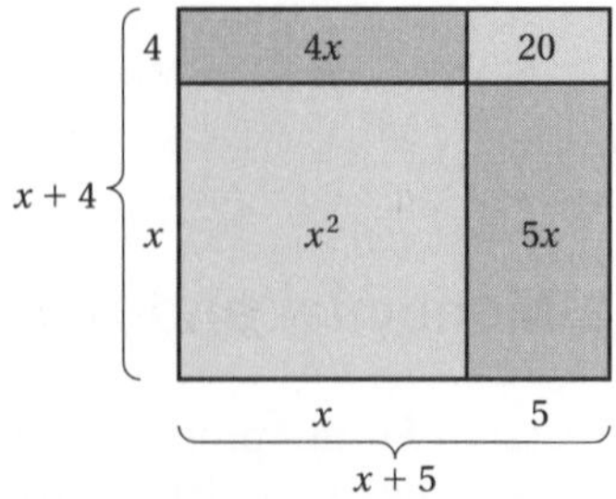

The total area can be expressed as $(x + 5)(x + 4)$ or, by adding the four smaller areas, $x^2 + 4x + 5x + 20$, or $x^2 + 9x + 20$.

Do Exercises 12–14.

EXAMPLE 8 Multiply: $(4x + 3)(x - 2)$.

$$(4x + 3)(x - 2) = 4x(x - 2) + 3(x - 2)$$ Using a distributive law

$$= 4x \cdot x - 4x \cdot 2 + 3 \cdot x - 3 \cdot 2$$ Using a distributive law on each part

$$= 4x^2 - 8x + 3x - 6$$ Multiplying the monomials

$$= 4x^2 - 5x - 6$$ Collecting like terms

Do Exercises 15 and 16.

Multiply.

15. $(5x + 3)(x - 4)$

16. $(2x - 3)(3x - 5)$

d Multiplying Any Two Polynomials

Let's consider the product of a binomial and a trinomial. We use a distributive law four times. You may see ways to skip some steps and do the work mentally.

EXAMPLE 9 Multiply: $(x^2 + 2x - 3)(x^2 + 4)$.

$$(x^2 + 2x - 3)(x^2 + 4) = x^2(x^2 + 4) + 2x(x^2 + 4) - 3(x^2 + 4)$$

$$= x^2 \cdot x^2 + x^2 \cdot 4 + 2x \cdot x^2 + 2x \cdot 4 - 3 \cdot x^2 - 3 \cdot 4$$

$$= x^4 + 4x^2 + 2x^3 + 8x - 3x^2 - 12$$

$$= x^4 + 2x^3 + x^2 + 8x - 12$$

Do Exercises 17 and 18.

Multiply.

17. $(x^2 + 3x - 4)(x^2 + 5)$

18. $(3y^2 - 7)(2y^3 - 2y + 5)$

PRODUCT OF TWO POLYNOMIALS

To multiply two polynomials P and Q, select one of the polynomials—say, P. Then multiply each term of P by every term of Q and collect like terms.

To use columns for long multiplication, multiply each term in the top row by every term in the bottom row. We write like terms in columns, and then add the results. Such multiplication is like multiplying with whole numbers.

3 2 1	300 + 20 + 1	
× 1 2	× 10 + 2	
6 4 2	600 + 40 + 2	Multiplying the top row by 2
3 2 1	3000 + 200 + 10	Multiplying the top row by 10
3 8 5 2	3000 + 800 + 50 + 2	Adding

EXAMPLE 10 Multiply: $(4x^3 - 2x^2 + 3x)(x^2 + 2x)$.

$4x^3 - 2x^2 + 3x$	
$x^2 + 2x$	
$8x^4 - 4x^3 + 6x^2$	Multiplying the top row by $2x$
$4x^5 - 2x^4 + 3x^3$	Multiplying the top row by x^2
$4x^5 + 6x^4 - x^3 + 6x^2$	Collecting like terms
	Line up like terms in columns.

Answers on page A-23

Multiply.

19. $\begin{array}{r} 3x^2 - 2x + 4 \\ \underline{x + 5} \end{array}$

20. $\begin{array}{r} -5x^2 + 4x + 2 \\ \underline{-4x^2 - 8} \end{array}$

21. Multiply.

$\begin{array}{r} 3x^2 - 2x - 5 \\ \underline{2x^2 + x - 2} \end{array}$

Answers on page A-23

EXAMPLE 11 Multiply: $(5x^3 - 3x + 4)(-2x^2 - 3)$.

When missing terms occur, it helps to leave spaces for them and align like terms as we multiply.

$$\begin{array}{rrrrrl} & 5x^3 & & -3x & +4 & \\ & & -2x^2 & & -3 & \\ \hline & -15x^3 & & +9x & -12 & \text{Multiplying by } -3 \\ -10x^5 & +6x^3 & -8x^2 & & & \text{Multiplying by } -2x^2 \\ \hline -10x^5 & -9x^3 & -8x^2 & +9x & -12 & \text{Collecting like terms} \end{array}$$

Do Exercises 19 and 20.

EXAMPLE 12 Multiply: $(2x^2 + 3x - 4)(2x^2 - x + 3)$.

$$\begin{array}{rrrrrl} & & 2x^2 & +3x & -4 & \\ & & 2x^2 & -x & +3 & \\ \hline & & 6x^2 & +9x & -12 & \text{Multiplying by } 3 \\ & -2x^3 & -3x^2 & +4x & & \text{Multiplying by } -x \\ 4x^4 & +6x^3 & -8x^2 & & & \text{Multiplying by } 2x^2 \\ \hline 4x^4 & +4x^3 & -5x^2 & +13x & -12 & \text{Collecting like terms} \end{array}$$

Do Exercise 21.

CALCULATOR CORNER

Checking Multiplication of Polynomials A partial check of multiplication of polynomials can be performed graphically on the TI-84 Plus graphing calculator. Consider the product $(x + 3)(x - 2) = x^2 + x - 6$. We will use two graph styles to determine whether this product is correct. First, we press MODE to determine whether SEQUENTIAL mode is selected. If it is not, we position the blinking cursor over SEQUENTIAL and then press ENTER. Next, on the Y = screen, we enter $y_1 = (x + 3)(x - 2)$ and $y_2 = x^2 + x - 6$. We will select the line-graph style for y_1 and the path style for y_2. To select these graph styles, we use ◀ to position the cursor over the icon to the left of the equation and press ENTER repeatedly until the desired style of icon appears, as shown below.

```
NORMAL SCI ENG
FLOAT 0123456789
RADIAN DEGREE
FUNC PAR POL SEQ
CONNECTED DOT
SEQUENTIAL SIMUL
REAL a+bi re^θi
FULL HORIZ G–T
```

```
Plot1  Plot2  Plot3
\Y1 = (X+3)(X−2)
-0Y2 = X2+X−6
\Y3 =
\Y4 =
\Y5 =
\Y6 =
\Y7 =
```

$y_1 = (x + 3)(x - 2),\ y_2 = x^2 + x - 6$

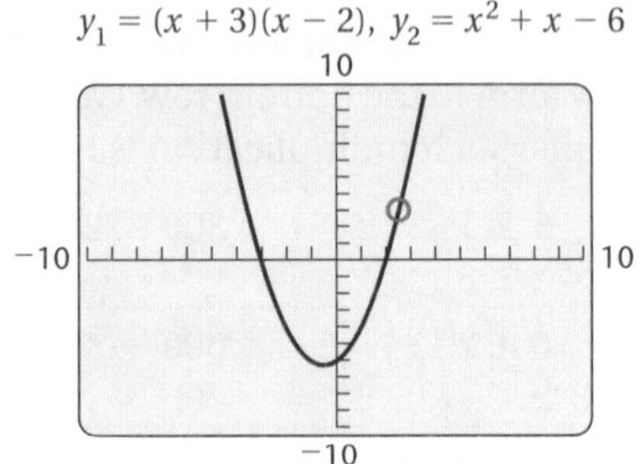

The graphing calculator will graph y_1 first as a solid line. Then it will graph y_2 as the circular cursor traces the leading edge of the graph, allowing us to determine visually whether the graphs coincide. In this case, the graphs appear to coincide, so the factorization is probably correct.

A table can also be used to perform a partial check of a product. See the Calculator Corner on p. 344 for the procedure.

Exercises: Determine graphically whether the product is correct.

1. $(x + 5)(x + 4) = x^2 + 9x + 20$
2. $(4x + 3)(x - 2) = 4x^2 - 5x - 6$
3. $(5x + 3)(x - 4) = 5x^2 + 17x - 12$
4. $(2x - 3)(3x - 5) = 6x^2 - 19x - 15$

4.5 EXERCISE SET

For Extra Help

MathXL | MyMathLab | InterAct Math | Math Tutor Center | Digital Video Tutor CD 3 Videotape 5 | Student's Solutions Manual

a Multiply.

1. $(8x^2)(5)$

2. $(4x^2)(-2)$

3. $(-x^2)(-x)$

4. $(-x^3)(x^2)$

5. $(8x^5)(4x^3)$

6. $(10a^2)(2a^2)$

7. $(0.1x^6)(0.3x^5)$

8. $(0.3x^4)(-0.8x^6)$

9. $\left(-\frac{1}{5}x^3\right)\left(-\frac{1}{3}x\right)$

10. $\left(-\frac{1}{4}x^4\right)\left(\frac{1}{5}x^8\right)$

11. $(-4x^2)(0)$

12. $(-4m^5)(-1)$

3. $(3x^2)(-4x^3)(2x^6)$

14. $(-2y^5)(10y^4)(-3y^3)$

b Multiply.

5. $2x(-x+5)$

16. $3x(4x-6)$

17. $-5x(x-1)$

18. $-3x(-x-1)$

9. $x^2(x^3+1)$

20. $-2x^3(x^2-1)$

21. $3x(2x^2-6x+1)$

22. $-4x(2x^3-6x^2-5x+1)$

3. $(-6x^2)(x^2+x)$

24. $(-4x^2)(x^2-x)$

25. $(3y^2)(6y^4+8y^3)$

26. $(4y^4)(y^3-6y^2)$

c Multiply.

7. $(x+6)(x+3)$

28. $(x+5)(x+2)$

29. $(x+5)(x-2)$

30. $(x+6)(x-2)$

1. $(x-4)(x-3)$

32. $(x-7)(x-3)$

33. $(x+3)(x-3)$

34. $(x+6)(x-6)$

5. $(5-x)(5-2x)$

36. $(3+x)(6+2x)$

37. $(2x+5)(2x+5)$

38. $(3x-4)(3x-4)$

9. $\left(x-\frac{5}{2}\right)\left(x+\frac{2}{5}\right)$

40. $\left(x+\frac{4}{3}\right)\left(x+\frac{3}{2}\right)$

41. $(x-2.3)(x+4.7)$

42. $(2x+0.13)(2x-0.13)$

Vrite an algebraic expression that represents the total area of the four smaller rectangles.

3.

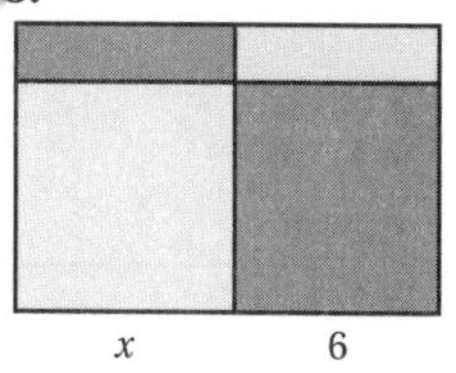

44.

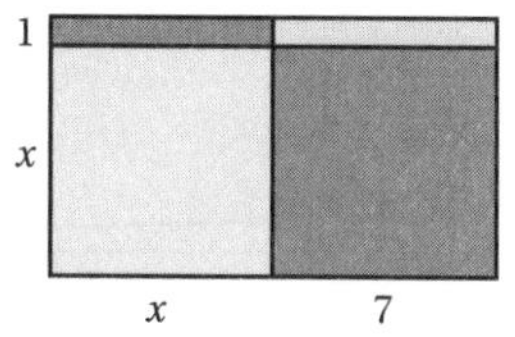

45.

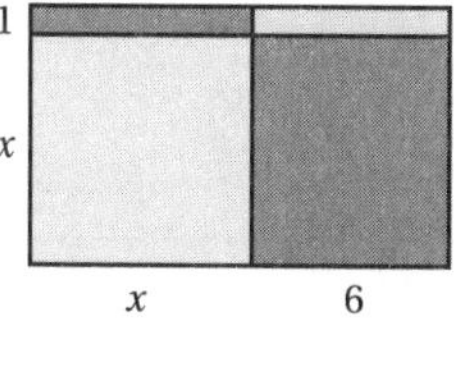

46.

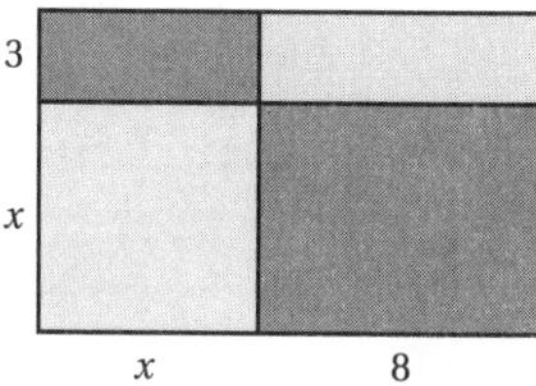

raw and label rectangles similar to the one following Example 7 to illustrate each product.

7. $x(x+5)$

48. $x(x+2)$

49. $(x+1)(x+2)$

0. $(x+3)(x+1)$

51. $(x+5)(x+3)$

52. $(x+4)(x+6)$

d Multiply.

53. $(x^2 + x + 1)(x - 1)$

54. $(x^2 + x - 2)(x + 2)$

55. $(2x + 1)(2x^2 + 6x + 1)$

56. $(3x - 1)(4x^2 - 2x - 1)$

57. $(y^2 - 3)(3y^2 - 6y + 2)$

58. $(3y^2 - 3)(y^2 + 6y + 1)$

59. $(x^3 + x^2)(x^3 + x^2 - x)$

60. $(x^3 - x^2)(x^3 - x^2 + x)$

61. $(-5x^3 - 7x^2 + 1)(2x^2 - x)$

62. $(-4x^3 + 5x^2 - 2)(5x^2 + 1)$

63. $(1 + x + x^2)(-1 - x + x^2)$

64. $(1 - x + x^2)(1 - x + x^2)$

65. $(2t^2 - t - 4)(3t^2 + 2t - 1)$

66. $(3a^2 - 5a + 2)(2a^2 - 3a + 4)$

67. $(x - x^3 + x^5)(x^2 - 1 + x^4)$

68. $(x - x^3 + x^5)(3x^2 + 3x^6 + 3x^4)$

69. $(x^3 + x^2 + x + 1)(x - 1)$

70. $(x + 2)(x^3 - x^2 + x - 2)$

71. $(x + 1)(x^3 + 7x^2 + 5x + 4)$

72. $(x + 2)(x^3 + 5x^2 + 9x + 3)$

73. $\left(x - \frac{1}{2}\right)\left(2x^3 - 4x^2 + 3x - \frac{2}{5}\right)$

74. $\left(x + \frac{1}{3}\right)\left(6x^3 - 12x^2 - 5x + \frac{1}{2}\right)$

75. **D$_W$** Under what conditions will the product of two binomials be a trinomial?

76. **D$_W$** How can the following figure be used to show that $(x + 3)^2 \neq x^2 + 9$?

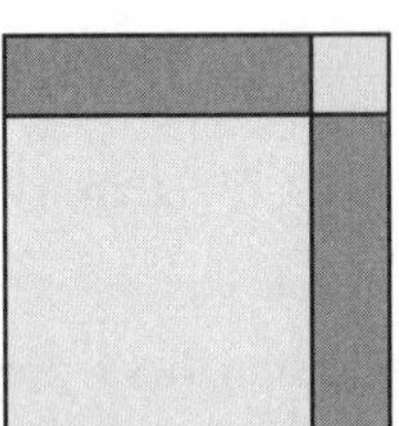

SKILL MAINTENANCE

Simplify.

77. $-\frac{1}{4} - \frac{1}{2}$ [1.4a]

78. $-3.8 - (-10.2)$ [1.4a]

79. $(10 - 2)(10 + 2)$ [1.8d]

80. $10 - 2 + (-6)^2 \div 3 \cdot$ [1.8d]

Factor. [1.7d]

81. $15x - 18y + 12$

82. $16x - 24y + 36$

83. $-9x - 45y + 15$

84. $100x - 100y + 1000a$

85. Graph: $y = \frac{1}{2}x - 3.$ [3.5a]

86. Solve: $4(x - 3) = 5(2 - 3x) + 1.$ [2.3c]

SYNTHESIS

nd a polynomial for the shaded area of the figure.

7.

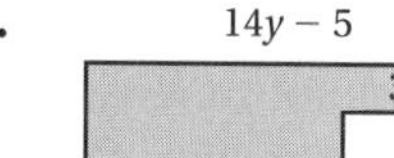

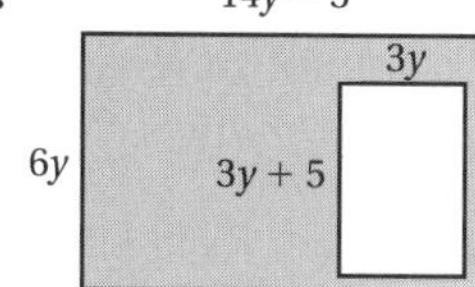

88.

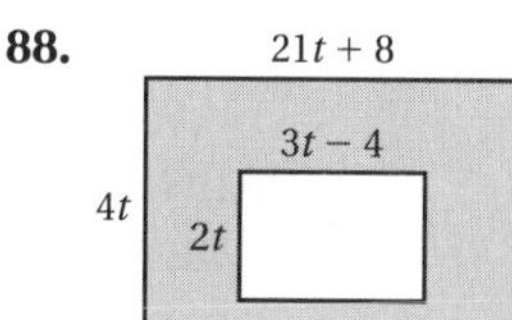

. A box with a square bottom is to be made from a 12-in.-square piece of cardboard. Squares with side x are cut out of the corners and the sides are folded up. Find the polynomials for the volume and the outside surface area of the box.

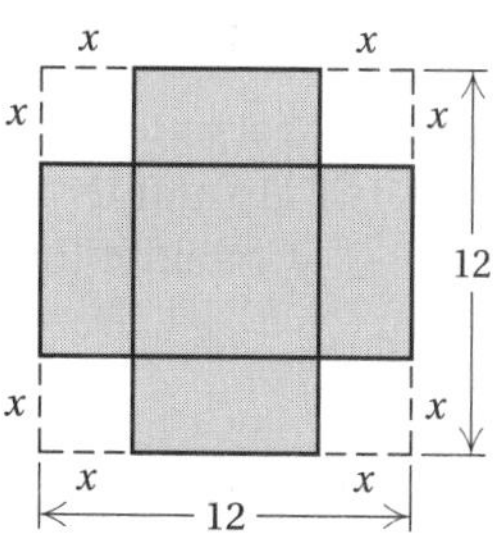

r each figure, determine what the missing number must be in order for the figure to have the given area.

. Area $= x^2 + 7x + 10$

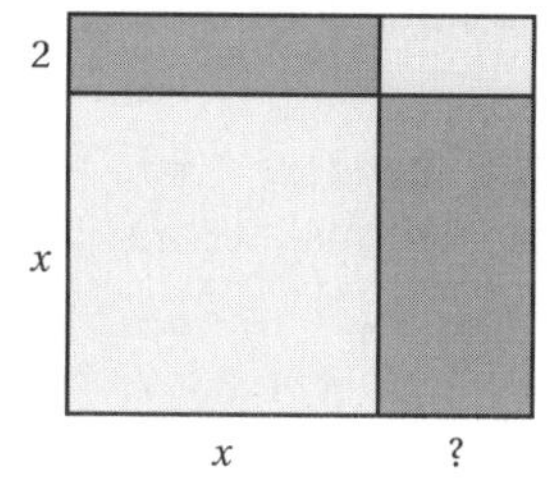

91. Area $= x^2 + 8x + 15$

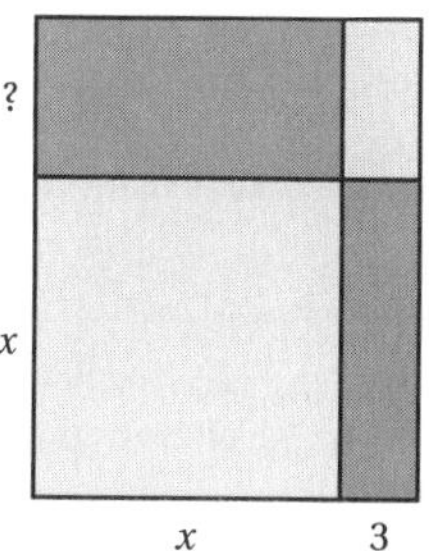

. An open wooden box is a cube with side x cm. The box, including its bottom, is made of wood that is 1 cm thick. Find a polynomial for the interior volume of the cube.

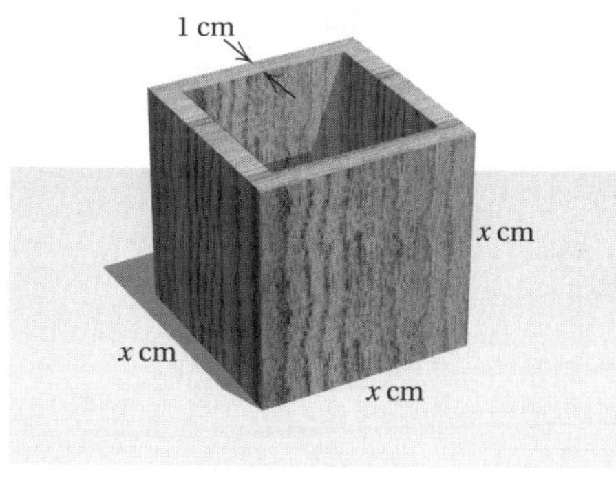

93. Find a polynomial for the volume of the solid shown below.

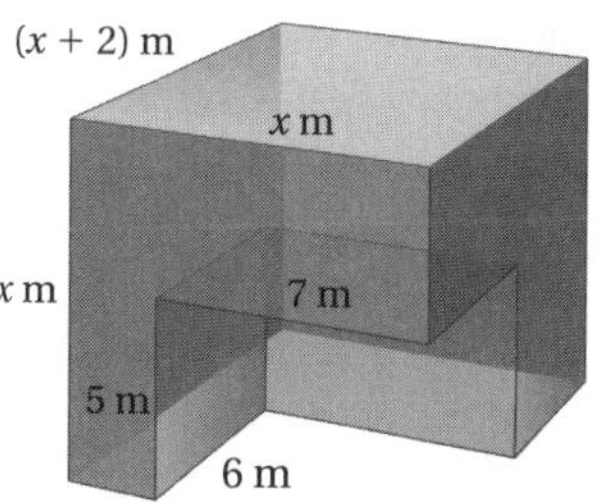

mpute and simplify.

. $(x + 3)(x + 6) + (x + 3)(x + 6)$

95. $(x - 2)(x - 7) - (x - 7)(x - 2)$

. $(x + 5)^2 - (x - 3)^2$

. Extend the pattern and simplify:

$$(x - a)(x - b)(x - c)(x - d) \cdots (x - z).$$

98. Use a graphing calculator to check your answers to Exercises 15, 29, and 53. Use graphs, tables, or both, as directed by your instructor.

4.6 SPECIAL PRODUCTS

Objectives

a Multiply two binomials mentally using the FOIL method.

b Multiply the sum and the difference of two terms mentally.

c Square a binomial mentally.

d Find special products when polynomial products are mixed together.

We encounter certain products so often that it is helpful to have faste methods of computing. Such techniques are called *special products*. We no consider special ways of multiplying any two binomials.

a Products of Two Binomials Using FOIL

To multiply two binomials, we can select one binomial and multiply eac term of that binomial by every term of the other. Then we collect like term Consider the product $(x + 3)(x + 7)$:

$$\begin{aligned}(x + 3)(x + 7) &= x(x + 7) + 3(x + 7)\\ &= x \cdot x + x \cdot 7 + 3 \cdot x + 3 \cdot 7\\ &= x^2 + 7x + 3x + 21\\ &= x^2 + 10x + 21.\end{aligned}$$

This example illustrates a special technique for finding the product of tw binomials:

First terms	Outside terms	Inside terms	Last terms

$$(x + 3)(x + 7) = x \cdot x + 7 \cdot x + 3 \cdot x + 3 \cdot 7.$$

To remember this method of multiplying, we use the initials **FOIL.**

THE FOIL METHOD

To multiply two binomials, $A + B$ and $C + D$, multiply the First terms AC, the Outside terms AD, the Inside terms BC, and then the Last terms BD. Then collect like terms, if possible.

$$(A + B)(C + D) = AC + AD + BC + BD$$

1. Multiply First terms: AC.
2. Multiply Outside terms: AD.
3. Multiply Inside terms: BC.
4. Multiply Last terms: BD.

FOIL

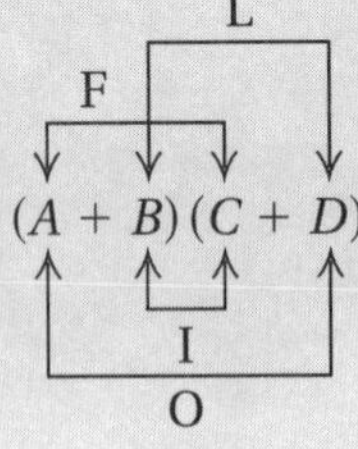

EXAMPLE 1 Multiply: $(x + 8)(x^2 - 5)$.

We have

$$\begin{aligned}&\quad\ \ \text{F}\qquad\quad\ \text{O}\qquad\quad\ \ \text{I}\qquad\quad \text{L}\\(x + 8)(x^2 - 5) &= x \cdot x^2 + x \cdot (-5) + 8 \cdot x^2 + 8(-5)\\ &= x^3 - 5x + 8x^2 - 40\\ &= x^3 + 8x^2 - 5x - 40.\end{aligned}$$

Since each of the original binomials is in descending order, we write t product in descending order, as is customary, but this is not a "must."

Study Tips

CHECKLIST

The foundation of all your study skills is TIME!

- ☐ Have you tried using the audio recordings?
- ☐ Are you taking the time to include all the steps when working your homework and the tests?
- ☐ Are you using the time-management suggestions we have given so you have the proper amount of time to study mathematics?
- ☐ Have you been using the supplements for the text such as the *Student's Solutions Manual* and the AW Math Tutor Center?
- ☐ Have you memorized the rules for special products of polynomials and for manipulating expressions with exponents?

Often we can collect like terms after we have multiplied.

XAMPLES Multiply.

2. $(x + 6)(x - 6) = x^2 - 6x + 6x - 36$ Using FOIL
$= x^2 - 36$ Collecting like terms

3. $(x + 7)(x + 4) = x^2 + 4x + 7x + 28$
$= x^2 + 11x + 28$

4. $(y - 3)(y - 2) = y^2 - 2y - 3y + 6$
$= y^2 - 5y + 6$

5. $(x^3 - 5)(x^3 + 5) = x^6 + 5x^3 - 5x^3 - 25$
$= x^6 - 25$

6. $(4t^3 + 5)(3t^2 - 2) = 12t^5 - 8t^3 + 15t^2 - 10$

o Exercises 1–8.

XAMPLES Multiply.

7. $\left(x - \frac{2}{3}\right)\left(x + \frac{2}{3}\right) = x^2 + \frac{2}{3}x - \frac{2}{3}x - \frac{4}{9}$
$= x^2 - \frac{4}{9}$

8. $(x^2 - 0.3)(x^2 - 0.3) = x^4 - 0.3x^2 - 0.3x^2 + 0.09$
$= x^4 - 0.6x^2 + 0.09$

9. $(3 - 4x)(7 - 5x^3) = 21 - 15x^3 - 28x + 20x^4$
$= 21 - 28x - 15x^3 + 20x^4$

(*Note*: If the original polynomials are in ascending order, it is natural to write the product in ascending order, but this is not a "must.")

. $(5x^4 + 2x^3)(3x^2 - 7x) = 15x^6 - 35x^5 + 6x^5 - 14x^4$
$= 15x^6 - 29x^5 - 14x^4$

Exercises 9–12.

We can show the FOIL method geometrically as follows.

The area of the large rectangle is $(A + B)(C + D)$.

The area of rectangle ① is AC.
The area of rectangle ② is AD.
The area of rectangle ③ is BC.
The area of rectangle ④ is BD.

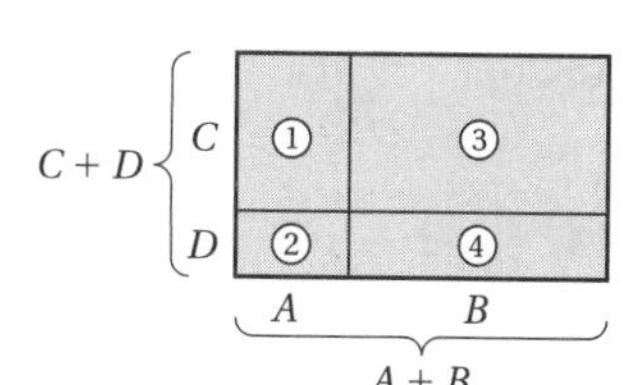

The area of the large rectangle is the sum of the areas of the smaller rectangles. Thus,

$$(A + B)(C + D) = AC + AD + BC + BD.$$

Multiplying Sums and Differences of Two Terms

nsider the product of the sum and the difference of the same two terms, ch as

$$(x + 2)(x - 2).$$

Multiply mentally, if possible. If you need extra steps, be sure to use them.

1. $(x + 3)(x + 4)$

2. $(x + 3)(x - 5)$

3. $(2x - 1)(x - 4)$

4. $(2x^2 - 3)(x - 2)$

5. $(6x^2 + 5)(2x^3 + 1)$

6. $(y^3 + 7)(y^3 - 7)$

7. $(t + 5)(t + 3)$

8. $(2x^4 + x^2)(-x^3 + x)$

Multiply.

9. $\left(x + \frac{4}{5}\right)\left(x - \frac{4}{5}\right)$

10. $(x^3 - 0.5)(x^2 + 0.5)$

11. $(2 + 3x^2)(4 - 5x^2)$

12. $(6x^3 - 3x^2)(5x^2 - 2x)$

Answers on page A-23

Multiply.

13. $(x + 5)(x - 5)$

14. $(2x - 3)(2x + 3)$

Since this is the product of two binomials, we can use FOIL. This type of product occurs so often, however, that it would be valuable if we could use an even faster method. To find a faster way to compute such a product, look for a pattern in the following:

a) $(x + 2)(x - 2) = x^2 - 2x + 2x - 4$ Using FOIL
$= x^2 - 4;$

b) $(3x - 5)(3x + 5) = 9x^2 + 15x - 15x - 25$
$= 9x^2 - 25.$

Do Exercises 13 and 14.

Perhaps you discovered in each case that when you multiply the two binomials, two terms are opposites, or additive inverses, which add to 0 and "drop out."

Multiply.

15. $(x + 2)(x - 2)$

16. $(x - 7)(x + 7)$

17. $(6 - 4y)(6 + 4y)$

18. $(2x^3 - 1)(2x^3 + 1)$

19. $\left(x - \frac{2}{5}\right)\left(x + \frac{2}{5}\right)$

Answers on page A-23

PRODUCT OF THE SUM AND THE DIFFERENCE

The product of the sum and the difference of the same two terms is the square of the first term minus the square of the second term:

$$(A + B)(A - B) = A^2 - B^2.$$

It is helpful to memorize this rule in both words and symbols. (If you do forget it, you can, of course, use FOIL.)

EXAMPLES Multiply. (Carry out the rule and say the words as you go.)

$$(A + B)(A - B) = A^2 - B^2$$

11. $(x + 4)(x - 4) = x^2 - 4^2$ "The square of the first term, x^2, minus the square of the second, 4^2"
$= x^2 - 16$ Simplifying

12. $(5 + 2w)(5 - 2w) = 5^2 - (2w)^2$
$= 25 - 4w^2$

13. $(3x^2 - 7)(3x^2 + 7) = (3x^2)^2 - 7^2$
$= 9x^4 - 49$

14. $(-4x - 10)(-4x + 10) = (-4x)^2 - 10^2$
$= 16x^2 - 100$

15. $\left(x + \frac{3}{8}\right)\left(x - \frac{3}{8}\right) = x^2 - \left(\frac{3}{8}\right)^2 = x^2 - \frac{9}{64}$

Do Exercises 15–19.

C Squaring Binomials

Consider the square of a binomial, such as $(x + 3)^2$. This can be expressed as $(x + 3)(x + 3)$. Since this is the product of two binomials, we can again use FOIL. But again, this type of product occurs so often that we would like to use an even faster method. Look for a pattern in the following:

) $(x+3)^2 = (x+3)(x+3)$
$= x^2 + 3x + 3x + 9$
$= x^2 + 6x + 9;$

b) $(x-3)^2 = (x-3)(x-3)$
$= x^2 - 3x - 3x + 9$
$= x^2 - 6x + 9;$

) $(5+3p)^2 = (5+3p)(5+3p)$
$= 25 + 15p + 15p + 9p^2$
$= 25 + 30p + 9p^2;$

d) $(3x-5)^2 = (3x-5)(3x-5)$
$= 9x^2 - 15x - 15x + 25$
$= 9x^2 - 30x + 25.$

o Exercises 20 and 21.

Multiply.

20. $(x+8)(x+8)$

21. $(x-5)(x-5)$

When squaring a binomial, we multiply a binomial by itself. Perhaps you oticed that two terms are the same and when added give twice the product f the terms in the binomial. The other two terms are squares.

SQUARE OF A BINOMIAL

The square of a sum or a difference of two terms is the square of the first term, plus or minus twice the product of the two terms, plus the square of the last term:

$$(A+B)^2 = A^2 + 2AB + B^2; \qquad (A-B)^2 = A^2 - 2AB + B^2.$$

It is helpful to memorize this rule in both words and symbols.

XAMPLES Multiply. (Carry out the rule and say the words as you go.)

$(A+B)^2 = A^2 + 2 \cdot A \cdot B + B^2$

5. $(x+3)^2 = x^2 + 2 \cdot x \cdot 3 + 3^2$ "x^2 plus 2 times x times 3 plus 3^2"
$= x^2 + 6x + 9$

$(A-B)^2 = A^2 - 2 \cdot A \cdot B + B^2$

. $(t-5)^2 = t^2 - 2 \cdot t \cdot 5 + 5^2$ "t^2 minus 2 times t times 5 plus 5^2"
$= t^2 - 10t + 25$

. $(2x+7)^2 = (2x)^2 + 2 \cdot 2x \cdot 7 + 7^2 = 4x^2 + 28x + 49$

. $(5x-3x^2)^2 = (5x)^2 - 2 \cdot 5x \cdot 3x^2 + (3x^2)^2 = 25x^2 - 30x^3 + 9x^4$

. $(2.3 - 5.4m)^2 = 2.3^2 - 2(2.3)(5.4m) + (5.4m)^2$
$= 5.29 - 24.84m + 29.16m^2$

) Exercises 22–27.

Multiply.

22. $(x+2)^2$

23. $(a-4)^2$

24. $(2x+5)^2$

25. $(4x^2-3x)^2$

26. $(7.8+1.2y)(7.8+1.2y)$

27. $(3x^2-5)(3x^2-5)$

Caution!

Although the square of a product is the product of the squares, the square of a sum is *not* the sum of the squares. That is, $(AB)^2 = A^2B^2$, but

The term $2AB$ is missing.

$$(A+B)^2 \neq A^2 + B^2.$$

To confirm this inequality, note, using the rules for order of operations, that

$$(7+5)^2 = 12^2 = 144,$$

whereas

$$7^2 + 5^2 = 49 + 25 = 74, \quad \text{and} \quad 74 \neq 144.$$

Answers on page A-23

28. In the figure at right, describe in terms of area the sum $A^2 + B^2$. How can the figure be used to verify that $(A + B)^2 \neq A^2 + B^2$?

Answer on page A-23

We can look at the rule for finding $(A + B)^2$ geometrically as follows. Th area of the large square is

$$(A + B)(A + B) = (A + B)^2.$$

This is equal to the sum of the areas of the smaller rectangles:

$$A^2 + AB + AB + B^2 = A^2 + 2AB + B^2.$$

Thus, $(A + B)^2 = A^2 + 2AB + B^2$.

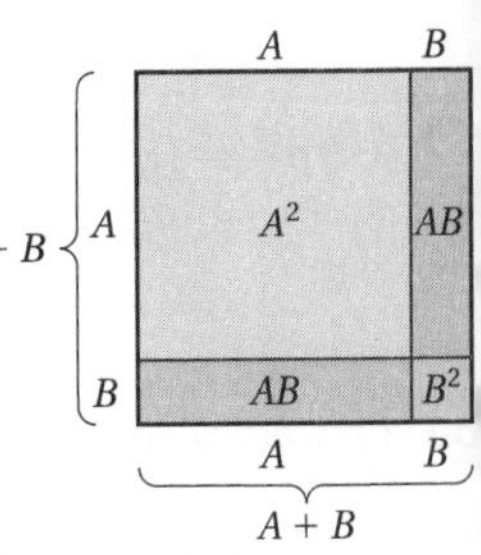

Do Exercise 28.

d Multiplication of Various Types

Let's now try several types of multiplications mixed together so that we ca learn to sort them out. When you multiply, first see what kind of multiplic tion you have. Then use the best method.

MULTIPLYING TWO POLYNOMIALS

1. Is it the product of a monomial and a polynomial? If so, multiply each term of the polynomial by the monomial.
   Example: $5x(x + 7) = 5x \cdot x + 5x \cdot 7 = 5x^2 + 35x$
2. Is it the product of the sum and the difference of the *same* two terms? If so, use the following:
   $$(A + B)(A - B) = A^2 - B^2.$$
   The product of the sum and the difference of the same two terms is the difference of the squares. [The answer has 2 terms.]
   Example: $(x + 7)(x - 7) = x^2 - 7^2 = x^2 - 49$
3. Is the product the square of a binomial? If so, use the following:
   $$(A + B)(A + B) = (A + B)^2 = A^2 + 2AB + B^2,$$
   or $$(A - B)(A - B) = (A - B)^2 = A^2 - 2AB + B^2.$$
   The square of a binomial is the square of the first term, plus or minus *twice* the product of the two terms, plus the square of the last term. [The answer has 3 terms.]
   Example: $(x + 7)(x + 7) = (x + 7)^2$
   $= x^2 + 2 \cdot x \cdot 7 + 7^2 = x^2 + 14x + 49$
4. Is it the product of two binomials other than those above? If so, use FOIL. [The answer will have 3 or 4 terms.]
   Example: $(x + 7)(x - 4) = x^2 - 4x + 7x - 28 = x^2 + 3x - 28$
5. Is it the product of two polynomials other than those above? If so, multiply each term of one by every term of the other. Use columns if you wish. [The answer will have 2 or more terms, usually more than 2 terms.]
   Example:
   $$\begin{aligned}(x^2 - 3x + 2)(x + 7) &= x^2(x + 7) - 3x(x + 7) + 2(x + 7)\\ &= x^2 \cdot x + x^2 \cdot 7 - 3x \cdot x - 3x \cdot 7\\ &\quad + 2 \cdot x + 2 \cdot 7\\ &= x^3 + 7x^2 - 3x^2 - 21x + 2x + 14\\ &= x^3 + 4x^2 - 19x + 14\end{aligned}$$

Remember that FOIL will *always* work for two binomials. You can use instead of either of rules 2 and 3, but those rules will make your work go fast

Study Tips

MEMORIZING FORMULAS

Memorizing can be a very helpful tool in the study of mathematics. Don't underestimate its power as you consider the special products. Consider putting the rules, in words and in math symbols, on index cards and go over them many times.

XAMPLE 21 Multiply: $(x + 3)(x - 3)$.

$(x + 3)(x - 3) = x^2 - 9$ Using method 2 (the product of the sum and the difference of two terms)

XAMPLE 22 Multiply: $(t + 7)(t - 5)$.

$(t + 7)(t - 5) = t^2 + 2t - 35$ Using method 4 (the product of two binomials, but neither the square of a binomial nor the product of the sum and the difference of two terms)

XAMPLE 23 Multiply: $(x + 6)(x + 6)$.

$(x + 6)(x + 6) = x^2 + 2(6)x + 36$ Using method 3 (the square of a binomial sum)

$= x^2 + 12x + 36$

XAMPLE 24 Multiply: $2x^3(9x^2 + x - 7)$.

$2x^3(9x^2 + x - 7) = 18x^5 + 2x^4 - 14x^3$ Using method 1 (the product of a monomial and a trinomial; multiplying each term of the trinomial by the monomial)

XAMPLE 25 Multiply: $(5x^3 - 7x)^2$.

$(5x^3 - 7x)^2 = 25x^6 - 2(5x^3)(7x) + 49x^2$ Using method 3 (the square of a binomial difference)

$= 25x^6 - 70x^4 + 49x^2$

XAMPLE 26 Multiply: $\left(3x + \frac{1}{4}\right)^2$.

$\left(3x + \frac{1}{4}\right)^2 = 9x^2 + 2(3x)\left(\frac{1}{4}\right) + \frac{1}{16}$ Using method 3 (the square of a binomial sum. To get the middle term, we multiply $3x$ by $\frac{1}{4}$ and double.)

$= 9x^2 + \frac{3}{2}x + \frac{1}{16}$

XAMPLE 27 Multiply: $\left(4x - \frac{3}{4}\right)^2$.

$\left(4x - \frac{3}{4}\right)^2 = 16x^2 - 2(4x)\left(\frac{3}{4}\right) + \frac{9}{16}$ Using method 3 (the square of a binomial difference)

$= 16x^2 - 6x + \frac{9}{16}$

XAMPLE 28 Multiply: $(p + 3)(p^2 + 2p - 1)$.

$$\begin{array}{r}p^2 + 2p - 1\\ p + 3\\ \hline 3p^2 + 6p - 3\\ p^3 + 2p^2 - p\quad\\ \hline p^3 + 5p^2 + 5p - 3\end{array}$$

Using method 5 (the product of two polynomials)

Multiplying by 3

Multiplying by p

Exercises 29–36.

Multiply.

29. $(x + 5)(x + 6)$

30. $(t - 4)(t + 4)$

31. $4x^2(-2x^3 + 5x^2 + 10)$

32. $(9x^2 + 1)^2$

33. $(2a - 5)(2a + 8)$

34. $\left(5x + \frac{1}{2}\right)^2$

35. $\left(2x - \frac{1}{2}\right)^2$

36. $(x^2 - x + 4)(x - 2)$

Answers on page A-23

Visualizing for Success

1

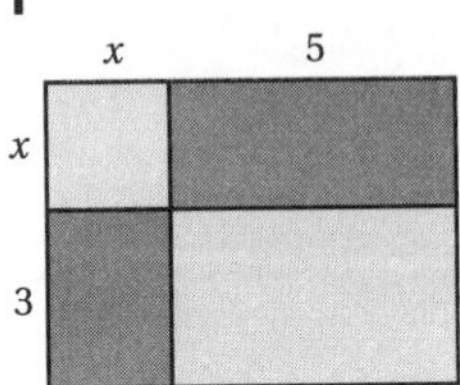

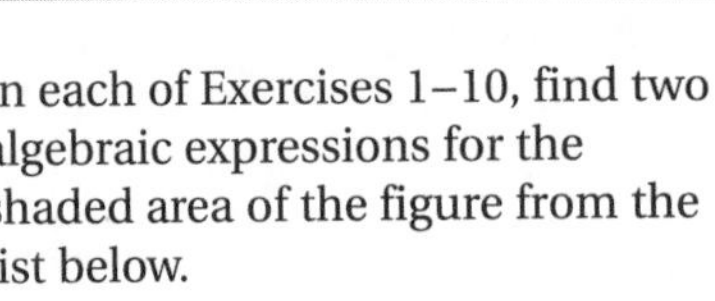

In each of Exercises 1–10, find two algebraic expressions for the shaded area of the figure from the list below.

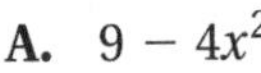

A. $9 - 4x^2$
B. $x^2 - (x - 6)^2$
C. $(x + 3)(x - 3)$
D. $10^2 + 2^2$
E. $x^2 + 8x + 15$
F. $(x + 5)(x + 3)$
G. $x^2 - 6x + 9$
H. $(3 - 2x)^2 + 4x(3 - 2x)$
I. $(x + 3)^2$
J. $(5x + 3)^2$
K. $(5 - 2x)^2 + 4x(5 - 2x)$
L. $x^2 - 9$
M. 104
N. $x^2 - 15$
O. $12x - 36$
P. $25x^2 + 30x + 9$
Q. $(x - 5)(x - 3) + 3(x - 5) + 5(x - 3)$
R. $(x - 3)^2$
S. $25 - 4x^2$
T. $x^2 + 6x + 9$

Answers on page A-23

2

3
3
x
x

3

5
x
x
5
x
x

4

3
x
3
x

5

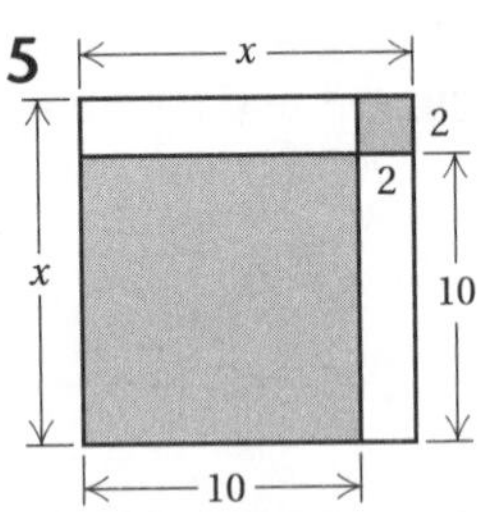

6

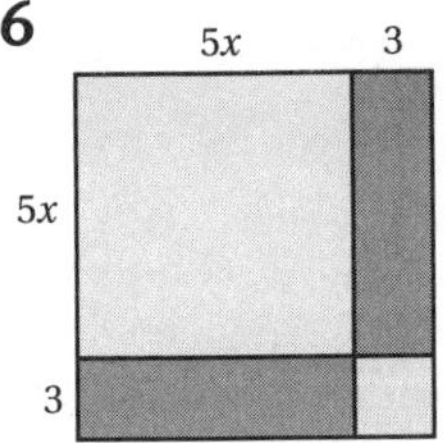

7

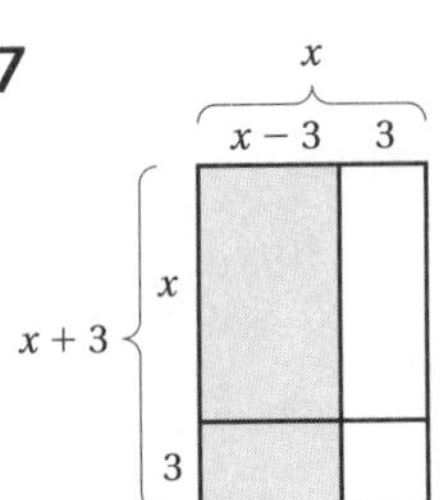

8

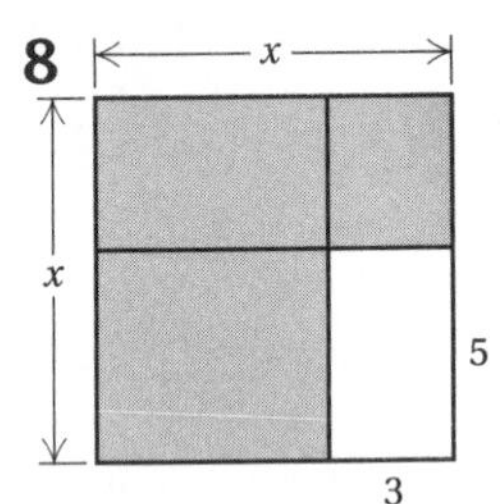

9

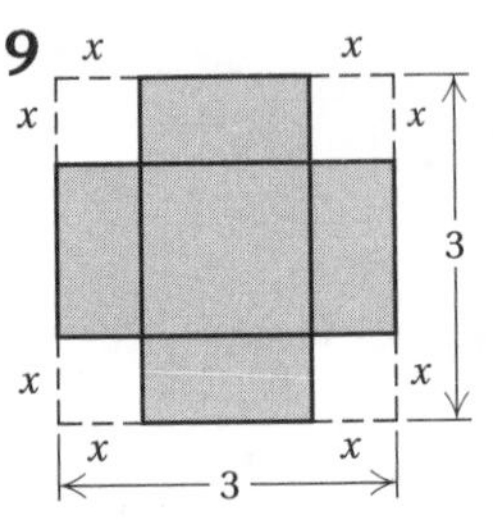

10

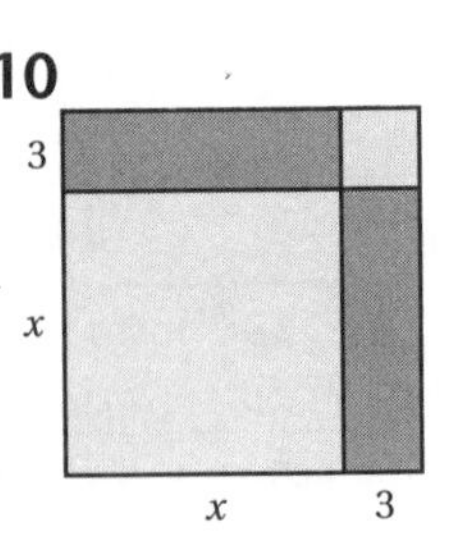

4.6 EXERCISE SET

For Extra Help

MathXL | MyMathLab | InterAct Math | Math Tutor Center | Digital Video Tutor CD 3 Videotape 5 | Student's Solutions Manual

a Multiply. Try to write only the answer. If you need more steps, be sure to use them.

1. $(x+1)(x^2+3)$

2. $(x^2-3)(x-1)$

3. $(x^3+2)(x+1)$

4. $(x^4+2)(x+10)$

5. $(y+2)(y-3)$

6. $(a+2)(a+3)$

7. $(3x+2)(3x+2)$

8. $(4x+1)(4x+1)$

9. $(5x-6)(x+2)$

10. $(x-8)(x+8)$

11. $(3t-1)(3t+1)$

12. $(2m+3)(2m+3)$

3. $(4x-2)(x-1)$

14. $(2x-1)(3x+1)$

15. $\left(p-\frac{1}{4}\right)\left(p+\frac{1}{4}\right)$

16. $\left(q+\frac{3}{4}\right)\left(q+\frac{3}{4}\right)$

7. $(x-0.1)(x+0.1)$

18. $(x+0.3)(x-0.4)$

19. $(2x^2+6)(x+1)$

20. $(2x^2+3)(2x-1)$

1. $(-2x+1)(x+6)$

22. $(3x+4)(2x-4)$

23. $(a+7)(a+7)$

24. $(2y+5)(2y+5)$

5. $(1+2x)(1-3x)$

26. $(-3x-2)(x+1)$

27. $\left(\frac{3}{8}y-\frac{5}{6}\right)\left(\frac{3}{8}y-\frac{5}{6}\right)$

28. $\left(\frac{1}{5}x-\frac{2}{7}\right)\left(\frac{1}{5}x+\frac{2}{7}\right)$

9. $(x^2+3)(x^3-1)$

30. $(x^4-3)(2x+1)$

31. $(3x^2-2)(x^4-2)$

2. $(x^{10}+3)(x^{10}-3)$

33. $(2.8x-1.5)(4.7x+9.3)$

34. $\left(x-\frac{3}{8}\right)\left(x+\frac{4}{7}\right)$

35. $(3x^5 + 2)(2x^2 + 6)$

36. $(1 - 2x)(1 + 3x^2)$

37. $(8x^3 + 1)(x^3 + 8)$

38. $(4 - 2x)(5 - 2x^2)$

39. $(4x^2 + 3)(x - 3)$

40. $(7x - 2)(2x - 7)$

41. $(4y^4 + y^2)(y^2 + y)$

42. $(5y^6 + 3y^3)(2y^6 + 2y^3)$

b Multiply mentally, if possible. If you need extra steps, be sure to use them.

43. $(x + 4)(x - 4)$

44. $(x + 1)(x - 1)$

45. $(2x + 1)(2x - 1)$

46. $(x^2 + 1)(x^2 - 1)$

47. $(5m - 2)(5m + 2)$

48. $(3x^4 + 2)(3x^4 - 2)$

49. $(2x^2 + 3)(2x^2 - 3)$

50. $(6x^5 - 5)(6x^5 + 5)$

51. $(3x^4 - 4)(3x^4 + 4)$

52. $(t^2 - 0.2)(t^2 + 0.2)$

53. $(x^6 - x^2)(x^6 + x^2)$

54. $(2x^3 - 0.3)(2x^3 + 0.3)$

55. $(x^4 + 3x)(x^4 - 3x)$

56. $\left(\frac{3}{4} + 2x^3\right)\left(\frac{3}{4} - 2x^3\right)$

57. $(x^{12} - 3)(x^{12} + 3)$

58. $(12 - 3x^2)(12 + 3x$

59. $(2y^8 + 3)(2y^8 - 3)$

60. $\left(m - \frac{2}{3}\right)\left(m + \frac{2}{3}\right)$

61. $\left(\frac{5}{8}x - 4.3\right)\left(\frac{5}{8}x + 4.3\right)$

62. $(10.7 - x^3)(10.7 + x^3)$

c Multiply mentally, if possible. If you need extra steps, be sure to use them.

63. $(x + 2)^2$

64. $(2x - 1)^2$

65. $(3x^2 + 1)^2$

66. $\left(3x + \frac{3}{4}\right)^2$

67. $\left(a - \frac{1}{2}\right)^2$

68. $\left(2a - \frac{1}{5}\right)^2$

69. $(3 + x)^2$

70. $(x^3 - 1)^2$

1. $(x^2 + 1)^2$

72. $(8x - x^2)^2$

73. $(2 - 3x^4)^2$

74. $(6x^3 - 2)^2$

5. $(5 + 6t^2)^2$

76. $(3p^2 - p)^2$

77. $\left(x - \frac{5}{8}\right)^2$

78. $(0.3y + 2.4)^2$

d Multiply mentally, if possible.

9. $(3 - 2x^3)^2$

80. $(x - 4x^3)^2$

81. $4x(x^2 + 6x - 3)$

82. $8x(-x^5 + 6x^2 + 9)$

3. $\left(2x^2 - \frac{1}{2}\right)\left(2x^2 - \frac{1}{2}\right)$

84. $(-x^2 + 1)^2$

85. $(-1 + 3p)(1 + 3p)$

86. $(-3q + 2)(3q + 2)$

7. $3t^2(5t^3 - t^2 + t)$

88. $-6x^2(x^3 + 8x - 9)$

89. $(6x^4 + 4)^2$

90. $(8a + 5)^2$

1. $(3x + 2)(4x^2 + 5)$

92. $(2x^2 - 7)(3x^2 + 9)$

93. $(8 - 6x^4)^2$

94. $\left(\frac{1}{5}x^2 + 9\right)\left(\frac{3}{5}x^2 - 7\right)$

5. $(t - 1)(t^2 + t + 1)$

96. $(y + 5)(y^2 - 5y + 25)$

ompute each of the following and compare.

7. $3^2 + 4^2; (3 + 4)^2$

98. $6^2 + 7^2; (6 + 7)^2$

99. $9^2 - 5^2; (9 - 5)^2$

100. $11^2 - 4^2; (11 - 4)^2$

nd the total area of all the shaded rectangles.

1.

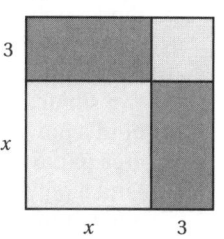

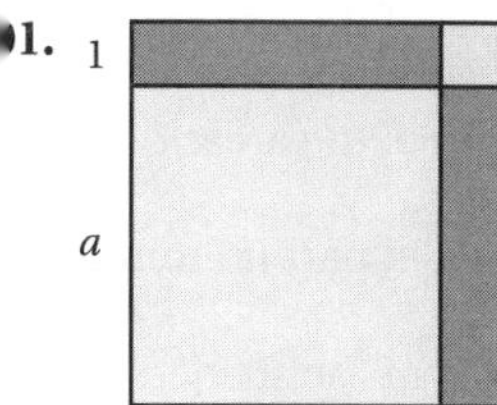

102.

3
x
x
3

103.

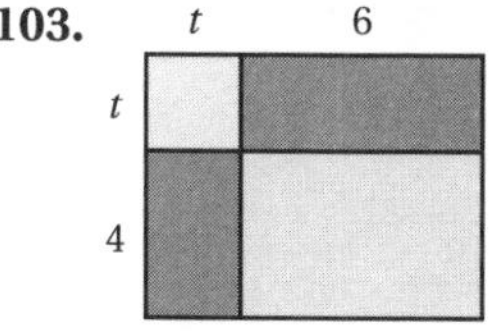

104.

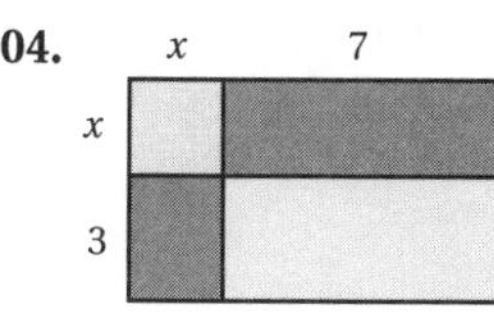

5. ^{D}W Under what conditions is the product of two binomials a binomial?

106. ^{D}W Brittney feels that since the FOIL method can be used to find the product of any two binomials, she needn't study the other special products. What advice would you give her?

SKILL MAINTENANCE

107. *Electricity Usage.* In apartment 3B, lamps, an air conditioner, and a television set are all operating at the same time. The lamps use 10 times as many watts of electricity as the television set, and the air conditioner uses 40 times as many watts as the television set. The total wattage used in the apartment is 2550. How many watts are used by each appliance? [2.6

Solve. [2.3c]

108. $3x - 8x = 4(7 - 8x)$

109. $3(x - 2) = 5(2x + 7)$

110. $5(2x - 3) - 2(3x - 4) = 20$

Solve. [2.4b]

111. $3x - 2y = 12$, for y

112. $3a - 5d = 4$, for a

SYNTHESIS

Multiply.

113. $5x(3x - 1)(2x + 3)$

114. $[(2x - 3)(2x + 3)](4x^2 + 9)$

115. $[(a - 5)(a + 5)]^2$

116. $(a - 3)^2(a + 3)^2$
(*Hint*: Examine Exercise 115.)

117. $(3t^4 - 2)^2(3t^4 + 2)^2$
(*Hint*: Examine Exercise 115.)

118. $[3a - (2a - 3)][3a + (2a - 3)]$

Solve.

119. $(x + 2)(x - 5) = (x + 1)(x - 3)$

120. $(2x + 5)(x - 4) = (x + 5)(2x - 4)$

121. *Factors and Sums.* To *factor* a number is to express it as a product. Since $12 = 4 \cdot 3$, we say that 12 is *factored* and that 4 and 3 are *factors* of 12. In the following table, the top number has been factored in such a way that the sum of the factors is the bottom number. For example, in the first column, 40 has been factored as $5 \cdot 8$, and $5 + 8 = 13$, the bottom number. Such thinking is important in algebra when we factor trinomials of the type $x^2 + bx + c$. Find the missing numbers in the table.

Product	40	63	36	72	−140	−96	48	168	110			
Factor	5									−9	−24	−3
Factor	8									−10	18	
Sum	13	16	−20	−38	−4	4	−14	−29	−21			18

122. A factored polynomial for the shaded area in this rectangle is $(A + B)(A - B)$.

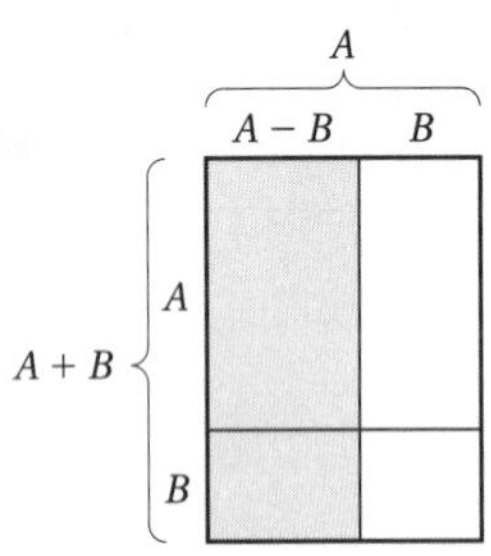

a) Find a polynomial for the area of the entire rectangle.

b) Find a polynomial for the sum of the areas of the two small unshaded rectangles.

c) Find a polynomial for the area in part (a) minus the area in part (b).

d) Find a polynomial for the area of the shaded region and compare this with the polynomial found in part (c).

Use the TABLE or GRAPH feature to check whether each of the following is correct.

123. $(x - 1)^2 = x^2 - 2x + 1$

124. $(x - 2)^2 = x^2 - 4x - 4$

125. $(x - 3)(x + 3) = x^2 - 6$

126. $(x - 3)(x + 2) = x^2 - x - 6$

5.1 INTRODUCTION TO FACTORING

Objectives

a. Find the greatest common factor, the GCF, of monomials.

b. Factor polynomials when the terms have a common factor, factoring out the greatest common factor.

c. Factor certain expressions with four terms using factoring by grouping.

We introduce factoring with a review of factoring natural numbers. Co sider the product $15 = 3 \cdot 5$. We say that 3 and 5 are **factors** of 15 and th $3 \cdot 5$ is a **factorization** of 15. Since $15 = 15 \cdot 1$, we also know that 15 and 1 a factors of 15 and that $15 \cdot 1$ is a factorization of 15.

a Finding the Greatest Common Factor

The numbers 20 and 30 have several factors in common, among them 2 a 5. The greatest of the common factors is called the **greatest common facto GCF.** One way to find the GCF is by making a list of factors of each number.

List all the factors of 20: 1, 2, 4, 5, 10, and 20.

List all the factors of 30: 1, 2, 3, 5, 6, 10, 15, and 30.

Now list the numbers common to both lists, the common factors:

1, 2, 5, and 10.

Then the greatest common factor, the GCF, is 10, the largest number in t common list.

The preceding procedure gives meaning to the notion of a GCF, but t following method, using prime factorizations, is generally faster.

EXAMPLE 1 Find the GCF of 20 and 30.

We find the prime factorization of each number. Then we draw lines b tween the common factors.

$$20 = 2 \cdot 2 \cdot 5$$

$$30 = 2 \cdot 3 \cdot 5$$

The GCF $= 2 \cdot 5 = 10$.

EXAMPLE 2 Find the GCF of 180 and 420.

We find the prime factorization of each number. Then we draw lines b tween the common factors.

$$180 = 2 \cdot 2 \cdot 3 \cdot 3 \cdot 5 = 2^2 \cdot 3^2 \cdot 5^1$$

$$420 = 2 \cdot 2 \cdot 3 \cdot 5 \cdot 7 = 2^2 \cdot 3^1 \cdot 5^1 \cdot 7^1$$

The GCF $= 2 \cdot 2 \cdot 3 \cdot 5 = 2^2 \cdot 3^1 \cdot 5^1 = 60$. Note how we can use the exp nents to determine the GCF. There are 2 lines for the 2's, 1 line for the 1 line for the 5, and no line for the 7.

EXAMPLE 3 Find the GCF of 30 and 77.

We find the prime factorization of each number. Then we draw lines b tween the common factors, if any exist.

$$30 = 2 \cdot 3 \cdot 5 = 2^1 \cdot 3^1 \cdot 5^1$$

$$77 = 7 \cdot 11 = 7^1 \cdot 11^1$$

Since there is no common prime factor, the GCF is 1.

XAMPLE 4 Find the GCF of 54, 90, and 252.

We find the prime factorization of each number. Then we draw lines beveen the common factors.

$$54 = 2 \cdot 3 \cdot 3 \cdot 3 = 2^1 \cdot 3^3,$$

$$90 = 2 \cdot 3 \cdot 3 \cdot 5 = 2^1 \cdot 3^2 \cdot 5^1,$$

$$252 = 2 \cdot 2 \cdot 3 \cdot 3 \cdot 7 = 2^2 \cdot 3^2 \cdot 7^1$$

he GCF $= 2^1 \cdot 3^2 = 18$.

Find the GCF.

1. 40, 100

ɔ *Exercises 1–4.*

Consider the product

$$12x^3(x^2 - 6x + 2) = 12x^5 - 72x^4 + 24x^3.$$

ɔ factor the polynomial on the right, we reverse the process of multiplication:

$$12x^5 - 72x^4 + 24x^3 = 12x^3(x^2 - 6x + 2).$$

2. 7, 21

FACTOR; FACTORIZATION

To **factor** a polynomial is to express it as a product.

A **factor** of a polynomial P is a polynomial that can be used to express P as a product.

A **factorization** of a polynomial is an expression that names that polynomial as a product.

3. 72, 360, 432

In the factorization

$$12x^5 - 72x^4 + 24x^3 = 12x^3(x^2 - 6x + 2),$$

ɪe monomial $12x^3$ is called the GCF of the terms, $12x^5$, $-72x^4$, and $24x^3$. The
:st step in factoring polynomials is to find the GCF of the terms.

Consider the monomials

$$x^3,\ x^4,\ x^6,\ \text{and}\ x^7.$$

ɪe GCF of these monomials is x^3, found by noting that the smallest expo-
ent of x is 3.

Consider

$$20x^2 \text{ and } 30x^5.$$

4. 3, 5, 22

ɪe GCF of 20 and 30 is 10. The GCF of x^2 and x^5 is x^2. Then the GCF of $20x^2$
ɪd $30x^5$ is the product of the individual GCFs, $10x^2$.

Answers on page A-26

Find the GCF.

5. $12x^2, \ -16x^3$

6. $3y^6, \ -5y^3, \ 2y^2$

7. $-24m^5n^6, \ 12mn^3, \ -16m^2n^2, \ 8m^4n^4$

8. $-35x^7, \ -49x^6, \ -14x^5, \ -63x^3$

Answers on page A-26

EXAMPLE 5 Find the GCF of $15x^5$, $-12x^4$, $27x^3$, and $-3x^2$.

First, we find a prime factorization of the coefficients, attaching a fact of -1 for the negative coefficients.

$$\begin{aligned} 15x^5 &= 3 \cdot 5 \cdot x^5, \\ -12x^4 &= -1 \cdot 2 \cdot 2 \cdot 3 \cdot x^4, \\ 27x^3 &= 3 \cdot 3 \cdot 3 \cdot x^3, \\ -3x^2 &= -1 \cdot 3 \cdot x^2 \end{aligned}$$

The greatest *positive* common factor of the coefficients is 3.

Then we find the GCF of the powers of x. That GCF is x^2, because 2 is tl smallest exponent of x. Thus the GCF of the set of monomials is $3x^2$.

What about the -1 factors in Example 5? Strictly speaking, both 1 and - are factors of any number or expression. We see this as follows:

$$3x^2 = 1 \cdot 3x^2 = (-1)(-3x^2).$$

Because the coefficient -3 is less than the coefficient 3, we consider $3x^2$, a not $-3x^2$, the GCF.

EXAMPLE 6 Find the GCF of $14p^2y^3$, $-8py^2$, $2py$, and $4p^3$.

We have

$$\begin{aligned} 14p^2y^3 &= 2 \cdot 7 \cdot p^2 \cdot y^3, \\ -8py^2 &= -1 \cdot 2 \cdot 2 \cdot 2 \cdot p \cdot y^2, \\ 2py &= 2 \cdot p \cdot y, \\ 4p^3 &= 2 \cdot 2 \cdot p^3. \end{aligned}$$

The greatest positive common factor of the coefficients is 2, the GCF of tl powers of p is p, and the GCF of the powers of y is 1 since there is no y-fact in the last monomial. Thus the GCF is $2p$.

TO FIND THE GCF OF TWO OR MORE MONOMIALS

1. Find the prime factorization of the coefficients, including -1 as a factor if any coefficient is negative.
2. Determine any common prime factors of the coefficients. For each one that occurs, include it as a factor of the GCF. If none occurs, use 1 as a factor.
3. Examine each of the variables as factors. If any appear as a factor of all the monomials, include it as a factor, using the smallest exponent of the variable. If none occurs in all the monomials, use 1 as a factor.
4. The GCF is the product of the results of steps (2) and (3).

Do Exercises 5–8.

Factoring When Terms Have a Common Factor

he polynomials we consider most when factoring are those with more than ne term. To multiply a monomial and a polynomial with more than one erm, we multiply each term of the polynomial by the monomial using the istributive laws:

$$a(b + c) = ab + ac \quad \text{and} \quad a(b - c) = ab - ac.$$

To factor, we do the reverse. We express a polynomial as a product using ne distributive laws in reverse:

$$ab + ac = a(b + c) \quad \text{and} \quad ab - ac = a(b - c).$$

ompare.

ultiply	*Factor*
$x(x^2 + 2x - 4)$	$3x^3 + 6x^2 - 12x$
$= 3x \cdot x^2 + 3x \cdot 2x - 3x \cdot 4$	$= 3x \cdot x^2 + 3x \cdot 2x - 3x \cdot 4$
$= 3x^3 + 6x^2 - 12x$	$= 3x(x^2 + 2x - 4)$

Caution!

Consider the following:

$$3x^3 + 6x^2 - 12x = 3 \cdot x \cdot x \cdot x + 2 \cdot 3 \cdot x \cdot x - 2 \cdot 2 \cdot 3 \cdot x.$$

The terms of the polynomial, $3x^3$, $6x^2$, and $-12x$, have been factored but the polynomial itself has not been factored. This is not what we mean by a factorization of the polynomial. The *factorization* is

$$3x(x^2 + 2x - 4). \leftarrow \text{A product}$$

The expressions $3x$ and $x^2 + 2x - 4$ are *factors* of $3x^3 + 6x^2 - 12x$.

o Exercises 9 and 10.

To factor, we first find the GCF of all terms. It may be 1.

XAMPLE 7 Factor: $7x^2 + 14$.

We have

$7x^2 + 14 = 7 \cdot x^2 + 7 \cdot 2$ Factoring each term

$= 7(x^2 + 2).$ Factoring out the GCF, 7

heck: We multiply to check:

$$7(x^2 + 2) = 7 \cdot x^2 + 7 \cdot 2 = 7x^2 + 14.$$

9. a) Multiply: $3(x + 2)$.

b) Factor: $3x + 6$.

10. a) Multiply: $2x(x^2 + 5x + 4)$.

b) Factor: $2x^3 + 10x^2 + 8x$.

Answers on page A-26

Factor. Check by multiplying.

11. $x^2 + 3x$

12. $3y^6 - 5y^3 + 2y^2$

13. $9x^4y^2 - 15x^3y + 3x^2y$

14. $\frac{3}{4}t^3 + \frac{5}{4}t^2 + \frac{7}{4}t + \frac{1}{4}$

15. $35x^7 - 49x^6 + 14x^5 - 63x^3$

16. $84x^2 - 56x + 28$

Factor.

17. $x^2(x + 7) + 3(x + 7)$

18. $x^2(a + b) + 2(a + b)$

Answers on page A-26

EXAMPLE 8 Factor: $16x^3 + 20x^2$.

$$16x^3 + 20x^2 = (4x^2)(4x) + (4x^2)(5) \quad \text{Factoring each term}$$
$$= 4x^2(4x + 5) \quad \text{Factoring out the GCF, } 4x^2$$

Suppose in Example 8 that you had not recognized the GCF and removed only part of it, as follows:

$$16x^3 + 20x^2 = (2x^2)(8x) + (2x^2)(10)$$
$$= 2x^2(8x + 10).$$

Note that $8x + 10$ still has a common factor of 2. You need not begin again. Just continue factoring out common factors, as follows, until finished:

$$= 2x^2(2 \cdot 4x + 2 \cdot 5)$$
$$= 2x^2[2(4x + 5)]$$
$$= 4x^2(4x + 5).$$

EXAMPLE 9 Factor: $15x^5 - 12x^4 + 27x^3 - 3x^2$.

$$15x^5 - 12x^4 + 27x^3 - 3x^2 = (3x^2)(5x^3) - (3x^2)(4x^2) + (3x^2)(9x) - (3x^2)(1)$$
$$= 3x^2(5x^3 - 4x^2 + 9x - 1) \quad \text{Factoring out the GCF, } 3x^2$$

Caution!

Don't forget the term -1.

Check: We multiply to check:

$$3x^2(5x^3 - 4x^2 + 9x - 1)$$
$$= (3x^2)(5x^3) - (3x^2)(4x^2) + (3x^2)(9x) - (3x^2)(1)$$
$$= 15x^5 - 12x^4 + 27x^3 - 3x^2.$$

As you become more familiar with factoring, you will be able to spot the GCF without factoring each term. Then you can write just the answer.

EXAMPLES Factor.

10. $24x^2 + 12x - 36 = 12(2x^2 + x - 3)$

11. $8m^3 - 16m = 8m(m^2 - 2)$

12. $14p^2y^3 - 8py^2 + 2py = 2py(7py^2 - 4y + 1)$

13. $\frac{4}{5}x^2 + \frac{1}{5}x + \frac{2}{5} = \frac{1}{5}(4x^2 + x + 2)$

Do Exercises 11–16.

There are two important points to keep in mind as we study this chapter.

TIPS FOR FACTORING

- Before doing any other kind of factoring, first try to factor out the GCF.
- Always check the result of factoring by multiplying.

C Factoring by Grouping: Four Terms

Certain polynomials with four terms can be factored using a method called *factoring by grouping.*

EXAMPLE 14 Factor: $x^2(x + 1) + 2(x + 1)$.

The binomial $x + 1$ is common to both terms:

$$x^2(x + 1) + 2(x + 1) = (x^2 + 2)(x + 1).$$

The factorization is $(x^2 + 2)(x + 1)$.

Do Exercises 17 and 18 on the preceding page.

Consider the four-term polynomial

$$x^3 + x^2 + 2x + 2.$$

There is no factor other than 1 that is common to all the terms. We can, however, factor $x^3 + x^2$ and $2x + 2$ separately:

$$x^3 + x^2 = x^2(x + 1); \qquad \text{Factoring } x^3 + x^2$$

$$2x + 2 = 2(x + 1). \qquad \text{Factoring } 2x + 2$$

We have grouped certain terms and factored each polynomial separately:

$$\begin{aligned} x^3 + x^2 + 2x + 2 &= (x^3 + x^2) + (2x + 2) \\ &= x^2(x + 1) + 2(x + 1) \\ &= (x^2 + 2)(x + 1), \end{aligned}$$

as in Example 14. This method is called **factoring by grouping.** We began with a polynomial with four terms. After grouping and removing common factors, we obtained a polynomial with two parts, each having a common factor $x + 1$. Not all polynomials with four terms can be factored by this procedure, but it does give us a method to try.

Study Tips

CHECKLIST

The foundation of all your study skills is TIME!

- ☐ Are you staying on schedule and on time for class and adapting your study time and class schedule to your personality?
- ☐ Did you study the examples in this chapter carefully?
- ☐ Are you asking questions at appropriate times in class and with your tutors?
- ☐ Are you doing exercises without answers as part of every homework assignment to prepare you for tests?

Factor by grouping.

19. $x^3 + 7x^2 + 3x + 21$

20. $8t^3 + 2t^2 + 12t + 3$

21. $3m^5 - 15m^3 + 2m^2 - 10$

22. $3x^3 - 6x^2 - x + 2$

23. $4x^3 - 6x^2 - 6x + 9$

24. $y^4 - 2y^3 - 2y - 10$

Answers on page A-26

EXAMPLES Factor by grouping.

15. $6x^3 - 9x^2 + 4x - 6$

$= (6x^3 - 9x^2) + (4x - 6)$

$= 3x^2(2x - 3) + 2(2x - 3)$ Factoring each binomial

$= (3x^2 + 2)(2x - 3)$ Factoring out the common factor $2x - 3$

We think through this process as follows:

$$6x^3 - 9x^2 + 4x - 6 = 3x^2(2x - 3) \ \square \ (2x - 3)$$

(1) Factor the first two terms.

(2) The factor $2x - 3$ gives us a hint to the factorization of the last two terms.

(3) Now we ask ourselves, "What times $2x - 3$ is $4x - 6$?" The answer is $+2$.

16. $x^3 + x^2 + x + 1 = (x^3 + x^2) + (x + 1)$

$= x^2(x + 1) + 1(x + 1)$ Factoring each binomial

$= (x^2 + 1)(x + 1)$ Factoring out the common factor $x + 1$

Caution!

Don't forget the 1.

17. $2x^3 - 6x^2 - x + 3$

$= (2x^3 - 6x^2) + (-x + 3)$ Separating into two binomials

$= 2x^2(x - 3) - 1(x - 3)$ *Check*: $-1(x - 3) = -x + 3$.

$= (2x^2 - 1)(x - 3)$ Factoring out the common factor $x -$

We can think through this process as follows.

(1) Factor the first two terms: $2x^3 - 6x^2 = 2x^2(x - 3)$.

(2) The factor $x - 3$ gives us a hint for factoring the last two terms:

$$2x^3 - 6x^2 - x + 3 = 2x^2(x - 3) \ \square \ (x - 3).$$

(3) Now we ask ourselves, "What times $x - 3$ is $-x + 3$?" The answer is -1.

18. $12x^5 + 20x^2 - 21x^3 - 35 = 4x^2(3x^3 + 5) - 7(3x^3 + 5)$

$= (4x^2 - 7)(3x^3 + 5)$

19. $x^3 + x^2 + 2x - 2 = x^2(x + 1) + 2(x - 1)$

This polynomial is not factorable using factoring by grouping. It may be factorable, but not by methods that we will consider in this text.

Do Exercises 19–24.

5.1 EXERCISE SET

For Extra Help

MathXL | MyMathLab | InterAct Math | Math Tutor Center | Digital Video Tutor CD 3 Videotape 6 | Student's Solutions Manual

a Find the GCF.

1. $x^2, \ -6x$

2. $x^2, \ 5x$

3. $3x^4, \ x^2$

4. $8x^4, \ -24x^2$

5. $2x^2, \ 2x, \ -8$

6. $8x^2, \ -4x, \ -20$

7. $-17x^5y^3, \ 34x^3y^2, \ 51xy$

8. $16p^6q^4, \ 32p^3q^3, \ -48pq^2$

9. $-x^2, \ -5x, \ -20x^3$

10. $-x^2, \ -6x, \ -24x^5$

11. $x^5y^5, \ x^4y^3, \ x^3y^3, \ -x^2y^2$

12. $-x^9y^6, \ -x^7y^5, \ x^4y^4, \ x^3y^3$

b Factor. Check by multiplying.

13. $x^2 - 6x$

14. $x^2 + 5x$

15. $2x^2 + 6x$

16. $8y^2 - 8y$

17. $x^3 + 6x^2$

18. $3x^4 - x^2$

19. $8x^4 - 24x^2$

20. $5x^5 + 10x^3$

21. $2x^2 + 2x - 8$

22. $8x^2 - 4x - 20$

23. $17x^5y^3 + 34x^3y^2 + 51xy$

24. $16p^6q^4 + 32p^5q^3 - 48pq^2$

25. $6x^4 - 10x^3 + 3x^2$

26. $5x^5 + 10x^2 - 8x$

27. $x^5y^5 + x^4y^3 + x^3y^3 - x^2y^2$

28. $x^9y^6 - x^7y^5 + x^4y^4 + x^3y^3$

29. $2x^7 - 2x^6 - 64x^5 + 4x^3$

30. $8y^3 - 20y^2 + 12y - 16$

31. $1.6x^4 - 2.4x^3 + 3.2x^2 + 6.4x$

32. $2.5x^6 - 0.5x^4 + 5x^3 + 10x^2$

33. $\frac{5}{3}x^6 + \frac{4}{3}x^5 + \frac{1}{3}x^4 + \frac{1}{3}x^3$

34. $\frac{5}{9}x^7 + \frac{2}{9}x^5 - \frac{4}{9}x^3 - \frac{1}{9}x$

c Factor.

35. $x^2(x + 3) + 2(x + 3)$

36. $3z^2(2z + 1) + (2z + 1)$

37. $5a^3(2a - 7) - (2a - 7)$

38. $m^4(8 - 3m) - 7(8 - 3m)$

Factor by grouping.

39. $x^3 + 3x^2 + 2x + 6$

40. $6z^3 + 3z^2 + 2z + 1$

41. $2x^3 + 6x^2 + x + 3$

42. $3x^3 + 2x^2 + 3x + 2$

43. $8x^3 - 12x^2 + 6x - 9$

44. $10x^3 - 25x^2 + 4x - 10$

45. $12p^3 - 16p^2 + 3p - 4$

46. $18x^3 - 21x^2 + 30x - 35$

47. $5x^3 - 5x^2 - x + 1$

48. $7x^3 - 14x^2 - x + 2$

49. $x^3 + 8x^2 - 3x - 24$

50. $2x^3 + 12x^2 - 5x - 30$

51. $2x^3 - 8x^2 - 9x + 36$

52. $20g^3 - 4g^2 - 25g + 5$

53. $\mathbf{D_W}$ Josh says that there is no need to print answers for Exercises 13–52 at the back of the book. Is he correct in saying this? Why or why not?

54. $\mathbf{D_W}$ Explain how one could construct a polynomial with four terms that can be factored by grouping.

SKILL MAINTENANCE

Solve.

55. $-2x < 48$ [2.7d]

56. $4x - 8x + 16 \geq 6(x - 2)$ [2.7e]

57. Divide: $\dfrac{-108}{-4}$. [1.6a]

58. Solve $A = \dfrac{p + q}{2}$ for p. [2.4b]

Multiply. [4.6d]

59. $(y + 5)(y + 7)$

60. $(y + 7)^2$

61. $(y + 7)(y - 7)$

62. $(y - 7)^2$

Find the intercepts of the equation. Then graph the equation. [3.2a]

63. $x + y = 4$

64. $x - y = 3$

65. $5x - 3y = 15$

66. $y - 3x = 6$

SYNTHESIS

Factor.

67. $4x^5 + 6x^3 + 6x^2 + 9$

68. $x^6 + x^4 + x^2 + 1$

69. $x^{12} + x^7 + x^5 + 1$

70. $x^3 - x^2 - 2x + 5$

71. $p^3 + p^2 - 3p + 10$

5.2 FACTORING TRINOMIALS OF THE TYPE $x^2 + bx + c$

Objective

a Factor trinomials of the type $x^2 + bx + c$ by examining the constant term c.

a Factoring $x^2 + bx + c$

'e now begin a study of the factoring of trinomials. We first factor trinomi-s like

$$x^2 + 5x + 6 \quad \text{and} \quad x^2 + 3x - 10$$

a refined *trial-and-error process*. In this section, we restrict our attention to inomials of the type $ax^2 + bx + c$, where $a = 1$. The coefficient a is often lled the **leading coefficient.**

To understand the factoring that follows, compare the following ultiplications:

$$\begin{aligned}
&\quad\;\; \text{F} \quad \text{O} \quad \text{I} \quad \text{L} \\
(x + 2)(x + 5) &= x^2 + 5x + 2x + 2 \cdot 5 \\
&= x^2 + 7x + 10; \\
(x - 2)(x - 5) &= x^2 - 5x - 2x + 2 \cdot 5 \\
&= x^2 - 7x + 10; \\
(x + 3)(x - 7) &= x^2 - 7x + 3x + 3(-7) \\
&= x^2 - 4x - 21; \\
(x - 3)(x + 7) &= x^2 + 7x - 3x + (-3)7 \\
&= x^2 + 4x - 21.
\end{aligned}$$

Note that for all four products:

- The product of the two binomials is a trinomial.
- The coefficient of x in the trinomial is the sum of the constant terms in the binomials.
- The constant term in the trinomial is the product of the constant terms in the binomials.

iese observations lead to a method for factoring certain trinomials. The first pe we consider has a positive constant term, just as in the first two multi-ications above.

ONSTANT TERM POSITIVE

factor $x^2 + 7x + 10$, we think of FOIL in reverse. We multiplied x times x get the first term of the trinomial, so we know that the first term of each bi-omial factor is x. Next, we look for numbers p and q such that

$$x^2 + 7x + 10 = (x + p)(x + q).$$

get the middle term and the last term of the trinomial, we look for two umbers p and q whose product is 10 and whose sum is 7. Those numbers are and 5. Thus the factorization is

$$(x + 2)(x + 5).$$

ieck: $(x + 2)(x + 5) = x^2 + 5x + 2x + 10$
$= x^2 + 7x + 10.$

1. Consider the trinomial $x^2 + 7x + 12$.

a) Complete the following table.

PAIRS OF FACTORS	SUMS OF FACTORS
1, 12	13
−1, −12	
2, 6	
−2, −6	
3, 4	
−3, −4	

b) Explain why you need to consider only positive factors, as in the following table.

PAIRS OF FACTORS	SUMS OF FACTORS
1, 12	
2, 6	
3, 4	

c) Factor: $x^2 + 7x + 12$.

2. Factor: $x^2 + 13x + 36$.

Answers on page A-26

3. Explain why you would *not* consider the pairs of factors listed below in factoring $y^2 - 8y + 12$.

PAIRS OF FACTORS	SUMS OF FACTORS
1, 12	
2, 6	
3, 4	

Factor.

4. $x^2 - 8x + 15$

5. $t^2 - 9t + 20$

Answers on page A-26

EXAMPLE 1 Factor: $x^2 + 5x + 6$.

Think of FOIL in reverse. The first term of each factor is x: $(x + \quad)(x + \quad)$. Next, we look for two numbers whose product is 6 and whose sum is 5. All the pairs of factors of 6 are shown in the table on the left below. Since both the product, 6, and the sum, 5, of the pair of numbers must be positive, we need consider only the positive factors, listed in the table on the right.

PAIRS OF FACTORS	SUMS OF FACTORS
1, 6	7
−1, −6	−7
2, 3	5
−2, −3	−5

PAIRS OF FACTORS	SUMS OF FACTORS
1, 6	7
2, 3	5

The numbers we need are 2 and 3.

The factorization is $(x + 2)(x + 3)$. We can check by multiplying to see whether we get the original trinomial.

Check: $(x + 2)(x + 3) = x^2 + 3x + 2x + 6 = x^2 + 5x + 6$.

Do Exercises 1 and 2 on the preceding page.

Compare these multiplications:

$$(x - 2)(x - 5) = x^2 - 5x - 2x + 10 = x^2 - 7x + 10;$$
$$(x + 2)(x + 5) = x^2 + 5x + 2x + 10 = x^2 + 7x + 10.$$

TO FACTOR $x^2 + bx + c$ WHEN c IS POSITIVE

When the constant term of a trinomial is positive, look for two numbers with the same sign. The sign is that of the middle term:

$$x^2 - 7x + 10 = (x - 2)(x - 5);$$

$$x^2 + 7x + 10 = (x + 2)(x + 5).$$

EXAMPLE 2 Factor: $y^2 - 8y + 12$.

Since the constant term, 12, is positive and the coefficient of the middle term, −8, is negative, we look for a factorization of 12 in which both factors are negative. Their sum must be −8.

PAIRS OF FACTORS	SUMS OF FACTORS
−1, −12	−13
−2, −6	**−8**
−3, −4	−7

The numbers we need are −2 and −6.

The factorization is $(y - 2)(y - 6)$. The student should check by multiplying.

Do Exercises 3–5.

ONSTANT TERM NEGATIVE

s we saw in two of the multiplications earlier in this section, the product of vo binomials can have a negative constant term:

$$(x + 3)(x - 7) = x^2 - 4x - 21$$

nd

$$(x - 3)(x + 7) = x^2 + 4x - 21.$$

ote that when the signs of the constants in the binomials are reversed, only e sign of the middle term in the product changes.

XAMPLE 3 Factor: $x^2 - 8x - 20$.

The constant term, -20, must be expressed as the product of a negative umber and a positive number. Since the sum of these two numbers must be egative (specifically, -8), the negative number must have the greater ab- olute value.

PAIRS OF FACTORS	SUMS OF FACTORS
1, −20	−19
2, −10	**−8**
4, −5	−1
5, −4	1
10, −2	8
20, −1	19

The numbers we need are 2 and −10.

Because these sums are all positive, for this problem all of the corresponding pairs can be disregarded. Note that in all three pairs, the positive number has the greater absolute value.

he numbers that we are looking for are 2 and 10. The factorization is $(x + 2)(x - 10)$.

neck: $(x + 2)(x - 10) = x^2 - 10x + 2x - 20$
$= x^2 - 8x - 20.$

TO FACTOR $x^2 + bx + c$ WHEN c IS NEGATIVE

When the constant term of a trinomial is negative, look for two numbers whose product is negative. One must be positive and the other negative:

$$x^2 - 4x - 21 = (x + 3)(x - 7);$$

$$x^2 + 4x - 21 = (x - 3)(x + 7).$$

Consider pairs of numbers for which the number with the larger absolute value has the same sign as b, the coefficient of the middle term.

o Exercises 6 and 7. (Exercise 7 is on the following page.)

6. Consider $x^2 - 5x - 24$.

a) Explain why you would *not* consider the pairs of factors listed below in factoring $x^2 - 5x - 24$.

PAIRS OF FACTORS	SUMS OF FACTORS
−1, 24	
−2, 12	
−3, 8	
−4, 6	

b) Explain why you *would* consider the pairs of factors listed below in factoring $x^2 - 5x - 24$.

PAIRS OF FACTORS	SUMS OF FACTORS
1, −24	
2, −12	
3, −8	
4, −6	

c) Factor: $x^2 - 5x - 24$.

Answers on page A-26

7. Consider $x^2 + 10x - 24$.

a) Explain why you would *not* consider the pairs of factors listed below in factoring $x^2 + 10x - 24$.

PAIRS OF FACTORS	SUMS OF FACTORS
1, −24	
2, −12	
3, −8	
4, −6	

b) Explain why you *would* consider the pairs of factors listed below in factoring $x^2 + 10x - 24$.

PAIRS OF FACTORS	SUMS OF FACTORS
−1, 24	
−2, 12	
−3, 8	
−4, 6	

c) Factor: $x^2 + 10x - 24$.

Factor.

8. $a^2 - 24 + 10a$

9. $-24 - 10t + t^2$

Answers on page A-26

EXAMPLE 4 Factor: $t^2 - 24 + 5t$.

It helps to first write the trinomial in descending order: $t^2 + 5t - 2$
Since the constant term, -24, is negative, we look for a factorization of -24 i
which one factor is positive and one factor is negative. Their sum must be
so the positive factor must have the larger absolute value. Thus we conside
only pairs of factors in which the positive term has the larger absolute valu

PAIRS OF FACTORS	SUMS OF FACTORS
−1, 24	23
−2, 12	10
−3, 8	**5** ← The numbers we need are −3 and 8.
−4, 6	2

The factorization is $(t - 3)(t + 8)$. The check is left to the student.

Do Exercises 8 and 9.

EXAMPLE 5 Factor: $x^4 - x^2 - 110$.

Consider this trinomial as $(x^2)^2 - x^2 - 110$. We look for numbers p an
q such that

$$x^4 - x^2 - 110 = (x^2 + p)(x^2 + q).$$

Since the constant term, -110, is negative, we look for a factorization of -11
in which one factor is positive and one factor is negative. Their sum must b
-1. The middle-term coefficient, -1, is small compared to -110. This tells u
that the desired factors are close to each other in absolute value. The numbe
we want are 10 and -11. The factorization is

$$(x^2 + 10)(x^2 - 11).$$

EXAMPLE 6 Factor: $a^2 + 4ab - 21b^2$.

We consider the trinomial in the equivalent form

$$a^2 + 4ba - 21b^2.$$

This way we think of $-21b^2$ as the "constant" term and $4b$ as the "coefficien
of the middle term. Then we try to express $-21b^2$ as a product of two facto
whose sum is $4b$. Those factors are $-3b$ and $7b$. The factorization
$(a - 3b)(a + 7b)$.

Check: $(a - 3b)(a + 7b) = a^2 + 7ab - 3ba - 21b^2$
$= a^2 + 4ab - 21b^2.$

There are polynomials that are not factorable.

EXAMPLE 7 Factor: $x^2 - x + 5$.

Since 5 has very few factors, we can easily check all possibilities.

PAIRS OF FACTORS	SUMS OF FACTORS
5, 1	6
−5, −1	−6

here are no factors whose sum is -1. Thus the polynomial is *not* factorable nto factors that are polynomials.

In this text, a polynomial like $x^2 - x + 5$ that cannot be factored further s said to be **prime.** In more advanced courses, polynomials like $x^2 - x + 5$ an be factored and are not considered prime.

o Exercises 10–12.

Often factoring requires two or more steps. In general, when told to factor, we should *factor completely.* This means that the final factorization hould not contain any factors that can be factored further.

XAMPLE 8 Factor: $2x^3 - 20x^2 + 50x$.

Always look first for a common factor. This time there is one, $2x$, which we actor out first:

$$2x^3 - 20x^2 + 50x = 2x(x^2 - 10x + 25).$$

ow consider $x^2 - 10x + 25$. Since the constant term is positive and the coefficient of the middle term is negative, we look for a factorization of 25 in hich both factors are negative. Their sum must be -10.

PAIRS OF FACTORS	SUMS OF FACTORS
$-25, -1$	-26
$-5, -5$	-10 ← The numbers we need are -5 and -5.

he factorization of $x^2 - 10x + 25$ is $(x - 5)(x - 5)$, or $(x - 5)^2$. The final actorization is $2x(x - 5)^2$. We check by multiplying:

$$\begin{aligned} 2x(x-5)^2 &= 2x(x^2 - 10x + 25) \\ &= (2x)(x^2) - (2x)(10x) + (2x)(25) \\ &= 2x^3 - 20x^2 + 50x. \end{aligned}$$

o Exercises 13–15.

Once any common factors have been factored out, the following sum- nary can be used to factor $x^2 + bx + c$.

TO FACTOR $x^2 + bx + c$

1. First arrange in descending order.
2. Use a trial-and-error process that looks for factors of c whose sum is b.
3. If c is positive, the signs of the factors are the same as the sign of b.
4. If c is negative, one factor is positive and the other is negative. If the sum of two factors is the opposite of b, changing the sign of each factor will give the desired factors whose sum is b.
5. Check by multiplying.

Factor.

10. $y^2 - 12 - 4y$

11. $t^4 + 5t^2 - 14$

12. $x^2 + 2x + 7$

Factor.

13. $x^3 + 4x^2 - 12x$

14. $p^2 - pq - 3pq^2$

15. $3x^3 + 24x^2 + 48x$

Answers on page A-26

Factor.

16. $14 + 5x - x^2$

17. $-x^2 + 3x + 18$

Answers on page A-26

LEADING COEFFICIENT −1

EXAMPLE 9 Factor: $10 - 3x - x^2$.

Note that the polynomial is written in ascending order. When we write in descending order, we get

$$-x^2 - 3x + 10,$$

which has a leading coefficient of -1. Before factoring in such a case, we ca factor out a -1, as follows:

$$-x^2 - 3x + 10 = -1(x^2 + 3x - 10).$$

Then we proceed to factor $x^2 + 3x - 10$. We get

$$-x^2 - 3x + 10 = -1(x^2 + 3x - 10) = -1(x + 5)(x - 2).$$

We can also express this answer in two other ways by multiplying either bino mial by -1. Thus each of the following is a correct answer:

$$-x^2 - 3x + 10 = -1(x + 5)(x - 2)$$

$$= (-x - 5)(x - 2) \quad \text{Multiplying } x + 5 \text{ by } -1$$

$$= (x + 5)(-x + 2). \quad \text{Multiplying } x - 2 \text{ by } -1$$

Do Exercises 16 and 17.

Study Tips

TIME MANAGEMENT (PART 2)

Here are some additional tips to help you with time management. (See also the Study Tips on time management in Sections 2.2 and 5.6.)

- **Are you a morning or an evening person?** If you are an evening person, it might be best to avoid scheduling early-morning classes. If you are a morning person, do the opposite, but go to bed earlier to compensate. Nothing can drain your study time and effectiveness like fatigue.
- **Keep on schedule.** Your course syllabus provides a plan for the semester's schedule. Use a write-on calendar, daily planner, Palm Pilot or other PDA, or laptop computer to outline your time for the semester. Be sure to note deadlines involving term papers and exams so you can begin a task early, breaking it down into smaller segments that can be accomplished more easily.
- **Balance your class schedule.** You may be someone who prefers large blocks of time for study on the off days. In that case, it might be advantageous for you to take courses that meet only three days a week. Keep in mind, however, that this might be a problem when tests in more than one course are scheduled for the same day.

"Time is our most important asset, yet we tend to waste it, kill it, and spend it rather than invest it."

Jim Rohn, motivational speaker

5.2 EXERCISE SET

For Extra Help

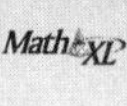
MathXL

MyMathLab

InterAct Math

Math Tutor Center

Digital Video Tutor CD 3 Videotape 6

Student's Solutions Manual

a Factor. Remember that you can check by multiplying.

1. $x^2 + 8x + 15$

PAIRS OF FACTORS	SUMS OF FACTORS

2. $x^2 + 5x + 6$

PAIRS OF FACTORS	SUMS OF FACTORS

3. $x^2 + 7x + 12$

PAIRS OF FACTORS	SUMS OF FACTORS

4. $x^2 + 9x + 8$

PAIRS OF FACTORS	SUMS OF FACTORS

5. $x^2 - 6x + 9$

PAIRS OF FACTORS	SUMS OF FACTORS

6. $y^2 - 11y + 28$

PAIRS OF FACTORS	SUMS OF FACTORS

7. $x^2 - 5x - 14$

PAIRS OF FACTORS	SUMS OF FACTORS

8. $a^2 + 7a - 30$

PAIRS OF FACTORS	SUMS OF FACTORS

9. $b^2 + 5b + 4$

PAIRS OF FACTORS	SUMS OF FACTORS

10. $z^2 - 8z + 7$

PAIRS OF FACTORS	SUMS OF FACTORS

11. $x^2 + \frac{2}{3}x + \frac{1}{9}$

PAIRS OF FACTORS	SUMS OF FACTORS

12. $x^2 - \frac{2}{5}x + \frac{1}{25}$

PAIRS OF FACTORS	SUMS OF FACTORS

13. $d^2 - 7d + 10$

14. $t^2 - 12t + 35$

15. $y^2 - 11y + 10$

16. $x^2 - 4x - 21$

17. $x^2 + x + 1$

18. $x^2 + 5x + 3$

19. $x^2 - 7x - 18$

20. $y^2 - 3y - 28$

21. $x^3 - 6x^2 - 16x$

22. $x^3 - x^2 - 42x$

23. $y^3 - 4y^2 - 45y$

24. $x^3 - 7x^2 - 60x$

25. $-2x - 99 + x^2$

26. $x^2 - 72 + 6x$

27. $c^4 + c^2 - 56$

28. $b^4 + 5b^2 - 24$

29. $a^4 + 2a^2 - 35$

30. $x^4 - x^2 - 6$

31. $x^2 + x - 42$

32. $x^2 + 2x - 15$

33. $7 - 2p + p^2$

34. $11 - 3w + w^2$

35. $x^2 + 20x + 100$

36. $a^2 + 19a + 88$

37. $30 + 7x - x^2$

38. $45 + 4x - x^2$

39. $24 - a^2 - 10a$

40. $-z^2 + 36 - 9z$

1. $x^4 - 21x^3 - 100x^2$

42. $x^4 - 20x^3 + 96x^2$

43. $x^2 - 21x - 72$

44. $4x^2 + 40x + 100$

45. $x^2 - 25x + 144$

46. $y^2 - 21y + 108$

47. $a^2 + a - 132$

48. $a^2 + 9a - 90$

49. $120 - 23x + x^2$

50. $96 + 22d + d^2$

51. $108 - 3x - x^2$

52. $112 + 9y - y^2$

53. $y^2 - 0.2y - 0.08$

54. $t^2 - 0.3t - 0.10$

55. $p^2 + 3pq - 10q^2$

56. $a^2 + 2ab - 3b^2$

57. $84 - 8t - t^2$

58. $72 - 6m - m^2$

59. $m^2 + 5mn + 4n^2$

60. $x^2 + 11xy + 24y^2$

61. $s^2 - 2st - 15t^2$

62. $p^2 + 5pq - 24q^2$

63. $6a^{10} - 30a^9 - 84a^8$

64. $7x^9 - 28x^8 - 35x^7$

65. ^D_W Gwyneth factors $x^3 - 8x^2 + 15x$ as $(x^2 - 5x)(x - 3)$. Is she wrong? Why or why not? What advice would you offer?

66. ^D_W When searching for a factorization, why do we list pairs of numbers with the correct *product* instead of pairs of numbers with the correct *sum*?

67. ^D_W Without multiplying $(x - 17)(x - 18)$, explain why it cannot possibly be a factorization of $x^2 + 35x + 306$.

68. ^D_W What is the advantage of writing out the prime factorization of c when factoring $x^2 + bx + c$ with a large value of c?

SKILL MAINTENANCE

Multiply. [4.6d]

69. $8x(2x^2 - 6x + 1)$

70. $(7w + 6)(4w - 11)$

71. $(7w + 6)^2$

72. $(4w - 11)^2$

73. $(4w - 11)(4w + 11)$

74. $-y(-y^2 + 3y - 5)$

75. $(3x - 5y)(2x + 7y)$

76. Simplify: $(3x^4)^3$. [4.2a, b]

Solve. [2.3a]

77. $3x - 8 = 0$

78. $2x + 7 = 0$

Solve.

79. *Arrests for Counterfeiting.* In a recent year, 29,200 people were arrested for counterfeiting. This number was down 1.2% from the preceding year. How many people were arrested the preceding year? [2.5a]

80. The first angle of a triangle is four times as large as the second. The measure of the third angle is 30° greater than that of the second. Find the angle measures. [2.6a]

SYNTHESIS

81. Find all integers m for which $y^2 + my + 50$ can be factored.

82. Find all integers b for which $a^2 + ba - 50$ can be factored.

Factor completely.

83. $x^2 - \frac{1}{2}x - \frac{3}{16}$

84. $x^2 - \frac{1}{4}x - \frac{1}{8}$

85. $x^2 + \frac{30}{7}x - \frac{25}{7}$

86. $\frac{1}{3}x^3 + \frac{1}{3}x^2 - 2x$

87. $b^{2n} + 7b^n + 10$

88. $a^{2m} - 11a^m + 28$

Find a polynomial in factored form for the shaded area. (Leave answers in terms of π.)

89.

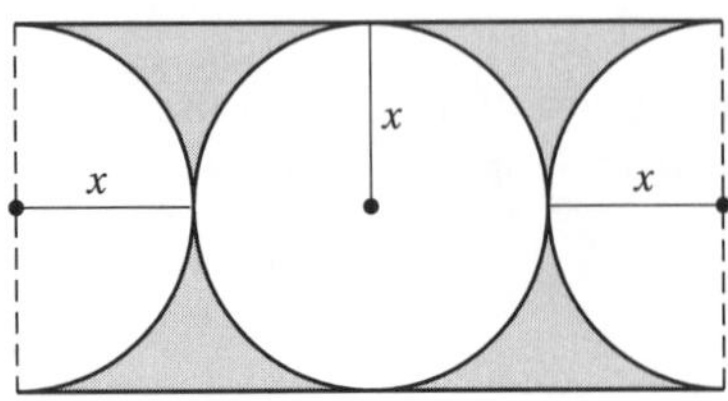

90.

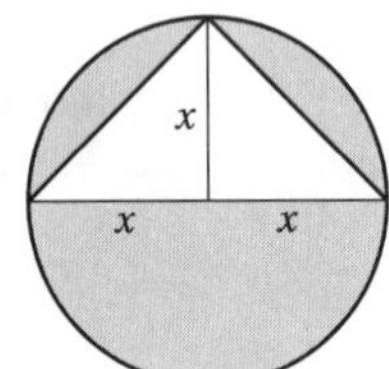

5.5 FACTORING TRINOMIAL SQUARES AND DIFFERENCES OF SQUARES

Objectives

a Recognize trinomial squares.

b Factor trinomial squares.

c Recognize differences of squares.

d Factor differences of squares, being careful to factor completely.

It would be helpful to memorize this table of perfect squares.

NUMBER, N	PERFECT SQUARE, N^2
1	1
2	4
3	9
4	16
5	25
6	36
7	49
8	64
9	81
10	100
11	121
12	144
13	169
14	196
15	225
16	256
17	289
18	324
19	361
20	400
21	441
22	484
23	529
24	576
25	625

In this section, we first learn to factor trinomials that are squares of bino-mials. Then we factor binomials that are differences of squares.

a Recognizing Trinomial Squares

Some trinomials are squares of binomials. For example, the trinomial $x^2 + 10x + 25$ is the square of the binomial $x + 5$. To see this, we can calculate $(x + 5)^2$. It is $x^2 + 2 \cdot x \cdot 5 + 5^2$, or $x^2 + 10x + 25$. A trinomial that is the square of a binomial is called a **trinomial square,** or a **perfect-square trinomial.**

In Chapter 4, we considered squaring binomials as special-product rules:

$$(A + B)^2 = A^2 + 2AB + B^2;$$
$$(A - B)^2 = A^2 - 2AB + B^2.$$

We can use these equations in reverse to factor trinomial squares.

TRINOMIAL SQUARES

$$A^2 + 2AB + B^2 = (A + B)^2;$$
$$A^2 - 2AB + B^2 = (A - B)^2$$

How can we recognize when an expression to be factored is a trinomial square? Look at $A^2 + 2AB + B^2$ and $A^2 - 2AB + B^2$. In order for an expression to be a trinomial square:

a) The two expressions A^2 and B^2 must be squares, such as

$$4, \quad x^2, \quad 25x^4, \quad 16t^2.$$

When the coefficient is a perfect square and the power(s) of the variable(s) is (are) even, then the expression is a perfect square.

b) There must be no minus sign before A^2 or B^2.

c) If we multiply A and B and double the result, $2 \cdot AB$, we get either the remaining term or its opposite.

EXAMPLE 1 Determine whether $x^2 + 6x + 9$ is a trinomial square.

a) We know that x^2 and 9 are squares.

b) There is no minus sign before x^2 or 9.

c) If we multiply the square roots, x and 3, and double the product, we get the remaining term: $2 \cdot x \cdot 3 = 6x$.

Thus, $x^2 + 6x + 9$ is the square of a binomial. In fact, $x^2 + 6x + 9 = (x + 3)^2$.

EXAMPLE 2 Determine whether $x^2 + 6x + 11$ is a trinomial square.

The answer is no, because only one term, x^2, is a square.

XAMPLE 3 Determine whether $16x^2 + 49 - 56x$ is a trinomial square.

It helps to first write the trinomial in descending order:

$$16x^2 - 56x + 49.$$

We know that $16x^2$ and 49 are squares.

There is no minus sign before $16x^2$ or 49.

If we multiply the square roots, $4x$ and 7, and double the product, we get the opposite of the remaining term: $2 \cdot 4x \cdot 7 = 56x$; $56x$ is the opposite of $-56x$.

ıus, $16x^2 + 49 - 56x$ is a trinomial square. In fact, $16x^2 - 56x + 49 =$ $x - 7)^2$.

ɔ Exercises 1–8.

ɔ Factoring Trinomial Squares

e can use the factoring methods from Sections 5.2–5.4 to factor trinomial uares, but there is a faster method using the following equations.

FACTORING TRINOMIAL SQUARES

$A^2 + 2AB + B^2 = (A + B)^2$;

$A^2 - 2AB + B^2 = (A - B)^2$

We consider 3 to be a square root of 9 because $3^2 = 9$. Similarly, A is a uare root of A^2. We use square roots of the squared terms and the sign of the maining term to factor a trinomial square.

KAMPLE 4 Factor: $x^2 + 6x + 9$.

$$x^2 + 6x + 9 = x^2 + 2 \cdot x \cdot 3 + 3^2 = (x + 3)^2$$

$$A^2 + 2 \quad A \quad B + B^2 = (A + B)^2$$

The sign of the middle term is positive.

KAMPLE 5 Factor: $x^2 + 49 - 14x$.

$x^2 + 49 - 14x = x^2 - 14x + 49$ Changing to descending order

$= x^2 - 2 \cdot x \cdot 7 + 7^2$ The sign of the middle term is negative.

$= (x - 7)^2$

AMPLE 6 Factor: $16x^2 - 40x + 25$.

$$16x^2 - 40x + 25 = (4x)^2 - 2 \cdot 4x \cdot 5 + 5^2 = (4x - 5)^2$$

$$A^2 \quad - 2 \quad A \quad B + B^2 = (A - B)^2$$

Exercises 9–13.

Determine whether each is a trinomial square. Write "yes" or "no."

1. $x^2 + 8x + 16$
2. $25 - x^2 + 10x$
3. $t^2 - 12t + 4$
4. $25 + 20y + 4y^2$
5. $5x^2 + 16 - 14x$
6. $16x^2 + 40x + 25$
7. $p^2 + 6p - 9$
8. $25a^2 + 9 - 30a$

Factor.

9. $x^2 + 2x + 1$
10. $1 - 2x + x^2$
11. $4 + t^2 + 4t$
12. $25x^2 - 70x + 49$
13. $49 - 56y + 16y^2$

Answers on page A-28

Factor.

14. $48m^2 + 75 + 120m$

15. $p^4 + 18p^2 + 81$

16. $4z^5 - 20z^4 + 25z^3$

17. $9a^2 + 30ab + 25b^2$

Answers on page A-28

EXAMPLE 7 Factor: $t^4 + 20t^2 + 100$.

$$t^4 + 20t^2 + 100 = (t^2)^2 + 2(t^2)(10) + 10^2$$
$$= (t^2 + 10)^2$$

EXAMPLE 8 Factor: $75m^3 + 210m^2 + 147m$.

Always look first for a common factor. This time there is one, $3m$:

$$75m^3 + 210m^2 + 147m = 3m[25m^2 + 70m + 49]$$
$$= 3m[(5m)^2 + 2(5m)(7) + 7^2]$$
$$= 3m(5m + 7)^2.$$

EXAMPLE 9 Factor: $4p^2 - 12pq + 9q^2$.

$$4p^2 - 12pq + 9q^2 = (2p)^2 - 2(2p)(3q) + (3q)^2$$
$$= (2p - 3q)^2$$

Do Exercises 14–17.

C Recognizing Differences of Squares

The following polynomials are *differences of squares*:

$$x^2 - 9, \quad 4t^2 - 49, \quad a^2 - 25b^2.$$

To factor a difference of squares such as $x^2 - 9$, think about the formula w
used in Chapter 4:

$$(A + B)(A - B) = A^2 - B^2.$$

Equations are reversible, so we also know the following.

DIFFERENCE OF SQUARES

$$A^2 - B^2 = (A + B)(A - B)$$

Thus,

$$x^2 - 9 = (x + 3)(x - 3).$$

To use this formula, we must be able to recognize when it applies. A **diffe-
ence of squares** is an expression like the following:

$$A^2 - B^2.$$

How can we recognize such expressions? Look at $A^2 - B^2$. In order for a bin
mial to be a difference of squares:

a) There must be two expressions, both squares, such as

$$4x^2, \quad 9, \quad 25t^4, \quad 1, \quad x^6, \quad 49y^8.$$

b) The terms must have different signs.

XAMPLE 10 Is $9x^2 - 64$ a difference of squares?

) The first expression is a square: $9x^2 = (3x)^2$.
The second expression is a square: $64 = 8^2$.

) The terms have different signs, $+9x^2$ and -64.

hus we have a difference of squares, $(3x)^2 - 8^2$.

XAMPLE 11 Is $25 - t^3$ a difference of squares?

) The expression t^3 is not a square.

he expression is not a difference of squares.

XAMPLE 12 Is $-4x^2 + 16$ a difference of squares?

) The expressions $4x^2$ and 16 are squares: $4x^2 = (2x)^2$ and $16 = 4^2$.

) The terms have different signs, $-4x^2$ and $+16$.

hus we have a difference of squares. We can also see this by rewriting in the quivalent form: $16 - 4x^2$.

o Exercises 18–24.

d Factoring Differences of Squares

o factor a difference of squares, we use the following equation.

FACTORING A DIFFERENCE OF SQUARES

$A^2 - B^2 = (A + B)(A - B)$

To factor a difference of squares $A^2 - B^2$, we find A and B, which are quare roots of the expressions A^2 and B^2. We then use A and B to form two ctors. One is the sum $A + B$, and the other is the difference $A - B$.

XAMPLE 13 Factor: $x^2 - 4$.

$$\begin{array}{ccccccc} x^2 - 4 = & x^2 & - & 2^2 & = & (x + 2)(x - 2) \\ & \uparrow & & \uparrow & & \uparrow\ \uparrow\ \uparrow\ \uparrow \\ & A^2 & - & B^2 & = & (A + B)(A - B) \end{array}$$

XAMPLE 14 Factor: $9 - 16t^4$.

$$\begin{array}{ccccccc} 9 - 16t^4 = & 3^2 & - & (4t^2)^2 & = & (3 + 4t^2)(3 - 4t^2) \\ & \uparrow & & \uparrow & & \uparrow\ \uparrow\ \uparrow\ \uparrow \\ & A^2 & - & B^2 & = & (A + B)(A - B) \end{array}$$

Determine whether each is a difference of squares. Write "yes" or "no."

18. $x^2 - 25$

19. $t^2 - 24$

20. $y^2 + 36$

21. $4x^2 - 15$

22. $16x^4 - 49$

23. $9w^6 - 1$

24. $-49 + 25t^2$

Answers on page A-28

Factor.

25. $x^2 - 9$

26. $4t^2 - 64$

27. $a^2 - 25b^2$

28. $64x^4 - 25x^6$

29. $5 - 20t^6$
[*Hint*: $1 = 1^2$, $t^6 = (t^3)^2$.]

Answers on page A-28

EXAMPLE 15 Factor: $m^2 - 4p^2$.

$$m^2 - 4p^2 = m^2 - (2p)^2 = (m + 2p)(m - 2p)$$

EXAMPLE 16 Factor: $x^2 - \frac{1}{9}$.

$$x^2 - \frac{1}{9} = x^2 - \left(\frac{1}{3}\right)^2 = \left(x + \frac{1}{3}\right)\left(x - \frac{1}{3}\right)$$

EXAMPLE 17 Factor: $18x^2 - 50x^6$.

Always look first for a factor common to all terms. This time there is one, $2x^2$.

$$\begin{aligned} 18x^2 - 50x^6 &= 2x^2(9 - 25x^4) \\ &= 2x^2[3^2 - (5x^2)^2] \\ &= 2x^2(3 + 5x^2)(3 - 5x^2) \end{aligned}$$

EXAMPLE 18 Factor: $49x^4 - 9x^6$.

$$\begin{aligned} 49x^4 - 9x^6 &= x^4(49 - 9x^2) \\ &= x^4(7 + 3x)(7 - 3x) \end{aligned}$$

Do Exercises 25–29.

Caution!

Note carefully in these examples that a difference of squares is *not* the square of the difference; that is,

$$A^2 - B^2 \neq (A - B)^2.$$

For example,

$$(45 - 5)^2 = 40^2 = 1600,$$

but

$$45^2 - 5^2 = 2025 - 25 = 2000.$$

Similarly,

$$A^2 - 2AB + B^2 \neq (A - B)(A + B).$$

For example,

$$(10 - 3)(10 + 3) = 7 \cdot 13 = 91,$$

but

$$\begin{aligned} 10^2 - 2 \cdot 10 \cdot 3 + 3^2 &= 100 - 2 \cdot 10 \cdot 3 + 9 \\ &= 100 - 60 + 9 \\ &= 49. \end{aligned}$$

ACTORING COMPLETELY

f a factor with more than one term can still be factored, you should do so. When no factor can be factored further, you have **factored completely.** Always factor completely whenever told to factor.

XAMPLE 19 Factor: $p^4 - 16$.

$$p^4 - 16 = (p^2)^2 - 4^2$$
$$= (p^2 + 4)(p^2 - 4) \quad \text{Factoring a difference of squares}$$
$$= (p^2 + 4)(p + 2)(p - 2) \quad \text{Factoring further; } p^2 - 4 \text{ is a difference of squares.}$$

The polynomial $p^2 + 4$ cannot be factored further into polynomials with eal coefficients.

Caution!

Apart from possibly removing a common factor, you cannot factor a sum of squares. In particular,

$$A^2 + B^2 \neq (A + B)^2.$$

Consider $25x^2 + 100$. Here a sum of squares has a common factor, 25. Factoring, we get $25(x^2 + 4)$, where $x^2 + 4$ is prime. For example,

$$x^2 + 4 \neq (x + 2)^2.$$

XAMPLE 20 Factor: $\frac{1}{16}x^8 - 81$.

$$\frac{1}{16}x^8 - 81 = \left(\frac{1}{4}x^4 + 9\right)\left(\frac{1}{4}x^4 - 9\right) \quad \text{Factoring a difference of squares}$$
$$= \left(\frac{1}{4}x^4 + 9\right)\left(\frac{1}{2}x^2 + 3\right)\left(\frac{1}{2}x^2 - 3\right) \quad \text{Factoring further. The factor } \tfrac{1}{4}x^4 - 9 \text{ is a difference of squares.}$$

The polynomial $\frac{1}{4}x^4 + 9$ cannot be factored further into polynomials with al coefficients.

XAMPLE 21 Factor: $y^4 - 16x^{12}$.

$$y^4 - 16x^{12} = (y^2 + 4x^6)(y^2 - 4x^6) \quad \text{Factoring a difference of squares}$$
$$= (y^2 + 4x^6)(y + 2x^3)(y - 2x^3) \quad \text{Factoring further. The factor } y^2 - 4x^6 \text{ is a difference of squares.}$$

TIPS FOR FACTORING

- Always look first for a common factor! If there is one, factor it out.
- Be alert for trinomial squares and differences of squares. Once recognized, they can be factored without trial and error.
- Always factor completely.
- Check by multiplying.

Exercises 30–32.

Factor completely.

30. $81x^4 - 1$

31. $16 - \frac{1}{81}y^8$

32. $49p^4 - 25q^6$

Answers on page A-28

5.5 EXERCISE SET

For Extra Help

MathXL | MyMathLab | InterAct Math | Math Tutor Center | Digital Video Tutor CD 3 Videotape 6 | Student's Solutions Manual

a Determine whether each of the following is a trinomial square.

1. $x^2 - 14x + 49$

2. $x^2 - 16x + 64$

3. $x^2 + 16x - 64$

4. $x^2 - 14x - 49$

5. $x^2 - 2x + 4$

6. $x^2 + 3x + 9$

7. $9x^2 - 36x + 24$

8. $36x^2 - 24x + 16$

b Factor completely. Remember to look first for a common factor and to check by multiplying.

9. $x^2 - 14x + 49$

10. $x^2 - 20x + 100$

11. $x^2 + 16x + 64$

12. $x^2 + 20x + 100$

13. $x^2 - 2x + 1$

14. $x^2 + 2x + 1$

15. $4 + 4x + x^2$

16. $4 + x^2 - 4x$

17. $q^4 - 6q^2 + 9$

18. $64 + 16a^2 + a^4$

19. $49 + 56y + 16y^2$

20. $75 + 48a^2 - 120a$

21. $2x^2 - 4x + 2$

22. $2x^2 - 40x + 200$

23. $x^3 - 18x^2 + 81x$

24. $x^3 + 24x^2 + 144x$

25. $12q^2 - 36q + 27$

26. $20p^2 + 100p + 125$

27. $49 - 42x + 9x^2$

28. $64 - 112x + 49x^2$

29. $5y^4 + 10y^2 + 5$

30. $a^4 + 14a^2 + 49$

31. $1 + 4x^4 + 4x^2$

32. $1 - 2a^5 + a^{10}$

33. $4p^2 + 12pq + 9q^2$

34. $25m^2 + 20mn + 4n^2$

35. $a^2 - 6ab + 9b^2$

36. $x^2 - 14xy + 49y^2$

37. $81a^2 - 18ab + b^2$

38. $64p^2 + 16pq + q^2$

39. $36a^2 + 96ab + 64b^2$

40. $16m^2 - 40mn + 25n^2$

c Determine whether each of the following is a difference of squares.

41. $x^2 - 4$

42. $x^2 - 36$

43. $x^2 + 25$

44. $x^2 + 9$

45. $x^2 - 45$

46. $x^2 - 80y^2$

47. $16x^2 - 25y^2$

48. $-1 + 36x^2$

d Factor completely. Remember to look first for a common factor.

49. $y^2 - 4$

50. $q^2 - 1$

51. $p^2 - 9$

52. $x^2 - 36$

53. $-49 + t^2$

54. $-64 + m^2$

55. $a^2 - b^2$

56. $p^2 - q^2$

57. $25t^2 - m^2$

58. $w^2 - 49z^2$

59. $100 - k^2$

60. $81 - w^2$

61. $16a^2 - 9$

62. $25x^2 - 4$

63. $4x^2 - 25y^2$

64. $9a^2 - 16b^2$

65. $8x^2 - 98$

66. $24x^2 - 54$

67. $36x - 49x^3$

68. $16x - 81x^3$

69. $\left(\frac{1}{16} - 49x^8\right)$

70. $\left(\frac{1}{625}x^8 - 49\right)$

71. $(0.09y^2 - 0.0004)$

72. $(0.16p^2 - 0.0025)$

73. $49a^4 - 81$

74. $25a^4 - 9$

75. $a^4 - 16$

76. $y^4 - 1$

77. $5x^4 - 405$

78. $4x^4 - 64$

79. $1 - y^8$

80. $x^8 - 1$

81. $x^{12} - 16$

82. $x^8 - 81$

83. $y^2 - \frac{1}{16}$

84. $x^2 - \frac{1}{25}$

85. $25 - \frac{1}{49}x^2$

86. $\frac{1}{4} - 9q^2$

87. $16m^4 - t^4$

88. $p^4q^4 - 1$

89. **DW** Explain in your own words how to determine whether a polynomial is a trinomial square.

90. **DW** Spiro concludes that since $x^2 - 9 = (x - 3)(x + 3)$, it must follow that $x^2 + 9 = (x + 3)(x + 3)$. What mistake is he making? How would you go about correcting the misunderstanding

SKILL MAINTENANCE

Divide. [1.6a, c]

91. $(-110) \div 10$

92. $-1000 \div (-2.5)$

93. $\left(-\frac{2}{3}\right) \div \frac{4}{5}$

94. $8.1 \div (-9)$

95. $-64 \div (-32)$

96. $-256 \div 1.6$

Find a polynomial for the shaded area. (Leave results in terms of π where appropriate.) [4.4d]

97.

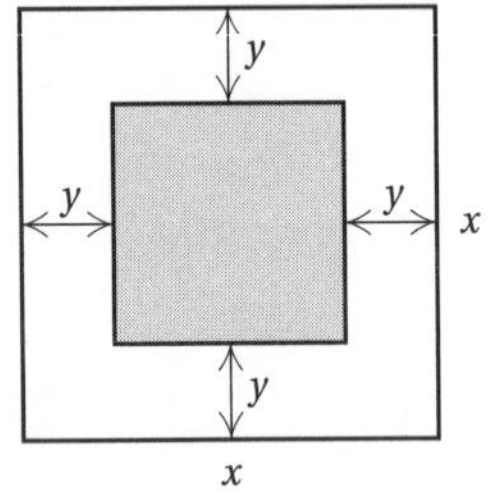

98.

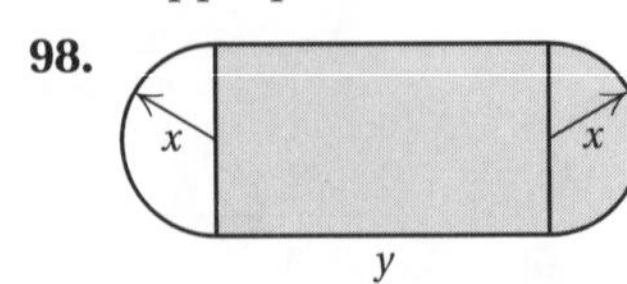

implify.

99. $y^5 \cdot y^7$ [4.1d]

100. $(5a^2b^3)^2$ [4.2a, b]

ind the intercepts. Then graph the equation. [3.2a]

01. $y - 6x = 6$

102. $3x - 5y = 15$

SYNTHESIS

actor completely, if possible.

03. $49x^2 - 216$

104. $27x^3 - 13x$

105. $x^2 + 22x + 121$

106. $x^2 - 5x + 25$

07. $18x^3 + 12x^2 + 2x$

108. $162x^2 - 82$

109. $x^8 - 2^8$

110. $4x^4 - 4x^2$

11. $3x^5 - 12x^3$

112. $3x^2 - \frac{1}{3}$

113. $18x^3 - \frac{8}{25}x$

114. $x^2 - 2.25$

15. $0.49p - p^3$

116. $3.24x^2 - 0.81$

117. $0.64x^2 - 1.21$

118. $1.28x^2 - 2$

19. $(x + 3)^2 - 9$

120. $(y - 5)^2 - 36q^2$

121. $x^2 - \left(\frac{1}{x}\right)^2$

122. $a^{2n} - 49b^{2n}$

23. $81 - b^{4k}$

124. $9x^{18} + 48x^9 + 64$

125. $9b^{2n} + 12b^n + 4$

126. $(x + 7)^2 - 4x - 24$

27. $(y + 3)^2 + 2(y + 3) + 1$

128. $49(x + 1)^2 - 42(x + 1) + 9$

ind c such that the polynomial is the square of a binomial.

29. $cy^2 + 6y + 1$

130. $cy^2 - 24y + 9$

Use the TABLE feature to determine whether the factorization is correct.

31. $x^2 + 9 = (x + 3)(x + 3)$

132. $x^2 - 49 = (x - 7)(x + 7)$

33. $x^2 + 9 = (x + 3)^2$

134. $x^2 - 49 = (x - 7)^2$

5.7 SOLVING QUADRATIC EQUATIONS BY FACTORING

Objectives

a Solve equations (already factored) using the principle of zero products.

b Solve quadratic equations by factoring and then using the principle of zero products.

Second-degree equations like $x^2 + x - 156 = 0$ and $9 - x^2 = 0$ are examples of *quadratic equations.*

QUADRATIC EQUATION

A **quadratic equation** is an equation equivalent to an equation of the type

$$ax^2 + bx + c = 0, \quad a \neq 0.$$

In order to solve quadratic equations, we need a new equation-solving principle.

a The Principle of Zero Products

The product of two numbers is 0 if one or both of the numbers is 0. Furthermore, *if any product is* 0, *then a factor must be* 0. For example:

If $7x = 0$, then we know that $x = 0$.

If $x(2x - 9) = 0$, then we know that $x = 0$ or $2x - 9 = 0$.

If $(x + 3)(x - 2) = 0$, then we know that $x + 3 = 0$ or $x - 2 = 0$.

Caution!

In a product such as $ab = 24$, we cannot conclude with certainty that a is 24 or that b is 24, but if $ab = 0$, we can conclude that $a = 0$ or $b = 0$.

EXAMPLE 1 Solve: $(x + 3)(x - 2) = 0$.

We have a product of 0. This equation will be true when either factor is 0. Thus it is true when

$$x + 3 = 0 \quad \text{or} \quad x - 2 = 0.$$

Here we have two simple equations that we know how to solve:

$$x = -3 \quad \text{or} \quad x = 2.$$

Each of the numbers -3 and 2 is a solution of the original equation, as we can see in the following checks.

Check: For -3:

$$\begin{array}{r|l} (x + 3)(x - 2) & = 0 \\ \hline (-3 + 3)(-3 - 2) & ?\ 0 \\ 0(-5) & \\ 0 & \quad \text{TRUE} \end{array}$$

For 2:

$$\begin{array}{r|l} (x + 3)(x - 2) & = 0 \\ \hline (2 + 3)(2 - 2) & ?\ 0 \\ 5(0) & \\ 0 & \quad \text{TRUE} \end{array}$$

Study Tips

WORKING WITH A CLASSMATE

If you are finding it difficult to master a particular topic or concept, try talking about it with a classmate. Verbalizing your questions about the material might help clarify it. If your classmate is also finding the material difficult, it is possible that the majority of the people in your class are confused and you can ask your instructor to explain the concept again.

We now have a principle to help in solving quadratic equations.

THE PRINCIPLE OF ZERO PRODUCTS

An equation $ab = 0$ is true if and only if $a = 0$ is true or $b = 0$ is true, or both are true. (A product is 0 if and only if one or both of the factors is 0.)

XAMPLE 2 Solve: $(5x + 1)(x - 7) = 0$.

We have

$$(5x + 1)(x - 7) = 0$$

$5x + 1 = 0$ *or* $x - 7 = 0$ Using the principle of zero products

$5x = -1$ *or* $x = 7$ Solving the two equations separately

$x = -\frac{1}{5}$ *or* $x = 7$.

eck: For $-\frac{1}{5}$:

$$\begin{array}{c|l} (5x + 1)(x - 7) = 0 & \\ \hline (5(-\frac{1}{5}) + 1)(-\frac{1}{5} - 7) \ ? \ 0 & \\ (-1 + 1)(-7\frac{1}{5}) & \\ 0(-7\frac{1}{5}) & \\ 0 & \text{TRUE} \end{array}$$

For 7:

$$\begin{array}{c|l} (5x + 1)(x - 7) = 0 & \\ \hline (5(7) + 1)(7 - 7) \ ? \ 0 & \\ (35 + 1) \cdot 0 & \\ 36 \cdot 0 & \\ 0 & \text{TRUE} \end{array}$$

e solutions are $-\frac{1}{5}$ and 7.

When you solve an equation using the principle of zero products, a check substitution, as in Examples 1 and 2, will detect errors in solving.

Exercises 1–3.

When some factors have only one term, you can still use the principle of ro products.

XAMPLE 3 Solve: $x(2x - 9) = 0$.

We have

$$x(2x - 9) = 0$$

$x = 0$ *or* $2x - 9 = 0$ Using the principle of zero products

$x = 0$ *or* $2x = 9$

$x = 0$ *or* $x = \frac{9}{2}$.

eck: For 0:

$$\begin{array}{c|l} x(2x - 9) = 0 & \\ \hline 0 \cdot (2 \cdot 0 - 9) \ ? \ 0 & \\ 0 \cdot (-9) & \\ 0 & \text{TRUE} \end{array}$$

For $\frac{9}{2}$:

$$\begin{array}{c|l} x(2x - 9) = 0 & \\ \hline \frac{9}{2} \cdot (2 \cdot \frac{9}{2} - 9) \ ? \ 0 & \\ \frac{9}{2} \cdot (9 - 9) & \\ \frac{9}{2} \cdot 0 & \\ 0 & \text{TRUE} \end{array}$$

Exercise 4.

Solve using the principle of zero products.

1. $(x - 3)(x + 4) = 0$

2. $(x - 7)(x - 3) = 0$

3. $(4t + 1)(3t - 2) = 0$

4. Solve: $y(3y - 17) = 0$.

Answers on page A-28

5. Solve: $x^2 - x - 6 = 0$.

Solve.

6. $x^2 - 3x = 28$

7. $x^2 = 6x - 9$

Solve.

8. $x^2 - 4x = 0$

9. $9x^2 = 16$

Answers on page A-28

b Using Factoring to Solve Equations

Using factoring and the principle of zero products, we can solve some ne kinds of equations. Thus we have extended our equation-solving abilities.

EXAMPLE 4 Solve: $x^2 + 5x + 6 = 0$.

There are no like terms to collect, and we have a squared term. We fir factor the polynomial. Then we use the principle of zero products.

$$x^2 + 5x + 6 = 0$$

$$(x + 2)(x + 3) = 0 \quad \text{Factoring}$$

$$x + 2 = 0 \quad or \quad x + 3 = 0 \quad \text{Using the principle of zero products}$$

$$x = -2 \quad or \quad x = -3$$

Check: For -2:

$$\begin{array}{c|c} x^2 + 5x + 6 & 0 \\ \hline (-2)^2 + 5(-2) + 6 \ ? & 0 \\ 4 - 10 + 6 & \\ -6 + 6 & \\ 0 & \end{array} \quad \text{TRUE}$$

For -3:

$$\begin{array}{c|c} x^2 + 5x + 6 & 0 \\ \hline (-3)^2 + 5(-3) + 6 \ ? & 0 \\ 9 - 15 + 6 & \\ -6 + 6 & \\ 0 & \end{array} \quad \text{TR}$$

The solutions are -2 and -3.

Caution!

Keep in mind that you *must* have 0 on one side of the equation before you can use the principle of zero products. Get all nonzero terms on one side and 0 on the other.

Do Exercise 5.

EXAMPLE 5 Solve: $x^2 - 8x = -16$.

We first add 16 to get a 0 on one side:

$$x^2 - 8x = -16$$

$$x^2 - 8x + 16 = 0 \quad \text{Adding 16}$$

$$(x - 4)(x - 4) = 0 \quad \text{Factoring}$$

$$x - 4 = 0 \quad or \quad x - 4 = 0 \quad \text{Using the principle of zero product}$$

$$x = 4 \quad or \quad x = 4. \quad \text{Solving each equation}$$

There is only one solution, 4. The check is left to the student.

Do Exercises 6 and 7.

EXAMPLE 6 Solve: $x^2 + 5x = 0$.

$$x^2 + 5x = 0$$

$$x(x + 5) = 0 \quad \text{Factoring out a common factor}$$

$$x = 0 \quad or \quad x + 5 = 0 \quad \text{Using the principle of zero products}$$

$$x = 0 \quad or \quad x = -5$$

The solutions are 0 and -5. The check is left to the student.

XAMPLE 7 Solve: $4x^2 = 25$.

$$4x^2 = 25$$
$$4x^2 - 25 = 0 \quad \text{Subtracting 25 on both sides to get 0 on one side}$$
$$(2x - 5)(2x + 5) = 0 \quad \text{Factoring a difference of squares}$$
$$2x - 5 = 0 \quad or \quad 2x + 5 = 0$$
$$2x = 5 \quad or \quad 2x = -5 \quad \text{Solving each equation}$$
$$x = \frac{5}{2} \quad or \quad x = -\frac{5}{2}$$

he solutions are $\frac{5}{2}$ and $-\frac{5}{2}$. The check is left to the student.

o Exercises 8 and 9 on the preceding page.

Solve.

10. $-2x^2 + 13x - 21 = 0$

XAMPLE 8 Solve: $-5x^2 + 2x + 3 = 0$.

In this case, the leading coefficient of the trinomial is negative. Thus we rst multiply by -1 and then proceed as we have in Examples 1–7.

$$-5x^2 + 2x + 3 = 0$$
$$-1(-5x^2 + 2x + 3) = -1 \cdot 0 \quad \text{Multiplying by } -1$$
$$5x^2 - 2x - 3 = 0 \quad \text{Simplifying}$$
$$(5x + 3)(x - 1) = 0 \quad \text{Factoring}$$
$$5x + 3 = 0 \quad or \quad x - 1 = 0 \quad \text{Using the principle of zero products}$$
$$5x = -3 \quad or \quad x = 1$$
$$x = -\frac{3}{5} \quad or \quad x = 1$$

ne solutions are $-\frac{3}{5}$ and 1. The check is left to the student.

o Exercises 10 and 11.

11. $10 - 3x - x^2 = 0$

12. Solve: $(x + 1)(x - 1) = 8$.

XAMPLE 9 Solve: $(x + 2)(x - 2) = 5$.

Be careful with an equation like this one! It might be tempting to set each ctor equal to 5. **Remember: We must have a 0 on one side.** We first carry out e product on the left. Then we subtract 5 on both sides to get 0 on one side. nen we proceed with the principle of zero products.

$$(x + 2)(x - 2) = 5$$
$$x^2 - 4 = 5 \quad \text{Multiplying on the left}$$
$$x^2 - 4 - 5 = 5 - 5 \quad \text{Subtracting 5}$$
$$x^2 - 9 = 0 \quad \text{Simplifying}$$
$$(x + 3)(x - 3) = 0 \quad \text{Factoring}$$
$$x + 3 = 0 \quad or \quad x - 3 = 0 \quad \text{Using the principle of zero products}$$
$$x = -3 \quad or \quad x = 3$$

ne solutions are -3 and 3. The check is left to the student.

o Exercise 12.

Answers on page A-28

13. Find the x-intercepts of the graph shown below.

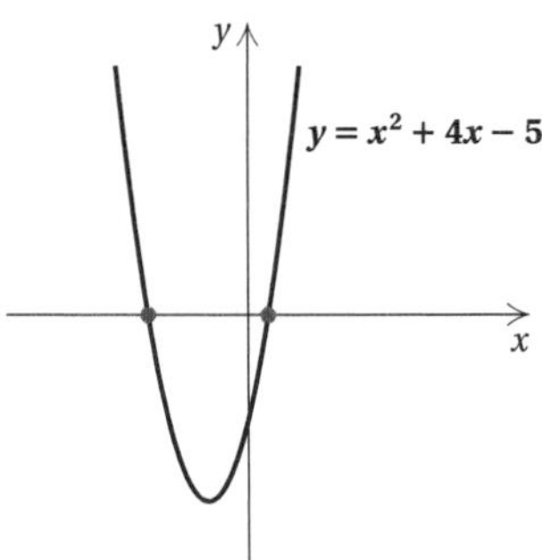

14. Use *only* the graph shown below to solve $3x - x^2 = 0$.

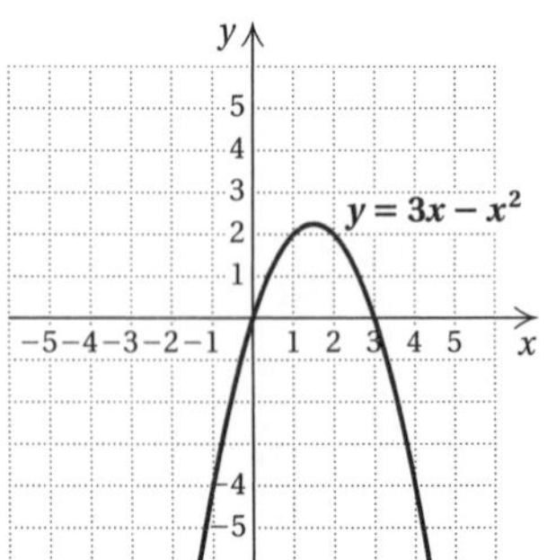

AG ALGEBRAIC–GRAPHICAL CONNECTION

In Chapter 3, we graphed linear equations of the type $y = mx + b$ and $Ax + By = C$. Recall that to find the x-intercept, we replaced y with 0 and solved for x. This procedure can also be used to find the x-intercepts when an equation of the form $y = ax^2 + bx + c$, $a \neq 0$, is to be graphed. Although the details of creating such graphs will be left to Chapter 9, we consider them briefly here from the standpoint of finding the x-intercepts. The graphs are shaped like the following curves. Note that each x-intercept represents a solution of $ax^2 + bx + c = 0$.

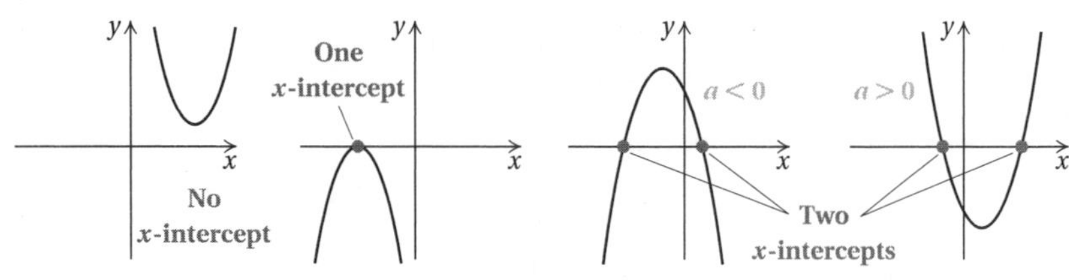

EXAMPLE 10 Find the x-intercepts of the graph of $y = x^2 - 4x - 5$ shown at right. (The grid is intentionally not included.)

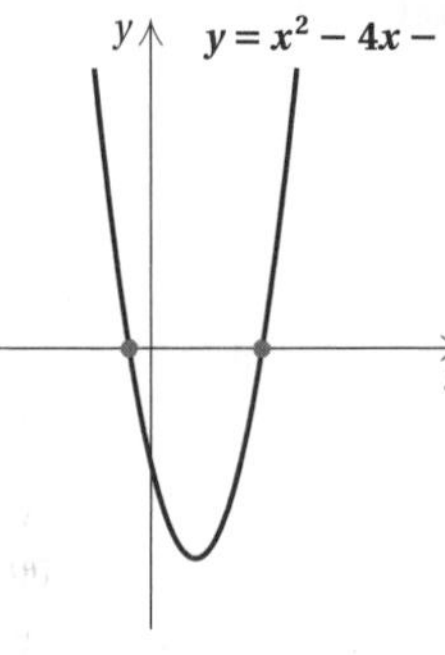

To find the x-intercepts, we let $y = 0$ and solve for x:

$$y = x^2 - 4x - 5$$

$$0 = x^2 - 4x - 5 \quad \text{Substituting 0 for } y$$

$$0 = (x - 5)(x + 1) \quad \text{Factoring}$$

$$x - 5 = 0 \quad or \quad x + 1 = 0 \quad \text{Using the principle of zero products}$$

$$x = 5 \quad or \quad x = -1.$$

The solutions of the equation $0 = x^2 - 4x - 5$ are 5 and -1. The x-intercepts of the graph of $y = x^2 - 4x - 5$ are $(5, 0)$ and $(-1, 0)$. We can now label them on the graph.

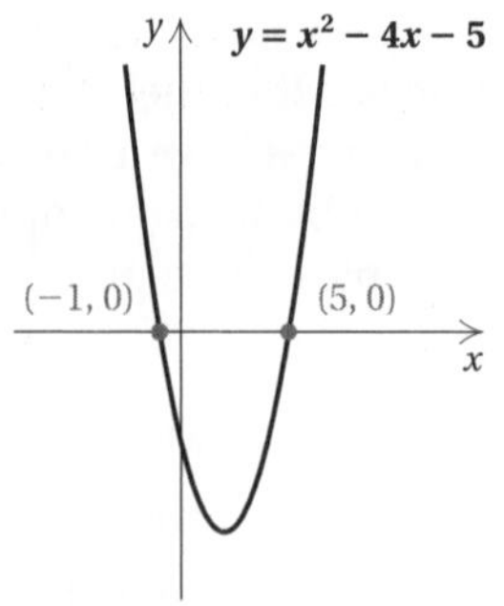

Do Exercises 13 and 14.

Answers on page A-28

CALCULATOR CORNER

Solving Quadratic Equations We can solve quadratic equations graphically. Consider the equation $x^2 + 2x = 8$. First, we must write the equation with 0 on one side. To do this, we subtract 8 on both sides of the equation; we get $x^2 + 2x - 8 = 0$. Next, we graph $y = x^2 + 2x - 8$ in a window that shows the x-intercepts. The standard window works well in this case.

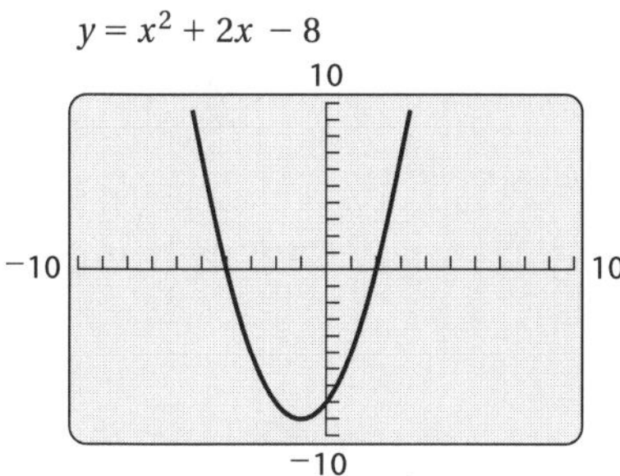

The solutions of the equation are the values of x for which $x^2 + 2x - 8 = 0$. These are also the first coordinates of the x-intercepts of the graph. We use the ZERO feature from the CALC menu to find these numbers. To find the solution corresponding to the leftmost x-intercept, we first press 2ND CALC 2 to select the ZERO feature. The prompt "Left Bound?" appears. Next, we use the ◁ or the ▷ key to move the cursor to the left of the intercept and press ENTER. Now the prompt "Right Bound?" appears. Then we move the cursor to the right of the intercept and press ENTER. The prompt "Guess?" appears. We move the cursor close to the intercept and press ENTER again. We now see the cursor positioned at the leftmost x-intercept and the coordinates of that point, $x = -4$, $y = 0$, are displayed. Thus, $x^2 + 2x - 8 = 0$ when $x = -4$. This is one solution of the equation.

We can repeat this procedure to find the first coordinate of the other x-intercept. We see that $x = 2$ at that point. Thus the solutions of the equation $x^2 + 2x - 8 = 0$ are -4 and 2. Note that the x-intercepts of the graph of $y = x^2 + 2x - 8$ are $(-4, 0)$ and $(2, 0)$.

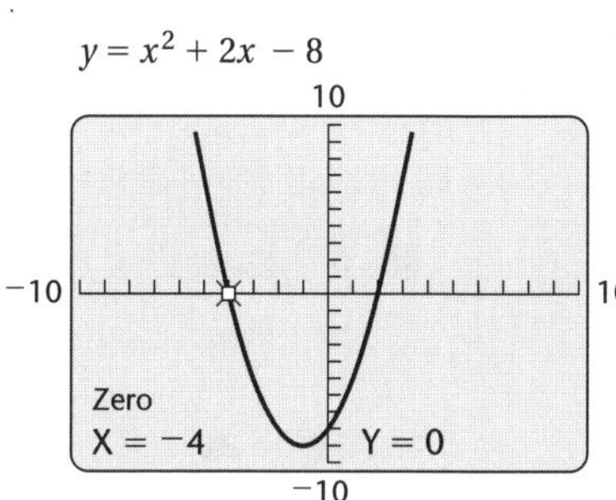

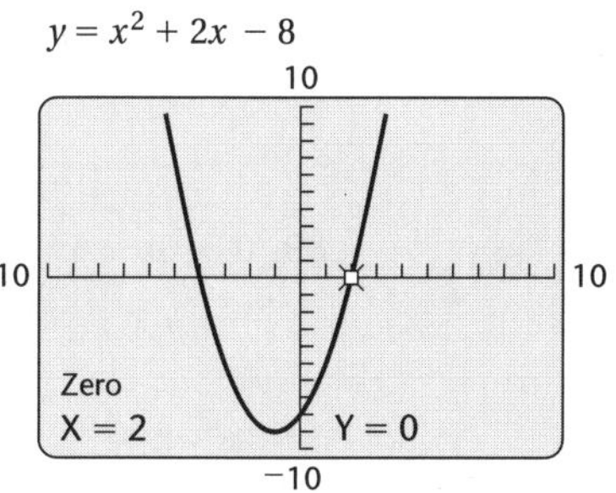

Exercises:

1. Solve each of the equations in Examples 4–8 graphically.

5.7 EXERCISE SET

For Extra Help

MathXL | MyMathLab | InterAct Math | Math Tutor Center | Digital Video Tutor CD 3 Videotape 6 | Student's Solutions Manual

a Solve using the principle of zero products.

1. $(x + 4)(x + 9) = 0$

2. $(x + 2)(x - 7) = 0$

3. $(x + 3)(x - 8) = 0$

4. $(x + 6)(x - 8) = 0$

5. $(x + 12)(x - 11) = 0$

6. $(x - 13)(x + 53) = 0$

7. $x(x + 3) = 0$

8. $y(y + 5) = 0$

9. $0 = y(y + 18)$

10. $0 = x(x - 19)$

11. $(2x + 5)(x + 4) = 0$

12. $(2x + 9)(x + 8) = 0$

13. $(5x + 1)(4x - 12) = 0$

14. $(4x + 9)(14x - 7) = 0$

15. $(7x - 28)(28x - 7) = 0$

16. $(13x + 14)(6x - 5) = 0$

17. $2x(3x - 2) = 0$

18. $55x(8x - 9) = 0$

19. $\left(\frac{1}{5} + 2x\right)\left(\frac{1}{9} - 3x\right) = 0$

20. $\left(\frac{7}{4}x - \frac{1}{16}\right)\left(\frac{2}{3}x - \frac{16}{15}\right) = 0$

21. $(0.3x - 0.1)(0.05x + 1) = 0$

22. $(0.1x + 0.3)(0.4x - 20) = 0$

23. $9x(3x - 2)(2x - 1) = 0$

24. $(x + 5)(x - 75)(5x - 1) = 0$

b Solve by factoring and using the principle of zero products. Remember to check.

25. $x^2 + 6x + 5 = 0$

26. $x^2 + 7x + 6 = 0$

27. $x^2 + 7x - 18 = 0$

28. $x^2 + 4x - 21 = 0$

29. $x^2 - 8x + 15 = 0$

30. $x^2 - 9x + 14 = 0$

31. $x^2 - 8x = 0$

32. $x^2 - 3x = 0$

33. $x^2 + 18x = 0$

34. $x^2 + 16x = 0$

35. $x^2 = 16$

36. $100 = x^2$

37. $9x^2 - 4 = 0$

38. $4x^2 - 9 = 0$

39. $0 = 6x + x^2 + 9$

40. $0 = 25 + x^2 + 10x$

41. $x^2 + 16 = 8x$

42. $1 + x^2 = 2x$

43. $5x^2 = 6x$

44. $7x^2 = 8x$

45. $6x^2 - 4x = 10$

46. $3x^2 - 7x = 20$

47. $12y^2 - 5y = 2$

48. $2y^2 + 12y = -10$

9. $t(3t + 1) = 2$

50. $x(x - 5) = 14$

51. $100y^2 = 49$

52. $64a^2 = 81$

3. $x^2 - 5x = 18 + 2x$

54. $3x^2 + 8x = 9 + 2x$

55. $10x^2 - 23x + 12 = 0$

56. $12x^2 + 17x - 5 = 0$

ind the x-intercepts for the graph of the equation. (The grids are intentionally not included.)

7.

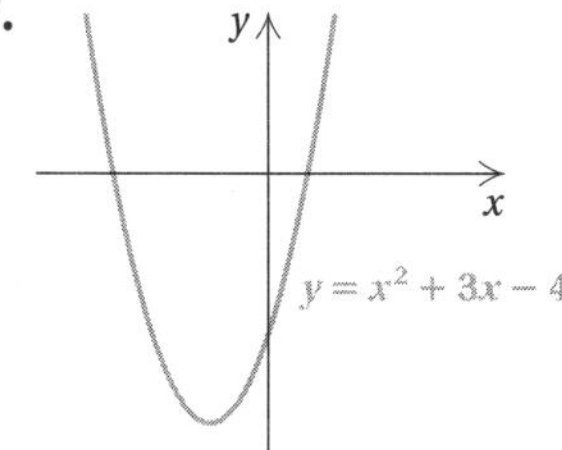

58.

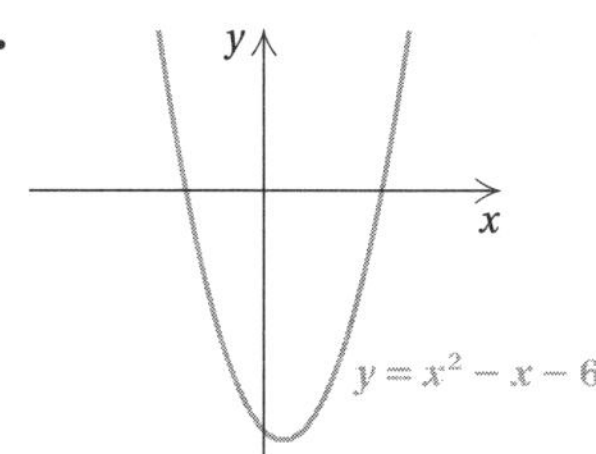

59.

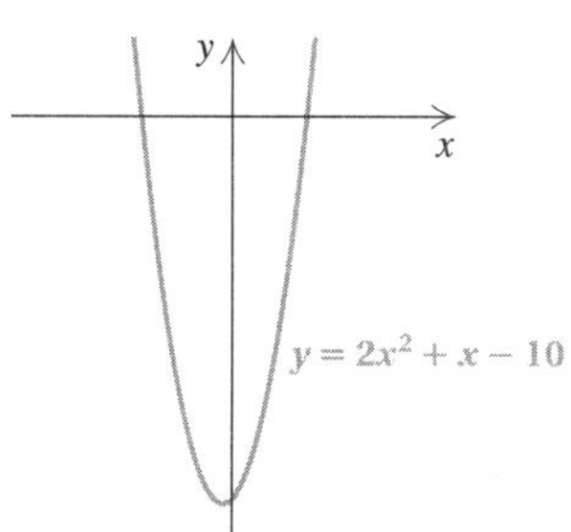

0.

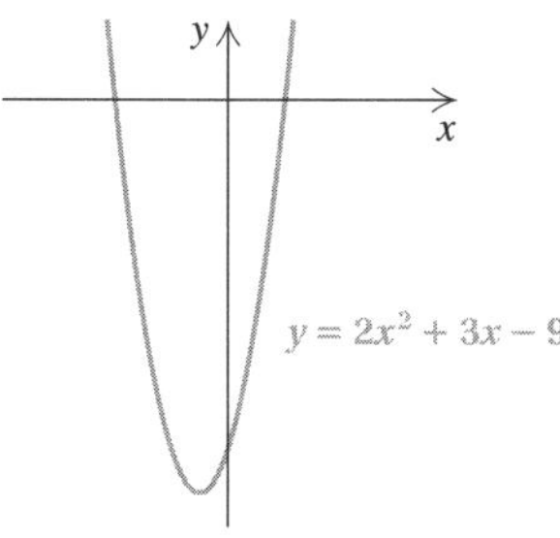

61.

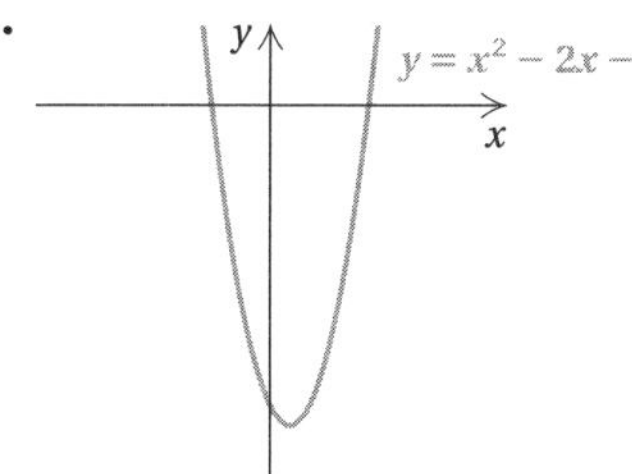

62.

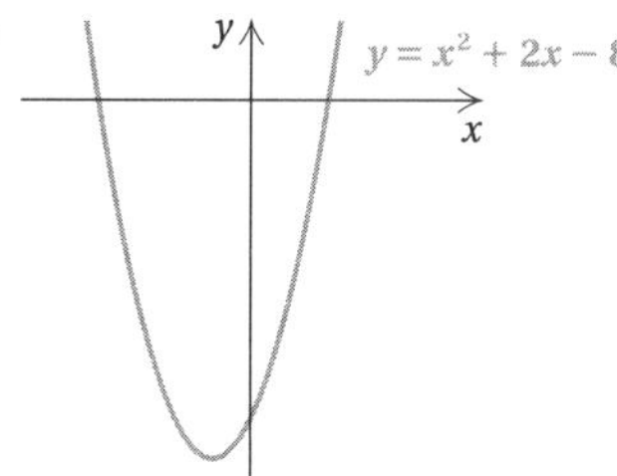

3. Use the following graph to solve $x^2 - 3x - 4 = 0$.

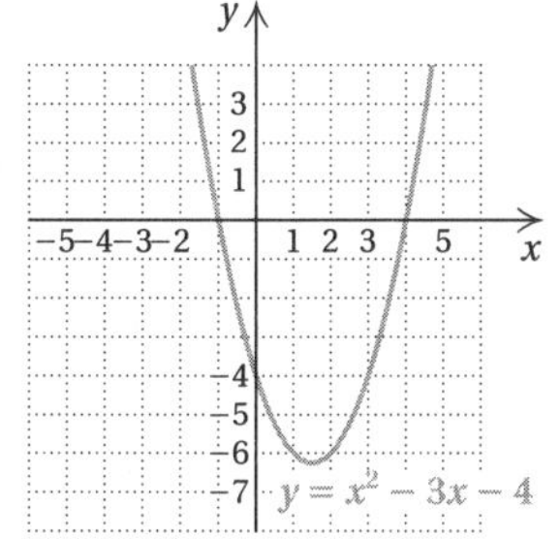

64. Use the following graph to solve $x^2 + x - 6 = 0$.

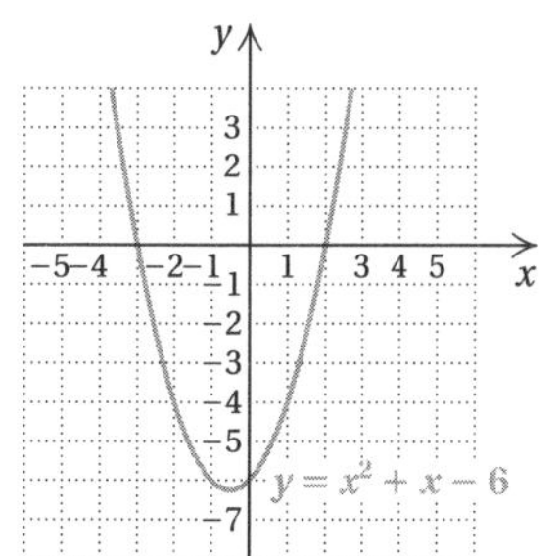

65. Use the following graph to solve $-x^2 + 2x + 3 = 0$.

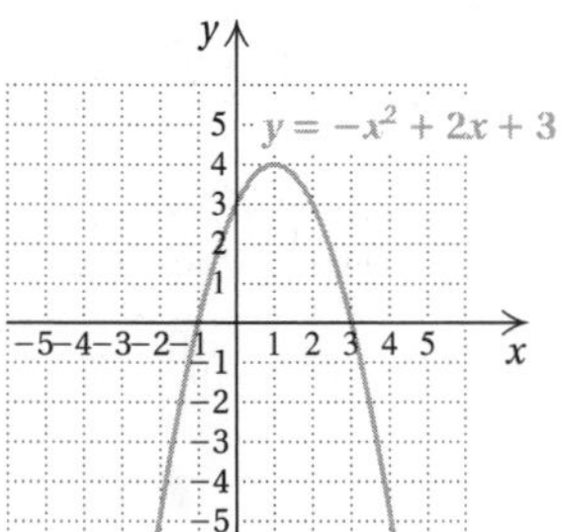

66. Use the following graph to solve $-x^2 - x + 6 = 0$.

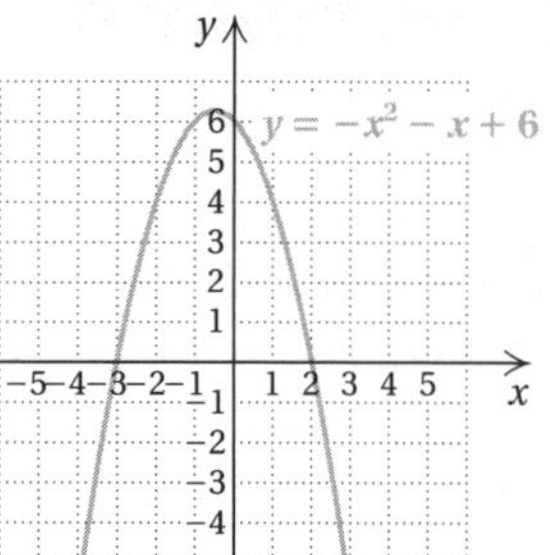

67. DW What is wrong with the following? Explain the correct method of solution.

$$(x - 3)(x + 4) = 8$$
$$x - 3 = 8 \quad or \quad x + 4 = 8$$
$$x = 11 \quad or \quad x = 4$$

68. DW What is incorrect about solving $x^2 = 3x$ by dividing by x on both sides?

SKILL MAINTENANCE

Translate to an algebraic expression. [1.1b]

69. The square of the sum of a and b

70. The sum of the squares of a and b

Divide. [1.6c]

71. $144 \div (-9)$

72. $-24.3 \div 5.4$

73. $-\frac{5}{8} \div \frac{3}{16}$

74. $-\frac{3}{16} \div \left(-\frac{5}{8}\right)$

SYNTHESIS

Solve.

75. $b(b + 9) = 4(5 + 2b)$

76. $y(y + 8) = 16(y - 1)$

77. $(t - 3)^2 = 36$

78. $(t - 5)^2 = 2(5 - t)$

79. $x^2 - \frac{1}{64} = 0$

80. $x^2 - \frac{25}{36} = 0$

81. $\frac{5}{16}x^2 = 5$

82. $\frac{27}{25}x^2 = \frac{1}{3}$

83. Find an equation that has the given numbers as solutions. For example, 3 and -2 are solutions of $x^2 - x - 6 = 0$.

a) $-3, 4$ **b)** $-3, -4$ **c)** $\frac{1}{2}, \frac{1}{2}$
d) $5, -5$ **e)** $0, 0.1, \frac{1}{4}$

84. *Matching.* Match each equation in the first column with the equivalent equation in the second column.

$x^2 + 10x - 2 = 0$	$4x^2 + 8x + 36 = 0$
$(x - 6)(x + 3) = 0$	$(2x + 8)(2x - 5) = 0$
$5x^2 - 5 = 0$	$9x^2 - 12x + 24 = 0$
$(2x - 5)(x + 4) = 0$	$(x + 1)(5x - 5) = 0$
$x^2 + 2x + 9 = 0$	$x^2 - 3x - 18 = 0$
$3x^2 - 4x + 8 = 0$	$2x^2 + 20x - 4 = 0$

Use a graphing calculator to find the solutions of the equation. Round solutions to the nearest hundredth.

85. $x^2 - 9.10x + 15.77 = 0$

86. $-x^2 + 0.63x + 0.22 = 0$

87. $0.84x^2 - 2.30x = 0$

88. $6.4x^2 - 8.45x - 94.06 = 0$

5.8 APPLICATIONS OF QUADRATIC EQUATIONS

Objective

a Solve applied problems involving quadratic equations that can be solved by factoring.

a Applied Problems, Quadratic Equations, and Factoring

We can now use our new method for solving quadratic equations and the five steps for solving problems.

EXAMPLE 1 *Manufacturing Marble Slabs.* Marble Supreme sells rectangular marble slabs used for tempering fudge in candy shops. The most popular slab that Marble Supreme sells is twice as long as it is wide and has an area of 7200 in^2. What are the dimensions of the slab?

1. **Familiarize.** We first make a drawing. Recall that the area of any rectangle is Length · Width. We let $x =$ the width of the slab, in inches. The length is then $2x$.

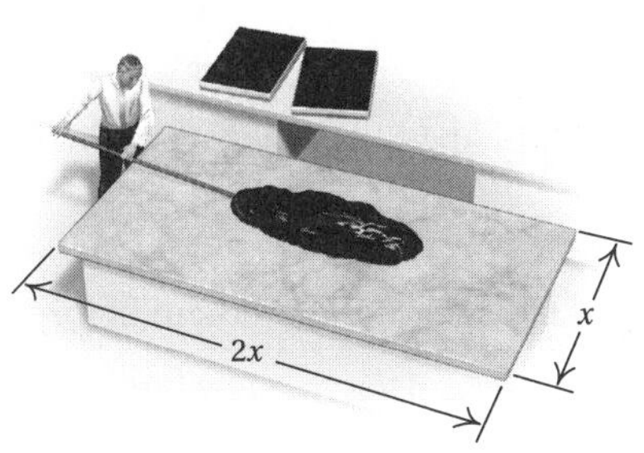

2. **Translate.** We reword and translate as follows:

Rewording: The area of the rectangle is 7200 cm^2.

Translating: $2x \cdot x = 7200$

3. **Solve.** We solve the equation as follows:

$$2x \cdot x = 7200$$
$$2x^2 = 7200$$
$$2x^2 - 7200 = 0 \quad \text{Subtracting 7200 to get 0 on one side}$$
$$2(x^2 - 3600) = 0 \quad \text{Removing a common factor of 2}$$
$$2(x - 60)(x + 60) = 0 \quad \text{Factoring a difference of squares}$$
$$(x - 60)(x + 60) = 0 \quad \text{Dividing by 2}$$
$$x - 60 = 0 \quad or \quad x + 60 = 0 \quad \text{Using the principle of zero products}$$
$$x = 60 \quad or \quad x = -60. \quad \text{Solving each equation}$$

4. **Check.** The solutions of the equation are 60 and -60. Since the width must be positive, -60 cannot be a solution. To check 60 in., we note that if the width is 60 in., then the length is $2 \cdot 60$ in. $= 120$ in., and the area is 60 in. · 120 in. $= 7200\ \text{in}^2$. Thus the solution 60 checks.

5. **State.** The slab is 60 in. wide and 120 in. long.

Do Exercise 1.

1. **Dimensions of Picture.** A rectangular picture is twice as long as it is wide. If the area of the picture is 288 in^2, find its dimensions.

Answer on page A-29

2. **Dimensions of a Sail.** The mainsail of Stacey's lightning-styled sailboat has an area of 125 ft^2. The sail is 15 ft taller than it is wide. Find the height and the width of the sail.

Answer on page A-29

EXAMPLE 2 *Racing Sailboat.* The height of a triangular sail on a racin sailboat is 9 ft more than the base. The area of the triangle is 110 ft^2. Find th height and the base of the sail.

Source: Whitney Gladstone, North Graphics, San Diego, CA

1. **Familiarize.** We first make a drawing. If you don't remember the for mula for the area of a triangle, look it up in the list of formulas at the bac of this book or in a geometry book. The area is $\frac{1}{2}$(base)(height).

   We let b = the base of the triangle. Then $b + 9$ = the height.

2. **Translate.** It helps to reword this problem before translating:

$$\begin{array}{cccccccl} \frac{1}{2} & \text{times} & \text{Base} & \text{times} & \underbrace{\text{Height}} & \text{is} & 110. & \text{Rewording} \\ \downarrow & \downarrow & \downarrow & \downarrow & \downarrow & \downarrow & \downarrow & \\ \frac{1}{2} & \cdot & b & \cdot & (b+9) & = & 110 & \text{Translating} \end{array}$$

3. **Solve.** We solve the equation as follows:

$$\frac{1}{2} \cdot b \cdot (b + 9) = 110$$

$$\frac{1}{2}(b^2 + 9b) = 110 \qquad \text{Multiplying}$$

$$2 \cdot \frac{1}{2}(b^2 + 9b) = 2 \cdot 110 \qquad \text{Multiplying by 2}$$

$$b^2 + 9b = 220 \qquad \text{Simplifying}$$

$$b^2 + 9b - 220 = 220 - 220 \qquad \text{Subtracting 220 to get 0 on one side}$$

$$b^2 + 9b - 220 = 0$$

$$(b - 11)(b + 20) = 0 \qquad \text{Factoring}$$

$$b - 11 = 0 \quad or \quad b + 20 = 0 \qquad \text{Using the principle of zero products}$$

$$b = 11 \quad or \quad b = -20.$$

4. **Check.** The base of a triangle cannot have a negative length, so −2 cannot be a solution. Suppose the base is 11 ft. The height is 9 ft mor than the base, so the height is 11 ft + 9 ft, or 20 ft, and the area i $\frac{1}{2}(11)(20)$, or 110 ft^2. These numbers check in the original problem.
5. **State.** The height is 20 ft and the base is 11 ft.

Do Exercise 2.

XAMPLE 3 *Games in a Sports League.* In a sports league of x teams in 'hich each team plays every other team twice, the total number N of games) be played is given by

$$x^2 - x = N.$$

Iaggie's basketball league plays a total of 240 games. How many teams are in ie league?

., 2. **Familiarize** and **Translate.** We are given that x is the number of teams in a league and N is the number of games. To familiarize yourself with this problem, reread Example 4 in Section 4.3 where we first considered it. To find the number of teams x in a league in which 240 games are played, we substitute 240 for N in the equation:

$$x^2 - x = 240. \qquad \text{Substituting 240 for } N$$

3. **Solve.** We solve the equation as follows:

$$x^2 - x = 240$$
$$x^2 - x - 240 = 240 - 240 \qquad \text{Subtracting 240 to get 0 on one side}$$
$$x^2 - x - 240 = 0$$
$$(x - 16)(x + 15) = 0 \qquad \text{Factoring}$$
$$x - 16 = 0 \quad or \quad x + 15 = 0 \qquad \text{Using the principle of zero products}$$
$$x = 16 \quad or \quad x = -15.$$

4. **Check.** The solutions of the equation are 16 and -15. Since the number of teams cannot be negative, -15 cannot be a solution. But 16 checks, since $16^2 - 16 = 256 - 16 = 240$.

5. **State.** There are 16 teams in the league.

o Exercise 3.

3. Use $N = x^2 - x$ for the following.

   a) **Volleyball League.** Amy's volleyball league has 19 teams. What is the total number of games to be played?

   b) **Softball League.** Barry's slow-pitch softball league plays a total of 72 games. How many teams are in the league?

Answers on page A-29

Study Tips

FIVE STEPS FOR PROBLEM SOLVING

Are you remembering to use the five steps for problem solving that were developed in Section 2.6?

1. **Familiarize** yourself with the situation.
   a) Carefully read and reread until you understand *what* you are being asked to find.
   b) Draw a diagram or see if there is a formula that applies.
   c) Assign a letter, or *variable,* to the unknown.
2. **Translate** the problem to an equation using the letter or variable.
3. **Solve** the equation.
4. **Check** the answer in the original wording of the problem.
5. **State** the answer to the problem clearly with appropriate units.

"Most worthwhile achievements are the result of many little things done in a simple direction."

Nido Quebin, speaker/entrepreneur

4. **Page Numbers.** The product of the page numbers on two facing pages of a book is 506. Find the page numbers.

Answer on page A-29

Study Tips

ASKING QUESTIONS

Don't be afraid to ask questions in class. Most instructors welcome this and encourage students to ask them. Other students probably have the same questions you do.

"Better to ask twice than lose your way once."

Danish proverb

EXAMPLE 4 *Athletic Numbers.* The product of the numbers of tw consecutive entrants in a marathon race is 156. Find the numbers.

1. **Familiarize.** The numbers are consecutive integers. Recall that consecu tive integers are next to each other, such as 49 and 50, or −6 and −5. L $x =$ the smaller integer; then $x + 1 =$ the larger integer.
2. **Translate.** It helps to reword the problem before translating:

First integer	times	Second integer	is	156.	Rewording
↓	↓	↓	↓	↓	
x	$\cdot$	$(x + 1)$	$=$	156	Translating

3. **Solve.** We solve the equation as follows:

$$x(x + 1) = 156$$

$$x^2 + x = 156 \quad \text{Multiplying}$$

$$x^2 + x - 156 = 156 - 156 \quad \text{Subtracting 156 to get 0 on one side}$$

$$x^2 + x - 156 = 0 \quad \text{Simplifying}$$

$$(x - 12)(x + 13) = 0 \quad \text{Factoring}$$

$$x - 12 = 0 \quad or \quad x + 13 = 0 \quad \text{Using the principle of zero products}$$

$$x = 12 \quad or \quad x = -13.$$

4. **Check.** The solutions of the equation are 12 and −13. When x is 12, the $x + 1$ is 13, and $12 \cdot 13 = 156$. The numbers 12 and 13 are consecutive in tegers that are solutions to the problem. When x is −13, then $x + 1$ is −1 and $(-13)(-12) = 156$. The numbers −13 and −12 are consecutive inte gers, but they are not solutions of the problem because negative numbe are not used as entry numbers.
5. **State.** The entry numbers are 12 and 13.

Do Exercise 4.

b The Pythagorean Theorem

The following problems involve the Pythagorean theorem, which relates th lengths of the sides of a *right* triangle. A triangle is a **right triangle** if it has 90°, or *right*, angle. The side opposite the 90° angle is called the **hypotenus** The other sides are called **legs.**

THE PYTHAGOREAN THEOREM

In any right triangle, if a and b are the lengths of the legs and c is the length of the hypotenuse, then

$$a^2 + b^2 = c^2.$$

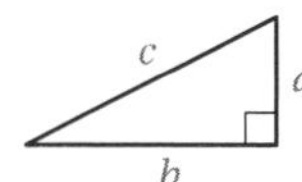

The symbol ⌈ denotes a 90° angle.

EXAMPLE 5 *Physical Education.* An outdoor-education ropes course includes a 25-ft cable that slopes downward from a height of 37 ft to a height of 30 ft. How far is it between the trees that the cable connects?

1. **Familiarize.** We make a drawing as above, noting that when we subtract 30 ft from 37 ft, we get the height of the right triangle that is formed. We let $b =$ the distance between the trees.

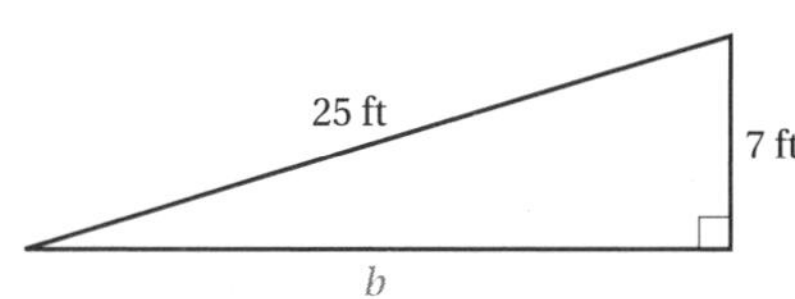

2. **Translate.** A right triangle is formed, so we can use the Pythagorean theorem:

$$a^2 + b^2 = c^2$$

$$7^2 + b^2 = 25^2.$$ Substituting 7 for the length of a leg and 25 for the length of the hypotenuse

3. **Solve.** We solve the equation as follows:

$$7^2 + b^2 = 25^2$$

$$49 + b^2 = 625 \quad \text{Squaring 7 and 25}$$

$$b^2 - 576 = 0 \quad \text{Subtracting 625}$$

$$(b - 24)(b + 24) = 0 \quad \text{Factoring}$$

$$b - 24 = 0 \quad or \quad b + 24 = 0 \quad \text{Using the principle of zero products}$$

$$b = 24 \quad or \quad b = -24.$$

4. **Check.** Since the distance between the trees cannot be negative, -24 cannot be a solution. If the distance is 24 ft, we have $7^2 + 24^2 = 49 + 576 = 625$, which is 25^2. Thus, 24 checks and is a solution.

5. **State.** The distance between the trees is 24 ft.

Do Exercise 5.

5. **Reach of a Ladder.** Twila has a 26-ft ladder leaning against her house. If the bottom of the ladder is 10 ft from the base of the house, how high does the ladder reach?

Answer on page A-29

6. **Right-Triangle Geometry.** The length of one leg of a right triangle is 1 m longer than the other. The length of the hypotenuse is 5 m. Find the lengths of the legs.

Answer on page A-29

EXAMPLE 6 *Ladder Settings.* A ladder of length 13 ft is placed against a building in such a way that the distance from the top of the ladder to the ground is 7 ft more than the distance from the bottom of the ladder to the building. Find both distances.

1. **Familiarize.** We first make a drawing. The ladder and the missing distances form the hypotenuse and legs of a right triangle. We let $x =$ the length of the side (leg) across the bottom. Then $x + 7 =$ the length of the other side (leg). The hypotenuse has length 13 ft.

2. **Translate.** Since a right triangle is formed, we can use the Pythagorean theorem:

$$a^2 + b^2 = c^2$$
$$x^2 + (x + 7)^2 = 13^2. \quad \text{Substituting}$$

3. **Solve.** We solve the equation as follows:

$$x^2 + (x^2 + 14x + 49) = 169 \quad \text{Squaring the binomial and 13}$$
$$2x^2 + 14x + 49 = 169 \quad \text{Collecting like terms}$$
$$2x^2 + 14x + 49 - 169 = 169 - 169 \quad \text{Subtracting 169 to get 0 on one side}$$
$$2x^2 + 14x - 120 = 0 \quad \text{Simplifying}$$
$$2(x^2 + 7x - 60) = 0 \quad \text{Factoring out a common factor}$$
$$x^2 + 7x - 60 = 0 \quad \text{Dividing by 2}$$
$$(x + 12)(x - 5) = 0 \quad \text{Factoring}$$
$$x + 12 = 0 \quad or \quad x - 5 = 0 \quad \text{Using the principle of zero products}$$
$$x = -12 \quad or \quad x = 5.$$

4. **Check.** The negative integer -12 cannot be the length of a side. When $x = 5$, $x + 7 = 12$, and $5^2 + 12^2 = 13^2$. So 5 and 12 check.

5. **State.** The distance from the top of the ladder to the ground is 12 ft. The distance from the bottom of the ladder to the building is 5 ft.

Do Exercise 6.

Translating for Success

ıgle Measures. The measures the angles of a triangle are ree consecutive integers. Find e measures of the angles.

ctangle Dimensions. The ea of a rectangle is 3599 ft^2. ıe length is 2 ft longer than the idth. Find the dimensions of e rectangle.

ıles Tax. Claire paid $40,704 r a new SUV. This included 6% r sales tax. How much did the JV cost before tax?

ire Cutting. A 180-m wire is ıt into three pieces. The third ece is 2 m longer than the first. ıe second is two-thirds as long the first. How long is each ece?

rimeter. The perimeter of a ctangle is 240 ft. The length is ft greater than the width. Find e length and the width.

The goal of these matching questions is to practice step (2), *Translate,* of the five-step problem-solving process. Translate each word problem to an equation and select a correct translation from equations A–O.

A. $2x \cdot x = 288$

B. $x(x + 60) = 7021$

C. $59 = x \cdot 60$

D. $x^2 + (x + 2)^2 = 3599$

E. $x^2 + (x + 70)^2 = 130^2$

F. $6\% \cdot x = 40{,}704$

G. $2(x + 2) + 2x = 240$

H. $\frac{1}{2}x(x - 1) = 1770$

I. $x + \frac{2}{3}x + (x + 2) = 180$

J. $59\% \cdot x = 60$

K. $x + 6\% \cdot x = 40{,}704$

L. $2x^2 + x = 288$

M. $x(x + 2) = 3599$

N. $x^2 + 60 = 7021$

O. $x + (x + 1) + (x + 2) = 180$

Answers on page A-29

6. *Cell-Phone Tower.* A guy wire on a cell-phone tower is 130 ft long and is attached to the top of the tower. The height of the tower is 70 ft longer than the distance from the point on the ground where the wire is attached to the bottom of the tower. Find the height of the tower.

7. *Sales Meeting Attendance.* PTQ Corporation holds a sales meeting in Tucson. Of the 60 employees, 59 of them attend the meeting. What percent attend the meeting?

8. *Dimensions of a Pool.* A rectangular swimming pool is twice as long as it is wide. The area of the surface is 288 ft^2. Find the dimensions of the pool.

9. *Dimensions of a Triangle.* The height of a triangle is 1 cm less than the length of the base. The area of the triangle is 1770 cm^2. Find the height and the length of the base.

10. *Width of a Rectangle.* The length of a rectangle is 60 ft longer than the width. Find the width if the area of the rectangle is 7021 ft^2.

5.8 EXERCISE SET

For Extra Help

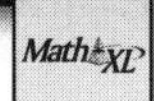

MathXL | MyMathLab | InterAct Math | Math Tutor Center | Digital Video Tutor CD 3 Videotape 6 | Student's Solutions Manual

a Solve.

1. *Design.* The screen of the TI-84 Plus graphing calculator is nearly rectangular. The length of the rectangle is 2 cm more than the width. If the area of the rectangle is 24 cm^2, find the length and the width.

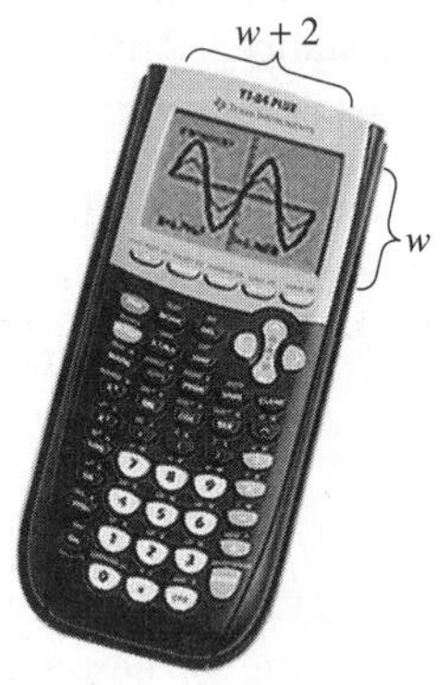

2. *Area of a Garden.* The length of a rectangular garden is 4 m greater than the width. The area of the garden is 96 m^2. Find the length and the width.

3. *Furnishings.* A rectangular table in Arlo's House of Tunes is six times as long as it is wide. The area of the table is 24 ft^2. Find the length and the width of the table.

4. *Dimensions of Picture.* A rectangular picture is three times as long as it is wide. The area of the picture is 588 in^2. Find the dimensions of the picture.

5. *Dimensions of a Triangle.* A triangle is 10 cm wider than it is tall. The area is 28 cm^2. Find the height and the base.

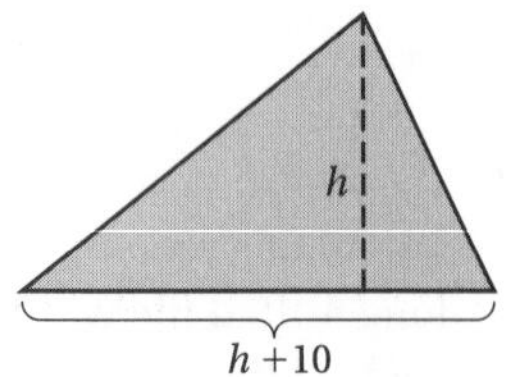

6. *Dimensions of a Triangle.* The height of a triangle is 3 cm less than the length of the base. The area of the triangle is 35 cm^2. Find the height and the length of the base.

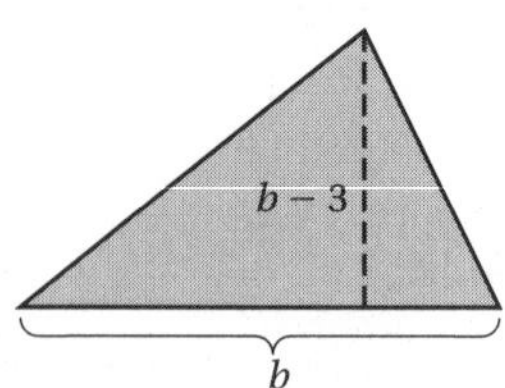

7. *Road Design.* A triangular traffic island has a base half as long as its height. The island has an area of 64 m^2. Find the base and the height.

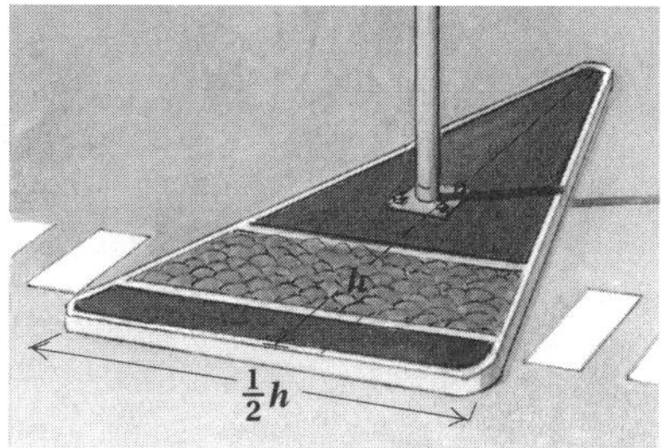

8. *Dimensions of a Sail.* The height of the jib sail on a Lightning sailboat is 5 ft greater than the length of its "foot." The area of the sail is 42 ft^2. Find the length of the foot and the height of the sail.

Games in a League. Use $x^2 - x = N$ for Exercises 9–12.

9. A chess league has 14 teams. What is the total number of games to be played if each team plays every other team twice?

10. A women's volleyball league has 23 teams. What is the total number of games to be played if each team plays every other team twice?

11. A slow-pitch softball league plays a total of 132 games. How many teams are in the league if each team plays every other team twice?

12. A basketball league plays a total of 90 games. How many teams are in the league if each team plays every other team twice?

Handshakes. A researcher wants to investigate the potential spread of germs by contact. She knows that the number of possible handshakes within a group of x people, assuming each person shakes every other person's hand only once, is given by

$$N = \frac{1}{2}(x^2 - x).$$

Use this formula for Exercises 13–16.

13. There are 100 people at a party. How many handshakes are possible?

14. There are 40 people at a meeting. How many handshakes are possible?

15. Everyone at a meeting shook hands with each other. There were 300 handshakes in all. How many people were at the meeting?

16. Everyone at a party shook hands with each other. There were 153 handshakes in all. How many people were at the party?

17. *Toasting.* During a toast at a party, there were 190 "clicks" of glasses. How many people took part in the toast?

18. *High-fives.* After winning the championship, all Detroit Pistons teammates exchanged "high-fives." Altogether there were 66 high-fives. How many players were there?

19. *Consecutive Page Numbers.* The product of the page numbers on two facing pages of a book is 210. Find the page numbers.

20. *Consecutive Page Numbers.* The product of the page numbers on two facing pages of a book is 420. Find the page numbers.

21. The product of two consecutive even integers is 168. Find the integers. (See Section 2.6.)

22. The product of two consecutive even integers is 224. Find the integers. (See Section 2.6.)

23. The product of two consecutive odd integers is 255. Find the integers.

24. The product of two consecutive odd integers is 143. Find the integers.

25. *Right-Triangle Geometry.* The length of one leg of a right triangle is 8 ft. The length of the hypotenuse is 2 ft longer than the other leg. Find the length of the hypotenuse and the other leg.

26. *Right-Triangle Geometry.* The length of one leg of a right triangle is 24 ft. The length of the other leg is 16 ft shorter than the hypotenuse. Find the length of the hypotenuse and the other leg.

27. *Roadway Design.* Elliott Street is 24 ft wide when it ends at Main Street in Brattleboro, Vermont. A 40-ft long diagonal crosswalk allows pedestrians to cross Main Street to or from either corner of Elliott Street (see the figure). Determine the width of Main Street.

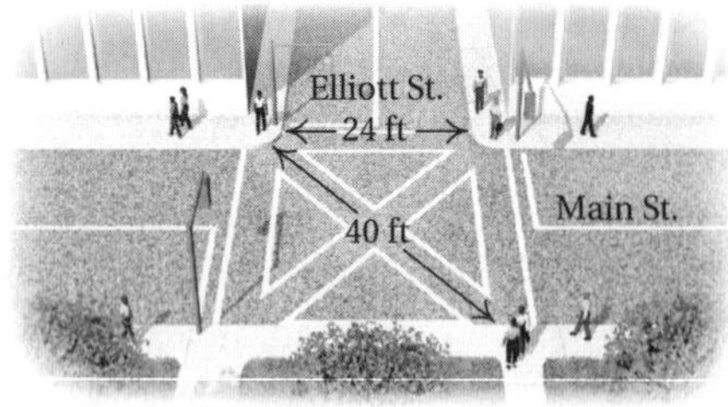

28. *Sailing.* The mainsail of a Lightning sailboat is a right triangle in which the hypotenuse is called the leech. If a 24-ft tall mainsail has a leech length of 26 ft and if Dacron® sailcloth costs $10 per square foot, find the cost of a new mainsail.

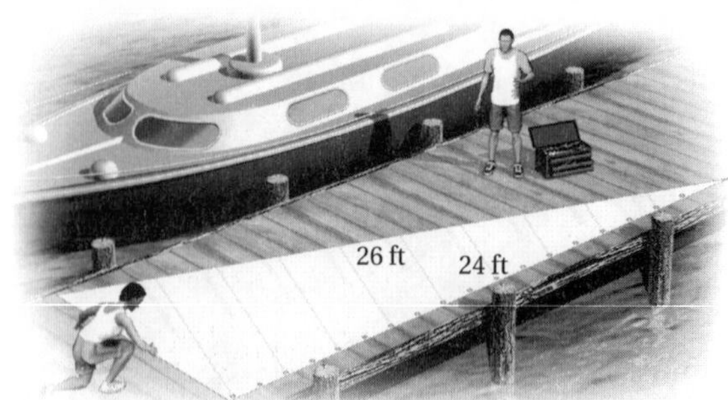

9. *Lookout Tower.* The diagonal braces in a lookout tower are 15 ft long and span a distance of 12 ft. How high does each brace reach vertically?

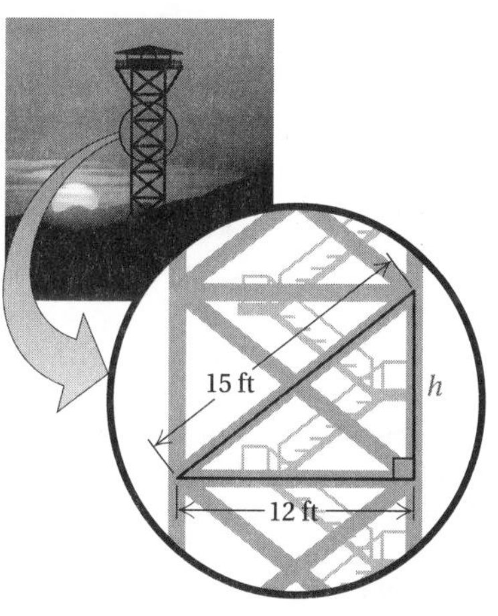

30. *Aviation.* Engine failure forced Geraldine to pilot her Cessna 150 to an emergency landing. To land, Geraldine's plane glided 17,000 ft over a 15,000-ft stretch of deserted highway. From what altitude did the descent begin?

1. *Architecture.* An architect has allocated a rectangular space of 264 ft^2 for a square dining room and a 10-ft wide kitchen, as shown in the figure. Find the dimensions of each room.

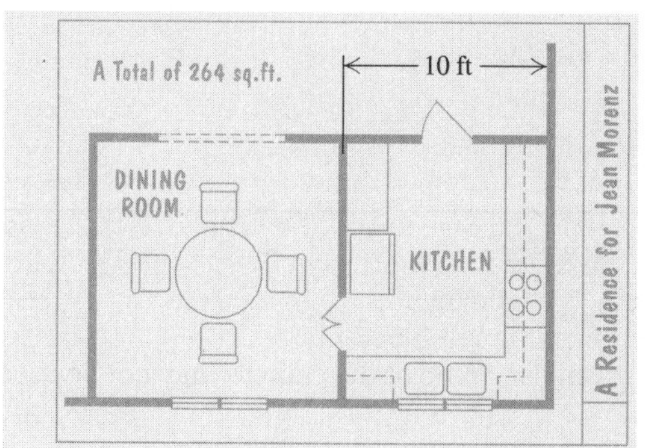

32. *Guy Wire.* The guy wire on a TV antenna is 1 m longer than the height of the antenna. If the guy wire is anchored 3 m from the foot of the antenna, how tall is the antenna?

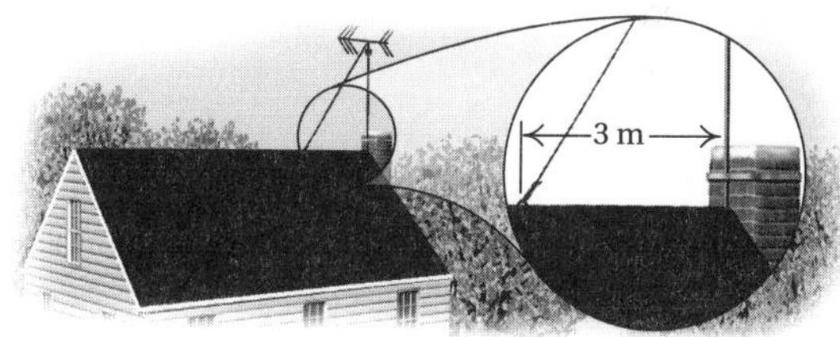

ocket Launch. A model rocket is launched with an initial locity of 180 ft/sec. Its height h, in feet, after t seconds is ven by the formula

$$h = 180t - 16t^2.$$

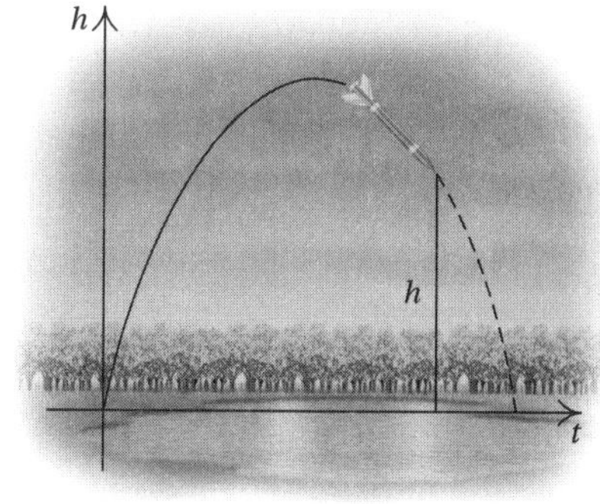

33. After how many seconds will the rocket first reach a height of 464 ft?

34. After how many seconds from launching will the rocket again be at that same height of 464 ft? (See Exercise 33.)

35. The sum of the squares of two consecutive odd positive integers is 74. Find the integers.

36. The sum of the squares of two consecutive odd positive integers is 130. Find the integers.

37. DW An archaeologist has measuring sticks of 3 ft, 4 ft, and 5 ft. Explain how she could draw a 7-ft by 9-ft rectangle on a piece of land being excavated.

38. DW Look closely at the problem-solving techniques developed in this chapter. What kinds of equations do we use? In order to solve these equations, what additional new skill do we need? Compare the skills learned in this chapter with those of Chapter 2.

SKILL MAINTENANCE

VOCABULARY REINFORCEMENT

In each of Exercises 39–46, fill in the blank with the correct term from the given list. Some of the choices may not be used and some may be used more than once.

39. To ______________ a polynomial is to express it as a product. [5.1b]

40. A(n) ______________ of a polynomial P is a polynomial that can be used to express P as a product. [5.1b]

41. A factorization of a polynomial is an expression that names that polynomial as a(n) ______________. [5.1b]

42. When factoring, always look first for the ______________. [5.1b]

43. The expression $-5x^2 + 8x - 7$ is an example of a ______________. [4.3a]

44. The ______________ asserts that when dividing with exponential notation, if the bases are the same, keep the base and subtract the exponent of the denominator from the exponent of the numerator. [4.1e]

45. For the graph of the equation $4x - 3y = 12$, the pair $(0, -4)$ is known as the ______________. [3.2a]

46. For the graph of the equation $4x - 3y = 12$, the number $\frac{4}{3}$ is known as the ______________. [3.3c]

- quotient rule
- product rule
- slope
- common factor
- common multiple
- factor
- x-intercept
- y-intercept
- binomial
- trinomial
- quotient
- product

SYNTHESIS

47. *Telephone Service.* Use the information in the figure below to determine the height of the telephone pole.

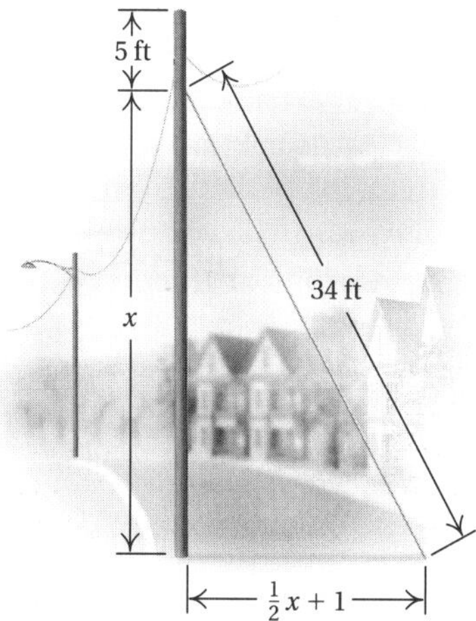

48. *Roofing.* A *square* of shingles covers 100 ft^2 of surface area. How many squares will be needed to reshingle the house shown?

49. *Pool Sidewalk.* A cement walk of constant width is built around a 20-ft by 40-ft rectangular pool. The total area of the pool and the walk is 1500 ft^2. Find the width of the walk.

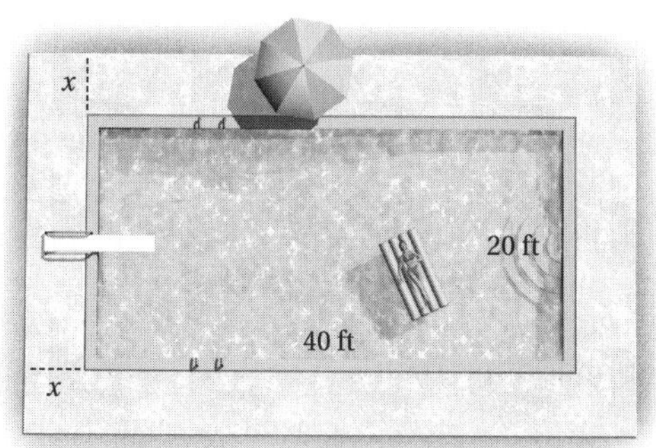

50. *Rain-Gutter Design.* An open rectangular gutter is made by turning up the sides of a piece of metal 20 in. wide. The area of the cross-section of the gutter is 50 in^2. Find the depth of the gutter.

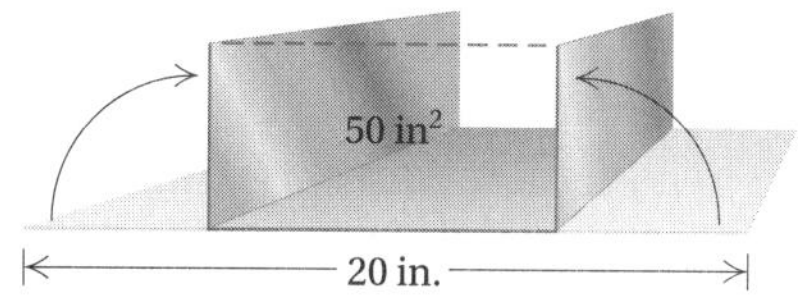

51. *Dimensions of an Open Box.* A rectangular piece of cardboard is twice as long as it is wide. A 4-cm square is cut out of each corner, and the sides are turned up to make a box with an open top. The volume of the box is 616 cm^3. Find the original dimensions of the cardboard.

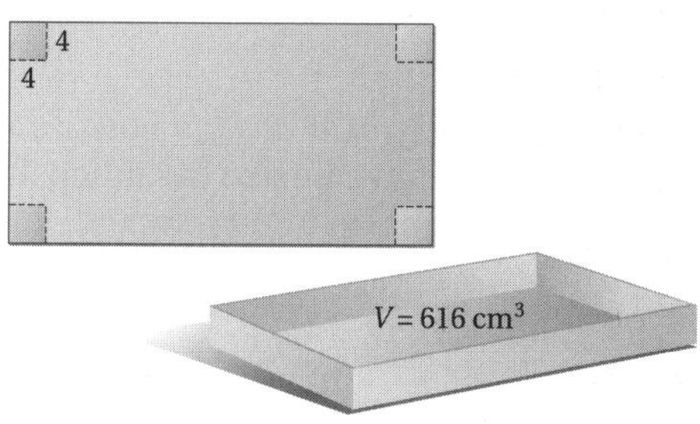

52. Solve for x.

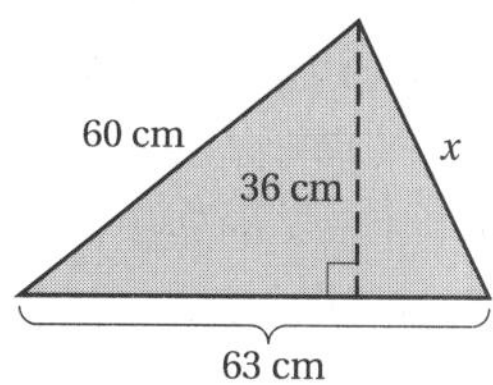

53. *Dimensions of a Closed Box.* The total surface area of a closed box is 350 ft^2. The box is 9 ft high and has a square base and lid. Find the length of a side of the base.

54. The ones digit of a number less than 100 is 4 greater than the tens digit. The sum of the number and the product of the digits is 58. Find the number.

6.1 MULTIPLYING AND SIMPLIFYING RATIONAL EXPRESSIONS

Objectives

a Find all numbers for which a rational expression is not defined.

b Multiply a rational expression by 1, using an expression such as A/A.

c Simplify rational expressions by factoring the numerator and the denominator and removing factors of 1.

d Multiply rational expressions and simplify.

Find all numbers for which the rational expression is not defined.

1. $\dfrac{16}{x - 3}$

2. $\dfrac{2x - 7}{x^2 + 5x - 24}$

3. $\dfrac{x + 5}{8}$

Answers on page A-30

a Rational Expressions and Replacements

Rational numbers are quotients of integers. Some examples are

$$\frac{2}{3}, \quad \frac{4}{-5}, \quad \frac{-8}{17}, \quad \frac{563}{1}.$$

The following are called **rational expressions** or **fraction expressions.** They are quotients, or ratios, of polynomials:

$$\frac{3}{4}, \quad \frac{z}{6}, \quad \frac{5}{x + 2}, \quad \frac{t^2 + 3t - 10}{7t^2 - 4}.$$

A rational expression is also a division. For example,

$$\frac{3}{4} \text{ means } 3 \div 4 \text{ and } \frac{x - 8}{x + 2} \text{ means } (x - 8) \div (x + 2).$$

Because rational expressions indicate division, we must be careful to avoid denominators of zero. When a variable is replaced with a number that produces a denominator equal to zero, the rational expression is not defined. For example, in the expression

$$\frac{x - 8}{x + 2},$$

when x is replaced with -2, the denominator is 0, and the expression is *not* defined:

$$\frac{x - 8}{x + 2} = \frac{-2 - 8}{-2 + 2} = \frac{-10}{0}. \leftarrow \text{Division by 0 is not defined.}$$

When x is replaced with a number other than -2, such as 3, the expression *is* defined because the denominator is nonzero:

$$\frac{x - 8}{x + 2} = \frac{3 - 8}{3 + 2} = \frac{-5}{5} = -1.$$

EXAMPLE 1 Find all numbers for which the rational expression

$$\frac{x + 4}{x^2 - 3x - 10}$$

is not defined.

The value of the numerator has no bearing on whether or not a rational expression is defined. To determine which numbers make the rational expression not defined, we set the *denominator* equal to 0 and solve:

$$x^2 - 3x - 10 = 0$$

$$(x - 5)(x + 2) = 0 \qquad \text{Factoring}$$

$$x - 5 = 0 \quad or \quad x + 2 = 0 \qquad \text{Using the principle of zero products (see Section 5.7)}$$

$$x = 5 \quad or \quad x = -2.$$

The rational expression is not defined for the replacement numbers 5 and -2.

Do Exercises 1–3.

b Multiplying by 1

We multiply rational expressions in the same way that we multiply fraction notation in arithmetic. For a review, see Section R.2. We saw that

$$\frac{3}{7} \cdot \frac{2}{5} = \frac{3 \cdot 2}{7 \cdot 5} = \frac{6}{35}.$$

MULTIPLYING RATIONAL EXPRESSIONS

To multiply rational expressions, multiply numerators and multiply denominators:

$$\frac{A}{B} \cdot \frac{C}{D} = \frac{AC}{BD}.$$

For example,

$$\frac{x-2}{3} \cdot \frac{x+2}{x+7} = \frac{(x-2)(x+2)}{3(x+7)}.$$ Multiplying the numerators and the denominators

Note that we leave the numerator, $(x-2)(x+2)$, and the denominator, $3(x+7)$, in factored form because it is easier to simplify if we do not multiply. In order to learn to simplify, we first need to consider multiplying the rational expression by 1.

Any rational expression with the same numerator and denominator is a symbol for 1:

$$\frac{19}{19} = 1, \qquad \frac{x+8}{x+8} = 1, \qquad \frac{3x^2-4}{3x^2-4} = 1, \qquad \frac{-1}{-1} = 1.$$

EQUIVALENT EXPRESSIONS

Expressions that have the same value for all allowable (or meaningful) replacements are called **equivalent expressions.**

We can multiply by 1 to obtain an *equivalent expression.* At this point, we select expressions for 1 arbitrarily. Later, we will have a system for our choices when we add and subtract.

EXAMPLES Multiply.

2. $\frac{3x+2}{x+1} \cdot 1 = \frac{3x+2}{x+1} \cdot \frac{2x}{2x} = \frac{(3x+2)2x}{(x+1)2x}$ Using the identity property of 1. We arbitrarily choose $2x/2x$ as a symbol for 1.

3. $\frac{x+2}{x-7} \cdot \frac{x+3}{x+3} = \frac{(x+2)(x+3)}{(x-7)(x+3)}$ We arbitrarily choose $(x+3)/(x+3)$ as a symbol for 1.

4. $\frac{2+x}{2-x} \cdot \frac{-1}{-1} = \frac{(2+x)(-1)}{(2-x)(-1)}$ Using $(-1)/(-1)$ as a symbol for 1

Do Exercises 4–6.

Multiply.

4. $\frac{2x+1}{3x-2} \cdot \frac{x}{x}$

5. $\frac{x+1}{x-2} \cdot \frac{x+2}{x+2}$

6. $\frac{x-8}{x-y} \cdot \frac{-1}{-1}$

Answers on page A-30

Simplify.

7. $\dfrac{5y}{y}$

8. $\dfrac{9x^2}{36x}$

Answers on page A-30

Study Tips

TUNE OUT DISTRACTIONS

Do you generally study in noisy places? If there is constant noise in your home, dorm, or other study area, consider finding a quiet place in the library—maybe an uncrowded place so you are not distracted with people-watching!

"The ability to concentrate and use your time well is everything."

Lee Iacocca, former CEO of Chrysler Corporation

C Simplifying Rational Expressions

Simplifying rational expressions is similar to simplifying fraction expressions in arithmetic. For a review, see Section R.2. We saw there, for example, that an expression like $\frac{15}{40}$ can be simplified as follows:

$$\frac{15}{40} = \frac{3 \cdot 5}{8 \cdot 5}$$ Factoring the numerator and the denominator. Note the common factor, 5.

$$= \frac{3}{8} \cdot \frac{5}{5}$$ Factoring the fraction expression

$$= \frac{3}{8} \cdot 1$$ $\frac{5}{5} = 1$

$$= \frac{3}{8}.$$ Using the identity property of 1, or "removing a factor of 1"

Similar steps are followed when simplifying rational expressions: We factor and remove a factor of 1, using the fact that

$$\frac{ab}{cb} = \frac{a}{c} \cdot \frac{b}{b} = \frac{a}{c} \cdot 1 = \frac{a}{c}.$$

In algebra, instead of simplifying

$$\frac{15}{40},$$

we may need to simplify an expression like

$$\frac{x^2 - 16}{x + 4}.$$

Just as factoring is important in simplifying in arithmetic, so too is it important in simplifying rational expressions. The factoring we use most is the factoring of polynomials, which we studied in Chapter 5.

To simplify, we can do the reverse of multiplying. We factor the numerator and the denominator and "remove" a factor of 1.

EXAMPLE 5 Simplify: $\dfrac{8x^2}{24x}$.

$$\frac{8x^2}{24x} = \frac{8 \cdot x \cdot x}{3 \cdot 8 \cdot x}$$ Factoring the numerator and the denominator. Note the common factor, $8x$.

$$= \frac{8x}{8x} \cdot \frac{x}{3}$$ Factoring the rational expression

$$= 1 \cdot \frac{x}{3}$$ $\frac{8x}{8x} = 1$

$$= \frac{x}{3}$$ We removed a factor of 1.

Do Exercises 7 and 8.

EXAMPLES Simplify.

6. $$\begin{aligned}\frac{5a + 15}{10} &= \frac{5(a + 3)}{5 \cdot 2} && \text{Factoring the numerator and the denominator}\\ &= \frac{5}{5} \cdot \frac{a + 3}{2} && \text{Factoring the rational expression}\\ &= 1 \cdot \frac{a + 3}{2} && \frac{5}{5} = 1\\ &= \frac{a + 3}{2} && \text{Removing a factor of 1}\end{aligned}$$

7. $$\begin{aligned}\frac{6a + 12}{7a + 14} &= \frac{6(a + 2)}{7(a + 2)} && \text{Factoring the numerator and the denominator}\\ &= \frac{6}{7} \cdot \frac{a + 2}{a + 2} && \text{Factoring the rational expression}\\ &= \frac{6}{7} \cdot 1 && \frac{a + 2}{a + 2} = 1\\ &= \frac{6}{7} && \text{Removing a factor of 1}\end{aligned}$$

8. $$\begin{aligned}\frac{6x^2 + 4x}{2x^2 + 2x} &= \frac{2x(3x + 2)}{2x(x + 1)} && \text{Factoring the numerator and the denominator}\\ &= \frac{2x}{2x} \cdot \frac{3x + 2}{x + 1} && \text{Factoring the rational expression}\\ &= 1 \cdot \frac{3x + 2}{x + 1} && \frac{2x}{2x} = 1\\ &= \frac{3x + 2}{x + 1} && \text{Removing a factor of 1}\end{aligned}$$

Caution!

Note in this step that you *cannot* remove the x's because x is not a factor of the entire numerator, $3x + 2$, and the entire denominator, $x + 1$.

9. $$\begin{aligned}\frac{x^2 + 3x + 2}{x^2 - 1} &= \frac{(x + 2)(x + 1)}{(x + 1)(x - 1)} && \text{Factoring the numerator and the denominator}\\ &= \frac{x + 1}{x + 1} \cdot \frac{x + 2}{x - 1} && \text{Factoring the rational expression}\\ &= 1 \cdot \frac{x + 2}{x - 1} && \frac{x + 1}{x + 1} = 1\\ &= \frac{x + 2}{x - 1} && \text{Removing a factor of 1}\end{aligned}$$

Simplify.

9. $\dfrac{2x^2 + x}{3x^2 + 2x}$

10. $\dfrac{x^2 - 1}{2x^2 - x - 1}$

11. $\dfrac{7x + 14}{7}$

12. $\dfrac{12y + 24}{48}$

Answers on page A-30

Simplify.

13. $\dfrac{x-8}{8-x}$

14. $\dfrac{c-d}{d-c}$

15. $\dfrac{-x-7}{x+7}$

Answers on page A-30

CANCELING

You may have encountered canceling when working with rational expressions. With great concern, we mention it as a possible way to speed up your work. Our concern is that canceling be done with care and understanding. Example 9 might have been done faster as follows:

$$\frac{x^2+3x+2}{x^2-1} = \frac{(x+2)(x+1)}{(x+1)(x-1)}$$ Factoring the numerator and the denominator

$$= \frac{(x+2)\cancel{(x+1)}}{\cancel{(x+1)}(x-1)}$$ When a factor of 1 is noted, it is canceled, as shown: $\frac{x+1}{x+1} = 1$.

$$= \frac{x+2}{x-1}.$$ Simplifying

Caution!

The difficulty with canceling is that it is often applied incorrectly, as in the following situations:

$$\frac{\cancel{x}+3}{\cancel{x}} = 3; \qquad \frac{\cancel{4}+1}{\cancel{4}+2} = \frac{1}{2}; \qquad \frac{1\cancel{5}}{\cancel{5}4} = \frac{1}{4}.$$

Wrong! Wrong! Wrong!

In each of these situations, the expressions canceled were *not* factors of 1. Factors are parts of products. For example, in $2 \cdot 3$, 2 and 3 are factors, but in $2 + 3$, 2 and 3 are *not* factors. If you can't factor, you can't cancel. If in doubt, don't cancel!

Do Exercises 9–12 on the preceding page.

OPPOSITES IN RATIONAL EXPRESSIONS

Expressions of the form $a - b$ and $b - a$ are opposites of each other. When either of these binomials is multiplied by -1, the result is the other binomial.

$$\left.\begin{aligned} -1(a-b) &= -a+b = b+(-a) = b-a; \\ -1(b-a) &= -b+a = a+(-b) = a-b. \end{aligned}\right\}$$ Multiplication by -1 reverses the order in which subtraction occurs.

Consider, for example,

$$\frac{x-4}{4-x}.$$

At first glance, it appears as though the numerator and the denominator do not have any common factors other than 1. But $x - 4$ and $4 - x$ are opposites, or additive inverses, of each other. Thus we can rewrite one as the opposite of the other by factoring out a -1.

EXAMPLE 10 Simplify: $\dfrac{x-4}{4-x}$.

$$\frac{x-4}{4-x} = \frac{x-4}{-(x-4)} = \frac{x-4}{-1(x-4)}$$ $4 - x = -(x-4)$; $4 - x$ and $x - 4$ are opposites.

$$= -1 \cdot \frac{x-4}{x-4}$$

$$= -1 \cdot 1$$

$$= -1$$

Do Exercises 13–15.

d Multiplying and Simplifying

We try to simplify after we multiply. That is why we leave the numerator and the denominator in factored form.

EXAMPLE 11 Multiply and simplify: $\frac{5a^3}{4} \cdot \frac{2}{5a}$.

$$\frac{5a^3}{4} \cdot \frac{2}{5a} = \frac{5a^3(2)}{4(5a)}$$ Multiplying the numerators and the denominators

$$= \frac{2 \cdot 5 \cdot a \cdot a \cdot a}{2 \cdot 2 \cdot 5 \cdot a}$$ Factoring the numerator and the denominator

$$= \frac{\cancel{2} \cdot \cancel{5} \cdot \cancel{a} \cdot a \cdot a}{\cancel{2} \cdot 2 \cdot \cancel{5} \cdot \cancel{a}}$$ Removing a factor of 1: $\frac{2 \cdot 5 \cdot a}{2 \cdot 5 \cdot a} = 1$

$$= \frac{a^2}{2}$$ Simplifying

EXAMPLE 12 Multiply and simplify: $\frac{x^2 + 6x + 9}{x^2 - 4} \cdot \frac{x - 2}{x + 3}$.

$$\frac{x^2 + 6x + 9}{x^2 - 4} \cdot \frac{x - 2}{x + 3} = \frac{(x^2 + 6x + 9)(x - 2)}{(x^2 - 4)(x + 3)}$$ Multiplying the numerators and the denominators

$$= \frac{(x + 3)(x + 3)(x - 2)}{(x + 2)(x - 2)(x + 3)}$$ Factoring the numerator and the denominator

$$= \frac{\cancel{(x + 3)}(x + 3)\cancel{(x - 2)}}{(x + 2)\cancel{(x - 2)}\cancel{(x + 3)}}$$ Removing a factor of 1: $\frac{(x + 3)(x - 2)}{(x + 3)(x - 2)} = 1$

$$= \frac{x + 3}{x + 2}$$ Simplifying

Do Exercise 16.

EXAMPLE 13 Multiply and simplify: $\frac{x^2 + x - 2}{15} \cdot \frac{5}{2x^2 - 3x + 1}$.

$$\frac{x^2 + x - 2}{15} \cdot \frac{5}{2x^2 - 3x + 1} = \frac{(x^2 + x - 2)5}{15(2x^2 - 3x + 1)}$$ Multiplying the numerators and the denominators

$$= \frac{(x + 2)(x - 1)5}{5(3)(x - 1)(2x - 1)}$$ Factoring the numerator and the denominator

$$= \frac{(x + 2)\cancel{(x - 1)}\cancel{5}}{\cancel{5}(3)\cancel{(x - 1)}(2x - 1)}$$ Removing a factor of 1: $\frac{(x - 1)5}{(x - 1)5} = 1$

$$= \frac{x + 2}{3(2x - 1)}$$ Simplifying

You need not carry out this multiplication.

Do Exercise 17.

16. Multiply and simplify:

$$\frac{a^2 - 4a + 4}{a^2 - 9} \cdot \frac{a + 3}{a - 2}.$$

17. Multiply and simplify:

$$\frac{x^2 - 25}{6} \cdot \frac{3}{x + 5}.$$

Answers on page A-30

CALCULATOR CORNER

Checking Multiplication and Simplification We can use the TABLE feature as a partial check that rational expressions have been multiplied and/or simplified correctly. To check the simplification in Example 9,

$$\frac{x^2 + 3x + 2}{x^2 - 1} = \frac{x + 2}{x - 1},$$

we first enter $y_1 = (x^2 + 3x + 2)/(x^2 - 1)$ and $y_2 = (x + 2)/(x - 1)$. Then, using AUTO mode, we look at a table of values of y_1 and y_2. If the simplification is correct, the values should be the same for all allowable replacements.

$y_1 = (x^2 + 3x + 2)/(x^2 - 1)$,
$y_2 = (x + 2)/(x - 1)$

X	Y1	Y2
−4	.4	.4
−3	.25	.25
−2	0	0
−1	ERROR	−.5
0	−2	−2
1	ERROR	ERROR
2	4	4

X = −4

The ERROR messages indicate that −1 and 1 are not allowable replacements in the first expression, and 1 is not an allowable replacement in the second. For all other numbers, we see that y_1 and y_2 are the same, so the simplification appears to be correct. Remember, this is only a partial check since we cannot check all possible values.

Exercises: Use the TABLE feature to determine whether each of the following appears to be correct.

1. $\frac{8x^2}{24x} = \frac{x}{3}$
2. $\frac{5x + 15}{10} = \frac{x + 3}{2}$
3. $\frac{x + 3}{x} = 3$
4. $\frac{x^2 + 3x - 4}{x^2 - 16} = \frac{x - 1}{x + 4}$
5. $\frac{x^2 + 2x - 3}{x^2 - 4} \cdot \frac{4x - 8}{x + 3} = \frac{4x - 1}{x + 2}$
6. $\frac{x^2 - 25}{6} \cdot \frac{3}{x + 5} = \frac{x - 5}{3}$
7. $\frac{x^2 + 6x + 9}{x^2 - 4} \cdot \frac{x - 2}{x + 3} = \frac{x + 3}{x + 2}$
8. $\frac{x^2}{x^2 - 3x} \cdot \frac{x^2 - 9}{3} = \frac{x(x + 3)}{3}$

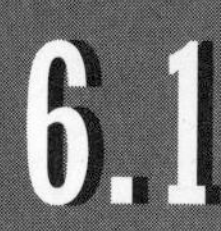

EXERCISE SET

For Extra Help

 MathXL
 MyMathLab
 InterAct Math
 Math Tutor Center

 Digital Video Tutor CD 4 Videotape 7
 Student's Solutions Manual

a Find all numbers for which the rational expression is not defined.

$\frac{-3}{2x}$

2. $\frac{24}{-8y}$

3. $\frac{5}{x-8}$

4. $\frac{y-4}{y+6}$

$\frac{3}{2y+5}$

6. $\frac{x^2-9}{4x-12}$

7. $\frac{x^2+11}{x^2-3x-28}$

8. $\frac{p^2-9}{p^2-7p+10}$

$\frac{m^3-2m}{m^2-25}$

10. $\frac{7-3x+x^2}{49-x^2}$

11. $\frac{x-4}{3}$

12. $\frac{x^2-25}{14}$

Multiply. Do not simplify. Note that in each case you are multiplying by 1.

$\frac{4x}{4x} \cdot \frac{3x^2}{5y}$

14. $\frac{5x^2}{5x^2} \cdot \frac{6y^3}{3z^4}$

15. $\frac{2x}{2x} \cdot \frac{x-1}{x+4}$

16. $\frac{2a-3}{5a+2} \cdot \frac{a}{a}$

$\frac{3-x}{4-x} \cdot \frac{-1}{-1}$

18. $\frac{x-5}{5-x} \cdot \frac{-1}{-1}$

19. $\frac{y+6}{y+6} \cdot \frac{y-7}{y+2}$

20. $\frac{x^2+1}{x^3-2} \cdot \frac{x-4}{x-4}$

Simplify.

$\frac{8x^3}{32x}$

22. $\frac{4x^2}{20x}$

23. $\frac{48p^7q^5}{18p^5q^4}$

$\frac{-76x^8y^3}{-24x^4y^3}$

25. $\frac{4x-12}{4x}$

26. $\frac{5a-40}{5}$

27. $\dfrac{3m^2 + 3m}{6m^2 + 9m}$

28. $\dfrac{4y^2 - 2y}{5y^2 - 5y}$

29. $\dfrac{a^2 - 9}{a^2 + 5a + 6}$

30. $\dfrac{t^2 - 25}{t^2 + t - 20}$

31. $\dfrac{a^2 - 10a + 21}{a^2 - 11a + 28}$

32. $\dfrac{x^2 - 2x - 8}{x^2 - x - 6}$

33. $\dfrac{x^2 - 25}{x^2 - 10x + 25}$

34. $\dfrac{x^2 + 8x + 16}{x^2 - 16}$

35. $\dfrac{a^2 - 1}{a - 1}$

36. $\dfrac{t^2 - 1}{t + 1}$

37. $\dfrac{x^2 + 1}{x + 1}$

38. $\dfrac{m^2 + 9}{m + 3}$

39. $\dfrac{6x^2 - 54}{4x^2 - 36}$

40. $\dfrac{8x^2 - 32}{4x^2 - 16}$

41. $\dfrac{6t + 12}{t^2 - t - 6}$

42. $\dfrac{4x + 32}{x^2 + 9x + 8}$

43. $\dfrac{2t^2 + 6t + 4}{4t^2 - 12t - 16}$

44. $\dfrac{3a^2 - 9a - 12}{6a^2 + 30a + 24}$

45. $\dfrac{t^2 - 4}{(t + 2)^2}$

46. $\dfrac{m^2 - 10m + 25}{m^2 - 25}$

7. $\dfrac{6 - x}{x - 6}$

48. $\dfrac{t - 3}{3 - t}$

49. $\dfrac{a - b}{b - a}$

50. $\dfrac{y - x}{-x + y}$

1. $\dfrac{6t - 12}{2 - t}$

52. $\dfrac{5a - 15}{3 - a}$

53. $\dfrac{x^2 - 1}{1 - x}$

54. $\dfrac{a^2 - b^2}{b^2 - a^2}$

d Multiply and simplify.

5. $\dfrac{4x^3}{3x} \cdot \dfrac{14}{x}$

56. $\dfrac{18}{x^3} \cdot \dfrac{5x^2}{6}$

57. $\dfrac{3c}{d^2} \cdot \dfrac{4d}{6c^3}$

8. $\dfrac{3x^2y}{2} \cdot \dfrac{4}{xy^3}$

59. $\dfrac{x^2 - 3x - 10}{x^2 - 4x + 4} \cdot \dfrac{x - 2}{x - 5}$

60. $\dfrac{t^2}{t^2 - 4} \cdot \dfrac{t^2 - 5t + 6}{t^2 - 3t}$

1. $\dfrac{a^2 - 9}{a^2} \cdot \dfrac{a^2 - 3a}{a^2 + a - 12}$

62. $\dfrac{x^2 + 10x - 11}{x^2 - 1} \cdot \dfrac{x + 1}{x + 11}$

63. $\dfrac{4a^2}{3a^2 - 12a + 12} \cdot \dfrac{3a - 6}{2a}$

4. $\dfrac{5v + 5}{v - 2} \cdot \dfrac{v^2 - 4v + 4}{v^2 - 1}$

65. $\dfrac{t^4 - 16}{t^4 - 1} \cdot \dfrac{t^2 + 1}{t^2 + 4}$

66. $\dfrac{x^4 - 1}{x^4 - 81} \cdot \dfrac{x^2 + 9}{x^2 + 1}$

67. $\dfrac{(x+4)^3}{(x+2)^3} \cdot \dfrac{x^2+4x+4}{x^2+8x+16}$

68. $\dfrac{(t-2)^3}{(t-1)^3} \cdot \dfrac{t^2-2t+1}{t^2-4t+4}$

69. $\dfrac{5a^2-180}{10a^2-10} \cdot \dfrac{20a+20}{2a-12}$

70. $\dfrac{2t^2-98}{4t^2-4} \cdot \dfrac{8t+8}{16t-112}$

71. **D$_W$** How is the process of canceling related to the identity property of 1?

72. **D$_W$** Explain how a rational expression can be formed for which -3 and 4 are not allowable replacements.

SKILL MAINTENANCE

Solve.

73. *Consecutive Even Integers.* The product of two consecutive even integers is 360. Find the integers. [5.8a]

74. *Chemistry.* About 5 L of oxygen can be dissolved in 100 L of water at 0°C. This is 1.6 times the amount that can be dissolved in the same volume of water at 20°C. How much oxygen can be dissolved in 100 L at 20°C? [2.6a]

Factor. [5.6a]

75. $x^2 - x - 56$

76. $a^2 - 16a + 64$

77. $x^5 - 2x^4 - 35x^3$

78. $2y^3 - 10y^2 + y - 5$

79. $16 - t^4$

80. $10x^2 + 80x + 70$

81. $x^2 - 9x + 14$

82. $x^2 + x + 7$

83. $16x^2 - 40xy + 25y^2$

84. $a^2 - 9ab + 14b^2$

SYNTHESIS

Simplify.

85. $\dfrac{x^4-16y^4}{(x^2+4y^2)(x-2y)}$

86. $\dfrac{(a-b)^2}{b^2-a^2}$

87. $\dfrac{t^4-1}{t^4-81} \cdot \dfrac{t^2-9}{t^2+1} \cdot \dfrac{(t-9)^2}{(t+1)^2}$

88. $\dfrac{(t+2)^3}{(t+1)^3} \cdot \dfrac{t^2+2t+1}{t^2+4t+4} \cdot \dfrac{t+1}{t+2}$

89. $\dfrac{x^2-y^2}{(x-y)^2} \cdot \dfrac{x^2-2xy+y^2}{x^2-4xy-5y^2}$

90. $\dfrac{x-1}{x^2+1} \cdot \dfrac{x^4-1}{(x-1)^2} \cdot \dfrac{x^2-1}{x^4-2x^2+1}$

91. Select any number x, multiply by 2, add 5, multiply by 5, subtract 25, and divide by 10. What do you get? Explain how this procedure can be used for a number trick.

6.2 DIVISION AND RECIPROCALS

Objectives

a Find the reciprocal of a rational expression.

b Divide rational expressions and simplify.

There is a similarity between what we do with rational expressions and hat we do with rational numbers. In fact, after variables have been replaced ith rational numbers, a rational expression represents a rational number.

a Finding Reciprocals

wo expressions are reciprocals of each other if their product is 1. The recipcal of a rational expression is found by interchanging the numerator and e denominator.

XAMPLES

1. The reciprocal of $\frac{2}{5}$ is $\frac{5}{2}$. $\left(\text{This is because } \frac{2}{5} \cdot \frac{5}{2} = \frac{10}{10} = 1.\right)$

2. The reciprocal of $\frac{2x^2 - 3}{x + 4}$ is $\frac{x + 4}{2x^2 - 3}$.

3. The reciprocal of $x + 2$ is $\frac{1}{x + 2}$. $\left(\text{Think of } x + 2 \text{ as } \frac{x + 2}{1}.\right)$

o Exercises 1–4.

Find the reciprocal.

1. $\frac{7}{2}$

2. $\frac{x^2 + 5}{2x^3 - 1}$

3. $x - 5$

4. $\frac{1}{x^2 - 3}$

b Division

'e divide rational expressions in the same way that we divide fraction notaon in arithmetic. For a review, see Section R.2.

DIVIDING RATIONAL EXPRESSIONS

To divide by a rational expression, multiply by its reciprocal:

$$\frac{A}{B} \div \frac{C}{D} = \frac{A}{B} \cdot \frac{D}{C} = \frac{AD}{BC}.$$

Then factor and, if possible, simplify.

XAMPLE 4 Divide: $\frac{3}{4} \div \frac{9}{5}$.

$\frac{3}{4} \div \frac{9}{5} = \frac{3}{4} \cdot \frac{5}{9}$ — Multiplying by the reciprocal of the divisor

$= \frac{3 \cdot 5}{4 \cdot 9} = \frac{3 \cdot 5}{2 \cdot 2 \cdot 3 \cdot 3}$ — Factoring

$= \frac{\cancel{3} \cdot 5}{2 \cdot 2 \cdot \cancel{3} \cdot 3}$ — Removing a factor of 1: $\frac{3}{3} = 1$

$= \frac{5}{12}$ — Simplifying

o Exercise 5.

5. Divide: $\frac{3}{5} \div \frac{7}{10}$.

Answers on page A-30

6. Divide: $\frac{x}{8} \div \frac{x}{5}$.

7. Divide:

$$\frac{x-3}{x+5} \div \frac{x+5}{x-2}.$$

8. Divide:

$$\frac{a^2+5a}{6} \div \frac{a^2-25}{18a}.$$

Answers on page A-30

EXAMPLE 5 Divide: $\frac{2}{x} \div \frac{3}{x}$.

$$\frac{2}{x} \div \frac{3}{x} = \frac{2}{x} \cdot \frac{x}{3}$$ Multiplying by the reciprocal of the divisor

$$= \frac{2 \cdot x}{x \cdot 3} = \frac{2 \cdot \cancel{x}}{\cancel{x} \cdot 3}$$ Removing a factor of 1: $\frac{x}{x} = 1$

$$= \frac{2}{3}$$

Do Exercise 6.

EXAMPLE 6 Divide: $\frac{x+1}{x+2} \div \frac{x-1}{x+3}$.

$$\frac{x+1}{x+2} \div \frac{x-1}{x+3} = \frac{x+1}{x+2} \cdot \frac{x+3}{x-1}$$ Multiplying by the reciprocal of the divisor

$$= \frac{(x+1)(x+3)}{(x+2)(x-1)}$$

We usually do not carry out the multiplication in the numerator or the denominator. It is not wrong to do so, but the factored form is often more useful.

Do Exercise 7.

EXAMPLE 7 Divide: $\frac{4}{x^2-7x} \div \frac{28x}{x^2-49}$.

$$\frac{4}{x^2-7x} \div \frac{28x}{x^2-49} = \frac{4}{x^2-7x} \cdot \frac{x^2-49}{28x}$$ Multiplying by the reciprocal

$$= \frac{4(x^2-49)}{(x^2-7x)(28x)}$$

$$= \frac{2 \cdot 2 \cdot (x-7)(x+7)}{x(x-7) \cdot 2 \cdot 2 \cdot 7 \cdot x}$$ Factoring the numerator and the denominator

$$= \frac{\cancel{2} \cdot \cancel{2} \cdot \cancel{(x-7)}(x+7)}{x\cancel{(x-7)} \cdot \cancel{2} \cdot \cancel{2} \cdot 7 \cdot x}$$ Removing a factor of 1: $\frac{2 \cdot 2 \cdot (x-7)}{2 \cdot 2 \cdot (x-7)} = 1$

$$= \frac{x+7}{7x^2}$$

Do Exercise 8.

XAMPLE 8 Divide and simplify: $\dfrac{x+1}{x^2-1} \div \dfrac{x+1}{x^2-2x+1}$.

$$\frac{x+1}{x^2-1} \div \frac{x+1}{x^2-2x+1}$$

$$= \frac{x+1}{x^2-1} \cdot \frac{x^2-2x+1}{x+1}$$ Multiplying by the reciprocal

$$= \frac{(x+1)(x^2-2x+1)}{(x^2-1)(x+1)}$$

$$= \frac{(x+1)(x-1)(x-1)}{(x-1)(x+1)(x+1)}$$ Factoring the numerator and the denominator

$$= \frac{\cancel{(x+1)}\cancel{(x-1)}(x-1)}{\cancel{(x-1)}\cancel{(x+1)}(x+1)}$$ Removing a factor of 1: $\dfrac{(x+1)(x-1)}{(x+1)(x-1)} = 1$

$$= \frac{x-1}{x+1}$$

XAMPLE 9 Divide and simplify: $\dfrac{x^2-2x-3}{x^2-4} \div \dfrac{x+1}{x+5}$.

$$\frac{x^2-2x-3}{x^2-4} \div \frac{x+1}{x+5}$$

$$= \frac{x^2-2x-3}{x^2-4} \cdot \frac{x+5}{x+1}$$ Multiplying by the reciprocal

$$= \frac{(x^2-2x-3)(x+5)}{(x^2-4)(x+1)}$$

$$= \frac{(x-3)(x+1)(x+5)}{(x-2)(x+2)(x+1)}$$ Factoring the numerator and the denominator

$$= \frac{(x-3)\cancel{(x+1)}(x+5)}{(x-2)(x+2)\cancel{(x+1)}}$$ Removing a factor of 1: $\dfrac{x+1}{x+1} = 1$

$$= \frac{(x-3)(x+5)}{(x-2)(x+2)}.$$

You need not carry out the multiplications in the numerator and the denominator.

o Exercises 9–11.

Divide and simplify.

9. $\dfrac{x-3}{x+5} \div \dfrac{x+2}{x+5}$

10. $\dfrac{x^2-5x+6}{x+5} \div \dfrac{x+2}{x+5}$

11. $\dfrac{y^2-1}{y+1} \div \dfrac{y^2-2y+1}{y+1}$

Answers on page A-30

6.2 EXERCISE SET

For Extra Help

MathXL · MyMathLab · InterAct Math · Math Tutor Center · Digital Video Tutor CD 4 Videotape 7 · Student's Solutions Manual

a Find the reciprocal.

1. $\frac{4}{x}$

2. $\frac{a+3}{a-1}$

3. $x^2 - y^2$

4. $x^2 - 5x + 7$

5. $\frac{1}{a+b}$

6. $\frac{x^2}{x^2-3}$

7. $\frac{x^2+2x-5}{x^2-4x+7}$

8. $\frac{(a-b)(a+b)}{(a+4)(a-5)}$

b Divide and simplify.

9. $\frac{2}{5} \div \frac{4}{3}$

10. $\frac{3}{10} \div \frac{3}{2}$

11. $\frac{2}{x} \div \frac{8}{x}$

12. $\frac{t}{3} \div \frac{t}{15}$

13. $\frac{a}{b^2} \div \frac{a^2}{b^3}$

14. $\frac{x^2}{y} \div \frac{x^3}{y^3}$

15. $\frac{a+2}{a-3} \div \frac{a-1}{a+3}$

16. $\frac{x-8}{x+9} \div \frac{x+2}{x-1}$

17. $\frac{x^2-1}{x} \div \frac{x+1}{x-1}$

18. $\frac{4y-8}{y+2} \div \frac{y-2}{y^2-4}$

19. $\frac{x+1}{6} \div \frac{x+1}{3}$

20. $\frac{a}{a-b} \div \frac{b}{a-b}$

21. $\frac{5x-5}{16} \div \frac{x-1}{6}$

22. $\frac{4y-12}{12} \div \frac{y-3}{3}$

23. $\frac{-6+3x}{5} \div \frac{4x-8}{25}$

24. $\frac{-12+4x}{4} \div \frac{-6+2x}{6}$

25. $\frac{a+2}{a-1} \div \frac{3a+6}{a-5}$

26. $\frac{t-3}{t+2} \div \frac{4t-12}{t+1}$

27. $\frac{x^2-4}{x} \div \frac{x-2}{x+2}$

28. $\frac{x+y}{x-y} \div \frac{x^2+y}{x^2-y^2}$

29. $\frac{x^2-9}{4x+12} \div \frac{x-3}{6}$

30. $\frac{a-b}{2a} \div \frac{a^2-b^2}{8a^3}$

31. $\frac{c^2+3c}{c^2+2c-3} \div \frac{c}{c+1}$

32. $\frac{y+5}{2y} \div \frac{y^2-25}{4y^2}$

3. $\dfrac{2y^2 - 7y + 3}{2y^2 + 3y - 2} \div \dfrac{6y^2 - 5y + 1}{3y^2 + 5y - 2}$

34. $\dfrac{x^2 + x - 20}{x^2 - 7x + 12} \div \dfrac{x^2 + 10x + 25}{x^2 - 6x + 9}$

5. $\dfrac{x^2 - 1}{4x + 4} \div \dfrac{2x^2 - 4x + 2}{8x + 8}$

36. $\dfrac{5t^2 + 5t - 30}{10t + 30} \div \dfrac{2t^2 - 8}{6t^2 + 36t + 54}$

7. **DW** Is the reciprocal of a product the product of the reciprocals? Why or why not?

38. **DW** Explain why 5, −1, and 7 are *not* allowable replacements in the division

$$\frac{x + 3}{x - 5} \div \frac{x - 7}{x + 1}.$$

SKILL MAINTENANCE

olve.

9. Bonnie is taking an astronomy course. In order to receive an A, she must average at least 90 after four exams. Bonnie scored 96, 98, and 89 on the first three tests. Determine (in terms of an inequality) what scores on the last test will earn her an A. [2.8b]

40. *Triangle Dimensions.* The base of a triangle is 4 in. less than twice the height. The area is 35 in^2. Find the height and the base. [5.8a]

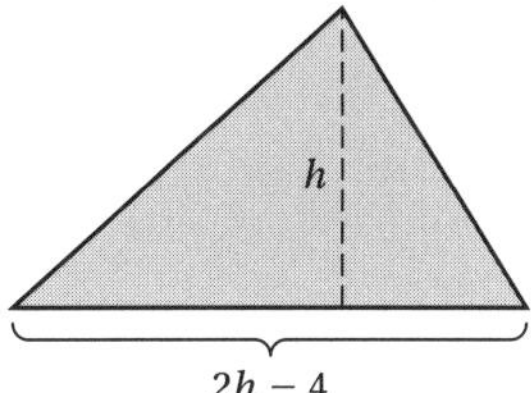

ubtract. [4.4c]

1. $(8x^3 - 3x^2 + 7) - (8x^2 + 3x - 5)$

42. $(3p^2 - 6pq + 7q^2) - (5p^2 - 10pq + 11q^2)$

implify. [4.2a, b]

3. $(2x^{-3}y^4)^2$

44. $(5x^6y^{-4})^3$

45. $\left(\dfrac{2x^3}{y^5}\right)^2$

46. $\left(\dfrac{a^{-3}}{b^4}\right)^5$

SYNTHESIS

implify.

7. $\dfrac{3a^2 - 5ab - 12b^2}{3ab + 4b^2} \div (3b^2 - ab)$

48. $\dfrac{3x + 3y + 3}{9x} \div \dfrac{x^2 + 2xy + y^2 - 1}{x^4 + x^2}$

49. $\dfrac{a^2b^2 + 3ab^2 + 2b^2}{a^2b^4 + 4b^4} \div (5a^2 + 10a)$

0. The volume of this rectangular solid is $x - 3$. What is its height?

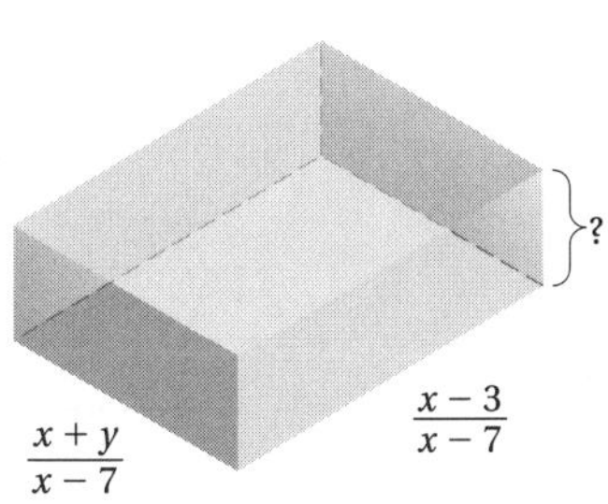

6.3 LEAST COMMON MULTIPLES AND DENOMINATORS

Objectives

a Find the LCM of several numbers by factoring.

b Add fractions, first finding the LCD.

c Find the LCM of algebraic expressions by factoring.

Find the LCM by factoring.

1. 16, 18

2. 6, 12

3. 2, 5

4. 24, 30, 20

Answers on page A-31

a Least Common Multiples

To add when denominators are different, we first find a common denominator. For a review, see Sections R.1 and R.2. We saw there, for example, that to add $\frac{5}{12}$ and $\frac{7}{30}$, we first look for the **least common multiple, LCM,** of both 12 and 30. That number becomes the **least common denominator, LCD.** To find the LCM of 12 and 30, we factor:

$$12 = 2 \cdot 2 \cdot 3;$$
$$30 = 2 \cdot 3 \cdot 5.$$

The LCM is the number that has 2 as a factor twice, 3 as a factor once, and 5 as a factor once:

$$\text{LCM} = 2 \cdot 2 \cdot 3 \cdot 5 = 60.$$

12 is a factor of the LCM.

30 is a factor of the LCM.

FINDING LCMS

To find the LCM, use each factor the greatest number of times that it appears in any one factorization.

EXAMPLE 1 Find the LCM of 24 and 36.

$$\left.\begin{aligned}24 &= 2 \cdot 2 \cdot 2 \cdot 3\\ 36 &= 2 \cdot 2 \cdot 3 \cdot 3\end{aligned}\right\} \quad \text{LCM} = 2 \cdot 2 \cdot 2 \cdot 3 \cdot 3, \text{ or } 72$$

Do Exercises 1–4.

b Adding Using the LCD

Let's finish adding $\frac{5}{12}$ and $\frac{7}{30}$:

$$\frac{5}{12} + \frac{7}{30} = \frac{5}{2 \cdot 2 \cdot 3} + \frac{7}{2 \cdot 3 \cdot 5}.$$

The least common denominator, LCD, is $2 \cdot 2 \cdot 3 \cdot 5$. To get the LCD in the first denominator, we need a 5. To get the LCD in the second denominator, we need another 2. We get these numbers by multiplying by forms of 1:

$$\frac{5}{12} + \frac{7}{30} = \frac{5}{2 \cdot 2 \cdot 3} \cdot \frac{5}{5} + \frac{7}{2 \cdot 3 \cdot 5} \cdot \frac{2}{2} \qquad \text{Multiplying by 1}$$

$$= \frac{25}{2 \cdot 2 \cdot 3 \cdot 5} + \frac{14}{2 \cdot 3 \cdot 5 \cdot 2} \qquad \text{Each denominator is now the LCD.}$$

$$= \frac{39}{2 \cdot 2 \cdot 3 \cdot 5} \qquad \text{Adding the numerators and keeping the LCD}$$

$$= \frac{\cancel{3} \cdot 13}{2 \cdot 2 \cdot \cancel{3} \cdot 5} \qquad \text{Factoring the numerator and removing a factor of 1: } \frac{3}{3} = 1$$

$$= \frac{13}{20}. \qquad \text{Simplifying}$$

EXAMPLE 2 Add: $\frac{5}{12} + \frac{11}{18}$.

$$\left.\begin{aligned} 12 &= 2 \cdot 2 \cdot 3 \\ 18 &= 2 \cdot 3 \cdot 3 \end{aligned}\right\} \quad \text{LCD} = 2 \cdot 2 \cdot 3 \cdot 3, \text{ or } 36$$

$$\frac{5}{12} + \frac{11}{18} = \frac{5}{2 \cdot 2 \cdot 3} \cdot \frac{3}{3} + \frac{11}{2 \cdot 3 \cdot 3} \cdot \frac{2}{2} = \frac{15 + 22}{2 \cdot 2 \cdot 3 \cdot 3} = \frac{37}{36}$$

Do Exercises 5–8.

c LCMs of Algebraic Expressions

To find the LCM of two or more algebraic expressions, we factor them. Then we use each factor the greatest number of times that it occurs in any one expression. In Section 6.4, each LCM will become an LCD used to add rational expressions.

EXAMPLE 3 Find the LCM of $12x$, $16y$, and $8xyz$.

$$\left.\begin{aligned} 12x &= 2 \cdot 2 \cdot 3 \cdot x \\ 16y &= 2 \cdot 2 \cdot 2 \cdot 2 \cdot y \\ 8xyz &= 2 \cdot 2 \cdot 2 \cdot x \cdot y \cdot z \end{aligned}\right\} \quad \begin{aligned} \text{LCM} &= 2 \cdot 2 \cdot 2 \cdot 2 \cdot 3 \cdot x \cdot y \cdot z \\ &= 48xyz \end{aligned}$$

EXAMPLE 4 Find the LCM of $x^2 + 5x - 6$ and $x^2 - 1$.

$$\left.\begin{aligned} x^2 + 5x - 6 &= (x + 6)(x - 1) \\ x^2 - 1 &= (x + 1)(x - 1) \end{aligned}\right\} \quad \text{LCM} = (x + 6)(x - 1)(x + 1)$$

EXAMPLE 5 Find the LCM of $x^2 + 4$, $x + 1$, and 5.

These expressions do not share a common factor other than 1, so the LCM is their product:

$$5(x^2 + 4)(x + 1).$$

EXAMPLE 6 Find the LCM of $x^2 - 25$ and $2x - 10$.

$$\left.\begin{aligned} x^2 - 25 &= (x + 5)(x - 5) \\ 2x - 10 &= 2(x - 5) \end{aligned}\right\} \quad \text{LCM} = 2(x + 5)(x - 5)$$

EXAMPLE 7 Find the LCM of $x^2 - 4y^2$, $x^2 - 4xy + 4y^2$, and $x - 2y$.

$$\left.\begin{aligned} x^2 - 4y^2 &= (x - 2y)(x + 2y) \\ x^2 - 4xy + 4y^2 &= (x - 2y)(x - 2y) \\ x - 2y &= x - 2y \end{aligned}\right\} \quad \begin{aligned} \text{LCM} &= (x + 2y)(x - 2y)(x - 2y) \\ &= (x + 2y)(x - 2y)^2 \end{aligned}$$

Do Exercises 9–12.

Add, first finding the LCD. Simplify if possible.

5. $\frac{3}{16} + \frac{1}{18}$

6. $\frac{1}{6} + \frac{1}{12}$

7. $\frac{1}{2} + \frac{3}{5}$

8. $\frac{1}{24} + \frac{1}{30} + \frac{3}{20}$

Find the LCM.

9. $12xy^2$, $15x^3y$

10. $y^2 + 5y + 4$, $y^2 + 2y + 1$

11. $t^2 + 16$, $t - 2$, 7

12. $x^2 + 2x + 1$, $3x^2 - 3x$, $x^2 - 1$

Answers on page A-31

6.3 EXERCISE SET

For Extra Help

MathXL MyMathLab InterAct Math Math Tutor Center Digital Video Tutor CD 4 Videotape 7 Student's Solutions Manual

a Find the LCM.

1. 12, 27

2. 10, 15

3. 8, 9

4. 12, 18

5. 6, 9, 21

6. 8, 36, 40

7. 24, 36, 40

8. 4, 5, 20

9. 10, 100, 500

10. 28, 42, 60

b Add, first finding the LCD. Simplify if possible.

11. $\frac{7}{24} + \frac{11}{18}$

12. $\frac{7}{60} + \frac{2}{25}$

13. $\frac{1}{6} + \frac{3}{40}$

14. $\frac{5}{24} + \frac{3}{20}$

15. $\frac{1}{20} + \frac{1}{30} + \frac{2}{45}$

16. $\frac{2}{15} + \frac{5}{9} + \frac{3}{20}$

c Find the LCM.

17. $6x^2,\ 12x^3$

18. $2a^2b,\ 8ab^3$

19. $2x^2,\ 6xy,\ 18y^2$

20. $p^3q,\ p^2q,\ pq^2$

21. $2(y-3),\ 6(y-3)$

22. $5(m+2),\ 15(m+2)$

23. $t,\ t+2,\ t-2$

24. $y,\ y-5,\ y+5$

25. $x^2-4,\ x^2+5x+6$

26. $x^2-4,\ x^2-x-2$

27. $t^3+4t^2+4t,\ t^2-4t$

28. $m^4-m^2,\ m^3-m^2$

29. $a+1,\ (a-1)^2,\ a^2-1$

30. $a^2-2ab+b^2,\ a^2-b^2,\ 3a+3b$

31. $m^2-5m+6,\ m^2-4m+4$

32. $2x^2+5x+2,\ 2x^2-x-1$

33. $2+3x,\ 4-9x^2,\ 2-3x$

34. $9-4x^2,\ 3+2x,\ 3-2x$

35. $10v^2+30v,\ 5v^2+35v+60$

36. $12a^2+24a,\ 4a^2+20a+24$

7. $9x^3 - 9x^2 - 18x,\ 6x^5 - 24x^4 + 24x^3$

38. $x^5 - 4x^3,\ x^3 + 4x^2 + 4x$

9. $x^5 + 4x^4 + 4x^3,\ 3x^2 - 12,\ 2x + 4$

40. $x^5 + 2x^4 + x^3,\ 2x^3 - 2x,\ 5x - 5$

1. DW If the LCM of a binomial and a trinomial is the trinomial, what relationship exists between the two expressions?

42. DW Explain why the product of two numbers is not always their least common multiple.

SKILL MAINTENANCE

actor. [5.6a]

3. $x^2 - 6x + 9$

44. $6x^2 + 4x$

45. $x^2 - 9$

6. $x^2 + 4x - 21$

47. $x^2 + 6x + 9$

48. $x^2 - 4x - 21$

omplete the table finding the LCM, the GCF, and the product of each pair of expressions. [4.5a], [5.1a], [6.3a]

	EXPRESSIONS	LCM	GCF	PRODUCT
	$12x^3,\ 8x^2$	$24x^3$	$4x^2$	$96x^5$
49.	$40x^3,\ 24x^4$			
50.	$16x^5,\ 48x^6$			
51.	$20x^2,\ 10x$			
52.	$12ab,\ 16ab^3$			
53.	$10x^2,\ 24x^3$			
54.	$a^5,\ a^{15}$			

SYNTHESIS

5. *Running.* Pedro and Maria leave the starting point of a fitness loop at the same time. Pedro jogs a lap in 6 min and Maria jogs one in 8 min. Assuming they continue to run at the same pace, when will they next meet at the starting place?

56. Look for a pattern in Exercises 49–54. See if you can discover a formula connecting LCM and GCF.

6.4 ADDING RATIONAL EXPRESSIONS

Objective

a Add rational expressions.

Add.

1. $\frac{5}{9} + \frac{2}{9}$

2. $\frac{3}{x-2} + \frac{x}{x-2}$

3. $\frac{4x+5}{x-1} + \frac{2x-1}{x-1}$

Answers on page A-31

a Adding Rational Expressions

We add rational expressions as we do rational numbers.

ADDING RATIONAL EXPRESSIONS WITH LIKE DENOMINATORS

To add when the denominators are the same, add the numerators and keep the same denominator. Then simplify if possible.

EXAMPLES Add.

1. $\frac{x}{x+1} + \frac{2}{x+1} = \frac{x+2}{x+1}$

2. $\frac{2x^2+3x-7}{2x+1} + \frac{x^2+x-8}{2x+1} = \frac{(2x^2+3x-7)+(x^2+x-8)}{2x+1}$

$$= \frac{3x^2+4x-15}{2x+1}$$

3. $\frac{x-5}{x^2-9} + \frac{2}{x^2-9} = \frac{(x-5)+2}{x^2-9} = \frac{x-3}{x^2-9}$

$$= \frac{x-3}{(x-3)(x+3)} \quad \text{Factoring}$$

$$= \frac{\cancel{x-3}}{(\cancel{x-3})(x+3)} \quad \text{Removing a factor of 1: } \frac{x-3}{x-3} = 1$$

$$= \frac{1}{x+3} \quad \text{Simplifying}$$

As in Example 3, simplifying should be done if possible after adding.

Do Exercises 1–3.

When denominators are different, we find the least common denominator, LCD. The procedure we use is as follows.

ADDING RATIONAL EXPRESSIONS WITH DIFFERENT DENOMINATORS

To add rational expressions with different denominators:

1. Find the LCM of the denominators. This is the least common denominator (LCD).
2. For each rational expression, find an equivalent expression with the LCD. To do so, multiply by 1 using an expression for 1 made up of factors of the LCD that are missing from the original denominator.
3. Add the numerators. Write the sum over the LCD.
4. Simplify if possible.

XAMPLE 4 Add: $\frac{5x^2}{8} + \frac{7x}{12}$.

First, we find the LCD:

$$\left.\begin{array}{l} 8 = 2 \cdot 2 \cdot 2 \\ 12 = 2 \cdot 2 \cdot 3 \end{array}\right\} \quad \text{LCD} = 2 \cdot 2 \cdot 2 \cdot 3, \text{ or } 24.$$

ompare the factorization $8 = 2 \cdot 2 \cdot 2$ with the factorization of the LCD, $4 = 2 \cdot 2 \cdot 2 \cdot 3$. The factor of 24 that is missing from 8 is 3. Compare $2 = 2 \cdot 2 \cdot 3$ and $24 = 2 \cdot 2 \cdot 2 \cdot 3$. The factor of 24 that is missing from 12 is 2.

We multiply each term by a symbol for 1 to get the LCD in each expreson, and then add and, if possible, simplify:

$$\frac{5x^2}{8} + \frac{7x}{12} = \frac{5x^2}{2 \cdot 2 \cdot 2} + \frac{7x}{2 \cdot 2 \cdot 3}$$

$$= \frac{5x^2}{2 \cdot 2 \cdot 2} \cdot \frac{3}{3} + \frac{7x}{2 \cdot 2 \cdot 3} \cdot \frac{2}{2} \quad \text{Multiplying by 1 to get the same denominators}$$

$$= \frac{15x^2}{24} + \frac{14x}{24} = \frac{15x^2 + 14x}{24}.$$

XAMPLE 5 Add: $\frac{3}{8x} + \frac{5}{12x^2}$.

First, we find the LCD:

$$\left.\begin{array}{l} 8x = 2 \cdot 2 \cdot 2 \cdot x \\ 12x^2 = 2 \cdot 2 \cdot 3 \cdot x \cdot x \end{array}\right\} \quad \text{LCD} = 2 \cdot 2 \cdot 2 \cdot 3 \cdot x \cdot x, \text{ or } 24x^2.$$

he factors of the LCD missing from $8x$ are 3 and x. The factor of the LCD issing from $12x^2$ is 2. We multiply each term by 1 to get the LCD in each exression, and then add and, if possible, simplify:

$$\frac{3}{8x} + \frac{5}{12x^2} = \frac{3}{8x} \cdot \frac{3 \cdot x}{3 \cdot x} + \frac{5}{12x^2} \cdot \frac{2}{2}$$

$$= \frac{9x}{24x^2} + \frac{10}{24x^2} = \frac{9x + 10}{24x^2}.$$

o Exercises 4 and 5.

XAMPLE 6 Add: $\frac{2a}{a^2 - 1} + \frac{1}{a^2 + a}$.

First, we find the LCD:

$$\left.\begin{array}{l} a^2 - 1 = (a - 1)(a + 1) \\ a^2 + a = a(a + 1) \end{array}\right\} \quad \text{LCD} = a(a - 1)(a + 1).$$

'e multiply each term by 1 to get the LCD in each expression, and then add nd simplify:

$$\frac{2a}{(a - 1)(a + 1)} \cdot \frac{a}{a} + \frac{1}{a(a + 1)} \cdot \frac{a - 1}{a - 1}$$

$$= \frac{2a^2}{a(a - 1)(a + 1)} + \frac{a - 1}{a(a - 1)(a + 1)}$$

$$= \frac{2a^2 + a - 1}{a(a - 1)(a + 1)}$$

$$= \frac{(a + 1)(2a - 1)}{a(a - 1)(a + 1)}. \quad \text{Factoring the numerator in order to simplify}$$

Add.

4. $\frac{3x}{16} + \frac{5x^2}{24}$

5. $\frac{3}{16x} + \frac{5}{24x^2}$

6. Add:

$$\frac{3}{x^3 - x} + \frac{4}{x^2 + 2x + 1}.$$

Answers on page A-31

7. Add:

$$\frac{x-2}{x+3}+\frac{x+7}{x+8}.$$

8. Add:

$$\frac{5}{x^2+17x+16}+\frac{3}{x^2+9x+8}.$$

Answers on page A-31

Then

$$=\frac{\cancel{(a+1)}(2a-1)}{a(a-1)\cancel{(a+1)}} \qquad \text{Removing a factor of 1: } \frac{a+1}{a+1}=1$$

$$=\frac{2a-1}{a(a-1)}.$$

Do Exercise 6 on the preceding page.

EXAMPLE 7 Add: $\frac{x+4}{x-2}+\frac{x-7}{x+5}$.

First, we find the LCD. It is just the product of the denominators:

LCD $= (x-2)(x+5)$.

We multiply by 1 to get the LCD in each expression, and then add and simplif

$$\frac{x+4}{x-2}\cdot\frac{x+5}{x+5}+\frac{x-7}{x+5}\cdot\frac{x-2}{x-2}$$

$$=\frac{(x+4)(x+5)}{(x-2)(x+5)}+\frac{(x-7)(x-2)}{(x-2)(x+5)}$$

$$=\frac{x^2+9x+20}{(x-2)(x+5)}+\frac{x^2-9x+14}{(x-2)(x+5)}$$

$$=\frac{x^2+9x+20+x^2-9x+14}{(x-2)(x+5)}=\frac{2x^2+34}{(x-2)(x+5)}.$$

Do Exercise 7.

EXAMPLE 8 Add: $\frac{x}{x^2+11x+30}+\frac{-5}{x^2+9x+20}$.

$$\frac{x}{x^2+11x+30}+\frac{-5}{x^2+9x+20}$$

$$=\frac{x}{(x+5)(x+6)}+\frac{-5}{(x+5)(x+4)}$$ Factoring the denominators in order to find the LCD. The LCD is $(x+4)(x+5)(x+6)$.

$$=\frac{x}{(x+5)(x+6)}\cdot\frac{x+4}{x+4}+\frac{-5}{(x+5)(x+4)}\cdot\frac{x+6}{x+6}$$ Multiplyin by 1

$$=\frac{x(x+4)+(-5)(x+6)}{(x+4)(x+5)(x+6)}=\frac{x^2+4x-5x-30}{(x+4)(x+5)(x+6)}$$

$$=\frac{x^2-x-30}{(x+4)(x+5)(x+6)}$$

$$=\frac{(x-6)\cancel{(x+5)}}{(x+4)\cancel{(x+5)}(x+6)}$$

$$=\frac{(x-6)}{(x+4)(x+6)}$$

Always simplify at the end if possible: $\frac{x+5}{x+5}=1$.

Do Exercise 8.

DENOMINATORS THAT ARE OPPOSITES

When one denominator is the opposite of the other, we can first multipl either expression by 1 using $-1/-1$.

EXAMPLES

9. $\frac{x}{2}+\frac{3}{-2}=\frac{x}{2}+\frac{3}{-2}\cdot\frac{-1}{-1}$ Multiplying by 1 using $\frac{-1}{-1}$

$=\frac{x}{2}+\frac{-3}{2}$ The denominators are now the same.

$=\frac{x+(-3)}{2}=\frac{x-3}{2}$

10. $\frac{3x+4}{x-2}+\frac{x-7}{2-x}=\frac{3x+4}{x-2}+\frac{x-7}{2-x}\cdot\frac{-1}{-1}$

We could have chosen to multiply this expression by $-1/-1$. We multiply only one expression, *not* both.

$=\frac{3x+4}{x-2}+\frac{-x+7}{x-2}$ *Note:* $(2-x)(-1)=-2+x = x-2.$

$=\frac{(3x+4)+(-x+7)}{x-2}=\frac{2x+11}{x-2}$

Do Exercises 9 and 10.

Add.

9. $\frac{x}{4}+\frac{5}{-4}$

10. $\frac{2x+1}{x-3}+\frac{x+2}{3-x}$

FACTORS THAT ARE OPPOSITES

Suppose that when we factor to find the LCD, we find factors that are opposites. The easiest way to handle this is to first go back and multiply by $-1/-1$ appropriately to change factors so that they are not opposites.

EXAMPLE 11 Add: $\frac{x}{x^2-25}+\frac{3}{10-2x}$.

First, we factor to find the LCD:

$x^2-25=(x-5)(x+5);$

$10-2x=2(5-x).$

We note that there is an $x-5$ as one factor of x^2-25 and a $5-x$ as one factor of $10-2x$. If the denominator of the second expression were $2x-10$, this situation would not occur. To rewrite the second expression with a denominator of $2x-10$, we multiply by 1 using $-1/-1$, and then continue as before:

$$\frac{x}{x^2-25}+\frac{3}{10-2x}=\frac{x}{(x-5)(x+5)}+\frac{3}{10-2x}\cdot\frac{-1}{-1}$$

$$=\frac{x}{(x-5)(x+5)}+\frac{-3}{2x-10}$$

$$=\frac{x}{(x-5)(x+5)}+\frac{-3}{2(x-5)}\qquad \text{LCD}=2(x-5)(x+5)$$

$$=\frac{x}{(x-5)(x+5)}\cdot\frac{2}{2}+\frac{-3}{2(x-5)}\cdot\frac{x+5}{x+5}$$

$$=\frac{2x}{2(x-5)(x+5)}+\frac{-3(x+5)}{2(x-5)(x+5)}$$

$$=\frac{2x-3(x+5)}{2(x-5)(x+5)}=\frac{2x-3x-15}{2(x-5)(x+5)}$$

$$=\frac{-x-15}{2(x-5)(x+5)}.\qquad \text{Collecting like terms}$$

Do Exercise 11.

11. Add:

$\frac{x+3}{x^2-16}+\frac{5}{12-3x}$.

Answers on page A-31

6.4 EXERCISE SET

For Extra Help

MathXL | MyMathLab | InterAct Math | Math Tutor Center | Digital Video Tutor CD 4 Videotape 7 | Student's Solution Manual

a Add. Simplify if possible.

1. $\frac{5}{8} + \frac{3}{8}$

2. $\frac{3}{16} + \frac{5}{16}$

3. $\frac{1}{3 + x} + \frac{5}{3 + x}$

4. $\frac{4x + 6}{2x - 1} + \frac{5 - 8x}{-1 + 2x}$

5. $\frac{x^2 + 7x}{x^2 - 5x} + \frac{x^2 - 4x}{x^2 - 5x}$

6. $\frac{4}{x + y} + \frac{9}{y + x}$

7. $\frac{2}{x} + \frac{5}{x^2}$

8. $\frac{3}{y^2} + \frac{6}{y}$

9. $\frac{5}{6r} + \frac{7}{8r}$

10. $\frac{13}{18x} + \frac{7}{24x}$

11. $\frac{4}{xy^2} + \frac{6}{x^2y}$

12. $\frac{8}{ab^3} + \frac{3}{a^2b}$

13. $\frac{2}{9t^3} + \frac{1}{6t^2}$

14. $\frac{5}{c^2d^3} + \frac{-4}{7cd^2}$

15. $\frac{x + y}{xy^2} + \frac{3x + y}{x^2y}$

16. $\frac{2c - d}{c^2d} + \frac{c + d}{cd^2}$

17. $\frac{3}{x - 2} + \frac{3}{x + 2}$

18. $\frac{2}{y + 1} + \frac{2}{y - 1}$

19. $\frac{3}{x + 1} + \frac{2}{3x}$

20. $\frac{4}{5y} + \frac{7}{y - 2}$

21. $\frac{2x}{x^2 - 16} + \frac{x}{x - 4}$

2. $\frac{4x}{x^2 - 25} + \frac{x}{x + 5}$

23. $\frac{5}{z + 4} + \frac{3}{3z + 12}$

24. $\frac{t}{t - 3} + \frac{5}{4t - 12}$

5. $\frac{3}{x - 1} + \frac{2}{(x - 1)^2}$

26. $\frac{8}{(y + 3)^2} + \frac{5}{y + 3}$

27. $\frac{4a}{5a - 10} + \frac{3a}{10a - 20}$

8. $\frac{9x}{6x - 30} + \frac{3x}{4x - 20}$

29. $\frac{x + 4}{x} + \frac{x}{x + 4}$

30. $\frac{a}{a - 3} + \frac{a - 3}{a}$

1. $\frac{4}{a^2 - a - 2} + \frac{3}{a^2 + 4a + 3}$

32. $\frac{a}{a^2 - 2a + 1} + \frac{1}{a^2 - 5a + 4}$

33. $\frac{x + 3}{x - 5} + \frac{x - 5}{x + 3}$

4. $\frac{3x}{2y - 3} + \frac{2x}{3y - 2}$

35. $\frac{a}{a^2 - 1} + \frac{2a}{a^2 - a}$

36. $\frac{3x + 2}{3x + 6} + \frac{x - 2}{x^2 - 4}$

7. $\frac{7}{8} + \frac{5}{-8}$

38. $\frac{5}{-3} + \frac{11}{3}$

39. $\frac{3}{t} + \frac{4}{-t}$

0. $\frac{5}{-a} + \frac{8}{a}$

41. $\frac{2x + 7}{x - 6} + \frac{3x}{6 - x}$

42. $\frac{2x - 7}{5x - 8} + \frac{6 + 10x}{8 - 5x}$

43. $\dfrac{y^2}{y-3}+\dfrac{9}{3-y}$

44. $\dfrac{t^2}{t-2}+\dfrac{4}{2-t}$

45. $\dfrac{b-7}{b^2-16}+\dfrac{7-b}{16-b^2}$

46. $\dfrac{a-3}{a^2-25}+\dfrac{a-3}{25-a^2}$

47. $\dfrac{a^2}{a-b}+\dfrac{b^2}{b-a}$

48. $\dfrac{x^2}{x-7}+\dfrac{49}{7-x}$

49. $\dfrac{x+3}{x-5}+\dfrac{2x-1}{5-x}+\dfrac{2(3x-1)}{x-5}$

50. $\dfrac{3(x-2)}{2x-3}+\dfrac{5(2x+1)}{2x-3}+\dfrac{3(x+1)}{3-2x}$

51. $\dfrac{2(4x+1)}{5x-7}+\dfrac{3(x-2)}{7-5x}+\dfrac{-10x-1}{5x-7}$

52. $\dfrac{5(x-2)}{3x-4}+\dfrac{2(x-3)}{4-3x}+\dfrac{3(5x+1)}{4-3x}$

53. $\dfrac{x+1}{(x+3)(x-3)}+\dfrac{4(x-3)}{(x-3)(x+3)}+\dfrac{(x-1)(x-3)}{(3-x)(x+3)}$

54. $\dfrac{2(x+5)}{(2x-3)(x-1)}+\dfrac{3x+4}{(2x-3)(1-x)}+\dfrac{x-5}{(3-2x)(x-1)}$

55. $\dfrac{6}{x-y}+\dfrac{4x}{y^2-x^2}$

56. $\dfrac{a-2}{3-a}+\dfrac{4-a^2}{a^2-9}$

57. $\dfrac{4-a}{25-a^2}+\dfrac{a+1}{a-5}$

58. $\dfrac{x+2}{x-7}+\dfrac{3-x}{49-x^2}$

59. $\dfrac{2}{t^2+t-6}+\dfrac{3}{t^2-9}$

60. $\dfrac{10}{a^2-a-6}+\dfrac{3a}{a^2+4a+4}$

61. **DW** Explain why the expressions

$$\frac{1}{3-x} \quad \text{and} \quad \frac{1}{x-3}$$

are opposites.

62. **DW** A student insists on finding a common denominator by always multiplying the denominators of the expressions being added. How could this approach be improved?

SKILL MAINTENANCE

ubtract. [4.4c]

3. $(x^2 + x) - (x + 1)$

64. $(4y^3 - 5y^2 + 7y - 24) - (-9y^3 + 9y^2 - 5y + 49)$

implify. [4.2a, b]

5. $(2x^4y^3)^{-3}$

66. $\left(\frac{x^3}{5y}\right)^2$

67. $\left(\frac{x^{-4}}{y^7}\right)^3$

68. $(5x^{-2}y^{-3})^2$

raph.

9. $y = \frac{1}{2}x - 5$ [3.1d], [3.3a]

70. $2y + x + 10 = 0$ [3.1d], [3.3a]

71. $y = 3$ [3.2b]

72. $x = -5$ [3.2b]

olve.

3. $3x - 7 = 5x + 9$ [2.3b]

74. $2a + 8 = 13 - 4a$ [2.3b]

5. $x^2 - 8x + 15 = 0$ [5.7b]

76. $x^2 - 7x = 18$ [5.7b]

SYNTHESIS

ind the perimeter and the area of the figure.

7.

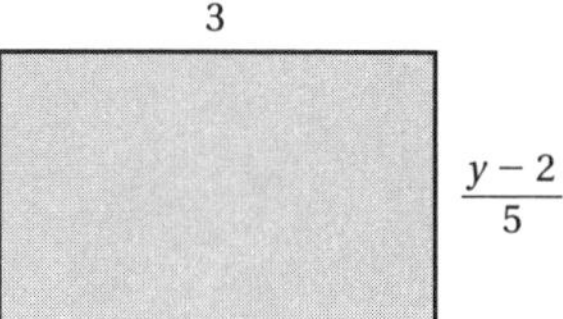

78.

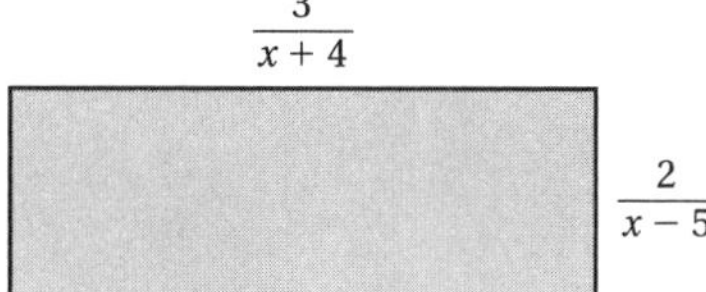

dd. Simplify if possible.

9. $\frac{5}{z+2} + \frac{4z}{z^2-4} + 2$

80. $\frac{-2}{y^2-9} + \frac{4y}{(y-3)^2} + \frac{6}{3-y}$

81. $\frac{3z^2}{z^4-4} + \frac{5z^2-3}{2z^4+z^2-6}$

2. Find an expression equivalent to

$$\frac{a-3b}{a-b}$$

that is a sum of two rational expressions. Answers may vary.

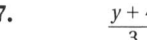

83.–86. Use the TABLE feature to check the additions in Exercises 29–32.

6.5 SUBTRACTING RATIONAL EXPRESSIONS

Objectives

a Subtract rational expressions.

b Simplify combined additions and subtractions of rational expressions.

Subtract.

1. $\frac{7}{11} - \frac{3}{11}$

2. $\frac{7}{y} - \frac{2}{y}$

3. $\frac{2x^2 + 3x - 7}{2x + 1} - \frac{x^2 + x - 8}{2x + 1}$

Answers on page A-31

a Subtracting Rational Expressions

We subtract rational expressions as we do rational numbers.

SUBTRACTING RATIONAL EXPRESSIONS WITH LIKE DENOMINATORS

To subtract when the denominators are the same, subtract the numerators and keep the same denominator. Then simplify if possible.

EXAMPLE 1 Subtract: $\frac{8}{x} - \frac{3}{x}$.

$$\frac{8}{x} - \frac{3}{x} = \frac{8 - 3}{x} = \frac{5}{x}$$

EXAMPLE 2 Subtract: $\frac{3x}{x + 2} - \frac{x - 2}{x + 2}$.

$$\frac{3x}{x + 2} - \frac{x - 2}{x + 2} = \frac{3x - (x - 2)}{x + 2}$$

$$= \frac{3x - x + 2}{x + 2} \quad \text{Removing parentheses}$$

$$= \frac{2x + 2}{x + 2}$$

Caution!

The parentheses are important to make sure that you subtract the entire numerator.

Do Exercises 1–3.

To subtract rational expressions with different denominators, we use procedure similar to what we used for addition, except that we subtrac numerators and write the difference over the LCD.

SUBTRACTING RATIONAL EXPRESSIONS WITH DIFFERENT DENOMINATORS

To subtract rational expressions with different denominators:

1. Find the LCM of the denominators. This is the least common denominator (LCD).
2. For each rational expression, find an equivalent expression with the LCD. To do so, multiply by 1 using a symbol for 1 made up of factors of the LCD that are missing from the original denominator.
3. Subtract the numerators. Write the difference over the LCD.
4. Simplify if possible.

XAMPLE 3 Subtract: $\frac{x+2}{x-4} - \frac{x+1}{x+4}$.

The LCD $= (x-4)(x+4)$.

$$\frac{x+2}{x-4} \cdot \frac{x+4}{x+4} - \frac{x+1}{x+4} \cdot \frac{x-4}{x-4}$$ Multiplying by 1

$$= \frac{(x+2)(x+4)}{(x-4)(x+4)} - \frac{(x+1)(x-4)}{(x-4)(x+4)}$$

$$= \frac{x^2+6x+8}{(x-4)(x+4)} - \frac{x^2-3x-4}{(x-4)(x+4)}$$

Subtracting this numerator. Don't forget the parentheses.

$$= \frac{x^2+6x+8-(x^2-3x-4)}{(x-4)(x+4)}$$

$$= \frac{x^2+6x+8-x^2+3x+4}{(x-4)(x+4)}$$ Removing parentheses

$$= \frac{9x+12}{(x-4)(x+4)}$$

ɔ *Exercise 4.*

4. Subtract:

$$\frac{x-2}{3x} - \frac{2x-1}{5x}.$$

XAMPLE 4 Subtract: $\frac{x}{x^2+5x+6} - \frac{2}{x^2+3x+2}$.

$$\frac{x}{^2+5x+6} - \frac{2}{x^2+3x+2}$$

$$= \frac{x}{(x+2)(x+3)} - \frac{2}{(x+2)(x+1)}$$ LCD $= (x+1)(x+2)(x+3)$

$$= \frac{x}{(x+2)(x+3)} \cdot \frac{x+1}{x+1} - \frac{2}{(x+2)(x+1)} \cdot \frac{x+3}{x+3}$$

$$= \frac{x^2+x}{(x+1)(x+2)(x+3)} - \frac{2x+6}{(x+1)(x+2)(x+3)}$$

Subtracting this numerator. Don't forget the parentheses.

$$= \frac{x^2+x-(2x+6)}{(x+1)(x+2)(x+3)}$$

$$= \frac{x^2+x-2x-6}{(x+1)(x+2)(x+3)}$$

$$= \frac{x^2-x-6}{(x+1)(x+2)(x+3)}$$

$$= \frac{(x+2)(x-3)}{(x+1)(x+2)(x+3)}$$

$$= \frac{\cancel{(x+2)}(x-3)}{(x+1)\cancel{(x+2)}(x+3)}$$ Simplifying by removing a factor of 1: $\frac{x+2}{x+2} = 1$

$$= \frac{x-3}{(x+1)(x+3)}.$$

ɔ *Exercise 5.*

5. Subtract:

$$\frac{x}{x^2+15x+56} - \frac{6}{x^2+13x+42}.$$

ENOMINATORS THAT ARE OPPOSITES

hen one denominator is the opposite of the other, we can first multiply one pression by $-1/-1$ to obtain a common denominator.

Answers on page A-31

Subtract.

6. $\frac{x}{3} - \frac{2x - 1}{-3}$

7. $\frac{3x}{x - 2} - \frac{x - 3}{2 - x}$

Answers on page A-31

EXAMPLE 5 Subtract: $\frac{x}{5} - \frac{3x - 4}{-5}$.

$$\frac{x}{5} - \frac{3x - 4}{-5} = \frac{x}{5} - \frac{3x - 4}{-5} \cdot \frac{-1}{-1}$$ Multiplying by 1 using $\frac{-1}{-1}$ ← This is equal to 1 (not -1).

$$= \frac{x}{5} - \frac{(3x - 4)(-1)}{(-5)(-1)}$$

$$= \frac{x}{5} - \frac{4 - 3x}{5}$$

$$= \frac{x - (4 - 3x)}{5}$$ Remember the parentheses!

$$= \frac{x - 4 + 3x}{5} = \frac{4x - 4}{5}$$

EXAMPLE 6 Subtract: $\frac{5y}{y - 5} - \frac{2y - 3}{5 - y}$.

$$\frac{5y}{y - 5} - \frac{2y - 3}{5 - y} = \frac{5y}{y - 5} - \frac{2y - 3}{5 - y} \cdot \frac{-1}{-1}$$

$$= \frac{5y}{y - 5} - \frac{(2y - 3)(-1)}{(5 - y)(-1)}$$

$$= \frac{5y}{y - 5} - \frac{3 - 2y}{y - 5}$$

$$= \frac{5y - (3 - 2y)}{y - 5}$$ Remember the parentheses!

$$= \frac{5y - 3 + 2y}{y - 5} = \frac{7y - 3}{y - 5}$$

Do Exercises 6 and 7.

FACTORS THAT ARE OPPOSITES

Suppose that when we factor to find the LCD, we find factors that are opposites. Then we multiply by $-1/-1$ appropriately to change factors so that they are not opposites.

EXAMPLE 7 Subtract: $\frac{p}{64 - p^2} - \frac{5}{p - 8}$.

Factoring $64 - p^2$, we get $(8 - p)(8 + p)$. Note that the factors $8 - p$ in the first denominator and $p - 8$ in the second denominator are opposites. We multiply the first expression by $-1/-1$ to avoid this situation. Then we proceed as before.

$$\frac{p}{64 - p^2} - \frac{5}{p - 8} = \frac{p}{64 - p^2} \cdot \frac{-1}{-1} - \frac{5}{p - 8}$$

$$= \frac{-p}{p^2 - 64} - \frac{5}{p - 8}$$

$$= \frac{-p}{(p - 8)(p + 8)} - \frac{5}{p - 8}$$ LCD $= (p - 8)(p + 8)$

$$= \frac{-p}{(p - 8)(p + 8)} - \frac{5}{p - 8} \cdot \frac{p + 8}{p + 8}$$

ultiplying, we have

$$\frac{-p}{(p-8)(p+8)} - \frac{5p+40}{(p-8)(p+8)}$$

Subtracting this numerator. Don't forget the parentheses.

$$= \frac{-p-(5p+40)}{(p-8)(p+8)}$$

$$= \frac{-p-5p-40}{(p-8)(p+8)} = \frac{-6p-40}{(p-8)(p+8)}.$$

Exercise 8.

8. Subtract:

$$\frac{y}{16-y^2} - \frac{7}{y-4}.$$

Combined Additions and Subtractions

ow let's look at some combined additions and subtractions.

XAMPLE 8 Perform the indicated operations and simplify:

$$\frac{x+9}{x^2-4} + \frac{5-x}{4-x^2} - \frac{2+x}{x^2-4}.$$

$$\frac{x+9}{x^2-4} + \frac{5-x}{4-x^2} - \frac{2+x}{x^2-4}$$

$$= \frac{x+9}{x^2-4} + \frac{5-x}{4-x^2}\cdot\frac{-1}{-1} - \frac{2+x}{x^2-4}$$

$$= \frac{x+9}{x^2-4} + \frac{x-5}{x^2-4} - \frac{2+x}{x^2-4} = \frac{(x+9)+(x-5)-(2+x)}{x^2-4}$$

$$= \frac{x+9+x-5-2-x}{x^2-4} = \frac{x+2}{x^2-4}$$

$$= \frac{\cancel{(x+2)}\cdot 1}{\cancel{(x+2)}(x-2)} = \frac{1}{x-2}.$$

Exercise 9.

9. Perform the indicated operations and simplify:

$$\frac{x+2}{x^2-9} - \frac{x-7}{9-x^2} + \frac{-8-x}{x^2-9}.$$

XAMPLE 9 Perform the indicated operations and simplify:

$$\frac{1}{x} - \frac{1}{x^2} + \frac{2}{x+1}.$$

The LCD $= x\cdot x(x+1)$, or $x^2(x+1)$.

$$\frac{1}{x}\cdot\frac{x(x+1)}{x(x+1)} - \frac{1}{x^2}\cdot\frac{(x+1)}{(x+1)} + \frac{2}{x+1}\cdot\frac{x^2}{x^2}$$

$$= \frac{x(x+1)}{x^2(x+1)} - \frac{x+1}{x^2(x+1)} + \frac{2x^2}{x^2(x+1)}$$

Subtracting this numerator. Don't forget the parentheses.

$$= \frac{x(x+1)-(x+1)+2x^2}{x^2(x+1)}$$

$$= \frac{x^2+x-x-1+2x^2}{x^2(x+1)}$$ Removing parentheses

$$= \frac{3x^2-1}{x^2(x+1)}$$

Exercise 10.

10. Perform the indicated operations and simplify:

$$\frac{1}{x} - \frac{5}{3x} + \frac{2x}{x+1}.$$

Answers on page A-31

6.5 EXERCISE SET

For Extra Help

MathXL | MyMathLab | InterAct Math | Math Tutor Center | Digital Video Tutor CD 4 Videotape 7 | Student's Solutions Manual

a Subtract. Simplify if possible.

1. $\frac{7}{x} - \frac{3}{x}$

2. $\frac{5}{a} - \frac{8}{a}$

3. $\frac{y}{y-4} - \frac{4}{y-4}$

4. $\frac{t^2}{t+5} - \frac{25}{t+5}$

5. $\frac{2x-3}{x^2+3x-4} - \frac{x-7}{x^2+3x-4}$

6. $\frac{x+1}{x^2-2x+1} - \frac{5-3x}{x^2-2x+1}$

7. $\frac{a-2}{10} - \frac{a+1}{5}$

8. $\frac{y+3}{2} - \frac{y-4}{4}$

9. $\frac{4z-9}{3z} - \frac{3z-8}{4z}$

10. $\frac{a-1}{4a} - \frac{2a+3}{a}$

11. $\frac{4x+2t}{3xt^2} - \frac{5x-3t}{x^2t}$

12. $\frac{5x+3y}{2x^2y} - \frac{3x+4y}{xy^2}$

13. $\frac{5}{x+5} - \frac{3}{x-5}$

14. $\frac{3t}{t-1} - \frac{8t}{t+1}$

15. $\frac{3}{2t^2-2t} - \frac{5}{2t-2}$

16. $\frac{11}{x^2-4} - \frac{8}{x+2}$

17. $\frac{2s}{t^2-s^2} - \frac{s}{t-s}$

18. $\frac{3}{12+x-x^2} - \frac{2}{x^2-9}$

9. $\frac{y-5}{y} - \frac{3y-1}{4y}$

20. $\frac{3x-2}{4x} - \frac{3x+1}{6x}$

21. $\frac{a}{x+a} - \frac{a}{x-a}$

2. $\frac{a}{a-b} - \frac{a}{a+b}$

23. $\frac{11}{6} - \frac{5}{-6}$

24. $\frac{5}{9} - \frac{7}{-9}$

5. $\frac{5}{a} - \frac{8}{-a}$

26. $\frac{8}{x} - \frac{3}{-x}$

27. $\frac{4}{y-1} - \frac{4}{1-y}$

. $\frac{5}{a-2} - \frac{3}{2-a}$

29. $\frac{3-x}{x-7} - \frac{2x-5}{7-x}$

30. $\frac{t^2}{t-2} - \frac{4}{2-t}$

. $\frac{a-2}{a^2-25} - \frac{6-a}{25-a^2}$

32. $\frac{x-8}{x^2-16} - \frac{x-8}{16-x^2}$

33. $\frac{4-x}{x-9} - \frac{3x-8}{9-x}$

. $\frac{4x-6}{x-5} - \frac{7-2x}{5-x}$

35. $\frac{5x}{x^2-9} - \frac{4}{3-x}$

36. $\frac{8x}{16-x^2} - \frac{5}{x-4}$

37. $\frac{t^2}{2t^2 - 2t} - \frac{1}{2t - 2}$

38. $\frac{4}{5a^2 - 5a} - \frac{2}{5a - 5}$

39. $\frac{x}{x^2 + 5x + 6} - \frac{2}{x^2 + 3x + 2}$

40. $\frac{a}{a^2 + 11a + 30} - \frac{5}{a^2 + 9a + 20}$

b Perform the indicated operations and simplify.

41. $\frac{3(2x + 5)}{x - 1} - \frac{3(2x - 3)}{1 - x} + \frac{6x - 1}{x - 1}$

42. $\frac{a - 2b}{b - a} - \frac{3a - 3b}{a - b} + \frac{2a - b}{a - b}$

43. $\frac{x - y}{x^2 - y^2} + \frac{x + y}{x^2 - y^2} - \frac{2x}{x^2 - y^2}$

44. $\frac{x - 3y}{2(y - x)} + \frac{x + y}{2(x - y)} - \frac{2x - 2y}{2(x - y)}$

45. $\frac{2(x - 1)}{2x - 3} - \frac{3(x + 2)}{2x - 3} - \frac{x - 1}{3 - 2x}$

46. $\frac{5(2y + 1)}{2y - 3} - \frac{3(y - 1)}{3 - 2y} - \frac{3(y - 2)}{2y - 3}$

47. $\frac{10}{2y - 1} - \frac{6}{1 - 2y} + \frac{y}{2y - 1} + \frac{y - 4}{1 - 2y}$

48. $\frac{(x + 1)(2x - 1)}{(2x - 3)(x - 3)} - \frac{(x - 3)(x + 1)}{(3 - x)(3 - 2x)} + \frac{(2x + 1)(x + 3)}{(3 - 2x)(x - 3)}$

49. $\frac{a + 6}{4 - a^2} - \frac{a + 3}{a + 2} + \frac{a - 3}{2 - a}$

50. $\frac{4t}{t^2 - 1} - \frac{2}{t} - \frac{2}{t + 1}$

51. $\frac{2z}{1 - 2z} + \frac{3z}{2z + 1} - \frac{3}{4z^2 - 1}$

52. $\frac{1}{x - y} - \frac{2x}{x^2 - y^2} + \frac{1}{x + y}$

53. $\frac{1}{x + y} - \frac{1}{x - y} + \frac{2x}{x^2 - y^2}$

54. $\frac{2b}{a^2 - b^2} - \frac{1}{a + b} + \frac{1}{a - b}$

5. DW Are parentheses as important when adding rational expressions as they are when subtracting? Why or why not?

56. DW Is it possible to add or subtract rational expressions without knowing how to factor? Why or why not?

SKILL MAINTENANCE

Simplify.

57. $\frac{x^8}{x^3}$ [4.1e]

58. $3x^4 \cdot 10x^8$ [4.1d]

59. $(a^2b^{-5})^{-4}$ [4.2a, b]

60. $\frac{54x^{10}}{3x^7}$ [4.1e]

61. $\frac{66x^2}{11x^5}$ [4.1e]

62. $5x^{-7} \cdot 2x^4$ [4.1d]

Find a polynomial for the shaded area of the figure. [4.4d]

63.

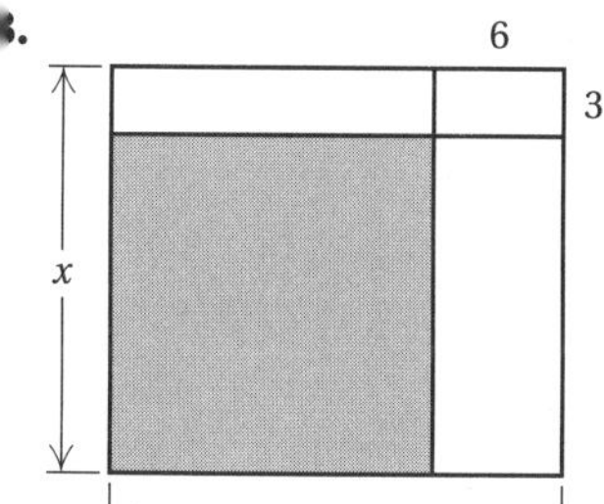

64.

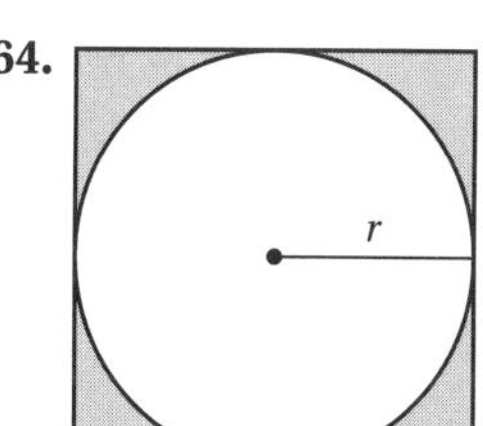

SYNTHESIS

Perform the indicated operations and simplify.

65. $\frac{2x+11}{x-3} \cdot \frac{3}{x+4} + \frac{2x+1}{4+x} \cdot \frac{3}{3-x}$

66. $\frac{x^2}{3x^2-5x-2} - \frac{2x}{3x+1} \cdot \frac{1}{x-2}$

67. $\frac{x}{x^4-y^4} - \left(\frac{1}{x+y}\right)^2$

68. $\left(\frac{a}{a-b} + \frac{b}{a+b}\right)\left(\frac{1}{3a+b} + \frac{2a+6b}{9a^2-b^2}\right)$

69. The perimeter of the following right triangle is $2a + 5$. Find the length of the missing side and the area.

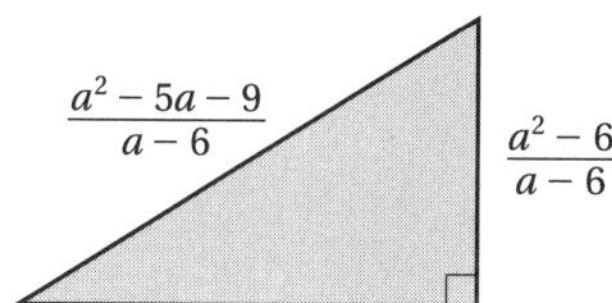

70.–73. Use the TABLE feature to check the subtractions in Exercises 15, 16, 19, and 20.

6.6 SOLVING RATIONAL EQUATIONS

Objective

a Solve rational equations.

1. Solve: $\frac{3}{4} + \frac{5}{8} = \frac{x}{12}$.

Answer on page A-32

Study Tips

RECORDING YOUR LECTURES

Consider recording your lectures and playing them back when convenient (for example, while commuting to campus). It can even be advantageous to record math lectures. (Be sure to get permission from your instructor before doing so, however.) Important points can be emphasized verbally. We consider this idea so worthwhile that we provide a series of audio recordings in the MyMathLab that accompanies the book. (See the Preface for more information.)

a Rational Equations

In Sections 6.1–6.5, we studied operations with *rational expressions.* These e pressions have no equals signs. We can add, subtract, multiply, or divide ar simplify expressions, but we cannot solve if there are no equals signs—as, f example, in

$$\frac{x^2 + 6x + 9}{x^2 - 4} \cdot \frac{x - 2}{x + 3}, \quad \frac{x + y}{x - y} \div \frac{x^2 + y}{x^2 - y^2}, \quad \text{and} \quad \frac{a + 3}{a^2 - 16} + \frac{5}{12 - 3a}.$$

Operation signs occur. There are no equals signs!

Most often, the result of our calculation is another rational expression th has not been cleared of fractions.

Equations *do have* equals signs, and we can clear them of fractions as w did in Section 2.3. A **rational,** or **fraction, equation,** is an equation containi one or more rational expressions. Here are some examples:

$$\frac{2}{3} + \frac{5}{6} = \frac{x}{9}, \quad x + \frac{6}{x} = -5, \quad \text{and} \quad \frac{x^2}{x - 1} = \frac{1}{x - 1}.$$

There are equals signs as well as operation signs.

SOLVING RATIONAL EQUATIONS

To solve a rational equation, the first step is to clear the equation of fractions. To do this, multiply all terms on both sides of the equation by the LCM of all the denominators. Then carry out the equation-solving process as we learned it in Chapter 2.

When clearing an equation of fractions, we use the terminology LCM i stead of LCD because we are *not* adding or subtracting rational expressio

EXAMPLE 1 Solve: $\frac{2}{3} + \frac{5}{6} = \frac{x}{9}$.

The LCM of all denominators is $2 \cdot 3 \cdot 3$, or 18. We multiply all terms both sides by 18:

$$18\left(\frac{2}{3} + \frac{5}{6}\right) = 18 \cdot \frac{x}{9} \qquad \text{Multiplying by the LCM on both sides}$$

$$18 \cdot \frac{2}{3} + 18 \cdot \frac{5}{6} = 18 \cdot \frac{x}{9} \qquad \text{Multiplying each term by the LCM to remove parentheses}$$

$$12 + 15 = 2x \qquad \text{Simplifying. Note that we have now cleared fractions.}$$

$$27 = 2x$$

$$\frac{27}{2} = x.$$

The solution is $\frac{27}{2}$.

Do Exercise 1.

XAMPLE 2 Solve: $\frac{x}{6} - \frac{x}{8} = \frac{1}{12}$.

2. Solve: $\frac{x}{4} - \frac{x}{6} = \frac{1}{8}$.

The LCM is 24. We multiply all terms on both sides by 24:

$$\frac{x}{6} - \frac{x}{8} = \frac{1}{12}$$

$$24\left(\frac{x}{6} - \frac{x}{8}\right) = 24 \cdot \frac{1}{12} \quad \text{Multiplying by the LCM on both sides}$$

$$24 \cdot \frac{x}{6} - 24 \cdot \frac{x}{8} = 24 \cdot \frac{1}{12} \quad \text{Multiplying to remove parentheses}$$

Be sure to multiply each term by the LCM.

$$4x - 3x = 2 \quad \text{Simplifying}$$

$$x = 2.$$

heck:

$\frac{x}{6} - \frac{x}{8} = \frac{1}{12}$	
$\frac{2}{6} - \frac{2}{8}$	$\frac{1}{12}$
$\frac{1}{3} - \frac{1}{4}$	
$\frac{4}{12} - \frac{3}{12}$	
$\frac{1}{12}$	TRUE

his checks, so the solution is 2.

o *Exercise 2.*

3. Solve: $\frac{1}{x} = \frac{1}{6 - x}$.

XAMPLE 3 Solve: $\frac{1}{x} = \frac{1}{4 - x}$.

The LCM is $x(4 - x)$. We multiply all terms on both sides by $x(4 - x)$:

$$\frac{1}{x} = \frac{1}{4 - x}$$

$$x(4 - x) \cdot \frac{1}{x} = x(4 - x) \cdot \frac{1}{4 - x} \quad \text{Multiplying by the LCM on both sides}$$

$$4 - x = x \quad \text{Simplifying}$$

$$4 = 2x$$

$$x = 2.$$

eck:

$\frac{1}{x} = \frac{1}{4 - x}$	
$\frac{1}{2}$	$\frac{1}{4 - 2}$
	$\frac{1}{2}$ TRUE

is checks, so the solution is 2.

Answers on page A-32

) *Exercise 3.*

4. Solve: $\frac{1}{2x}+\frac{1}{x}=-12.$

AC ALGEBRAIC–GRAPHICAL CONNECTION

We can obtain a visual check of the solutions of a rational equation by graphing. For example, consider the equation

$$\frac{x}{4}+\frac{x}{2}=6.$$

We can examine the solution by graphing the equations

$$y=\frac{x}{4}+\frac{x}{2} \quad \text{and} \quad y=6$$

using the same set of axes.

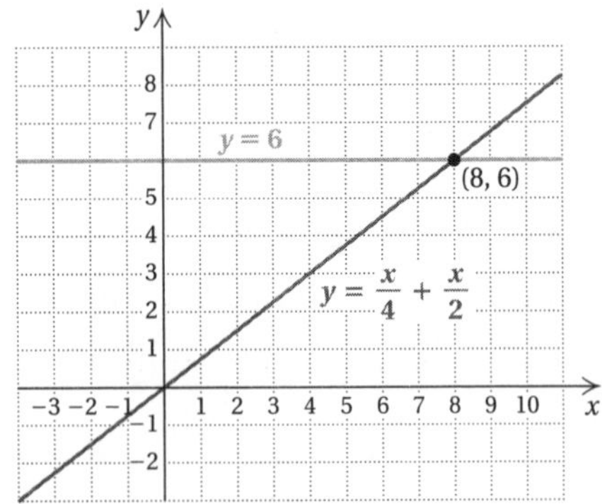

The y-values for each equation will be the same where the graphs intersect. The x-value of that point will yield that value, so it will be the solution of the equation. It appears from the graph that when $x=8$, the value of $x/4+x/2$ is 6. We can check by substitution:

$$\frac{x}{4}+\frac{x}{2}=\frac{8}{4}+\frac{8}{2}=2+4=6.$$

Thus the solution is 8.

Caution!

We have introduced a new use of the LCM in this section. We previously used the LCM in adding or subtracting rational expressions. *Now* we have equations with equals signs. We clear fractions by multiplying both sides of the equation by the LCM. This eliminates the denominators. Do *not* make the mistake of trying to clear fractions when you do not have an equation.

EXAMPLE 4 Solve: $\frac{2}{3x}+\frac{1}{x}=10.$

The LCM is $3x$. We multiply all terms on both sides by $3x$:

$$\frac{2}{3x}+\frac{1}{x}=10$$

$$3x\left(\frac{2}{3x}+\frac{1}{x}\right)=3x\cdot 10 \qquad \text{Multiplying by the LCM on both sides}$$

$$3x\cdot\frac{2}{3x}+3x\cdot\frac{1}{x}=3x\cdot 10 \qquad \text{Multiplying to remove parentheses}$$

$$2+3=30x \qquad \text{Simplifying}$$

$$5=30x$$

$$\frac{5}{30}=x$$

$$\frac{1}{6}=x.$$

The check is left to the student. The solution is $\frac{1}{6}$.

Do Exercise 4.

Answer on page A-32

XAMPLE 5 Solve: $x + \frac{6}{x} = -5.$

The LCM is x. We multiply all terms on both sides by x:

$$x + \frac{6}{x} = -5$$

$$x\left(x + \frac{6}{x}\right) = -5x \qquad \text{Multiplying by } x \text{ on both sides}$$

$$x \cdot x + x \cdot \frac{6}{x} = -5x \qquad \text{Note that each rational expression on the left is now multiplied by } x.$$

$$x^2 + 6 = -5x \qquad \text{Simplifying}$$

$$x^2 + 5x + 6 = 0 \qquad \text{Adding } 5x \text{ to get a 0 on one side}$$

$$(x + 3)(x + 2) = 0 \qquad \text{Factoring}$$

$$x + 3 = 0 \quad or \quad x + 2 = 0 \qquad \text{Using the principle of zero products}$$

$$x = -3 \quad or \quad x = -2.$$

eck: For -3:

$$x + \frac{6}{x} = -5$$

$-3 + \frac{6}{-3}$	-5
$-3 - 2$	
-5	TRUE

For -2:

$$x + \frac{6}{x} = -5$$

$-2 + \frac{6}{-2}$	-5
$-2 - 3$	
-5	TRUE

th of these check, so there are two solutions, -3 and -2.

Exercise 5.

CHECKING POSSIBLE SOLUTIONS

When we multiply both sides of an equation by the LCM, the resulting equation might have solutions that are *not* solutions of the original equation. Thus we must *always* check possible solutions in the original equation.

1. If you have carried out all algebraic procedures correctly, you need only check if a number makes a denominator 0 in the original equation. If it does make a denominator 0, it is *not* a solution.
2. To be sure that no computational errors have been made and that you indeed have a solution, a complete check is necessary, as we did in Chapter 2.

5. Solve: $x + \frac{1}{x} = 2.$

6. Solve: $\frac{x^2}{x + 2} = \frac{4}{x + 2}.$

7. Solve: $\frac{4}{x - 2} + \frac{1}{x + 2} = \frac{26}{x^2 - 4}.$

Answers on page A-32

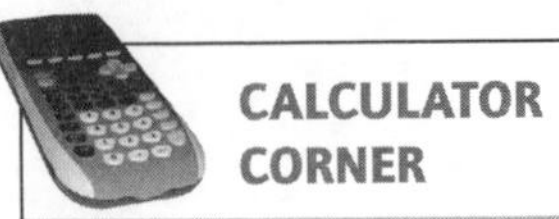

CALCULATOR CORNER

Checking Solutions of Rational Equations We can use a table to check possible solutions of rational equations. Consider the equation in Example 6 and the possible solutions that were found, 1 and −1. To check these solutions, we enter $y_1 = x^2/(x-1)$ and $y_2 = 1/(x-1)$ on the equation-editor screen. Then, with a table set in ASK mode, we enter $x = 1$. The ERROR messages indicate that 1 is not a solution because it is not an allowable replacement for x in the equation. Next, we enter $x = -1$. Since y_1 and y_2 have the same value, we know that the equation is true when $x = -1$, and thus −1 is a solution.

$y_1 = x^2/(x-1)$,
$y_2 = 1/(x-1)$

X	Y1	Y2
1	ERROR	ERROR
−1	−.5	−.5

X =

Exercises: Use a graphing calculator to check the possible solutions in each of the following.

1. Examples 1, 3, 5, and 7
2. Margin Exercises 1, 3, 6, and 7

Example 6 illustrates the importance of checking all possible solution

EXAMPLE 6 Solve: $\dfrac{x^2}{x-1} = \dfrac{1}{x-1}$.

The LCM is $x - 1$. We multiply all terms on both sides by $x - 1$:

$$\frac{x^2}{x-1} = \frac{1}{x-1}$$

$$(x-1)\cdot\frac{x^2}{x-1} = (x-1)\cdot\frac{1}{x-1} \quad \text{Multiplying by } x-1 \text{ on both sid}$$

$$x^2 = 1 \quad \text{Simplifying}$$

$$x^2 - 1 = 0 \quad \text{Subtracting 1 to get a 0 on one si}$$

$$(x-1)(x+1) = 0 \quad \text{Factoring}$$

$$x - 1 = 0 \quad or \quad x + 1 = 0 \quad \text{Using the principle of zero products}$$

$$x = 1 \quad or \quad x = -1.$$

The numbers 1 and −1 are possible solutions.

Check: For 1:

$$\frac{x^2}{x-1} = \frac{1}{x-1}$$
$$\frac{1^2}{1-1} \;\Big|\; \frac{1}{1-1}$$
$$\frac{1}{0} \;\Big|\; \frac{1}{0} \quad \text{NOT DEFINED}$$

For −1:

$$\frac{x^2}{x-1} = \frac{1}{x-1}$$
$$\frac{(-1)^2}{(-1)-1} \;\Big|\; \frac{1}{(-1)-1}$$
$$\frac{1}{-2} \;\Big|\; \frac{1}{-2}$$
$$-\frac{1}{2} \;\Big|\; -\frac{1}{2} \quad \text{TRUE}$$

We look at the original equation and see that 1 makes a denominato and is therefore not a solution. The number −1 checks and is a solution.

Do Exercise 6 on the preceding page.

EXAMPLE 7 Solve: $\dfrac{3}{x-5} + \dfrac{1}{x+5} = \dfrac{2}{x^2-25}$.

The LCM is $(x-5)(x+5)$. We multiply all terms on both sides $(x-5)(x+5)$:

$$(x-5)(x+5)\left(\frac{3}{x-5} + \frac{1}{x+5}\right) = (x-5)(x+5)\left(\frac{2}{x^2-2\text{5}}\right.$$

Multiplying by the LCM on both sic

$$(x-5)(x+5)\cdot\frac{3}{x-5} + (x-5)(x+5)\cdot\frac{1}{x+5} = (x-5)(x+5)\cdot\frac{2}{x^2-2}$$

$$3(x+5) + (x-5) = 2 \quad \text{Simplifying}$$

$$3x + 15 + x - 5 = 2 \quad \text{Removing parenthe}$$

$$4x + 10 = 2$$

$$4x = -8$$

$$x = -2.$$

The check is left to the student. The number −2 checks and is the solution

Do Exercise 7 on the preceding page.

ARE YOU CALCULATING OR SOLVING?

One of the common difficulties with this chapter is knowing for sure the task at hand. Are you combining expressions using operations to get another *rational expression,* or are you solving equations for which the results are numbers that are *solutions* of an equation? To learn to make these decisions, complete the following list by writing in the blank the type of answer you should get: "Rational expression" or "Solutions." You need not complete the mathematical operations.

TASK	ANSWER (Just write "Rational expression" or "Solutions.")
1. Add: $\frac{4}{x-2}+\frac{1}{x+2}$.	
2. Solve: $\frac{4}{x-2}=\frac{1}{x+2}$.	
3. Subtract: $\frac{4}{x-2}-\frac{1}{x+2}$.	
4. Multiply: $\frac{4}{x-2}\cdot\frac{1}{x+2}$.	
5. Divide: $\frac{4}{x-2}\div\frac{1}{x+2}$.	
6. Solve: $\frac{4}{x-2}+\frac{1}{x+2}=\frac{26}{x^2-4}$.	
7. Perform the indicated operations and simplify: $\frac{4}{x-2}+\frac{1}{x+2}-\frac{26}{x^2-4}$.	
8. Solve: $\frac{x^2}{x-1}=\frac{1}{x-1}$.	
9. Solve: $\frac{2}{y^2-25}=\frac{3}{y-5}+\frac{1}{y-5}$.	
10. Solve: $\frac{x}{x+4}-\frac{4}{x-4}=\frac{x^2+16}{x^2-16}$.	
11. Perform the indicated operations and simplify: $\frac{x}{x+4}-\frac{4}{x-4}-\frac{x^2+16}{x^2-16}$.	
12. Solve: $\frac{5}{y-3}-\frac{30}{y^2-9}=1$.	
13. Add: $\frac{5}{y-3}+\frac{30}{y^2-9}+1$.	

6.6 EXERCISE SET

For Extra Help

MathXL | MyMathLab | InterAct Math | Math Tutor Center | Digital Video Tutor CD 4 Videotape 7 | Student's Solutions Manual

a Solve. Don't forget to check!

1. $\frac{4}{5} - \frac{2}{3} = \frac{x}{9}$

2. $\frac{x}{20} = \frac{3}{8} - \frac{4}{5}$

3. $\frac{3}{5} + \frac{1}{8} = \frac{1}{x}$

4. $\frac{2}{3} + \frac{5}{6} = \frac{1}{x}$

5. $\frac{3}{8} + \frac{4}{5} = \frac{x}{20}$

6. $\frac{3}{5} + \frac{2}{3} = \frac{x}{9}$

7. $\frac{1}{x} = \frac{2}{3} - \frac{5}{6}$

8. $\frac{1}{x} = \frac{1}{8} - \frac{3}{5}$

9. $\frac{1}{6} + \frac{1}{8} = \frac{1}{t}$

10. $\frac{1}{8} + \frac{1}{12} = \frac{1}{t}$

11. $x + \frac{4}{x} = -5$

12. $\frac{10}{x} - x = 3$

13. $\frac{x}{4} - \frac{4}{x} = 0$

14. $\frac{x}{5} - \frac{5}{x} = 0$

15. $\frac{5}{x} = \frac{6}{x} - \frac{1}{3}$

$\frac{4}{x} = \frac{5}{x} - \frac{1}{2}$

17. $\frac{5}{3x} + \frac{3}{x} = 1$

18. $\frac{5}{2y} + \frac{8}{y} = 1$

$\frac{t-2}{t+3} = \frac{3}{8}$

20. $\frac{x-7}{x+2} = \frac{1}{4}$

21. $\frac{2}{x+1} = \frac{1}{x-2}$

$\frac{8}{y-3} = \frac{6}{y+4}$

23. $\frac{x}{6} - \frac{x}{10} = \frac{1}{6}$

24. $\frac{x}{8} - \frac{x}{12} = \frac{1}{8}$

$\frac{t+2}{5} - \frac{t-2}{4} = 1$

26. $\frac{x+1}{3} - \frac{x-1}{2} = 1$

27. $\frac{5}{x-1} = \frac{3}{x+2}$

$\frac{x-7}{x-9} = \frac{2}{x-9}$

29. $\frac{a-3}{3a+2} = \frac{1}{5}$

30. $\frac{x+7}{8x-5} = \frac{2}{3}$

31. $\dfrac{x-1}{x-5}=\dfrac{4}{x-5}$

32. $\dfrac{y+11}{y+8}=\dfrac{3}{y+8}$

33. $\dfrac{2}{x+3}=\dfrac{5}{x}$

34. $\dfrac{6}{y}=\dfrac{5}{y-8}$

35. $\dfrac{x-2}{x-3}=\dfrac{x-1}{x+1}$

36. $\dfrac{t+5}{t-2}=\dfrac{t-2}{t+4}$

37. $\dfrac{1}{x+3}+\dfrac{1}{x-3}=\dfrac{1}{x^2-9}$

38. $\dfrac{4}{x-3}+\dfrac{2x}{x^2-9}=\dfrac{1}{x+3}$

39. $\dfrac{x}{x+4}-\dfrac{4}{x-4}=\dfrac{x^2+16}{x^2-16}$

40. $\dfrac{5}{y-3}-\dfrac{30}{y^2-9}=1$

41. $\dfrac{4-a}{8-a}=\dfrac{4}{a-8}$

42. $\dfrac{3}{x-7}=\dfrac{x+10}{x-7}$

43. $2-\dfrac{a-2}{a+3}=\dfrac{a^2-4}{a+3}$

44. $\dfrac{5}{x-1}+x+1=\dfrac{5x+4}{x-1}$

olve.

5. $\frac{x+1}{x+2} = \frac{x+3}{x+4}$

46. $\frac{x^2}{x^2-4} = \frac{x}{x+2} - \frac{2x}{2-x}$

7. $4a - 3 = \frac{a+13}{a+1}$

48. $\frac{3x-9}{x-3} = \frac{5x-4}{2}$

9. $\frac{4}{y-2} - \frac{2y-3}{y^2-4} = \frac{5}{y+2}$

50. $\frac{y^2-4}{y+3} = 2 - \frac{y-2}{y+3}$

1. DW Why is it especially important to check the possible solutions to a rational equation?

52. DW How can a graph be used to determine how many solutions an equation has?

SKILL MAINTENANCE

VOCABULARY REINFORCEMENT

n each of Exercises 53–60, fill in the blank with the correct term from the given list. Some of the choices may not be used.

3. A rational expression is a(n) ______________ of two polynomials. [6.1a]

4. A factor of a polynomial P is a polynomial that can be used to express P as a(n) ______________. [5.1a]

5. Two expressions are ______________ of each other if their product is 1. [1.6b]

6. When ______________, always remember to look first for the greatest common factor. [5.1b]

7. To find the LCM, use each factor the ______________ number of times that it appears in any one factorization. [6.3a]

8. When solving rational equations, always check a possible solution to see if it makes a denominator 0. If it does, it is ______________ a solution. [6.6a]

9. The quotient rule asserts that when dividing with exponential notation, if the bases are the same, keep the base and ______________ the exponent of the denominator from the exponent of the numerator. [4.1e]

0. Two expressions are ______________ of each other if their sum is 0. [1.3b]

not
always
factor
add
subtract
sum
product
smallest
greatest
factoring
quotient
reciprocals
additive inverses
exponents

SYNTHESIS

olve.

1. $\frac{x}{x^2+3x-4} + \frac{x+1}{x^2+6x+8} = \frac{2x}{x^2+x-2}$

62. $\frac{3a-5}{a^2+4a+3} + \frac{2a+2}{a+3} = \frac{a-3}{a+1}$

3. Use a graphing calculator to check the solutions to Exercises 1–4.

64. Use a graphing calculator to check the solutions to Exercises 13, 15, and 25.

6.7 APPLICATIONS USING RATIONAL EQUATIONS AND PROPORTIONS

Objectives

a Solve applied problems using rational equations.

b Solve proportion problems.

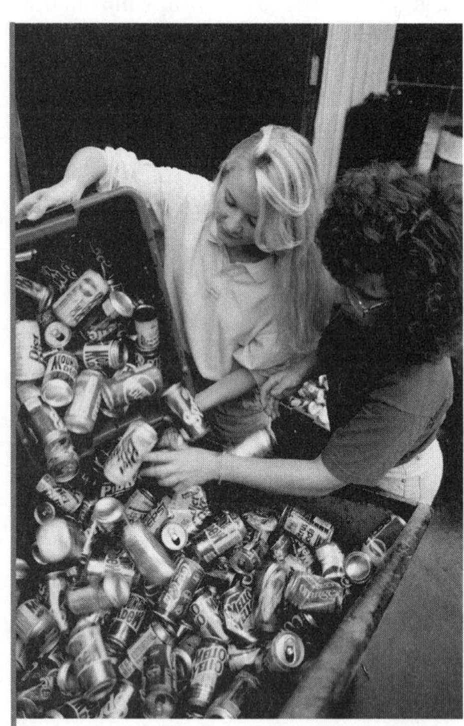

In many areas of study, applications involving rates, proportions, or re ciprocals translate to rational equations. By using the five steps for problen solving and the skills of Sections 6.1–6.6, we can now solve such problems.

a Solving Applied Problems

PROBLEMS INVOLVING WORK

EXAMPLE 1 *Recyclable Work.* Erin and Tara work as volunteers at community recycling depot. Erin can sort a morning's accumulation c recyclables in 4 hr, while Tara requires 6 hr to do the same job. How lon would it take them, working together, to sort the recyclables?

1. **Familiarize.** We familiarize ourselves with the problem by consid ering two *incorrect* ways of translating the problem to mathematica language.

   a) A common *incorrect* way to translate the problem is to add th two times: 4 hr + 6 hr = 10 hr. Let's think about this. Erin can d the job alone in 4 hr. If Erin and Tara work together, whateve time it takes them should be *less* than 4 hr. Thus we reject 10 h as a solution, but we do have a partial check on any answer w get. The answer should be less than 4 hr.

   b) Another *incorrect* way to translate the problem is as follows. Sup pose the two people split up the sorting job in such a way tha Erin does half the sorting and Tara does the other half. Then

   Erin sorts $\frac{1}{2}$ the recyclables in $\frac{1}{2}$(4 hr), or 2 hr,

   and Tara sorts $\frac{1}{2}$ the recyclables in $\frac{1}{2}$(6 hr), or 3 hr.

   But time is wasted since Erin would finish 1 hr earlier than Tara In effect, they have not worked together to get the job done a fast as possible. If Erin helps Tara after completing her half, th entire job could be done in a time somewhere between 2 hr an 3 hr.

We proceed to a translation by considering how much of the job i finished in 1 hr, 2 hr, 3 hr, and so on. It takes Erin 4 hr to do the sort ing job alone. Then, in 1 hr, she can do $\frac{1}{4}$ of the job. It takes Tara 6 h to do the job alone. Then, in 1 hr, he can do $\frac{1}{6}$ of the job. Working to gether, they can do

$$\frac{1}{4} + \frac{1}{6}, \text{ or } \frac{5}{12} \text{ of the job in 1 hr.}$$

In 2 hr, Erin can do $2(\frac{1}{4})$ of the job and Tara can do $2(\frac{1}{6})$ of the job Working together, they can do

$$2\left(\frac{1}{4}\right) + 2\left(\frac{1}{6}\right), \text{ or } \frac{5}{6} \text{ of the job in 2 hr.}$$

Study Tips

BEING A TUTOR

Try being a tutor for a fellow student. You can maximize your understanding and retention of concepts if you explain the material to someone else.

Continuing this reasoning, we can create a table like the following one.

TIME	FRACTION OF THE JOB COMPLETED		
	ERIN	TARA	TOGETHER
1 hr	$\frac{1}{4}$	$\frac{1}{6}$	$\frac{1}{4} + \frac{1}{6}$, or $\frac{5}{12}$
2 hr	$2\left(\frac{1}{4}\right)$	$2\left(\frac{1}{6}\right)$	$2\left(\frac{1}{4}\right) + 2\left(\frac{1}{6}\right)$, or $\frac{5}{6}$
3 hr	$3\left(\frac{1}{4}\right)$	$3\left(\frac{1}{6}\right)$	$3\left(\frac{1}{4}\right) + 3\left(\frac{1}{6}\right)$, or $1\frac{1}{4}$
t hr	$t\left(\frac{1}{4}\right)$	$t\left(\frac{1}{6}\right)$	$t\left(\frac{1}{4}\right) + t\left(\frac{1}{6}\right)$

From the table, we see that if they work 3 hr, the fraction of the job completed is $1\frac{1}{4}$, which is more of the job than needs to be done. We see again that the answer is somewhere between 2 hr and 3 hr. What we want is a number t such that the fraction of the job that gets completed is 1; that is, the job is just completed.

2. **Translate.** From the table, we see that the time we want is some number t for which

$$t\left(\frac{1}{4}\right) + t\left(\frac{1}{6}\right) = 1, \quad \text{or} \quad \frac{t}{4} + \frac{t}{6} = 1,$$

where 1 represents the idea that the entire job is completed in time t.

3. **Solve.** We solve the equation:

$$12\left(\frac{t}{4} + \frac{t}{6}\right) = 12 \cdot 1$$

Multiplying by the LCM, which is $2 \cdot 2 \cdot 3$, or 12

$$12 \cdot \frac{t}{4} + 12 \cdot \frac{t}{6} = 12$$

$$3t + 2t = 12$$

$$5t = 12$$

$$t = \frac{12}{5}, \text{ or } 2\frac{2}{5} \text{ hr.}$$

4. **Check.** The check can be done by recalculating:

$$\frac{12}{5}\left(\frac{1}{4}\right) + \frac{12}{5}\left(\frac{1}{6}\right) = \frac{3}{5} + \frac{2}{5} = \frac{5}{5} = 1.$$

We also have another check in what we learned from the *Familiarize* step. The answer, $2\frac{2}{5}$ hr, is between 2 hr and 3 hr (see the table), and it is less than 4 hr, the time it takes Erin working alone.

5. **State.** It takes $2\frac{2}{5}$ hr for them to do the sorting, working together.

1. **Wall Construction.** By checking work records, a contractor finds that it takes Eduardo 6 hr to construct a wall of a certain size. It takes Yolanda 8 hr to construct the same wall. How long would it take if they worked together?

Answer on page A-32

Study Tips

TEST TAKING: MORE ON DOING EVEN-NUMBERED EXERCISES

In an earlier study tip (p. 270), as a way to improve your test-taking skills, we encouraged you to build some even-numbered exercises into your homework. Here we explore this issue further.

Working a test is different from working your homework, when the answers are provided. When taking the test, you are "on your own," so to speak. Keep the following tips in mind when taking your next test or quiz.

1. Work a bit slower and deliberately, taking a fresh piece of paper to redo the problem. Check your work against your previous work to see if there is a difference and why. This is especially helpful if you finish the test early and have extra time.
2. Use estimation techniques to solve the problem as a check.
3. Do the checks to applied problems that we so often discuss in the book.

THE WORK PRINCIPLE

Suppose a = the time it takes A to do a job, b = the time it takes B to do the same job, and t = the time it takes them to do the same job working together. Then

$$\frac{t}{a} + \frac{t}{b} = 1, \quad \text{or} \quad \frac{1}{a} + \frac{1}{b} = \frac{1}{t}.$$

Do Exercise 1.

PROBLEMS INVOLVING MOTION

Problems that deal with distance, speed (or rate), and time are called **motion problems.** Translation of these problems involves the distance formula $d = r \cdot t$, and/or the equivalent formulas $r = d/t$ and $t = d/r$.

MOTION FORMULAS

The following are the formulas for motion problems:

$d = rt$; Distance = Rate · Time (basic formula)

$r = \dfrac{d}{t}$; Rate = Distance/Time

$t = \dfrac{d}{r}$. Time = Distance/Rate

EXAMPLE 2 *Animal Speeds.* A zebra can run 15 mph faster than an elephant. A zebra can run 8 mi in the same time that an elephant can run 5 mi. Find the speed of each animal.

Source: *World Almanac*, 2005, p. 179

1. **Familiarize.** We first make a drawing. Let r = the speed of the elephant. Then $r + 15$ = the speed of the zebra.

Recall that sometimes we need to find a formula in order to solve an application. A formula that relates the notions of distance, speed, and time is $d = rt$, or

Distance = Speed · Time.

(Indeed, you may need to look up such a formula.)

Since each animal travels for the same length of time, we can use just t for time. We organize the information in a chart, as follows.

$d = r \cdot t$

	DISTANCE	SPEED	TIME	
Elephant	5	r	t	$\rightarrow 5 = rt$
Zebra	8	$r + 15$	t	$\rightarrow 8 = (r + 15)t$

2. Translate. We can apply the formula $d = rt$ along the rows of the table to obtain two equations:

$5 = rt,$ **(1)**

$8 = (r + 15)t.$ **(2)**

We know that the animals travel for the same length of time. Thus if we solve each equation for t and set the results equal to each other, we get an equation in terms of r.

Solving $5 = rt$ for t: $t = \frac{5}{r}$

Solving $8 = (r + 15)t$ for t: $t = \frac{8}{r + 15}$

Since the times are the same, we have the following equation:

$$\frac{5}{r} = \frac{8}{r + 15}.$$

3. Solve. To solve the equation, we first multiply both sides by the LCM, which is $r(r + 15)$:

$$r(r + 15) \cdot \frac{5}{r} = r(r + 15) \cdot \frac{8}{r + 15}$$ Multiplying both sides by the LCM, which is $r(r + 15)$

$$5(r + 15) = 8r$$ Simplifying

$$5r + 75 = 8r$$ Removing parentheses

$$75 = 3r$$

$$25 = r.$$

We now have a possible solution. The speed of the elephant is 25 mph, and the speed of the zebra is $r + 15 = 25 + 15$, or 40 mph.

4. Check. We first reread the problem to see what we were to find. We check the speeds of 25 for the elephant and 40 for the zebra. The zebra does travel 15 mph faster than the elephant and will travel farther than the elephant, which runs at a slower speed. If the zebra runs 8 mi at 40 mph, the time it has traveled is $\frac{8}{40}$, or $\frac{1}{5}$ hr. If the elephant runs 5 mi at 25 mph, the time it has traveled is $\frac{5}{25}$, or $\frac{1}{5}$ hr. Since the times are the same, the speeds check.

5. State. The speed of the elephant is 25 mph and the speed of the zebra is 40 mph.

Do Exercise 2.

2. Driving speed. Nancy drives 20 mph faster than her father, Greg. In the same time that Nancy travels 180 mi, her father travels 120 mi. Find their speeds.

Answer on page A-32

3. Find the ratio of 145 km to 2.5 liters (L).

4. **Batting Average.** Recently, a baseball player got 7 hits in 25 times at bat. What was the rate, or batting average, in hits per times at bat?

5. Impulses in nerve fibers travel 310 km in 2.5 hr. What is the rate, or speed, in kilometers per hour?

6. A lake of area 550 yd^2 contains 1320 fish. What is the population density of the lake in number of fish per square yard?

7. **Automotive Mileage.** In highway driving, a Chrysler PT Cruiser will travel 377 mi on 14.5 gal of gasoline. How much gas will be required for a 900-mi trip?

Source: DaimlerChrysler Corporation

Answers on page A-32

b Applications Involving Proportions

We now consider applications with proportions. A **proportion** involves ratios. A **ratio** of two quantities is their quotient. For example, 73% is the ratio of 73 to 100, $\frac{73}{100}$. The ratio of two different kinds of measure is called a **rate.** Suppose an animal travels 720 ft in 2.5 hr. Its **rate,** or **speed,** is then

$$\frac{720 \text{ ft}}{2.5 \text{ hr}} = 288 \frac{\text{ft}}{\text{hr}}.$$

Do Exercises 3–6.

PROPORTION

An equality of ratios, $A/B = C/D$, is called a **proportion.** The numbers within a proportion are said to be **proportional** to each other.

EXAMPLE 3 *Mileage.* A 2004 Toyota Prius is a gasoline–electric car that travels 240 mi in city driving on 4 gal of gas. Find the amount of gas required for 360 mi of city driving.

Source: *Motor Trend*, May 2004, p. 89

1. **Familiarize.** We know that the Toyota can travel 240 mi on 4 gal of gas. Thus we can set up a ratio, letting x = the amount of gas required to drive 360 mi.
2. **Translate.** We assume that the car uses gas at the same rate in all city driving. Thus the ratios are the same and we can write a proportion. Note that the units of *mileage* are in the numerators and the units of *gasoline* are in the denominators.

$$\begin{matrix} \text{Miles} \rightarrow \\ \text{Gas} \rightarrow \end{matrix} \frac{240}{4} = \frac{360}{x} \begin{matrix} \leftarrow \text{Miles} \\ \leftarrow \text{Gas} \end{matrix}$$

3. **Solve.** To solve for x, we multiply both sides by the LCM, which is $4x$:

$$4x \cdot \frac{240}{4} = 4x \cdot \frac{360}{x} \quad \text{Multiplying by } 4x$$
$$240x = 1440 \quad \text{Simplifying}$$
$$\frac{240x}{240} = \frac{1440}{240} \quad \text{Dividing by 240}$$
$$x = 6. \quad \text{Simplifying}$$

We can also use cross products to solve the proportion:

$$\frac{240}{4} = \frac{360}{x} \quad 240x \text{ and } 4 \cdot 360 \text{ are cross products.}$$

$$240x = 4 \cdot 360 \quad \text{Equating cross products}$$
$$\frac{240x}{240} = \frac{4 \cdot 360}{240} \quad \text{Dividing by 240}$$
$$x = 6.$$

4. **Check.** The check is left to the student.
5. **State.** The Toyota Prius will require 6 gal of gas for 360 mi of city driving.

o Exercise 7 on the preceding page.

XAMPLE 4 *Environmental Science.* To determine the number of fish in lake, a park ranger catches 225 fish, tags them, and throws them back into he lake. Later, 108 fish are caught, and 15 of them are found to be tagged. Estimate how many fish are in the lake.

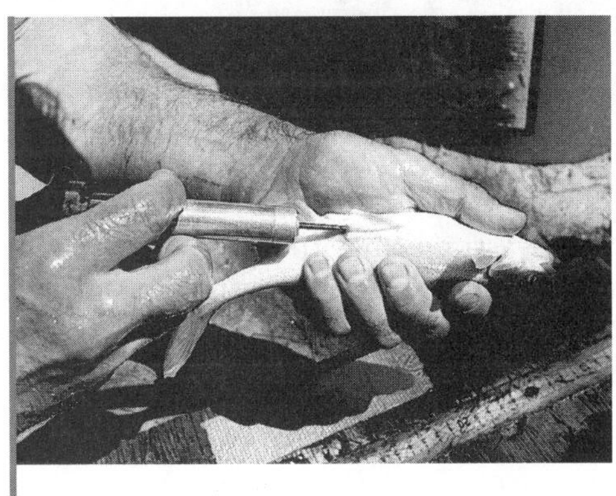

1. **Familiarize.** The ratio of the number of fish tagged to the total number of fish in the lake, F, is $\frac{225}{F}$. Of the 108 fish caught later, 15 fish were tagged. The ratio of fish tagged to fish caught is $\frac{15}{108}$.
2. **Translate.** Assuming that the two ratios are the same, we can translate to a proportion.

$$\begin{array}{r} \text{Fish tagged originally} \longrightarrow \\ \text{Fish in lake} \longrightarrow \end{array} \frac{225}{F} = \frac{15}{108} \begin{array}{l} \longleftarrow \text{Tagged fish caught later} \\ \longleftarrow \text{Fish caught later} \end{array}$$

3. **Solve.** We solve the proportion. We multiply by the LCM, which is $108F$:

$$108F \cdot \frac{225}{F} = 108F \cdot \frac{15}{108} \qquad \text{Multiplying by } 108F$$

$$108 \cdot 225 = F \cdot 15$$

$$\frac{108 \cdot 225}{15} = F \qquad \text{Dividing by 15}$$

$$1620 = F.$$

4. **Check.** The check is left to the student.
5. **State.** We estimate that there are about 1620 fish in the lake.

Do Exercise 8.

In the following example, we predict whether an important home-run record can be broken.

XAMPLE 5 *Home Runs by the Chicago Cubs.* After 14 games of the 2004 Major League Baseball season, which consists of 162 games, the Chicago Cubs had hit 30 home runs. The club record for a season (1998) was 212 home runs. At the pace they were hitting home runs in 2004, would the Cubs break their club record?

Source: Major League Baseball

8. **Environmental Science.** To determine the number of humpback whales in a pod, a marine biologist, using tail markings, identifies 27 members of the pod. Several weeks later, 40 whales from the pod are randomly sighted. Of the 40 sighted, 12 are from the 27 originally identified. Estimate the number of whales in the pod.

Answer on page A-32

9. Barry Bonds' Walks. Barry Bonds of the San Francisco Giants set a major league record in 2002 by getting 198 walks in 143 games. After playing in 122 games in 2004, he had 191 walks. Assuming he played in 143 games in 2004, would he break his record? (Barry Bonds actually got 232 walks in 147 games in 2004.)

Answer on page A-32

1. **Familiarize.** Let's assume that the pace of hitting 30 home runs in 14 games continues for the entire 162-game season. We let $H =$ the number of home runs that the Cubs hit in 162 games.
2. **Translate.** Assuming the rate continues, the ratios are the same and we have the proportion

   $$\text{Number of home runs} \rightarrow \frac{H}{162} = \frac{30}{14} \leftarrow \text{Number of home runs}$$
   (Number of games → 162; 14 ← Number of games)

3. **Solve.** We solve the proportion:

   $$\frac{H}{162} = \frac{30}{14}$$
   $$14H = 162 \cdot 30 \quad \text{Equating cross products}$$
   $$\frac{14H}{14} = \frac{162 \cdot 30}{14} \quad \text{Dividing by 14}$$
   $$H \approx 347.$$

4. **Check.** The check is left to the student.
5. **State.** Since $347 > 212$, we could predict that the Cubs would break their team record of 212. (The Cubs actually got 235 home runs in 2004.)

Do Exercise 9.

SIMILAR TRIANGLES

Proportions arise in geometry when we are studying *similar triangles.* If two triangles are **similar,** then their corresponding angles have the same measure and their corresponding sides are proportional. To illustrate, if triangle *ABC* is similar to triangle *RST*, then angles *A* and *R* have the same measure, angles *B* and *S* have the same measure, angles *C* and *T* have the same measure, and

$$\frac{a}{r} = \frac{b}{s} = \frac{c}{t}.$$

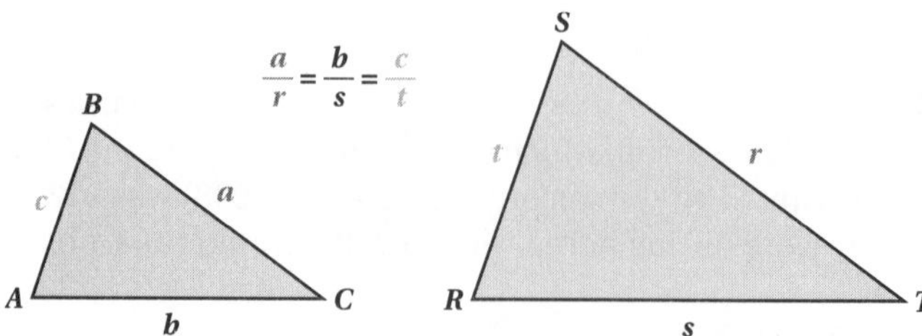

SIMILAR TRIANGLES

In **similar triangles,** corresponding angles have the same measure and the lengths of corresponding sides are proportional.

XAMPLE 6 *Similar Triangles.* Triangles ABC and XYZ below are similar iangles. Solve for z if $x = 10$, $a = 8$, and $c = 5$.

We make a sketch, write a proportion, and then solve. Note that side a is lways opposite angle A, side x is always opposite angle X, and so on.

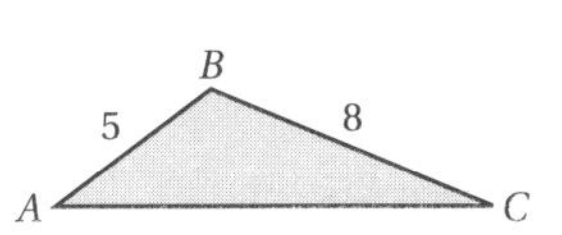

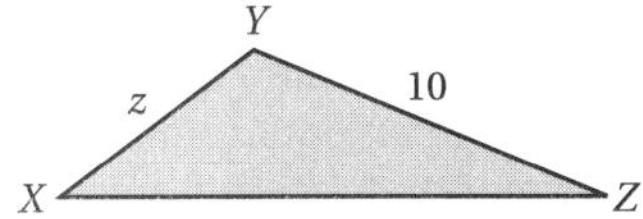

We have

$$\frac{z}{5} = \frac{10}{8} \qquad \text{The proportion } \frac{5}{z} = \frac{8}{10} \text{ could also be used.}$$

$$40 \cdot \frac{z}{5} = 40 \cdot \frac{10}{8} \qquad \text{Multiplying by 40}$$

$$8z = 50$$

$$z = \frac{50}{8}, \text{ or } 6.25. \qquad \text{Dividing by 8}$$

XAMPLE 7 *F-106 Blueprint.* A blueprint for an F-106 Delta Dart fighter lane is a scale drawing, as shown below. Each wing has a triangular shape. he blueprint shows similar triangles. Find the length of side a of the wing.

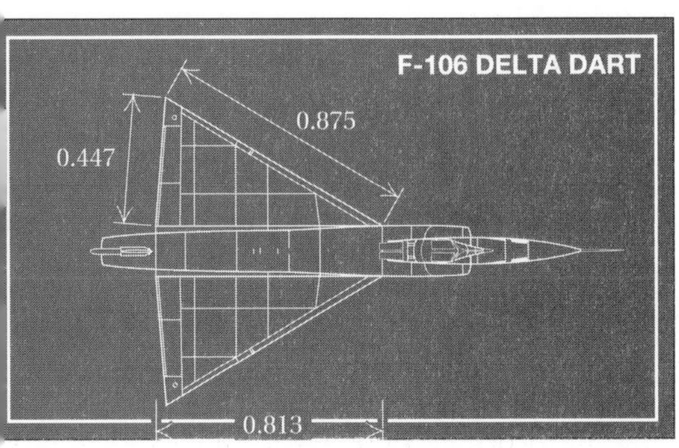

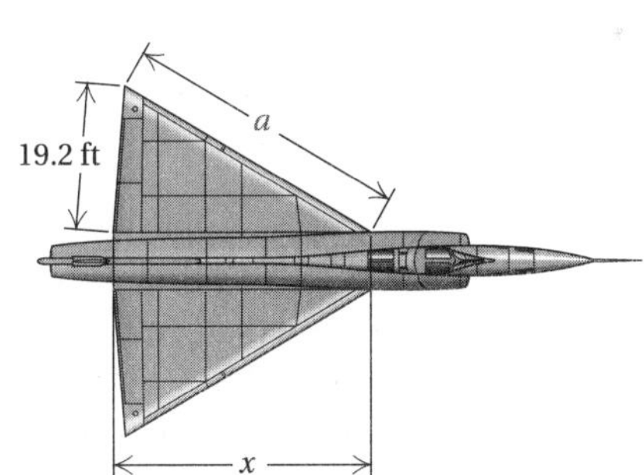

We let $a =$ the length of the wing. Thus we have the proportion

$$\begin{array}{r} \text{Length on the blueprint} \rightarrow \\ \text{Length of the wing} \rightarrow \end{array} \frac{0.447}{19.2} = \frac{0.875}{a}. \begin{array}{l} \leftarrow \text{Length on the blueprint} \\ \leftarrow \text{Length of the wing} \end{array}$$

olve: $0.447 \cdot a = 19.2 \cdot 0.875$ Equating cross products

$$a = \frac{19.2 \cdot 0.875}{0.447} \qquad \text{Dividing by 0.447}$$

$$a \approx 37.6 \text{ ft}$$

he length of side a of the wing is about 37.6 ft.

o Exercises 10 and 11.

10. Height of a Flagpole. How high is a flagpole that casts a 45-ft shadow at the same time that a 5.5-ft woman casts a 10-ft shadow?

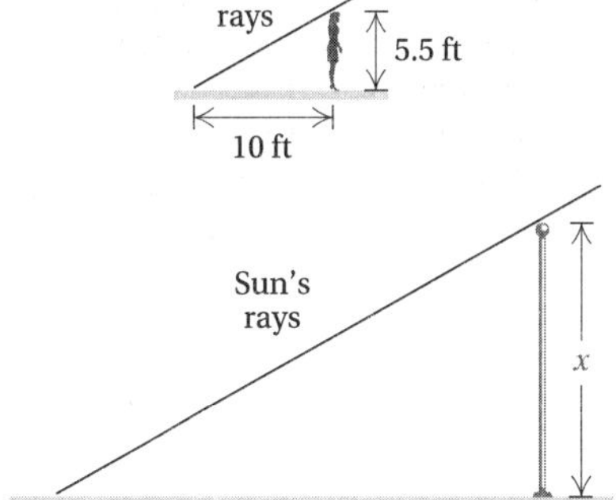

11. F-106 Blueprint. Referring to Example 7, find the length x on the plane.

Answers on page A-32

Translating for Success

1. *Search Engine Ads.* In 2005, it was estimated that \$3.6 billion was spent in advertising on Internet search engines such as Google® and Yahoo®. This was a 25% increase over the amount spent in 2004. How much was spent in 2004?

   Source: Forrester Research

2. *Cycling Distance.* A bicyclist traveled 197 mi in 7 days. At this rate, how many miles could the cyclist travel in 30 days?

3. *Bicycling.* The speed of one bicyclist is 2 km/h faster than the speed of another bicyclist. The first bicyclist travels 60 km in the same amount of time that it takes the second to travel 50 km. Find the speed of each bicyclist.

4. *Filling Time.* A swimming pool can be filled in 5 hr by hose A alone and in 6 hr by hose B alone. How long would it take to fill the tank if both hoses were working?

5. *Office Budget.* Emma has \$36 budgeted for office stationery. Engraved stationery costs \$20 for the first 25 sheets and \$0.08 for each additional sheet. How many engraved sheets of stationery can Emma order and still stay within her budget?

The goal of these matching questions is to practice step (2), *Translate,* of the five-step problem-solving process. Translate each word problem to an equation and select a correct translation from equations A–O.

A. $2x + 2(x + 1) = 613$

B. $x^2 + (x + 1)^2 = 613$

C. $\dfrac{60}{x + 2} = \dfrac{50}{x}$

D. $20 + 0.08(x - 25) = 36$

E. $\dfrac{197}{7} = \dfrac{x}{30}$

F. $x + (x + 1) = 613$

G. $\dfrac{7}{197} = \dfrac{x}{30}$

H. $x^2 + (x + 2)^2 = 612$

I. $x^2 + (x + 1)^2 = 612$

J. $\dfrac{50}{x + 2} = \dfrac{60}{x}$

K. $x + 25\% \cdot x = 3.6$

L. $t + 5 = 7$

M. $x^2 + (x + 1)^2 = 452$

N. $\dfrac{1}{5} + \dfrac{1}{6} = \dfrac{1}{t}$

O. $x^2 + (x + 2)^2 = 452$

Answers on page A-32

6. *Sides of a Square.* If the si[des of] a square are increased by 2 [ft,] the area of the original squ[are] plus the area of the enlarge[d] square is 452 ft^2. Find the l[ength] of a side of the original squ[are.]

7. *Consecutive Integers.* The [sum] of two consecutive integers [is] 613. Find the integers.

8. *Sums of Squares.* The sum [of] the squares of two consecu[tive] odd integers is 612. Find th[e] integers.

9. *Sums of Squares.* The sum [of] the squares of two consecu[tive] integers is 613. Find the integers.

10. *Rectangle Dimensions.* Th[e] length of a rectangle is 1 ft longer than its width. Find [the] dimensions of the rectangl[e] such that the perimeter of [the] rectangle is 613 ft.

6.7 EXERCISE SET

For Extra Help

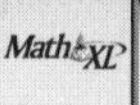

MathXL

MyMathLab

InterAct Math

Math Tutor Center

Digital Video Tutor CD 4 Videotape 7

Student's Solutions Manual

a Solve.

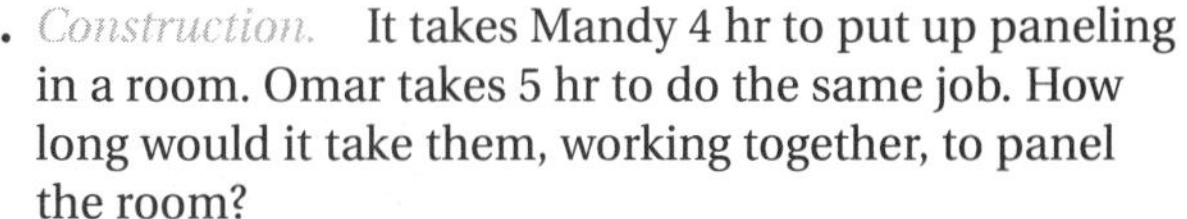

1. *Construction.* It takes Mandy 4 hr to put up paneling in a room. Omar takes 5 hr to do the same job. How long would it take them, working together, to panel the room?

2. *Carpentry.* By checking work records, a carpenter finds that Juanita can build a small shed in 12 hr. Anton can do the same job in 16 hr. How long would it take if they worked together?

3. *Shoveling.* Vern can shovel the snow from his driveway in 45 min. Nina can do the same job in 60 min. How long would it take Nina and Vern to shovel the driveway if they worked together?

4. *Raking.* Zoë can rake her yard in 4 hr. Steffi does the same job in 3 hr. How long would it take the two of them, working together, to rake the yard?

5. *Wiring.* By checking work records, a contractor finds that Kenny Dewitt can wire a room addition in 9 hr. It takes Betty Wohnt 7 hr to wire the same room. How long would it take if they worked together?

6. *Plumbing.* By checking work records, a plumber finds that Raul can plumb a house in 48 hr. Mira can do the same job in 36 hr. How long would it take if they worked together?

7. *Gardening.* Nicole can weed her vegetable garden in 50 min. Glen can weed the same garden in 40 min. How long would it take if they worked together?

8. *Harvesting.* Bobbi can pick a quart of raspberries in 20 min. Blanche can pick a quart in 25 min. How long would it take if Bobbi and Blanche worked together?

9. *Office Printers.* The HP Officejet 4215 All-In-One printer, fax, scanner, and copier can print in black one copy of a company's year-end report in 10 min. The HP Officejet 7410 All-In-One can print the same report in 6 min. How long would it take the two printers, working together, to print one copy of the report?

10. *Office Copiers.* The HP Officejet 7410 All-In-One printer, fax, scanner, and copier can copy in color a sta training manual in 9 min. The HP Officejet 4215 All-In-One can copy the same report in 15 min. How long would it take the two copiers, working together, to mak one copy of the manual?

11. *Car Speed.* Rick drives his four-wheel-drive truck 40 km/h faster than Sarah drives her Saturn. While Sarah travels 150 km, Rick travels 350 km. Find their speeds.

Complete this table and the equations as part of the *Familiarize* step.

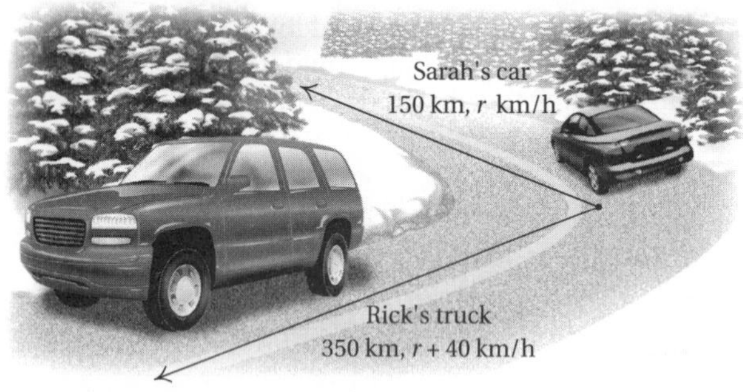

$d = r \cdot t$

	DISTANCE	SPEED	TIME	
Car	150	r		→ $150 = r($
Truck	350		t	→ $350 = ($

12. *Car Speed.* A passenger car travels 30 km/h faster than a delivery truck. While the car goes 400 km, the truck goes 250 km. Find their speeds.

13. *Train Speed.* The speed of a B & M freight train is 14 mph slower than the speed of an Amtrak passenger train. The freight train travels 330 mi in the same time that it takes the passenger train to travel 400 mi. Find the speed of each train.

Complete this table and the equations as part of the *Familiarize* step.

$d = r \cdot t$

	DISTANCE	SPEED	TIME	
B & M	330		t	→ $330 =$
Amtrak	400	r		→ $400 =$

4. *Train Speed.* The speed of a freight train is 15 mph slower than the speed of a passenger train. The freight train travels 390 mi in the same time that it takes the passenger train to travel 480 mi. Find the speed of each train.

5. *Trucking Speed.* A long-distance trucker traveled 120 mi in one direction during a snowstorm. The return trip in rainy weather was accomplished at double the speed and took 3 hr less time. Find the speed going.

16. *Car Speed.* After driving 126 mi, a person found that the drive would have taken 1 hr less time by increasing the speed by 8 mph. What was the actual speed?

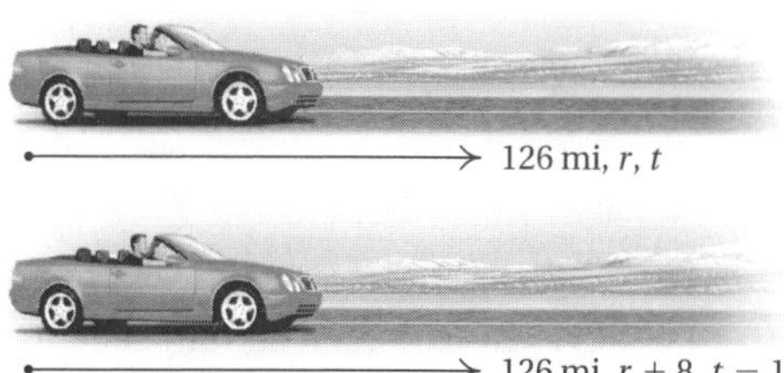

7. *Bicycle Speed.* Hank bicycles 5 km/h slower than Kelly. In the time that it takes Hank to bicycle 42 km, Kelly can bicycle 57 km. How fast does each bicyclist travel?

18. *Driving Speed.* Hillary's Lexus travels 30 mph faster than Bill's Harley. In the same time that Bill travels 75 mi, Hillary travels 120 mi. Find their speeds.

9. *Walking Speed.* Bonnie power walks 3 km/h faster than Ralph. In the time that it takes Ralph to walk 7.5 km, Bonnie walks 12 km. Find their speeds.

20. *Cross-Country Skiing.* Gerard cross-country skis 4 km/h faster than Sally. In the time that it takes Sally to ski 18 km, Gerard skis 24 km. Find their speeds.

11. *Tractor Speed.* Manley's tractor is just as fast as Caledonia's. It takes Manley 1 hr more than it takes Caledonia to drive to town. If Manley is 20 mi from town and Caledonia is 15 mi from town, how long does it take Caledonia to drive to town?

22. *Boat Speed.* Tory and Emilio's motorboats both travel at the same speed. Tory pilots her boat 40 km before docking. Emilio continues for another 2 hr, traveling a total of 100 km before docking. How long did it take Tory to navigate the 40 km?

b Find the ratio of the following. Simplify if possible.

23. 10 divorces, 18 marriages

24. 800 mi, 50 gal

25. *Speed of Black Racer.* A black racer snake travels 4.6 km in 2 hr. What is the speed in kilometers per hour?

26. *Speed of Light.* Light travels 558,000 mi in 3 sec. What is the speed in miles per second?

Solve.

27. *Protein Needs.* A 120-lb person should eat a minimum of 44 g of protein each day. How much protein should a 180-lb person eat each day?

28. *Coffee Beans.* The coffee beans from 14 trees are required to produce 7.7 kg of coffee (this is the average amount that each person in the United States drinks each year). How many trees are required to produce 320 kg of coffee?

29. *Hemoglobin.* A normal 10-cc specimen of human blood contains 1.2 g of hemoglobin. How much hemoglobin would 16 cc of the same blood contain?

30. *Walking Speed.* Wanda walked 234 km in 14 days. At this rate, how far would she walk in 42 days?

31. *Honey Bees.* Making 1 lb of honey requires 20,000 trips by bees to flowers to gather nectar. How many pounds of honey would 35,000 trips produce?

Source: Tom Turpin, Professor of Entomology, Purdue University

32. *Cockroaches and Horses.* A cockroach can run about 2 mi/hr (mph). The average body length of a cockroach is 1 in. The average body length of a horse is 8 ft (96 in.). If we assume that a horse's speed-to-length ratio is the same as that of a cockroach, how fast can a horse run?

Source: Tom Turpin, Professor of Entomology, Purdue University

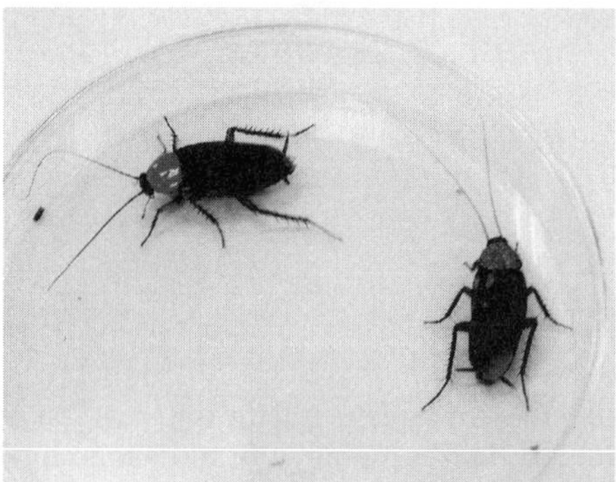

Professor Turpin founded the annual cockroach race at Purdue University.

33. *Money.* The ratio of the weight of copper to the weight of zinc in a U.S. penny is $\frac{1}{39}$. If 50 kg of zinc is being turned into pennies, how much copper is needed?

34. *Baking.* In a potato bread recipe, the ratio of milk to flour is $\frac{3}{13}$. If 5 cups of milk are used, how many cups of flour are used?

35. *Ichiro Suzuki.* In the 2004 Major League Baseball season, Ichiro Suzuki, playing for the Seattle Mariners of the American League, collected 72 hits in 217 at-bats in his first 48 games.

a) The ratio of number of hits to number of at-bats, rounded to the nearest thousandth, is a player's *batting average.* What was Suzuki's batting average in his first 48 games?
b) Based on the ratio of number of hits to number of games, how many hits would he get in the 162-game season?
c) Based on the ratio of number of hits to number of at-bats and assuming he bats 700 times in 2004, how many hits would he get?*

36. *Barry Bonds.* In the 2004 Major League Baseball season, Barry Bonds, playing for the San Francisco Giants of the National League, collected 44 hits in 117 at-bats in his first 49 games.

a) The ratio of number of hits to number of at-bats, rounded to the nearest thousandth, is a player's *batting average.* What was Bonds' batting average in his first 49 games?
b) Based on the ratio of number of hits to number of games, how many hits would he get in the 162-game season?
c) Based on the ratio of number of hits to number of at-bats and assuming he bats 400 times in 2004, how many hits would he get?†

Hat Sizes. Hat sizes are determined by measuring the circumference of one's head in either inches or centimeters. Use ratio and proportion to complete the missing parts of the following table.

	HAT SIZE	HEAD CIRCUMFERENCE (in inches)	HEAD CIRCUMFERENCE (in centimeters)
	$6\frac{3}{4}$	$21\frac{1}{5}$ in.	53.8 cm
37.	7		
38.			56.8 cm
39.		$22\frac{4}{5}$ in.	
40.	$7\frac{3}{8}$		
41.			59.8 cm
42.		24 in.	

*Ichiro Suzuki finished the 2004 American League baseball season with 262 hits in 704 at-bats and the highest 2004 American League season batting average of 0.372.
†Barry Bonds finished the 2004 National League baseball season with 135 hits in 373 at-bats and the highest 2004 National League batting average of 0.362.

43. *Estimating Trout Population.* To determine the number of trout in a lake, a conservationist catches 112 trout, tags them, and throws them back into the lake. Later, 82 trout are caught; 32 of them are tagged. Estimate the number of trout in the lake.

44. *Grass Seed.* It takes 60 oz of grass seed to seed 3000 ft^2 of lawn. At this rate, how much would be needed to seed 5000 ft^2 of lawn?

45. *Quality Control.* A sample of 144 firecrackers contained 9 "duds." How many duds would you expect in a sample of 3200 firecrackers?

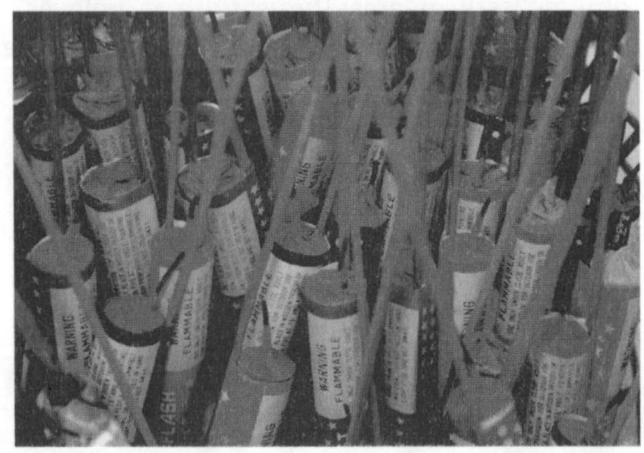

46. *Frog Population.* To estimate how many frogs there are in a rain forest, a research team tags 600 frogs and then releases them. Later the team catches 300 frogs and notes that 25 of them have been tagged. Estimate the total frog population in the rain forest.

47. *Weight on Mars.* The ratio of the weight of an object on Mars to the weight of the same object on Earth is 0.4 to 1.

a) How much would a 12-ton rocket weigh on Mars?
b) How much would a 120-lb astronaut weigh on Mars?

48. *Weight on Moon.* The ratio of the weight of an object on the moon to the weight of the same object on Earth is 0.16 to 1.

a) How much would a 12-ton rocket weigh on the moon?
b) How much would a 180-lb astronaut weigh on the moon?

Geometry. For each pair of similar triangles, find the length of the indicated side.

49. b:

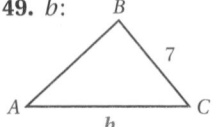

B 7 A C b

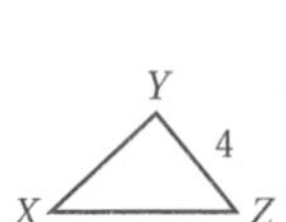

50. a:

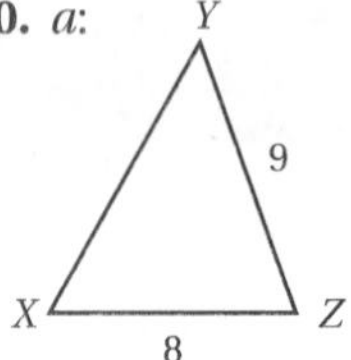

B a A C 6

51. f:

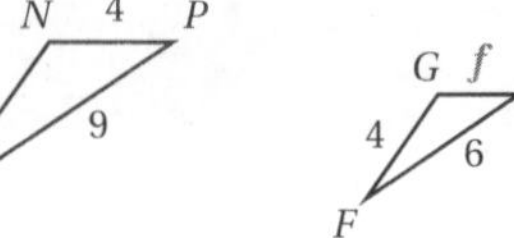

52. r:

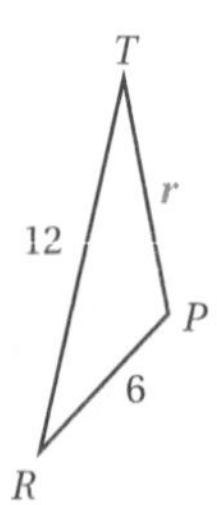

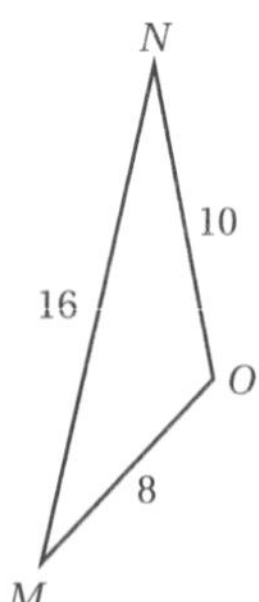

53. h:

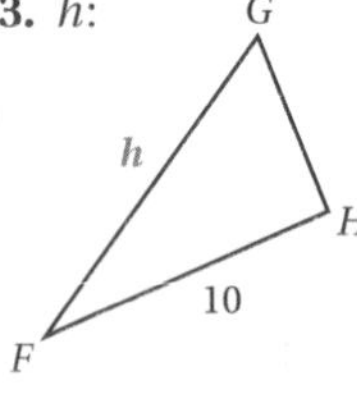

S 7 T R 6

54. n:

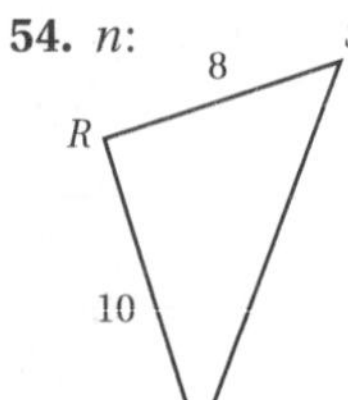

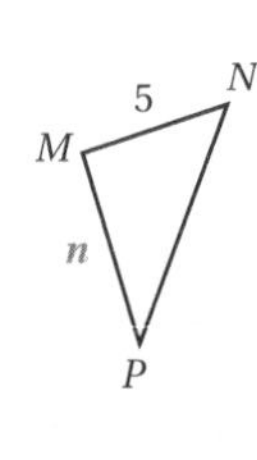

5. l:

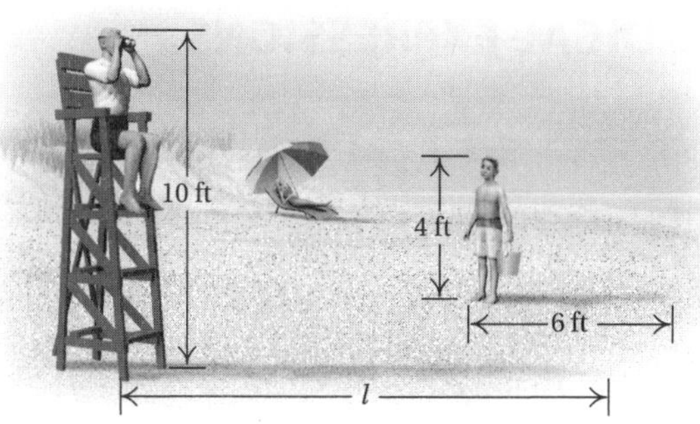

56. h:

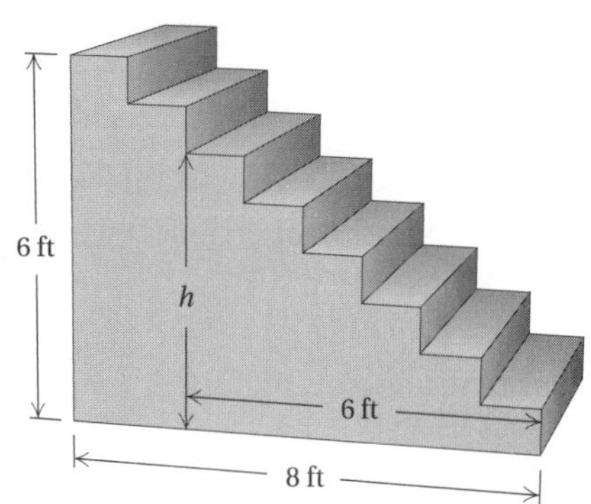

7. DW Look over Example 2 of Section 6.7. What new equation-solving skill have we developed in this chapter that enables us to solve this problem? How do these equations differ from others in the preceding parts of this book?

58. DW Look over Example 2 of Section 6.7. In order to solve the equation, what other skills of this chapter are required?

SKILL MAINTENANCE

implify. [4.1d]

9. $x^5 \cdot x^6$

60. $x^{-5} \cdot x^6$

61. $x^{-5} \cdot x^{-6}$

62. $x^5 \cdot x^{-6}$

raph. [3.1d]

3. $y = 2x - 6$

64. $y = -2x + 6$

65. $3x + 2y = 12$

6. $x - 3y = 6$

67. $y = -\frac{3}{4}x + 2$

68. $y = \frac{2}{5}x - 4$

SYNTHESIS

9. Ann and Betty work together and complete a sales report in 4 hr. It would take Betty 6 hr longer, working alone, to do the job than it would Ann. How long would it take each of them to do the job working alone?

1. How soon, in minutes, after 5 o'clock will the hands on a clock first be together?

70. Express 100 as the sum of two numbers for which the ratio of one number, increased by 5, to the other number, decreased by 5, is 4.

72. Rachel allows herself 1 hr to reach a sales appointment 50 mi away. After she has driven 30 mi, she realizes that she must increase her speed by 15 mph in order to get there on time. What was her speed for the first 30 mi?

73. Solve $\frac{t}{a} + \frac{t}{b} = 1$ for t.

8.1 INTRODUCTION TO RADICAL EXPRESSIONS

Objectives

a. Find the principal square roots and their opposites of the whole numbers from 0^2 to 25^2.

b. Approximate square roots of real numbers using a calculator.

c. Solve applied problems involving square roots.

d. Identify radicands of radical expressions.

e. Identify whether a radical expression represents a real number.

f. Simplify a radical expression with a perfect-square radicand.

Find the square roots.

1. 36 **2.** 64

3. 121 **4.** 144

Find the following.

5. $\sqrt{16}$ **6.** $\sqrt{49}$

7. $\sqrt{100}$ **8.** $\sqrt{441}$

9. $-\sqrt{49}$ **10.** $-\sqrt{169}$

Use a calculator to approximate each of the following square roots to three decimal places.

11. $\sqrt{15}$ **12.** $\sqrt{30}$

13. $\sqrt{980}$ **14.** $-\sqrt{667.8}$

15. $\sqrt{\frac{2}{3}}$ **16.** $-\sqrt{\frac{203.4}{67.82}}$

Answers on page A-37

a Square Roots

When we raise a number to the second power, we have squared the numbe Sometimes we may need to find the number that was squared. We call thi process finding a square root of a number.

SQUARE ROOT

The number c is a **square root** of a if $c^2 = a$.

Every positive number has two square roots. For example, the squa roots of 25 are 5 and -5 because $5^2 = 25$ and $(-5)^2 = 25$. The positiv square root is also called the **principal square root.** The symbol $\sqrt{\ }$ is calle a **radical*** (or **square root**) symbol. The radical symbol represents only th principal square root. Thus, $\sqrt{25} = 5$. To name the negative square root of number, we use $-\sqrt{\ }$. The number 0 has only one square root, 0.

EXAMPLE 1 Find the square roots of 81.

The square roots are 9 and -9.

EXAMPLE 2 Find $\sqrt{225}$.

There are two square roots of 225, 15 and -15. We want the principal, c positive, square root since this is what $\sqrt{\ }$ represents. Thus, $\sqrt{225} = 15$.

EXAMPLE 3 Find $-\sqrt{64}$.

The symbol $\sqrt{64}$ represents the positive square root. Then $-\sqrt{64}$ repre sents the negative square root. That is, $\sqrt{64} = 8$, so $-\sqrt{64} = -8$.

Do Exercises 1–10.

We can think of the processes of "squaring" and "finding square roots" a inverses of each other. We square a number and get one answer. When we fin the square roots of the answer, we get the original number *and* its opposit

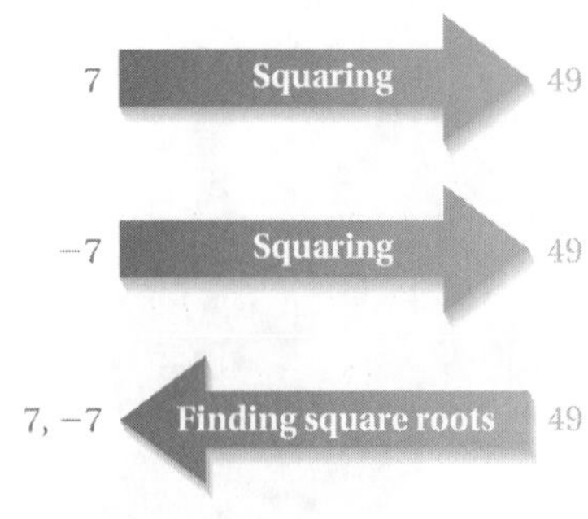

*Radicals can be other than square roots, but we will consider only square-root radicals i Chapter 8. See Appendix C for other types of radicals.

D Approximating Square Roots

We often need to use rational numbers to *approximate* square roots that are irrational. Such approximations can be found using a calculator with a square-root key ($\sqrt{\ }$).

EXAMPLES Use a calculator to approximate each of the following.

	Number	*Using a calculator with a 10-digit readout*	*Rounded to three decimal places*
4.	$\sqrt{10}$	3.162277660	3.162
5.	$-\sqrt{583.8}$	−24.16195356	−24.162
6.	$\sqrt{\frac{48}{55}}$	0.934198733	0.934

Do Exercises 11–16 on the preceding page.

C Applications of Square Roots

We now consider an application involving a formula with a radical expression.

EXAMPLE 7 *Speed of a Skidding Car.* After an accident, how do police determine the speed at which the car had been traveling? The formula $r = 2\sqrt{5L}$ can be used to approximate the speed r, in miles per hour, of a car that has left a skid mark of length L, in feet. What was the speed of a car that left skid marks of length **(a)** 30 ft? **(b)** 150 ft?

We substitute 30 for L and find an approximation:

$$r = 2\sqrt{5L} = 2\sqrt{5 \cdot 30} = 2\sqrt{150} \approx 24.495.$$

The speed of the car was about 24.5 mph.

CALCULATOR CORNER

Approximating Square Roots We can use a graphing calculator to approximate square roots. To approximate $\sqrt{18}$, for example, we press 2ND ($\sqrt{\ }$) 1 8) ENTER. ($\sqrt{\ }$ is the second operation associated with the x^2 key.) Although it is not necessary for this example to include the left parenthesis, we do so here in order to close the set of parentheses that are opened when the graphing calculator displays "$\sqrt{\ }$(." To approximate $-\sqrt{8.65}$, we press (−) 2ND ($\sqrt{\ }$) 8 . 6 5) ENTER. We see that $\sqrt{18} \approx 4.243$ and $-\sqrt{8.65} \approx -2.941$.

```
√(18)
              4.242640687
-√(8.65)
             -2.941088234
```

Exercises: Use a graphing calculator to approximate each of the following to three decimal places.

1. $\sqrt{43}$
2. $\sqrt{101}$
3. $\sqrt{10,467}$
4. $\sqrt{\frac{2}{5}}$
5. $-\sqrt{9406}$
6. $-\sqrt{\frac{11}{17}}$

17. Speed of a Skidding Car. Referring to Example 7, determine the speed of a car that left skid marks of length **(a)** 40 ft; **(b)** 123 ft.

Identify the radicand.

18. $\sqrt{227}$

19. $-\sqrt{45 + x}$

20. $\sqrt{\frac{x}{x + 2}}$

21. $8\sqrt{x^2 + 4}$

Determine whether the expression represents a real number. Write "yes" or "no."

22. $-\sqrt{25}$

23. $\sqrt{-25}$

24. $-\sqrt{-36}$

25. $-\sqrt{36}$

Answers on page A-37

b) We substitute 150 for L and find an approximation:

$$r = 2\sqrt{5L} = 2\sqrt{5 \cdot 150} \approx 54.772.$$

The speed of the car was about 54.8 mph.

Do Exercise 17.

d Radicands and Radical Expressions

When an expression is written under a radical, we have a **radical expressio**
Here are some examples:

$$\sqrt{14}, \quad \sqrt{x}, \quad 8\sqrt{x^2 + 4}, \quad \sqrt{\frac{x^2 - 5}{2}}.$$

The expression written under the radical is called the **radicand.**

EXAMPLES Identify the radicand in each expression.

8. $-\sqrt{105}$ The radicand is 105.

9. $\sqrt{x} + 2$ The radicand is x.

10. $\sqrt{x + 2}$ The radicand is $x + 2$.

11. $6\sqrt{y^2 - 5}$ The radicand is $y^2 - 5$.

12. $\sqrt{\frac{a - b}{a + b}}$ The radicand is $\frac{a - b}{a + b}$.

Do Exercises 18–21.

e Expressions That Are Meaningful as Real Numbers

The square of any nonzero number is always positive. For example, $8^2 =$ 6
and $(-11)^2 = 121$. There are no real numbers that when squared yield neg
tive numbers. For example, $\sqrt{-100}$ does not represent a real number becau
there are no real numbers that when squared yield -100. We can try to squa
10 and -10, but we know that $10^2 = 100$ and $(-10)^2 = 100$. Neither square
-100. Thus the following expressions do not represent real numbers (they a
meaningless as real numbers):

$$\sqrt{-100}, \quad \sqrt{-49}, \quad -\sqrt{-3}.$$

EXCLUDING NEGATIVE RADICANDS

Radical expressions with negative radicands do not represent real numbers.

Later in your study of mathematics, you may encounter a number syste
called the **complex numbers** in which negative numbers have square roo

Do Exercises 22–25.

f Perfect-Square Radicands

he expression $\sqrt{x^2}$, with a perfect-square radicand, x^2, can be troublesome to simplify. Recall that $\sqrt{}$ denotes the principal square root. That is, the answer is nonnegative (either positive or zero). If x represents a nonnegative umber, $\sqrt{x^2}$ simplifies to x. If x represents a negative number, $\sqrt{x^2}$ simplifies to $-x$ (the opposite of x), which is positive.

Suppose that $x = 3$. Then

$$\sqrt{x^2} = \sqrt{3^2} = \sqrt{9} = 3.$$

ippose that $x = -3$. Then

$$\sqrt{x^2} = \sqrt{(-3)^2} = \sqrt{9} = 3, \quad \text{the } \textit{opposite} \text{ of } -3.$$

ote that 3 is the *absolute value* of both 3 and -3. In general, when replacements for x are considered to be *any* real numbers, it follows that

$$\sqrt{x^2} = |x|,$$

nd when $x = 3$ or $x = -3$,

$$\sqrt{x^2} = \sqrt{3^2} = |3| = 3 \quad \text{and} \quad \sqrt{x^2} = \sqrt{(-3)^2} = |-3| = 3.$$

PRINCIPAL SQUARE ROOT OF A^2

For any real number A,

$$\sqrt{A^2} = |A|.$$

(That is, for any real number A, the principal square root of A^2 is the absolute value of A.)

XAMPLES Simplify. Assume that expressions under radicals represent any al number.

3. $\sqrt{10^2} = |10| = 10$

14. $\sqrt{(-7)^2} = |-7| = 7$

5. $\sqrt{(3x)^2} = |3x|$ Absolute-value notation is necessary.

6. $\sqrt{a^2b^2} = \sqrt{(ab)^2} = |ab|$

7. $\sqrt{x^2 + 2x + 1} = \sqrt{(x + 1)^2} = |x + 1|$

Exercises 26–31.

Fortunately, in many cases, it can be assumed that radicands that are riable expressions do not represent the square of a negative number. When is assumption is made, the need for absolute-value symbols disappears. hen

$$\text{for } x \geq 0, \quad \sqrt{x^2} = x,$$

nce x is nonnegative.

PRINCIPAL SQUARE ROOT OF A^2

For any nonnegative real number A,

$$\sqrt{A^2} = A.$$

(That is, for any nonnegative real number A, the principal square root of A^2 is A.)

Simplify. Assume that expressions under radicals represent any real number.

26. $\sqrt{(-13)^2}$

27. $\sqrt{(7w)^2}$

28. $\sqrt{(xy)^2}$

29. $\sqrt{x^2y^2}$

30. $\sqrt{(x - 11)^2}$

31. $\sqrt{x^2 + 8x + 16}$

Answers on page A-37

Simplify. Assume that radicands do not represent the square of a negative number.

32. $\sqrt{(xy)^2}$

33. $\sqrt{x^2y^2}$

34. $\sqrt{(x - 11)^2}$

35. $\sqrt{x^2 + 8x + 16}$

36. $\sqrt{25y^2}$

37. $\sqrt{\frac{1}{4}t^2}$

Answers on page A-37

EXAMPLES Simplify. Assume that radicands do not represent the square of a negative number.

18. $\sqrt{(3x)^2} = 3x$ — Since $3x$ is assumed to be nonnegative, $|3x| = 3x$.

19. $\sqrt{a^2b^2} = \sqrt{(ab)^2} = ab$ — Since ab is assumed to be nonnegative, $|ab| = ab$.

20. $\sqrt{x^2 + 2x + 1} = \sqrt{(x + 1)^2} = x + 1$ — Since $x + 1$ is assumed to be nonnegative

Do Exercises 32–37.

RADICALS AND ABSOLUTE VALUE

Henceforth, in this text we will assume that no radicands are formed by raising negative quantities to even powers.

We make this assumption in order to eliminate some confusion an because it is valid in many applications. As you study further in mathematic however, you will frequently have to make a determination about expressior under radicals being nonnegative or positive. This will often be necessa in calculus.

Study Tips

BEGINNING TO STUDY FOR THE FINAL EXAM (PART 2)

The best scenario for preparing for a final exam is to do so over a period of at least two weeks. Work in a diligent, disciplined manner, doing some final-exam preparation each day. Here is a detailed plan that many find useful.

1. **Begin by browsing through each chapter, reviewing the highlighted or boxed information regarding important formulas in both the text and the Summary and Review.** There may be some formulas that you will need to memorize.
2. **Retake each chapter test that you took in class, assuming your instructor has returned it. Otherwise, use the chapter test in the book.** Restudy the objectives in the text that correspond to each question you missed.
3. **Then work any Cumulative Review that covers chapters up to that point.** Be careful to avoid any questions corresponding to objectives not covered. Again, restudy the objectives in the text that correspond to each question you missed.
4. **If you are still missing questions, use the supplements for extra review.** For example, you might check out the videotapes or audio recordings, the *Student's Solutions Manual*, the InterAct Math Tutorial Web site, or MathXL.
5. **For remaining difficulties, see your instructor, go to a tutoring session, or participate in a study group.**
6. **Check for former final exams that may be on file in the math department or a study center, or with students who have already taken the course.** Use them for practice, being alert to trouble spots.
7. **Take the Final Examination in the text during the last couple of days before the final.** Set aside the same amount of time that you will have for the final. See how much of the final exam you can complete under test-like conditions.

"The door of opportunity won't open unless you do some pushing."

Anonymous

8.1 EXERCISE SET

For Extra Help

MathXL | MyMathLab | InterAct Math | Math Tutor Center | Digital Video Tutor CD 5 Videotape 9 | Student's Solutions Manual

a Find the square roots.

1. 4 **2.** 1 **3.** 9 **4.** 16 **5.** 100

6. 121 **7.** 169 **8.** 144 **9.** 256 **10.** 625

mplify.

11. $\sqrt{4}$ **12.** $\sqrt{1}$ **13.** $-\sqrt{9}$ **14.** $-\sqrt{25}$ **15.** $-\sqrt{36}$

16. $-\sqrt{81}$ **17.** $-\sqrt{225}$ **18.** $\sqrt{400}$ **19.** $\sqrt{361}$ **20.** $-\sqrt{441}$

b Use a calculator to approximate the square roots. Round to three decimal places.

21. $\sqrt{5}$ **22.** $\sqrt{8}$ **23.** $\sqrt{432}$ **24.** $-\sqrt{8196}$ **25.** $-\sqrt{347.7}$

26. $-\sqrt{204.788}$ **27.** $\sqrt{\frac{278}{36}}$ **28.** $-\sqrt{\frac{567}{788}}$ **29.** $-\sqrt{8 \cdot 9 \cdot 200}$ **30.** $\sqrt{\frac{47 \cdot 83}{947.03}}$

c *Parking-Lot Arrival Spaces.* The attendants at a parking lot park cars in temporary spaces before the cars are taken to permanent parking stalls. The number N of such spaces needed is approximated by the formula $N = 2.5\sqrt{A}$, where A is the average number of arrivals during peak hours.

31. Find the number of spaces needed when the average number of arrivals is **(a)** 25; **(b)** 89.

32. Find the number of spaces needed when the average number of arrivals is **(a)** 62; **(b)** 100.

Hang Time. An athlete's *hang time* (time airborne for a jump) T, in seconds, is given by $T = 0.144\sqrt{V}$, where V is the athlete's vertical leap, in inches.

Source: Peter Brancazio, "The Mechanics of a Slam Dunk," *Popular Mechanics*, November 1991. Courtesy of Peter Brancazio, Brooklyn College.

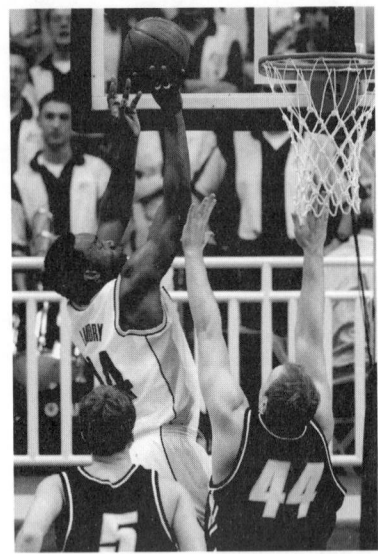

33. Carl Landry of the Purdue University basketball team can jump 33.5 in. vertically. Find his hang time.

34. Brandon McKnight of the Purdue University basketball team can jump 33 in. vertically. Find his hang time.

35. Jeff Trepagnier of the USC basketball team can jump 40 in. vertically. Find his hang time.

36. Keston Roberts of the Binghampton University basketball team can jump 38 in. vertically. Find his hang time.

d Identify the radicand.

37. $\sqrt{200}$

38. $\sqrt{16z}$

39. $-\sqrt{a-4}$

40. $\sqrt{3t+10}$

41. $5\sqrt{t^2+1}$

42. $-9\sqrt{x^2+16}$

43. $x^2y\sqrt{\dfrac{3}{x+2}}$

44. $ab^2\sqrt{\dfrac{a}{a+b}}$

e Determine whether the expression represents a real number. Write "yes" or "no."

45. $\sqrt{-16}$

46. $\sqrt{-81}$

47. $-\sqrt{81}$

48. $-\sqrt{64}$

49. $-\sqrt{-25}$

50. $\sqrt{-(-49)}$

f Simplify. Remember that we have assumed that radicands do not represent the square of a negative number.

51. $\sqrt{c^2}$

52. $\sqrt{x^2}$

53. $\sqrt{9x^2}$

54. $\sqrt{16y^2}$

55. $\sqrt{(8p)^2}$

56. $\sqrt{(7pq)^2}$

57. $\sqrt{(ab)^2}$

58. $\sqrt{(6y)^2}$

9. $\sqrt{(34d)^2}$

60. $\sqrt{(53b)^2}$

61. $\sqrt{(x+3)^2}$

62. $\sqrt{(d-3)^2}$

3. $\sqrt{a^2 - 10a + 25}$

64. $\sqrt{x^2 + 2x + 1}$

65. $\sqrt{4a^2 - 20a + 25}$

66. $\sqrt{9p^2 + 12p + 4}$

7. DW What is the difference between "**the** square root of 10" and "**a** square root of 10"?

68. DW Explain the difference between the two descriptions of the principal square root of A^2 given on p. 613.

SKILL MAINTENANCE

olve. [7.4a]

9. *Supplementary Angles.* Two angles are supplementary. One angle is 3° less than twice the other. Find the measures of the angles.

70. *Complementary Angles.* Two angles are complementary. The sum of the measure of the first angle and half the measure of the second is 64°. Find the measures of the angles.

1. *Food Expenses.* The amount F that a family spends on food varies directly as its income I. A family making $39,200 a year will spend $10,192 on food. At this rate, how much would a family making $41,000 spend on food? [6.9b]

ivide and simplify. [6.2b]

2. $\dfrac{x-3}{x+4} \div \dfrac{x^2-9}{x+4}$

73. $\dfrac{x^2+10x-11}{x^2-1} \div \dfrac{x+11}{x+1}$

74. $\dfrac{x^4-16}{x^4-1} \div \dfrac{x^2+4}{x^2+1}$

SYNTHESIS

5. Use only the graph of $y = \sqrt{x}$, shown below, to approximate $\sqrt{3}$, $\sqrt{5}$, and $\sqrt{7}$. Answers may vary.

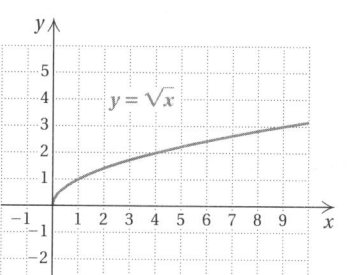

76. Between what two consecutive integers is $\sqrt{78}$?

lve.

. $\sqrt{x^2} = 16$

78. $\sqrt{y^2} = -7$

79. $t^2 = 49$

. Suppose that the area of a square is 3. Find the length of a side.

9.1 INTRODUCTION TO QUADRATIC EQUATIONS

Objectives

a Write a quadratic equation in standard form $ax^2 + bx + c = 0, a > 0$, and determine the coefficients a, b, and c.

b Solve quadratic equations of the type $ax^2 + bx = 0$, where $b \neq 0$, by factoring.

c Solve quadratic equations of the type $ax^2 + bx + c = 0$, where $b \neq 0$ and $c \neq 0$, by factoring.

d Solve applied problems involving quadratic equations.

AG *ALGEBRAIC–GRAPHICAL CONNECTION*

Before we begin this chapter, let's look back at some algebraic–graphical equation-solving concepts and their interrelationships. In Chapter 3, we considered the graph of a *linear equation* $y = mx + b$. For example, the graph of the equation $y = \frac{5}{2}x - 4$ and its x-intercept are shown below.

If $y = 0$, then $x = \frac{8}{5}$. Thus the x-intercept is $\left(\frac{8}{5}, 0\right)$. This point is also the intersection of the graphs of $y = \frac{5}{2}x - 4$ and $y = 0$.

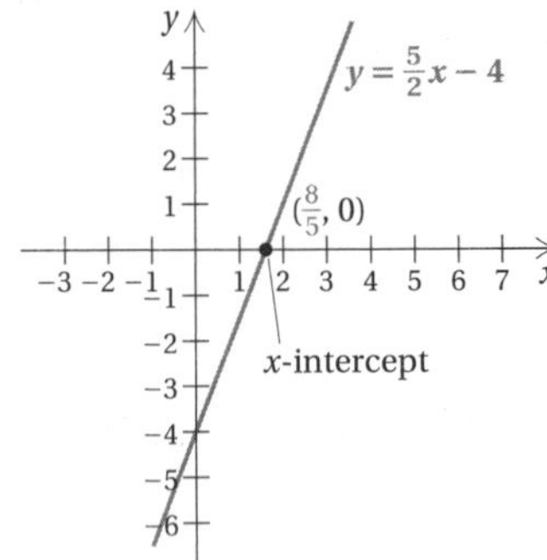

In Chapter 2, we learned how to solve linear equations like $0 = \frac{5}{2}x - 4$ algebraically (using algebra). We proceeded as follows:

$$0 = \frac{5}{2}x - 4$$

$$4 = \frac{5}{2}x \qquad \text{Adding 4}$$

$$8 = 5x \qquad \text{Multiplying by 2}$$

$$\frac{8}{5} = x. \qquad \text{Dividing by 5}$$

We see that $\frac{8}{5}$, the solution of $0 = \frac{5}{2}x - 4$, is the first coordinate of the x-intercept of the graph of $y = \frac{5}{2}x - 4$.

Do Exercise 1.

In this chapter, we build on these ideas by applying them to quadratic equations. In Section 5.7, we briefly considered the graph of a *quadratic equation*

$$y = ax^2 + bx + c, \quad a \neq 0.$$

For example, the graph of the equation $y = x^2 + 6x + 8$ and its x-intercepts are shown below.

The x-intercepts are $(-4, 0)$ and $(-2, 0)$. We will develop in detail the creation of such graphs in Section 9.6. The points $(-4, 0)$ and $(-2, 0)$ are the intersections of the graphs of $y = x^2 + 6x + 8$ and $y = 0$.

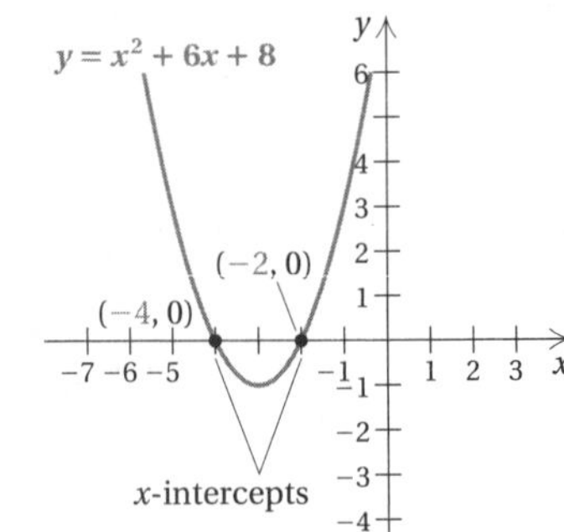

1. a) Consider the linear equation $y = -\frac{2}{3}x - 3$. Find the intercepts and graph the equation.

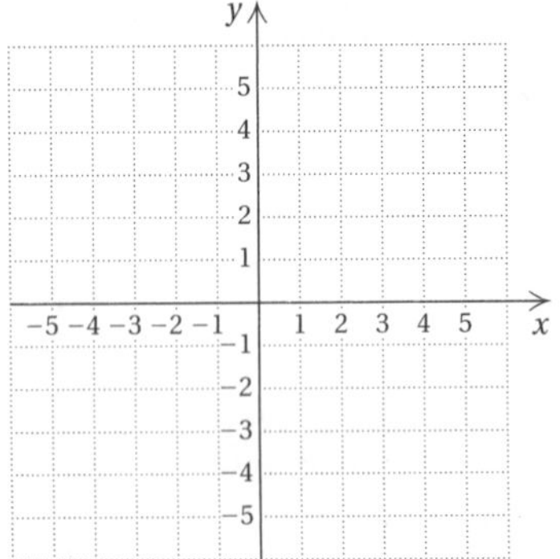

b) Solve the equation

$$0 = -\frac{2}{3}x - 3.$$

c) Complete: The solution of the equation $0 = -\frac{2}{3}x - 3$ is ________. This value is the ________ of the x-intercept, (____, ____), of the graph of $y = -\frac{2}{3}x - 3$.

Answers on page A-40

We began studying the solution of quadratic equations like

$$x^2 + 6x + 8 = 0$$

ı Section 5.7. There we used factoring for such solutions:

$x^2 + 6x + 8 = 0$

$\kappa + 4)(x + 2) = 0$ Factoring

$x + 4 = 0$ *or* $x + 2 = 0$ Using the principle of zero products

$x = -4$ *or* $x = -2$.

/e see that the solutions of $x^2 + 6x + 8 = 0$, -4 and -2, are the first ɔordinates of the x-intercepts, $(-4, 0)$ and $(-2, 0)$, of the graph of $y =$ $^2 + 6x + 8$.

o Exercise 2.

We will enhance our ability to solve quadratic equations in ections 9.1–9.3.

a Standard Form

he following are **quadratic equations.** They contain polynomials of sec- ıd degree.

$$4x^2 + 7x - 5 = 0,$$
$$3t^2 - \frac{1}{2}t = 9,$$
$$5y^2 = -6y,$$
$$5m^2 = 15$$

The quadratic equation $4x^2 + 7x - 5 = 0$ is said to be in **standard form.** though the quadratic equation $4x^2 = 5 - 7x$ is equivalent to the preceding quation, it is *not* in standard form.

QUADRATIC EQUATION

A **quadratic equation** is an equation equivalent to an equation of the type

$$ax^2 + bx + c = 0, \quad a > 0,$$

where a, b, and c are real-number constants. We say that the preceding is the **standard form of a quadratic equation.**

We define $a > 0$ to ease the proof of the quadratic formula, which we con- ler later, and to ease solving by factoring, which we review in this section. ıppose we are studying an equation like $-3x^2 + 8x - 2 = 0$. It is not in ındard form. We can find an equivalent equation that is in standard form by ultiplying by -1 on both sides:

$$-1(-3x^2 + 8x - 2) = -1(0)$$
$$3x^2 - 8x + 2 = 0. \quad \text{Standard form}$$

2. Consider the quadratic equation $y = x^2 - 2x - 3$ and its graph shown below.

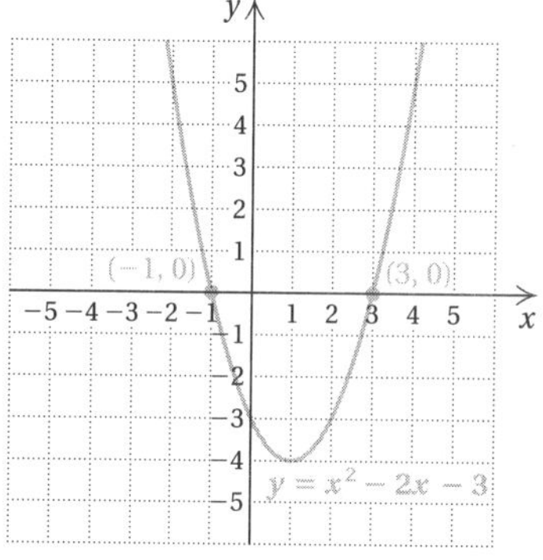

a) Solve the equation

$$x^2 - 2x - 3 = 0.$$

(*Hint*: Use the principle of zero products.)

b) Complete: The solutions of the equation $x^2 - 2x - 3 = 0$ are ____ and ____. These values are the _______ of the x-intercepts, (____, ____) and (____, ____), of the graph of $y = x^2 - 2x - 3$.

Answers on page A-40

Write in standard form and determine a, b, and c.

3. $6x^2 = 3 - 7x$

4. $y^2 = 8y$

5. $3 - x^2 = 9x$

6. $3x + 5x^2 = x^2 - 4 + 2x$

7. $5x^2 = 21$

Solve.

8. $2x^2 + 8x = 0$

9. $10x^2 - 6x = 0$

Answers on page A-40

EXAMPLES Write in standard form and determine a, b, and c.

1. $4x^2 + 7x - 5 = 0$ The equation is already in standard form.

$a = 4; \quad b = 7; \quad c = -5$

2. $3x^2 - 0.5x = 9$

$3x^2 - 0.5x - 9 = 0$ Subtracting 9. This is standard form.

$a = 3; \quad b = -0.5; \quad c = -9$

3. $-4y^2 = 5y$

$-4y^2 - 5y = 0$ Subtracting $5y$

Not positive!

$4y^2 + 5y = 0$ Multiplying by -1. This is standard form.

$a = 4; \quad b = 5; \quad c = 0$

Do Exercises 3–7.

b Solving Quadratic Equations of the Type $ax^2 + bx = 0$

Sometimes we can use factoring and the principle of zero products to solve quadratic equations. We are actually reviewing methods that we introduced in Section 5.7.

When $c = 0$ and $b \neq 0$, we can always factor and use the principle of zero products (see Section 5.7 for a review).

EXAMPLE 4 Solve: $7x^2 + 2x = 0$.

$$7x^2 + 2x = 0$$

$$x(7x + 2) = 0 \quad \text{Factoring}$$

$$x = 0 \quad or \quad 7x + 2 = 0 \quad \text{Using the principle of zero products}$$

$$x = 0 \quad or \quad 7x = -2$$

$$x = 0 \quad or \quad x = -\tfrac{2}{7}$$

Check: For 0:

$$\begin{array}{c|c} 7x^2 + 2x & 0 \\ \hline 7 \cdot 0^2 + 2 \cdot 0 & ?\ 0 \\ 0 & \end{array} \quad \text{TRUE}$$

For $-\frac{2}{7}$:

$$\begin{array}{c|c} 7x^2 + 2x & 0 \\ \hline 7(-\frac{2}{7})^2 + 2(-\frac{2}{7}) & ?\ 0 \\ 7(\frac{4}{49}) - \frac{4}{7} & \\ \frac{4}{7} - \frac{4}{7} & \\ 0 & \end{array} \quad \text{TR}$$

The solutions are 0 and $-\frac{2}{7}$.

Caution!

You may be tempted to divide each term in an equation like the one in Example 4 by x. This method would yield the equation

$$7x + 2 = 0,$$

whose only solution is $-\frac{2}{7}$. In effect, since 0 is also a solution of the original equation, we have divided by 0. The error of such division means the loss of one of the solutions.

XAMPLE 5 Solve: $4x^2 - 8x = 0$.

We have

$$4x^2 - 8x = 0$$
$$4x(x-2) = 0 \quad \text{Factoring}$$
$$4x = 0 \quad or \quad x - 2 = 0 \quad \text{Using the principle of zero products}$$
$$x = 0 \quad or \quad x = 2.$$

he solutions are 0 and 2.

A quadratic equation of the type $ax^2 + bx = 0$, where $c = 0$ and $b \neq 0$, will always have 0 as one solution and a nonzero number as the other solution.

o Exercises 8 and 9 on the preceding page.

AC ***ALGEBRAIC–GRAPHICAL CONNECTION***

Let's visualize the solutions in Example 5.

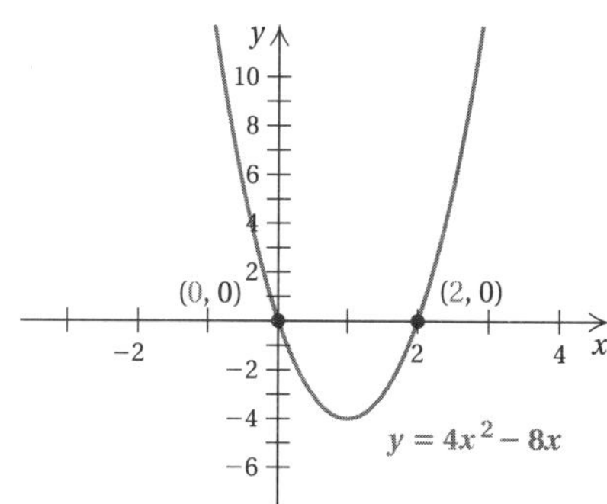

We see that the solutions of $4x^2 - 8x = 0$, 0 and 2, are the first coordinates of the x-intercepts, $(0, 0)$ and $(2, 0)$, of the graph of $y = 4x^2 - 8x$.

C Solving Quadratic Equations of the Type $ax^2 + bx + c = 0$

/hen neither b nor c is 0, we can sometimes solve by ıctoring.

XAMPLE 6 Solve: $2x^2 - x - 21 = 0$.

We have

$$2x^2 - x - 21 = 0$$
$$(2x-7)(x+3) = 0 \quad \text{Factoring}$$
$$2x - 7 = 0 \quad or \quad x + 3 = 0 \quad \text{Using the principle of zero products}$$
$$2x = 7 \quad or \quad x = -3$$
$$x = \tfrac{7}{2} \quad or \quad x = -3.$$

he solutions are $\frac{7}{2}$ and -3.

XAMPLE 7 Solve: $(y-3)(y-2) = 6(y-3)$.

We write the equation in standard form and then try factor:

$$y^2 - 5y + 6 = 6y - 18 \quad \text{Multiplying}$$
$$y^2 - 11y + 24 = 0 \quad \text{Standard form}$$
$$(y-8)(y-3) = 0 \quad \text{Factoring}$$
$$y - 8 = 0 \quad or \quad y - 3 = 0 \quad \text{Using the principle of zero products}$$
$$y = 8 \quad or \quad y = 3.$$

he solutions are 8 and 3.

o Exercises 10 and 11 on the following page.

AC ***ALGEBRAIC–GRAPHICAL CONNECTION***

Let's visualize the solutions in Example 6.

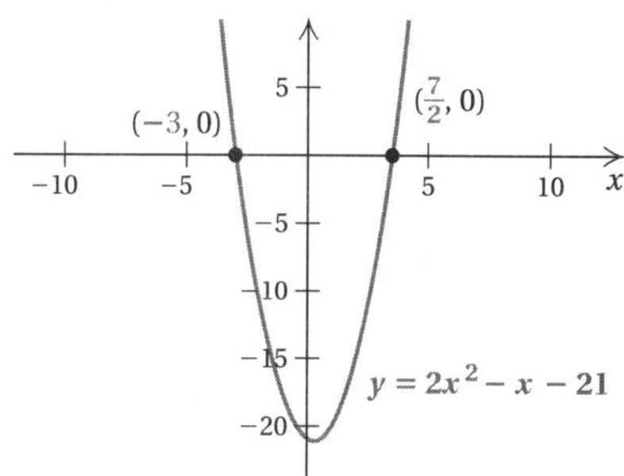

We see that the solutions of $2x^2 - x - 21 = 0$, -3 and $\frac{7}{2}$, are the first coordinates of the x-intercepts, $(-3, 0)$ and $(\frac{7}{2}, 0)$, of the graph of $y = 2x^2 - x - 21$.

Solve.

10. $4x^2 + 5x - 6 = 0$

11. $(x-1)(x+1) = 5(x-1)$

12. Solve:

$$\frac{20}{x+5} - \frac{1}{x-4} = 1.$$

Answers on page A-40

Recall that to solve a rational equation, we multiply both sides by th LCM of all the denominators. We may obtain a quadratic equation after a fe steps. When that happens, we know how to finish solving, but we mu remember to check possible solutions because a replacement may result i division by 0. See Section 6.6.

EXAMPLE 8 Solve: $\frac{3}{x-1} + \frac{5}{x+1} = 2.$

We multiply by the LCM, which is $(x-1)(x+1)$:

$$(x-1)(x+1) \cdot \left(\frac{3}{x-1} + \frac{5}{x+1}\right) = 2 \cdot (x-1)(x+1).$$

We use the distributive law on the left:

$$(x-1)(x+1) \cdot \frac{3}{x-1} + (x-1)(x+1) \cdot \frac{5}{x+1} = 2(x-1)(x+1)$$

$$3(x+1) + 5(x-1) = 2(x-1)(x+1)$$

$$3x + 3 + 5x - 5 = 2(x^2 - 1)$$

$$8x - 2 = 2x^2 - 2$$

$$0 = 2x^2 - 8x$$

$$0 = 2x(x-4) \quad \text{Factoring}$$

$$2x = 0 \quad or \quad x - 4 = 0$$

$$x = 0 \quad or \quad x = 4.$$

Check: For 0:

$$\frac{3}{x-1} + \frac{5}{x+1} = 2$$

$$\frac{3}{0-1} + \frac{5}{0+1} \; ? \; 2$$

$$\frac{3}{-1} + \frac{5}{1}$$

$$-3 + 5$$

$$2 \qquad \text{TRUE}$$

For 4:

$$\frac{3}{x-1} + \frac{5}{x+1} = 2$$

$$\frac{3}{4-1} + \frac{5}{4+1} \; ? \; 2$$

$$\frac{3}{3} + \frac{5}{5}$$

$$1 + 1$$

$$2 \qquad \text{TR}$$

The solutions are 0 and 4.

Do Exercise 12.

d Solving Applied Problems

EXAMPLE 9 *Diagonals of a Polygon.* The number of diagonals d of a polygon of n sides is given by the formula

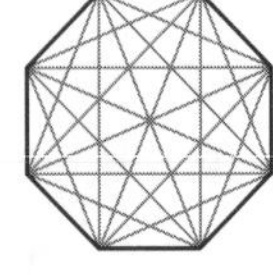

$$d = \frac{n^2 - 3n}{2}.$$

If a polygon has 27 diagonals, how many sides does it have?

1. **Familiarize.** We can make a drawing to familiarize ourselves with th problem. We draw an octagon (8 sides) and count the diagonals and se that there are 20. Let's check this in the formula. We evaluate the formu

for $n = 8$:

$$d = \frac{8^2 - 3(8)}{2} = \frac{64 - 24}{2} = \frac{40}{2} = 20.$$

2. **Translate.** We know that the number of diagonals is 27. We substitute 27 for d:

$$27 = \frac{n^2 - 3n}{2}.$$

3. **Solve.** We solve the equation for n, reversing the equation first for convenience:

$$\frac{n^2 - 3n}{2} = 27$$

$n^2 - 3n = 54$ Multiplying by 2 to clear fractions

$n^2 - 3n - 54 = 0$ Subtracting 54

$(n - 9)(n + 6) = 0$ Factoring

$n - 9 = 0$ *or* $n + 6 = 0$

$n = 9$ *or* $n = -6$.

4. **Check.** Since the number of sides cannot be negative, -6 cannot be a solution. We leave it to the student to show by substitution that 9 checks.

5. **State.** The polygon has 9 sides (it is a nonagon).

o Exercise 13 on the following page.

Study Tips

READ FOR SUCCESS

In his article "The Daily Dozen Disciplines for Massive Success in 2001 & Beyond," Jerry Clark comments, "Research has shown that 58% of high school graduates never read another book from cover to cover the rest of their adult lives, that 78% of the population have not been in a bookstore in the last 5 years, and that 97% of the population of the U.S. do not have library cards." Clark then suggests spending at least 15 minutes each day reading an empowering and uplifting book or article. The following books are some suggestions from your author. Their motivating words may empower you in your study of mathematics.

1. *Fish*, by Stephen C. Lundin, Harry Paul, and John Christensen (Hyperion). This was a Wall Street Journal Business Bestseller. Though it has a strange title, it discusses a remarkable way to boost morale and improve results.
2. *True Success: A New Philosophy of Excellence*, by Tom Morris (Grosset/Putnam). Morris was a well-loved philosophy professor at Notre Dame. Students, especially athletes, flocked to his classes.
3. *The Road Less Traveled, Abounding Grace*, by M. Scott Peck. Noted psychiatrist and author of many excellent books, Peck has amazing insights and wisdom about life.
4. *The Weight of Glory, The Great Divorce*, by C. S. Lewis. British author and scholar, noted for his philosophical exposition, Lewis also wrote science-fiction fantasies with moral overtones.

"Far worse than not reading books is not realizing that it matters!"

Jim Rohn, motivational speaker

13. Consider the following heptagon, that is, a polygon with 7 sides.

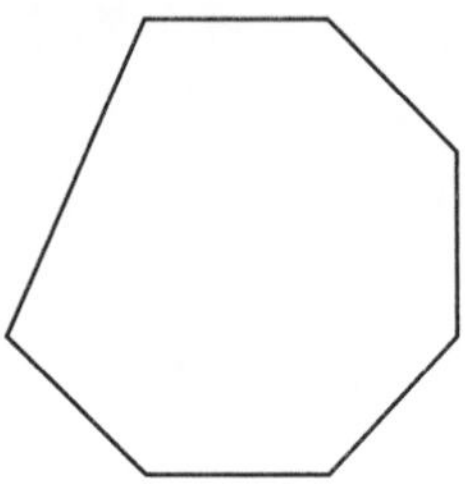

a) Draw all the diagonals and then count them.

b) Use the formula

$$d = \frac{n^2 - 3n}{2}$$

to check your answer to part (a) by evaluating the formula for $n = 7$.

c) A polygon has 44 diagonals. How many sides does it have?

Answers on page A-40

CALCULATOR CORNER

Solving Quadratic Equations A quadratic equation written with 0 on one side of the equals sign can be solved using the ZERO feature of a graphing calculator. (See the Calculator Corner on p. 449 for the procedure.)

We can also use the INTERSECT feature to solve a quadratic equation. Consider the equation in Margin Exercise 11,

$$(x - 1)(x + 1) = 5(x - 1).$$

First, we enter $y_1 = (x - 1)(x + 1)$ and $y_2 = 5(x - 1)$ on the equation-editor screen and graph the equations, using the window $[-5, 5, -5, 20]$, Yscl = 2. We see that there are two points of intersection, so the equation has two solutions.

Next, we use the INTERSECT feature to find the coordinates of the lefthand point of intersection. (See the Calculator Corner on p. 564 for the procedure.) The first coordinate of this point, 1, is one solution of the equation. We use the INTERSECT feature again to find the other solution, 4.

$y_1 = (x - 1)(x + 1), y_2 = 5(x - 1)$

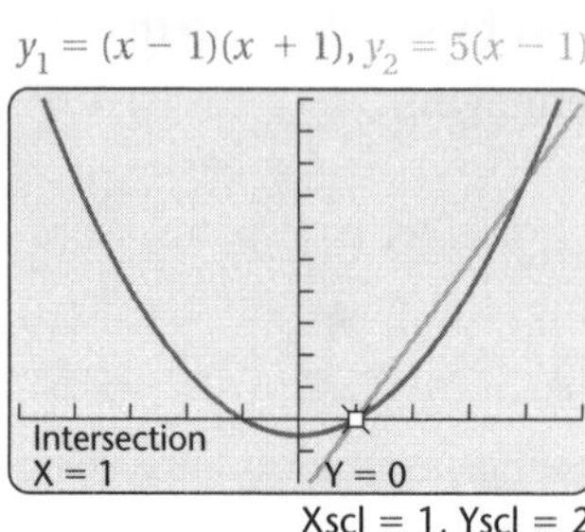

Xscl = 1, Yscl = 2

$y_1 = (x - 1)(x + 1), y_2 = 5(x - 1)$

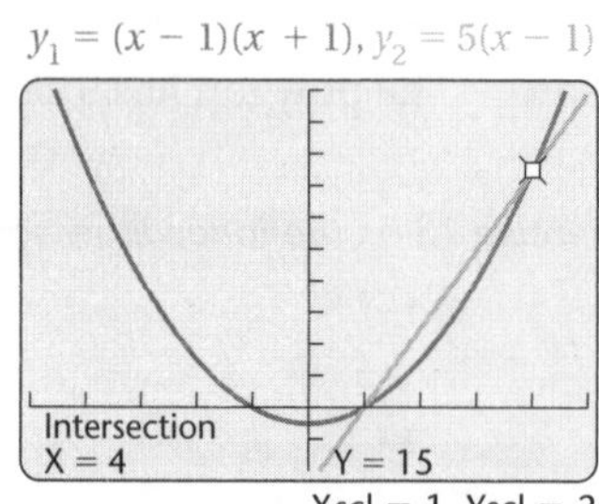

Xscl = 1, Yscl = 2

Note that we could use the ZERO feature to solve this equation if we first write it with 0 on one side, that is, $(x - 1)(x + 1) - 5(x - 1) = 0$.

Exercises: Solve.

1. $5x^2 - 8x + 3 = 0$
2. $2x^2 - 7x - 15 = 0$
3. $6(x - 3) = (x - 3)(x - 2)$
4. $(x + 1)(x - 4) = 3(x - 4)$

9.1 EXERCISE SET

For Extra Help

MathXL | MyMathLab | InterAct Math | Math Tutor Center | Digital Video Tutor CD 5 Videotape 10 | Student's Solutions Manual

a Write in standard form and determine a, b, and c.

1. $x^2 - 3x + 2 = 0$

2. $x^2 - 8x - 5 = 0$

3. $7x^2 = 4x - 3$

4. $9x^2 = x + 5$

5. $5 = -2x^2 + 3x$

6. $3x - 1 = 5x^2 + 9$

b Solve.

7. $x^2 + 5x = 0$

8. $x^2 + 7x = 0$

9. $3x^2 + 6x = 0$

10. $4x^2 + 8x = 0$

1. $5x^2 = 2x$

12. $11x = 3x^2$

13. $4x^2 + 4x = 0$

14. $8x^2 - 8x = 0$

5. $0 = 10x^2 - 30x$

16. $0 = 10x^2 - 50x$

17. $11x = 55x^2$

18. $33x^2 = -11x$

9. $14t^2 = 3t$

20. $6m = 19m^2$

1. $5y^2 - 3y^2 = 72y + 9y$

22. $63p - 16p^2 = 17p + 58p^2$

c Solve.

3. $x^2 + 8x - 48 = 0$

24. $x^2 - 16x + 48 = 0$

25. $5 + 6x + x^2 = 0$

26. $x^2 + 10 + 11x = 0$

7. $18 = 7p + p^2$

28. $t^2 + 14t = -24$

29. $-15 = -8y + y^2$

30. $q^2 + 14 = 9q$

1. $x^2 + 10x + 25 = 0$

32. $x^2 + 6x + 9 = 0$

33. $r^2 = 8r - 16$

34. $x^2 + 1 = 2x$

5. $6x^2 + x - 2 = 0$

36. $2x^2 - 11x + 15 = 0$

37. $3a^2 = 10a + 8$

38. $15b - 9b^2 = 4$

9. $6x^2 - 4x = 10$

40. $3x^2 - 7x = 20$

41. $2t^2 + 12t = -10$

42. $12w^2 - 5w = 2$

3. $t(t - 5) = 14$

44. $6z^2 + z - 1 = 0$

45. $t(9 + t) = 4(2t + 5)$

46. $3y^2 + 8y = 12y + 15$

7. $16(p - 1) = p(p + 8)$

48. $(2x - 3)(x + 1) = 4(2x - 3)$

9. $(t - 1)(t + 3) = t - 1$

50. $(x - 2)(x + 2) = x + 2$

Solve.

51. $\frac{24}{x-2} + \frac{24}{x+2} = 5$

52. $\frac{8}{x+2} + \frac{8}{x-2} = 3$

53. $\frac{1}{x} + \frac{1}{x+6} = \frac{1}{4}$

54. $\frac{1}{x} + \frac{1}{x+9} = \frac{1}{20}$

55. $1 + \frac{12}{x^2-4} = \frac{3}{x-2}$

56. $\frac{5}{t-3} - \frac{30}{t^2-9} = 1$

57. $\frac{r}{r-1} + \frac{2}{r^2-1} = \frac{8}{r+1}$

58. $\frac{x+2}{x^2-2} = \frac{2}{3-x}$

59. $\frac{x-1}{1-x} = -\frac{x+8}{x-8}$

60. $\frac{4-x}{x-4} + \frac{x+3}{x-3} = 0$

61. $\frac{5}{y+4} - \frac{3}{y-2} = 4$

62. $\frac{2z+11}{2z+8} = \frac{3z-1}{z-1}$

d Solve.

63. *Diagonals.* A decagon is a figure with 10 sides. How many diagonals does a decagon have?

64. *Diagonals.* A hexagon is a figure with 6 sides. How many diagonals does a hexagon have?

65. *Diagonals.* A polygon has 14 diagonals. How many sides does it have?

66. *Diagonals.* A polygon has 9 diagonals. How many sides does it have?

67. $^{\mathrm{D}}\mathrm{W}$ Explain how the graph of $y = (x - 2)(x + 3)$ is related to the solutions of the equation $(x - 2)(x + 3) = 0$.

68. $^{\mathrm{D}}\mathrm{W}$ Explain how you might go about constructing a quadratic equation whose solutions are -5 and 7.

SKILL MAINTENANCE

Simplify. [8.1a], [8.2a]

69. $\sqrt{64}$

70. $-\sqrt{169}$

71. $\sqrt{8}$

72. $\sqrt{12}$

73. $\sqrt{20}$

74. $\sqrt{88}$

75. $\sqrt{405}$

76. $\sqrt{1020}$

Use a calculator to approximate the square roots. Round to three decimal places. [8.1b]

77. $\sqrt{7}$

78. $\sqrt{23}$

79. $\sqrt{\frac{7}{3}}$

80. $\sqrt{524.77}$

SYNTHESIS

Solve.

81. $4m^2 - (m + 1)^2 = 0$

82. $x^2 + \sqrt{22}x = 0$

83. $\sqrt{5}x^2 - x = 0$

84. $\sqrt{7}x^2 + \sqrt{3}x = 0$

Use a graphing calculator to solve the equation.

85. $3x^2 - 7x = 20$

86. $x(x - 5) = 14$

87. $3x^2 + 8x = 12x + 15$

88. $(x - 2)(x + 2) = x + 2$

89. $(x - 2)^2 + 3(x - 2) = 4$

90. $(x + 3)^2 = 4$

91. $16(x - 1) = x(x + 8)$

92. $x^2 + 2.5x + 1.5625 = 9.61$

9.3 THE QUADRATIC FORMULA

Objectives

a Solve quadratic equations using the quadratic formula.

b Find approximate solutions of quadratic equations using a calculator.

We learn to complete the square to prove a general formula that can be used to solve quadratic equations even when they cannot be solved by factoring.

a Solving Using the Quadratic Formula

Each time you solve by completing the square, you perform nearly the same steps. When we repeat the same kind of computation many times, we look for a formula so we can speed up our work. Consider

$$ax^2 + bx + c = 0, \quad a > 0.$$

Let's solve by completing the square. As we carry out the steps, compare them with Example 10 in the preceding section.

$$x^2 + \frac{b}{a}x + \frac{c}{a} = 0 \qquad \text{Multiplying by } \frac{1}{a}$$

$$x^2 + \frac{b}{a}x = -\frac{c}{a} \qquad \text{Adding } -\frac{c}{a}$$

Half of $\frac{b}{a}$ is $\frac{b}{2a}$. The square is $\frac{b^2}{4a^2}$. Thus we add $\frac{b^2}{4a^2}$ on both sides.

$$x^2 + \frac{b}{a}x + \frac{b^2}{4a^2} = -\frac{c}{a} + \frac{b^2}{4a^2} \qquad \text{Adding } \frac{b^2}{4a^2}$$

$$\left(x + \frac{b}{2a}\right)^2 = -\frac{4ac}{4a^2} + \frac{b^2}{4a^2} \qquad \text{Factoring the left side and finding a common denominator on the right}$$

$$\left(x + \frac{b}{2a}\right)^2 = \frac{b^2 - 4ac}{4a^2}$$

$$x + \frac{b}{2a} = \sqrt{\frac{b^2 - 4ac}{4a^2}} \quad or \quad x + \frac{b}{2a} = -\sqrt{\frac{b^2 - 4ac}{4a^2}} \qquad \text{Using the principle of square roots}$$

Since $a > 0$, $\sqrt{4a^2} = 2a$, so we can simplify as follows:

$$x + \frac{b}{2a} = \frac{\sqrt{b^2 - 4ac}}{2a} \quad or \quad x + \frac{b}{2a} = -\frac{\sqrt{b^2 - 4ac}}{2a}.$$

Thus,

$$x = -\frac{b}{2a} + \frac{\sqrt{b^2 - 4ac}}{2a} \quad or \quad x = -\frac{b}{2a} - \frac{\sqrt{b^2 - 4ac}}{2a},$$

so $$x = -\frac{b}{2a} \pm \frac{\sqrt{b^2 - 4ac}}{2a},$$

or $$x = \frac{-b \pm \sqrt{b^2 - 4ac}}{2a}.$$

We now have the following.

THE QUADRATIC FORMULA

The solutions of $ax^2 + bx + c = 0$ are given by

$$x = \frac{-b \pm \sqrt{b^2 - 4ac}}{2a}.$$

The formula also holds when $a < 0$. A similar proof would show this, but e will not consider it here.

XAMPLE 1 Solve $5x^2 - 8x = -3$ using the quadratic formula.

We first find standard form and determine a, b, and c:

$$5x^2 - 8x + 3 = 0;$$
$$a = 5, \quad b = -8, \quad c = 3.$$

Ve then use the quadratic formula:

$$x = \frac{-b \pm \sqrt{b^2 - 4ac}}{2a}$$

$$x = \frac{-(-8) \pm \sqrt{(-8)^2 - 4 \cdot 5 \cdot 3}}{2 \cdot 5} \quad \text{Substituting}$$

Caution!

Be sure to write the fraction bar all the way across.

$$x = \frac{8 \pm \sqrt{64 - 60}}{10}$$

$$x = \frac{8 \pm \sqrt{4}}{10}$$

$$x = \frac{8 \pm 2}{10}$$

$$x = \frac{8 + 2}{10} \quad or \quad x = \frac{8 - 2}{10}$$

$$x = \frac{10}{10} \quad or \quad x = \frac{6}{10}$$

$$x = 1 \quad or \quad x = \frac{3}{5}.$$

he solutions are 1 and $\frac{3}{5}$.

o Exercise 1.

It would have been easier to solve the equation in Example 1 by factoring. Ve used the quadratic formula only to illustrate that it can be used to solve ny quadratic equation. The following is a general procedure for solving a uadratic equation.

SOLVING QUADRATIC EQUATIONS

To solve a quadratic equation:

1. Check to see if it is in the form $ax^2 = p$ or $(x + c)^2 = d$. If it is, use the principle of square roots as in Section 9.2.
2. If it is not in the form of (1), write it in standard form, $ax^2 + bx + c = 0$ with a and b nonzero.
3. Then try factoring.
4. If it is not possible to factor or if factoring seems difficult, use the quadratic formula.

The solutions of a quadratic equation can always be found using the quadratic formula. They cannot always be found by factoring. (When the radicand $b^2 - 4ac \geq 0$, the equation has real-number solutions. When $b^2 - 4ac < 0$, the equation has no real-number solutions.)

1. Solve using the quadratic formula:

$$2x^2 = 4 - 7x.$$

Answer on page A-40

AG ***ALGEBRAIC–GRAPHICAL CONNECTION***

Let's visualize the solutions in Example 2.

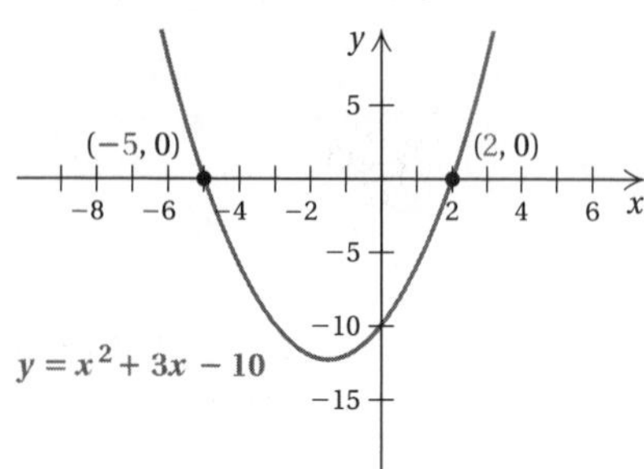

We see that the solutions of $x^2 + 3x - 10 = 0$, -5 and 2, are the first coordinates of the x-intercepts, $(-5, 0)$ and $(2, 0)$, of the graph of $y = x^2 + 3x - 10$.

EXAMPLE 2 Solve $x^2 + 3x - 10 = 0$ using the quadratic formula.

The equation is in standard form. So we determine a, b, and c:

$$x^2 + 3x - 10 = 0;$$
$$a = 1, \quad b = 3, \quad c = -10.$$

We then use the quadratic formula:

$$x = \frac{-b \pm \sqrt{b^2 - 4ac}}{2a}$$
$$= \frac{-3 \pm \sqrt{3^2 - 4 \cdot 1 \cdot (-10)}}{2 \cdot 1} \qquad \text{Substituting}$$
$$= \frac{-3 \pm \sqrt{9 + 40}}{2}$$
$$= \frac{-3 \pm \sqrt{49}}{2} = \frac{-3 \pm 7}{2}.$$

Thus,

$$x = \frac{-3 + 7}{2} = \frac{4}{2} = 2 \quad or \quad x = \frac{-3 - 7}{2} = \frac{-10}{2} = -5.$$

The solutions are 2 and -5.

Note that the radicand $(b^2 - 4ac = 49)$ in the quadratic formula is a perfect square, so we could have used factoring to solve.

Do Exercise 2.

2. Solve using the quadratic formula:

$$x^2 - 3x - 10 = 0.$$

EXAMPLE 3 Solve $x^2 = 4x + 7$ using the quadratic formula. Compare using the quadratic formula here with completing the square as we did in Example 8 of Section 9.2.

We first find standard form and determine a, b, and c:

$$x^2 - 4x - 7 = 0;$$
$$a = 1, \quad b = -4, \quad c = -7.$$

We then use the quadratic formula:

$$x = \frac{-b \pm \sqrt{b^2 - 4ac}}{2a} = \frac{-(-4) \pm \sqrt{(-4)^2 - 4 \cdot 1 \cdot (-7)}}{2 \cdot 1} \qquad \text{Substituting}$$
$$= \frac{4 \pm \sqrt{16 + 28}}{2} = \frac{4 \pm \sqrt{44}}{2}$$
$$= \frac{4 \pm \sqrt{4 \cdot 11}}{2} = \frac{4 \pm \sqrt{4}\sqrt{11}}{2}$$
$$= \frac{4 \pm 2\sqrt{11}}{2} = \frac{2 \cdot 2 \pm 2\sqrt{11}}{2 \cdot 1}$$
$$= \frac{2(2 \pm \sqrt{11})}{2 \cdot 1} = \frac{2}{2} \cdot \frac{2 \pm \sqrt{11}}{1} \qquad \text{Factoring out 2 in the numerator and the denominator}$$
$$= 2 \pm \sqrt{11}.$$

The solutions are $2 + \sqrt{11}$ and $2 - \sqrt{11}$, or $2 \pm \sqrt{11}$.

Do Exercise 3.

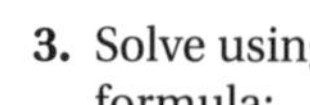

3. Solve using the quadratic formula:

$$x^2 + 4x = 7.$$

4. Solve using the quadratic formula:

$$x^2 = x - 1.$$

Answers on page A-40

XAMPLE 4 Solve $x^2 + x = -1$ using the quadratic formula.

We first find standard form and determine a, b, and c:

$$x^2 + x + 1 = 0;$$
$$a = 1, \quad b = 1, \quad c = 1.$$

/e then use the quadratic formula:

$$x = \frac{-b \pm \sqrt{b^2 - 4ac}}{2a} = \frac{-1 \pm \sqrt{1^2 - 4 \cdot 1 \cdot 1}}{2 \cdot 1} = \frac{-1 \pm \sqrt{-3}}{2}.$$

'ote that the radicand ($b^2 - 4ac = -3$) in the quadratic formula is negative. hus there are no real-number solutions because square roots of negative umbers do not exist as real numbers.

o Exercise 4 on the preceding page.

XAMPLE 5 Solve $3x^2 = 7 - 2x$ using the quadratic formula.

We first find standard form and determine a, b, and c:

$$3x^2 + 2x - 7 = 0;$$
$$a = 3, \quad b = 2, \quad c = -7.$$

/e then use the quadratic formula:

$$= \frac{-b \pm \sqrt{b^2 - 4ac}}{2a} = \frac{-2 \pm \sqrt{2^2 - 4 \cdot 3 \cdot (-7)}}{2 \cdot 3} = \frac{-2 \pm \sqrt{4 + 84}}{2 \cdot 3}$$
$$= \frac{-2 \pm \sqrt{88}}{6} = \frac{-2 \pm \sqrt{4 \cdot 22}}{6} = \frac{-2 \pm \sqrt{4}\sqrt{22}}{6} = \frac{-2 \pm 2\sqrt{22}}{6}$$
$$= \frac{2(-1 \pm \sqrt{22})}{2 \cdot 3} = \frac{2}{2} \cdot \frac{-1 \pm \sqrt{22}}{3} = \frac{-1 \pm \sqrt{22}}{3}.$$

he solutions are $\frac{-1 + \sqrt{22}}{3}$ and $\frac{-1 - \sqrt{22}}{3}$, or $\frac{-1 \pm \sqrt{22}}{3}$.

o Exercise 5.

b Approximate Solutions

. calculator can be used to approximate solutions.

XAMPLE 6 Use a calculator to approximate to the nearest tenth the solu- ons to the equation in Example 5.

Using a calculator, we have

$$\frac{-1 + \sqrt{22}}{3} \approx 1.230138587 \approx 1.2 \text{ to the nearest tenth, and}$$
$$\frac{-1 - \sqrt{22}}{3} \approx -1.896805253 \approx -1.9 \text{ to the nearest tenth.}$$

he approximate solutions are 1.2 and -1.9.

o Exercise 6 on the following page.

5. Solve using the quadratic formula:

$$5x^2 - 8x = 3.$$

Answer on page A-40

CALCULATOR CORNER

Visualizing Solutions of Quadratic Equations

To see that there are no real-number solutions of the equation in Example 4,

$$x^2 + x = -1,$$

we graph $y_1 = x^2 + x$ and $y_2 = -1$.

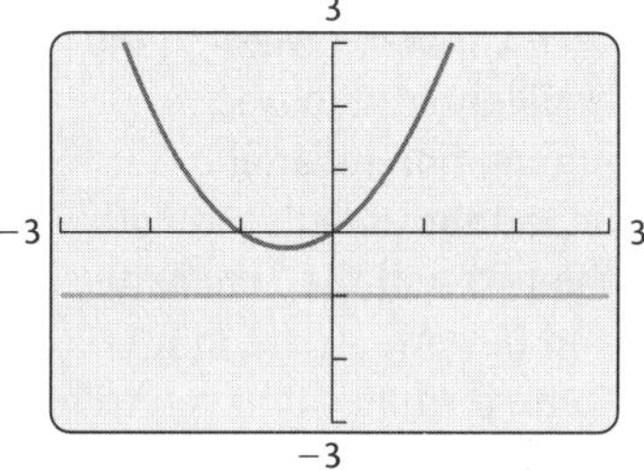

We see that the graphs do not intersect. Thus there is no real number for which $y_1 = y_2$, or $x^2 + x = -1$.

Exercises:

1. Explain how the graph of $y = x^2 + x + 1$ shows that the equation in Example 4, $x^2 + x = -1$, has no real-number solutions.
2. Use a graph to determine whether the equation $x^2 + x = 1$ has real-number solutions.
3. Use a graph to determine whether the equation $x^2 = x - 1$ has real-number solutions.

6. Approximate the solutions to the equation in Margin Exercise 5. Round to the nearest tenth.

Answer on page A-40

Study Tips

BEGINNING TO STUDY FOR THE FINAL EXAM (PART 4): ONE OR TWO DAYS OF STUDY TIME

1. **Begin by browsing through each chapter, reviewing the highlighted or boxed information regarding important formulas in both the text and the Summary and Review.** There may be some formulas that you will need to memorize.
2. **Take the Final Examination in the text during the last couple of days before the final.** Set aside the same amount of time that you will have for the final. See how much of the final exam you can complete under test-like conditions. Be careful to avoid any questions corresponding to objectives not covered. Restudy the objectives in the text that correspond to each question you missed.
3. **Attend a final-exam review session if one is available.**

"Great is the art of beginning, but greater is the art of ending."

Henry Wadsworth Longfellow, nineteenth-century American poet

CALCULATOR CORNER

Approximating Solutions of Quadratic Equations In Example 5, we found that the solutions of the equation $3x^2 = 7 - 2x$ are $\frac{-1 + \sqrt{22}}{3}$ and $\frac{-1 - \sqrt{22}}{3}$. We can use a graphing calculator to approximate these solutions. To approximate $\frac{-1 + \sqrt{22}}{3}$, we press

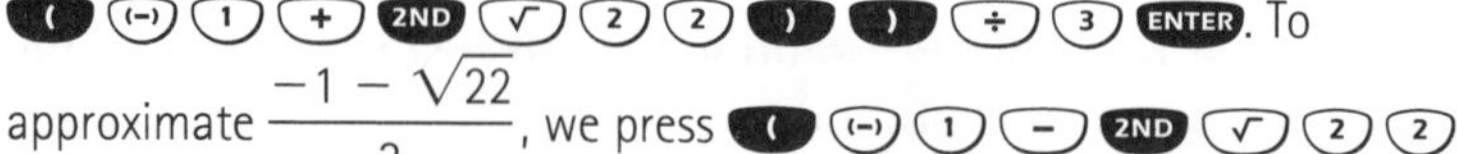

. To approximate $\frac{-1 - \sqrt{22}}{3}$, we press ((-) 1 − 2ND √ 2 2)) ÷ 3 ENTER. We see that the solutions are approximately 1.2 and −1.9.

```
(-1+√(22))/3
                 1.230138587
(-1-√(22))/3
                -1.896805253
```

Exercises: Use a graphing calculator to approximate the solutions to each of the following to the nearest tenth.

1. Example 3
2. Margin Exercise 3
3. Margin Exercise 5

COMPARING METHODS OF SOLVING QUADRATIC EQUATIONS

In Sections 9.1–9.3, we have studied three different methods of solving quadratic equations. Each of these methods has advantages and disadvantages, as outlined in the table below. Note that although the quadratic formula can be used to solve *any* quadratic equation, the other methods are sometimes faster and easier to use.

METHOD	ADVANTAGES	DISADVANTAGES
The quadratic formula	Can be used to solve *any* quadratic equation.	Can be slower than factoring or the principle of square roots.
The principle of square roots	Fastest way to solve equations of the form $ax^2 = p$, or $(x + k)^2 = p$. Can be used to solve *any* quadratic equation.	Can be slow when completing the square is required.
Factoring	Can be very fast.	Can be used only on certain equations. Many equations are difficult or impossible to solve by factoring.

9.3 EXERCISE SET

For Extra Help

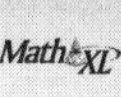
MathXL

MyMathLab

InterAct Math

Math Tutor Center

Digital Video Tutor CD 5 Videotape 10

Student's Solutions Manual

a Solve. Try factoring first. If factoring is not possible or is difficult, use the quadratic formula.

1. $x^2 - 4x = 21$

2. $x^2 + 8x = 9$

3. $x^2 = 6x - 9$

4. $x^2 = 24x - 144$

5. $3y^2 - 2y - 8 = 0$

6. $3y^2 - 7y + 4 = 0$

7. $4x^2 + 4x = 15$

8. $4x^2 + 12x = 7$

9. $x^2 - 9 = 0$

10. $x^2 - 16 = 0$

11. $x^2 - 2x - 2 = 0$

12. $x^2 - 2x - 11 = 0$

13. $y^2 - 10y + 22 = 0$

14. $y^2 + 6y - 1 = 0$

15. $x^2 + 4x + 4 = 7$

16. $x^2 - 2x + 1 = 5$

17. $3x^2 + 8x + 2 = 0$

18. $3x^2 - 4x - 2 = 0$

19. $2x^2 - 5x = 1$

20. $4x^2 + 4x = 5$

21. $2y^2 - 2y - 1 = 0$

22. $4y^2 + 4y - 1 = 0$

23. $2t^2 + 6t + 5 = 0$

24. $4y^2 + 3y + 2 = 0$

25. $3x^2 = 5x + 4$

26. $2x^2 + 3x = 1$

27. $2y^2 - 6y = 10$

28. $5m^2 = 3 + 11m$

29. $\frac{x^2}{x+3} - \frac{5}{x+3} = 0$

30. $\frac{x^2}{x-4} - \frac{7}{x-4} = 0$

31. $x + 2 = \frac{3}{x+2}$

32. $x - 3 = \frac{5}{x-3}$

33. $\frac{1}{x} + \frac{1}{x+1} = \frac{1}{3}$

34. $\frac{1}{x} + \frac{1}{x+6} = \frac{1}{5}$

b Solve using the quadratic formula. Use a calculator to approximate the solutions to the nearest tenth.

35. $x^2 - 4x - 7 = 0$

36. $x^2 + 2x - 2 = 0$

37. $y^2 - 6y - 1 = 0$

38. $y^2 + 10y + 22 = 0$

39. $4x^2 + 4x = 1$

40. $4x^2 = 4x + 1$

41. $3x^2 - 8x + 2 = 0$

42. $3x^2 + 4x - 2 = 0$

43. DW Write a quadratic equation in the form $y = ax^2 + bx + c$ that does not cross the x-axis.

44. DW Under what condition(s) would using the quadratic formula *not* be the easiest way to solve a quadratic equation?

SKILL MAINTENANCE

Add or subtract. [8.4a]

45. $\sqrt{40} - 2\sqrt{10} + \sqrt{90}$

46. $\sqrt{54} - \sqrt{24}$

47. $\sqrt{18} + \sqrt{50} - 3\sqrt{8}$

48. $\sqrt{81x^3} - \sqrt{4x}$

49. Simplify: $\sqrt{80}$. [8.2a]

50. Multiply and simplify: $\sqrt{3x^2}\sqrt{9x^3}$. [8.2c]

51. Simplify: $\sqrt{9000x^{10}}$. [8.2b]

52. Rationalize the denominator: $\sqrt{\frac{7}{3}}$. [8.3c]

53. Find an equation of variation in which y varies inversely as x, and $y = 235$ when $x = 0.6$. [6.9c]

54. The time T to do a certain job varies inversely as the number N of people working. It takes 5 hr for 24 people to wash and wax the floors in a building. How long would it take 36 people to do the job? [6.9d]

SYNTHESIS

Solve.

55. $5x + x(x - 7) = 0$

56. $x(3x + 7) - 3x = 0$

57. $3 - x(x - 3) = 4$

58. $x(5x - 7) = 1$

59. $(y + 4)(y + 3) = 15$

60. $(y + 5)(y - 1) = 27$

61. $x^2 + (x + 2)^2 = 7$

62. $x^2 + (x + 1)^2 = 5$

63.–70. Use a graphing calculator to approximate the solutions of the equations in Exercises 35–42. Compare your answers with those found using the quadratic formula.

EXERCISE SET

For Extra Help

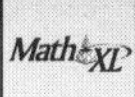

MathXL | MyMathLab | InterAct Math | Math Tutor Center | Digital Video Tutor CD 5 Videotape 10 | Student's Solutions Manual

a Solve.

1. *HDTV Dimensions.* A high-definition television (HDTV) features a larger screen and greater clarity than a standard television. An HDTV might have a 70-in. diagonal screen with the width 27 in. greater than the height. Find the width and the height of a 70-in. HDTV screen.

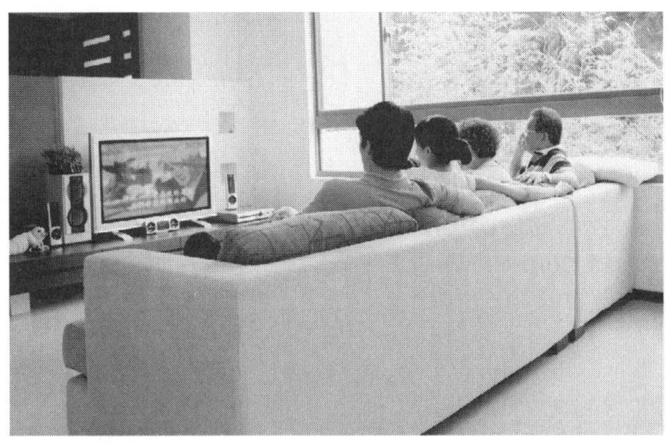

2. The length of a rectangular pine forest is 2 mi greater than the width. The area is 80 mi^2. Find the length and the width.

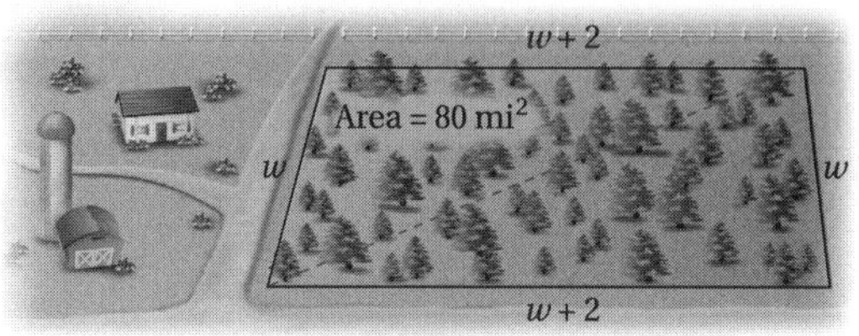

3. The length of a rectangular area rug is 3 ft greater than the width. The area is 70 ft^2. Find the length and the width.

4. *HDTV Dimensions.* When we say that a television is 42 in., we mean that the diagonal is 42 in. For a 42-in. television, the width is 15 in. more than the height. Find the dimensions of a 42-in. high-definition television.

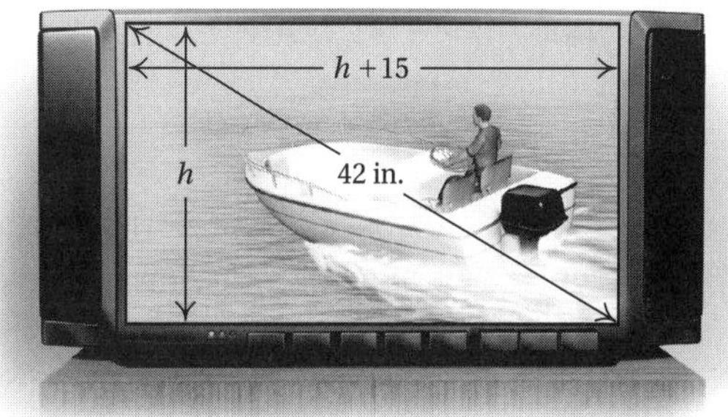

5. *Carpenter's Square.* A *square* is a carpenter's tool in the shape of a right triangle. One side, or leg, of a square is 8 in. longer than the other. The length of the hypotenuse is $8\sqrt{13}$ in. Find the lengths of the legs of the square.

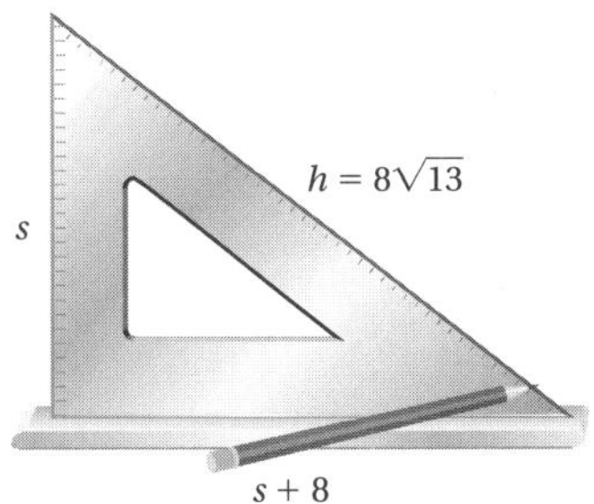

6. *Rectangle Dimensions.* The length of a rectangular lobby in a hotel is twice the width. The area is 50 m^2. Find the length and the width.

7. *Rectangle Dimensions.* The width of a rectangle is 4 cm less than the length. The area is 320 cm^2. Find the length and the width.

8. *Rectangle Dimensions.* The width of a rectangle is 3 cm less than the length. The area is 340 cm^2. Find the length and the width.

Find the approximate answers for Exercises 9–14. Round to the nearest tenth.

9. *Right-Triangle Dimensions.* The hypotenuse of a right triangle is 8 m long. One leg is 2 m longer than the other. Find the lengths of the legs.

10. *Right-Triangle Dimensions.* The hypotenuse of a right triangle is 5 cm long. One leg is 2 cm longer than the other. Find the lengths of the legs.

11. *Rectangle Dimensions.* The length of a rectangle is 2 in. greater than the width. The area is 20 in^2. Find the length and the width.

12. *Rectangle Dimensions.* The length of a rectangle is 3 ft greater than the width. The area is 15 ft^2. Find the length and the width.

13. *Rectangle Dimensions.* The length of a rectangle is twice the width. The area is 20 cm^2. Find the length and the width.

14. *Rectangle Dimensions.* The length of a rectangle is twice the width. The area is 10 m^2. Find the length and the width.

15. *Picture Frame.* A picture frame measures 25 cm by 20 cm. There is 266 cm^2 of picture showing. The frame is of uniform thickness. Find the thickness of the frame.

16. *Tablecloth.* A rectangular tablecloth measures 96 in. by 72 in. It is laid on a tabletop with an area of 5040 in^2, and hangs over the edge by the same amount on all sides. By how many inches does the cloth hang over the edge?

or Exercises 17–24, complete the table to help with the familiarization.

7. *Boat Speed.* The current in a stream moves at a speed of 3 km/h. A boat travels 40 km upstream and 40 km downstream in a total time of 14 hr. What is the speed of the boat in still water? Complete the following table to help with the familiarization.

	d	r	t
Upstream		$r - 3$	t_1
Downstream	40		t_2
Total Time			

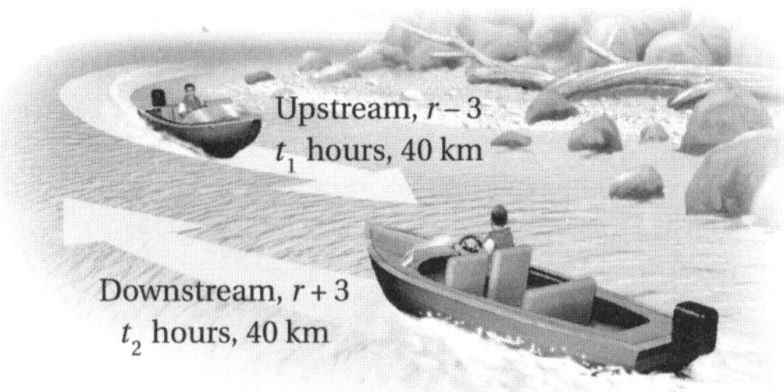

18. *Wind Speed.* An airplane flies 1449 mi against the wind and 1539 mi with the wind in a total time of 5 hr. The speed of the airplane in still air is 600 mph. What is the speed of the wind?

	d	r	t
With Wind	1539		
Against Wind		$600 - r$	
Total Time			5

9. *Wind Speed.* An airplane flies 520 km against the wind and 680 km with the wind in a total time of 4 hr. The speed of the airplane in still air is 300 km/h. What is the speed of the wind?

	d	r	t
With Wind		$300 + r$	
Against Wind	520		
Total Time			4

20. *Boat Speed.* The current in a stream moves at a speed of 4 mph. A boat travels 5 mi upstream and 13 mi downstream in a total time of 2 hr. What is the speed of the boat in still water?

	d	r	t
Upstream		$r - 4$	t_1
Downstream	13		t_2
Total Time			

1. *Speed of a Stream.* The speed of a boat in still water is 10 km/h. The boat travels 12 km upstream and 28 km downstream in a total time of 4 hr. What is the speed of the stream?

	d	r	t
Upstream			
Downstream			
Total Time			

22. *Speed of a Stream.* The speed of a boat in still water is 8 km/h. The boat travels 60 km upstream and 60 km downstream in a total time of 16 hr. What is the speed of the stream?

	d	r	t
Upstream			
Downstream			
Total Time			

23. *Boat Speed.* The current in a stream moves at a speed of 4 mph. A boat travels 4 mi upstream and 12 mi downstream in a total time of 2 hr. What is the speed of the boat in still water?

	d	r	t
Upstream			
Downstream			
Total Time			

24. *Boat Speed.* The current in a stream moves at a speed of 3 mph. A boat travels 45 mi upstream and 45 mi downstream in a total time of 8 hr. What is the speed of the boat in still water?

	d	r	t
Upstream			
Downstream			
Total Time			

25. *Speed of a Stream.* The speed of a boat in still water is 9 km/h. The boat travels 80 km upstream and 80 km downstream in a total time of 18 hr. What is the speed of the stream?

26. *Speed of a Stream.* The speed of a boat in still water is 10 km/h. The boat travels 48 km upstream and 48 km downstream in a total time of 10 hr. What is the speed of the stream?

DW Find and explain the error(s) in each of the following solutions of a quadratic equation.

27. $(x + 6)^2 = 16$
$x + 6 = \sqrt{16}$
$x + 6 = 4$
$x = -2$

28. $x^2 + 2x - 8 = 0$
$(x + 4)(x - 2) = 0$
$x = 4$ *or* $x = -2$

SKILL MAINTENANCE

Add or subtract. [8.4a]

29. $5\sqrt{2} + \sqrt{18}$

30. $7\sqrt{40} - 2\sqrt{10}$

31. $\sqrt{4x^3} - 7\sqrt{x}$

32. $\sqrt{24} - \sqrt{54}$

33. $\sqrt{2} + \sqrt{\frac{1}{2}}$

34. $\sqrt{3} - \sqrt{\frac{1}{3}}$

35. $\sqrt{24} + \sqrt{54} - \sqrt{48}$

36. $\sqrt{4x} + \sqrt{81x^3}$

SYNTHESIS

37. *Pizza.* What should the diameter d of a pizza be so that it has the same area as two 12-in. pizzas? Do you get more to eat with a 16-in. pizza or with two 12-in. pizzas?

38. *Golden Rectangle.* The so-called *golden rectangle* is said to be extremely pleasing visually and was used often by ancient Greek and Roman architects. The length of a golden rectangle is approximately 1.6 times the width. Find the dimensions of a golden rectangle if its area is 9000 m^2.

9.6 GRAPHS OF QUADRATIC EQUATIONS

Objectives

a Graph quadratic equations.

b Find the x-intercepts of a quadratic equation.

n this section, we will graph equations of the form

$$y = ax^2 + bx + c, \quad a \neq 0.$$

'he polynomial on the right side of the equation is of second degree, or **uadratic.** Examples of the types of equations we are going to graph are

$$y = x^2, \qquad y = x^2 + 2x - 3, \qquad y = -2x^2 + 3.$$

a Graphing Quadratic Equations of the Type $y = ax^2 + bx + c$

ɜraphs of quadratic equations of the type $y = ax^2 + bx + c$ (where $a \neq 0$) are lways cup-shaped. They have a **line of symmetry** like the dashed lines hown in the figures below. If we fold on this line, the two halves will match xactly. The curve goes on forever. 'he top or bottom point where the urve changes is called the **vertex.** 'he second coordinate is either the mallest value of y or the largest 'alue of y. The vertex is also hought of as a turning point. ɜraphs of quadratic equations re called **parabolas.**

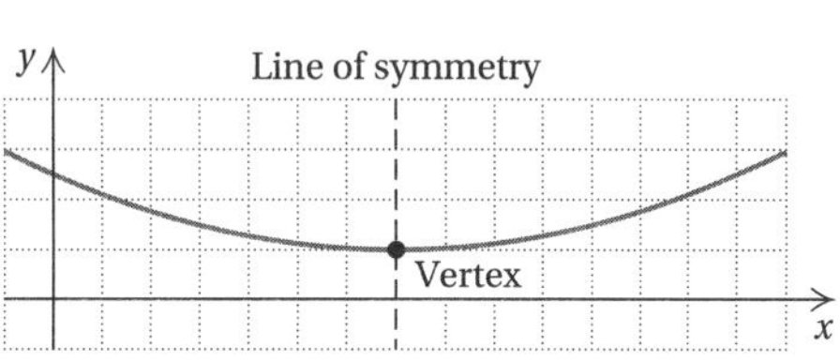

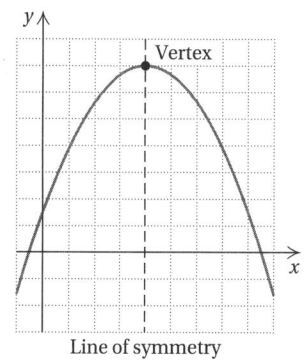

To graph a quadratic equation, we begin by choosing some numbers for and computing the corresponding values of y.

:XAMPLE 1 Graph: $y = x^2$.

We choose numbers for x and find the corresponding values for y. Then ve plot the ordered pairs (x, y) resulting from the computations and connect hem with a smooth curve.

For $x = -3$, $y = x^2 = (-3)^2 = 9$.
For $x = -2$, $y = x^2 = (-2)^2 = 4$.
For $x = -1$, $y = x^2 = (-1)^2 = 1$.
For $x = 0$, $y = x^2 = (0)^2 = 0$.
For $x = 1$, $y = x^2 = (1)^2 = 1$.
For $x = 2$, $y = x^2 = (2)^2 = 4$.
For $x = 3$, $y = x^2 = (3)^2 = 9$.

x	y	(x, y)
−3	9	(−3, 9)
−2	4	(−2, 4)
−1	1	(−1, 1)
0	0	(0, 0)
1	1	(1, 1)
2	4	(2, 4)
3	9	(3, 9)

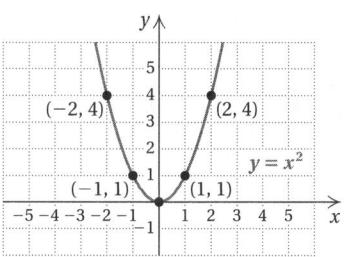

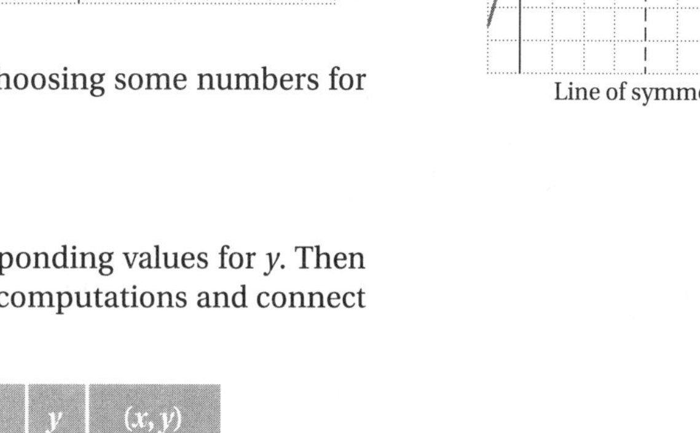

In Example 1, the vertex is the point $(0, 0)$. The second coordinate of the vertex, 0, is the smallest y-value. The y-axis ($x = 0$) is the line of symmetry. Parabolas whose equations are $y = ax^2$ always have the origin $(0, 0)$ as the vertex and the y-axis as the line of symmetry.

How do we graph a quadratic equation? There are many methods, some of which you will study in your next mathematics course. Our goal here is to give you a basic graphing technique that is fairly easy to apply. A key in the graphing is knowing the vertex. By graphing it and then choosing x-values on both sides of the vertex, we can compute more points and complete the graph.

FINDING THE VERTEX

For a parabola given by the quadratic equation $y = ax^2 + bx + c$:

1. The x-coordinate of the vertex is $-\dfrac{b}{2a}$.
   The line of symmetry is $x = -b/(2a)$.
2. The second coordinate of the vertex is found by substituting the x-coordinate into the equation and computing y.

The proof that the vertex can be found in this way can be shown by completing the square in a manner similar to the proof of the quadratic formula, but it will not be considered here.

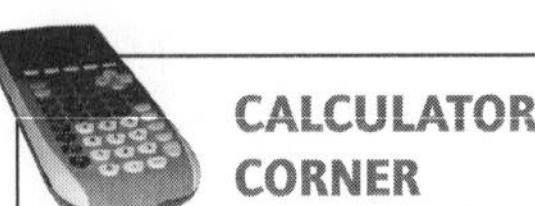

CALCULATOR CORNER

Graphing Quadratic Equations Use a graphing calculator to make a table of values for $y = x^2$. (See the Calculator Corner on p. 235 for the procedure.)

EXAMPLE 2 Graph: $y = -2x^2 + 3$.

We first find the vertex. The x-coordinate of the vertex is

$$-\frac{b}{2a} = -\frac{0}{2(-2)} = 0.$$

We substitute 0 for x into the equation to find the second coordinate of the vertex:

$$y = -2x^2 + 3 = -2(0)^2 + 3 = 3.$$

The vertex is $(0, 3)$. The line of symmetry is the y-axis ($x = 0$). We choose some x-values on both sides of the vertex and graph the parabola.

For $x = 1$, $y = -2x^2 + 3 = -2(1)^2 + 3 = -2 + 3 = 1$.
For $x = -1$, $y = -2x^2 + 3 = -2(-1)^2 + 3 = -2 + 3 = 1$.
For $x = 2$, $y = -2x^2 + 3 = -2(2)^2 + 3 = -8 + 3 = -5$.
For $x = -2$, $y = -2x^2 + 3 = -2(-2)^2 + 3 = -8 + 3 = -5$.

x	y	
0	3	← This is the vertex.
1	1	
−1	1	
2	−5	
−2	−5	

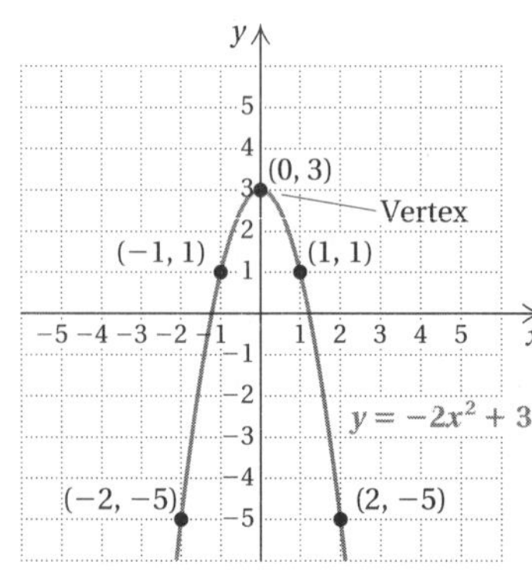

There are two other tips you might use when graphing quadratic equations. The first involves the coefficient of x^2. Note that a in $y = ax^2 + bx + c$ tells us whether the graph opens up or down. When a is positive, as in Example 1, the graph opens up; when a is negative, as in Example 2, the graph opens down. It is also helpful to plot the y-intercept. It occurs when $x = 0$.

TIPS FOR GRAPHING QUADRATIC EQUATIONS

1. Graphs of quadratic equations $y = ax^2 + bx + c$ are all parabolas. They are *smooth* cup-shaped symmetric curves, with no sharp points or kinks in them.
2. Find the vertex and the line of symmetry.
3. The graph of $y = ax^2 + bx + c$ opens up if $a > 0$. It opens down if $a < 0$.
4. Find the y-intercept. It occurs when $x = 0$, and it is easy to compute.

EXAMPLE 3 Graph: $y = x^2 + 2x - 3$.

We first find the vertex. The x-coordinate of the vertex is

$$-\frac{b}{2a} = -\frac{2}{2(1)} = -1.$$

We substitute -1 for x into the equation to find the second coordinate of the vertex:

$$\begin{aligned} y &= x^2 + 2x - 3 \\ &= (-1)^2 + 2(-1) - 3 \\ &= 1 - 2 - 3 \\ &= -4. \end{aligned}$$

The vertex is $(-1, -4)$. The line of symmetry is $x = -1$.

We choose some x-values on both sides of $x = -1$—say, -2, -3, -4 and 0, 1, 2—and graph the parabola. Since the coefficient of x^2 is 1, which is positive, we know that the graph opens up. Be sure to find y when $x = 0$. This gives the y-intercept.

x	y	
-1	-4	← Vertex
0	-3	← y-intercept
-2	-3	
1	0	
-3	0	
2	5	
-4	5	

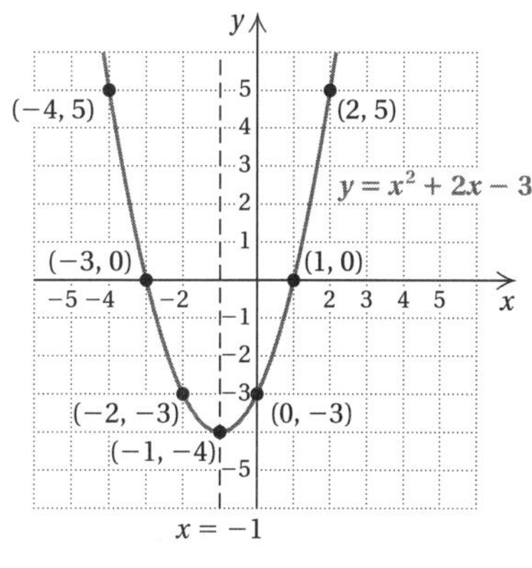

Do Exercises 1–3.

Graph. List the ordered pair for the vertex.

1. $y = x^2 - 3$

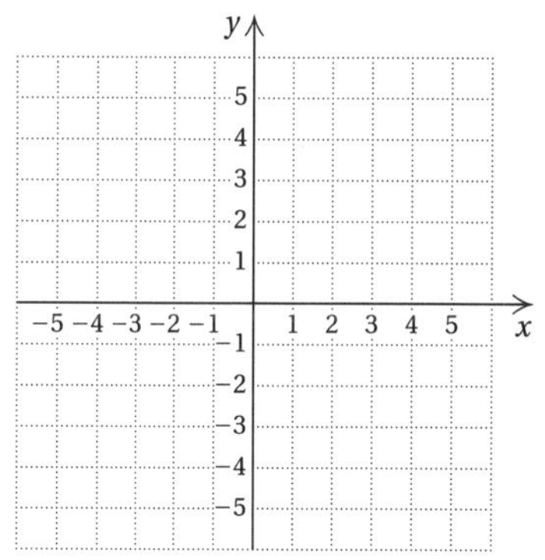

2. $y = -3x^2 + 6x$

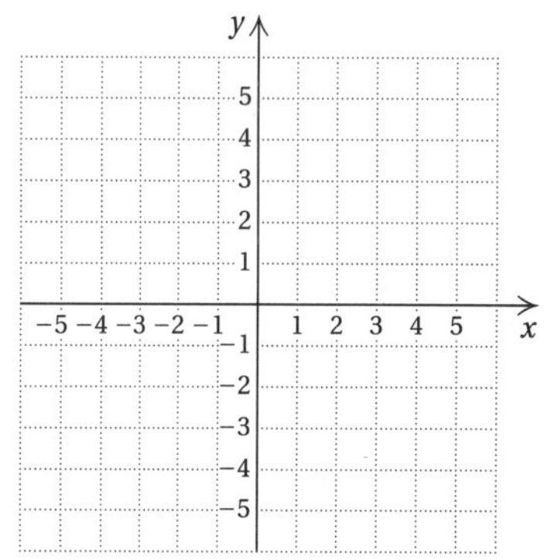

3. $y = x^2 - 4x + 4$

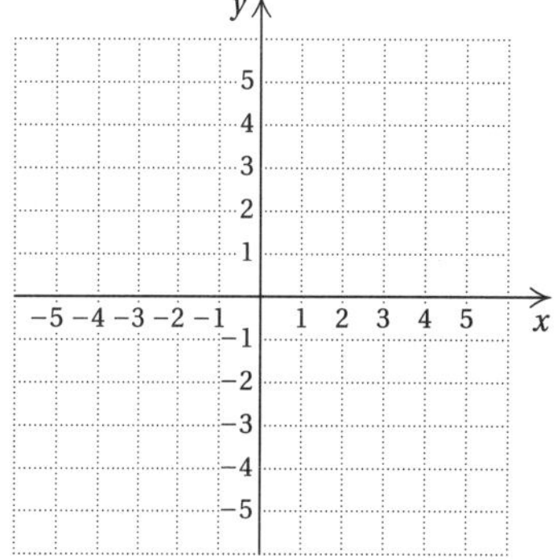

Answers on page A-41

CALCULATOR CORNER

Graphing Quadratic Equations Use a graphing calculator to graph each of the equations in Margin Exercises 1–3.

b Finding the x-Intercepts of a Quadratic Equation

The x-intercepts of $y = ax^2 + bx + c$ occur at those values of x for which $y = 0$. Thus the first coordinates of the x-intercepts are solutions of the equation

$$0 = ax^2 + bx + c.$$

We have been studying how to find such numbers in Sections 9.1–9.3.

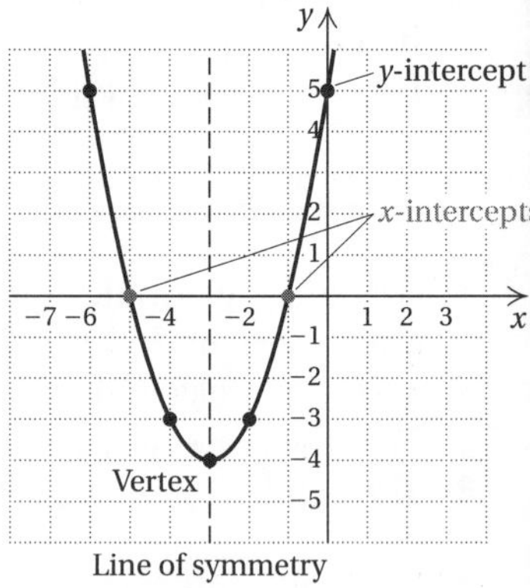

Find the x-intercepts.

4. $y = x^2 - 3$

5. $y = x^2 + 6x + 8$

6. $y = -2x^2 - 4x + 1$

7. $y = x^2 + 3$

EXAMPLE 4 Find the x-intercepts of $y = x^2 - 4x + 1$.

We solve the equation

$$x^2 - 4x + 1 = 0.$$

Factoring is not convenient, so we use the quadratic formula:

$$a = 1, \quad b = -4, \quad c = 1$$

$$x = \frac{-b \pm \sqrt{b^2 - 4ac}}{2a}$$

$$= \frac{-(-4) \pm \sqrt{(-4)^2 - 4(1)(1)}}{2(1)}$$

$$= \frac{4 \pm \sqrt{16 - 4}}{2}$$

$$= \frac{4 \pm \sqrt{12}}{2} = \frac{4 \pm \sqrt{4 \cdot 3}}{2}$$

$$= \frac{4 \pm 2\sqrt{3}}{2} = \frac{2 \cdot 2 \pm 2\sqrt{3}}{2 \cdot 1}$$

$$= \frac{2}{2} \cdot \frac{2 \pm \sqrt{3}}{1} = 2 \pm \sqrt{3}.$$

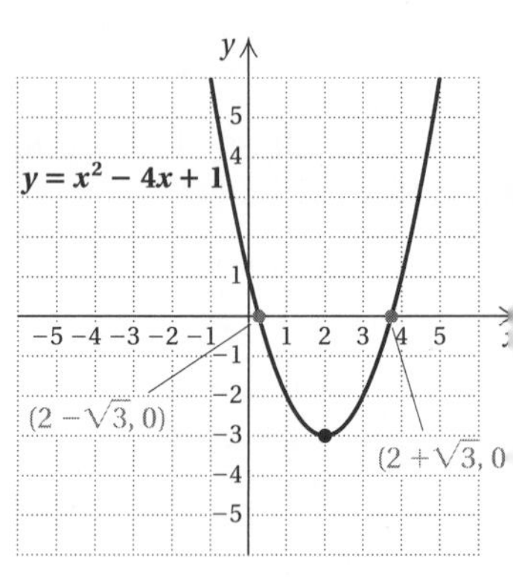

The x-intercepts are $(2 - \sqrt{3}, 0)$ and $(2 + \sqrt{3}, 0)$.

In the quadratic formula $x = \dfrac{-b \pm \sqrt{b^2 - 4ac}}{2a}$, the radicand $b^2 - 4ac$ is called the **discriminant.** The discriminant tells how many real-number solutions the equation $0 = ax^2 + bx + c$ has, so it also tells how many x-intercepts there are.

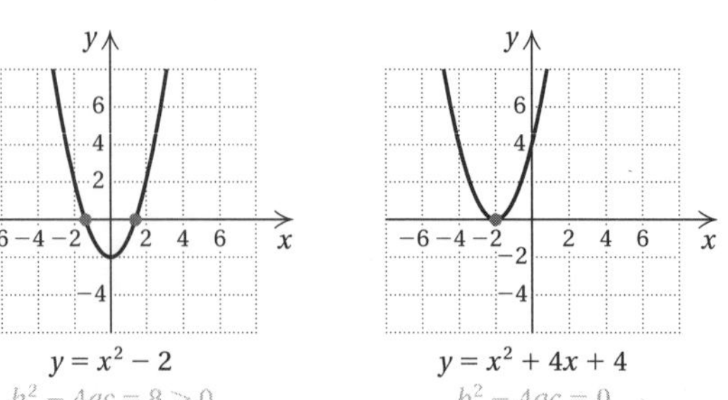

$y = x^2 - 2$
$b^2 - 4ac = 8 > 0$
Two real solutions
Two x-intercepts

$y = x^2 + 4x + 4$
$b^2 - 4ac = 0$
One real solution
One x-intercept

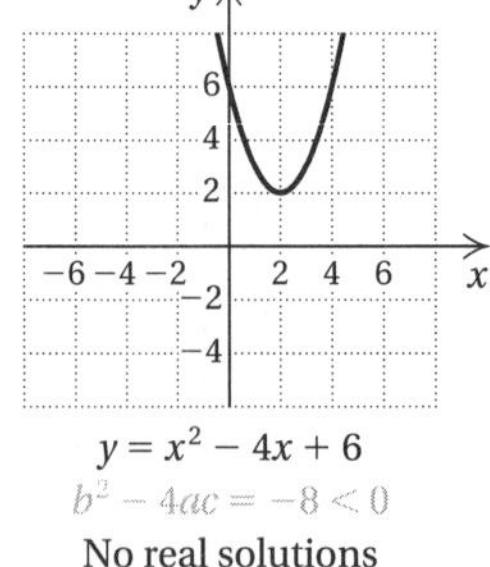

$y = x^2 - 4x + 6$
$b^2 - 4ac = -8 < 0$
No real solutions
No x-intercepts

Do Exercises 4–7.

Answers on page A-41

Visualizing for Success

Match each equation or inequality with its graph.

1. $y = -4 + 4x - x^2$
2. $y = 5 - x^2$
3. $5x + 2y = -10$
4. $5x + 2y \leq 10$
5. $y < 5x$
6. $y = x^2 - 3x - 2$
7. $2x - 5y = 10$
8. $5x - 2y = 10$
9. $2x + 5y = 10$
10. $y = x^2 + 3x - 2$

Answers on page A-42

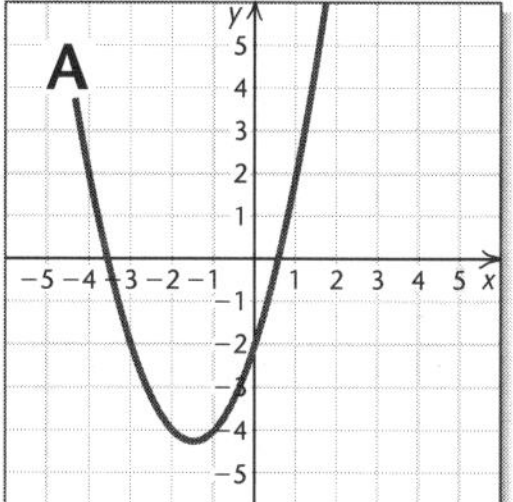

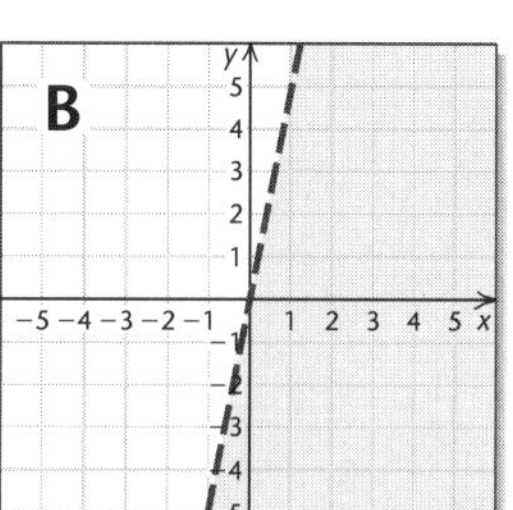

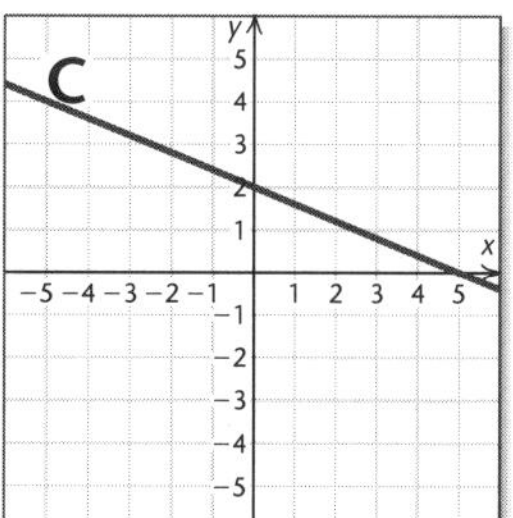

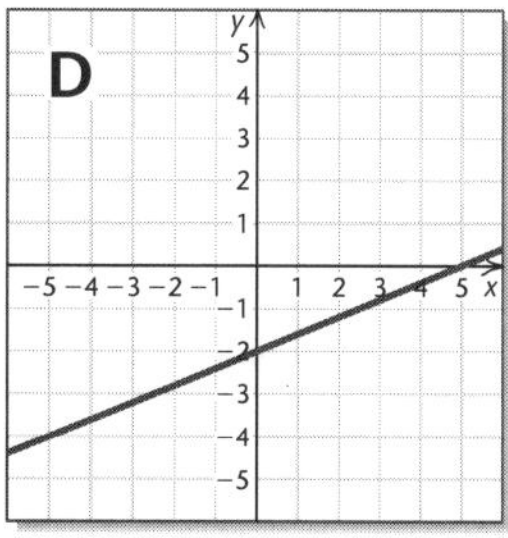

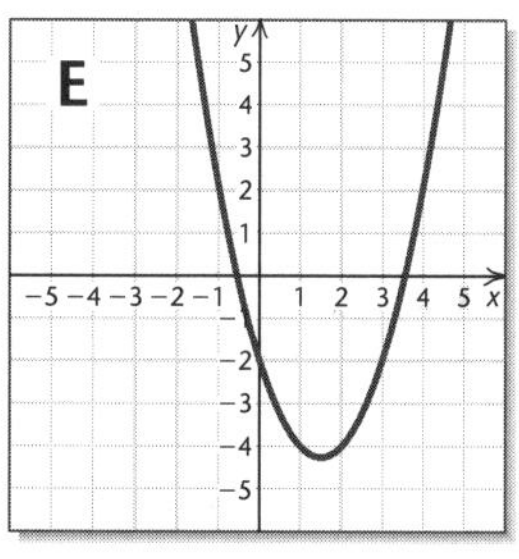

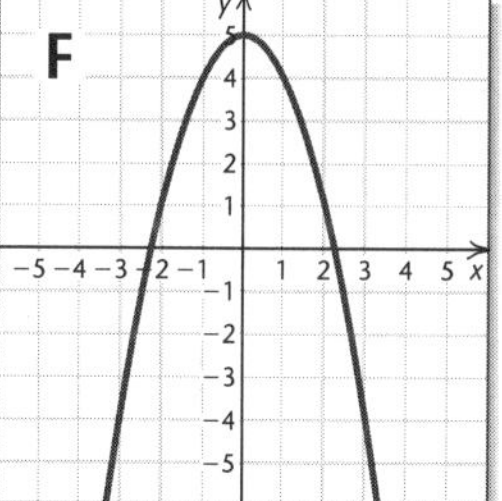

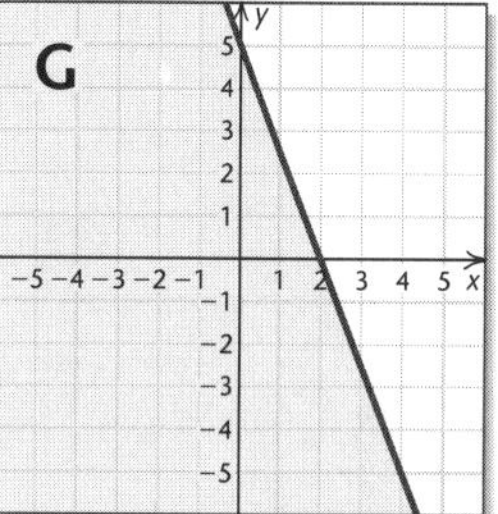

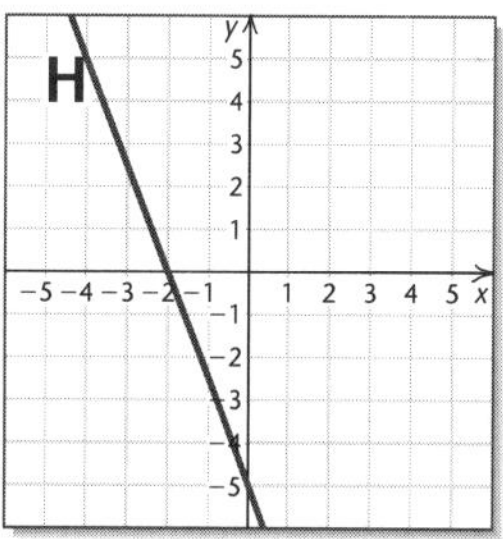

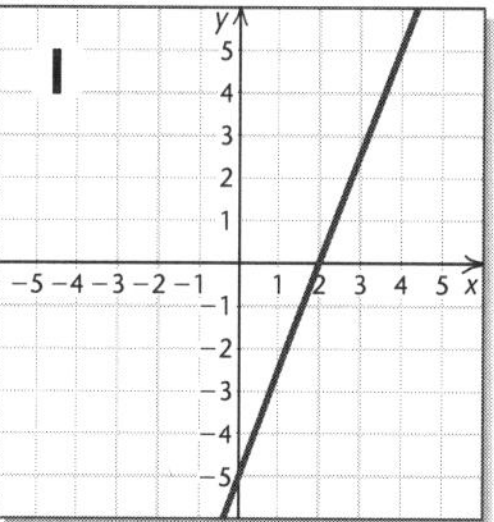

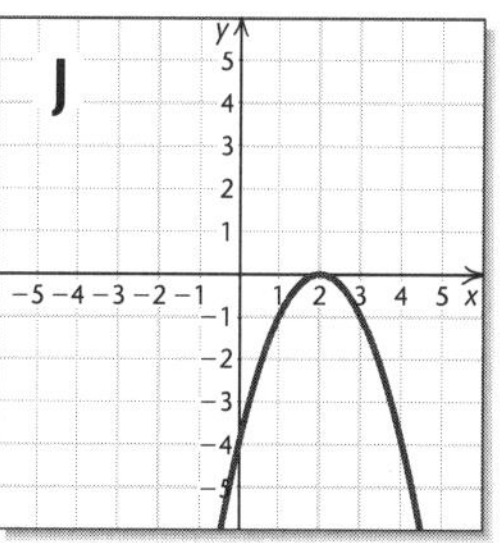

9.6 EXERCISE SET

For Extra Help

MathXL | MyMathLab | InterAct Math | Math Tutor Center | Digital Video Tutor CD 5 Videotape 10 | Student's Solutions Manual

a Graph the quadratic equation. In Exercises 1–8, label the ordered pairs for the vertex and the y-intercept.

1. $y = x^2 + 1$

x	y
-2	
-1	
0	
1	
2	
3	

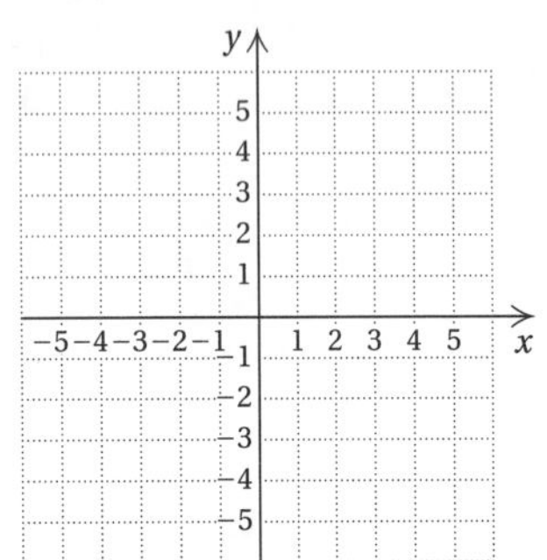

2. $y = 2x^2$

x	y
-2	
-1	
0	
1	
2	
3	

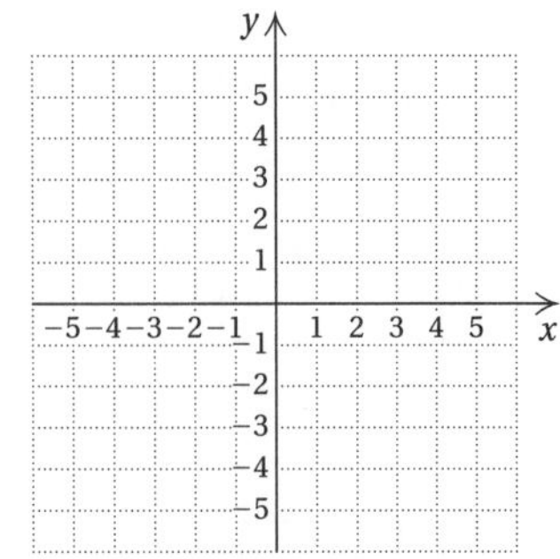

3. $y = -1 \cdot x^2$

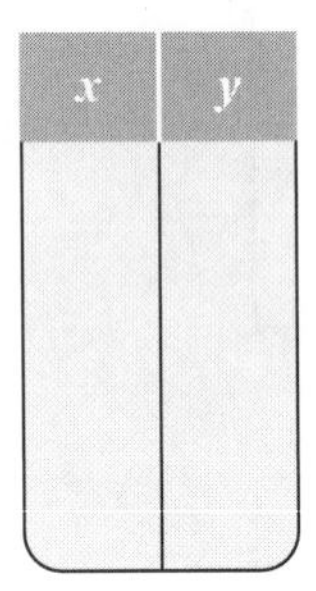

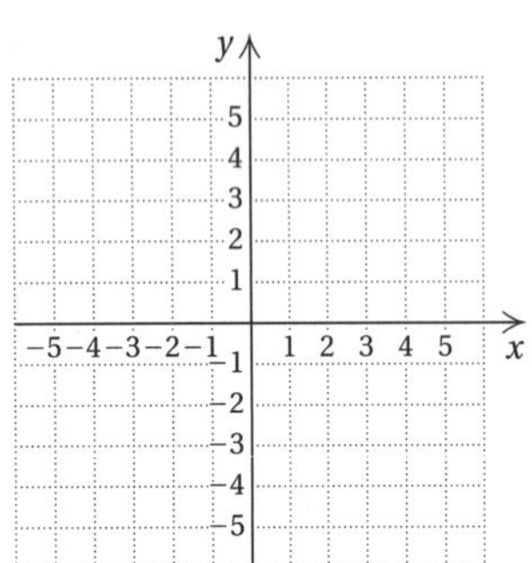

4. $y = x^2 - 1$

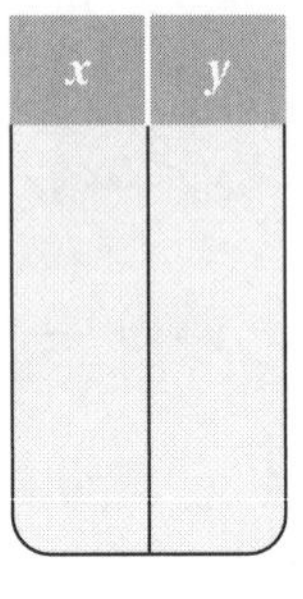

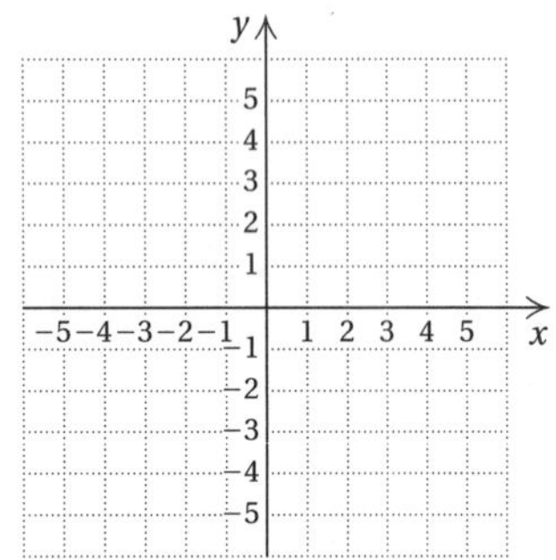

5. $y = -x^2 + 2x$

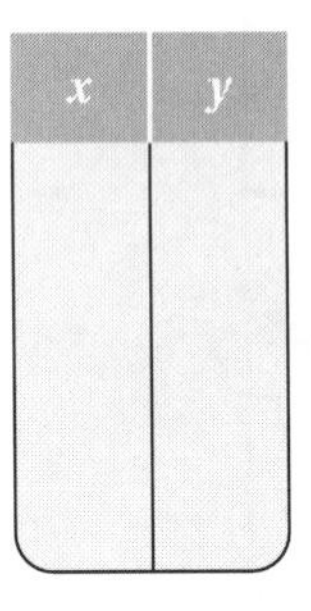

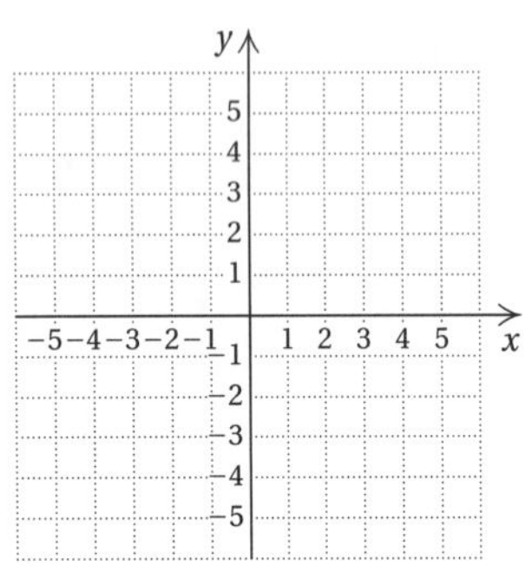

6. $y = x^2 + x - 2$

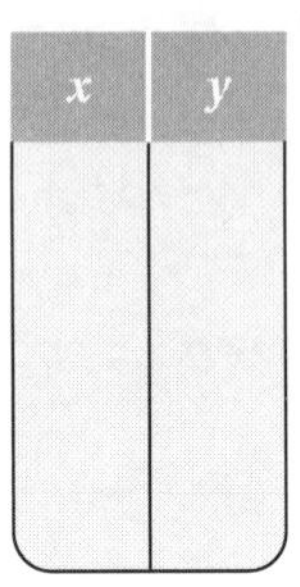

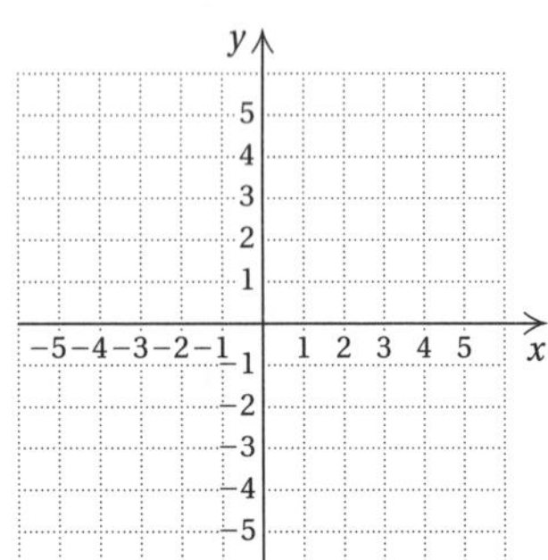

7. $y = 5 - x - x^2$

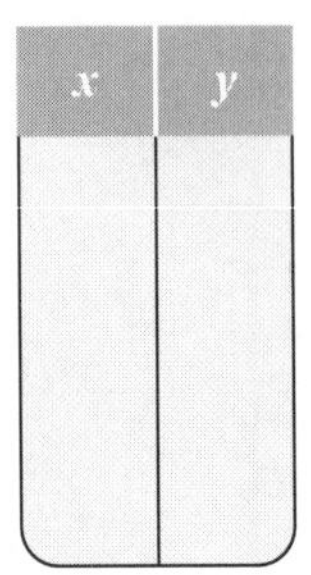

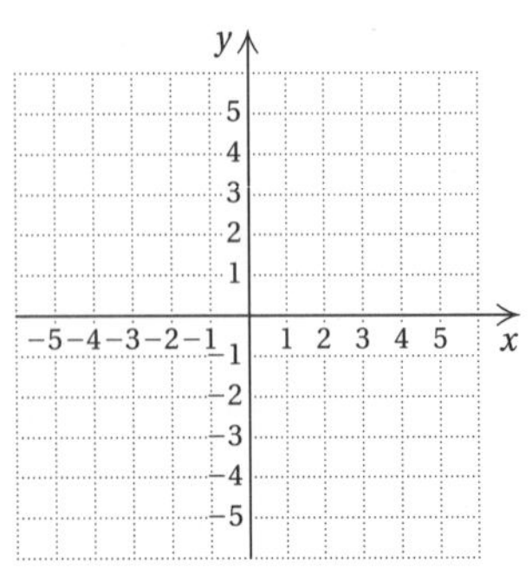

8. $y = x^2 + 2x + 1$

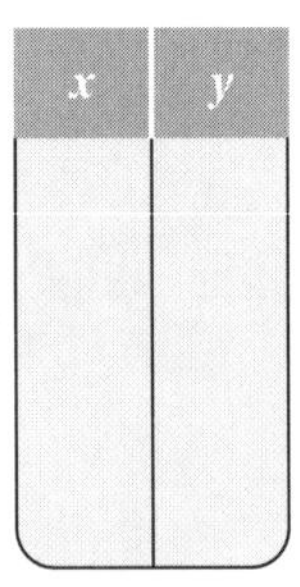

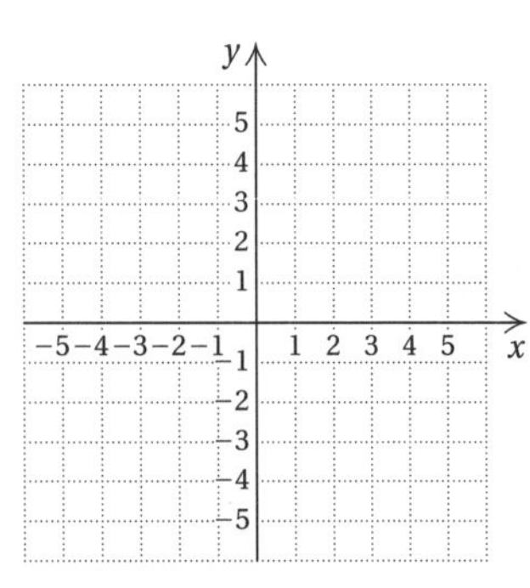

9. $y = x^2 - 2x + 1$

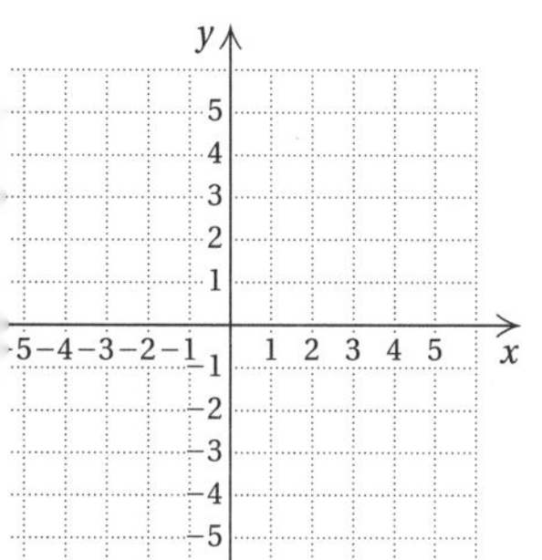

10. $y = -\frac{1}{2}x^2$

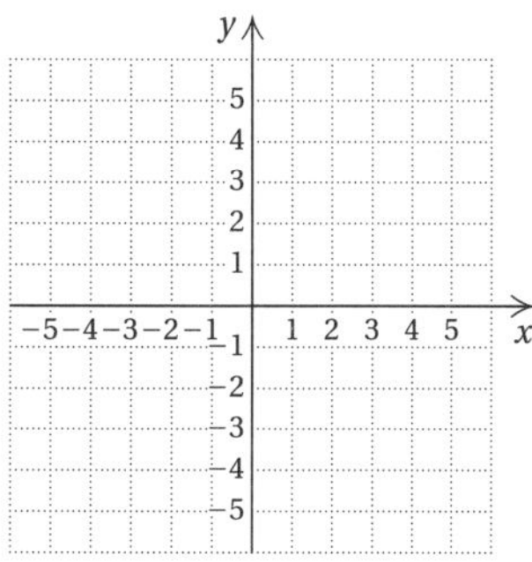

11. $y = -x^2 + 2x + 3$

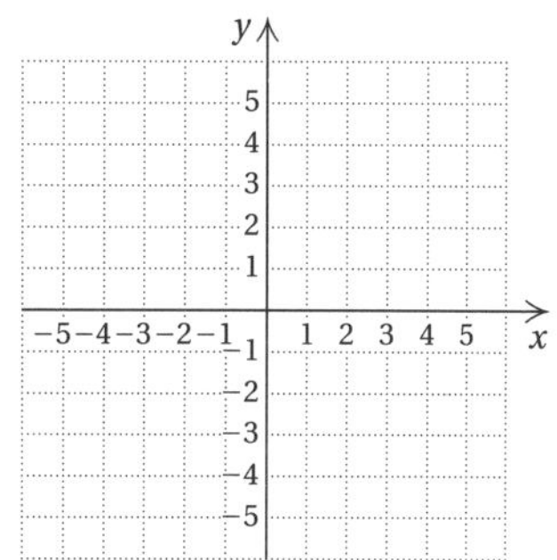

12. $y = -x^2 - 2x + 3$

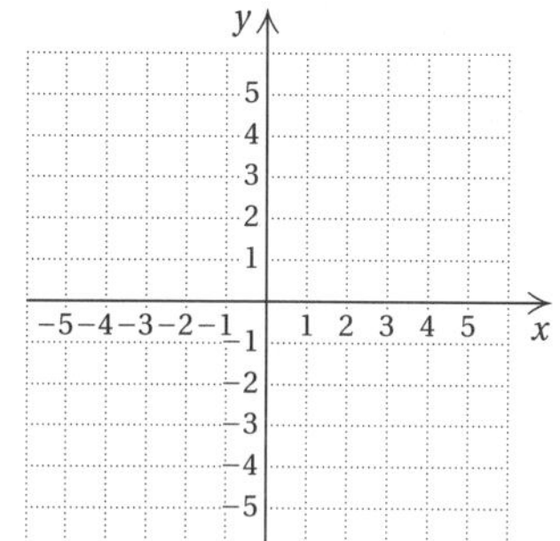

3. $y = -2x^2 - 4x + 1$

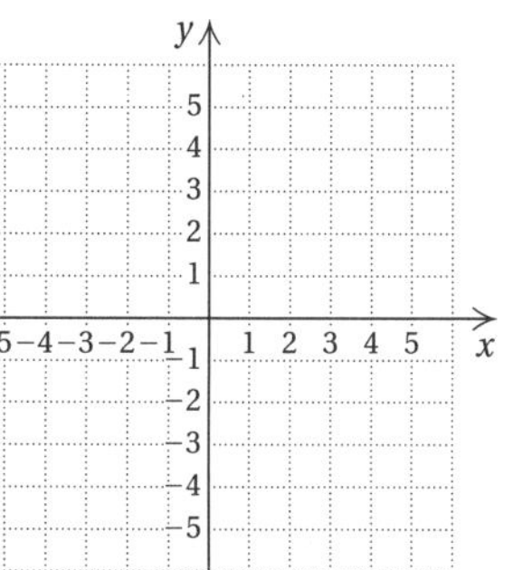

14. $y = 2x^2 + 4x - 1$

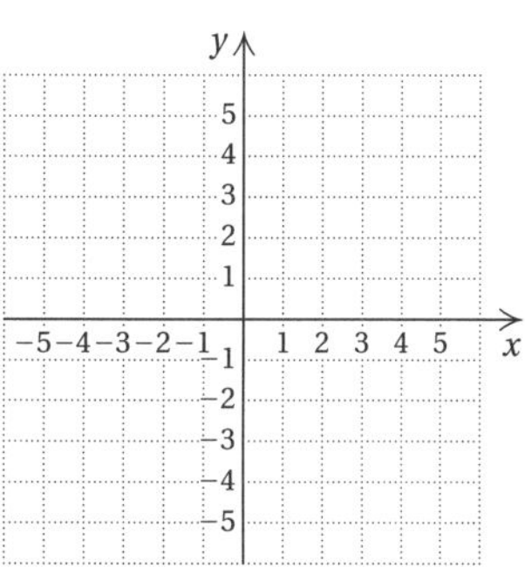

15. $y = 5 - x^2$

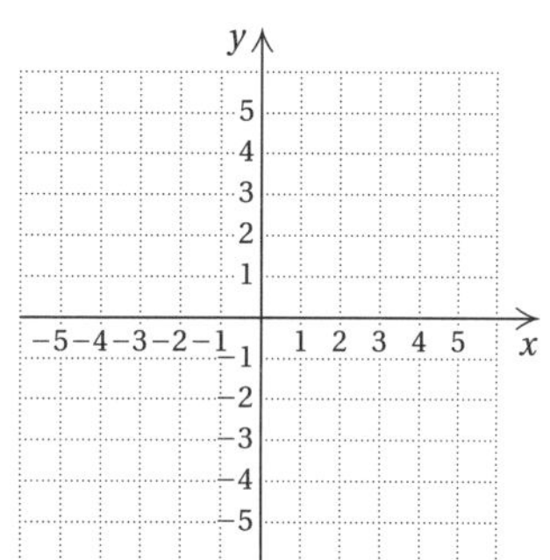

16. $y = 4 - x^2$

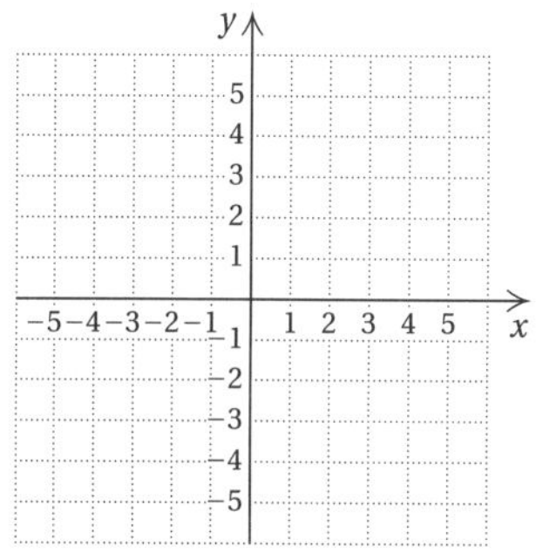

7. $y = \frac{1}{4}x^2$

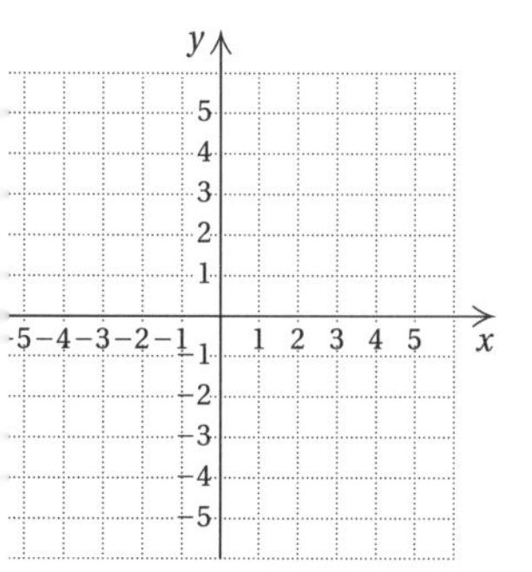

18. $y = -0.1x^2$

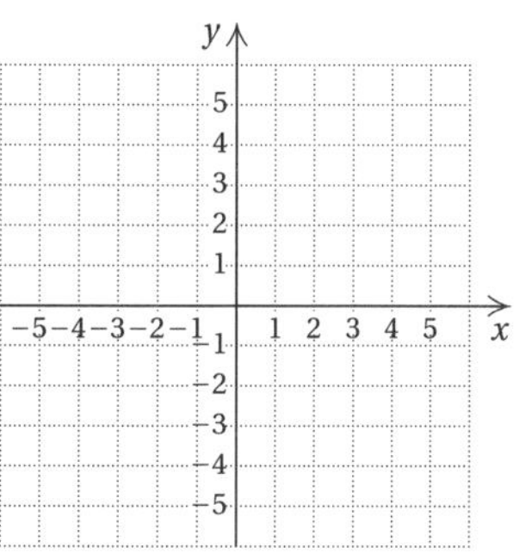

19. $y = -x^2 + x - 1$

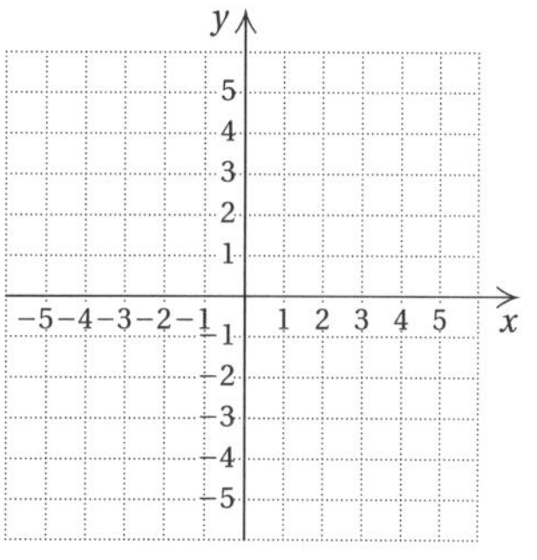

20. $y = x^2 + 2x$

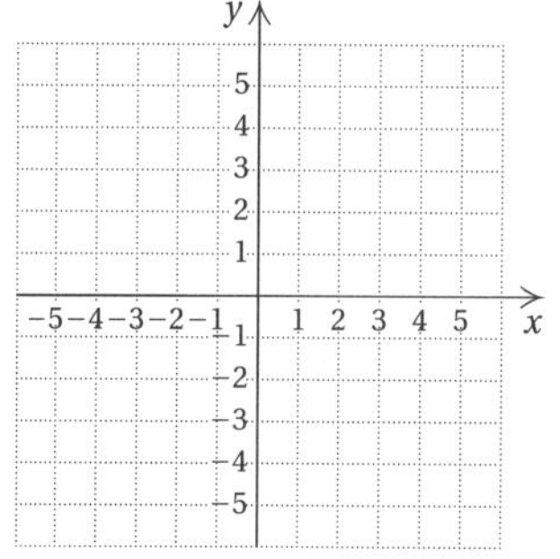

1. $y = -2x^2$

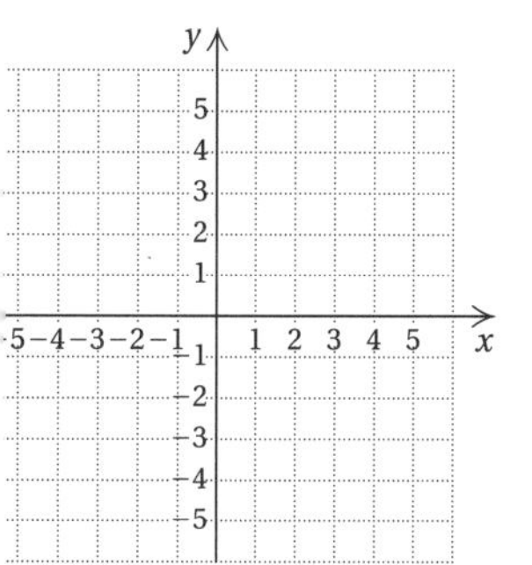

22. $y = -x^2 - 1$

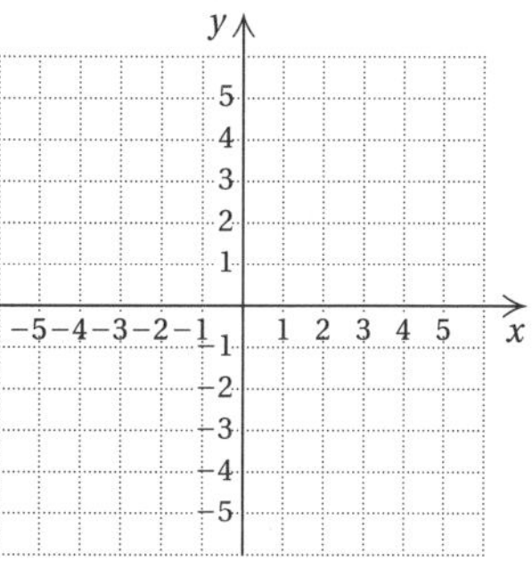

23. $y = x^2 - x - 6$

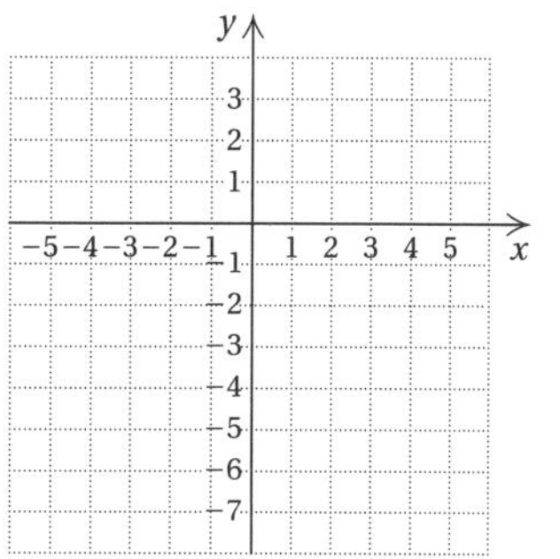

24. $y = 6 + x - x^2$

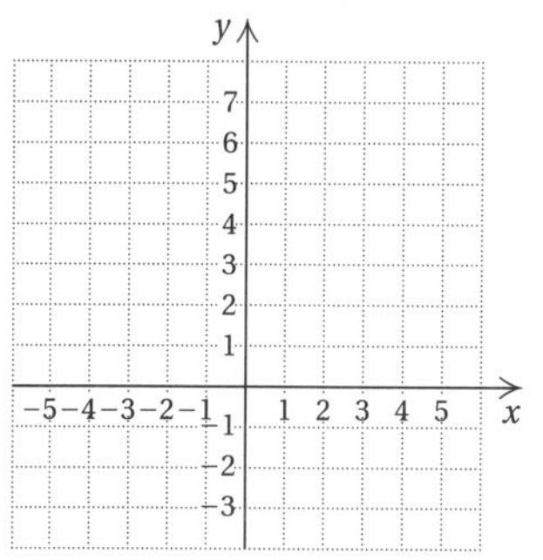

b Find the x-intercepts.

25. $y = x^2 - 2$

26. $y = x^2 - 7$

27. $y = x^2 + 5x$

28. $y = x^2 - 4x$

29. $y = 8 - x - x^2$

30. $y = 8 + x - x^2$

31. $y = x^2 - 6x + 9$

32. $y = x^2 + 10x + 25$

33. $y = -x^2 - 4x + 1$

34. $y = x^2 + 4x - 1$

35. $y = x^2 + 9$

36. $y = x^2 + 1$

37. $\mathbf{D_W}$ Suppose that the x-intercepts of a parabola are $(a_1, 0)$ and $(a_2, 0)$. What is the easiest way to find an equation for the line of symmetry? to find the coordinates of the vertex?

38. $\mathbf{D_W}$ Discuss the effect of the sign of a on the graph of $y = ax^2 + bx + c$.

SKILL MAINTENANCE

39. Add: $\sqrt{8} + \sqrt{50} + \sqrt{98} + \sqrt{128}$. [8.4a]

40. Multiply and simplify: $\sqrt{5y^4}\,\sqrt{125y}$. [8.2c]

41. Find an equation of variation in which y varies inversely as x and $y = 12.4$ when $x = 2.4$. [6.9c]

42. Evaluate $3x^4 + 3x - 7$ when $x = -2$. [4.3a]

SYNTHESIS

43. *Height of a Projectile.* The height H, in feet, of a projectile with an initial velocity of 96 ft/sec is given by the equation

$$H = -16t^2 + 96t,$$

where t is the time, in seconds. Use the graph of this equation, shown here, or any equation-solving technique to answer the following questions.

a) How many seconds after launch is the projectile 128 ft above ground?
b) When does the projectile reach its maximum height?
c) How many seconds after launch does the projectile return to the ground?

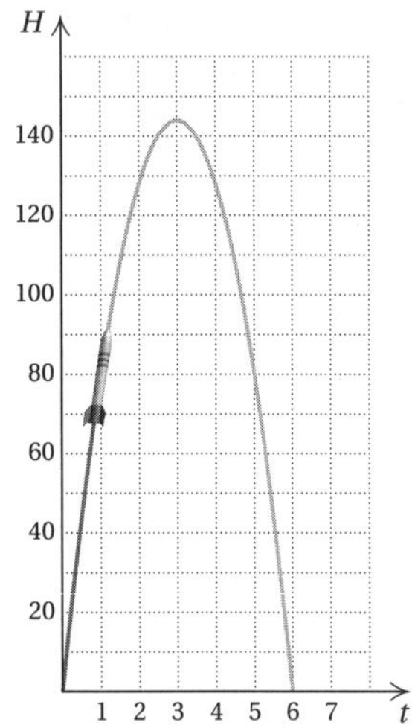

For each equation in Exercises 44–47, evaluate the discriminant $b^2 - 4ac$. Then use the answer to state how many real-number solutions exist for the equation.

44. $y = x^2 + 8x + 16$

45. $y = x^2 + 2x - 3$

46. $y = -2x^2 + 4x - 3$

47. $y = -0.02x^2 + 4.7x - 2300$

Answers

CHAPTER 1

Margin Exercises, Section 1.1, pp. 58–62

1. $14{,}410 + x = 15{,}300$; 890 ft **2.** 64 **3.** 28 **4.** 60
5. 192 ft^2 **6.** 25 **7.** 16 **8.** 12 hr **9.** $x - 8$
10. $y + 8$, or $8 + y$ **11.** $m - 4$ **12.** $\frac{1}{2}p$
13. $6 + 8x$, or $8x + 6$ **14.** $a - b$
15. $59\%x$, or $0.59x$ **16.** $xy - 200$ **17.** $p + q$

Calculator Corner, p. 60

1. 56 **2.** 11.9 **3.** 1.8 **4.** 34,427.16 **5.** 20.1
6. 29.9

Exercise Set 1.1, p. 63

1. 32 min; 69 min; 81 min **3.** 1935 m^2 **5.** 260 mi
7. 24 ft^2 **9.** 56 **11.** 8 **13.** 1 **15.** 6 **17.** 2
19. $b + 7$, or $7 + b$ **21.** $c - 12$ **23.** $q + 4$, or $4 + q$
25. $a + b$, or $b + a$ **27.** $x \div y$, or $\frac{x}{y}$, or x/y, or $x \cdot \frac{1}{y}$
29. $x + w$, or $w + x$ **31.** $n - m$ **33.** $x + y$, or $y + x$
35. $2z$ **37.** $3m$ **39.** $4a + 6$, or $6 + 4a$ **41.** $xy - 8$
43. $2t - 5$ **45.** $3n + 11$, or $11 + 3n$
47. $4x + 3y$, or $3y + 4x$
49. $89\%s$, or $0.89s$, where s is the salary **51.** $s + 0.05s$
53. $65t$ miles **55.** $\$50 - x$ **57.** DW **59.** $2 \cdot 3 \cdot 3 \cdot 3$
60. $2 \cdot 2 \cdot 2 \cdot 2 \cdot 2$ **61.** $2 \cdot 2 \cdot 3 \cdot 3 \cdot 3$
62. $2 \cdot 2 \cdot 2 \cdot 2 \cdot 2 \cdot 2 \cdot 3$ **63.** $3 \cdot 11 \cdot 31$ **64.** 18
65. 96 **66.** 60 **67.** 96 **68.** 396 **69.** $\frac{1}{4}$ **71.** 0

Margin Exercises, Section 1.2, pp. 68–74

1. 8; −5 **2.** 125; −50 **3.** −3 **4.** −10; 156
5. −120; 50; −80 **6.**

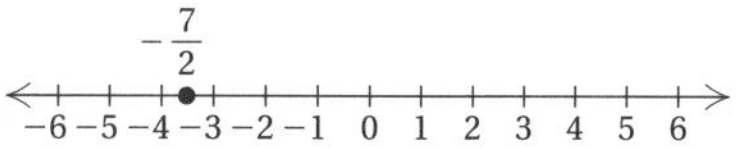

7.

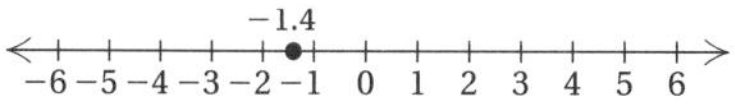

8.

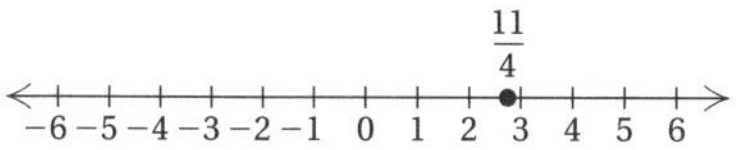

9. −0.375

10. $-0.\overline{54}$ **11.** $1.\overline{3}$ **12.** < **13.** < **14.** > **15.** >
16. > **17.** < **18.** < **19.** > **20.** $7 > -5$
21. $4 < x$ **22.** False **23.** True **24.** True **25.** 8
26. 9 **27.** $\frac{2}{3}$ **28.** 5.6

Calculator Corner, p. 69

1. −0.75 **2.** −0.45 **3.** −0.125 **4.** −1.8 **5.** − 0.675
6. −0.6875 **7.** −3.5 **8.** −0.76

Calculator Corner, p. 70

1. 8.717797887 **2.** 17.80449381 **3.** 67.08203932
4. 35.4807407 **5.** 3.141592654 **6.** 91.10618695
7. 530.9291585 **8.** 138.8663978

Calculator Corner, p. 73

1. 5 **2.** 17 **3.** 0 **4.** 6.48 **5.** 12.7 **6.** 0.9
7. $\frac{5}{7}$ **8.** $\frac{4}{3}$

Exercise Set 1.2, p. 75

1. −34,000,000 **3.** 24; −2 **5.** 950,000,000; −460
7. Alley Cats: −34; Strikers: 34
9.

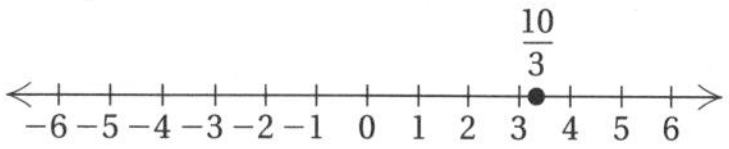

11.

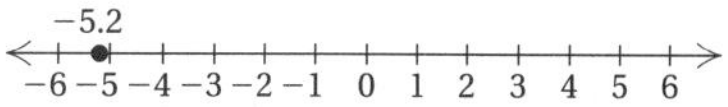

13.

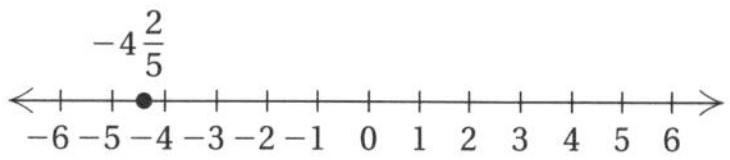

15. −0.875
17. $0.8\overline{3}$ **19.** $-1.1\overline{6}$ **21.** $0.\overline{6}$ **23.** 0.1 **25.** −0.5
27. 0.16 **29.** > **31.** < **33.** < **35.** < **37.** >
39. < **41.** > **43.** < **45.** < **47.** > **49.** <
51. < **53.** True **55.** False **57.** $x < -6$
59. $y \geq -10$ **61.** 3 **63.** 10 **65.** 0 **67.** 30.4
69. $\frac{2}{3}$ **71.** 0 **73.** $3\frac{5}{8}$ **75.** DW **77.** 0.63
78. 0.238 **79.** 1.1 **80.** 0.2276 **81.** 52% **82.** 125%
83. $83.\overline{3}\%$, or $83\frac{1}{3}\%$ **84.** 59.375%, or $59\frac{3}{8}\%$

85. $-\frac{5}{6}, -\frac{3}{4}, -\frac{2}{3}, \frac{1}{6}, \frac{3}{8}, \frac{1}{2}$
87. −8.76, −5.16, −4.24, −2.13, 1.85, 5.23
89. $\frac{1}{9}$ **91.** $5\frac{5}{9}$, or $\frac{50}{9}$

Margin Exercises, Section 1.3, pp. 78–82

1. −3 **2.** −3 **3.** −5 **4.** 4 **5.** 0 **6.** −2 **7.** −11 **8.** −12 **9.** 2 **10.** −4 **11.** −2 **12.** 0 **13.** −22 **14.** 3 **15.** 0.53 **16.** 2.3 **17.** −7.7 **18.** −6.2 **19.** $-\frac{2}{9}$ **20.** $-\frac{19}{20}$ **21.** −58 **22.** −56 **23.** −14 **24.** −12 **25.** 4 **26.** −8.7 **27.** 7.74 **28.** $\frac{8}{9}$ **29.** 0 **30.** −12 **31.** −14; 14 **32.** −1; 1 **33.** 19; −19 **34.** 1.6; −1.6 **35.** $-\frac{2}{3}; \frac{2}{3}$ **36.** $\frac{9}{8}; -\frac{9}{8}$ **37.** 4 **38.** 13.4 **39.** 0 **40.** $-\frac{1}{4}$ **41.** −2 students

Exercise Set 1.3, p. 83

1. −7 **3.** −6 **5.** 0 **7.** −8 **9.** −7 **11.** −27 **13.** 0 **15.** −42 **17.** 0 **19.** 0 **21.** 3 **23.** −9 **25.** 7 **27.** 0 **29.** 35 **31.** −3.8 **33.** −8.1 **35.** $-\frac{1}{5}$ **37.** $-\frac{7}{9}$ **39.** $-\frac{3}{8}$ **41.** $-\frac{19}{24}$ **43.** $\frac{1}{24}$ **45.** $\frac{8}{15}$ **47.** $\frac{16}{45}$ **49.** 37 **51.** 50 **53.** −1409 **55.** −24 **57.** 26.9 **59.** −8 **61.** $\frac{13}{8}$ **63.** −43 **65.** $\frac{4}{3}$ **67.** 24 **69.** $\frac{3}{8}$ **71.** 13,796 ft **73.** −3°F **75.** −\$20,300 **77.** He owes \$85. **79.** DW **81.** 0.713 **82.** 0.92875 **83.** 12.5% **84.** 40.625% **85.** $\frac{8}{5}$ **86.** $\frac{1}{4}$ **87.** All positive **89.** (b)

Margin Exercises, Section 1.4, pp. 86–88

1. −10 **2.** 3 **3.** −5 **4.** −1 **5.** 2 **6.** −4 **7.** −2 **8.** −11 **9.** 4 **10.** −2 **11.** −6 **12.** −16 **13.** 7.1 **14.** 3 **15.** 0 **16.** $\frac{3}{2}$ **17.** −8 **18.** 7 **19.** −3 **20.** −23.3 **21.** 0 **22.** −9 **23.** $-\frac{6}{5}$ **24.** 12.7 **25.** 214°F higher

Exercise Set 1.4, p. 89

1. −7 **3.** −6 **5.** 0 **7.** −4 **9.** −7 **11.** −6 **13.** 0 **15.** 14 **17.** 11 **19.** −14 **21.** 5 **23.** −1 **25.** 18 **27.** −3 **29.** −21 **31.** 5 **33.** −8 **35.** 12 **37.** −23 **39.** −68 **41.** −73 **43.** 116 **45.** 0 **47.** −1 **49.** $\frac{1}{12}$ **51.** $-\frac{17}{12}$ **53.** $\frac{1}{8}$ **55.** 19.9 **57.** −8.6 **59.** −0.01 **61.** −193 **63.** 500 **65.** −2.8 **67.** −3.53 **69.** $-\frac{1}{2}$ **71.** $\frac{6}{7}$ **73.** $-\frac{41}{30}$ **75.** $-\frac{2}{15}$ **77.** $-\frac{1}{48}$ **79.** $-\frac{43}{60}$ **81.** 37 **83.** −62 **85.** −139 **87.** 6 **89.** 108.5 **91.** $\frac{1}{4}$ **93.** 2319 m **95.** \$347.94 **97.** (a) 77; (b) −41 **99.** 381 ft **101.** DW **103.** 100.5 **104.** 226 **105.** 13 **106.** 50 **107.** $\frac{11}{12}$ **108.** $\frac{41}{64}$ **109.** False; $3 - 0 \neq 0 - 3$ **111.** True **113.** True

Margin Exercises, Section 1.5, pp. 93–96

1. 20; 10; 0; −10; −20; −30 **2.** −18 **3.** −100 **4.** −8 **5.** $-\frac{5}{9}$ **6.** −30.033 **7.** $-\frac{7}{10}$ **8.** −10; 0; 10; 20; 30 **9.** 27 **10.** 32 **11.** 35 **12.** $\frac{20}{63}$ **13.** $\frac{2}{3}$ **14.** 13.455 **15.** −30 **16.** 30 **17.** 0 **18.** $-\frac{8}{3}$ **19.** 0 **20.** 0 **21.** −30 **22.** −30.75 **23.** $-\frac{5}{3}$ **24.** 120 **25.** −120 **26.** 6 **27.** 4; −4 **28.** 9; −9 **29.** 48; 48 **30.** 55°C

Exercise Set 1.5, p. 97

1. −8 **3.** −48 **5.** −24 **7.** −72 **9.** 16 **11.** 42 **13.** −120 **15.** −238 **17.** 1200 **19.** 98 **21.** −72 **23.** −12.4 **25.** 30 **27.** 21.7 **29.** $-\frac{2}{5}$ **31.** $\frac{1}{12}$ **33.** −17.01 **35.** $-\frac{5}{12}$ **37.** 420 **39.** $\frac{2}{7}$ **41.** −60 **43.** 150 **45.** $-\frac{2}{45}$ **47.** 1911 **49.** 50.4 **51.** $\frac{10}{189}$ **53.** −960 **55.** 17.64 **57.** $-\frac{5}{784}$ **59.** 0 **61.** −720 **63.** −30,240 **65.** 1 **67.** 16, −16; 16, −16 **69.** 441; −147 **71.** 20; 20 **73.** −2; 2 **75.** −20 lb **77.** −54°C **79.** \$12.71 **81.** −32 m **83.** DW **85.** 180 **86.** $2 \cdot 2 \cdot 2 \cdot 2 \cdot 2 \cdot 2 \cdot 2 \cdot 2 \cdot 2 \cdot 3 \cdot 3$ **87.** $\frac{2}{3}$ **88.** $\frac{8}{9}$ **89.** $\frac{6}{11}$ **90.** $\frac{41}{265}$ **91.** $\frac{11}{32}$ **92.** $\frac{37}{67}$ **93.** $\frac{1}{24}$ **94.** 6 **95.** (a)

97.

$x-2y$ $-y$ $-x$ $x-y$ $2x$ $x+y$ $3x$ $2y$

0 x y

Margin Exercises, Section 1.6, pp. 100–105

1. -2 **2.** 5 **3.** -3 **4.** 8 **5.** -6 **6.** $-\frac{30}{7}$

7. Not defined **8.** 0 **9.** $\frac{3}{2}$ **10.** $-\frac{4}{5}$ **11.** $-\frac{1}{3}$

12. -5 **13.** $\frac{1}{1.6}$ **14.** $\frac{2}{3}$

15.

NUMBER	OPPOSITE	RECIPROCAL
$\frac{2}{3}$	$-\frac{2}{3}$	$\frac{3}{2}$
$-\frac{5}{4}$	$\frac{5}{4}$	$-\frac{4}{5}$
0	0	Not defined
1	-1	1
-8	8	$-\frac{1}{8}$
-4.5	4.5	$-\frac{1}{4.5}$

6. $\frac{4}{7} \cdot \left(-\frac{5}{3}\right)$ **17.** $5 \cdot \left(-\frac{1}{8}\right)$ **18.** $(a - b) \cdot \left(\frac{1}{7}\right)$

9. $-23 \cdot a$ **20.** $-5 \cdot \left(\frac{1}{7}\right)$ **21.** $-\frac{20}{21}$ **22.** $-\frac{12}{5}$

3. $\frac{16}{7}$ **24.** -7 **25.** $\frac{5}{-6}, -\frac{5}{6}$ **26.** $\frac{-8}{7}, \frac{8}{-7}$

7. $\frac{-10}{3}, -\frac{10}{3}$ **28.** -3.4°F per minute

Calculator Corner, p. 105

. -4 **2.** -0.3 **3.** -12 **4.** -9.5 **5.** -12 **6.** 2.7
. -2 **8.** -5.7 **9.** -32 **10.** -1.8 **11.** 35
2. 14.44 **13.** -2 **14.** -0.8 **15.** 1.4 **16.** 4

Exercise Set 1.6, p. 106

. -8 **3.** -14 **5.** -3 **7.** 3 **9.** -8 **11.** 2

3. -12 **15.** -8 **17.** Not defined **19.** 0 **21.** $\frac{7}{15}$

3. $-\frac{13}{47}$ **25.** $\frac{1}{13}$ **27.** $\frac{1}{4.3}$ **29.** -7.1 **31.** $\frac{q}{p}$

3. $4y$ **35.** $\frac{3b}{2a}$ **37.** $4 \cdot \left(\frac{1}{17}\right)$ **39.** $8 \cdot \left(-\frac{1}{13}\right)$

1. $13.9 \cdot \left(-\frac{1}{1.5}\right)$ **43.** $x \cdot y$ **45.** $(3x + 4)\left(\frac{1}{5}\right)$

47. $(5a - b)\left(\frac{1}{\quad}\right.$ **49.** $-\frac{9}{8}$ **51.** $\frac{5}{3}$ **53.** $\frac{9}{14}$

55. $\frac{9}{64}$ **57.** -2 **59.** $\frac{11}{13}$ **61.** -16.2 **63.** Not defined

65. 44.3% **67.** -5.1% **69.** D_W **71.** 33 **72.** 129

73. 1 **74.** 1296 **75.** $\frac{22}{39}$ **76.** 0.477 **77.** 87.5%

78. $\frac{2}{3}$ **79.** $\frac{9}{8}$ **80.** $\frac{128}{625}$ **81.** $\frac{1}{-10.5}$; -10.5, the reciprocal of the reciprocal is the original number

83. Negative **85.** Positive **87.** Negative

Margin Exercises, Section 1.7, pp. 109–117

1.

Value	$x + x$	$2x$
$x = 3$	6	6
$x = -6$	-12	-12
$x = 4.8$	9.6	9.6

2.

Value	$x + 3x$	$5x$
$x = 2$	8	10
$x = -6$	-24	-30
$x = 4.8$	19.2	24

3. $\frac{6}{8}$ **4.** $\frac{3t}{4t}$ **5.** $\frac{3}{4}$ **6.** $-\frac{4}{3}$ **7.** $\frac{x}{8}$ **8.** $\frac{3}{4q}$ **9.** 1; 1
10. -10; -10 **11.** $9 + x$ **12.** qp
13. $t + xy$, or $yx + t$, or $t + yx$ **14.** 19; 19 **15.** 150; 150
16. $(r + s) + 7$ **17.** $(9a)b$
18. $(4t)u$, $(tu)4$, $t(4u)$; answers may vary
19. $(2 + r) + s$, $(r + s) + 2$, $s + (r + 2)$; answers may vary
20. **(a)** 63; **(b)** 63 **21.** **(a)** 80; **(b)** 80 **22.** **(a)** 28; **(b)** 28
23. **(a)** 8; **(b)** 8 **24.** **(a)** -4; **(b)** -4 **25.** **(a)** -25; **(b)** -25
26. $5x$, $-8y$, 3 **27.** $-4y$, $-2x$, $3z$ **28.** $3x - 15$
29. $5x + 5$ **30.** $\frac{3}{5}p + \frac{3}{5}q - \frac{3}{5}t$ **31.** $-2x + 6$
32. $5x - 10y + 20z$ **33.** $-5x + 10y - 20z$
34. Associative law of multiplication
35. Identity property of 1
36. Commutative law of addition
37. Distributive law of multiplication over addition
38. Identity property of 0
39. Commutative law of multiplication
40. Associative law of addition
41. $6(x - 2)$ **42.** $3(x - 2y + 3)$ **43.** $b(x + y - z)$
44. $2(8a - 18b + 21)$ **45.** $\frac{1}{8}(3x - 5y + 7)$
46. $-4(3x - 8y + 4z)$ **47.** $3x$ **48.** $6x$ **49.** $-8x$
50. $0.59x$ **51.** $3x + 3y$ **52.** $-4x - 5y - 7$
53. $-\frac{2}{3} + \frac{1}{10}x + \frac{7}{9}y$

Exercise Set 1.7, p. 118

1. $\frac{3y}{5y}$ **3.** $\frac{10x}{15x}$ **5.** $\frac{2x}{x^2}$ **7.** $-\frac{3}{2}$ **9.** $-\frac{7}{6}$ **11.** $\frac{4s}{3}$
13. $8 + y$ **15.** nm **17.** $xy + 9$, or $9 + yx$
19. $c + ab$, or $ba + c$ **21.** $(a + b) + 2$ **23.** $8(xy)$
25. $a + (b + 3)$ **27.** $(3a)b$
29. $2 + (b + a), (2 + a) + b, (b + 2) + a$; answers may vary **31.** $(5 + w) + v$; $(v + 5) + w$; $(w + v) + 5$; answers may vary
33. $(3x)y, y(x \cdot 3), 3(yx)$; answers may vary
35. $a(7b), b(7a), (7b)a$; answers may vary **37.** $2b + 10$
39. $7 + 7t$ **41.** $30x + 12$ **43.** $7x + 28 + 42y$
45. $7x - 21$ **47.** $-3x + 21$ **49.** $\frac{2}{3}b - 4$
51. $7.3x - 14.6$ **53.** $-\frac{3}{5}x + \frac{3}{5}y - 6$
55. $45x + 54y - 72$ **57.** $-4x + 12y + 8z$
59. $-3.72x + 9.92y - 3.41$ **61.** $4x, 3z$ **63.** $7x, 8y, -9z$
65. $2(x + 2)$ **67.** $5(6 + y)$ **69.** $7(2x + 3y)$
71. $5(x + 2 + 3y)$ **73.** $8(x - 3)$
75. $4(-y + 8)$, or $-4(y - 8)$ **77.** $2(4x + 5y - 11)$
79. $a(x - 1)$ **81.** $a(x - y - z)$
83. $6(-3x + 2y + 1)$, or $-6(3x - 2y - 1)$
85. $\frac{1}{3}(2x - 5y + 1)$ **87.** $19a$ **89.** $9a$ **91.** $8x + 9z$
93. $7x + 15y^2$ **95.** $-19a + 88$ **97.** $4t + 6y - 4$
99. b **101.** $\frac{13}{4}y$ **103.** $8x$ **105.** $5n$ **107.** $-16y$
109. $17a - 12b - 1$ **111.** $4x + 2y$ **113.** $7x + y$
115. $0.8x + 0.5y$ **117.** $\frac{35}{6}a + \frac{3}{2}b - 42$ **119.** DW
121. 144 **122.** 72 **123.** 144 **124.** 60 **125.** 32
126. 72 **127.** 90 **128.** 108 **129.** $\frac{89}{48}$ **130.** $\frac{5}{24}$
131. $-\frac{5}{24}$ **132.** 30% **133.** Not equivalent; $3 \cdot 2 + 5 \neq 3 \cdot 5 + 2$ **135.** Equivalent; commutative law of addition **137.** $q(1 + r + rs + rst)$

Margin Exercises, Section 1.8, pp. 122–127

1. $-x - 2$ **2.** $-5x - 2y - 8$ **3.** $-6 + t$ **4.** $-x + y$
5. $4a - 3t + 10$ **6.** $-18 + m + 2n - 4z$ **7.** $2x - 9$
8. $3y + 2$ **9.** $2x - 7$ **10.** $3y + 3$ **11.** $-2a + 8b - 3c$
12. $-9x - 8y$ **13.** $-16a + 18$ **14.** $-26a + 41b - 48c$
15. $3x - 7$ **16.** $-18.6x - 19y$ **17.** 2 **18.** 18 **19.** 6
20. 17 **21.** $5x - y - 8$ **22.** −1237 **23.** 8 **24.** 4
25. 317 **26.** −12

Calculator Corner, p. 126

1. −11 **2.** 9 **3.** 114 **4.** 117,649 **5.** −1,419,857
6. −1,124,864 **7.** −117,649 **8.** −1,419,857
9. −1,124,864 **10.** −4 **11.** −2 **12.** 787

Exercise Set 1.8, p. 128

1. $-2x - 7$ **3.** $-8 + x$ **5.** $-4a + 3b - 7c$
7. $-6x + 8y - 5$ **9.** $-3x + 5y + 6$ **11.** $8x + 6y + 43$
13. $5x - 3$ **15.** $-3a + 9$ **17.** $5x - 6$ **19.** $-19x + 2$
21. $9y - 25z$ **23.** $-7x + 10y$ **25.** $37a - 23b + 35c$
27. 7 **29.** −40 **31.** 19 **33.** $12x + 30$ **35.** $3x + 30$
37. $9x - 18$ **39.** $-4x - 64$ **41.** −7 **43.** −7
45. −16 **47.** −334 **49.** 14 **51.** 1880 **53.** 12
55. 8 **57.** −86 **59.** 37 **61.** −1 **63.** −10
65. −67 **67.** −7988 **69.** −3000 **71.** 60 **73.** 1
75. 10 **77.** $-\frac{13}{45}$ **79.** $-\frac{23}{18}$ **81.** −122 **83.** DW
85. Integers **86.** Additive inverses
87. Commutative law **88.** Identity property of 1
89. Associative law **90.** Associative law
91. Multiplicative inverses **92.** Identity property of 0
93. $6y - (-2x + 3a - c)$ **95.** $6m - (-3n + 5m - 4b)$
97. $-2x - f$ **99.** (a) 52; 52; 28.130169; (b) −24; −24; −108.307025 **101.** −6

Concept Reinforcement, p. 132

1. True **2.** True **3.** False **4.** True **5.** False
6. True **7.** False

Summary and Review: Chapter 1, p. 132

1. 4 **2.** $19\%x$, or $0.19x$ **3.** −45, 72 **4.** 38
5.
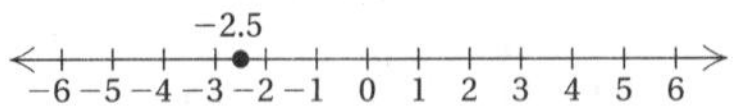

6.
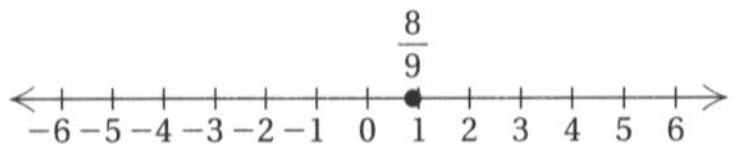

7. $<$ **8.** $>$
9. $>$ **10.** $<$ **11.** −3.8 **12.** $\frac{3}{4}$ **13.** $\frac{8}{3}$ **14.** $-\frac{1}{7}$
15. 34 **16.** 5 **17.** −3 **18.** −4 **19.** −5 **20.** 1
21. $-\frac{7}{5}$ **22.** −7.9 **23.** 54 **24.** −9.18 **25.** $-\frac{2}{7}$
26. −210 **27.** −7 **28.** −3 **29.** $\frac{3}{4}$ **30.** 40.4
31. −2 **32.** 2 **33.** −9 **34.** 8-yd gain **35.** −$130
36. $4.64 **37.** $18.95 **38.** $15x - 35$ **39.** $-8x + 10$
40. $4x + 15$ **41.** $-24 + 48x$ **42.** $2(x - 7)$
43. $6(-x + 1)$, or $-6(x - 1)$ **44.** $5(x + 2)$
45. $3(-x + 4y - 4)$, or $-3(x - 4y + 4)$ **46.** $7a - 3b$
47. $-2x + 5y$ **48.** $5x - y$ **49.** $-a + 8b$ **50.** $-3a +$
51. $-2b + 21$ **52.** 6 **53.** $12y - 34$ **54.** $5x + 24$
55. $-15x + 25$ **56.** True **57.** False **58.** $x > -3$
59. DW If the sum of two numbers is 0, they are opposites, or additive inverses of each other. For every real number a, the opposite of a can be named $-a$, and $a + (-a) = (-a) + a = 0$. **60.** DW No; $|0| = 0$, and 0 is not positive. **61.** $-\frac{5}{8}$ **62.** −2.1 **63.** 1000
64. $4a + 2b$

est: Chapter 1, p. 135

. [1.1a] 6 **2.** [1.1b] $x - 9$ **3.** [1.1a] 240 ft^2
. [1.2d] < **5.** [1.2d] > **6.** [1.2d] > **7.** [1.2d] <
. [1.2e] 7 **9.** [1.2e] $\frac{9}{4}$ **10.** [1.2e] 2.7 **11.** [1.3b] $-\frac{2}{3}$
2. [1.3b] 1.4 **13.** [1.3b] 8 **14.** [1.6b] $-\frac{1}{2}$
5. [1.6b] $\frac{7}{4}$ **16.** [1.4a] 7.8 **17.** [1.3a] -8
8. [1.3a] $\frac{7}{40}$ **19.** [1.4a] 10 **20.** [1.4a] -2.5
1. [1.4a] $\frac{7}{8}$ **22.** [1.5a] -48 **23.** [1.5a] $\frac{3}{16}$
4. [1.6a] -9 **25.** [1.6c] $\frac{3}{4}$ **26.** [1.6c] -9.728
7. [1.8d] -173 **28.** [1.8d] -5 **29.** [1.4b] 14°F
0. [1.3c], [1.4b] Up 15 points **31.** [1.5b] 16,080
2. [1.6d] $\frac{33}{35}$°C per minute **33.** [1.7c] $18 - 3x$
4. [1.7c] $-5y + 5$ **35.** [1.7d] $2(6 - 11x)$
6. [1.7d] $7(x + 3 + 2y)$ **37.** [1.4a] 12
8. [1.8b] $2x + 7$ **39.** [1.8b] $9a - 12b - 7$
0. [1.8c] $68y - 8$ **41.** [1.8d] -4 **42.** [1.8d] 448
3. [1.2d] $-2 \geq x$ **44.** [1.2e], [1.8d] 15
5. [1.8c] $4a$ **46.** [R.6a], [1.7e] $4x + 4y$

HAPTER 2

argin Exercises, Section 2.1, pp. 138–141

. False **2.** True **3.** Neither **4.** Yes **5.** No
No **7.** Yes **8.** 9 **9.** -13 **10.** 22 **11.** 13.2
2. -6.5 **13.** -2 **14.** $\frac{31}{8}$

xercise Set 2.1, p. 142

. Yes **3.** No **5.** No **7.** Yes **9.** No **11.** No
3. 4 **15.** -20 **17.** -14 **19.** -18 **21.** 15
3. -14 **25.** 2 **27.** 20 **29.** -6 **31.** $6\frac{1}{2}$ **33.** 19.9
5. $\frac{7}{3}$ **37.** $-\frac{7}{4}$ **39.** $\frac{41}{24}$ **41.** $-\frac{1}{20}$ **43.** 5.1 **45.** 12.4
7. -5 **49.** $1\frac{5}{6}$ **51.** $-\frac{10}{21}$ **53.** DW **55.** -11 **56.** 5
7. $-\frac{5}{12}$ **58.** $\frac{1}{3}$ **59.** $-\frac{3}{2}$ **60.** -5.2 **61.** $-\frac{1}{24}$
2. 172.72 **63.** \$83 $- x$ **64.** $65t$ miles **65.** 342.246
7. $-\frac{26}{15}$ **69.** -10 **71.** All real numbers **73.** $-\frac{5}{17}$
5. 13, -13

argin Exercises, Section 2.2, pp. 144–147

15 **2.** $-\frac{7}{4}$ **3.** -18 **4.** 10 **5.** 10 **6.** $-\frac{4}{5}$
7800 **8.** -3 **9.** 28

xercise Set 2.2, p. 148

6 **3.** 9 **5.** 12 **7.** -40 **9.** 1 **11.** -7 **13.** -6
5. 6 **17.** -63 **19.** 36 **21.** -21 **23.** $-\frac{3}{5}$ **25.** $-\frac{3}{2}$
27. $\frac{9}{2}$ **29.** 7 **31.** -7 **33.** 8 **35.** 15.9 **37.** -50
39. -14 **41.** DW **43.** $7x$ **44.** $-x + 5$ **45.** $8x + 11$
46. $-32y$ **47.** $x - 4$ **48.** $-5x - 23$ **49.** $-10y - 42$
50. $-22a + 4$ **51.** $8r$ miles **52.** $\frac{1}{2}b \cdot 10\ \text{m}^2$, or $5b\ \text{m}^2$
53. -8655 **55.** No solution **57.** No solution
59. $\frac{b}{3a}$ **61.** $\frac{4b}{a}$

Margin Exercises, Section 2.3, pp. 150–156

1. 5 **2.** 4 **3.** 4 **4.** 39 **5.** $-\frac{3}{2}$ **6.** -4.3 **7.** -3
8. 800 **9.** 1 **10.** 2 **11.** 2 **12.** $\frac{17}{2}$ **13.** $\frac{8}{3}$
14. $-\frac{43}{10}$, or -4.3 **15.** 2 **16.** 3 **17.** -2 **18.** $-\frac{1}{2}$
19. Yes **20.** Yes **21.** Yes **22.** Yes **23.** No
24. No **25.** No **26.** No **27.** All real numbers
28. No solution

Calculator Corner, p. 157

1. Left to the student **2.** Left to the student

Exercise Set 2.3, p. 158

1. 5 **3.** 8 **5.** 10 **7.** 14 **9.** -8 **11.** -8 **13.** -7
15. $\frac{2}{3}$ **17.** 6 **19.** 4 **21.** 6 **23.** -3 **25.** 1
27. 6 **29.** -20 **31.** 7 **33.** 2 **35.** 5 **37.** 2
39. 10 **41.** 4 **43.** 0 **45.** -1 **47.** $-\frac{4}{3}$ **49.** $\frac{2}{5}$
51. -2 **53.** -4 **55.** $\frac{4}{5}$ **57.** $-\frac{28}{27}$ **59.** 6 **61.** 2
63. No solution **65.** All real numbers **67.** 6 **69.** 8
71. 1 **73.** All real numbers **75.** No solution
77. 17 **79.** $-\frac{5}{3}$ **81.** -3 **83.** 2 **85.** $\frac{4}{7}$
87. No solution **89.** All real numbers **91.** $-\frac{51}{31}$
93. DW **95.** -6.5 **96.** -75.14 **97.** $7(x - 3 - 2y)$
98. $8(y - 11x + 1)$ **99.** -160 **100.** $-17x + 18$
101. $91x - 242$ **102.** 0.25 **103.** $-\frac{5}{32}$ **105.** $\frac{52}{45}$

Margin Exercises, Section 2.4, pp. 162–165

1. 2.8 mi **2.** 280,865 socks **3.** 341 mi **4.** $q = 3B$
5. $r = \frac{d}{t}$ **6.** $I = \frac{E}{R}$ **7.** $x = y - 5$ **8.** $x = y + 7$
9. $x = y + b$ **10.** $y = \frac{5x}{9}$, or $\frac{5}{9}x$ **11.** $p = \frac{bq}{a}$
12. $x = \frac{y - b}{m}$ **13.** $Q = \frac{a + p}{t}$ **14.** $D = \frac{C}{\pi}$
15. $c = 4A - a - b - d$

Exercise Set 2.4, p. 166

1. **(a)** 57,000 Btu's; **(b)** $a = \frac{B}{30}$ **3.** **(a)** $1\frac{3}{5}$ mi; **(b)** $t = 5M$
5. **(a)** 1423 students; **(b)** $n = 15f$
7. 10.5 calories per ounce **9.** 42 games **11.** $x = \frac{y}{5}$
13. $c = \frac{a}{b}$ **15.** $x = y - 13$ **17.** $x = y - b$

19. $x = 5 - y$ **21.** $x = a - y$ **23.** $y = \frac{5x}{8}$, or $\frac{5}{8}x$
25. $x = \frac{By}{A}$ **27.** $t = \frac{W - b}{m}$ **29.** $x = \frac{y - c}{b}$
31. $b = 3A - a - c$ **33.** $t = \frac{A - b}{a}$ **35.** $h = \frac{A}{b}$
37. $w = \frac{P - 2l}{2}$, or $\frac{1}{2}P - l$ **39.** $a = 2A - b$
41. $a = \frac{F}{m}$ **43.** $c^2 = \frac{E}{m}$ **45.** $x = \frac{c - By}{A}$ **47.** $t = \frac{3k}{v}$
49. DW **51.** 0.92 **52.** −90 **53.** −9.325 **54.** 44
55. −13.2 **56.** $-21a + 12b$ **57.** 0.031 **58.** 0.671
59. $\frac{1}{6}$ **60.** $-\frac{3}{2}$
61. **(a)** 1901 calories;
(b) $a = \frac{917 + 6w + 6h - K}{6}$;
$h = \frac{K - 917 - 6w + 6a}{6}$;
$w = \frac{K - 917 - 6h + 6a}{6}$
63. $b = \frac{Ha - 2}{H}$, or $a - \frac{2}{H}$; $a = \frac{2 + Hb}{H}$, or $\frac{2}{H} + b$
65. A quadruples. **67.** A increases by $2h$ units.

Margin Exercises, Section 2.5, pp. 170–173

1. $13\% \cdot 80 = a$ **2.** $a = 60\% \cdot 70$ **3.** $43 = 20\% \cdot b$
4. $110\% \cdot b = 30$ **5.** $16 = n \cdot 80$ **6.** $n \cdot 94 = 10.5$
7. 1.92 **8.** 115 **9.** 36% **10.** 111,416 mi^2
11. About 1.2 million **12.** About 58%

Exercise Set 2.5, p. 174

1. 20% **3.** 150 **5.** 546 **7.** 24% **9.** 2.5 **11.** 5%
13. 25% **15.** 84 **17.** 24% **19.** 16% **21.** $46\frac{2}{3}$
23. 0.8 **25.** 5 **27.** 40 **29.** \$198 **31.** \$1584
33. \$528 **35.** Japan: 44.3%; Germany: 24.9%
37. About 603 at-bats **39.** \$195 **41.** **(a)** 16%; **(b)** \$29
43. **(a)** \$3.75; **(b)** \$28.75 **45.** **(a)** \$28.80; **(b)** \$33.12
47. 200 women **49.** About 31.5 lb **51.** \$655; 196%
53. \$2190; \$1455 **55.** \$3935; 261% **57.** DW
59. 181.52 **60.** 0.4538 **61.** 12.0879 **62.** 844.1407
63. $a + c$ **64.** $7x - 9y$ **65.** −3.9 **66.** $-6\frac{1}{8}$
67. Division; subtraction **68.** Exponential; division; subtraction **69.** 6 ft 7 in.

Margin Exercises, Section 2.6, pp. 179–188

1. $62\frac{2}{3}$ mi **2.** Jenny: 8 in.; Emma: 4 in.; Sarah: 6 in.
3. 313 and 314 **4.** 60,417 copies
5. Length: 84 ft; width: 50 ft **6.** First: 30°; second: 90°; third: 60° **7.** Second: 80; third: 89 **8.** \$8400 **9.** \$658

Translating for Success, p. 189

1. B **2.** H **3.** G **4.** N **5.** J **6.** C **7.** L **8.** E
9. F **10.** D

Exercise Set 2.6, p. 190

1. 180 in.; 60 in. **3.** \$4.29 **5.** \$6.3 billion **7.** $699\frac{1}{3}$ n
9. 1204 and 1205 **11.** 41, 42, 43 **13.** 61, 63, 65
15. Length: 48 ft; width: 14 ft **17.** \$75 **19.** \$85
21. 11 visits **23.** 28°, 84°, 68° **25.** 33°, 38°, 109°
27. \$350 **29.** \$852.94 **31.** 12 mi **33.** \$36
35. \$25 and \$50 **37.** DW **39.** $-\frac{47}{40}$ **40.** $-\frac{17}{40}$
41. $-\frac{3}{10}$ **42.** $-\frac{32}{15}$ **43.** −10 **44.** 1.6 **45.** 409.6
46. −9.6 **47.** −41.6 **48.** 0.1 **49.** 120 apples
51. About 0.65 in. **53.** \$9.17, not \$9.10

Margin Exercises, Section 2.7, pp. 195–202

1. **(a)** No; **(b)** no; **(c)** no; **(d)** yes; **(e)** no; **(f)** no
2. **(a)** Yes; **(b)** yes; **(c)** yes; **(d)** no; **(e)** yes; **(f)** yes
3.
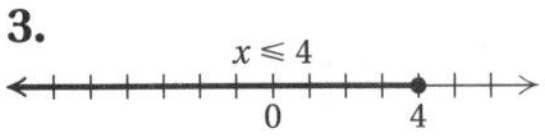

4.
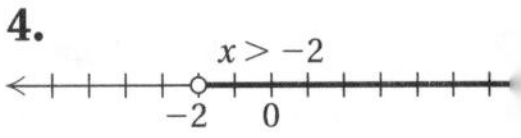

5.
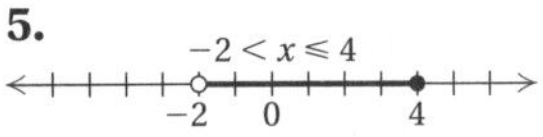

6. $\{x \mid x > 2\}$;
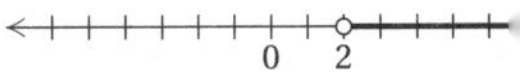

7. $\{x \mid x \le 3\}$;

8. $\{x \mid x < -3\}$;
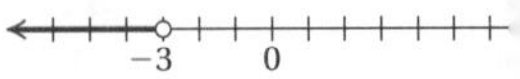

9. $\left\{x \middle| x \ge \frac{2}{15}\right\}$ **10.** $\{y \mid y \le -3\}$
11. $\{x \mid x < 8\}$;
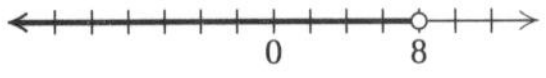

12. $\{y \mid y \ge 32\}$;
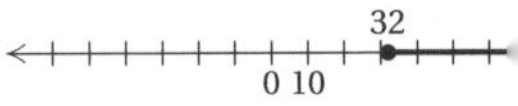

13. $\{x \mid x \ge -6\}$ **14.** $\left\{y \middle| y < -\frac{13}{5}\right\}$
15. $\left\{x \middle| x > -\frac{1}{4}\right\}$ **16.** $\left\{y \middle| y \ge \frac{19}{9}\right\}$ **17.** $\left\{y \middle| y \ge \frac{19}{9}\right\}$
18. $\{x \mid x \ge -2\}$ **19.** $\{x \mid x \ge -4\}$ **20.** $\left\{x \middle| x > \frac{8}{3}\right\}$

Exercise Set 2.7, p. 203

1. **(a)** Yes; **(b)** yes; **(c)** no; **(d)** yes; **(e)** yes
3. **(a)** No; **(b)** no; **(c)** no; **(d)** yes; **(e)** no
5.
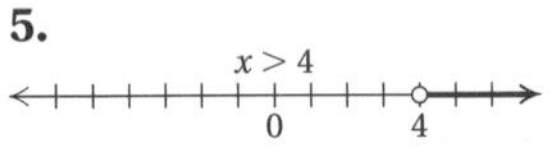

7.
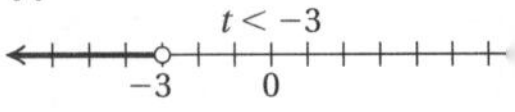

9.
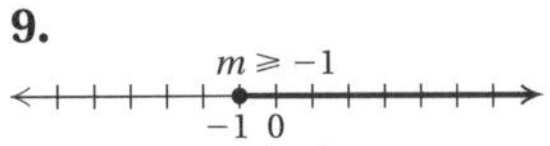

11.
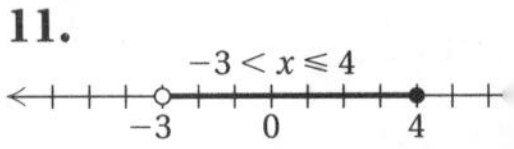

13.
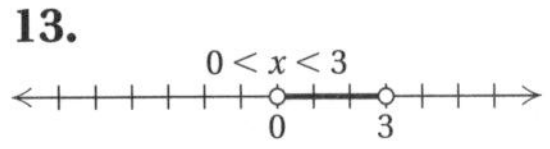

15. $\{x \mid x > -5\}$;
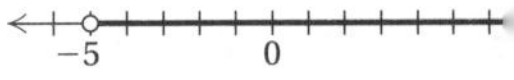

17. $\{x \mid x \le -18\}$;
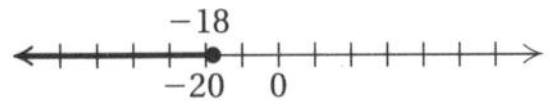

19. $\{y \mid y > -5\}$
21. $\{x \mid x > 2\}$ **23.** $\{x \mid x \le -3\}$ **25.** $\{x \mid x < 4\}$
27. $\{t \mid t > 14\}$ **29.** $\left\{y \middle| y \le \frac{1}{4}\right\}$ **31.** $\left\{x \middle| x > \frac{7}{12}\right\}$
33. $\{x \mid x < 7\}$;
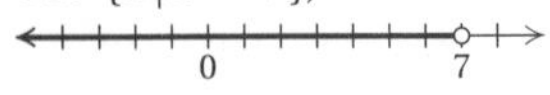

35. $\{x \mid x < 3\}$;
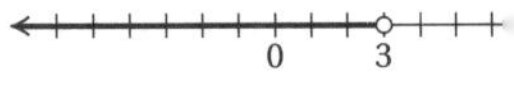

37. $\left\{y \middle| y \ge -\frac{2}{5}\right\}$ **39.** $\{x \mid x \ge -6\}$ **41.** $\{y \mid y \le 4\}$
43. $\left\{x \middle| x > \frac{17}{3}\right\}$ **45.** $\left\{y \middle| y < -\frac{1}{14}\right\}$ **47.** $\left\{x \middle| x \le \frac{3}{10}\right\}$
49. $\{x \mid x < 8\}$ **51.** $\{x \mid x \le 6\}$ **53.** $\{x \mid x < -3\}$
55. $\{x \mid x > -3\}$ **57.** $\{x \mid x \le 7\}$ **59.** $\{x \mid x > -10\}$

61. $\{y|y < 2\}$ **63.** $\{y|y \geq 3\}$ **65.** $\{y|y > -2\}$ **67.** $\{x|x > -4\}$ **69.** $\{x|x \leq 9\}$ **71.** $\{y|y \leq -3\}$ **73.** $\{y|y < 6\}$ **75.** $\{m|m \geq 6\}$ **77.** $\{t|t < -\frac{5}{3}\}$ **79.** $\{r|r > -3\}$ **81.** $\{x|x \geq -\frac{57}{34}\}$ **83.** $\{x|x > -2\}$ **85.** DW **87.** -74 **88.** 4.8 **89.** $-\frac{5}{8}$ **90.** -1.11 **91.** -38 **92.** $-\frac{7}{8}$ **93.** -9.4 **94.** 1.11 **95.** 140 **96.** 41 **97.** $-2x - 23$ **98.** $37x - 1$ **99.** **(a)** Yes; **(b)** yes; **(c)** no; **(d)** no; **(e)** no; **(f)** yes; **(g)** yes **101.** No solution

Margin Exercises, Section 2.8, pp. 207–209

1. $m \geq 92$ **2.** $c \geq 4000$ **3.** $p \leq 21{,}900$ **4.** $45 < t < 55$ **5.** $d > 15$ **6.** $w < 110$ **7.** $n > -2$ **8.** $c \leq 12{,}500$ **9.** $d \leq 11.4\%$ **10.** $s \geq 23$ **11.** $\frac{9}{5}C + 32 < 88; \{C|C < 31\frac{1}{9}°\}$

12. $\frac{91 + 86 + 89 + s}{4} \geq 90; \{s|s \geq 94\}$

Exercise Set 2.8, p. 210

1. $n \geq 7$ **3.** $w > 2$ kg **5.** 90 mph $< s <$ 110 mph **7.** $a \leq 1{,}200{,}000$ **9.** $c \geq \$1.50$ **11.** $x > 8$ **13.** $y \leq -4$ **15.** $n \geq 1300$ **17.** $A \leq 500$ L **19.** $3x + 2 < 13$ **21.** $\{x|x \geq 84\}$ **23.** $\{C|C < 1063°\}$ **25.** $\{Y|Y \geq 1935\}$ **27.** $\{L|L \geq 5 \text{ in.}\}$ **29.** 15 or fewer copies **31.** 5 min or more **33.** 2 courses **35.** 4 servings or more **37.** Lengths greater than or equal to 92 ft; lengths less than or equal to 92 ft **39.** Lengths less than 21.5 cm **41.** The blue-book value is greater than or equal to $10,625. **43.** It has at least 16 g of fat. **45.** Dates at least 6 weeks after July 1 **47.** Heights greater than or equal to 4 ft **49.** 21 calls or more **51.** DW **53.** Even **54.** Odd **55.** Additive **56.** Multiplicative **57.** Equivalent **58.** Addition principle **59.** Multiplication principle; is reversed **60.** Solution **61.** Temperatures between $-15°$C and $-9\frac{4}{9}°$C **63.** They contain at least 7.5 g of fat per serving.

Concept Reinforcement, p. 215

1. True **2.** True **3.** True **4.** False **5.** True **6.** False

Summary and Review: Chapter 2, p. 215

1. -22 **2.** 1 **3.** 25 **4.** 9.99 **5.** $\frac{1}{4}$ **6.** 7 **7.** -192 **8.** $-\frac{7}{3}$ **9.** $-\frac{15}{64}$ **10.** -8 **11.** 4 **12.** -5 **13.** $-\frac{1}{3}$ **14.** 3 **15.** 4 **16.** 16 **17.** All real numbers **18.** 6 **19.** -3 **20.** 28 **21.** 4 **22.** No solution **23.** Yes **24.** No **25.** Yes **26.** $\{y|y \geq -\frac{1}{2}\}$ **27.** $\{x|x \geq 7\}$ **28.** $\{y|y > 2\}$ **29.** $\{y|y \leq -4\}$ **30.** $\{x|x < -11\}$ **31.** $\{y|y > -7\}$ **32.** $\{x|x > -\frac{9}{11}\}$ **33.** $\{x|x \geq -\frac{1}{12}\}$

34.

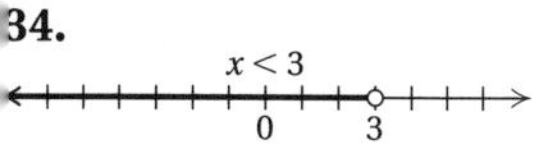

35.

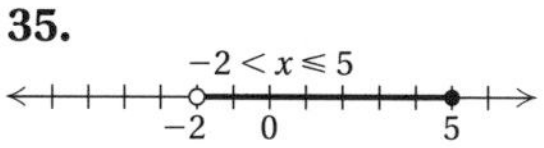

36.

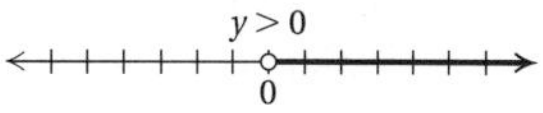

37. $d = \frac{C}{\pi}$ **38.** $B = \frac{3V}{h}$

39. $a = 2A - b$ **40.** $x = \frac{y - b}{m}$ **41.** Length: 365 mi; width: 275 mi **42.** 345, 346 **43.** $2117 **44.** 27 appliances **45.** 35°, 85°, 60° **46.** 15 **47.** 18.75% **48.** 600 **49.** About 26% **50.** $220 **51.** $53,400 **52.** $138.95 **53.** 86 **54.** $\{w|w > 17 \text{ cm}\}$ **55.** DW The end result is the same either way. If s is the original salary, the new salary after a 5% raise followed by an 8% raise is $1.08(1.05s)$. If the raises occur the other way around, the new salary is $1.05(1.08s)$. By the commutative and associative laws of multiplication, we see that these are equal. However, it would be better to receive the 8% raise first, because this increase yields a higher salary initially than a 5% raise. **56.** DW The inequalities are equivalent by the multiplication principle for inequalities. If we multiply both sides of one inequality by -1, the other inequality results. **57.** 23, -23 **58.** 20, -20

59. $a = \frac{y - 3}{2 - b}$

Test: Chapter 2, p. 218

1. [2.1b] 8 **2.** [2.1b] 26 **3.** [2.2a] -6 **4.** [2.2a] 49 **5.** [2.3b] -12 **6.** [2.3a] 2 **7.** [2.3a] -8 **8.** [2.1b] $-\frac{7}{20}$ **9.** [2.3c] 7 **10.** [2.3c] $\frac{5}{3}$ **11.** [2.3b] $\frac{5}{2}$ **12.** [2.3c] No solution **13.** [2.3c] All real numbers **14.** [2.7c] $\{x|x \leq -4\}$ **15.** [2.7c] $\{x|x > -13\}$ **16.** [2.7d] $\{x|x \leq 5\}$ **17.** [2.7d] $\{y|y \leq -13\}$ **18.** [2.7d] $\{y|y \geq 8\}$ **19.** [2.7d] $\{x|x \leq -\frac{1}{20}\}$ **20.** [2.7e] $\{x|x < -6\}$ **21.** [2.7e] $\{x|x \leq -1\}$

22. [2.7b]

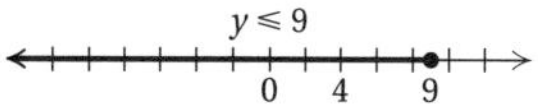

23. [2.7b, e]

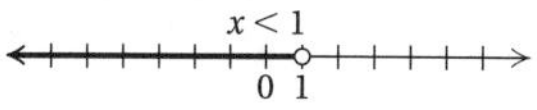

24. [2.7b]

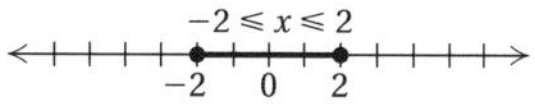

25. [2.5a] 18

26. [2.5a] 16.5% **27.** [2.5a] 40,000 **28.** [2.5a] About 53.4% **29.** [2.6a] Width: 7 cm; length: 11 cm **30.** [2.5a] About $240.7 billion **31.** [2.6a] 2509, 2510, 2511 **32.** [2.6a] $880 **33.** [2.6a] 3 m, 5 m **34.** [2.8b] $\{l|l \geq 174 \text{ yd}\}$ **35.** [2.8b] $\{b|b \leq \$105\}$ **36.** [2.8a] $\{c|c \leq 143{,}750\}$

37. [2.4b] $r = \frac{A}{2\pi h}$ **38.** [2.4b] $x = \frac{y - b}{8}$

39. [2.4b] $d = \frac{1 - ca}{-c}$, or $\frac{ca - 1}{c}$

40. [1.2e], [2.3a] 15, -15 **41.** [2.6a] 60 tickets

Cumulative Review: Chapters 1–2, p. 220

1. [1.1a] $\frac{3}{2}$ **2.** [1.1a] $\frac{15}{4}$ **3.** [1.1a] 0 **4.** [1.1b] $2w - 4$ **5.** [1.2d] $>$ **6.** [1.2d] $>$ **7.** [1.2d] $<$ **8.** [1.3b], [1.6b] $-\frac{2}{5}, \frac{5}{2}$ **9.** [1.2e] 3 **10.** [1.2e] $\frac{3}{4}$ **11.** [1.2e] 0 **12.** [1.3a] -4.4

13. [1.4a] $-\frac{5}{2}$ **14.** [1.5a] $\frac{5}{6}$ **15.** [1.5a] -105
16. [1.6a] -9 **17.** [1.6c] -3 **18.** [1.6c] $\frac{32}{125}$
19. [1.7c] $15x + 25y + 10z$ **20.** [1.7c] $-12x - 8$
21. [1.7c] $-12y + 24x$ **22.** [1.7d] $2(32 + 9x + 12y)$
23. [1.7d] $8(2y - 7)$ **24.** [1.7d] $5(a - 3b + 5)$
25. [1.7e] $15b + 22y$ **26.** [1.7e] $4 + 9y + 6z$
27. [1.7e] $1 - 3a - 9d$ **28.** [1.7e] $-2.6x - 5.2y$
29. [1.8b] $3x - 1$ **30.** [1.8b] $-2x - y$
31. [1.8b] $-7x + 6$ **32.** [1.8b] $8x$ **33.** [1.8c] $5x - 13$
34. [2.1b] 4.5 **35.** [2.2a] $\frac{4}{25}$ **36.** [2.1b] 10.9
37. [2.1b] $3\frac{5}{6}$ **38.** [2.2a] -48 **39.** [2.2a] 12
40. [2.2a] -6.2 **41.** [2.3a] -3 **42.** [2.3b] $-\frac{12}{5}$
43. [2.3b] 8 **44.** [2.3c] 7 **45.** [2.3b] $-\frac{4}{5}$
46. [2.3b] $-\frac{10}{3}$ **47.** [2.3c] All real numbers
48. [2.3c] No solution **49.** [2.3c] All real numbers
50. [2.7c] $\{x \mid x < 2\}$ **51.** [2.7e] $\{y \mid y \geq 4\}$
52. [2.7e] $\{y \mid y < -3\}$ **53.** [2.4b] $m = 65 - H$
54. [2.4b] $P = \dfrac{I}{rt}$ **55.** [2.5a] 25.2 **56.** [2.5a] 45%
57. [2.5a] \$363.56 **58.** [2.5a] 174.6 million
59. [2.8b] $\{s \mid s \geq 84\}$ **60.** [2.6a] \$45 **61.** [2.6a] \$1050
62. [2.6a] 50 m, 53 m, 40 m **63.** [2.8b] $\{d \mid d \leq 128\frac{1}{3}\text{ mi}\}$
64. [2.6a] \$24.60 **65.** [1.8d] (c) **66.** [1.8c] (d)
67. [2.4b] (b) **68.** [2.5a] \$45,200 **69.** [2.5a] 30%
70. [1.2e], [2.3a] 4, -4 **71.** [2.3b] 3
72. [2.4b] $Q = \dfrac{2 - pm}{p}$

CHAPTER 3

Margin Exercises, Section 3.1, pp. 224–234

1.–8.

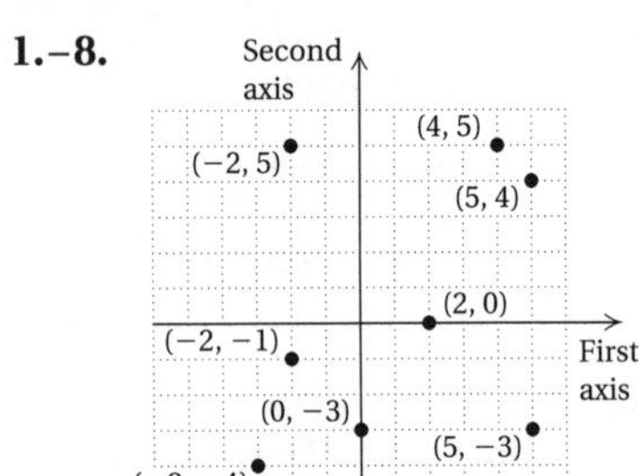

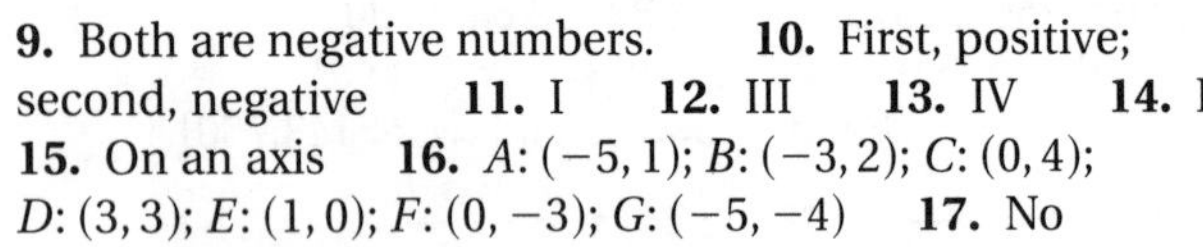

9. Both are negative numbers. **10.** First, positive; second, negative **11.** I **12.** III **13.** IV **14.** II
15. On an axis **16.** A: $(-5, 1)$; B: $(-3, 2)$; C: $(0, 4)$; D: $(3, 3)$; E: $(1, 0)$; F: $(0, -3)$; G: $(-5, -4)$ **17.** No
18. Yes **19.** $(-2, -3)$, $(1, 3)$; answers may vary

20.

x	y	(x, y)
-3	6	$(-3, 6)$
-1	2	$(-1, 2)$
0	0	$(0, 0)$
1	-2	$(1, -2)$
3	-6	$(3, -6)$

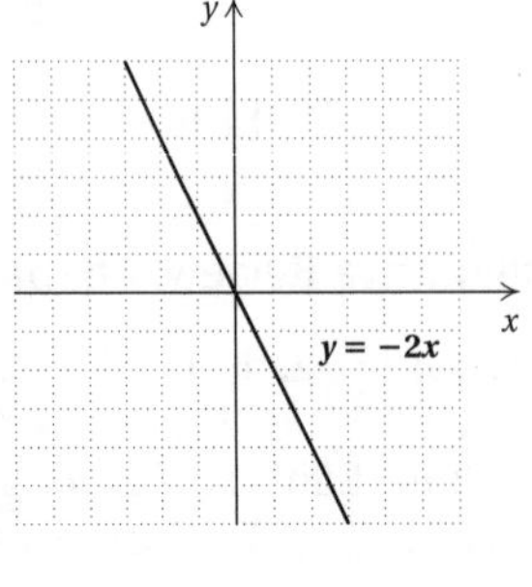

21.

x	y	(x, y)
4	2	$(4, 2)$
2	1	$(2, 1)$
0	0	$(0, 0)$
-2	-1	$(-2, -1)$
-4	-2	$(-4, -2)$
-1	$-\frac{1}{2}$	$(-1, -\frac{1}{2})$

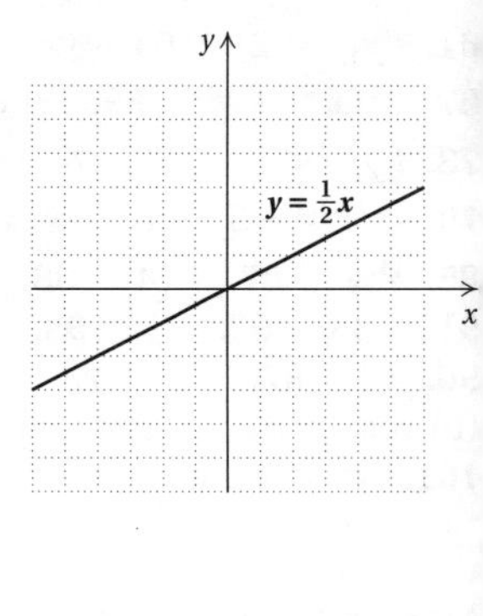

22.

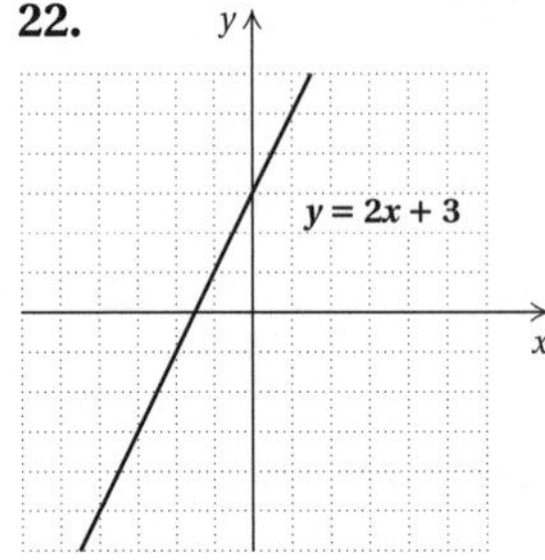

23.

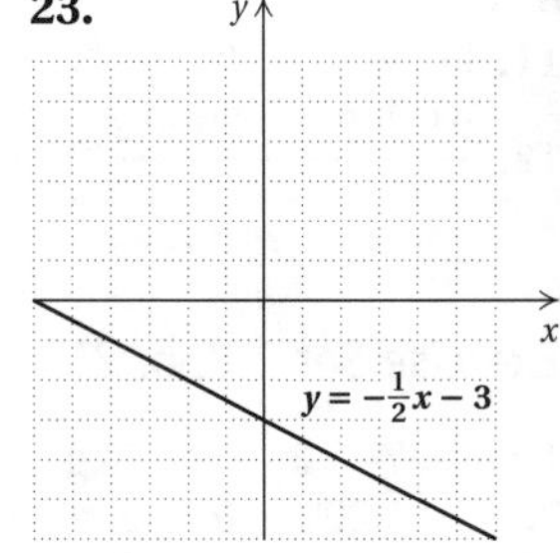

24.

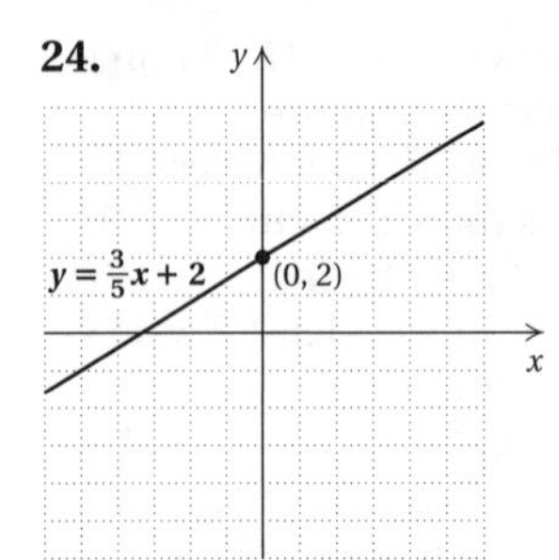

25.

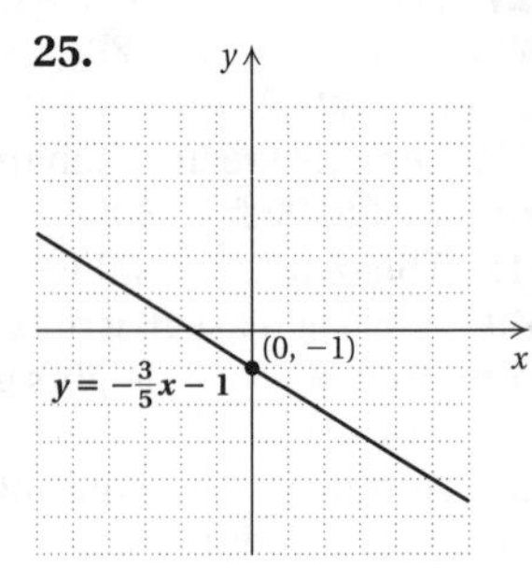

26.

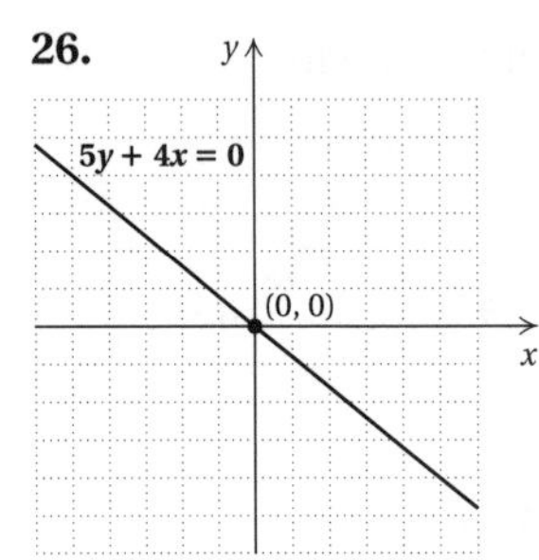

27.

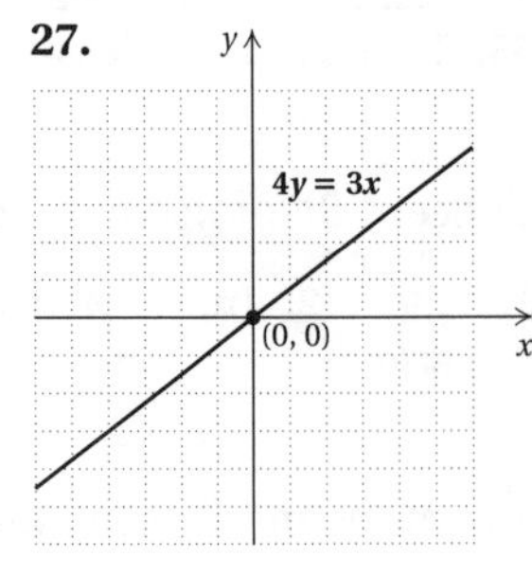

28.

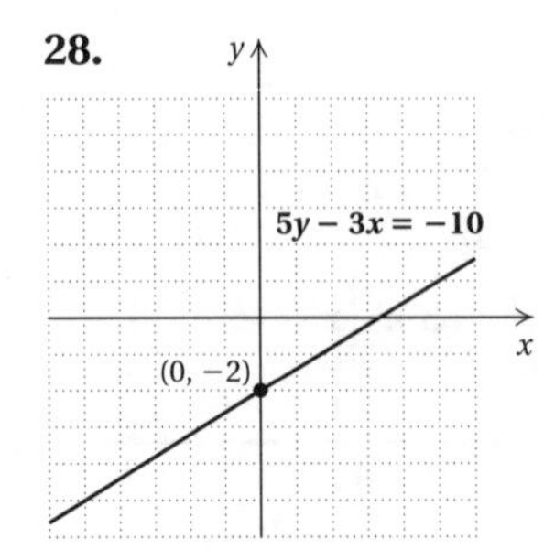

29.

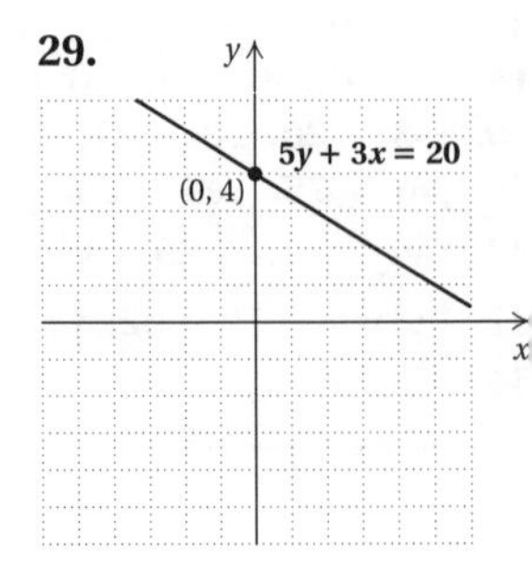

(a) \$2720; \$2040; \$680; \$0;
) about \$1700;
) about 2.8 yr

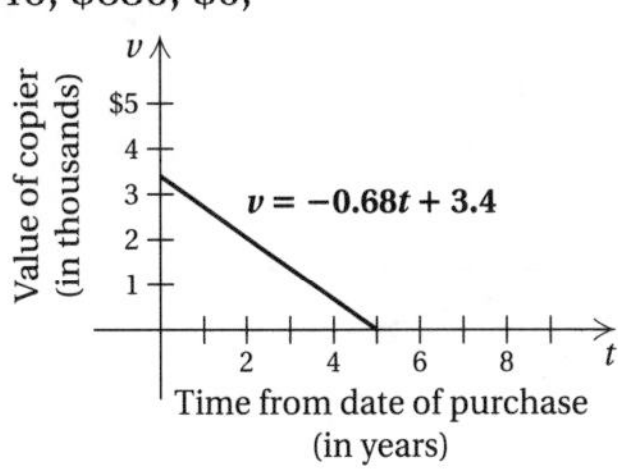

alculator Corner, p. 230

Left to the student

alculator Corner, p. 235

$y = 2x + 1$

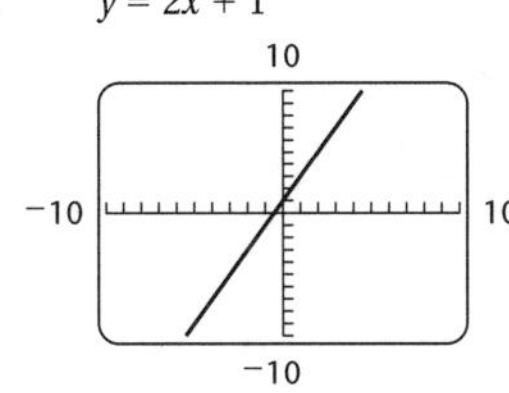

2. $y = -3x + 1$

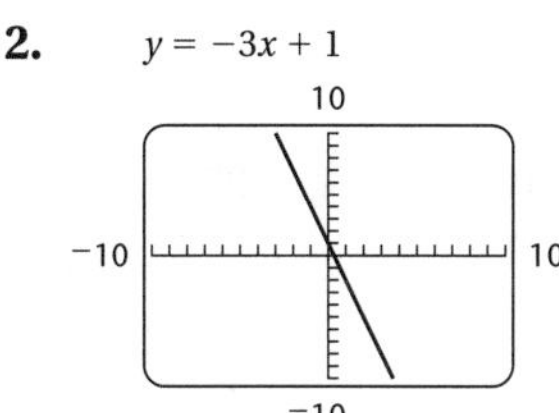

$y = -5x + 3$

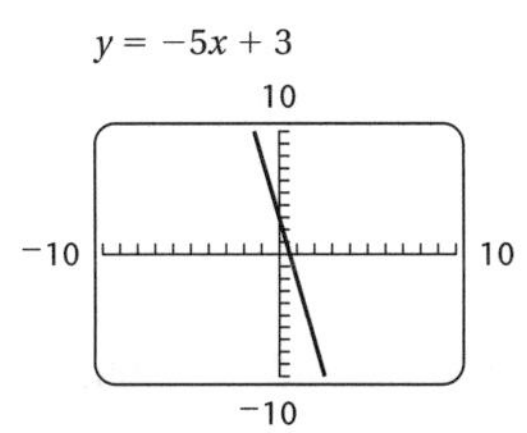

4. $y = 4x - 5$

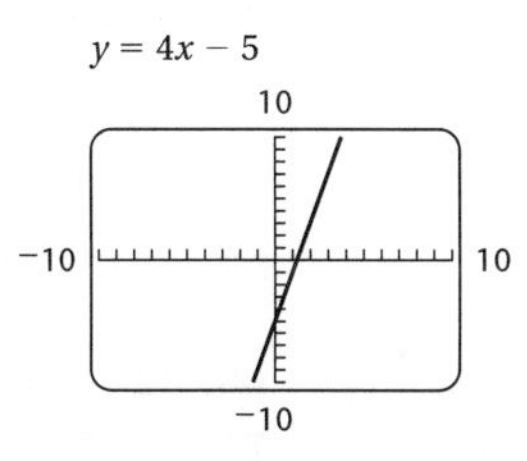

$y = \frac{4}{5}x + 2$

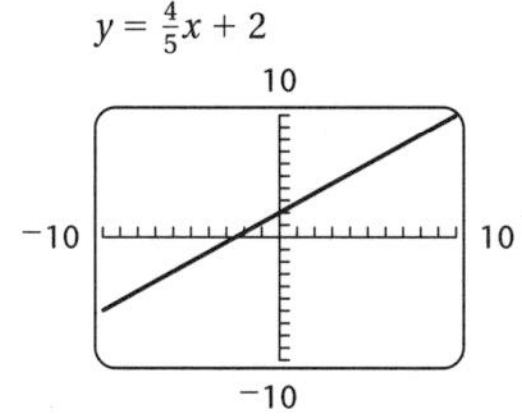

6. $y = -\frac{3}{5}x - 1$

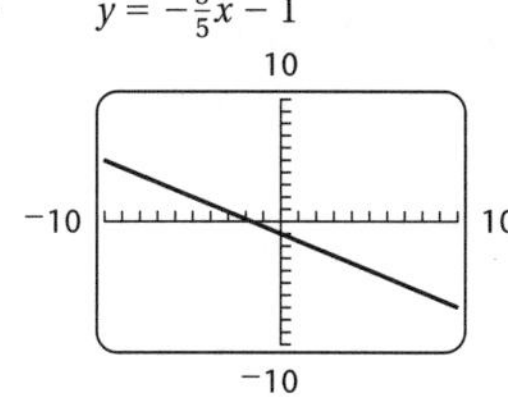

$y = 2.085x + 5.08$

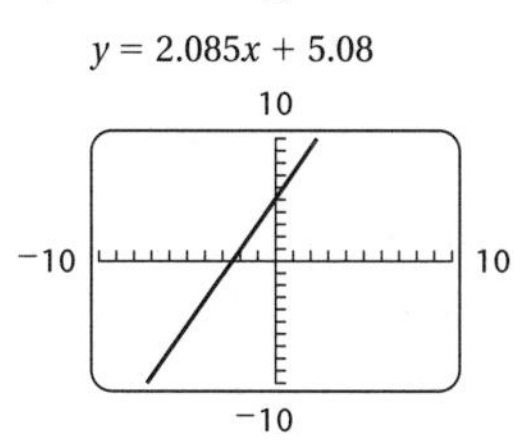

8. $y = -3.45x - 1.68$

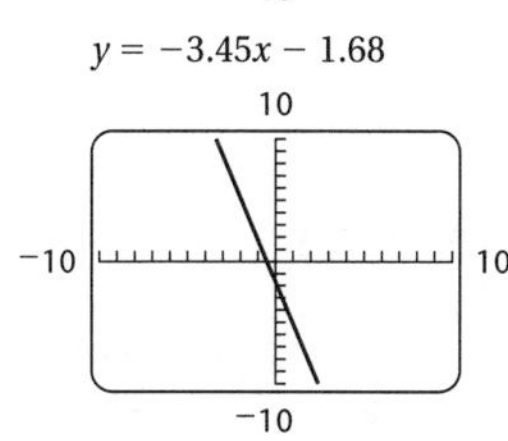

xercise Set 3.1, p. 236

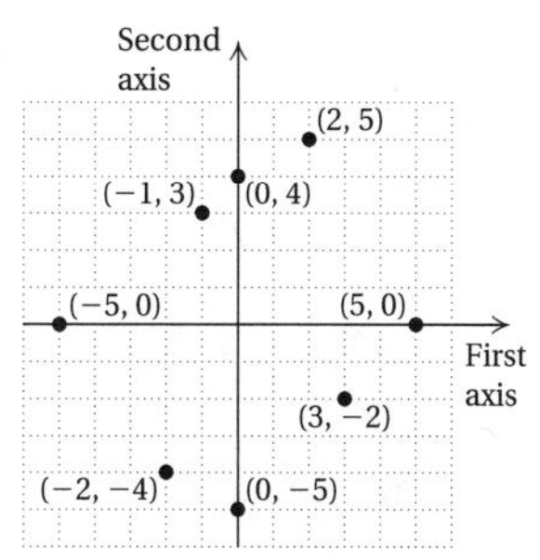

3. II **5.** IV **7.** III
9. On an axis **11.** II
13. IV **15.** II
17. I, IV **19.** I, III

1. A: $(3, 3)$; B: $(0, -4)$; C: $(-5, 0)$; D: $(-1, -1)$; E: $(2, 0)$

23. No **25.** No **27.** Yes

29.

$$\begin{array}{c|l} \multicolumn{2}{c}{y = x - 5} \\ \hline -1 \;?\; & 4 - 5 \\ & -1 \quad \text{TRUE} \end{array}$$

$$\begin{array}{c|l} \multicolumn{2}{c}{y = x - 5} \\ \hline -4 \;?\; & 1 - 5 \\ & -4 \quad \text{TRUE} \end{array}$$

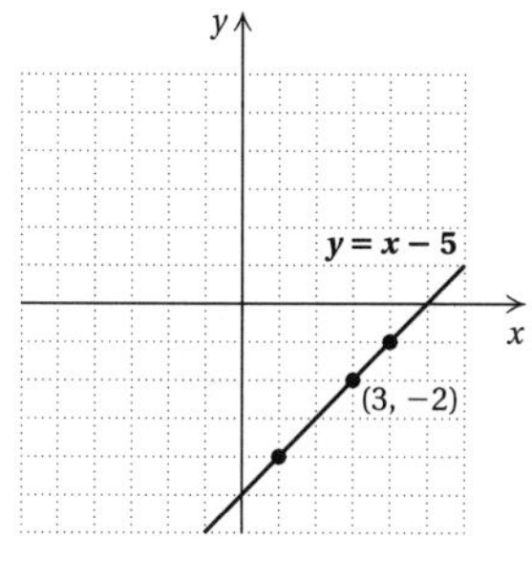

31.

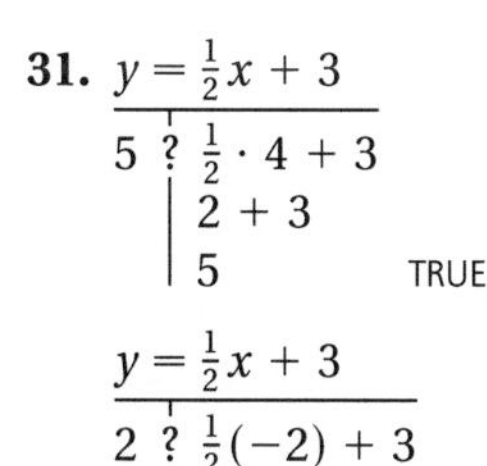

$$\begin{array}{c|l} \multicolumn{2}{c}{y = \frac{1}{2}x + 3} \\ \hline 5 \;?\; & \frac{1}{2} \cdot 4 + 3 \\ & 2 + 3 \\ & 5 \quad \text{TRUE} \end{array}$$

$$\begin{array}{c|l} \multicolumn{2}{c}{y = \frac{1}{2}x + 3} \\ \hline 2 \;?\; & \frac{1}{2}(-2) + 3 \\ & -1 + 3 \\ & 2 \quad \text{TRUE} \end{array}$$

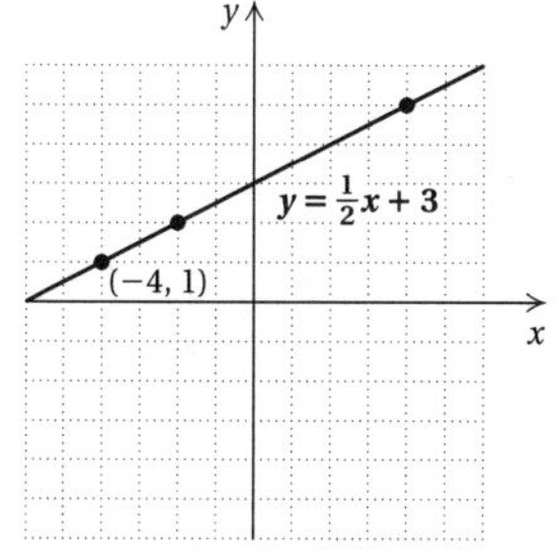

33.

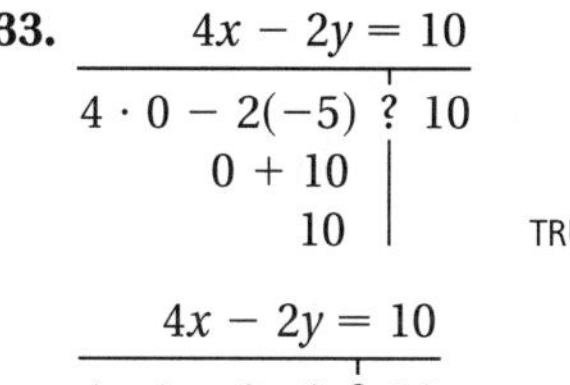

$$\begin{array}{r|l} \multicolumn{2}{c}{4x - 2y = 10} \\ \hline 4 \cdot 0 - 2(-5) & ?\; 10 \\ 0 + 10 & \\ 10 & \quad \text{TRUE} \end{array}$$

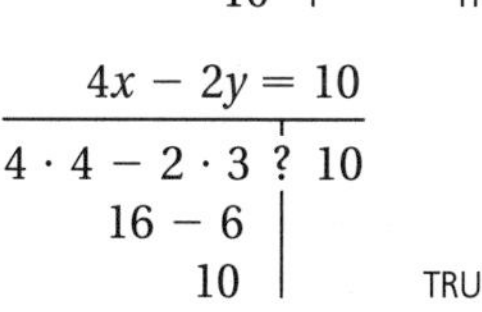

$$\begin{array}{r|l} \multicolumn{2}{c}{4x - 2y = 10} \\ \hline 4 \cdot 4 - 2 \cdot 3 & ?\; 10 \\ 16 - 6 & \\ 10 & \quad \text{TRUE} \end{array}$$

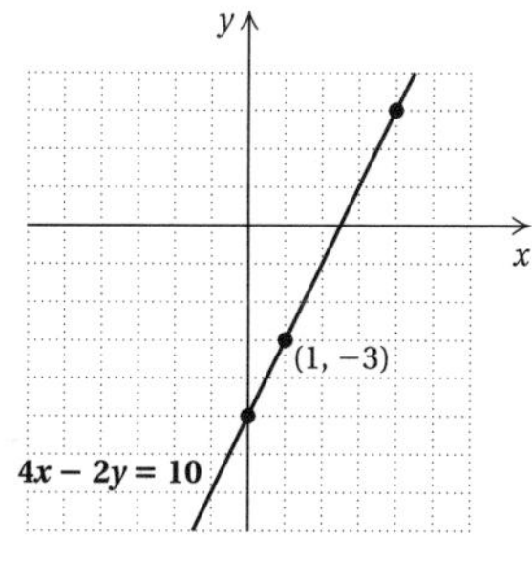

35.

x	y
−2	−1
−1	0
0	1
1	2
2	3
3	4

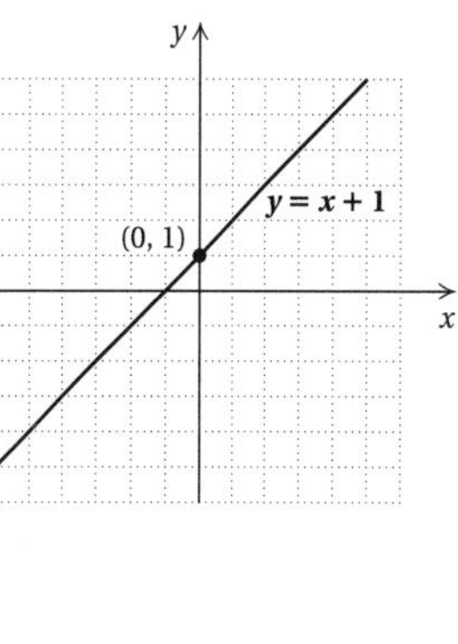

37.

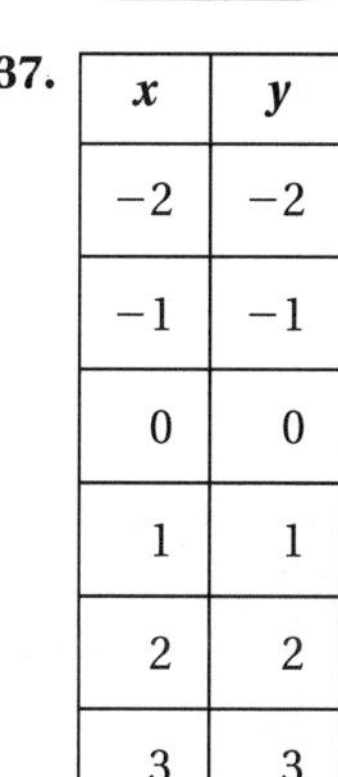

x	y
−2	−2
−1	−1
0	0
1	1
2	2
3	3

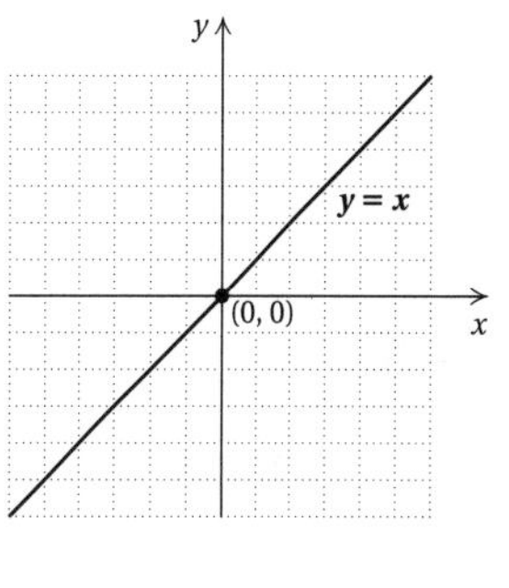

39.

x	y
-2	-1
0	0
4	2

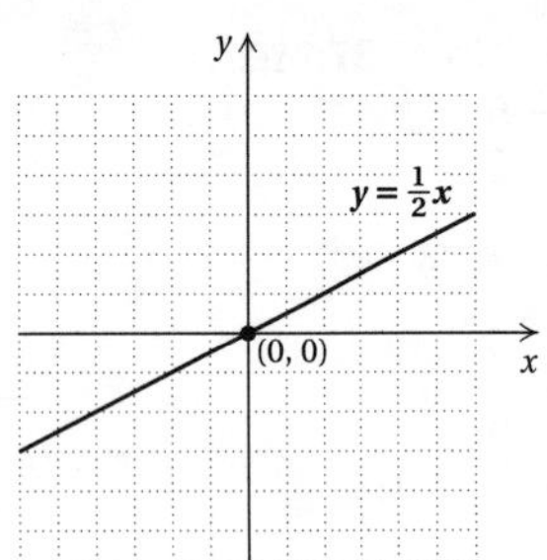

41.

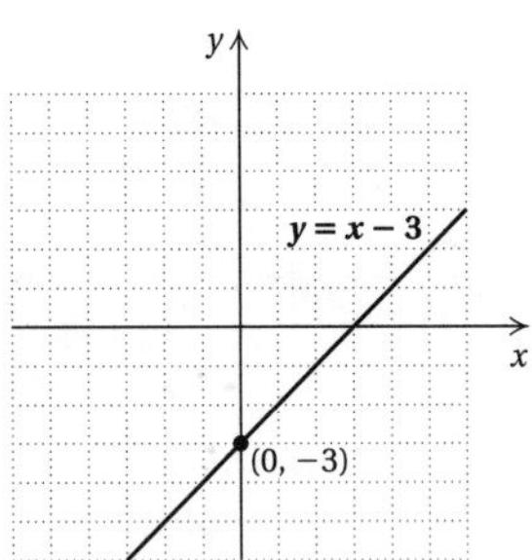

43.

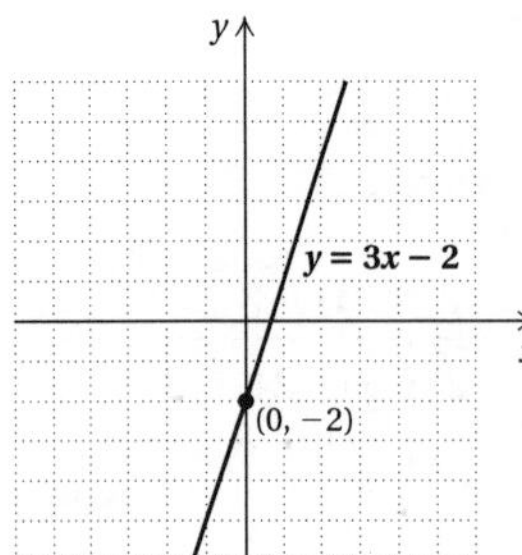

45.

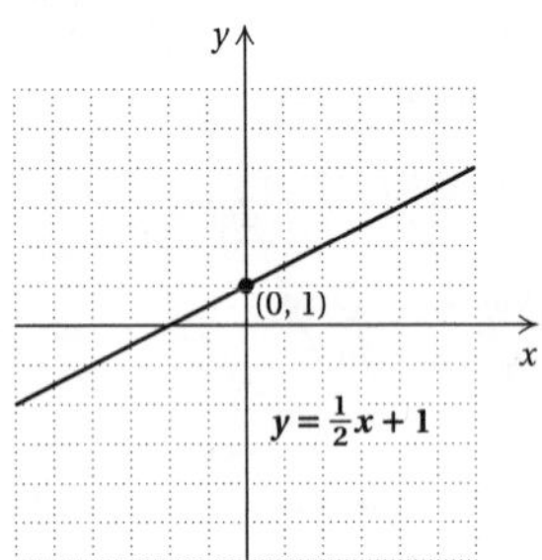

47.

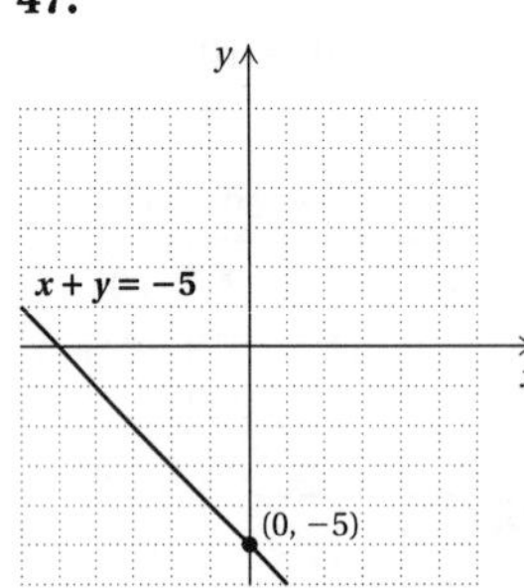

49.

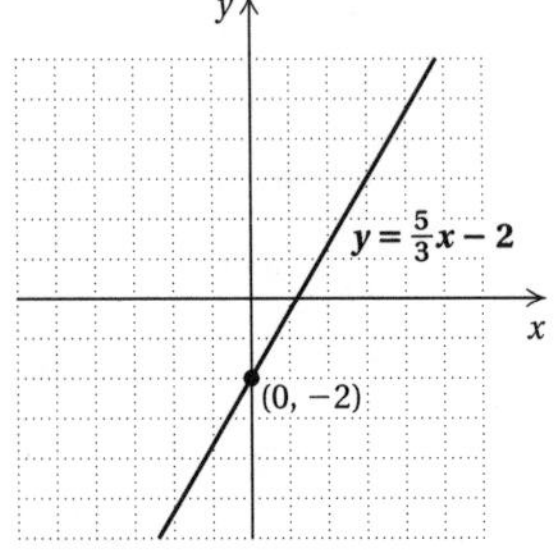

51.

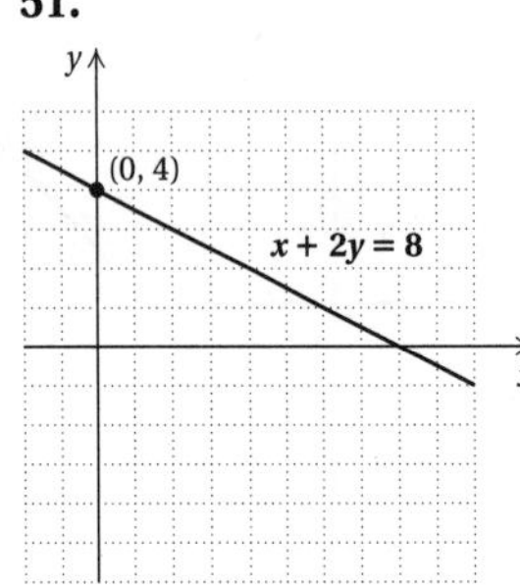

53.

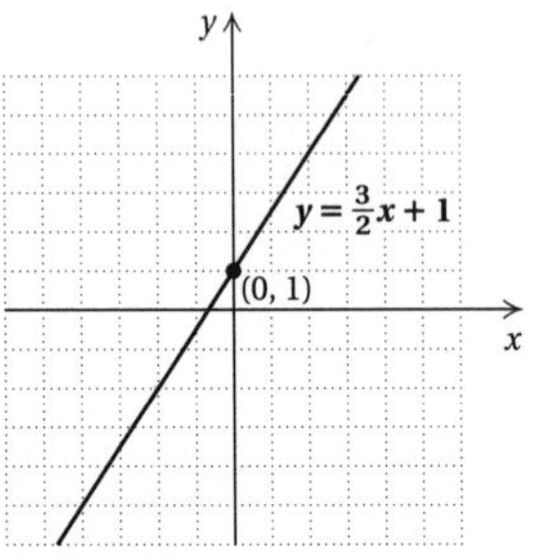

55.

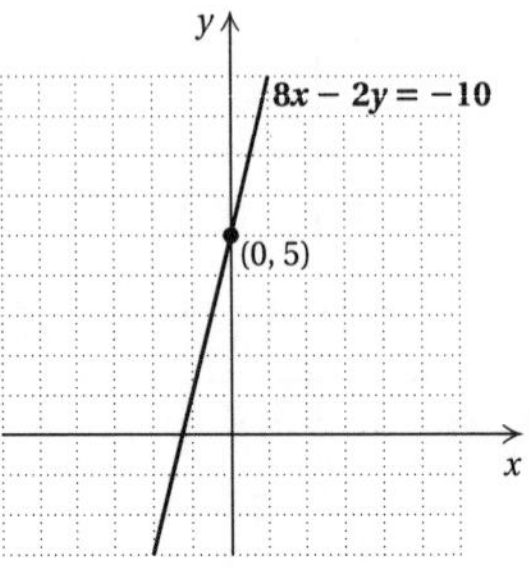

57.

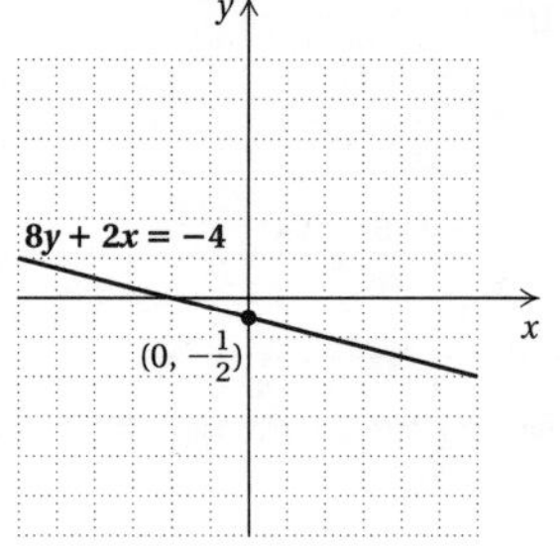

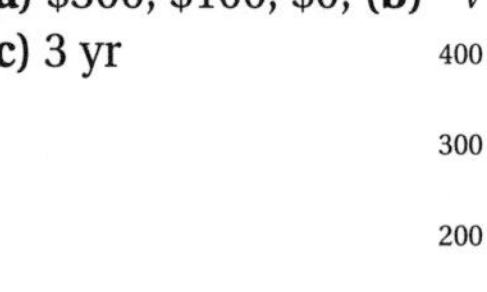

59. **(a)** \$300, \$100, \$0; **(b)** **(c)** 3 yr

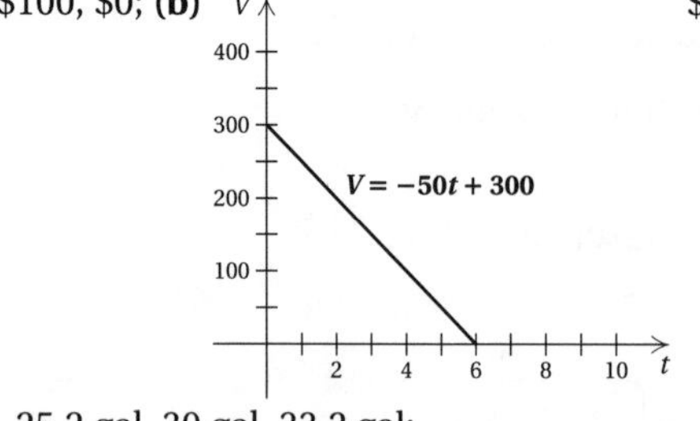

\$5

61. **(a)** 22 gal, 25.2 gal, 30 gal, 33.2 gal; **(b)** 27 gal; **(c)** in 13 yr, or in 2008

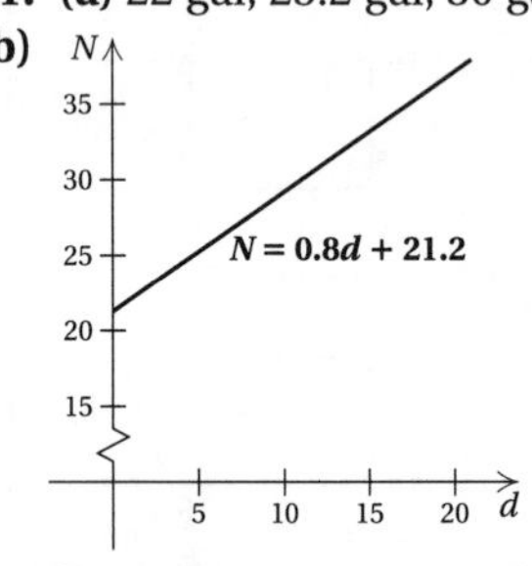

63. DW **65.** 12 **66.** 4.89 **67.** 0 **68.** $\frac{4}{5}$ **69.** 3.4 **70.** $\sqrt{2}$ **71.** $\frac{2}{3}$ **72.** $\frac{7}{8}$ **73.** \$16.81 **74.** \$18.40

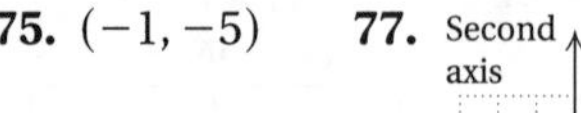

75. $(-1, -5)$ **77.**

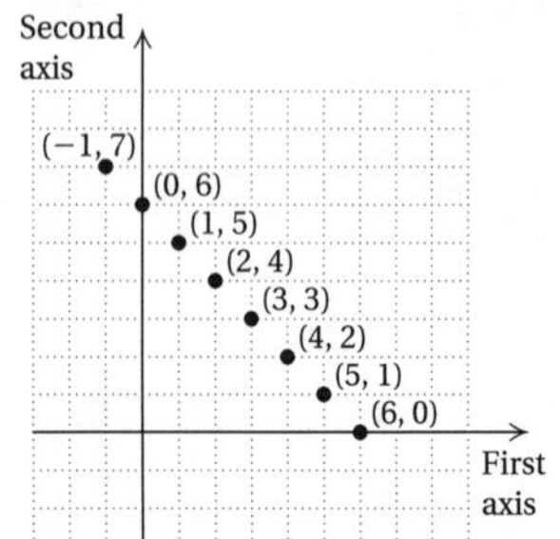

79. 26 linear units **81.** *A*: (10, 18); *B*: (8, 15); *C*: (3, 13); *D*: (8, 11); *E*: (3, 8); *F*: (8, 5); *G*: (12, 5); *H*: (17, 8); *I*: (12, 11); *J*: (17, 13); *K*: (12, 15)
83. The figure is translated 3 units down.

Margin Exercises, Section 3.2, pp. 243–247

1. **(a)** (0, 3); **(b)** (4, 0)

2.

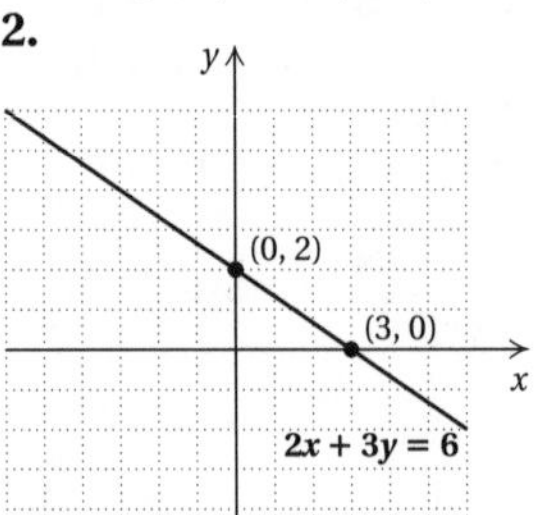

3.

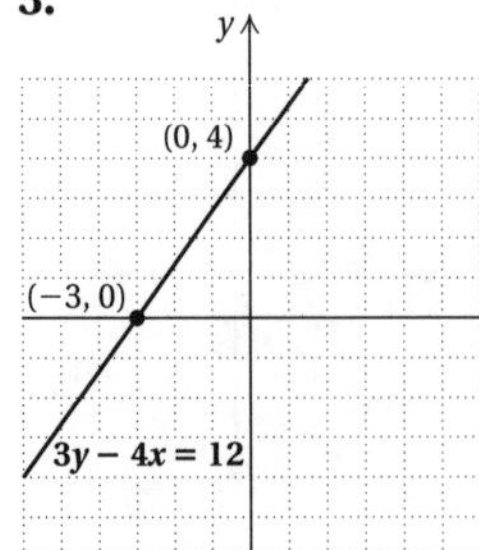

4.

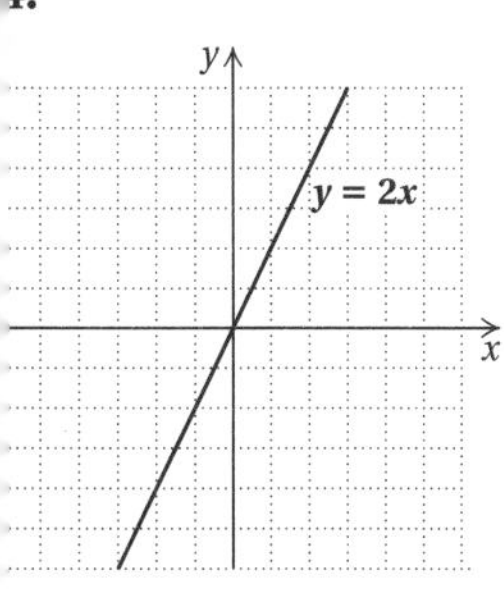

5.

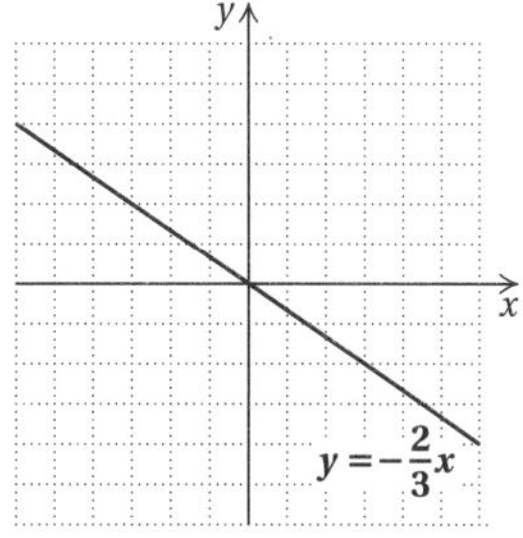

6.

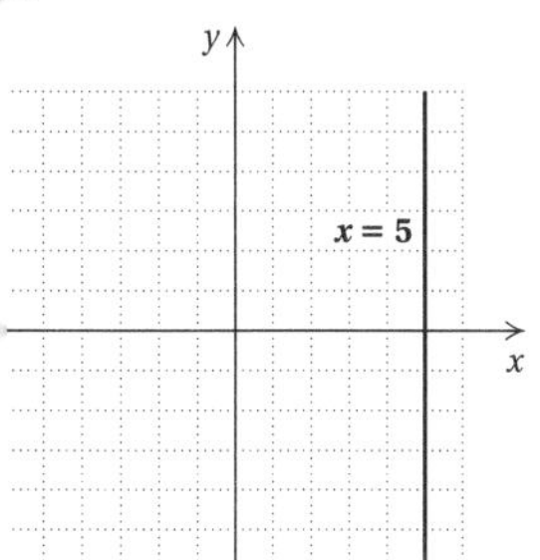

7.

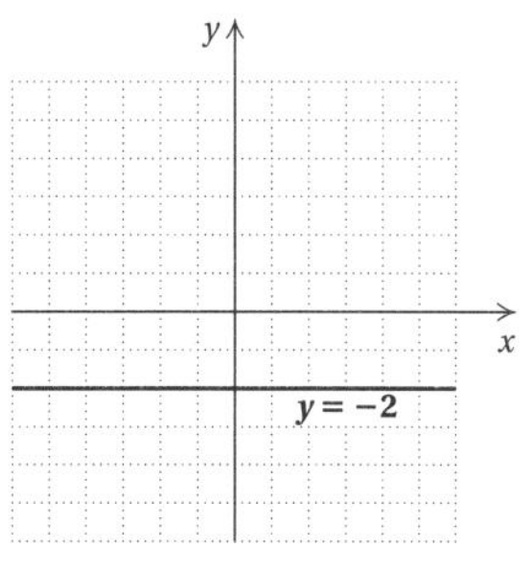

8.

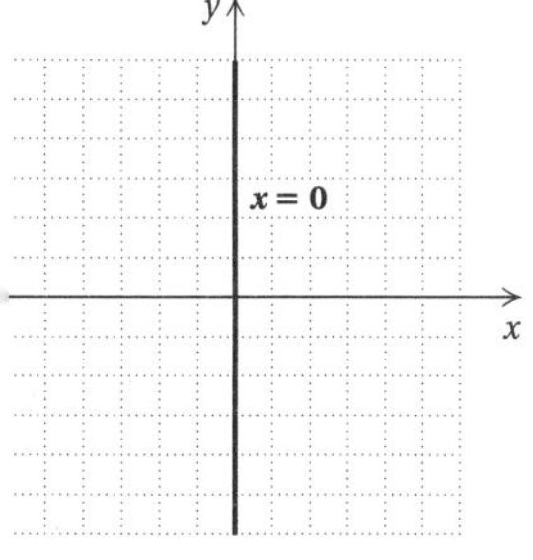

9.

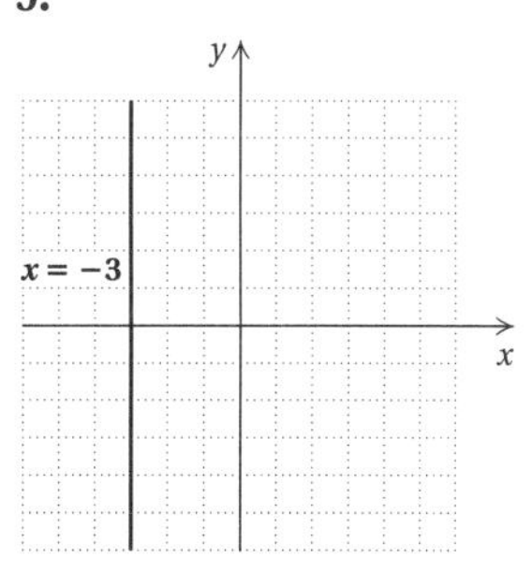

Calculator Corner, p. 245

1. y-intercept: $(0, -15)$; x-intercept: $(-2, 0)$;

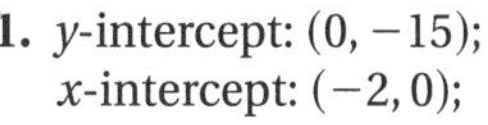

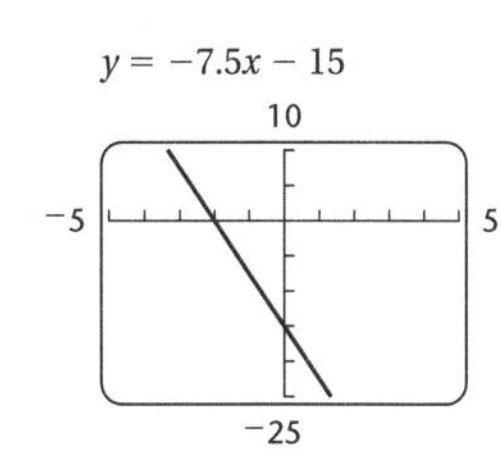

2. y-intercept: $(0, 43)$; x-intercept: $(-20, 0)$;

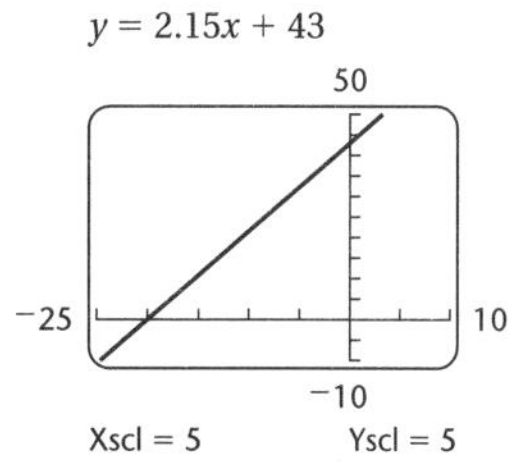

3. y-intercept: $(0, -30)$; x-intercept: $(25, 0)$;

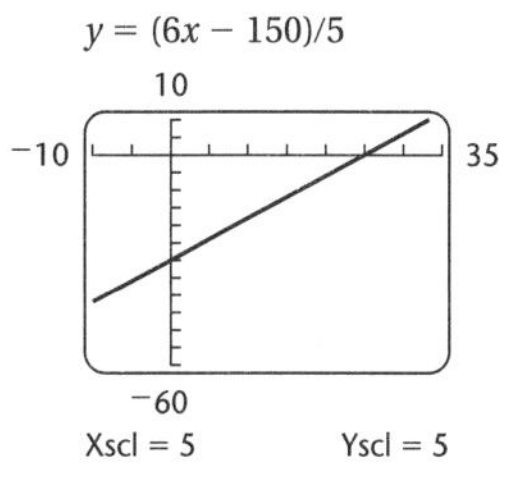

4. y-intercept: $(0, -4)$; x-intercept: $(20, 0)$;

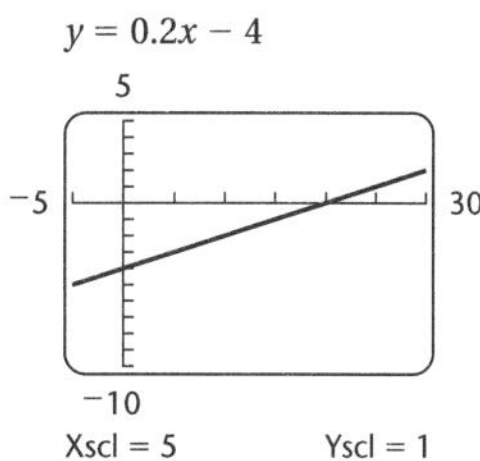

5. y-intercept: $(0, -15)$; x-intercept: $(10, 0)$;

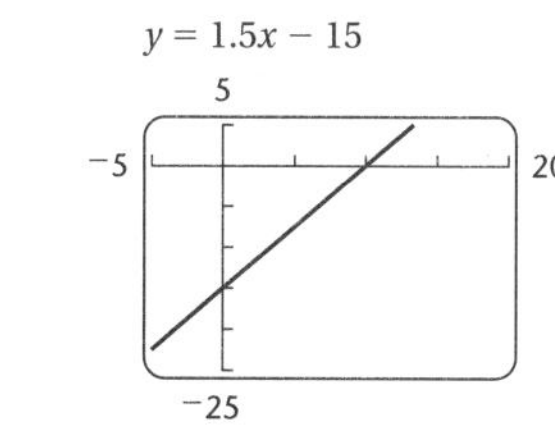

6. y-intercept: $\left(0, -\frac{1}{2}\right)$; x-intercept: $\left(\frac{2}{5}, 0\right)$;

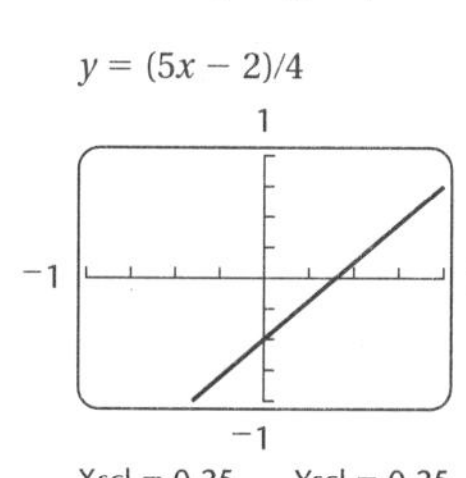

Visualizing for Success, p. 248

1. E **2.** C **3.** G **4.** A **5.** I **6.** D **7.** F **8.** J **9.** B **10.** H

Exercise Set 3.2, p. 249

1. **(a)** $(0, 5)$; **(b)** $(2, 0)$ **3.** **(a)** $(0, -4)$; **(b)** $(3, 0)$ **5.** **(a)** $(0, 3)$; **(b)** $(5, 0)$ **7.** **(a)** $(0, -14)$; **(b)** $(4, 0)$ **9.** **(a)** $\left(0, \frac{10}{3}\right)$; **(b)** $\left(-\frac{5}{2}, 0\right)$ **11.** **(a)** $\left(0, -\frac{1}{3}\right)$; **(b)** $\left(\frac{1}{2}, 0\right)$

13.

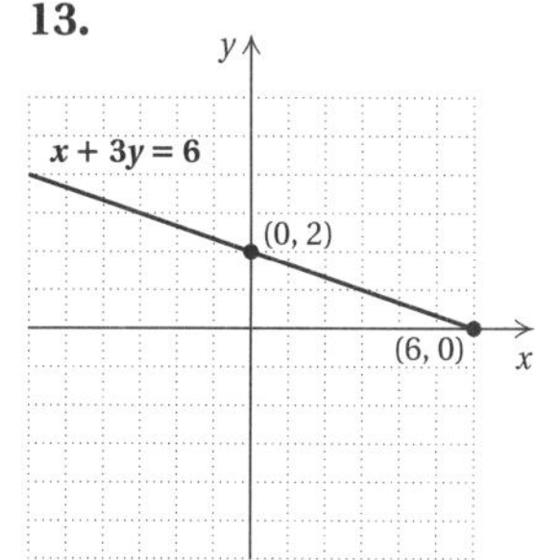

15.

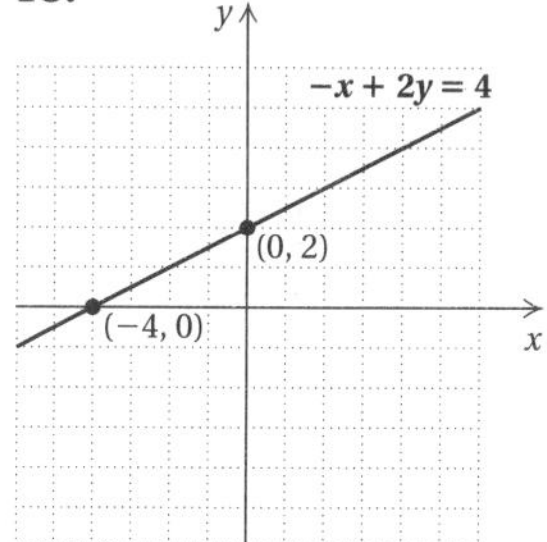

17.

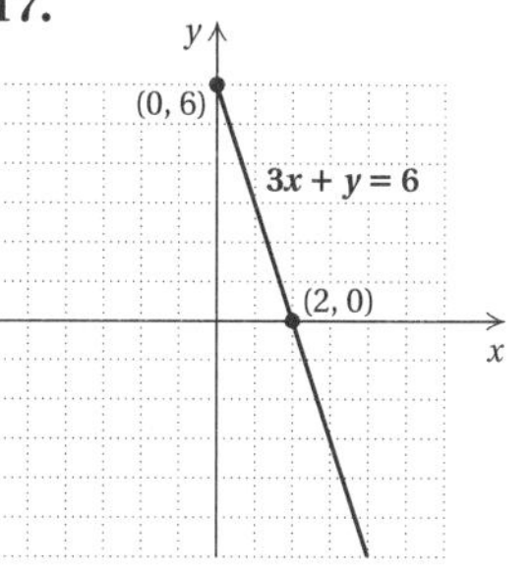

19.

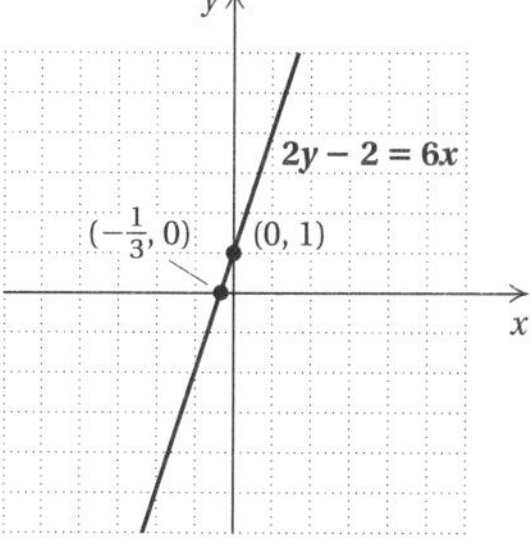

21.

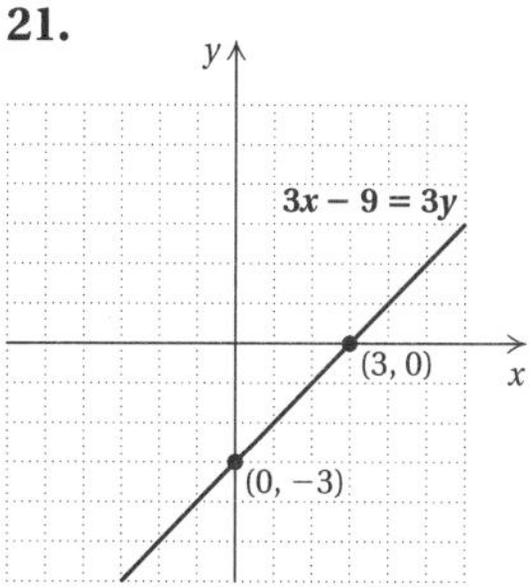

23.

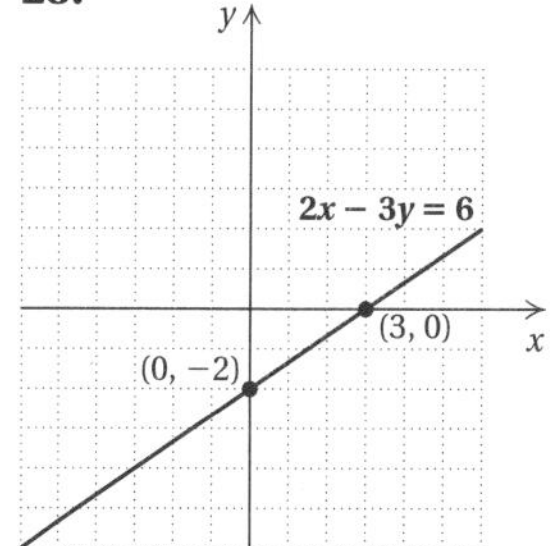

25.

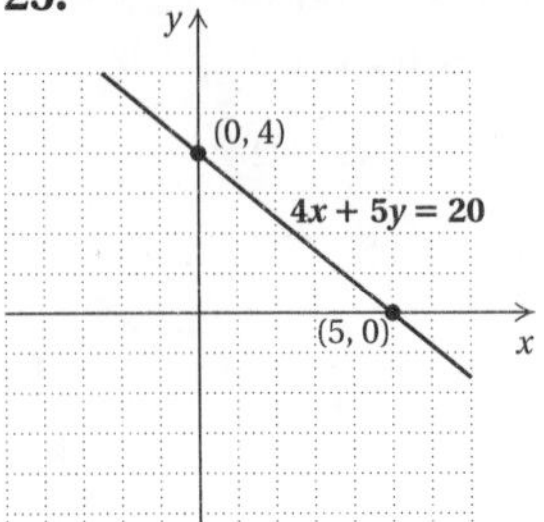

27.

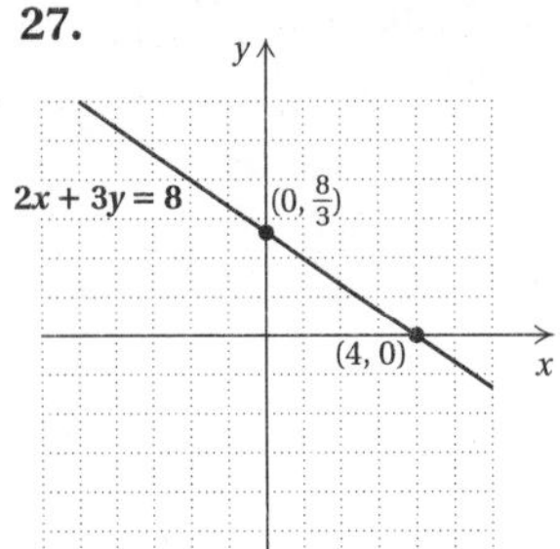

29.

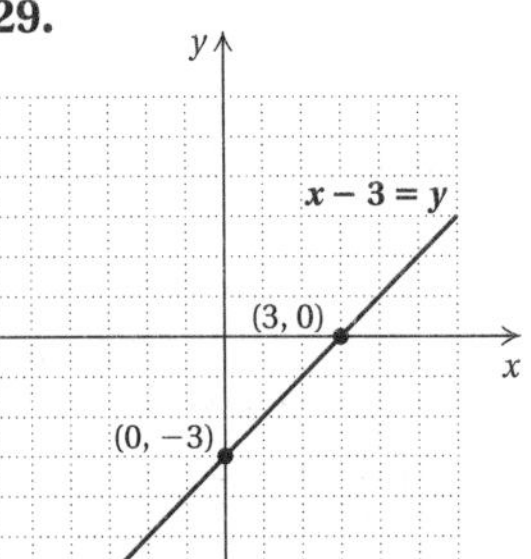

31.

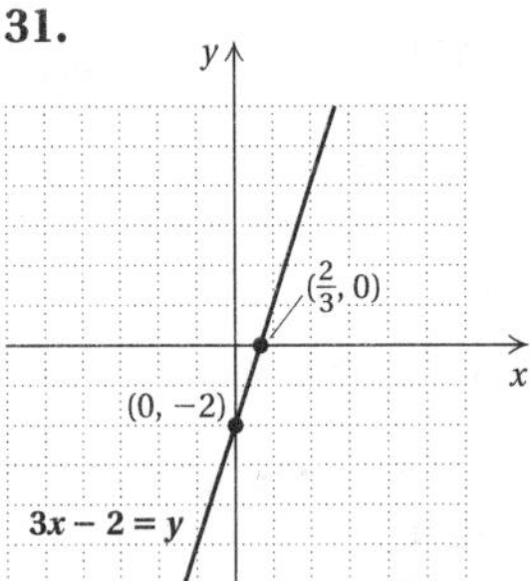

33.

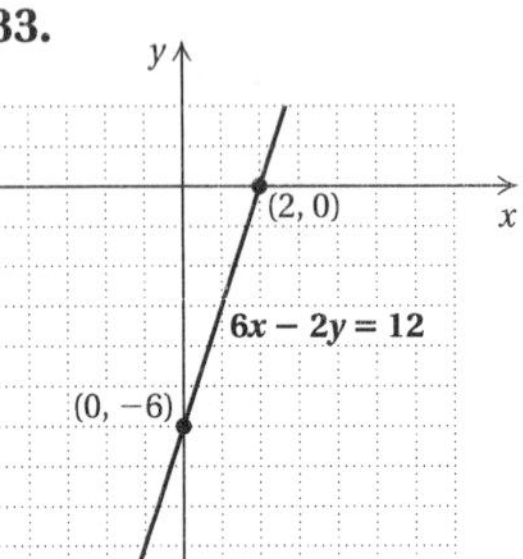

35.

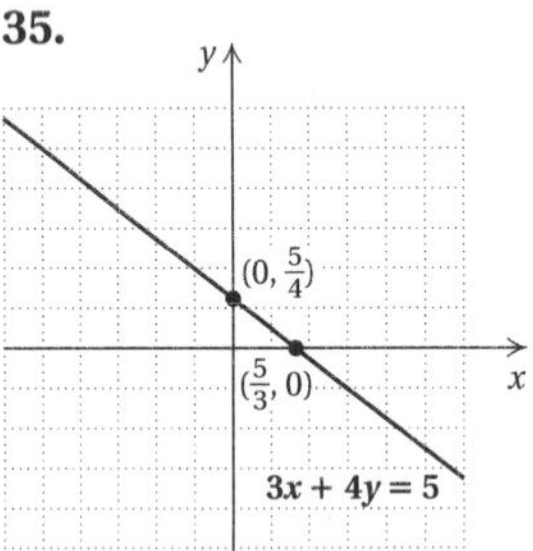

37.

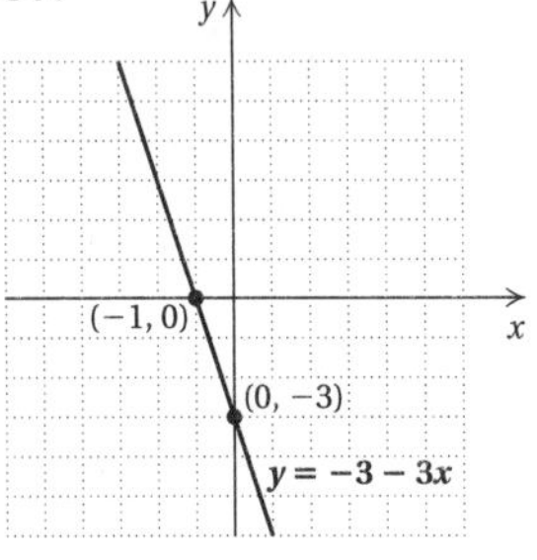

39.

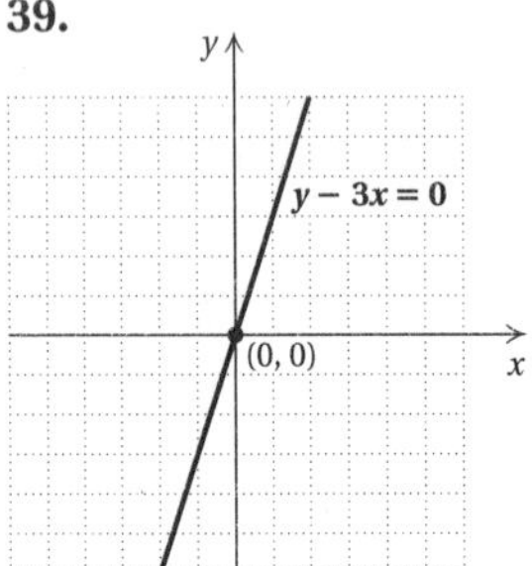

41.

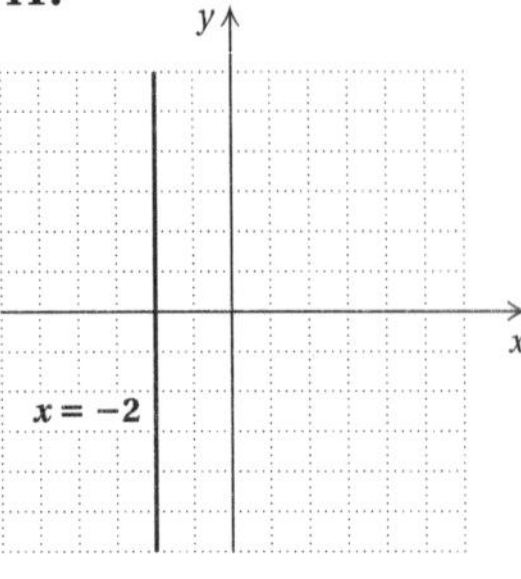

43.

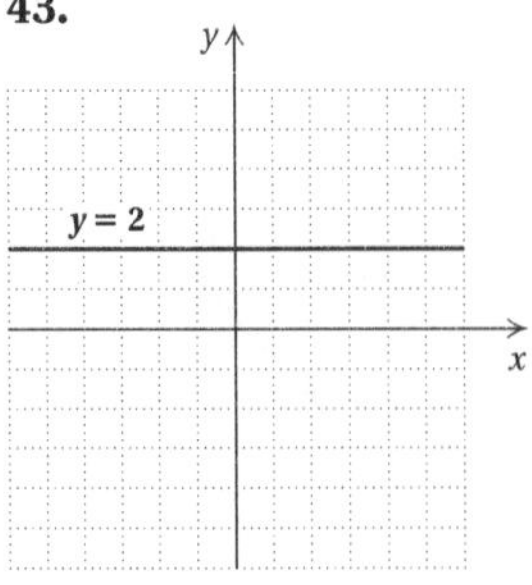

45.

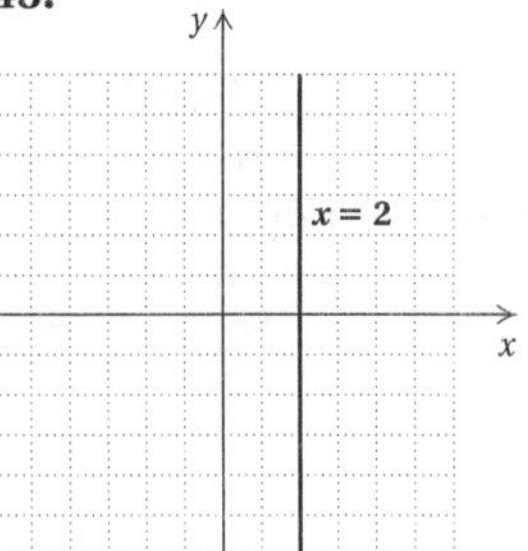

47.

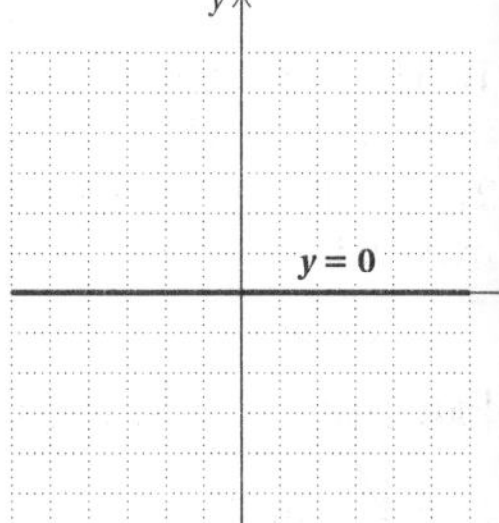

49.

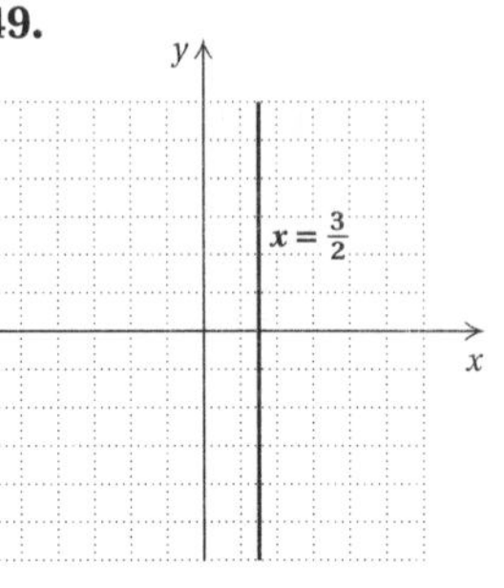

51.

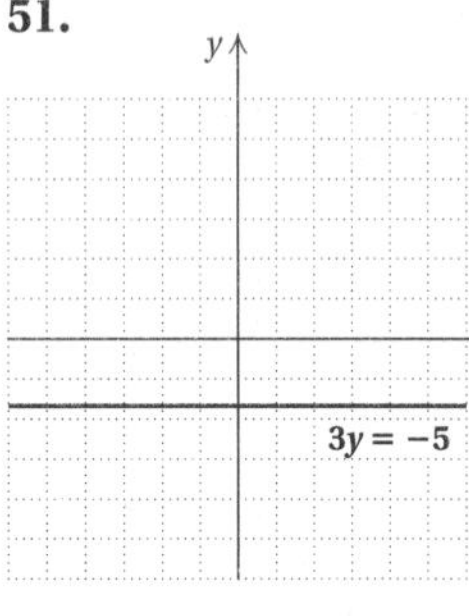

53.

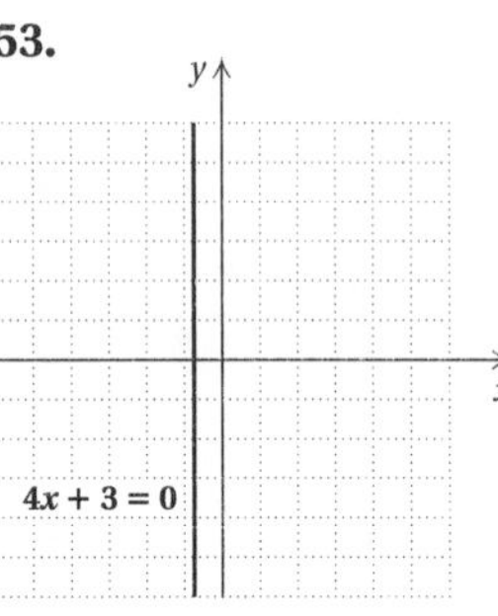

55.

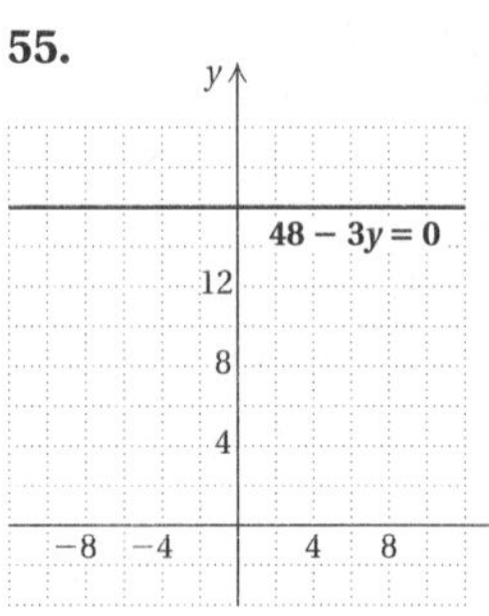

57. $y = -1$ **59.** $x = 4$ **61.** $^{\text{D}}\text{W}$ **63.** 16% **64.** \$32.50 **65.** $\{x \mid x > -40\}$ **66.** $\{x \mid x \le -7\}$ **67.** $\{x \mid x < 1\}$ **68.** $\{x \mid x \ge 2\}$ **69.** $y = -4$ **71.** $k = 12$

Margin Exercises, Section 3.3, pp. 256–261

1. $\frac{2}{5}$

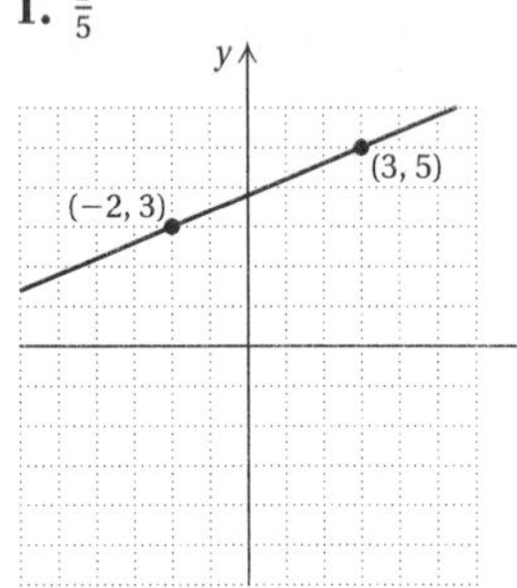

2. $-\frac{5}{3}$

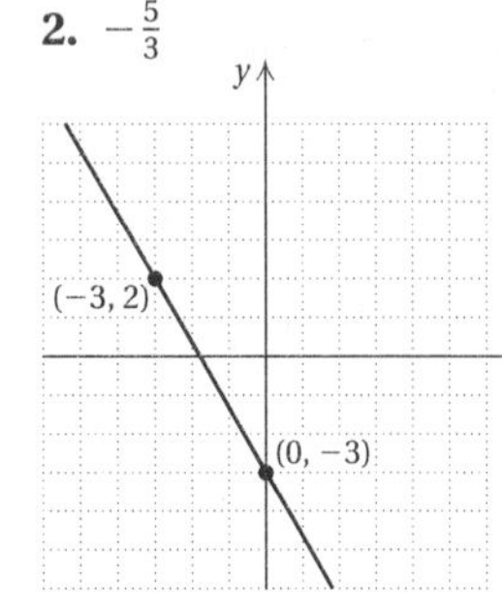

3. $63\frac{7}{11}\%$, or $63.\overline{63}\%$ **4.** 4.5 cents per minute **5.** −1700 deaths by firearms per year **6.** 4 **7.** −17 **8.** −1 **9.** $\frac{2}{3}$ **10.** −1 **11.** $\frac{5}{4}$ **12.** Not defined **13.**

Calculator Corner, p. 260

1. This line will pass through the origin and slant up from left to right. This line will be steeper than $y = 10x$.
2. This line will pass through the origin and slant up from left to right. This line will be less steep than $y = \frac{5}{32}x$.

Calculator Corner, p. 261

1. This line will pass through the origin and slant down from left to right. This line will be steeper than $y = -10x$. **2.** This line will pass through the origin and slant down from left to right. This line will be less steep than $y = -\frac{5}{32}x$.

Exercise Set 3.3, p. 262

1. $-\frac{3}{7}$ **3.** $\frac{2}{3}$ **5.** $\frac{3}{4}$ **7.** 0
9. $-\frac{4}{5}$;

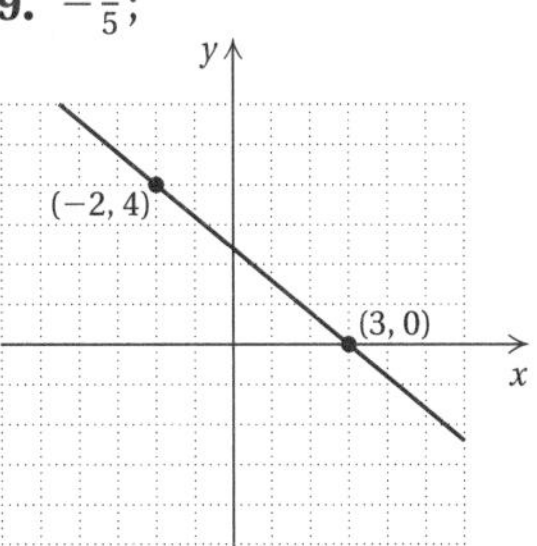

11. 3;

13. $-\frac{5}{6}$;

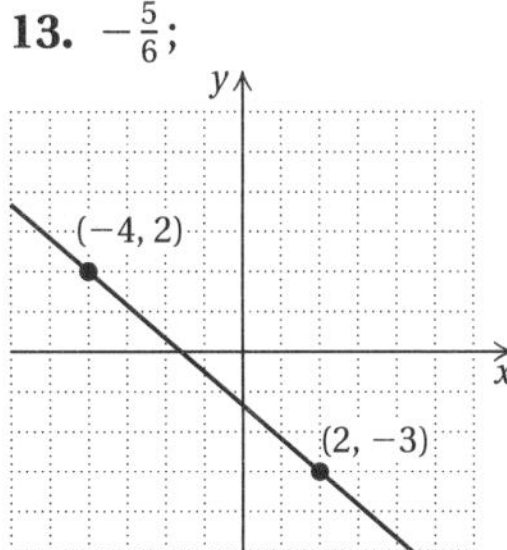

15. $\frac{7}{8}$;

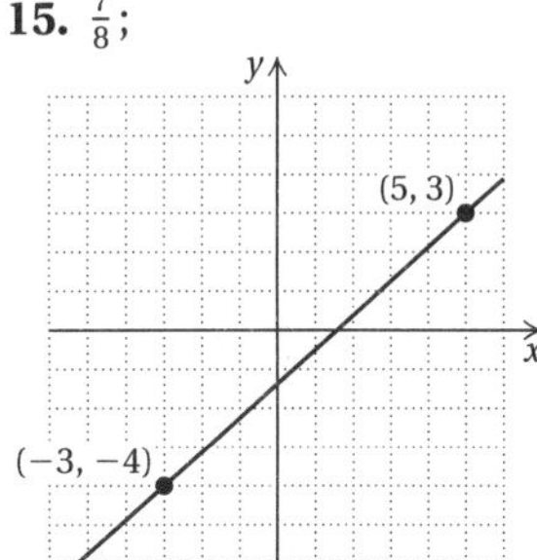

17. $\frac{2}{3}$ **19.** Not defined **21.** $-\frac{5}{13}$ **23.** 0 **25.** $\frac{12}{41}$ **27.** $\frac{28}{129}$ **29.** About 29.4% **31.** 25 miles per gallon **33.** −\$500 per year **35.** About 7600 people per year **37.** −10 **39.** 3.78 **41.** 3 **43.** $-\frac{1}{5}$ **45.** $-\frac{3}{2}$ **47.** Not defined **49.** −2.74 **51.** 3 **53.** $\frac{5}{4}$ **55.** 0 **57.** DW **59.** $\frac{4}{25}$ **60.** $\frac{1}{3}$ **61.** $\frac{3}{8}$ **62.** $\frac{3}{4}$ **63.** \$3.57 **64.** \$48.60 **65.** 20% **66.** \$18 **67.** \$45.15 **68.** \$55 **69.** $y = -x + 5$ **71.** $y = x + 2$

73.

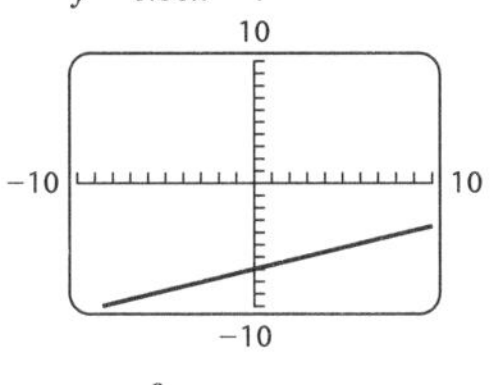

X	Y1
−10	−10.5
−9.9	−10.47
−9.8	−10.43
−9.7	−10.4
−9.6	−10.36
−9.5	−10.33
−9.4	−10.29

X = −10

75.

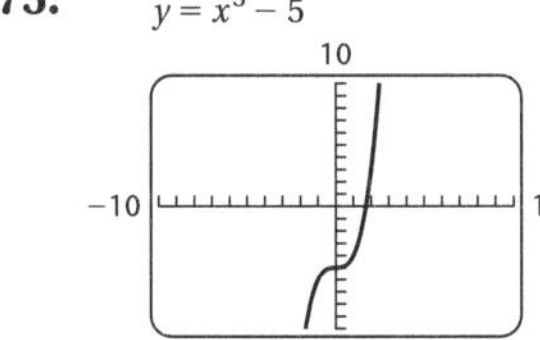

X	Y1
−10	−1005
−9.9	−975.3
−9.8	−946.2
−9.7	−917.7
−9.6	−889.7
−9.5	−862.4
−9.4	−835.6

X = −10

Margin Exercises, Section 3.4, pp. 267–270

1. Slope: 5; y-intercept: (0, 0)
2. Slope: $-\frac{3}{2}$; y-intercept: (0, −6)
3. Slope: $-\frac{3}{4}$; y-intercept: $\left(0, \frac{15}{4}\right)$
4. Slope: 2; y-intercept: $\left(0, -\frac{17}{2}\right)$
5. Slope: $-\frac{7}{5}$; y-intercept: $\left(0, -\frac{22}{5}\right)$
6. $y = 3.5x - 23$ **7.** $y = 13$ **8.** $y = -7.29x$ **9.** $y = 5x - 18$ **10.** $y = -3x - 5$ **11.** $y = 6x - 13$ **12.** $y = -\frac{2}{3}x + \frac{14}{3}$ **13.** $y = x + 2$ **14.** $y = 2x + 4$

Exercise Set 3.4, p. 271

1. Slope: −4; y-intercept: (0, −9)
3. Slope: 1.8; y-intercept: (0, 0)
5. Slope: $-\frac{8}{7}$; y-intercept: (0, −3)
7. Slope: $\frac{4}{9}$; y-intercept: $\left(0, -\frac{7}{9}\right)$
9. Slope: $-\frac{3}{2}$; y-intercept: $\left(0, -\frac{1}{2}\right)$
11. Slope: 0; y-intercept: (0, −17) **13.** $y = -7x - 13$ **15.** $y = 1.01x - 2.6$ **17.** $y = -2x - 6$ **19.** $y = \frac{3}{4}x + \frac{5}{2}$ **21.** $y = x - 8$ **23.** $y = -3x + 3$ **25.** $y = x + 4$ **27.** $y = -\frac{1}{2}x + 4$ **29.** $y = -\frac{3}{2}x + \frac{13}{2}$ **31.** $y = -4x - 11$ **33. (a)** $T = -0.75a + 165$; **(b)** −0.75 beat per minute per year; **(c)** 127.5 beats per minute **35.** DW **37.** $\frac{53}{7}$ **38.** $\frac{3}{8}$ **39.** $\frac{24}{19}$ **40.** $\frac{125}{7}$ **41.** $\frac{1}{3}$ **42.** $-\frac{1}{12}$ **43.** $\frac{42}{25}$ **44.** $\frac{5}{7}$ **45.** $y = 3x - 9$ **47.** $y = \frac{3}{2}x - 2$

Margin Exercises, Section 3.5, pp. 273–275

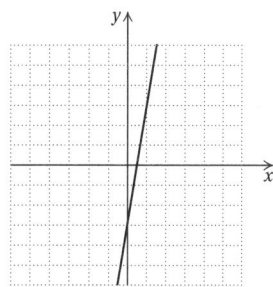

1.

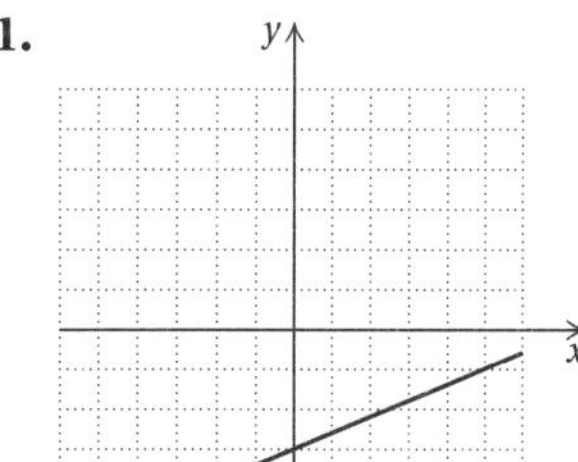

$y = \frac{2}{5}x - 3$

2.

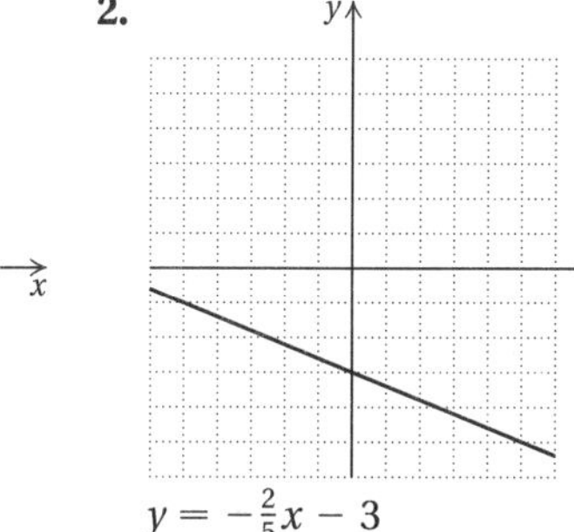

$y = -\frac{2}{5}x - 3$

3.

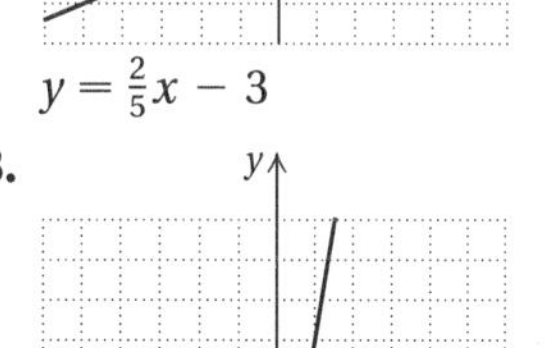

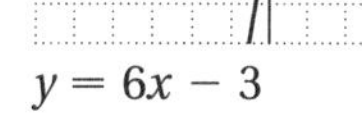

$y = 6x - 3$

4.

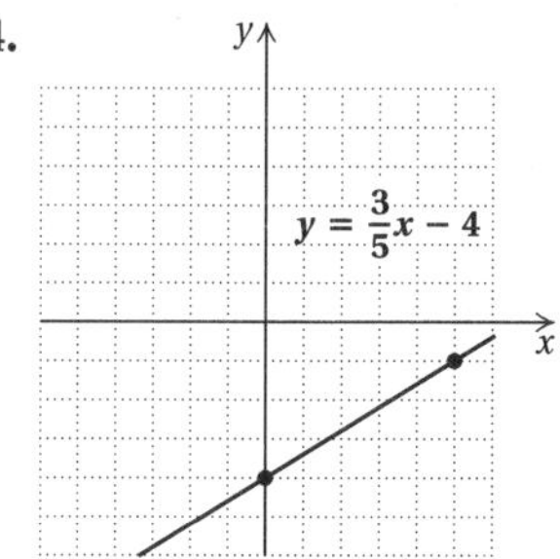

5.

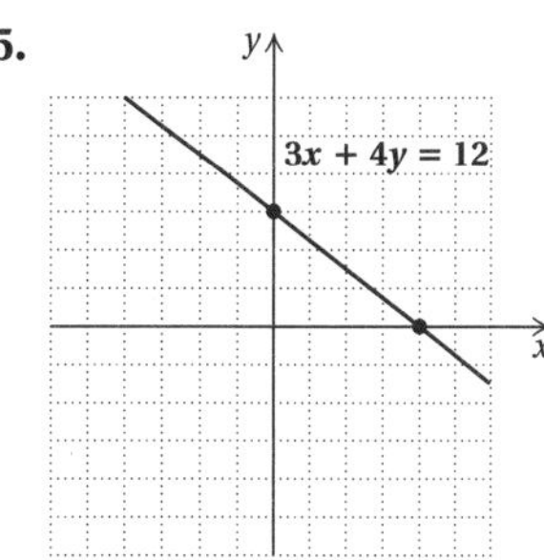

Exercise Set 3.5, p. 276

1.

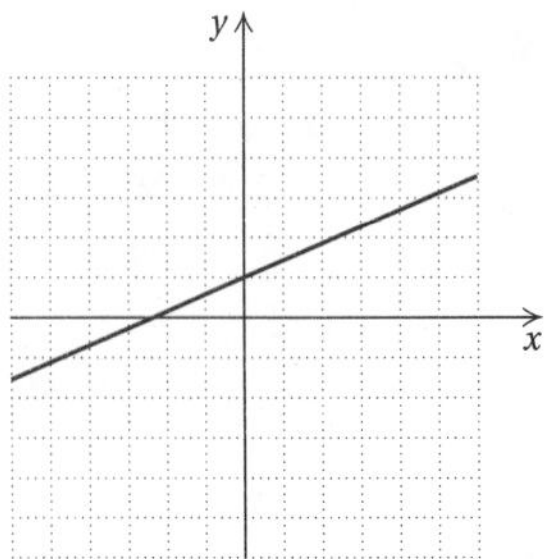

3.

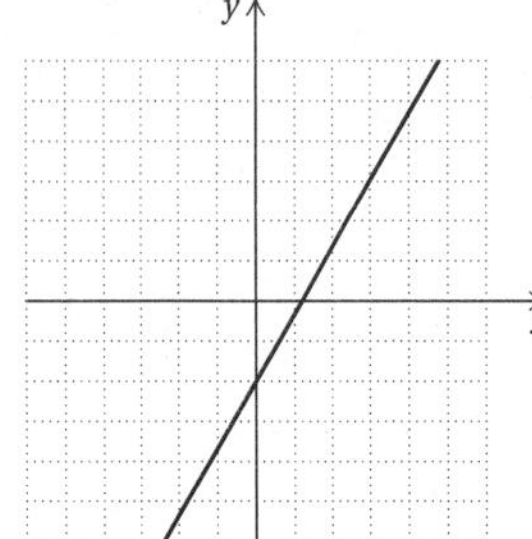

5.

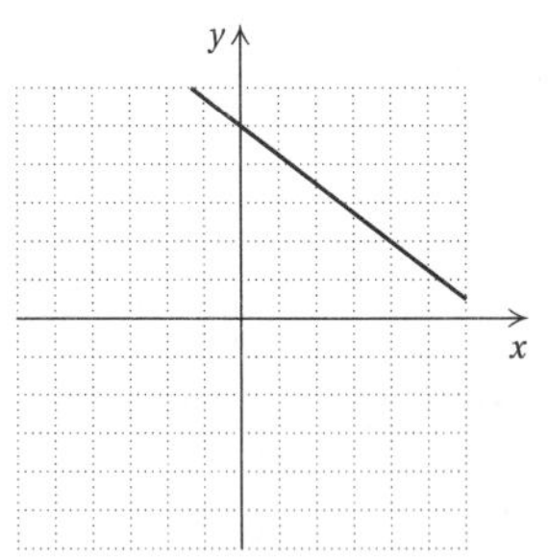

7.

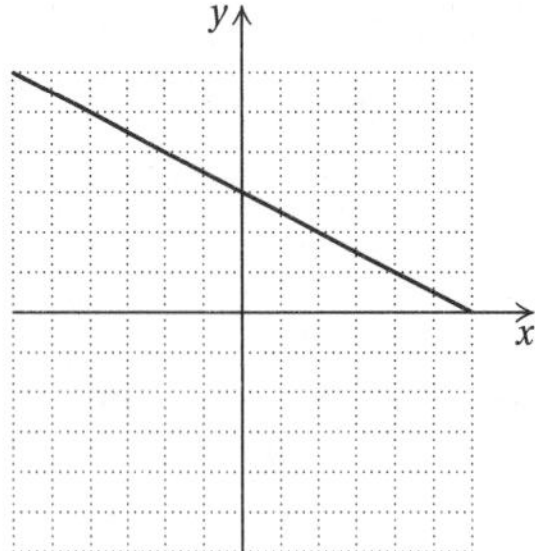

9.

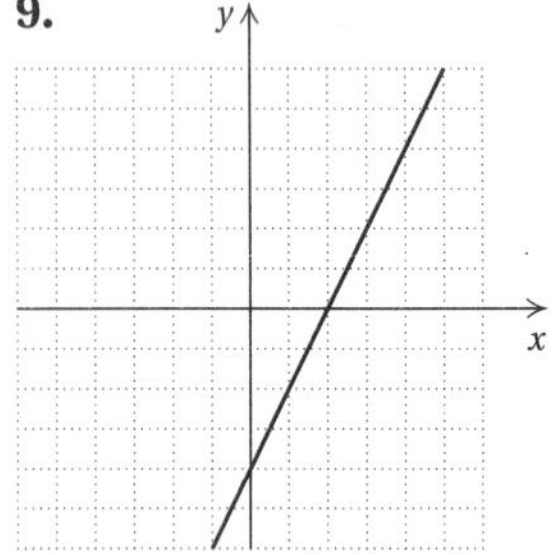

11.

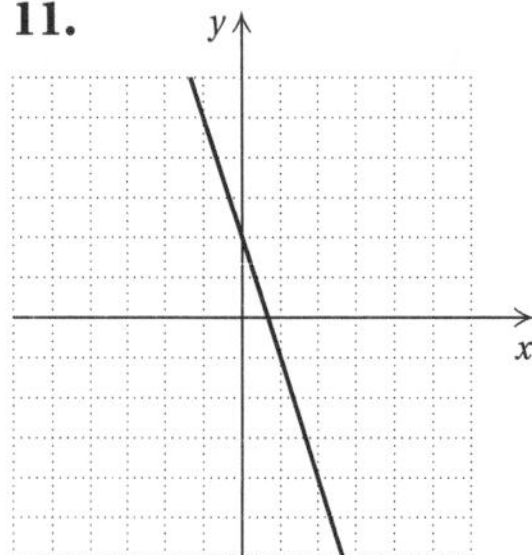

13.

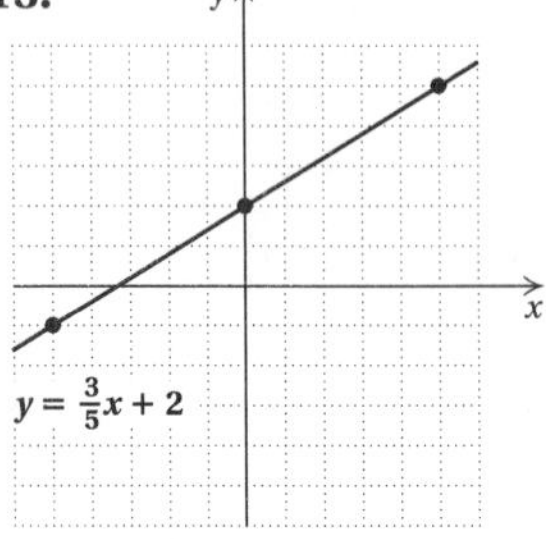

15.

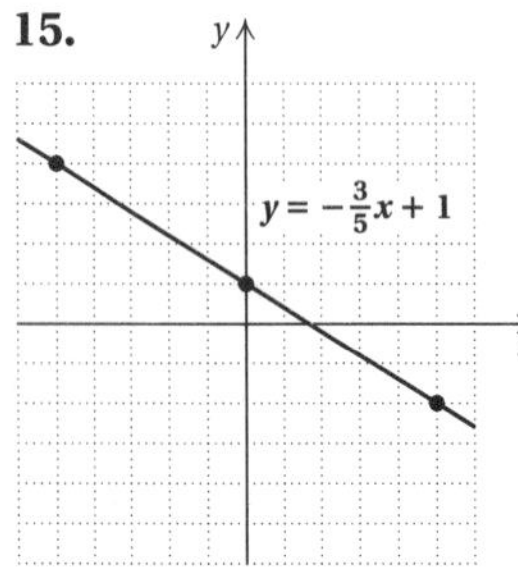

17.

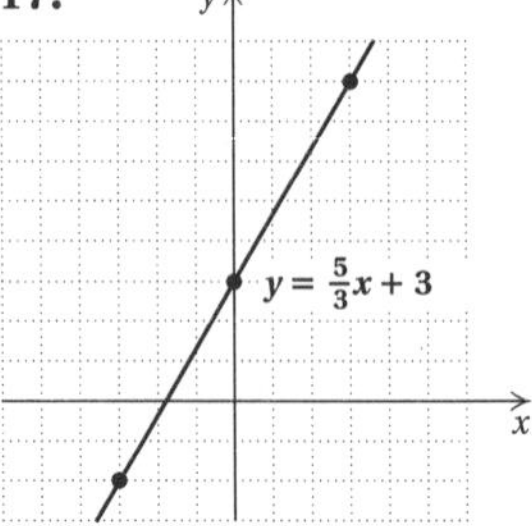

19.

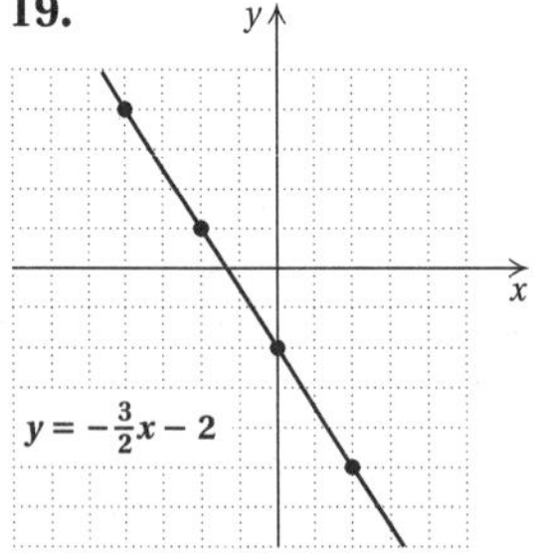

21.

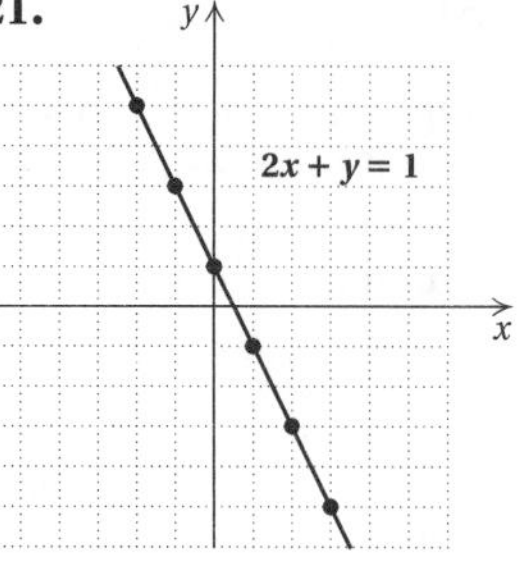

23.

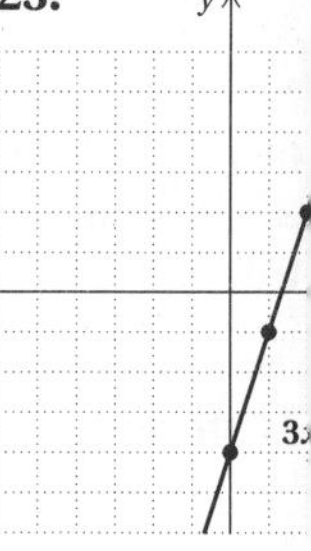

25.

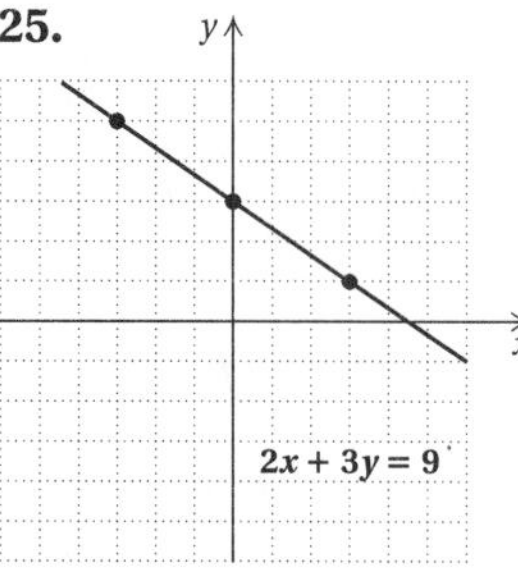

27.

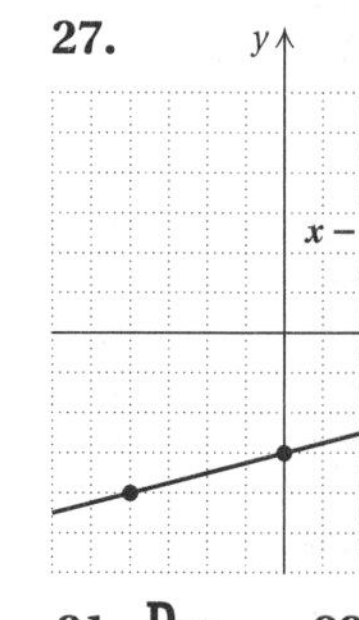

29.

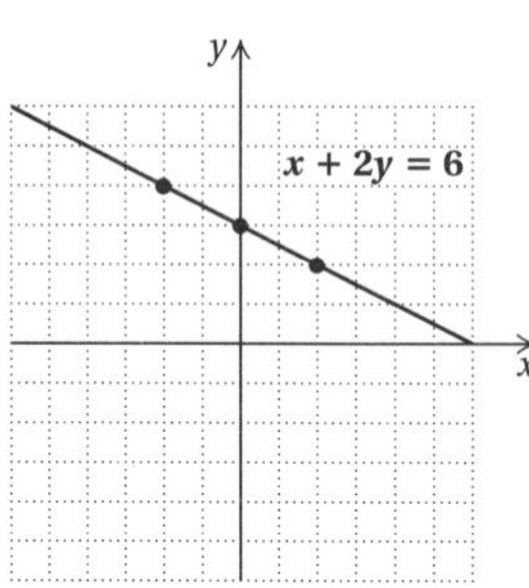

31. DW **33**

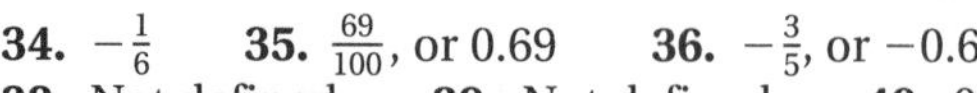

34. $-\frac{1}{6}$ **35.** $\frac{69}{100}$, or 0.69 **36.** $-\frac{3}{5}$, or -0.6
38. Not defined **39.** Not defined **40.** 0
41. Increase of about 416 kidney transplants per
42. Increase of about 264 liver transplants per ye
43. $y = 1.5x + 16$ **45.**

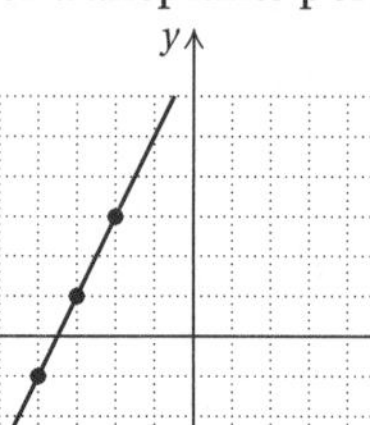

CHAPTER 4

Margin Exercises, Section 4.1, pp. 304–309

1. $5 \cdot 5 \cdot 5 \cdot 5$ **2.** $x \cdot x \cdot x \cdot x \cdot x$ **3.** $3t \cdot 3t$
5. $(-x) \cdot (-x) \cdot (-x) \cdot (-x)$ **6.** $-1 \cdot y \cdot y \cdot y$
8. 1 **9.** 8.4 **10.** 1 **11.** -1.4 **12.** 0 **13**
14. 160 **15.** 3215.36 cm^2 **16.** 119 **17.** 3; -
18. **(a)** 144; **(b)** 36; **(c)** no **19.** 3^{10} **20.** x^{10}
22. x^5 **23.** a^9b^8 **24.** 4^3 **25.** y^4 **26.** p^9
28. $\frac{1}{4^3} = \frac{1}{64}$ **29.** $\frac{1}{5^2} = \frac{1}{25}$ **30.** $\frac{1}{2^4} = \frac{1}{16}$

31. $\frac{1}{(-2)^3} = -\frac{1}{8}$ 32. $\frac{4}{p^3}$ 33. x^2 34. 5^2 35. $\frac{1}{x^7}$
36. $\frac{1}{7^5}$ 37. b 38. t^6

Exercise Set 4.1, p. 310

1. $3 \cdot 3 \cdot 3 \cdot 3$ 3. $(-1.1)(-1.1)(-1.1)(-1.1)(-1.1)$
5. $\left(\frac{2}{3}\right)\left(\frac{2}{3}\right)\left(\frac{2}{3}\right)\left(\frac{2}{3}\right)$ 7. $(7p)(7p)$ 9. $8 \cdot k \cdot k \cdot k$
11. $-6 \cdot y \cdot y \cdot y \cdot y$ 13. 1 15. b 17. 1
19. -7.03 21. 1 23. ab 25. a 27. 27 29. 19
31. -81 33. 256 35. 93 37. 136 39. 10; 4
41. 3629.84 ft^2 43. $\frac{1}{3^2} = \frac{1}{9}$ 45. $\frac{1}{10^3} = \frac{1}{1000}$
47. $\frac{1}{7^3} = \frac{1}{343}$ 49. $\frac{1}{a^3}$ 51. $8^2 = 64$ 53. y^4 55. z^n
57. 4^{-3} 59. x^{-3} 61. a^{-5} 63. 2^7 65. 8^{14} 67. x^7
69. 9^{38} 71. $(3y)^{12}$ 73. $(7y)^{17}$ 75. 3^3 77. $\frac{1}{x}$
79. x^{17} 81. $\frac{1}{x^{13}}$ 83. $\frac{1}{a^{10}}$ 85. 1 87. 7^3 89. 8^6
91. y^4 93. $\frac{1}{16^6}$ 95. $\frac{1}{m^6}$ 97. $\frac{1}{(8x)^4}$ 99. 1 101. x^2
103. x^9 105. $\frac{1}{z^4}$ 107. x^3 109. 1
111. $5^2 = 25; 5^{-2} = \frac{1}{25}; \left(\frac{1}{5}\right)^2 = \frac{1}{25}; \left(\frac{1}{5}\right)^{-2} = 25; -5^2 = -25;$
$(-5)^2 = 25; -\left(-\frac{1}{5}\right)^2 = -\frac{1}{25}; \left(-\frac{1}{5}\right)^{-2} = 25$ 113. $\mathbf{D_W}$
115. 8 in., 4 in. 116. 228, 229 117. 25,543.75 ft^2
118. 51°, 27°, 102° 119. $\frac{23}{14}$ 120. $\frac{11}{10}$
121. $4(x - 3 + 6y)$ 122. $2(128 - a - 2b)$ 123. No
125. No 127. y^{5x} 129. a^{4t} 131. 1 133. >
135. < 137. $-\frac{1}{10,000}$

Margin Exercises, Section 4.2, pp. 314–321

1. 3^{20} 2. $\frac{1}{x^{12}}$ 3. y^{15} 4. $\frac{1}{x^{32}}$ 5. $\frac{16x^{20}}{y^{12}}$ 6. $\frac{25x^{10}}{y^{12}z^6}$
7. x^{74} 8. $\frac{27z^{24}}{y^6x^{15}}$ 9. $-\frac{1}{y^{24}}$ 10. $-\frac{1}{8x^{12}}$ 11. $-\frac{y^{15}}{27x^6}$
12. $\frac{x^{12}}{25}$ 13. $\frac{8t^{15}}{w^{12}}$ 14. $\frac{9}{x^8}$ 15. 5.17×10^{-4}
16. 5.23×10^8 17. 689,300,000,000 18. 0.0000567
19. 5.6×10^{-15} 20. 7.462×10^{-13} 21. 2.0×10^3
22. 5.5×10^2 23. 1.884672×10^{11} L
24. The mass of Saturn is 9.5×10 times the mass of Earth.

Calculator Corner, p. 319

1. 1.3545×10^{-4} 2. 9.044×10^5 3. 3.2×10^5
4. 3.6×10^{12} 5. 3×10^{-6} 6. 4×10^5 7. 8×10^{-26}
8. 3×10^{13}

Exercise Set 4.2, p. 322

1. 2^6 3. $\frac{1}{5^6}$ 5. x^{12} 7. $\frac{1}{a^{18}}$ 9. t^{18} 11. $\frac{1}{t^{12}}$
13. x^8 15. a^3b^3 17. $\frac{1}{a^3b^3}$ 19. $\frac{1}{m^3n^6}$ 21. $16x^6$
23. $\frac{9}{x^8}$ 25. $\frac{1}{x^{12}y^{15}}$ 27. $x^{24}y^8$ 29. $\frac{a^{10}}{b^{35}}$ 31. $\frac{25t^6}{r^8}$
33. $\frac{b^{21}}{a^{15}c^6}$ 35. $\frac{9x^6}{y^{16}z^6}$ 37. $\frac{16x^6}{y^4}$ 39. $a^{12}b^8$ 41. $\frac{y^6}{4}$
43. $\frac{a^8}{b^{12}}$ 45. $\frac{8}{y^6}$ 47. $49x^6$ 49. $\frac{x^6y^3}{z^3}$ 51. $\frac{c^2d^6}{a^4b^2}$
53. 2.8×10^{10} 55. 9.07×10^{17} 57. 3.04×10^{-6}
59. 1.8×10^{-8} 61. 10^{11} 63. 2.96×10^8 65. 10^{-7}
67. 87,400,000 69. 0.00000005704 71. 10,000,000
73. 0.00001 75. 6×10^9 77. 3.38×10^4
79. 8.1477×10^{-13} 81. 2.5×10^{13} 83. 5.0×10^{-4}
85. 3.0×10^{-21} 87. Approximately 1.325×10^{14} ft^3
89. The mass of Jupiter is 3.18×10^2 times the mass of Earth.
91. 1×10^{22} 93. The mass of the sun is 3.33×10^5 times the mass of Earth. 95. 4.375×10^2 days 97. $\mathbf{D_W}$
99. $9(x - 4)$ 100. $2(2x - y + 8)$ 101. $3(s + t + 8)$
102. $-7(x + 2)$ 103. $\frac{7}{4}$ 104. 2 105. $-\frac{12}{7}$ 106. $-\frac{11}{2}$
107.

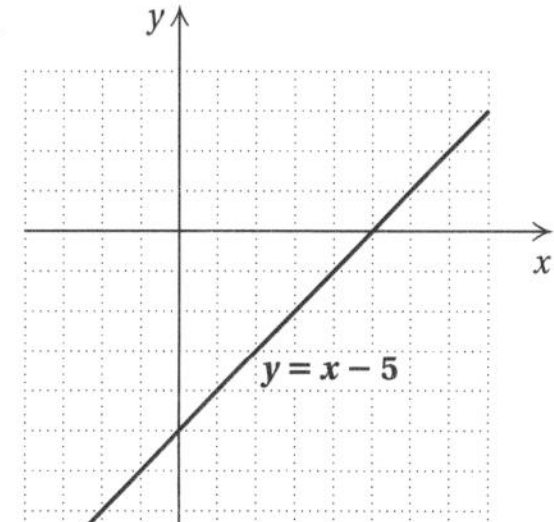

108.

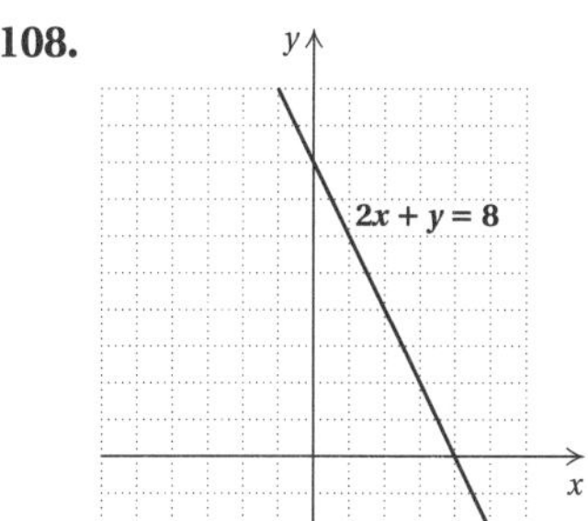

109. 2.478125×10^{-1} 111. $\frac{1}{5}$ 113. 3^{11} 115. 7
117. $\frac{1}{0.4}$, or 2.5 119. False 121. False 123. True

Margin Exercises, Section 4.3, pp. 327–334

1. $4x^2 - 3x + \frac{5}{4}; 15y^3; -7x^3 + 1.1$; answers may vary
2. -19 3. -104 4. -18 5. 21 6. 6; -4
7. 132 games 8. 360 ft 9. (a) 7.55 parts per million; (b) When $t = 3$, $C \approx 7.5$; so the value found in part (a) appears to be correct. 10. 20 parts per million
11. $-9x^3 + (-4x^5)$ 12. $-2y^3 + 3y^7 + (-7y) + (-9)$
13. $3x^2, 6x, \frac{1}{2}$ 14. $-4y^5, 7y^2, -3y, -2$ 15. $4x^3$ and $-x^3$
16. $4t^4$ and $-7t^4$; $-9t^3$ and $10t^3$ 17. $5x^2$ and $7x^2$; $3x$ and $-8x$; -10 and 11 18. 2, -7, -8.5, 10, -4 19. $8x^2$
20. $2x^3 + 7$ 21. $-\frac{1}{4}x^5 + 2x^2$ 22. $-4x^3$ 23. $5x^3$
24. $25 - 3x^5$ 25. $6x$ 26. $4x^3 + 4$
27. $-\frac{1}{4}x^3 + 4x^2 + 7$ 28. $x^5 - \frac{9}{20}x^4 + \frac{49}{5}$
29. $6x^7 + 3x^5 - 2x^4 + 4x^3 + 5x^2 + x$
30. $7x^5 - 5x^4 + 2x^3 + 4x^2 - 3$
31. $14t^7 - 10t^5 + 7t^2 - 14$ 32. $-2x^2 - 3x + 2$
33. $10x^4 - 8x - \frac{1}{2}$ 34. 4, 2, 1, 0; 4 35. 0, 3, 6, 5; 6
36. x 37. x^3, x^2, x, x^0 38. x^2, x 39. x^3

40. $2x^3 + 4x^2 + 0x - 2$; $2x^3 + 4x^2 \qquad - 2$
41. $a^4 + 0a^3 + 0a^2 + 0a + 10$; $a^4 \qquad + 10$
42. Monomial 43. None of these 44. Binomial
45. Trinomial

Calculator Corner, p. 330

1. 3; 2.25; −27 2. 44; 0; 9.28 3. 13; −3.32; 7
4. −1; −7; −40.6

Exercise Set 4.3, p. 335

1. −18; 7 3. 19; 14 5. −12; −7 7. $\frac{13}{3}$; 5 9. 9; 1
11. 56; −2 13. 1112 ft 15. (a) 1138.34 billion kilowatt-hours, 1499.46 billion kilowatt-hours, 1950.86 billion kilowatt-hours, 2402.26 billion kilowatt-hours, 3305.06 billion kilowatt-hours; (b) left to the student
17. \$18,750; \$24,000 19. −4, 4, 5, 2.75, 1
21. 1,820,000; 3,660,000 23. 9 words 25. 6 27. 15
29. $2, -3x, x^2$ 31. $-2x^4, \frac{1}{3}x^3, -x, 3$ 33. $6x^2$ and $-3x^2$
35. $2x^4$ and $-3x^4$; $5x$ and $-7x$ 37. $3x^5$ and $14x^5$; $-7x$ and $-2x$; 8 and −9 39. −3, 6 41. 5, $\frac{3}{4}$, 3
43. −5, 6, −2.7, 8, −2 45. $-3x$ 47. $-8x$
49. $11x^3 + 4$ 51. $x^3 - x$ 53. $4b^5$ 55. $\frac{3}{4}x^5 - 2x - 42$
57. x^4 59. $\frac{15}{16}x^3 - \frac{7}{6}x^2$ 61. $x^5 + 6x^3 + 2x^2 + x + 1$
63. $15y^9 + 7y^8 + 5y^3 - y^2 + y$ 65. $x^6 + x^4$
67. $13x^3 - 9x + 8$ 69. $-5x^2 + 9x$ 71. $12x^4 - 2x + \frac{1}{4}$
73. 1, 0; 1 75. 2, 1, 0; 2 77. 3, 2, 1, 0; 3 79. 2, 1, 6, 4; 6

81.

TERM	COEFFICIENT	DEGREE OF THE TERM	DEGREE OF THE POLYNOMIAL
$-7x^4$	−7	4	
$6x^3$	6	3	
$-3x^2$	−3	2	4
$8x$	8	1	
−2	−2	0	

83. x^2, x 85. x^3, x^2, x^0 87. None missing
89. $x^3 + 0x^2 + 0x - 27$; $x^3 \qquad - 27$
91. $x^4 + 0x^3 + 0x^2 - x + 0x^0$; $x^4 \qquad - x$
93. None missing 95. Trinomial 97. None of these
99. Binomial 101. Monomial 103. DW
105. 27 apples 106. −19 107. $-\frac{17}{24}$ 108. $\frac{5}{8}$
109. −2.6 110. $\frac{15}{2}$ 111. $b = \dfrac{C + r}{a}$ 112. 45%; 37.5%; 17.5% 113. $3(x - 5y + 21)$ 115. $3x^6$ 117. 10
119. −4, 4, 5, 2.75, 1 121. 1,820,000; 3,660,000

Margin Exercises, Section 4.4, pp. 341–344

1. $x^2 + 7x + 3$ 2. $-4x^5 + 7x^4 + x^3 + 2x^2 + 4$
3. $24x^4 + 5x^3 + x^2 + 1$ 4. $2x^3 + \frac{10}{3}$ 5. $2x^2 - 3x - 1$
6. $8x^3 - 2x^2 - 8x + \frac{5}{2}$ 7. $-8x^4 + 4x^3 + 12x^2 + 5x - 8$
8. $-x^3 + x^2 + 3x + 3$ 9. $-4x^3 + 6x - 3$
10. $-5x^4 - 3x^2 - 7x + 5$
11. $-14x^{10} + \frac{1}{2}x^5 - 5x^3 + x^2 - 3x$ 12. $2x^3 + 2x + 8$
13. $x^2 - 6x - 2$ 14. $-8x^4 - 5x^3 + 8x^2 - 1$
15. $x^3 - x^2 - \frac{4}{3}x - 0.9$ 16. $2x^3 + 5x^2 - 2x - 5$
17. $-x^5 - 2x^3 + 3x^2 - 2x + 2$ 18. Sum of perimeters: $13x$; sum of areas: $\frac{7}{2}x^2$ 19. $(x^2 - 64)$ ft^2

Calculator Corner, p. 344

1. Yes 2. Yes 3. No 4. Yes 5. No 6. Yes

Exercise Set 4.4, p. 345

1. $-x + 5$ 3. $x^2 - \frac{11}{2}x - 1$ 5. $2x^2$ 7. $5x^2 + 3x - 3$
9. $-2.2x^3 - 0.2x^2 - 3.8x + 23$ 11. $6 + 12x^2$
13. $-\frac{1}{2}x^4 + \frac{2}{3}x^3 + x^2$
15. $0.01x^5 + x^4 - 0.2x^3 + 0.2x + 0.06$
17. $9x^8 + 8x^7 - 6x^4 + 8x^2 + 4$
19. $1.05x^4 + 0.36x^3 + 14.22x^2 + x + 0.97$ 21. $5x$
23. $x^2 - \frac{3}{2}x + 2$ 25. $-12x^4 + 3x^3 - 3$ 27. $-3x + 7$
29. $-4x^2 + 3x - 2$ 31. $4x^4 - 6x^2 - \frac{3}{4}x + 8$
33. $7x - 1$ 35. $-x^2 - 7x + 5$ 37. −18
39. $6x^4 + 3x^3 - 4x^2 + 3x - 4$
41. $4.6x^3 + 9.2x^2 - 3.8x - 23$ 43. $\frac{3}{4}x^3 - \frac{1}{2}x$
45. $0.06x^3 - 0.05x^2 + 0.01x + 1$ 47. $3x + 6$
49. $11x^4 + 12x^3 - 9x^2 - 8x - 9$ 51. $x^4 - x^3 + x^2 - x$
53. $\frac{23}{2}a + 12$ 55. $5x^2 + 4x$ 57. $(r + 11)(r + 9)$; $9r + 99 + 11r + r^2$, or $r^2 + 20r + 99$
59. $(x + 3)(x + 3)$, or $(x + 3)^2$; $x^2 + 3x + 9 + 3x$, or $x^2 + 6x + 9$ 61. $\pi r^2 - 25\pi$ 63. $18z - 64$ 65. DW
67. 6 68. −19 69. $-\frac{7}{22}$ 70. 5 71. 5 72. 1
73. $\frac{39}{2}$ 74. $\frac{37}{2}$ 75. $\{x \mid x \geq -10\}$ 76. $\{x \mid x < 0\}$
77. $20w + 42$ 79. $2x^2 + 20x$ 81. $y^2 - 4y + 4$
83. $12y^2 - 23y + 21$ 85. $-3y^4 - y^3 + 5y - 2$

Margin Exercises, Section 4.5, pp. 349–352

1. $-15x$ 2. $-x^2$ 3. x^2 4. $-x^5$ 5. $12x^7$ 6. $-8y$
7. $7y^5$ 8. 0 9. $8x^2 + 16x$ 10. $-15t^3 + 6t^2$
11. $-5x^6 - 25x^5 + 30x^4 - 40x^3$
12. (a) $(y + 2)(y + 7) = y \cdot (y + 7) + 2(y + 7)$
$= y \cdot y + y \cdot 7 + 2 \cdot y + 2 \cdot 7$
$= y^2 + 7y + 2y + 14$
$= y^2 + 9y + 14$;
(b) $(y + 2)(y + 7)$, or $y^2 + 2y + 7y + 14$, or $y^2 + 9y + 14$
13. $x^2 + 13x + 40$ 14. $x^2 + x - 20$
15. $5x^2 - 17x - 12$ 16. $6x^2 - 19x + 15$
17. $x^4 + 3x^3 + x^2 + 15x - 20$
18. $6y^5 - 20y^3 + 15y^2 + 14y - 35$
19. $3x^3 + 13x^2 - 6x + 20$
20. $20x^4 - 16x^3 + 32x^2 - 32x - 16$
21. $6x^4 - x^3 - 18x^2 - x + 10$

Calculator Corner, p. 352

1. Correct **2.** Correct **3.** Not correct **4.** Not correct

Exercise Set 4.5, p. 353

1. $40x^2$ **3.** x^3 **5.** $32x^8$ **7.** $0.03x^{11}$ **9.** $\frac{1}{15}x^4$ **11.** 0 **13.** $-24x^{11}$ **15.** $-2x^2 + 10x$ **17.** $-5x^2 + 5x$ **19.** $x^5 + x^2$ **21.** $6x^3 - 18x^2 + 3x$ **23.** $-6x^4 - 6x^3$ **25.** $18y^6 + 24y^5$ **27.** $x^2 + 9x + 18$ **29.** $x^2 + 3x - 10$ **31.** $x^2 - 7x + 12$ **33.** $x^2 - 9$ **35.** $25 - 15x + 2x^2$ **37.** $4x^2 + 20x + 25$ **39.** $x^2 - \frac{21}{10}x - 1$ **41.** $x^2 + 2.4x - 10.81$ **43.** $(x + 2)(x + 6)$, $x^2 + 8x + 12$ **45.** $(x + 1)(x + 6)$, $x^2 + 7x + 6$ **47.**

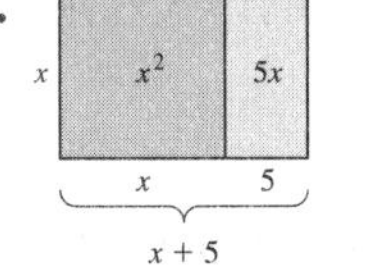

49.

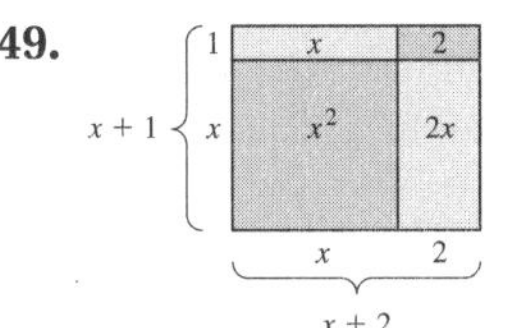

51.

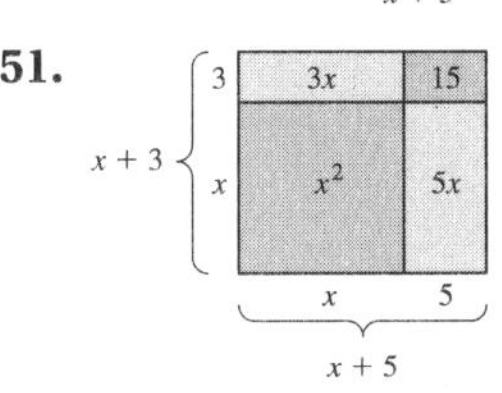

53. $x^3 - 1$ **55.** $4x^3 + 14x^2 + 8x + 1$ **57.** $3y^4 - 6y^3 - 7y^2 + 18y - 6$ **59.** $x^6 + 2x^5 - x^3$ **61.** $-10x^5 - 9x^4 + 7x^3 + 2x^2 - x$ **63.** $-1 - 2x - x^2 + x^4$ **65.** $6t^4 + t^3 - 16t^2 - 7t + 4$ **67.** $x^9 - x^5 + 2x^3 - x$ **69.** $x^4 - 1$ **71.** $x^4 + 8x^3 + 12x^2 + 9x + 4$ **73.** $2x^4 - 5x^3 + 5x^2 - \frac{19}{10}x + \frac{1}{5}$ **75.** DW **77.** $-\frac{3}{4}$ **78.** 6.4 **79.** 96 **80.** 32 **81.** $3(5x - 6y + 4)$ **82.** $4(4x - 6y + 9)$ **83.** $-3(3x + 15y - 5)$ **84.** $100(x - y + 10a)$ **85.**

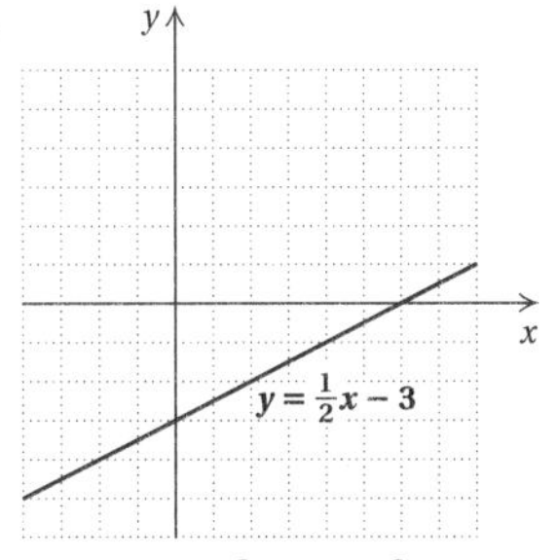

86. $\frac{23}{19}$ **87.** $75y^2 - 45y$ **89.** $V = (4x^3 - 48x^2 + 144x)$ in^3; $S = (-4x^2 + 144)$ in^2 **91.** 5 **93.** $(x^3 + 2x^2 - 210)$ m^3 **95.** 0 **97.** 0

Margin Exercises, Section 4.6, pp. 357–361

1. $x^2 + 7x + 12$ **2.** $x^2 - 2x - 15$ **3.** $2x^2 - 9x + 4$ **4.** $2x^3 - 4x^2 - 3x + 6$ **5.** $12x^5 + 10x^3 + 6x^2 + 5$ **6.** $y^6 - 49$ **7.** $t^2 + 8t + 15$ **8.** $-2x^7 + x^5 + x^3$ **9.** $x^2 - \frac{16}{25}$ **10.** $x^5 + 0.5x^3 - 0.5x^2 - 0.25$ **11.** $8 + 2x^2 - 15x^4$ **12.** $30x^5 - 27x^4 + 6x^3$ **13.** $x^2 - 25$ **14.** $4x^2 - 9$ **15.** $x^2 - 4$ **16.** $x^2 - 49$ **17.** $36 - 16y^2$ **18.** $4x^6 - 1$ **19.** $x^2 - \frac{4}{25}$ **20.** $x^2 + 16x + 64$ **21.** $x^2 - 10x + 25$ **22.** $x^2 + 4x + 4$ **23.** $a^2 - 8a + 16$ **24.** $4x^2 + 20x + 25$ **25.** $16x^4 - 24x^3 + 9x^2$ **26.** $60.84 + 18.72y + 1.44y^2$ **27.** $9x^4 - 30x^2 + 25$ **28.** $(A + B)^2$ represents the area of the large square. This includes all four sections. $A^2 + B^2$ represents only two of the sections. **29.** $x^2 + 11x + 30$ **30.** $t^2 - 16$ **31.** $-8x^5 + 20x^4 + 40x^2$ **32.** $81x^4 + 18x^2 + 1$ **33.** $4a^2 + 6a - 40$ **34.** $25x^2 + 5x + \frac{1}{4}$ **35.** $4x^2 - 2x + \frac{1}{4}$ **36.** $x^3 - 3x^2 + 6x - 8$

Visualizing for Success, p. 362

1. E, F **2.** B, O **3.** S, K **4.** R, G **5.** D, M **6.** J, P **7.** C, L **8.** N, Q **9.** A, H **10.** I, T

Exercise Set 4.6, p. 363

1. $x^3 + x^2 + 3x + 3$ **3.** $x^4 + x^3 + 2x + 2$ **5.** $y^2 - y - 6$ **7.** $9x^2 + 12x + 4$ **9.** $5x^2 + 4x - 12$ **11.** $9t^2 - 1$ **13.** $4x^2 - 6x + 2$ **15.** $p^2 - \frac{1}{16}$ **17.** $x^2 - 0.01$ **19.** $2x^3 + 2x^2 + 6x + 6$ **21.** $-2x^2 - 11x + 6$ **23.** $a^2 + 14a + 49$ **25.** $1 - x - 6x^2$ **27.** $\frac{9}{64}y^2 - \frac{5}{8}y + \frac{25}{36}$ **29.** $x^5 + 3x^3 - x^2 - 3$ **31.** $3x^6 - 2x^4 - 6x^2 + 4$ **33.** $13.16x^2 + 18.99x - 13.95$ **35.** $6x^7 + 18x^5 + 4x^2 + 12$ **37.** $8x^6 + 65x^3 + 8$ **39.** $4x^3 - 12x^2 + 3x - 9$ **41.** $4y^6 + 4y^5 + y^4 + y^3$ **43.** $x^2 - 16$ **45.** $4x^2 - 1$ **47.** $25m^2 - 4$ **49.** $4x^4 - 9$ **51.** $9x^8 - 16$ **53.** $x^{12} - x^4$ **55.** $x^8 - 9x^2$ **57.** $x^{24} - 9$ **59.** $4y^{16} - 9$ **61.** $\frac{25}{64}x^2 - 18.49$ **63.** $x^2 + 4x + 4$ **65.** $9x^4 + 6x^2 + 1$ **67.** $a^2 - a + \frac{1}{4}$ **69.** $9 + 6x + x^2$ **71.** $x^4 + 2x^2 + 1$ **73.** $4 - 12x^4 + 9x^8$ **75.** $25 + 60t^2 + 36t^4$ **77.** $x^2 - \frac{5}{4}x + \frac{25}{64}$ **79.** $9 - 12x^3 + 4x^6$ **81.** $4x^3 + 24x^2 - 12x$ **83.** $4x^4 - 2x^2 + \frac{1}{4}$ **85.** $9p^2 - 1$ **87.** $15t^5 - 3t^4 + 3t^3$ **89.** $36x^8 + 48x^4 + 16$ **91.** $12x^3 + 8x^2 + 15x + 10$ **93.** $64 - 96x^4 + 36x^8$ **95.** $t^3 - 1$ **97.** 25; 49 **99.** 56; 16 **101.** $a^2 + 2a + 1$ **103.** $t^2 + 10t + 24$ **105.** DW **107.** Lamps: 500 watts; air conditioner: 2000 watts; television: 50 watts **108.** $\frac{28}{27}$ **109.** $-\frac{41}{7}$ **110.** $\frac{27}{4}$ **111.** $y = \dfrac{3x - 12}{2}$, or $y = \dfrac{3}{2}x - 6$ **112.** $a = \dfrac{5d + 4}{3}$, or $a = \dfrac{5}{3}d + \dfrac{4}{3}$ **113.** $30x^3 + 35x^2 - 15x$ **115.** $a^4 - 50a^2 + 625$ **117.** $81t^{16} - 72t^8 + 16$ **119.** -7 **121.** First row: 90, -432, -63; second row: 7, -18, -36, -14, 12, -6, -21, -11; third row: 9, -2, -2, 10, -8, -8, -8, -10, 21; fourth row: -19, -6 **123.** Yes **125.** No

CHAPTER 5

Margin Exercises, Section 5.1, pp. 393–398

1. 20 **2.** 7 **3.** 72 **4.** 1 **5.** $4x^2$ **6.** y^2 **7.** $4mn^2$ **8.** $7x^3$ **9.** (a) $3x + 6$; (b) $3(x + 2)$ **10.** (a) $2x^3 + 10x^2 + 8x$; (b) $2x(x^2 + 5x + 4)$ **11.** $x(x + 3)$ **12.** $y^2(3y^4 - 5y + 2)$ **13.** $3x^2y(3x^2y - 5x + 1)$ **14.** $\frac{1}{4}(3t^3 + 5t^2 + 7t + 1)$ **15.** $7x^3(5x^4 - 7x^3 + 2x^2 - 9)$ **16.** $28(3x^2 - 2x + 1)$ **17.** $(x^2 + 3)(x + 7)$ **18.** $(x^2 + 2)(a + b)$ **19.** $(x^2 + 3)(x + 7)$ **20.** $(2t^2 + 3)(4t + 1)$ **21.** $(3m^3 + 2)(m^2 - 5)$ **22.** $(3x^2 - 1)(x - 2)$ **23.** $(2x^2 - 3)(2x - 3)$ **24.** Not factorable using factoring by grouping

Exercise Set 5.1, p. 399

1. x **3.** x^2 **5.** 2 **7.** $17xy$ **9.** x **11.** x^2y^2
13. $x(x-6)$ **15.** $2x(x+3)$ **17.** $x^2(x+6)$
19. $8x^2(x^2-3)$ **21.** $2(x^2+x-4)$
23. $17xy(x^4y^2+2x^2y+3)$ **25.** $x^2(6x^2-10x+3)$
27. $x^2y^2(x^3y^3+x^2y+xy-1)$
29. $2x^3(x^4-x^3-32x^2+2)$
31. $0.8x(2x^3-3x^2+4x+8)$
33. $\frac{1}{3}x^3(5x^3+4x^2+x+1)$ **35.** $(x^2+2)(x+3)$
37. $(5a^3-1)(2a-7)$ **39.** $(x^2+2)(x+3)$
41. $(2x^2+1)(x+3)$ **43.** $(4x^2+3)(2x-3)$
45. $(4p^2+1)(3p-4)$ **47.** $(5x^2-1)(x-1)$
49. $(x^2-3)(x+8)$ **51.** $(2x^2-9)(x-4)$ **53.** D_W
55. $\{x|x>-24\}$ **56.** $\{x|x \le \frac{14}{5}\}$ **57.** 27
58. $p=2A-q$ **59.** $y^2+12y+35$ **60.** $y^2+14y+49$
61. y^2-49 **62.** $y^2-14y+49$

63.

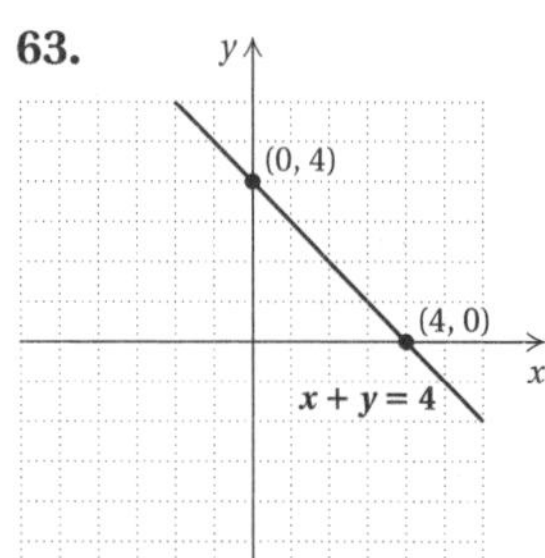

64.

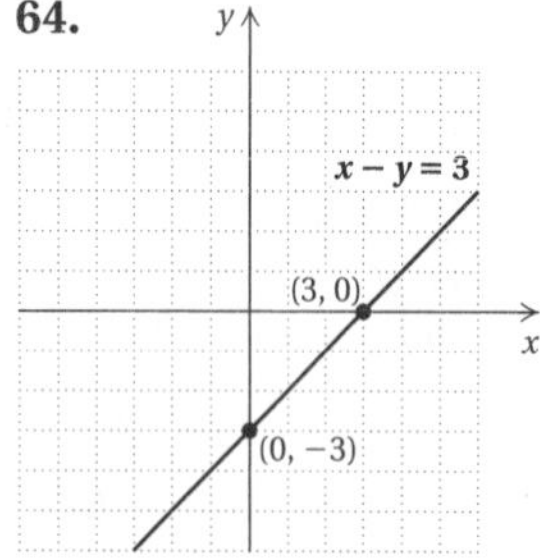

65.

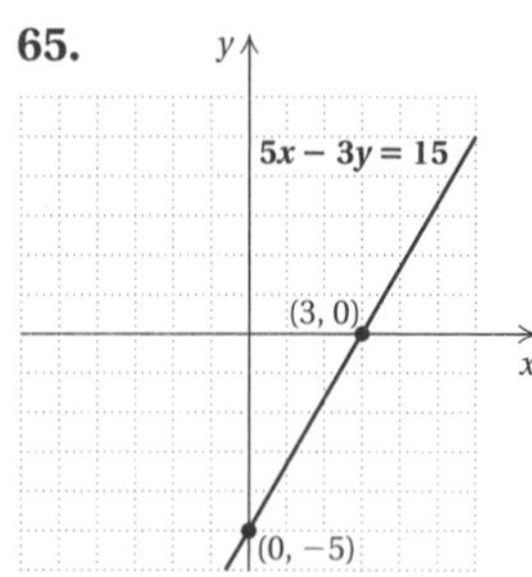

66.

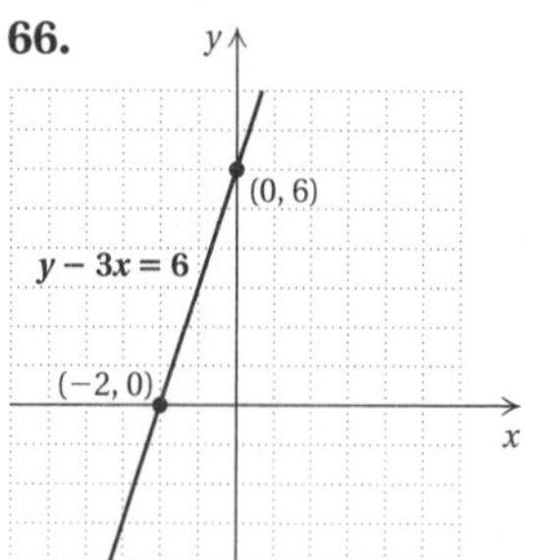

67. $(2x^3+3)(2x^2+3)$ **69.** $(x^7+1)(x^5+1)$
71. Not factorable by grouping

Margin Exercises, Section 5.2, pp. 401–406

1. **(a)** −13, 8, −8, 7, −7; **(b)** 13, 8, 7; both 7 and 12 are positive; **(c)** $(x+3)(x+4)$ **2.** $(x+9)(x+4)$
3. The coefficient of the middle term, −8, is negative.
4. $(x-5)(x-3)$ **5.** $(t-5)(t-4)$ **6.** **(a)** 23, 10, 5, 2; the positive factor has the larger absolute value; **(b)** −23, −10, −5, −2; the negative factor has the larger absolute value; **(c)** $(x+3)(x-8)$ **7.** **(a)** −23, −10, −5, −2; the negative factor has the larger absolute value; **(b)** 23, 10, 5, 2; the positive factor has the larger absolute value;
(c) $(x-2)(x+12)$ **8.** $(a-2)(a+12)$
9. $(t+2)(t-12)$ **10.** $(y-6)(y+2)$
11. $(t^2+7)(t^2-2)$ **12.** Prime **13.** $x(x+6)(x-2)$
14. $p(p-q-3q^2)$ **15.** $3x(x+4)^2$
16. $-1(x+2)(x-7)$, or $(-x-2)(x-7)$, or $(x+2)(-x+7)$ **17.** $-1(x+3)(x-6)$, or $(-x-3)(x-6)$, or $(x+3)(-x+6)$

Exercise Set 5.2, p. 407

1.

PAIRS OF FACTORS	SUMS OF FACTORS
1, 15	16
−1, −15	−16
3, 5	8
−3, −5	−8

$(x+3)(x+5)$

3.

PAIRS OF FACTORS	SUMS OF FACTORS
1, 12	13
−1, −12	−13
2, 6	8
−2, −6	−8
3, 4	7
−3, −4	−7

$(x+3)(x+4)$

5.

PAIRS OF FACTORS	SUMS OF FACTORS
1, 9	10
−1, −9	−10
3, 3	6
−3, −3	−6

$(x-3)^2$

7.

PAIRS OF FACTORS	SUMS OF FACTORS
−1, 14	13
1, −14	−13
−2, 7	5
2, −7	−5

$(x+2)(x-7)$

9.

PAIRS OF FACTORS	SUMS OF FACTORS
1, 4	5
−1, −4	−5
2, 2	4
−2, −2	−4

$(b+1)(b+4)$

11.

PAIRS OF FACTORS	SUMS OF FACTORS
$\frac{1}{3}, \frac{1}{3}$	$\frac{2}{3}$
$-\frac{1}{3}, -\frac{1}{3}$	$-\frac{2}{3}$
$1, \frac{1}{9}$	$\frac{10}{9}$
$-1, -\frac{1}{9}$	$-\frac{10}{9}$

$(x+\frac{1}{3})^2$

3. $(d-2)(d-5)$ 15. $(y-1)(y-10)$ 17. Prime 9. $(x-9)(x+2)$ 21. $x(x-8)(x+2)$ 23. $y(y-9)(y+5)$ 25. $(x-11)(x+9)$ 27. $(c^2+8)(c^2-7)$ 29. $(a^2+7)(a^2-5)$ 31. $(x-6)(x+7)$ 33. Prime 35. $(x+10)^2$ 37. $-1(x-10)(x+3)$, or $(-x+10)(x+3)$, or $(x-10)(-x-3)$ 39. $-1(a-2)(a+12)$, or $(-a+2)(a+12)$, or $(a-2)(-a-12)$ 41. $x^2(x-25)(x+4)$ 43. $(x-24)(x+3)$ 45. $(x-9)(x-16)$ 47. $(a+12)(a-11)$ 49. $(x-15)(x-8)$ 51. $-1(x+12)(x-9)$, or $(-x-12)(x-9)$, or $(x+12)(-x+9)$ 53. $(y-0.4)(y+0.2)$ 55. $(p+5q)(p-2q)$ 57. $-1(t+14)(t-6)$, or $(-t-14)(t-6)$, or $(t+14)(-t+6)$ 59. $(m+4n)(m+n)$ 61. $(s+3t)(s-5t)$ 63. $6a^8(a+2)(a-7)$ 65. DW 67. DW 69. $16x^3-48x^2+8x$ 70. $28w^2-53w-66$ 71. $49w^2+84w+36$ 72. $16w^2-88w+121$ 73. $16w^2-121$ 74. y^3-3y^2+5y 75. $6x^2+11xy-35y^2$ 76. $27x^{12}$ 77. $\frac{8}{3}$ 78. $-\frac{7}{2}$ 79. 29,555 80. 100°, 25°, 55° 81. 15, −15, 27, −27, 51, −51 83. $\left(x+\frac{1}{4}\right)\left(x-\frac{3}{4}\right)$ 85. $(x+5)\left(x-\frac{5}{7}\right)$ 87. $(b^n+5)(b^n+2)$ 89. $2x^2(4-\pi)$

Margin Exercises, Section 5.5, pp. 427–431

1. Yes 2. No 3. No 4. Yes 5. No 6. Yes 7. No 8. Yes 9. $(x+1)^2$ 10. $(x-1)^2$ 11. $(t+2)^2$ 12. $(5x-7)^2$ 13. $(7-4y)^2$ 14. $3(4m+5)^2$ 15. $(p^2+9)^2$ 16. $z^3(2z-5)^2$ 17. $(3a+5b)^2$ 18. Yes 19. No 20. No 21. No 22. Yes 23. Yes 24. Yes 25. $(x+3)(x-3)$ 26. $4(t+4)(t-4)$ 27. $(a+5b)(a-5b)$ 28. $x^4(8+5x)(8-5x)$ 29. $5(1+2t^3)(1-2t^3)$ 30. $(9x^2+1)(3x+1)(3x-1)$ 31. $\left(4+\frac{1}{9}y^4\right)\left(2-\frac{1}{3}y^2\right)\left(2+\frac{1}{3}y^2\right)$ 32. $(7p^2+5q^3)(7p^2-5q^3)$

Exercise Set 5.5, p. 432

1. Yes 3. No 5. No 7. No 9. $(x-7)^2$ 11. $(x+8)^2$ 13. $(x-1)^2$ 15. $(x+2)^2$ 17. $(q^2-3)^2$ 19. $(4y+7)^2$ 21. $2(x-1)^2$ 23. $x(x-9)^2$ 25. $3(2q-3)^2$ 27. $(7-3x)^2$ 29. $5(y^2+1)^2$ 31. $(1+2x^2)^2$ 33. $(2p+3q)^2$ 35. $(a-3b)^2$ 37. $(9a-b)^2$ 39. $4(3a+4b)^2$ 41. Yes 43. No 45. No 47. Yes 49. $(y+2)(y-2)$ 51. $(p+3)(p-3)$ 53. $(t+7)(t-7)$ 55. $(a+b)(a-b)$ 57. $(5t+m)(5t-m)$ 59. $(10+k)(10-k)$ 61. $(4a+3)(4a-3)$ 63. $(2x+5y)(2x-5y)$ 65. $2(2x+7)(2x-7)$ 67. $x(6+7x)(6-7x)$ 69. $\left(\frac{1}{4}+7x^4\right)\left(\frac{1}{4}-7x^4\right)$ 71. $(0.3y+0.02)(0.3y-0.02)$ 73. $(7a^2+9)(7a^2-9)$ 75. $(a^2+4)(a+2)(a-2)$ 77. $5(x^2+9)(x+3)(x-3)$ 79. $(1+y^4)(1+y^2)(1+y)(1-y)$ 81. $(x^6+4)(x^3+2)(x^3-2)$ 83. $\left(y+\frac{1}{4}\right)\left(y-\frac{1}{4}\right)$ 85. $\left(5+\frac{1}{7}x\right)\left(5-\frac{1}{7}x\right)$ 87. $(4m^2+t^2)(2m+t)(2m-t)$ 89. DW 91. −11 92. 400 93. $-\frac{5}{6}$ 94. −0.9 95. 2 96. −160 97. $x^2-4xy+4y^2$ 98. $\frac{1}{2}\pi x^2+2xy$

99. y^{12} 100. $25a^4b^6$ 101.

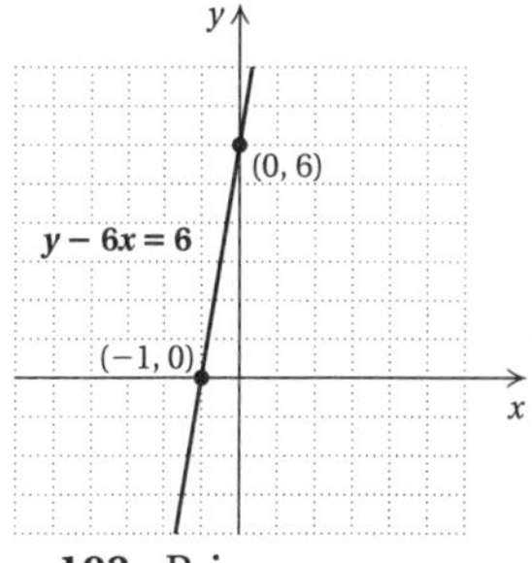

102.

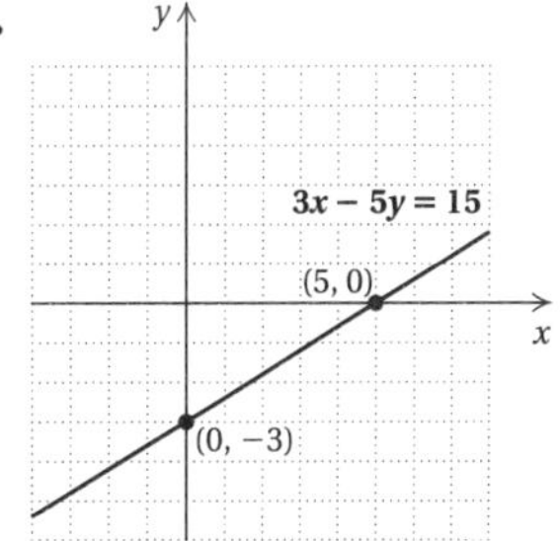

103. Prime

105. $(x+11)^2$ 107. $2x(3x+1)^2$ 109. $(x^4+2^4)(x^2+2^2)(x+2)(x-2)$ 111. $3x^3(x+2)(x-2)$ 113. $2x\left(3x+\frac{2}{5}\right)\left(3x-\frac{2}{5}\right)$ 115. $p(0.7+p)(0.7-p)$ 117. $(0.8x+1.1)(0.8x-1.1)$ 119. $x(x+6)$ 121. $\left(x+\frac{1}{x}\right)\left(x-\frac{1}{x}\right)$ 123. $(9+b^{2k})(3-b^k)(3+b^k)$ 125. $(3b^n+2)^2$ 127. $(y+4)^2$ 129. 9 131. Not correct 133. Not correct

Margin Exercises, Section 5.7, pp. 445–448

1. 3, −4 2. 7, 3 3. $-\frac{1}{4}, \frac{2}{3}$ 4. 0, $\frac{17}{3}$ 5. −2, 3 6. −4, 7 7. 3 8. 0, 4 9. $-\frac{4}{3}, \frac{4}{3}$ 10. 3, $\frac{7}{2}$ 11. −5, 2 12. −3, 3 13. (−5, 0), (1, 0) 14. 0, 3

Calculator Corner, p. 449

1. Left to the student

Exercise Set 5.7, p. 450

1. −4, −9 3. −3, 8 5. −12, 11 7. 0, −3 9. 0, −18 11. $-\frac{5}{2}$, −4 13. $-\frac{1}{5}$, 3 15. 4, $\frac{1}{4}$ 17. 0, $\frac{2}{3}$ 19. $-\frac{1}{10}, \frac{1}{27}$ 21. $\frac{1}{3}$, −20 23. 0, $\frac{2}{3}, \frac{1}{2}$ 25. −5, −1 27. −9, 2 29. 3, 5 31. 0, 8 33. 0, −18 35. −4, 4 37. $-\frac{2}{3}, \frac{2}{3}$ 39. −3 41. 4 43. 0, $\frac{6}{5}$ 45. −1, $\frac{5}{3}$ 47. $-\frac{1}{4}, \frac{2}{3}$ 49. −1, $\frac{2}{3}$ 51. $-\frac{7}{10}, \frac{7}{10}$ 53. −2, 9 55. $\frac{4}{5}, \frac{3}{2}$ 57. (−4, 0), (1, 0) 59. $\left(-\frac{5}{2}, 0\right)$, (2, 0) 61. (−3, 0), (5, 0) 63. −1, 4 65. −1, 3 67. DW 69. $(a+b)^2$ 70. a^2+b^2 71. −16 72. −4.5 73. $-\frac{10}{3}$ 74. $\frac{3}{10}$ 75. −5, 4 77. −3, 9 79. $-\frac{1}{8}, \frac{1}{8}$ 81. −4, 4 83. Answers may vary. **(a)** $x^2-x-12=0$; **(b)** $x^2+7x+12=0$; **(c)** $4x^2-4x+1=0$; **(d)** $x^2-25=0$; **(e)** $40x^3-14x^2+x=0$ 85. 2.33, 6.77 87. 0, 2.74

Exercises, Section 5.8, pp. 453–458

1. Length: 24 in.; width: 12 in. **2.** Height: 25 ft; width: 10 ft **3.** (a) 342 games; (b) 9 teams **4.** 22 and 23 **5.** 24 ft **6.** 3 m, 4 m

Translating for Success, p. 459

1. O **2.** M **3.** K **4.** I **5.** G **6.** E **7.** C **8.** A **9.** H **10.** B

Exercise Set 5.8, p. 460

1. Length: 6 cm; width: 4 cm **3.** Length: 12 ft; width: 2 ft **5.** Height: 4 cm; base: 14 cm **7.** Base: 8 m; height: 16 m **9.** 182 games **11.** 12 teams **13.** 4950 handshakes **15.** 25 people **17.** 20 people **19.** 14 and 15 **21.** 12 and 14; −12 and −14 **23.** 15 and 17; −15 and −17 **25.** Hypotenuse: 17 ft; leg: 15 ft **27.** 32 ft **29.** 9 ft **31.** Dining room: 12 ft by 12 ft; kitchen: 12 ft by 10 ft **33.** 4 sec **35.** 5 and 7 **37.** DW **39.** Factor **40.** Factor **41.** Product **42.** Common factor **43.** Trinomial **44.** Quotient rule **45.** y-intercept **46.** Slope **47.** 35 ft **49.** 5 ft **51.** 30 cm by 15 cm **53.** 7 ft

CHAPTER 6

Margin Exercises, Section 6.1, pp. 472–477

1. 3 **2.** −8, 3 **3.** None **4.** $\frac{(2x+1)x}{(3x-2)x}$ **5.** $\frac{(x+1)(x+2)}{(x-2)(x+2)}$ **6.** $\frac{(x-8)(-1)}{(x-y)(-1)}$ **7.** 5 **8.** $\frac{x}{4}$ **9.** $\frac{2x+1}{3x+2}$ **10.** $\frac{x+1}{2x+1}$ **11.** $x+2$ **12.** $\frac{y+2}{4}$ **13.** −1 **14.** −1 **15.** −1 **16.** $\frac{a-2}{a-3}$ **17.** $\frac{x-5}{2}$

Calculator Corner, p. 478

1. Correct **2.** Correct **3.** Not correct **4.** Not correct **5.** Not correct **6.** Not correct **7.** Correct **8.** Correct

Exercise Set 6.1, p. 479

1. 0 **3.** 8 **5.** $-\frac{5}{2}$ **7.** −4, 7 **9.** −5, 5 **11.** None **13.** $\frac{(4x)(3x^2)}{(4x)(5y)}$ **15.** $\frac{2x(x-1)}{2x(x+4)}$ **17.** $\frac{-1(3-x)}{-1(4-x)}$ **19.** $\frac{(y+6)(y-7)}{(y+6)(y+2)}$ **21.** $\frac{x^2}{4}$ **23.** $\frac{8p^2q}{3}$ **25.** $\frac{x-3}{x}$ **27.** $\frac{m+1}{2m+3}$ **29.** $\frac{a-3}{a+2}$ **31.** $\frac{a-3}{a-4}$ **33.** $\frac{x+5}{x-5}$ **35.** $a+1$ **37.** $\frac{x^2+1}{x+1}$ **39.** $\frac{3}{2}$ **41.** $\frac{6}{t-3}$ **43.** $\frac{t+2}{2(t-4)}$ **45.** $\frac{t-2}{t+2}$ **47.** −1 **49.** −1 **51.** −6 **53.** $-x-1$ **55.** $\frac{56x}{3}$ **57.** $\frac{2}{dc^2}$ **59.** $\frac{x+2}{x-2}$ **61.** $\frac{(a+3)(a-3)}{a(a+4)}$ **63.** $\frac{2a}{a-2}$ **65.** $\frac{(t+2)(t-2)}{(t+1)(t-1)}$ **67.** $\frac{x+4}{x+2}$ **69.** $\frac{5(a+6)}{a-1}$ **71.** DW **73.** 18 and 20; −18 and −20 **74.** 3.125 L **75.** $(x-8)(x+7)$ **76.** $(a-8)^2$ **77.** $x^3(x-7)(x+5)$ **78.** $(2y^2+1)(y-5)$ **79.** $(2+t)(2-t)(4+t^2)$ **80.** $10(x+7)(x+1)$ **81.** $(x-7)(x-2)$ **82.** Prime **83.** $(4x-5y)^2$ **84.** $(a-7b)(a-2b)$ **85.** $x+2y$ **87.** $\frac{(t-9)^2(t-1)}{(t^2+9)(t+1)}$ **89.** $\frac{x-y}{x-5y}$

91.
$$\frac{5(2x+5)-25}{10} = \frac{10x+25-25}{10} = \frac{10x}{10} = x$$

You get the same number you selected. To do a number trick, ask someone to select a number and then perform these operations. The person will probably be surprised that the result is the original number.

Margin Exercises, Section 6.2, pp. 483–485

1. $\frac{2}{7}$ **2.** $\frac{2x^3-1}{x^2+5}$ **3.** $\frac{1}{x-5}$ **4.** x^2-3 **5.** $\frac{6}{7}$ **6.** $\frac{5}{8}$ **7.** $\frac{(x-3)(x-2)}{(x+5)(x+5)}$ **8.** $\frac{3a^2}{a-5}$ **9.** $\frac{x-3}{x+2}$ **10.** $\frac{(x-3)(x-2)}{x+2}$ **11.** $\frac{y+1}{y-1}$

Exercise Set 6.2, p. 486

1. $\frac{x}{4}$ **3.** $\frac{1}{x^2-y^2}$ **5.** $a+b$ **7.** $\frac{x^2-4x+7}{x^2+2x-5}$ **9.** $\frac{3}{10}$ **11.** $\frac{1}{4}$ **13.** $\frac{b}{a}$ **15.** $\frac{(a+2)(a+3)}{(a-3)(a-1)}$ **17.** $\frac{(x-1)^2}{x}$ **19.** $\frac{1}{2}$ **21.** $\frac{15}{8}$ **23.** $\frac{15}{4}$ **25.** $\frac{a-5}{3(a-1)}$ **27.** $\frac{(x+2)^2}{x}$ **29.** $\frac{3}{2}$ **31.** $\frac{c+1}{c-1}$ **33.** $\frac{y-3}{2y-1}$ **35.** $\frac{x+1}{x-1}$ **37.** DW **39.** $\{x \mid x \geq 77\}$ **40.** Height: 7 in.; base: 10 in. **41.** $8x^3-11x^2-3x+12$ **42.** $-2p^2+4pq-4q^2$ **43.** $\frac{4y^8}{x^6}$ **44.** $\frac{125x^{18}}{y^{12}}$ **45.** $\frac{4x^6}{y^{10}}$ **46.** $\frac{1}{a^{15}b^{20}}$ **47.** $-\frac{1}{b^2}$ **49.** $\frac{a+1}{5ab^2(a^2+4)}$

Margin Exercises, Section 6.3, pp. 488–489

1. 144 **2.** 12 **3.** 10 **4.** 120 **5.** $\frac{35}{144}$ **6.** $\frac{1}{4}$ **7.** $\frac{11}{10}$ **8.** $\frac{9}{40}$ **9.** $60x^3y^2$ **10.** $(y+1)^2(y+4)$ **11.** $7(t^2+16)(t-2)$ **12.** $3x(x+1)^2(x-1)$